GLENCOE

WORLD
GEOGRAPHY

A Physical and Cultural Approach

**NATIONAL
GEOGRAPHIC
SOCIETY**

Richard G. Boehm, Ph.D.
Professor of Geography
Southwest Texas State University

GLENCOE
McGraw-Hill

New York, New York   Columbus, Ohio   Woodland Hills, California   Peoria, Illinois

About The Authors

NATIONAL GEOGRAPHIC SOCIETY
The National Geographic Society, founded in 1888 for the increase and diffusion of geographic knowledge, is the world's largest nonprofit scientific and educational organization. Since its earliest days, the Society has used sophisticated communication technologies, from color photography to holography, to convey geographic knowledge to a worldwide membership. The Educational Media Division supports the Society's mission by developing innovative educational programs—ranging from traditional print materials to multimedia programs including CD-ROMS, videodiscs, and software.

RICHARD G. BOEHM
Richard G. Boehm, Ph.D., was one of seven authors of *Geography for Life*, national standards in geography, prepared under Goals 2000: Educate America Act. He was also one of the authors of the *Guidelines for Geographic Education,* in which the five themes of geography were first articulated. In 1990 Dr. Boehm was designated "Distinguished Geography Educator" by the National Geographic Society. In 1991 he received the George J. Miller award from the National Council for Geographic Education (NCGE) for distinguished service to geographic education. He was President of the NCGE and has twice won the *Journal of Geography* award for best article. He has received the NCGE's "Distinguished Teaching Achievement" award and is presently Professor of Geography at Southwest Texas State University in San Marcos, Texas.

Contributing Writers

SARAH W. BEDNARZ, PH.D.
Visiting Assistant Professor of Geography
Department of Geography
Texas A & M University
College Station, Texas

ROBERT BEDNARZ, PH.D.
Associate Professor of Geography
Department of Geography
Texas A & M University
College Station, Texas

JAMES L. SWANSON
Teacher and Chairperson,
 History Department
Marin Country Day School
Corte Madera, California

Glencoe/McGraw-Hill
A Division of The McGraw-Hill Companies

Copyright © 1997, 1995 by The McGraw-Hill Companies, Inc. All rights reserved.
Except as permitted under the United States Copyright Act, no part of this publication may be reproduced or distributed in any form or by any means, or stored in a database or retrieval system, without prior written permission of the publisher.

Send all inquiries to:
Glencoe/McGraw-Hill, 936 Eastwind Drive, Westerville, Ohio 43081

ISBN 0-02-821713-6 (Student Edition)   ISBN 0-02-821714-4 (Teacher's Wraparound Edition)

Printed in the United States of America.

9 10 11 12 13   071/043   02 01 00 99

Consultants

General Content Consultant
THEODORE M. BLACK, SR.
Chancellor Emeritus
New York State Board of Regents

Geography Consultant
SARAH W. BEDNARZ, PH.D.
Visiting Assistant Professor
  of Geography
Department of Geography
Texas A & M University
College Station, Texas

Multicultural Consultant
RICARDO L. GARCÍA, ED.D.
Professor
University of Wisconsin
Stevens Point, Wisconsin

Religion Consultants
JOHN L. ESPOSITO, PH.D.
Professor of Religion and
International Affairs Director
Georgetown University
Washington, D.C.
SAYYID M. SYEED, PH.D.
Secretary General
Islamic Society of
  North America
Plainfield, Indiana

Introduction to Geography
BURRELL E. MONTZ, PH.D.
Associate Professor of Geography
  and Environmental Studies
Binghamton University
Binghamton, New York

United States and Canada
DAVID A. LANEGRAN, PH.D.
Professor of Geography
Macalester College
St. Paul, Minnesota

Latin America
GERALD T. HANSON, PH.D.
Professor of Geography
University of Arkansas
Little Rock, Arkansas

Europe
GAIL L. HOBBS, PH.D.
Associate Professor of Geography
Pierce College
Woodland Hills, California

Russia and the Eurasian Republics
SUSAN W. HARDWICK, PH.D.
Professor of Geography
California State University
Chico, California
PAVEL PANKIN
Principal
School No. 1741
Western District
Moscow, Russia

North Africa and Southwest Asia
THEODORE H. SCHMUDDE, PH.D.
Professor of Geography
University of Tennessee
Knoxville, Tennessee
JERROLD D. GREEN, PH.D.
Director
Middle East Studies Center
University of Arizona
Tucson, Arizona

Africa South of the Sahara
WILLIAM R. BROWN, PH.D.
Assistant Professor of Geography
  and Departmental Head
Prairie View A & M University
Prairie View, Texas

South Asia
GARY J. HAUSLADEN, PH.D.
Associate Professor of Geography
University of Nevada
Reno, Nevada

East Asia
KENJI KENNETH OSHIRO, PH.D.
Professor of Geography
  and Departmental Chair
Wright State University
Dayton, Ohio

Southeast Asia
JULIE A. TUASON, PH.D.
Rutgers University
New Brunswick, N.J.

Australia, Oceania, and Antarctica
LAURIE MOLINA, PH.D.
Program Director
Geography Education and Technology
  Program
Florida State University
Tallahassee, Florida

Teacher Reviewers

ROSEMARY M. BREWER
Secondary Social Studies Teacher
Hall High School
Little Rock, Arkansas

JOSEPH BRYAN
World Geography Teacher
John Jay High School
Northside Independent School District
San Antonio, Texas

RUSSELL PARKER BUSH
Social Studies Department Chairperson
Buckhannon-Upshur Middle School
Buckhannon, West Virginia

REBECCA A. CORLEY
Social Studies Teacher
Evans Junior High School
Lubbock, Texas

MARY REAL D'ANGELO
Social Studies Teacher and
Departmental Chair
Boys Town High School
Boys Town, Nebraska

KEVIN DAVIS
Social Studies Teacher
Jacksonville High School
Jacksonville, Arkansas

ROBERT E. EDISON
History Instructor
Pearl C. Anderson Middle School
Dallas, Texas

MOUNIR A. FARAH, PH.D.
Associate Director,
Middle East Studies Program
University of Arkansas
Fayetteville, Arkansas

MARY JANE FRASER, PH.D.
Teacher and Social Studies
Curriculum Project Leader
Seattle School District
Seattle, Washington

SHERRY KAY HENDERSON
World Geography Teacher
Northbrook High School
Houston, Texas

FRED H. HUDDLESTON
Department Chairperson Social Studies
McCollum High School
Harlandale Independent School District
San Antonio, Texas

MARIANNE KENNEY
Social Studies Specialist
Colorado Department of Education
Denver, Colorado

WARDELL RICHARDS
Social Studies Teacher
and Departmental Chair
W.W. Sammuell High School
Dallas, Texas

JUDITH ROSENSTOCK
Middle School Principal
Trinity Preparatory School
Winter Park, Florida

RUTH W. STAS
K-12 Social Studies Coordinator
Manheim Township School District
Lancaster, Pennsylvania

DALE ZELLMER
K-12 Social Studies Consultant
Department of Curriculum
Anoka-Hennepin School District
Coon Rapids, Minnesota

Contents

Reference Atlas   A1

The World	A2
United States	A4
Canada	A6
Mexico, the Caribbean, and Central America	A8
North America	A10
South America	A11
Europe	A12
Russia and the Eurasian Republics	A14
The Middle East	A16
South Asia	A18
Africa	A19
East Asia	A20
Southeast Asia	A22
Oceania	A24
The Pacific Rim	A26
Polar Regions	A28
World Facts	1

UNIT 1 Looking at the World   2-83

CHAPTER 1
How Geographers Look at the World   **4**
1 Themes of Geography	5
▼ Geography Skills Handbook	11

CHAPTER 2
Looking at the Earth   **26**
1 Planet Earth	27
2 Earth's Features	33
3 Earth's Resources	37

CHAPTER 3
Climates of the Earth   **44**
1 Earth-Sun Relationships	45
2 Factors Affecting Climate	48
3 World Climate Patterns	52

CHAPTER 4
Environments, Peoples, and Cultures   **62**
1 Limits and Opportunities	63
2 Cultural Expressions	69
3 World Culture Regions Today	74

UNIT 2 The United States and Canada 84-149

UNIT 2 ATLAS **86**
The United States and Canada: Country Profile **90**

CHAPTER 5
The Physical Geography of the United States and Canada **92**
  1 The Land   93
  2 The Climate and Vegetation   98

CHAPTER 6
The Cultural Geography of the United States and Canada **106**
  1 Population Patterns   107
  2 History and Government   111
  3 Cultures and Lifestyles   120

CHAPTER 7
The United States and Canada Today **128**
  1 Living in the United States and Canada   129
  2 People and Their Environment   137

UNIT 3 Latin America 150-211

UNIT 3 ATLAS **152**
Latin America: Country Profile **156**

CHAPTER 8
The Physical Geography of Latin America **160**
  1 The Land   161
  2 The Climate and Vegetation   166

CHAPTER 9
The Cultural Geography of Latin America **174**
  1 Population Patterns   175
  2 History and Government   181
  3 Cultures and Lifestyles   186

CHAPTER 10
Latin America Today **194**
  1 Living in Latin America   195
  2 People and Their Environment   202

UNIT 4 Europe

212-281

UNIT 4 ATLAS	**214**
Europe: Country Profile	**218**

CHAPTER 11
The Physical Geography of Europe — **222**
1 The Land — 223
2 The Climate and Vegetation — 230

CHAPTER 12
The Cultural Geography of Europe — **238**
1 Population Patterns — 239
2 History and Government — 244
3 Cultures and Lifestyles — 251

CHAPTER 13
Europe Today — **260**
1 Living in Europe — 261
2 People and Their Environment — 270

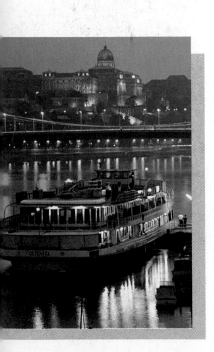

UNIT 5 Russia and the Eurasian Republics

282-347

UNIT 5 ATLAS	**284**
Russia and the Eurasian Republics: Country Profile	**288**

CHAPTER 14
The Physical Geography of Russia and the Eurasian Republics — **290**
1 The Land — 291
2 The Climate and Vegetation — 296

CHAPTER 15
The Cultural Geography of Russia and the Eurasian Republics — **304**
1 Population Patterns — 305
2 History and Government — 311
3 Cultures and Lifestyles — 317

CHAPTER 16
Russia and the Eurasian Republics Today — **326**
1 Living in Russia and the Eurasian Republics — 327
2 People and Their Environment — 336

UNIT 6 North Africa and Southwest Asia 348-407

UNIT 6 ATLAS 350
North Africa and Southwest Asia: Country Profile 354

CHAPTER 17
The Physical Geography of North Africa and Southwest Asia 356
  1 The Land 357
  2 The Climate and Vegetation 362

CHAPTER 18
The Cultural Geography of North Africa and Southwest Asia 370
  1 Population Patterns 371
  2 History and Government 376
  3 Cultures and Lifestyles 382

CHAPTER 19
North Africa and Southwest Asia Today 390
  1 Living in North Africa and Southwest Asia 391
  2 People and Their Environment 398

UNIT 7 Africa South of the Sahara 408-467

UNIT 7 ATLAS 410
Africa South of the Sahara: Country Profile 414

CHAPTER 20
The Physical Geography of Africa South of the Sahara 418
  1 The Land 419
  2 The Climate and Vegetation 424

CHAPTER 21
The Cultural Geography of Africa South of the Sahara 432
  1 Population Patterns 433
  2 History and Government 438
  3 Cultures and Lifestyles 442

CHAPTER 22
Africa South of the Sahara Today 450
  1 Living in Africa South of the Sahara 451
  2 People and Their Environment 458

UNIT 8 South Asia 468-527

UNIT 8 ATLAS	**470**
South Asia: Country Profile	**474**

CHAPTER 23
The Physical Geography of South Asia — **476**
1 The Land — 477
2 The Climate and Vegetation — 482

CHAPTER 24
The Cultural Geography of South Asia — **490**
1 Population Patterns — 491
2 History and Government — 496
3 Cultures and Lifestyles — 501

CHAPTER 25
South Asia Today — **510**
1 Living in South Asia — 511
2 People and Their Environment — 518

UNIT 9 East Asia 528-587

UNIT 9 ATLAS	**530**
East Asia: Country Profile	**534**

CHAPTER 26
The Physical Geography of East Asia — **536**
1 The Land — 537
2 The Climate and Vegetation — 542

CHAPTER 27
The Cultural Geography of East Asia — **550**
1 Population Patterns — 551
2 History and Government — 556
3 Cultures and Lifestyles — 561

CHAPTER 28
East Asia Today — **570**
1 Living in East Asia — 571
2 People and Their Environment — 577

UNIT 10 Southeast Asia   588-645

| UNIT 10 ATLAS | 590 |
| Southeast Asia: Country Profile | 594 |

CHAPTER 29
The Physical Geography of Southeast Asia   **596**
  1 The Land   597
  2 The Climate and Vegetation   602

CHAPTER 30
The Cultural Geography of Southeast Asia   **610**
  1 Population Patterns   611
  2 History and Government   615
  3 Cultures and Lifestyles   620

CHAPTER 31
Southeast Asia Today   **628**
  1 Living in Southeast Asia   629
  2 People and Their Environment   635

UNIT 11 Australia, Oceania, and Antarctica   646-703

| UNIT 11 ATLAS | 648 |
| Australia, Oceania, Antarctica: Country Profile | 652 |

CHAPTER 32
**The Physical Geography of Australia, Oceania,
and Antarctica**   **654**
  1 The Land   655
  2 The Climate and Vegetation   660

CHAPTER 33
**The Cultural Geography of Australia, Oceania,
and Antarctica**   **668**
  1 Population Patterns   669
  2 History and Government   673
  3 Cultures and Lifestyles   678

CHAPTER 34
Australia, Oceania, and Antarctica Today   **686**
  1 Living in Australia, Oceania, and Antarctica 687
  2 People and Their Environment   694

Appendix   **704**
  English Glossary   705
  Spanish Handbook
    Spanish Glossary   715
    Spanish Summaries   727
  Gazetteer   761
  Index   771
  Acknowledgments   785

NATIONAL GEOGRAPHIC SOCIETY

PICTURING THE WORLD

Looking at the World	2	Africa South of the Sahara	408
The United States and Canada	84	South Asia	468
Latin America	150	East Asia	528
Europe	212	Southeast Asia	588
Russia and the Eurasian Republics	282	Australia, Oceania, and Antarctica	646
North Africa and Southwest Asia	348		

SKILLS

MAP AND GRAPH SKILLS

Geography Skills Handbook	11
Understanding Scale	58
Interpreting a Climate Graph	78
Understanding Latitude and Longitude	102
Reading a Cartogram	144
Reading a Relief Map	170
Interpreting a Population Pyramid	190
Reading a Vegetation Map	206
Reading a Climate Map	234
Interpreting a Political Map	300
Reading a Bar Graph	322
Interpreting a Special-Purpose Map	386
Reading a Circle Graph	446
Reading a Land-Use Map	462
Reading a Line Graph	506
Interpreting a Contour Map	546
Reading a Population Density Map	566
Reading an Economic Activity Map	582

Understanding Time Zones	640
Interpreting Routes on a Map	664
Reading Tables and Analyzing Statistics	682

CRITICAL THINKING SKILLS

Analyzing Information	276
Distinguishing Fact From Opinion	342
Making Comparisons	402
Evaluating Information	428
Drawing Conclusions	486
Making Generalizations	522
Determining Cause and Effect	606
Predicting Consequences	698

STUDY AND WRITING SKILLS

Outlining	124
Writing a Topic Sentence	256
Writing a Paragraph	366
Interpreting Primary Sources	624

CASE STUDIES

Out of Ozone	72	Moving to Lagos	456
Not in My Backyard!	142	The Ganges: Plagued by Pollution	516
Rain Forests for Farmlands	200	Troublesome Tremors	580
Protecting the Netherlands	268	Logging in Thailand	638
The Dying Aral Sea	334	Preserving the Great Barrier Reef	692
The War for Water	396		

Where is the World's Largest Mountain
Range? 40

What is the Tallest Living Thing
on Earth? 110

Where is the Deepest Canyon
on Earth? 180

What is the Smallest Country
on Earth? 243

Where is the Most Polluted Place
on Earth? 310

Where is the Lowest Point on Earth? 375

Where is the World's Fishiest Lake? 437

What is the World's Most
Useful Tree? 495

Where is the World's Longest
Escalator? 555

Where are the World's Newest
Mammals? 614

What is the Most Poisonous Animal? 672

GEOGRAPHY AND HISTORY

Canada's Two Languages 119

Buenos Aires, Argentina's Gateway 185

Chunnel Vision 250

The Unconquerable Russian Winter 316

The Sahara: Growing or Shifting? 381

Africa: European Colonies 441

Nepal and Bhutan: Isolated
by Geography 500

Hong Kong: Harbor of Free Enterprise 560

Singapore: Model of Prosperity 619

Living in Antarctica 677

GEOGRAPHY CONNECTIONS

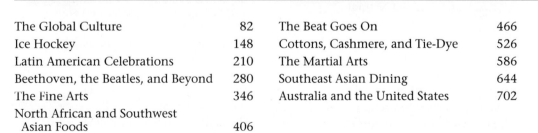

The Global Culture 82

Ice Hockey 148

Latin American Celebrations 210

Beethoven, the Beatles, and Beyond 280

The Fine Arts 346

North African and Southwest
Asian Foods 406

The Beat Goes On 466

Cottons, Cashmere, and Tie-Dye 526

The Martial Arts 586

Southeast Asian Dining 644

Australia and the United States 702

MAPS

REFERENCE ATLAS

The World — A2

United States — A4

Canada — A6

Mexico, the Caribbean, and Central America — A8

North America — A10

South America — A11

Europe — A12

Russia and the Eurasian Republics — A14

The Middle East — A16

South Asia — A18

Africa — A19

East Asia — A20

Southeast Asia — A22

Oceania — A24

The Pacific Rim — A26

Polar Regions — A28

World Facts — 1

Robinson Projection — 19, 23

Gall-Peters Projection — 19

Locating Places: The World — 25

Plates and Plate Movement — 30

Locating Places: The World — 43

Ocean Currents and Continents — 49

The World: Climate Regions — 53

The World: Natural Vegetation — 55

Southeastern United States; West Palm Beach, Florida — 58

Locating Places: The World — 61

The World: Economic Activity — 64

The World: Population Density — 66

Great Wall of China — 70

Culture Hearths — 71

The World: Culture Regions — 75

The World: Language Families — 76

The World: Religions — 77

Locating Places: The World — 81

UNIT 1
LOOKING AT THE WORLD

The Global Grid — 6

The Hemispheres — 7

Relative Location of Dallas, TX — 9

Different Map Scales: Mexico and Mexico City — 12

France — 13

Mexico: Physical — 14

Mexico: Political — 14

United States: Oil and Natural Gas Fields — 15

A Great Circle Route — 16

Mercator Projection — 17

Conic Projection — 17

Sinusoidal Projection — 18

Polar (Azimuthal) Projection — 18

Goode's Interrupted Equal-Area Projection — 18

UNIT 2
THE UNITED STATES AND CANADA

United States and Canada: Political — 86

United States and Canada: Population Density — 87

United States and Canada: Physical Features — 88

United States and Canada: Natural Resources — 89

The St. Lawrence Seaway — 91

Comparing Lands: The United States and Canada — 94

The United States and Canada: Physical-Political — 95

Mississippi River — 96, 103

The United States and Canada: Climate Regions — 99

The United States and Canada: Natural Vegetation — 101

The United States and Canada: Political — 102

Locating Places: The United States and Canada — 105

Major Languages of Canada — 119

Locating Places: The United States and Canada — 127

The United States and Canada: Economic Activity — 130

Acid Rain — 138

Locating Places: The United States and Canada — 147

UNIT 3
LATIN AMERICA

Latin America: Political — 152

Latin America: Population Density — 153

Latin America: Physical Features — 154

Latin America: Natural Resources — 155

Comparing Lands: Latin America and the United States — 162

Latin America: Physical-Political — 163

Desert Areas of Chile — 165

Latin America: Climate Regions — 167

Latin America: Natural Vegetation — 169

Peru — 170

Locating Places: Latin America — 173

Latin America: Major Languages — 177

Native American Empires — 182

European Colonial Empires — 183

Panama Canal — 184

Locating Places: Latin America — 193

Latin America: Economic Activity — 197

Forested Regions in Costa Rica — 200

Amazon Basin — 203

Latin America: Natural Vegetation — 206

Locating Places: Latin America — 209

UNIT 4
EUROPE

Europe: Political — 214

Europe: Population Density — 215

Europe: Physical Features — 216

Europe: Natural Resources — 217

Comparing Lands: Europe and the United States — 224

Norwegian Fjords — 224

Europe: Physical-Political — 225

Europe: Climate Regions — 231, 234

Europe: Natural Vegetation — 232

Locating Places: Europe — 237

The Roman Empire, A.D. 117 — 245

Venice — 247

Europe, 1955; Europe, 1993 — 249

The Chunnel — 250

Europe: Languages — 252

Locating Places: Europe — 259

The European Union — 262

Europe: Economic Activity — 265

The Netherlands — 269

Locating Places: Mediterranean Region — 279

UNIT 5
RUSSIA AND THE EURASIAN REPUBLICS

Russia and the Eurasian Republics: Political — 284

Russia and the Eurasian Republics: Population Density — 285

Russia and the Eurasian Republics: Physical Features — 286

Russia and the Eurasian Republics: Natural Resources — 287

Ural Mountains — 292

Comparing Lands: Russia and the United States — 292

Russia and the Eurasian Republics: Physical-Political — 293

Russia and the Eurasian Republics: Climate Regions — 297

Russia and the Eurasian Republics: 1993 — 300

Locating Places: Russia and the
Eurasian Republics 303

Russian and Soviet Expansion 314

Locating Places: Russia and the
Eurasian Republics 325

Russia and the Eurasian Republics:
Economic Activity 329

Aral Sea 335

Chernobyl 337

Locating Places: Russia and the
Eurasian Republics 345

UNIT 6
NORTH AFRICA AND SOUTHWEST ASIA

North Africa and Southwest Asia:
Political 350

North Africa and Southwest Asia:
Population Density 351

North Africa and Southwest Asia:
Physical Features 352

North Africa and Southwest Asia:
Natural Resources 353

Comparing Lands: North
Africa/Southwest Asia and the
United States 358

North Africa and Southwest Asia:
Physical-Political 359

Nile River Valley 360

North Africa and Southwest Asia:
Climate Regions 363

North Africa and Southwest Asia:
Natural Vegetation 364

Locating Places: North Africa and
Southwest Asia 369

Early Hebrew Kingdoms 372

Early Civilizations 377

Muslim Empires 378

The Middle East After World War I 379

Literacy Rate in Southwest Asia 386

Locating Places: North Africa and
Southwest Asia 389

North Africa and Southwest Asia:
Economic Activity 393

Euphrates River Valley 397

North Africa and Southwest Asia:
Annual Precipitation 399

Persian Gulf Area 401

Locating Places: North Africa and
Southwest Asia 405

UNIT 7
AFRICA SOUTH OF THE SAHARA

Africa South of the Sahara: Political 410

Africa South of the Sahara: Population
Density 411

Africa South of the Sahara Physical
Features 412

Africa South of the Sahara Natural
Resources 413

Comparing Lands: Africa South of the
Sahara and the United States 420

Africa South of the Sahara:
Physical-Political 421

Victoria Falls 422

Africa South of the Sahara: Climate
Regions 425

Africa South of the Sahara: Natural
Vegetation 426

Locating Places: Africa South of
the Sahara 431

Africa South of the Sahara: Major
Ethnic and Culture Groups 435

Early States 438

The African Slave Trade 439

Africa: Colonial Rule, 1914 441

Locating Places: Africa South of
the Sahara 449

Africa South of Sahara: Economic
Activity 453

Lagos 457

Hunger in Africa 459

Africa South of Sahara: Land Use 462

Locating Places: Africa South of
the Sahara 465

UNIT 8
SOUTH ASIA
South Asia: Political 470
South Asia: Population Density 471
South Asia: Physical Features 472
South Asia: Natural Resources 473
Comparing Lands: South Asia and
the United States 478
South Asia: Physical-Political 479
South Asia: Climate Regions 483
South Asia: Natural Vegetation 484
Locating Places: South Asia 489
Indus Valley Civilization 497
South Asian Empires 498
South Asia: Languages 502
South Asia: Religions 503
Locating Places: South Asia 509
South Asia: Economic Activity 514
The Himalayas 519
South Asian Monsoons 520
Locating Places: South Asia 525

UNIT 9
EAST ASIA
East Asia: Political 530
East Asia: Population Density 531, 566
East Asia: Physical Features 532
East Asia: Natural Resources 533
Comparing Lands: East Asia and
the United States 538
East Asia: Physical-Political 539
East Asia: Climate Regions 543
East Asia: Natural Vegetation 544
Taiwan 546
Locating Places: East Asia 549
Chinese Empires 557
The Japanese Empire, 1945 558
Hong Kong 560
Locating Places: East Asia 569
East Asia: Economic Activity 574, 582
Huang He 579
Tectonic Plates Near Japan 581
Locating Places: East Asia 585

UNIT 10
SOUTHEAST ASIA
Southeast Asia: Political 590
Southeast Asia: Population Density 591
Southeast Asia: Physical Features 592
Southeast Asia: Natural Resources 593
Comparing Lands: Southeast Asia and
the United States 598
Southeast Asia: Physical-Political 599
Philippine Volcanoes 600
Southeast Asia: Climate Regions 603
Southeast Asia: Natural Vegetation 604
Locating Places: Southeast Asia 609
Kingdoms and Trade Routes in Southeast
Asia, A.D. 100-1400 616
Foreign Colonies in Southeast
Asia, 1914 617
Angkor Wat 618
Singapore 619
Southeast Asia: Religions 620
Locating Places: Southeast Asia 627
Bali 630
Southeast Asia: Economic Activity 631
World Time Zones 640
Locating Places: Southeast Asia 643

UNIT 11
AUSTRALIA, OCEANIA, AND ANTARCTICA
Australia and Oceania:
Political 648
Australia and Oceania: Population
Density 649
Australia, Oceania, and Antarctica:
Physical 650
Australia, Oceania, and Antarctica:
Natural Resources 651
Comparing Lands: Australia, Oceania,
and Antarctica and the United States 656
Australia and Oceania:
Physical-Political 657
North Island of New Zealand 658
Australia, Oceania, and Antarctica:
Climate Regions 661
Australia, Oceania, and Antarctica:
Natural Vegetation 662
Transportation Routes in Australia 664

Locating Places: Australia and
  New Zealand   667
Australia and Oceania:
  Colonies, 1900   674
Locating Places: Australia   685
Fiji Islands   688

Australia and Oceania
  Economic Activity   689
Great Barrier Reef   693
Antarctica: National Claims and
  Scientific Stations   697
Locating Places: Antarctica   701

GRAPHS, TABLES, AND DIAGRAMS

Road Map Symbols   11
Global Gores   16
Wheat Production in Selected Countries
  (bar graph)   20
United States: Population Growth   20
World Land Areas   21
Wheat Production in Selected Countries
  (pictograph)   21
The Continents of the World   22
How the Moon Seems to Change Shape   22
The Solar System   28
Inside the Earth   29
California Earthquake:
  January 17, 1994   31
Landforms and Water Bodies   34
The Water Cycle   35
The Seasons in the Northern
  Hemisphere   46
Zones of Latitude and Wind Patterns   50
Rain Shadow   51
World Population Growth   65
How CFCs Destroy Ozone   73
Climate Graph: Tokyo, Japan and
  Mogadishu, Somalia   78
Population: Canada and the
  United States   87
United States: Physical Profile;
  Canada: Physical Profile   89

The St. Lawrence Seaway   91
Levees and Dams   97
Comparing Climate Regions: Canada
  and the United States   100
Ethnic Origins of Americans, Ethnic
  Origins of Canadians   108
The National Governments of the
  United States and Canada   117
The United States and Canada:
  Religions   121
The United States and Canada:
  Social Indicators   134
What's In Our Trash? (diagram)   142
Current Population Comparisons
  (cartogram)   144
Population: Latin America and the
  United States   153
South America: Physical Profile   155
Comparing Climate Regions: Argentina
  and the United States   168
Ethnic Groups in Selected Latin
  American Countries   176
Latin America: Religions   186
Cuba: Age Distribution; Uruguay:
  Age Distribution   190
Population: Europe and the
  United States   215
Europe: Physical Profile   217

Comparing Climate Regions: Europe and the United States   233

Europe: Religions   254

The European Union's Share in World Trade   264

Population: Russia and the Eurasian Republics and the United States   285

Russia: Physical Profile   287

Comparing Climate Regions: Russia and the United States   298

Russia and the Eurasian Republics: Religions   318

Population: Moldova and Tajikistan; Average Annual Population Growth Rate: Selected Nations   322

Population: North Africa and Southwest Asia and the United States   351

North Africa and Southwest Asia: Physical Profile   353

North Africa and Southwest Asia: Religions   382

Land Use in Selected Countries of North Africa and Southwest Asia   392

World Oil Reserves   394

Crude Oil Production in Selected Countries of North Africa and Southwest Asia   395

Comparing Selected Countries of North Africa and Southwest Asia   402

Population: Africa South of the Sahara and the United States   411

Africa South of the Sahara: Physical Profile   413

Africa South of the Sahara: Metropolitan Areas   436

Africa South of the Sahara: Religions   443

Ethnic Groups of Kenya; Languages of Kenya   446

Agricultural Workforce (Selected Countries)   452

Wildlife Reserves (Selected Countries)   460

Population: South Asia and the United States   471

South Asia: Physical Profile   473

Comparing Climate Regions: India and the United States   485

Population of Bangladesh by Age and Gender   493

South Asia: Religions   502

Pakistan and India: Population Growth   506

India's Agricultural and Food Production   513

Population: East Asia and the United States   531

China and the Korean Peninsula: Physical Profile   533

East Asia: Religions   562

Population of Japan by Age and Sex; Population of China by Age and Sex   573

Japan's Balance of Trade   575

Population: Southeast Asia and the United States   591

Mainland Southeast Asia: Physical Profile   593

Southeast Asia: Rural and Urban Population (Selected Countries)   612

Southeast Asia: Religions   621

Population: Australia, Oceania, and Antarctica and the United States   649

Australia: Physical Profile   651

Australia, Oceania, and Antarctica: Religions   679

Ethnic Groups of Australia   680

Comparative Data (Selected Nations)   682

REFERENCE
ATLAS

Contents

The World A2

United States.. A4

Canada A6

Mexico, the Caribbean, and
  Central America A8

North America A10

South America A11

Europe A12

Russia and the Eurasian Republics ... A14

The Middle East A16

South Asia A18

Africa... A19

East Asia A20

Southeast Asia.................................. A22

Oceania A24

The Pacific Rim A26

Polar Regions A28

World Facts... 1

ATLAS KEY

PACK ICE

ICE CAP

TUNDRA

MOUNTAINS

EVERGREEN FOREST

MIXED FOREST

GRASSLAND

ARID

Shallow water

Shallow water

Inland water

3000 meters

5000 meters

3000 meters

5000 meters

ATLAS KEY

OCEANS AND SEAS

SYMBOL KEY

⊛ National capital
★ State/province capital
● Major city
○ Other city

——— International boundary
----- Disputed boundary
·········· Undefined boundary
——— State/province/republic boundary

Non-subject
⊥⊥⊥ Canal/waterway
Waterfall
▲ Peak

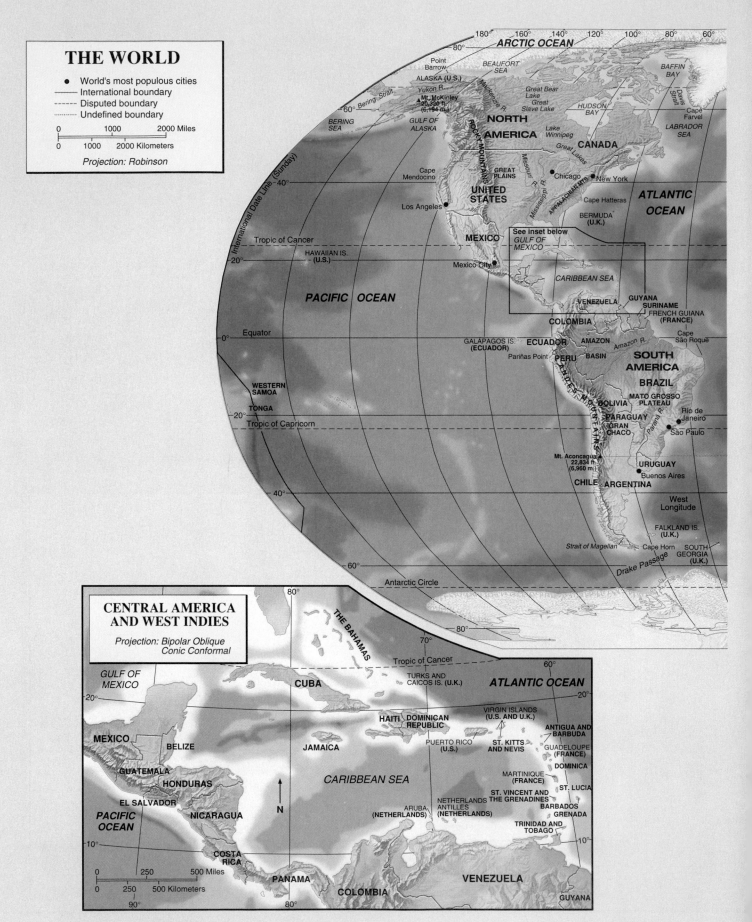

THE WORLD

- ● World's most populous cities
- ─── International boundary
- ----- Disputed boundary
- ········· Undefined boundary

0   1000   2000 Miles
0   1000   2000 Kilometers

Projection: Robinson

ARCTIC OCEAN

Point Barrow   BEAUFORT SEA   BAFFIN BAY

ALASKA (U.S.)   Great Bear Lake   Great Slave Lake   HUDSON BAY   Davis Strait

Bering Strait   Yukon R.   Mackenzie R.   Cape Farvel

Mt. McKinley 20,320 ft. (6,194 m.)   NORTH AMERICA   LABRADOR SEA

BERING SEA   GULF OF ALASKA   ROCKY MOUNTAINS   Lake Winnipeg   CANADA

Cape Mendocino   GREAT PLAINS   Great Lakes   Chicago   New York

International Date Line (Sunday)   UNITED STATES   Missouri R.   Mississippi R.   APPALACHIAN MTS.   Cape Hatteras   ATLANTIC OCEAN

Los Angeles   BERMUDA (U.K.)

Tropic of Cancer   MEXICO   See inset below   GULF OF MEXICO

HAWAIIAN IS. (U.S.)   Mexico City   CARIBBEAN SEA   GUYANA   SURINAME

PACIFIC OCEAN   VENEZUELA   FRENCH GUIANA (FRANCE)

COLOMBIA

Equator   GALÁPAGOS IS. (ECUADOR)   ECUADOR   AMAZON   Amazon R.   Cape São Roque

Pariñas Point   PERU   BASIN   SOUTH AMERICA

ANDES MOUNTAINS   BRAZIL

WESTERN SAMOA   MATO GROSSO PLATEAU

TONGA   BOLIVIA   Rio de Janeiro

PARAGUAY   Paraná R.

Tropic of Capricorn   GRAN CHACO   São Paulo

Mt. Aconcagua 22,834 ft. (6,960 m.)   URUGUAY

Buenos Aires

CHILE   ARGENTINA   West Longitude

FALKLAND IS. (U.K.)

Strait of Magellan   Cape Horn   SOUTH GEORGIA (U.K.)

Drake Passage

Antarctic Circle

CENTRAL AMERICA AND WEST INDIES

Projection: Bipolar Oblique Conic Conformal

GULF OF MEXICO   THE BAHAMAS   ATLANTIC OCEAN

CUBA   TURKS AND CAICOS IS. (U.K.)

Tropic of Cancer

MEXICO   VIRGIN ISLANDS (U.S. AND U.K.)   ANTIGUA AND BARBUDA

HAITI   DOMINICAN REPUBLIC

BELIZE   PUERTO RICO (U.S.)   ST. KITTS AND NEVIS

JAMAICA   GUADELOUPE (FRANCE)

GUATEMALA   DOMINICA

MARTINIQUE (FRANCE)   ST. LUCIA

HONDURAS   CARIBBEAN SEA   ST. VINCENT AND THE GRENADINES

EL SALVADOR   BARBADOS

N   GRENADA

PACIFIC OCEAN   NICARAGUA   ARUBA (NETHERLANDS)   NETHERLANDS ANTILLES (NETHERLANDS)   TRINIDAD AND TOBAGO

0   250   500 Miles
0   250   500 Kilometers

COSTA RICA

PANAMA   VENEZUELA

COLOMBIA   GUYANA

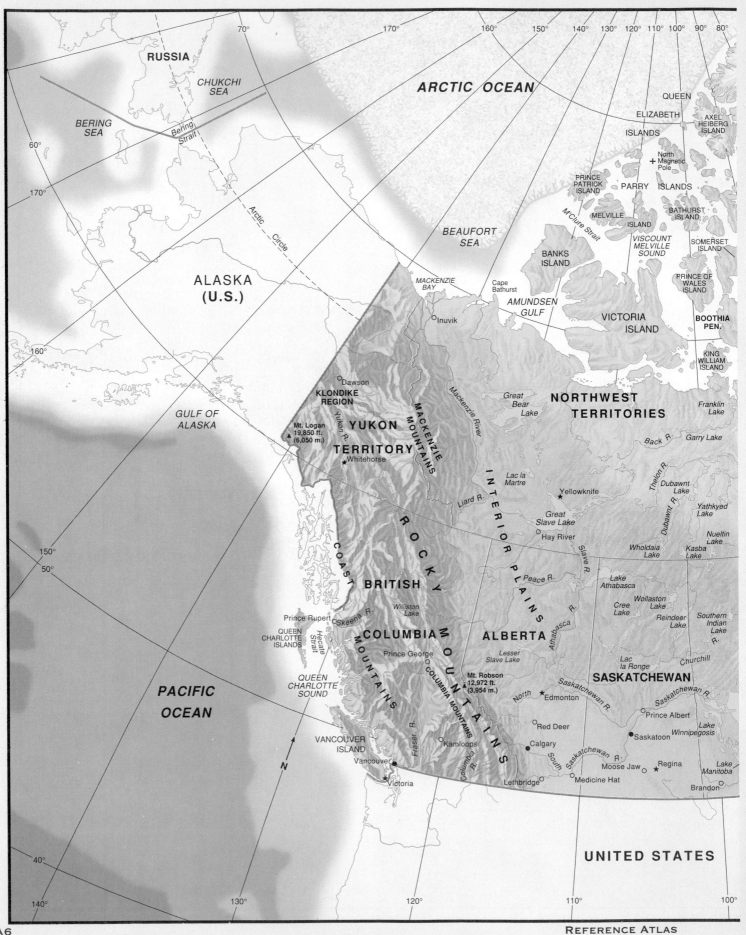

RUSSIA

CHUKCHI
SEA

BERING
SEA

Bering Strait

70°

170°

ARCTIC OCEAN

160° 150° 140° 130° 120° 110° 100° 90° 80°

QUEEN
ELIZABETH
ISLANDS

AXEL
HEIBERG
ISLAND

North
Magnetic
Pole

PRINCE
PATRICK
ISLAND

PARRY ISLANDS

MELVILLE
ISLAND

BATHURST
ISLAND

VISCOUNT
MELVILLE
SOUND

SOMERSET
ISLAND

M'Clure Strait

60°

170°

Arctic Circle

BEAUFORT
SEA

BANKS
ISLAND

AMUNDSEN
GULF

PRINCE OF
WALES
ISLAND

BOOTHIA
PEN.

Cape
Bathurst

ALASKA
(U.S.)

MACKENZIE
BAY

VICTORIA
ISLAND

160°

Inuvik

KING
WILLIAM
ISLAND

GULF OF
ALASKA

Dawson

KLONDIKE
REGION

Mt. Logan
19,850 ft.
(6,050 m.)

Yukon R.

YUKON

TERRITORY

Whitehorse

MACKENZIE MOUNTAINS

Mackenzie River

Great
Bear
Lake

NORTHWEST
TERRITORIES

Franklin
Lake

Back R.

Garry Lake

Thelon R.

Dubawnt
Lake

Yathkyed
Lake

INTERIOR PLAINS

Lac la
Martre

Yellowknife

Liard R.

Dubawnt R.

150°
50°

COAST

ROCKY

BRITISH

Great
Slave Lake

Hay River

Nueltin
Lake

Wholdaia
Lake

Kasba
Lake

Peace R.

Lake
Athabasca

Wollaston
Lake

Reindeer
Lake

Southern
Indian
Lake

Prince Rupert

QUEEN
CHARLOTTE
ISLANDS

Williston
Lake

Skeena R.

Hecate Strait

COLUMBIA

MOUNTAINS

Prince George

Lesser
Slave Lake

Mt. Robson
12,972 ft.
(3,954 m.)

COLUMBIA MOUNTAINS

ALBERTA

Athabasca R.

Cree
Lake

Lac
la Ronge

SASKATCHEWAN

Churchill

PACIFIC
OCEAN

QUEEN
CHARLOTTE
SOUND

MOUNTAINS

Fraser R.

Kamloops

Columbia R.

North Saskatchewan R.

Red Deer

Edmonton

Saskatchewan R.

Prince Albert

Lake
Winnipegosis

VANCOUVER
ISLAND

N

Vancouver

Victoria

Calgary

Saskatoon

Lethbridge

South Saskatchewan R.

Moose Jaw

Medicine Hat

Regina

Lake
Manitoba

Brandon

40°

140°

130°

120°

UNITED STATES

110°

100°

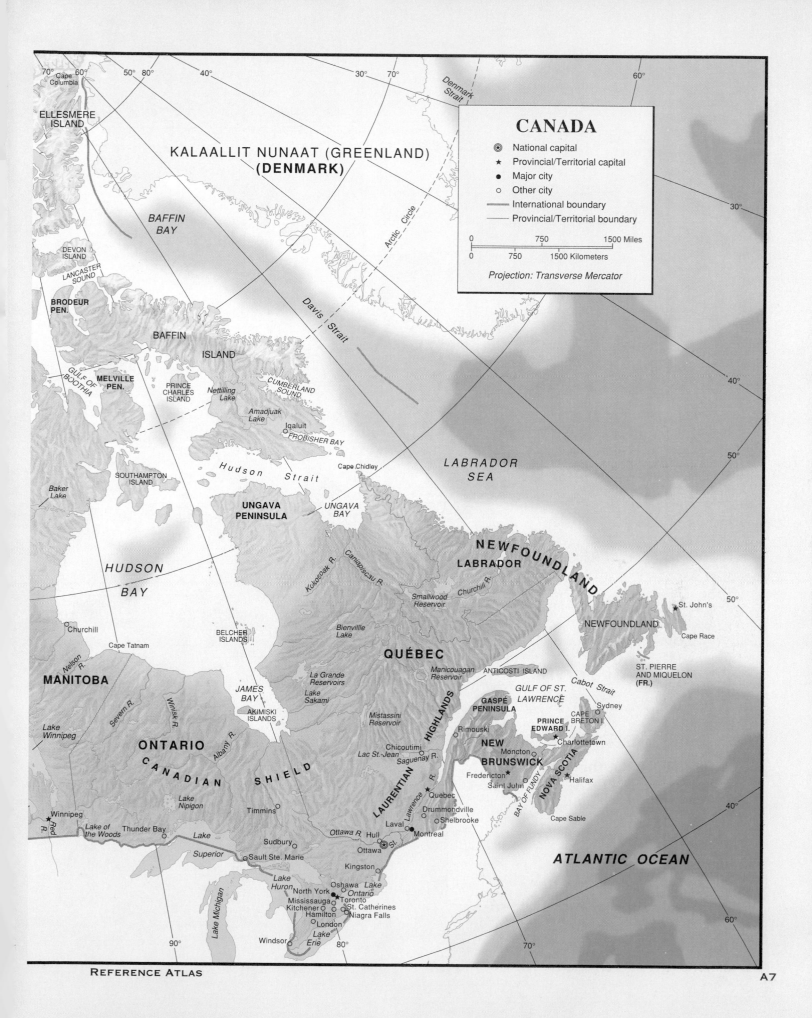

CANADA

- ⊛ National capital
- ★ Provincial/Territorial capital
- ● Major city
- ○ Other city
- ░░░ International boundary
- ── Provincial/Territorial boundary

| 0 | 750 | 1500 Miles |
| 0 | 750 | 1500 Kilometers |

Projection: Transverse Mercator

70° Cape Columbia 60° 50° 80° 40° 30° 70° Denmark Strait 60°

ELLESMERE ISLAND

KALAALLIT NUNAAT (GREENLAND) (DENMARK)

BAFFIN BAY

DEVON ISLAND

LANCASTER SOUND

BRODEUR PEN.

Arctic Circle 30°

BAFFIN ISLAND

GULF OF BOOTHIA

MELVILLE PEN.

PRINCE CHARLES ISLAND

Nettilling Lake

CUMBERLAND SOUND

Davis Strait 40°

Amadjuak Lake

Iqaluit ○ FROBISHER BAY

Baker Lake

SOUTHAMPTON ISLAND

Hudson Strait Cape Chidley

LABRADOR SEA 50°

UNGAVA PENINSULA

UNGAVA BAY

NEWFOUNDLAND

HUDSON BAY

LABRADOR

BELCHER ISLANDS

Smallwood Reservoir

Churchill R.

NEWFOUNDLAND

St. John's ★ 50°

Cape Race

Churchill ○

Cape Tatnam

Bienville Lake

QUÉBEC

Manicouagan Reservoir

ANTICOSTI ISLAND

Cabot Strait

ST. PIERRE AND MIQUELON (FR.)

MANITOBA

Nelson R.

Severn R.

Winisk R.

JAMES BAY

AKIMISKI ISLANDS

La Grande Reservoirs

Lake Sakami

Mistassini Reservoir

GASPÉ PENINSULA

GULF OF ST. LAWRENCE

Sydney ○

CAPE BRETON I.

Lake Winnipeg

ONTARIO

Albany R.

Rimouski ○

Chicoutimi ○

Lac St.-Jean

Saguenay R.

NEW BRUNSWICK

Moncton ○

PRINCE EDWARD I.

Charlottetown ★

CANADIAN SHIELD

Lake Nipigon

Timmins ○

LAURENTIAN HIGHLANDS

Fredericton ★

St. Lawrence R.

Quebec ★

Drummondville ○

Shelbrooke ○

Saint John ○

BAY OF FUNDY

NOVA SCOTIA

Halifax ★

Winnipeg ★

Red R.

Lake of the Woods

Thunder Bay ○

Lake Superior

Sudbury ○

Sault Ste. Marie ○

Ottawa R.

Hull ○

Laval ○

Montreal ●

Cape Sable

ATLANTIC OCEAN

40°

Ottawa ⊛

Kingston ○

Lake Michigan

Lake Huron

North York ●

Oshawa ○

Lake Ontario

Toronto ★

Mississauga ○

Kitchener ○

St. Catherines ○

Hamilton ○

Niagra Falls ○

London ○

Windsor ○

Lake Erie

80°

70°

60°

90°

MEXICO, the CARIBBEAN, and CENTRAL AMERICA

⊛ National capital
• Major city
— International boundary

0 ——— 250 ——— 500 Miles

0 ——— 250 ——— 500 Kilometers

Projection: Azimuthal Equal Area

**Labels on map:**

BAJA CALIFORNIA PENINSULA

GULF OF CALIFORNIA

SIERRA MADRE OCCIDENTAL

Ciudad Juárez

Chihuahua

MEXICAN PLATEAU

SIERRA MADRE ORIENTAL

Monterrey

Rio Grande

San Pedro River

Tampico

Tropic of Cancer

León

Guadalajara

MEXICO

Mexico City

Puebla

Balsas River

Veracruz

CAMPECHE BAY

GULF OF MEXICO

Mérida

YUCATÁN PENINSULA

SIERRA MADRE DEL SUR

PACIFIC OCEAN

N

Belize City

Belmopan

BELIZE

Dolores

GULF OF HONDURAS

GUATEMALA

El Progreso

Quezaltenango

Guatemala

Tegucigalpa

Santa Ana

San Salvador

EL SALVADOR

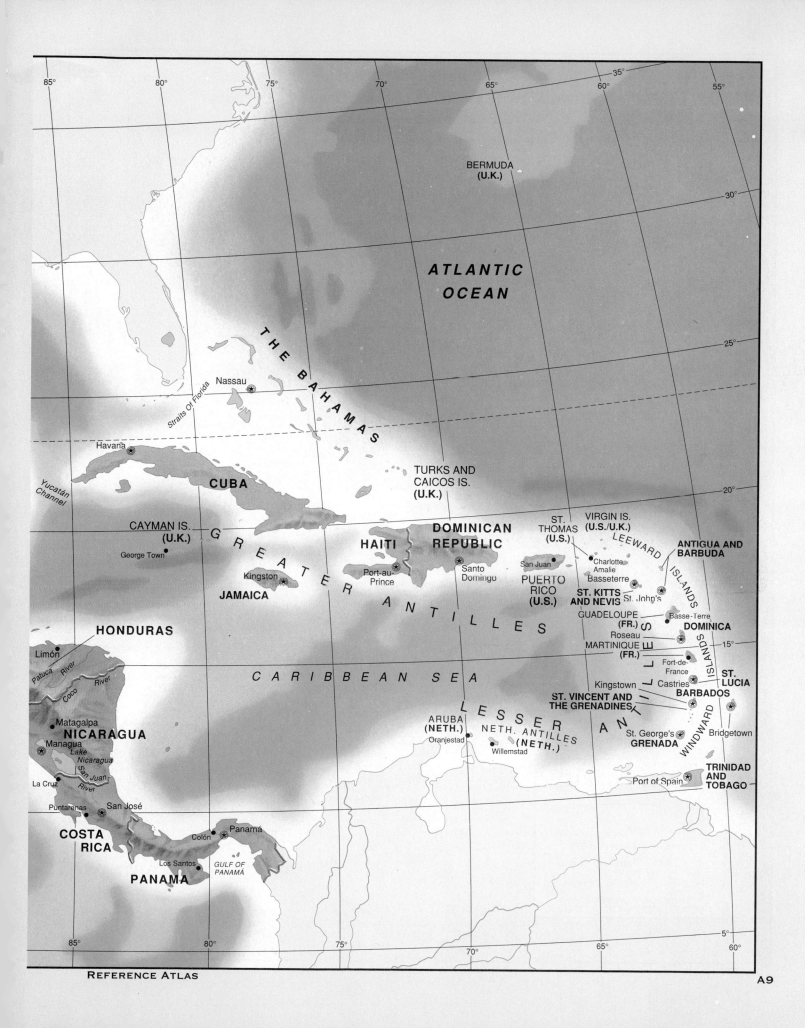

85°   80°   75°   70°   65°   60°   55°

35°

BERMUDA
(U.K.)

30°

ATLANTIC
OCEAN

25°

THE BAHAMAS

Nassau

Straits Of Florida

Havana

20°

Yucatán
Channel

CUBA

TURKS AND
CAICOS IS.
(U.K.)

CAYMAN IS.
(U.K.)

GREATER ANTILLES

DOMINICAN
REPUBLIC

HAITI

ST.
THOMAS
(U.S.)

VIRGIN IS.
(U.S./U.K.)

LEEWARD ISLANDS

ANTIGUA AND
BARBUDA

George Town

Kingston

Port-au-
Prince

Santo
Domingo

San Juan

Charlotte
Amalie

Basseterre

St. John's

JAMAICA

PUERTO
RICO
(U.S.)

ST. KITTS
AND NEVIS

GUADELOUPE
(FR.)

Basse-Terre

DOMINICA

HONDURAS

Limón

MARTINIQUE
(FR.)

Roseau

15°

Patuca   River

Coco   River

CARIBBEAN SEA

LESSER ANTILLES

Fort-de-
France

Castries

ST.
LUCIA

BARBADOS

Matagalpa

NICARAGUA

Kingstown

ST. VINCENT AND
THE GRENADINES

Managua
Lake
Nicaragua

ARUBA
(NETH.)

NETH. ANTILLES
(NETH.)

St. George's

WINDWARD

Bridgetown

San Juan
River

Oranjestad

GRENADA

La Cruz

Willemstad

TRINIDAD
AND
TOBAGO

Puntarenas

San José

Port of Spain

COSTA
RICA

Colón

Panamá

Los Santos

GULF OF
PANAMÁ

5°

PANAMA

85°   80°   75°   70°   65°   60°

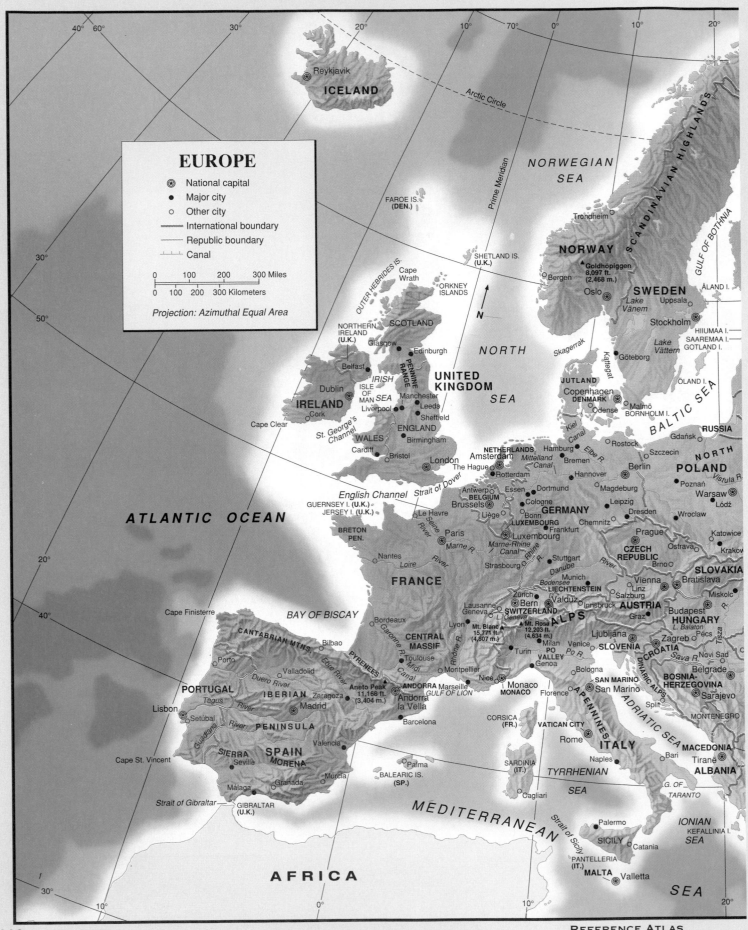

EUROPE

- ⊛ National capital
- ● Major city
- ○ Other city
- ⌗⌗⌗ International boundary
- —— Republic boundary
- ┼┼┼ Canal

0 100 200 300 Miles
0 100 200 300 Kilometers

Projection: Azimuthal Equal Area

ICELAND
Reykjavik

Arctic Circle

NORWEGIAN SEA

SCANDINAVIAN HIGHLANDS

Trondheim

NORWAY

▲ Goldhöpiggen
8,097 ft.
(2,468 m.)

GULF OF BOTHNIA

Bergen

SWEDEN

Oslo
Lake Vänem

Uppsala

ÅLAND I.

FAROE IS.
(DEN.)

SHETLAND IS.
(U.K.)

Cape Wrath

OUTER HEBRIDES IS.

ORKNEY ISLANDS

SCOTLAND

N

NORTHERN IRELAND
(U.K.)

Glasgow
Edinburgh

Belfast

IRISH SEA

PENNINE RANGE

UNITED KINGDOM

NORTH SEA

Skagerrak

Göteborg

Stockholm

Lake Vättern

HIIUMAA I.
SAAREMAA I.
GOTLAND I.

ÖLAND I.

Dublin

ISLE OF MAN

Manchester

IRELAND

Cork

Liverpool
Leeds
Sheffield

JUTLAND

Kattegat

Copenhagen
DENMARK

Malmö
BORNHOLM I.

BALTIC SEA

RUSSIA

Cape Clear

St. George's Channel

WALES

Cardiff

ENGLAND

Birmingham

Bristol

London

Kiel
Canal

Odense

Kiel

Rostock

Gdańsk

Szczecin

NORTH

POLAND

NETHERLANDS
Amsterdam

Hamburg
Elbe R.
Bremen

Berlin

Poznań

Warsaw

ATLANTIC OCEAN

English Channel

Strait of Dover

GUERNSEY I. (U.K.)
JERSEY I. (U.K.)

Le Havre
Seine River

The Hague
Rotterdam

Antwerp
BELGIUM
Brussels

Mittelland Canal

Essen
Dortmund

Liège
Cologne
Bonn

Hannover

Magdeburg

GERMANY

Leipzig

Dresden

Chemnitz

Łódź

Wrocław

Katowice

BRETON PEN.

Nantes

Loire River

Paris
Marne R.

LUXEMBOURG
Luxembourg

Frankfurt

Marne-Rhine Canal

Prague

CZECH REPUBLIC

Brno

Ostrava

Kraków

SLOVAKIA

FRANCE

Bordeaux

Garonne R.

CENTRAL MASSIF

Strasbourg

Stuttgart

Rhine R.

Danube River

Munich

Bodensee

Zürich

Bratislava

Linz

Vienna

Salzburg

Miskolc

BAY OF BISCAY

Cape Finisterre

Lyon

Mt. Blanc
15,771 ft.
(4,807 m.)

▲ Mt. Rosa
12,203 ft.
(4,634 m.)

ALPS

LIECHTENSTEIN

SWITZERLAND

Lausanne
Geneva
Bern

Valduz

Innsbruck

AUSTRIA

Graz

HUNGARY

Budapest

L. Balaton

Pécs

Tisza R.

CANTABRIAN MTNS.

Bilbao

PYRENEES

Toulouse
Canal du Midi

Montpellier

Nice

Turin

Milan

PO VALLEY

Po R.

Venice

Ljubljana

SLOVENIA

Zagreb

Sava R.

CROATIA

Novi Sad

Porto

PORTUGAL

Valladolid

Duero River

IBERIAN

Madrid

Zaragoza

Ebro River

Aneto Peak
11,168 ft.
(3,404 m.)

ANDORRA

Andorra la Vella

GULF OF LION

Marseille

Monaco
MONACO

Genoa

Bologna

Florence

SAN MARINO
San Marino

APENNINES

DINARIC ALPS

Belgrade

BOSNIA-HERZEGOVINA

Sarajevo

ADRIATIC SEA

Split

MONTENEGRO

Lisbon

Setúbal

Tagus River

PENINSULA

Guadiana River

SPAIN

SIERRA MORENA

Seville

Valencia

Barcelona

CORSICA
(FR.)

VATICAN CITY

Rome

ITALY

Naples

Bari

MACEDONIA

Tiranë

Cape St. Vincent

Granada

Murcia

Málaga

Palma

BALEARIC IS.
(SP.)

SARDINIA
(IT.)

TYRRHENIAN SEA

Cagliari

G. OF TARANTO

ALBANIA

IONIAN SEA

KEFALLINIA I.

Strait of Gibraltar

GIBRALTAR
(U.K.)

MEDITERRANEAN

Strait of Sicily

Palermo

SICILY

Catania

PANTELLERIA
(IT.)

MALTA
Valletta

AFRICA

SEA

North Cape
30° 40° 70° 50° 60° 70° 60° 80°

BARENTS SEA

Murmansk

KOLA PENINSULA

WHITE SEA

TIMAN RIDGE

Pechora R.

URAL MOUNTAINS

ASIA

Arkhangel'sk

Mt. Konzhakovskiy ▲
5,147 ft.
(1,569 m.)

N. Dvina River Vychegda River

White Sea-Baltic Waterway

FINLAND

Lake Onega

Sukhona River

Kama R.

Perm

Tampere
Lake Saimaa
Turku
Espoo Helsinki
St. Petersburg
GULF OF FINLAND
Tallinn
ESTONIA

Lake Ladoga

Volga-Baltic Waterway

Rybinsk Reservoir

Kama River

Ufa

70°

50°

Yaroslavl

Kazan

Chudskoye Lake

GULF OF RIGA

Volga River

Nizhniy Novgorod

Kuybyshev Reservoir

Orenburg

Ural River

LATVIA
Riga
W. Dvina River

EUROPEAN PLAIN

Volga-Baltic Waterway

Moscow

Samara

BALTIC PLAIN

LITHUANIA
Kaunas

Oka River

Tula

RUSSIA

VOLGA UPLAND

Volga River

Vilnius

Smolensk

CENTRAL RUSSIAN UPLAND

Saratov

Ural River

BELARUS
Minsk

Don R.

Kursk

Voronezh

Volgograd Reservoir

KAZAKSTAN

ARAL SEA

Pripet River

Desna R.

River

Volgograd

Volga River

DEPRESSION

Kiev

Kremenchug Reservoir

Kharkov

Tsimlyansk Reservoir

CASPIAN

Lvov

UKRAINE

Lugansk

Astrakhan

DNEIPER UPLAND

Dniester

Dnepropetrovsk

Donetsk

Don River

Delta of the Volga

40°

Krivoy Rog

Zaporozhye

Rostov

CASPIAN SEA

60°

MOLDOVA
Chisinau

DNIEPER LOWLAND
Prut River

Kakhovka Res.

Dnieper River

Debrecen

CARPATHIAN MTNS.

Odessa

SEA OF AZOV

Krasnodar

Grozny

Cluj-Napoca

CRIMEA

CAUCASUS MTNS.

ROMANIA
Timişoara
Braşov

Mt. Elbrus
18,510 ft.
(5,642 m.)

WALLACHIA PLAIN
Bucharest
Danube River

Constanta

BLACK SEA

SERBIA
Ruse

Niš
BULGARIA
Sofia Plovdiv
Burgas
Skopje Musala Peak
9,536 ft.
(2,926 m.)

Varna

Bosporus

PENINSULA TURKEY

Salonika

Dardanelles SEA OF MARMARA

BALKAN
Larissa

AEGEAN SEA

ASIA

GREECE

Patras Athens
Piraeus
PELOPONESE PEN.

RHODES

30°

CRETE (GR.)
Iráklion

30° 40° 50°

ARCTIC
OCEAN

FRANZ JOSEF
ISLANDS

E U R O P E

BARENTS SEA

Cape Zelaniya

Murmansk

BALTIC SEA

KOLA
PENINSULA

KARA SEA

GULF OF FINLAND

(RUSSIA)

Lake
Ladoga

Baltic-
White Sea
Canal

WHITE
SEA

Arkhangel'sk

Kara Strait

NOVAYA ZEMLYA

YAMAL
PEN.

St.
Petersburg

Lake Onega

GYDAN
PENINSULA

Minsk

VALDAI HILLS

Volga-Baltic
Waterway

N. Dvina

TIMAN RIDGE

Pechora River

Yenisey
River

BELARUS

Rybinsk Res.

Vologda

Sukhona R.

Vychegda

Lvov

DNIEPER
UPLAND

R.

Yaroslovl

NORTHERN HILLS

Ob River

WEST
SIBERIAN

Urengoy

Dnieper

Moscow

Ivanovo

Volga

Mt. Konzhakovskiy
5,147 ft.
(1,569 m.)

Kiev

Tula

DNIEPER
LOWLAND

Ryazan'

PLAIN

UKRAINE

Nizhniy Novgorod

Kamsk Res.

URAL

MOLDOVA

Chisinau

Kharkov

Kazan

Izhevsk

R.

Perm

Ob

Vakh

R.

Odessa

Nikolayev

Krivoy Rog

Voronezh

River

Ul'yanovsk

Kuybyshev Res.

Kama

Yekaterinburg

Dnepropetrovsk

Don

MOUNTAINS

Zaporozh'ye

VOLGA UPLAND

Saratov

Tol'yatti

Ufa

Tomsk

Donetsk

Lugansk

Penza

Chelyabinsk

Irtysh

R.

Mariupol

SEA OF
AZOV

Rostov

Samara

Tobol

River

Omsk

L. Chany

Kemerovo

BLACK
SEA

Volgograd
Reservoir

Volga

Ural

R.

Orenburg

Ishim

R.

Novosibirsk

Krasnodar

Tsimlyansk
Res.

Volgograd

Novosibirsk Res.
Novokuznetsk

CAUCASUS

CASPIAN DEPRESSION

Astrakhan

KYRGYZ

TURGAY
PLATEAU

Barnaul

Mt. Belukha
14,783 ft.
(4,506 m.)

Mt. Elbrus
18,510 ft.
(5,642 m.)

MTS.

STEPPE

KAZAKH

GEORGIA

KAZAKSTAN

Karaganda

UPLAND

Tbilisi

Semipalatinsk

ARMENIA

Yerevan

CASPIAN

ARAL
SEA

L. Zaysan

AZERBAIJAN

USTYURT
PLATEAU

Syr

BETPAK-DALA

AZERBAIJAN

Baku

SEA

Kzyl-Orda

Darya

Lake Balkhash

KARA BOGAZ
GOL GULF

PLAINS OF TURAN

DESERT

Ili R.

L. Alakol

A S I A

KARAKUM

Amu

Darya

UZBEKISTAN

Bishkek

Almaty

Ashkhabad

Tashkent

KYRGYZSTAN

TURKMENISTAN

Samarkand

L. Issyk-Kul

DESERT

Darya

ALAY MOUNTAINS

Dushanbe

Communism Pk.
24,590 ft.
(7,495 m.)

TAJIKISTAN

REFERENCE ATLAS

ARCTIC
OCEAN

+ North Pole

*CHUKCHI
SEA*

Bering Strait

BERING SEA

WRANGEL
ISLAND

80°   70°   60°   170°

CHUKOTSK
PEN.

Long Strait

KORYAK
MTNS.

EAST SIBERIAN
SEA

Anadyr R.

180°

KOLYMA
RANGE

NEW SIBERIAN
ISLANDS

Cherskiy

KOLYMA
PLAIN

Cape Arkticheski

SEVERNAYA
ZEMLYA

Sannikov Strait

Laptev Strait

Kolyma

170°

KARAGIN
ISLAND

Evensk

KOMANDORSKIY
ISLANDS

Vil'kitskiy Strait

LAPTEV SEA

River

SHELIKHOV
GULF

SREDINNY
RA.

TAYMYR
PEN.

BYRRANGA
MTNS.

CHERSKIY   RANGE

Indigirka

KAMCHATKA
PENINSULA

▲ Mt. Klyuchevsk
15,584 ft.
(4,750 m.)

L. Taymy

VERKHOYANSK

Verkhoyansk

S

River

160°

Noril'sk

Olenëk

Lena

RANGE

B

Magadan

Petropavlovsk-
Kamchatskiy

Kotuy R.

River

E

I

Cape Lopatka

CENTRAL SIBERIAN

Markha R.

Vilyuy R.

Yakutsk

R

SEA   OF   OKHOTSK

Tura Tunguska

Vilyuy

River

Vilyuysk
Reservoir

S

LENA PLATEAU

Cape Yelizavety

Lower

River

Aldan

SAKHALIN

150°

PLATEAU

River

ALDAN
MTNS.

Terpeniya Point

Yenisey

Angara

Vitim

STANOVOY RANGE

Uda R.

DZHUGDZHUR RA.

Tatar

ISLAND

KURIL

River

R.

STANOVOY
UPLAND

Komsomol'sk

Strait

ISLANDS

Lena

Bratsk

Lake
Baikal

R.

YABLONOVY RANGE

Amur

River

La Pérouse

Krasnoyarsk

Krasnoyarsk
Reservoir

Bratsk
Reservoir

Chita

R.

Khabarovsk

SIKHOTE-ALIN

Strait

RA.

140°

SAYAN

Irkutsk

Ulan-Ude

Shilka

L. Khanka

40°

MOUNTAINS

ALTAI MTNS.

ASIA

Vladivostok

SEA   OF   JAPAN

130°

RUSSIA AND
THE EURASIAN REPUBLICS

❂ National capital

● Major city

○ Other city

International boundary

0   250   500 Miles

0   250   500 Kilometers

Projection: Two-Point Equidistant

90°   100°   110°   120°   130°

30°

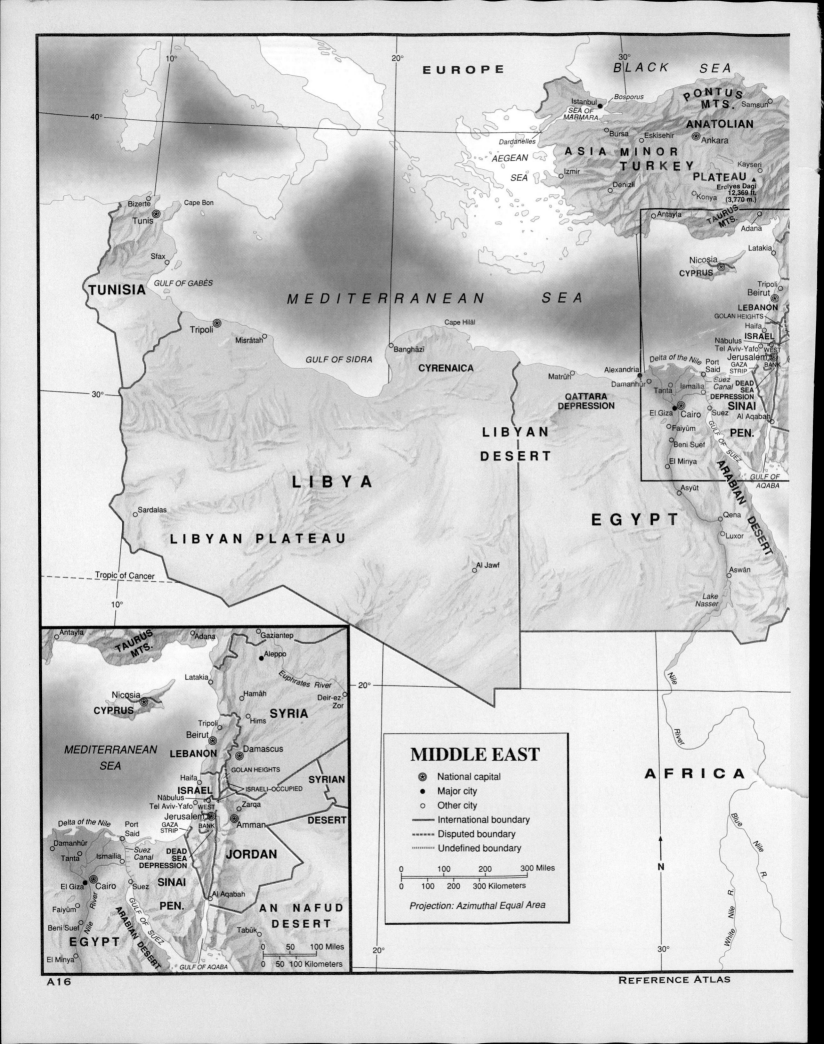

EUROPE

BLACK SEA

PONTUS MTS.

Samsun

Istanbul
SEA OF MARMARA
Bosporus

ASIA MINOR
TURKEY

ANATOLIAN

Bursa
Eskisehir
Ankara

Dardanelles

AEGEAN SEA

Izmir

Kayseri

Denizli

PLATEAU
Erciyes Dagi
12,369 ft.
(3,770 m.)

Konya

Antayla

TAURUS MTS.

Adana

MEDITERRANEAN   SEA

Latakia

Nicosia

CYPRUS

Tripoli
Beirut

LEBANON
GOLAN HEIGHTS

Haifa

ISRAEL

Nâbulus
Tel Aviv-Yafo
Jerusalem
WEST
BANK
GAZA STRIP

Bizerte
Cape Bon

Tunis

Sfax

GULF OF GABÈS

TUNISIA

Tripoli

Misrâtah

Cape Hilâl

Banghâzi

GULF OF SIDRA

CYRENAICA

Matrûh

Alexandria

Delta of the Nile

Port Said

Damanhûr

Tanta
Ismailia

Suez Canal

DEAD SEA DEPRESSION

SINAI
PEN.

El Giza   Cairo   Suez

Al Aqabah

LIBYAN
DESERT

QATTARA DEPRESSION

30°

LIBYA

Faiyûm

Beni Suef

El Minya

GULF OF SUEZ

ARABIAN DESERT

Sardalas

LIBYAN PLATEAU

EGYPT

Qena

Luxor

Al Jawf

Tropic of Cancer

10°

Aswân

Lake Nasser

Antayla

TAURUS MTS.

Adana
Gaziantep

Aleppo

Nicosia

Latakia

Euphrates River

CYPRUS

Hamâh

Deir-ez-Zor

MEDITERRANEAN SEA

Tripoli
Beirut

Hims

SYRIA

20°

Nile

Haifa

LEBANON

Damascus

GOLAN HEIGHTS

Nâbulus
Tel Aviv-Yafo
WEST
Jerusalem
BANK
GAZA STRIP

ISRAELI-OCCUPIED

Zarqa

SYRIAN

DESERT

AFRICA

Delta of the Nile
Damanhûr
Tanta

Port Said

Amman

Ismailia

Suez Canal

DEAD SEA DEPRESSION

JORDAN

N

El Giza   Cairo
Faiyûm

Suez

SINAI
PEN.

Al Aqabah

Beni Suef

EGYPT

Nile River

ARABIAN DESERT

GULF OF SUEZ

AN NAFUD DESERT

El Minya

Tabûk

GULF OF AQABA

Blue Nile R.

White Nile R.

Nile R.

MIDDLE EAST

⊛ National capital

● Major city

○ Other city

—— International boundary

----- Disputed boundary

········ Undefined boundary

0   100   200   300 Miles

0   100   200   300 Kilometers

Projection: Azimuthal Equal Area

0   50   100 Miles

0   50   100 Kilometers

20°

30°

ASIA

Trabzon

Erzurum • Mt. Ararat ▲
16,945 ft.
(5,165 m.)

Malatya

Diyarbakir
Lake
Van

Urmia
Lake
Urmia

Ardabīl

Tabrīz

Rasht

Mashhad •

ELBURZ MTNS.

Gaziantep

Aleppo •

Mosul

Irbīl

Kirkuk

Qazvin

Tehran ◎

▲ Mt. Demavend
18,386 ft.
(5,604 m.)

Hamāh

Deir-ez-
Zor

SYRIA

M
E
S
O
P
O
T
A
M
I
A

IRAQ

Hamadān

Qom

GREAT SALT DESERT

Hims •

Damascus ◎

SYRIAN

Tigris R.

Baghdad ◎

Bākhtarān

Arāk

ZAGROS

Esfahān •

PLATEAU

Bīrjand

ISRAELI-OCCUPIED

Euphrates R.

Karbalā

IRAN

OF

JORDAN

Zarqa

Al Hillah

Al Najaf

R.

An
Nāsirīyah

Ahvāz

MOUNTAINS

OF

Amman

DESERT

Abadan

Kermān

IRAN

Zāhedān

AN NAFUD
DESERT

Al Basrah

KUWAIT

Kuwait

Būshehr

Shīrāz

Tabūk

Hawalli

Al Ahmadī

See inset below

Ha'il

PERSIAN

NAJD PLATEAU

Buraydah

Ad Dammam

Manama ◎

BAHRAIN

GULF

Dubai

Bandar 'Abbās

Strait of Hormuz

GULF OF OMAN

RED

Madinah •

QATAR

Al Hufūf

Doha ◎

Abu
Dhabi •

Tropic of Cancer

Yanbu al Bahr

Riyadh ◎

UNITED ARAB
EMIRATES

Muscat ◎

Cape Al Hadd

SAUDI ARABIA

SEA

Jiddah

Makkah ◎

At Ta'if

ARABIAN PENINSULA

TUWAYQ MTS.

OMAN

RUB AL
KHALI

Duqm •

ĀSĪR MOUNTAINS

San'a ◎

▲ Mt. Nabī Shu'ayb
12,336 ft.
(3,760 m.)

YEMEN

Al Ghaydah

Salālah •

ARABIAN SEA

Al Hudaydah

Ta'izz •

Al Mukallā

Bab el Mandeb

Aden •

Lake
Tana

GULF OF ADEN

Cape Asir

SOCOTRA
(YEMEN)

SOUTH ASIA

⊛ National capital
● Major city
○ Other city
—— International boundary
----- Disputed boundary

0   250   500 Miles
0   250   500 Kilometers

Projection: Mercator

Mazār-i-Sharīf
HINDU KUSH
KARAKORAM RANGE
Godwin Austen Pk. (K-2)
28,251 ft.
(8,611 m.)
Herāt
⊛ Kabul
AFGHANISTAN
Peshāwar
Srīnagar
Rāwalpindi
⊛ Islāmābād
Siālkot
Jhelum R.
Gujrānwāla
Sargodha
Amritsar
Faisalabad
Lahore
Ravi R.
Quetta
Multān
SULAIMĀN RANGE
Sutlej River
Helmand River
Qandahār
PAKISTAN
BALUCHISTAN
THAR
DESERT
Delhi
⊛ New Delhi
Yamuna River
GANGES
Jaipur
Āgra
HIMALAYAS
Mt. Dhaulagiri
26,971 ft.
(8,221 m.)
NEPAL
Mt. Everest
29,028 ft.
(8,848 m.)
Mt. Kanchenjunga
28,208 ft.
(8,598 m.)
Kathmandu
⊛ Thimpu
BHUTAN
PĀTKAI
RANGE
Sukkur
Indus River
CENTRAL MAKRĀN RANGE
Hyderābād
Kānpur
Lucknow
Ghāghara River
Ganges River
Patna
Vārānasi
PLAIN
Brahmaputra River
Guwāhāti
Sylhet
Imphāl
Sonmiāni
Bay
Karāchi
RANN OF
KUTCH
Tropic of Cancer
GULF OF KUTCH
KĀTHIĀWAR
PENINSULA
Ahmadābād
Gāndhi
Reservoir
INDIA
VINDHYA RANGE
Indore
Narmada River
RANGE
Govind Ballaldh
Pant Res.
BANGLADESH
Dhaka
Haora
Calcutta
Khulna
Barisāl
Karnaphuli
Reservoir
Chittagong
Vadodara
SĀTPURA
Mahānadi River
Delta of The Ganges
(Sundarbans)
GULF OF
KHAMBHĀT
Sūrat
Tāpti River
DECCAN
Nāgpur
Palmyras
Point
Bombay
Pune
Godāvari River
PLATEAU
BAY OF
BENGAL
Solāpur
Bhima River
Hyderābād
Vishākhapatnam
ARABIAN
SEA
Krishna River
Vijayawāda
HINDUSTAN
N
WESTERN GHATS
Bangalore
EASTERN GHATS
Madras
Coromandel Coast
NORTH ANDAMAN
MIDDLE ANDAMAN
SOUTH ANDAMAN
ANDAMAN IS.
(INDIA)
LACCĀDIVE IS.
(INDIA)
Coimbatore
Calicut
Malabar
Madurai
Palk Strait
Point Calimere
Point Pedro
Jaffna
ANDAMAN
SEA
Cochin
Trincomalee
LACCADIVE
Coast
Cape
Comorin
GULF
OF
MANNAR
SRI
LANKA
Colombo ⊛
Dehiwala
NICOBAR IS.
(INDIA)
SEA
Moratuwa
Cape Dondra
GREAT
NICOBAR I.
⊛ Male
MALDIVES
Equator
INDIAN OCEAN

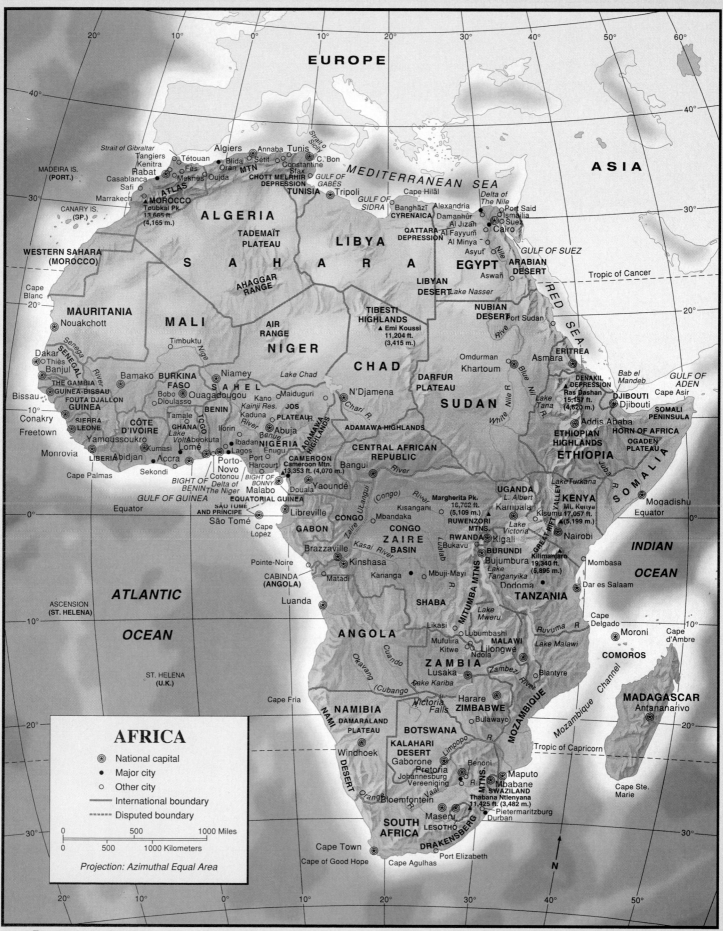

AFRICA

- ⊛ National capital
- ● Major city
- ○ Other city
- —— International boundary
- ----- Disputed boundary

Scale:
500 — 1000 Miles
500 — 1000 Kilometers

Projection: Azimuthal Equal Area

80°   90°   100°   110°

50°

L. Uvs
Ulaangom
L. Hyargas
ALTAI SHAN
L. Har Us
Dund-Us
Ertix L. Har
He (Irtysh R.)
Ulungur

L. Hövsgöl
Sühbaatar
Orhon R.
Ulaanbaatar ✪
Uliastay

MONGOLIA

DZUNGARIAN BASIN
Karamay
L. Ebinur

Bayanhongor

MONGOLIAN
PLATEAU

Ürümqi

TURFAN
DEPRESSION

Dalandzadgad

G O B I

TIAN SHAN
Pobedy Pk.
24,406 ft.
(7,439 m.)
He
L. Bosten
Tarim
Kongi He
Lop Nur

Kashi
Kongur Pk.
25,324 ft.
▲ (7,719 m.)
Yarkant He
Hotan He

Yumen
QILIAN
Mt. Qilian
18,198 ft.
▲ (5,547 m.)
SHAN
L. Har

CHINA

Yinchuan
HUANGTU
PLATEAU

TAKLIMAKAN
ALTUN SHAN
QAIDAM
BASIN
L.
Qinghai
Huang
Xining
He
Lanzhou

Godwin Austin Pk. (K-2)
28,251 ft.
▲ (8,611 m.)
KUNLUN SHAN
Golmud
A'NYÊMAQÊN SHAN

Jing He
Wei He
QIN LING

HOH XIL SHAN
L.
Ulan Ul
BAYAN HAR SHAN
Jinsha
Jiang
Yalong
Min Jiang

PLATEAU OF XIZANG

Jiang

T I B E T
TANGGULA SHAN
Siling L.
Nam L.

Chengdu
Jialing Jiang
SICHUAN
BASIN

H I M A L A Y A S
Mapam
L. Zhari
L. Tangra
Yarlung
Lhasa
Jiang
Zangbo
Mt. Everest
29,028 ft.
▲ (8,848 m.)
Mt. Kanchenjunga
28,208 ft.
▲ (8,598 m.)
Yamzho
L.
(Brahmaputra R.)
Nu Jiang
HENGDUAN SHAN
Mt. Gongga
24,790 ft.
(7,556 m.)
Chongqing

YUNGUI
Guiyang
PLATEAU
Kunming

Yuan Jiang
Nanpan Jiang
(Red R.)
You Jiang
Nanning

(Salween R.)

30°

BAY OF
BENGAL

20°

GULF
OF
TONKIN

80°   90°   100°

A20

EAST ASIA

- National capital
- Major city
- Other city
- International boundary

0   150   300 Miles
0 150 300 Kilometers

Projection: Robinson

SOUTHEAST ASIA

NEPAL
BHUTAN
CHINA
BANGLADESH
Tropic of Cancer
INDIA

90°
100°
110°

Chindwin R.

MYANMAR
Mandalay
Myingyan
R.
ARAKAN MTNS.
Irrawaddy
20°
Chiang Mai
LAOS
Red R.
Hanoi
Haiphong
GULF OF TONKIN

River
Salween
Vientiane
Black R.
I
N
D
O
C
H
I
N
A

Nan R.
ANNAMESE CORD.

Henzada
Pegu
KHORAT
PLATEAU
Mekong
Hue
Da Nang

Bassein
Yangon
Moulmein
THAILAND
Nakhon
Ratchasima
Savannakhet
VIETNAM

C. Negrais
GULF OF
MARTABAN
Chao Praya
Ping R.
Ubon
Ratchathani
River

Preparis
Channel
Tavoy
Krung Thep
(Bangkok)
Qui-Nhon

Coco Channel
Thonburi
CAMBODIA
Tonle Sap
Nha-Trang

ANDAMAN
ISLANDS
ANDAMAN
SEA
Phnom
Penh
Ho Chi Minh City

GULF OF
THAILAND
Long Xuyen

10°
ISTHMUS
OF
KRA
Pt. Bai Bung

SRI LANKA
NICOBAR
ISLANDS
Hat Yai
SOUTH CHINA
SEA

INDIAN
OCEAN
Great
Channel
George Town
MALAY
Ipoh
MALAYSIA

NATUNA
ISLANDS

PENINSULA
Kuala
Lumpur
ANAMBAS
IS.

Medan
C. Datu

Strait of Malacca

L. Toba
Johor Baharu
SINGAPORE
Singapore
Kapuas R.
Equator
0°
SUMATRA
Pontianak

Pekanbaru
Karimata Strait

Padang
BARISAN
Jambi

MTNS.
Palembang
JAVA
SEA

SOUTHEAST ASIA
⊚ National capital
● Major city
○ Other city
—— International boundary

0   200   400 Miles
0   200   400 Kilometers

Projection: Mercator

Sunda Strait
Jakarta
Bandung
JAVA
Surakarta
Semarang
Yogyakarta

10°

90°
100°
110°

A22

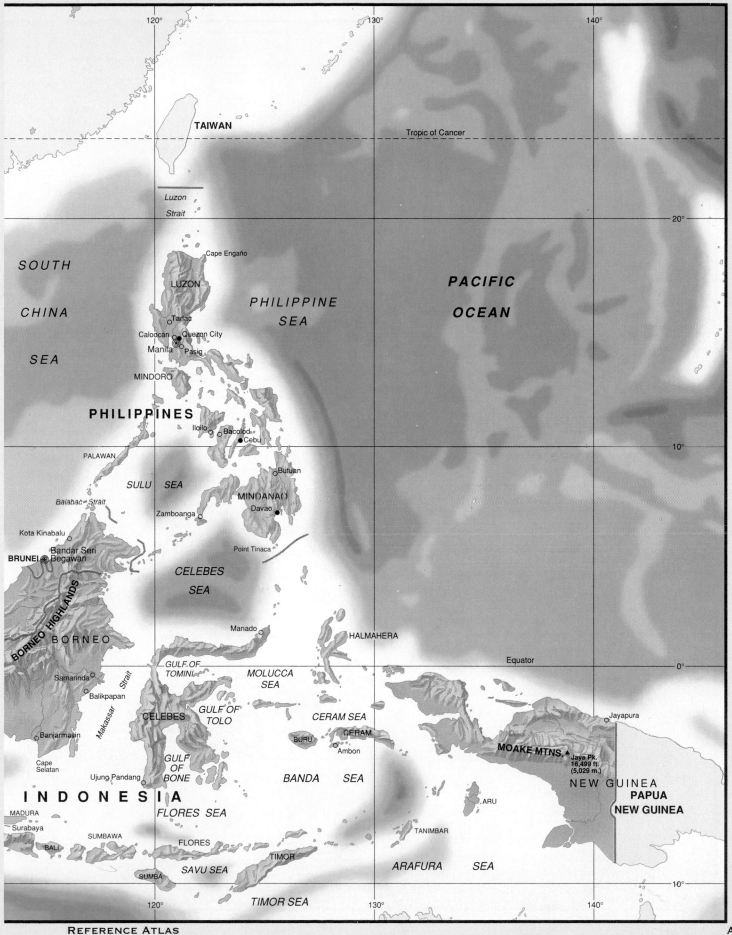

120° 130° 140°

TAIWAN

Tropic of Cancer

Luzon
Strait

20°

SOUTH

CHINA

SEA

Cape Engaño

LUZON

PHILIPPINE
SEA

PACIFIC

OCEAN

Tarlac
Caloocan Quezon City
Manila Pasig

MINDORO

PHILIPPINES

Iloilo Bacolod
Cebu

10°

PALAWAN

Butuan

SULU   SEA

MINDANAO

Balabac Strait

Zamboanga

Davao

Kota Kinabalu

Point Tinaca

Bandar Seri
BRUNEI Begawan

CELEBES

SEA

BORNEO HIGHLANDS

B O R N E O

Manado

HALMAHERA

Equator

0°

Samarinda

GULF OF
TOMINI

MOLUCCA
SEA

Makassar Strait

Balikpapan

GULF OF
TOLO

CERAM SEA

CELEBES

CERAM

Banjarmasin

BURU

Ambon

MOAKE MTNS.
Jaya Pk.
16,499 ft.
(5,029 m.)

Jayapura

Cape
Selatan

GULF
OF
BONE

Ujung Pandang

BANDA   SEA

N E W   G U I N E A

PAPUA
NEW GUINEA

I N D O N E S I A

FLORES SEA

ARU

MADURA

Surabaya

SUMBAWA

FLORES

TANIMBAR

BALI

TIMOR

ARAFURA   SEA

10°

SUMBA

SAVU SEA

TIMOR SEA

120° 130° 140°

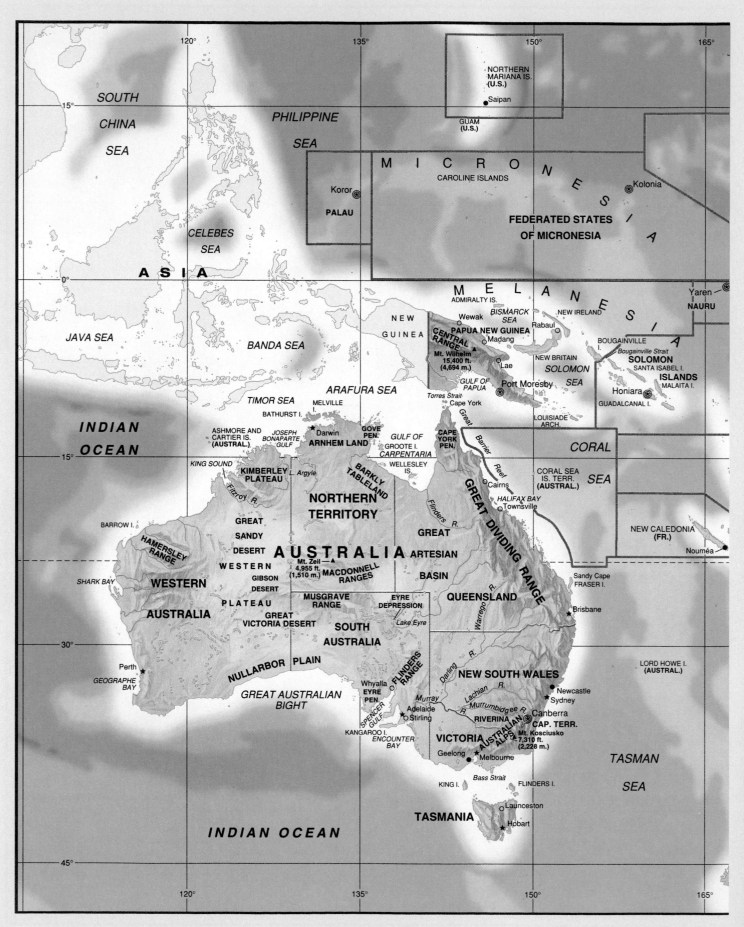

SOUTH
CHINA
SEA

PHILIPPINE

SEA

NORTHERN
MARIANA IS.
(U.S.)
• Saipan

GUAM
(U.S.)

15°

MICRONESIA

CAROLINE ISLANDS

⊛Kolonia

Koror⊛

PALAU

FEDERATED STATES

OF MICRONESIA

MICRONESIA

CELEBES
SEA

ASIA

0°

MELANESIA

Yaren ⊛
NAURU

ADMIRALTY IS.

NEW
GUINEA

BISMARCK
SEA

NEW IRELAND

JAVA SEA

BANDA SEA

Wewak
CENTRAL
RANGE
PAPUA NEW GUINEA
• Madang
Rabaul
○

BOUGAINVILLE
I.
Bougainville Strait

SOLOMON
SANTA ISABEL I.

INDIAN
OCEAN

TIMOR SEA

ARAFURA SEA

Mt. Wilhelm
15,400 ft.
(4,694 m.)
▲
NEW BRITAIN
• Lae
SOLOMON
SEA
ISLANDS
MALAITA I.

BATHURST I.
MELVILLE
I.

GULF OF
PAPUA
⊛ Port Moresby
Honiara ⊛

Torres Strait
Cape York
GUADALCANAL I.

LOUISIADE
ARCH.

15°

ASHMORE AND
CARTIER IS.
(AUSTRAL.)

JOSEPH
BONAPARTE
GULF
★ Darwin
GOVE
PEN.
GULF OF
CAPE
YORK
PEN.
Great

ARNHEM LAND
GROOTE I.
CARPENTARIA
Barrier

CORAL

CORAL SEA
IS. TERR.
(AUSTRAL.)

SEA

KING SOUND

KIMBERLEY
PLATEAU
L. Argyle
BARKLY
TABLELAND
WELLESLEY
IS.
Reef

Fitzroy R.

NORTHERN

TERRITORY

Flinders
R.

HALIFAX BAY
○ Townsville
Cairns
○

NEW CALEDONIA
(FR.)

BARROW I.

GREAT

GREAT

Nouméa
●

HAMERSLEY
RANGE

SANDY

AUSTRALIA
ARTESIAN

DIVIDING RANGE

SHARK BAY

DESERT

Mt. Zeil ▲
4,955 ft.
(1,510 m.) MACDONNELL
RANGES

BASIN

Sandy Cape
FRASER I.

WESTERN

GIBSON

WESTERN

DESERT

MUSGRAVE
RANGE
EYRE
DEPRESSION

Warrego R.

QUEENSLAND
● Brisbane

AUSTRALIA

PLATEAU
GREAT
VICTORIA DESERT
Lake Eyre
SOUTH

LORD HOWE I.
(AUSTRAL.)

30°

Perth
●
NULLARBOR
PLAIN
AUSTRALIA
Darling R.
NEW SOUTH WALES

GEOGRAPHE
BAY

FLINDERS
RANGE
Lachlan
R.
● Newcastle
Sydney ★

GREAT AUSTRALIAN

Whyalla
EYRE
PEN.

Murrumbidgee R.

BIGHT
Murray
R.
RIVERINA
Canberra
AUSTRALIAN ALPS CAP. TERR.

SPENCER
GULF
Adelaide
○ Stirling
★
Mt. Kosciusko
7,310 ft.
(2,228 m.)

KANGAROO I.
VICTORIA
ENCOUNTER
BAY
Geelong
○ ● Melbourne

TASMAN

SEA

KING I.
Bass Strait
FLINDERS I.

INDIAN OCEAN

TASMANIA
○ Launceston
★ Hobart

15°

120°

135°

150°

165°

45°

120°

135°

150°

165°

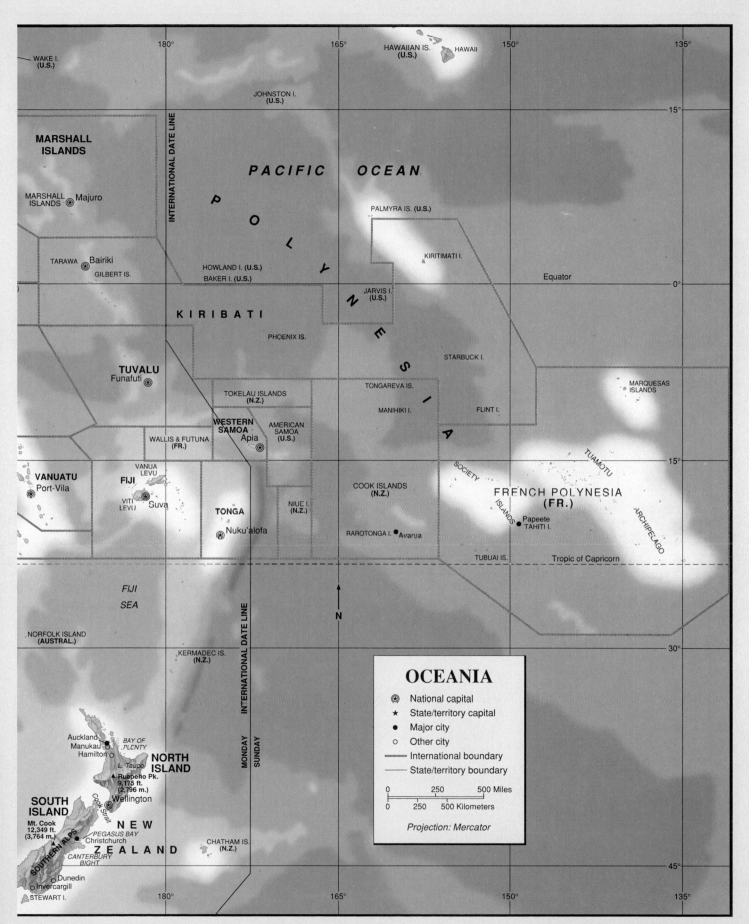

WAKE I.
(U.S.)

HAWAIIAN IS. HAWAII
(U.S.)

JOHNSTON I.
(U.S.)

180° 165° 150° 135°

15°

**MARSHALL
ISLANDS**

PACIFIC OCEAN

MARSHALL Majuro
ISLANDS

PALMYRA IS. (U.S.)

P
O
L
Y
N
E
S
I
A

TARAWA Bairiki
GILBERT IS.

KIRITIMATI I.

HOWLAND I. (U.S.)
BAKER I. (U.S.)

Equator 0°

JARVIS I.
(U.S.)

KIRIBATI

PHOENIX IS.

STARBUCK I.

TUVALU
Funafuti

TOKELAU ISLANDS
(N.Z.)

TONGAREVA IS.

MARQUESAS
ISLANDS

**WESTERN
SAMOA**
Apia

AMERICAN
SAMOA
(U.S.)

MANIHIKI I.

FLINT I.

WALLIS & FUTUNA
(FR.)

VANUATU
Port-Vila

VANUA
LEVU

SOCIETY

TUAMOTU

15°

FIJI

VITI
LEVU   Suva

NIUE I.
(N.Z.)

COOK ISLANDS
(N.Z.)

**FRENCH POLYNESIA
(FR.)**

ISLANDS

Papeete
TAHITI I.

ARCHIPELAGO

TONGA
Nuku'alofa

RAROTONGA I. Avarua

TUBUAI IS. Tropic of Capricorn

*FIJI
SEA*

INTERNATIONAL DATE LINE

N

NORFOLK ISLAND
(AUSTRAL.)

KERMADEC IS.
(N.Z.)

30°

INTERNATIONAL DATE LINE

MONDAY   SUNDAY

OCEANIA

⊛ National capital
★ State/territory capital
● Major city
○ Other city
── International boundary
── State/territory boundary

0   250   500 Miles
0   250   500 Kilometers

Projection: Mercator

Auckland
Manukau
Hamilton

BAY OF
PLENTY

**NORTH
ISLAND**

L. Taupo

▲ Ruapehu Pk.
9,175 ft.
(2,796 m.)

Wellington

**SOUTH
ISLAND**

Cook Strait

Mt. Cook
12,349 ft.
(3,764 m.)

PEGASUS BAY
Christchurch

N E W

SOUTHERN ALPS

CANTERBURY
BIGHT

Z E A L A N D

CHATHAM IS.
(N.Z.)

○ Dunedin
○ Invercargill

STEWART I.

45°

180° 165° 150° 135°

A26

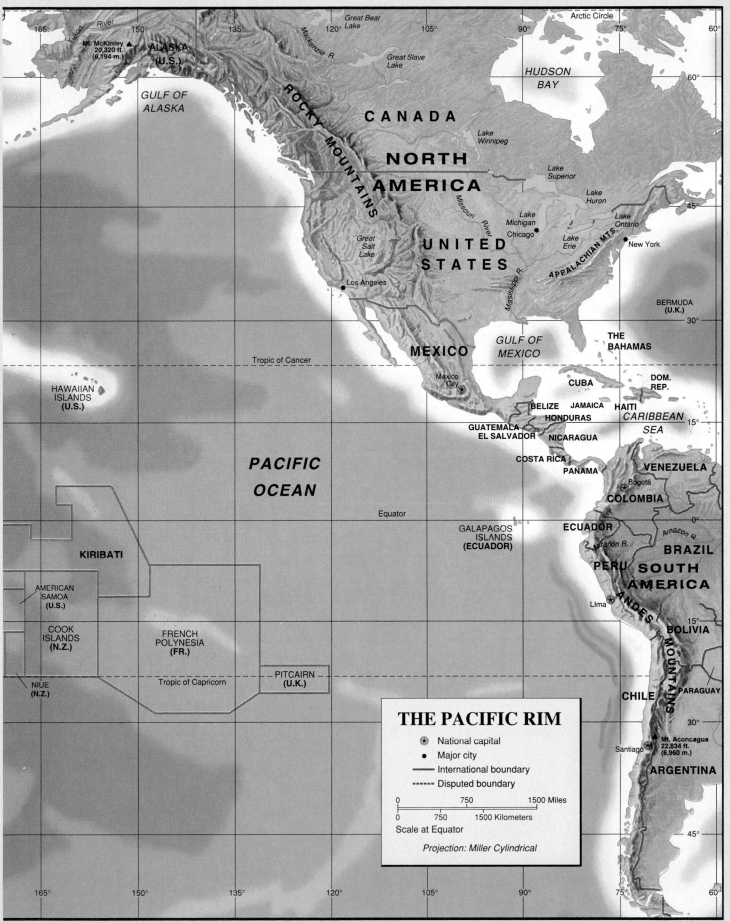

THE PACIFIC RIM

⊛ National capital
● Major city
── International boundary
----- Disputed boundary

| 0 | 750 | 1500 Miles |
| 0 | 750 | 1500 Kilometers |

Scale at Equator

Projection: Miller Cylindrical

POLAR REGIONS

○ City and town

—•— International boundary

0   250   500   750 Miles
0   250   500   750 Kilometers

Projection: Polar Azimuthal Equidistant

World Facts

WHAT IS THE . . .	ANSWER	LOCATION	SIZE
largest continent?	Asia	Eastern Hemisphere	17,400,000 sq. miles
smallest continent?	Australia	South Pacific	2,941,290 sq. miles
largest nation?	Russia and the Russian Federation	Europe-Asia	6,592,800 sq. miles
smallest nation?	Vatican City	Europe	.17 sq. miles
largest ocean?	Pacific		64,186,300 sq. miles
longest river?	Nile	East Africa	4,160 miles long
largest lake?	Caspian Sea	Eurasia	143,244 sq. miles
deepest lake?	Baikal	Asia	5,315 feet deep
highest mountain?	Mt. Everest	Nepal-Tibet	29,028 feet high
highest waterfall?	Angel Falls	Venezuela	3,212 feet high
largest desert?	Sahara	North Africa	3,500,000 sq. miles
highest continental point?	Mt. Everest	Nepal-Tibet	29,028 feet high
lowest continental point?	Dead Sea	Israel-Jordan	1,312 feet below sea level

Looking at the World

GeoJournal Activity

While studying world geography, think like a geographer. Take note of where things occur. Observe and describe the human and physical characteristics of places where you go. See how people have affected the environment and how the environment affects people.

David Doubilet

How Geographers Look at the World

CHAPTER FOCUS

Geographic Setting

The surface of the earth varies from place to place in terms of its physical features, climate, and resources. The people who inhabit our world vary as well.

Geographic Themes

Geographers use five geographic themes to analyze the earth and its patterns:

LOCATION "Where is it?"

PLACE "What is it like there?"

HUMAN/ENVIRONMENT INTERACTION "What is the relationship between people and their environment?"

MOVEMENT "How are people and places connected?"

REGION "How is a place similar to and different from other places?"

▲ Photograph: *Golden Gate Bridge, San Francisco, California*

NATIONAL GEOGRAPHIC SOCIETY

Picturing the World

A diver inspects a school of cardinalfish swimming through a forest of wire coral off the coast of Japan. Seventy percent of our planet is covered by water and only three percent of that is freshwater. The salty oceans contain most of the earth's water. To date, we have explored less than one percent of the deep seafloor. Look at the map on pages A2-A3.

1. Name the four oceans of the world.
2. What is the largest sea in Europe?
3. Now look at the photograph on page 26. What is the name of the large sea in the center of the photograph?

Picture Atlas CD-ROM Enrichment Corner

Create a file of ocean information. (See the *Picture Atlas of the World* User's Guide on how to use the Collector but-ton.) Include the essays for all the oceans and the caption in the western Pacific Ocean off the coast of Ecuador. Then answer the following questions:

1. What is the largest and deepest ocean in the world?
2. What ocean current brings warmth and moisture to Europe?
3. What is the name of the mountains on the floor of the Atlantic Ocean?
4. Which ocean is ringed by North America, Europe, and Asia?
5. What is the name of the system of warm water currents sometimes occurring in the eastern Pacific off the coast of Ecuador?

1 Themes of Geography

SETTING THE SCENE

Read to Discover . . .
- what geography is.
- how geographers see the world.
- how geography relates to other disciplines and to you personally.

Key Terms
- geography
- absolute location
- hemisphere
- latitude
- longitude
- grid system
- relative location
- interdependent
- culture

Identify and Locate
Equator, Tropic of Cancer, Tropic of Capricorn, Prime Meridian

The study of the earth and of the ways people live and work on it is called **geography.** The word "geography" comes from the Greek word *geographia*, which means "a description of the earth." Geographers are people who study the earth. They study the way places on the earth differ and the ways people organize themselves and use the earth's resources. Geography also deals with the location of these places and the complex relationships between people and their environments.

Five Geographic Themes

The study of geography can be organized around five themes: location, place, human/environment interaction, movement, and region. These five themes offer a structured way of thinking about the world and can be used to study all kinds of geographic issues at local, national, and global levels.

Location

The theme of location is concerned with the question "Where is it?" Geographers study the location and distribution of almost everything on the surface of the earth. The **absolute location** of a place—its precise position on the globe—is an important part of their study.

To determine absolute location, geographers use a network of imaginary lines around the earth. The Equator is an important line that circles the earth midway between the North Pole and the South Pole. It divides the earth into **hemispheres,** or two halves. The Northern Hemisphere includes all of the land and water between the Equator and the North Pole. The Southern Hemisphere includes all of the land and water between the Equator and the South Pole.

Latitude

Other imaginary lines called lines of **latitude,** or parallels, circle the earth parallel to the Equator and measure the distance north or south of the Equator in degrees. The Equator is measured at 0° latitude, while the Poles lie at latitudes 90° N (north) and 90° S (south).

Two lines of latitude are important indicators to geographers—the Tropic of Cancer located at 23½° N, and the Tropic of Capricorn at 23½° S. Because the earth is tilted 23½° in its revolutions around the sun, these two lines of

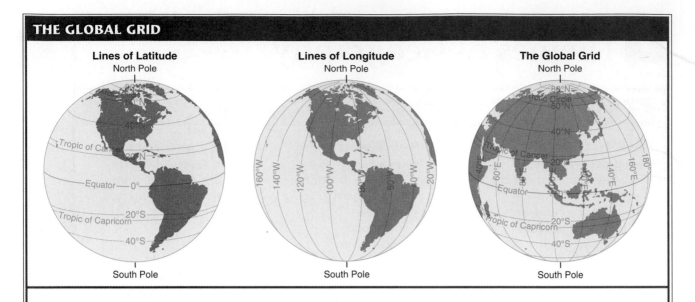

Lines of Latitude
North Pole ... South Pole

Lines of Longitude
North Pole ... South Pole

The Global Grid
North Pole ... South Pole

FOCUS ON GEOGRAPHIC THEMES

1. **Location:** At what lines of latitude on the globe are the Tropic of Cancer and the Tropic of Capricorn located?
2. **Location:** Between which lines of latitude is the Arctic Circle located?
3. **Place:** What are the northern and southern extremities of the globe?

latitude mark the limits of the areas—called tropics—on the earth that receive the most heat from the sun.

Longitude

A second set of imaginary lines is called lines of **longitude**, or meridians. These lines from Pole to Pole measure distances east or west of the starting line, which lies at 0° longitude and is called the Prime Meridian. By international agreement, the Prime Meridian is the line of longitude that runs through the Royal Observatory in Greenwich, England. Longitude is measured in degrees east and west of the Prime Meridian up to 180° in each direction.

Places east of the Prime Meridian up to 180° are known as east longitude. Places west of the Prime Meridian up to 180° are known as west longitude. It is important to indicate whether a location is east or west longitude. The distance between meridians is measured in degrees—the same as the distance between lines of latitude.

Absolute Location

The lines of latitude and longitude cross one another, forming a pattern called a **grid system.** This system makes it possible to find exact places on the earth's surface. Many places can be found along a line of latitude. Only one place, however, can be found at the point where a certain line of latitude crosses a certain line of longitude.

By using degrees and minutes, people can find the precise point where one line of latitude crosses one line of longitude. Thus, people can locate ships at sea, planes in the sky, and places on land. For example, a ship at sea might be located off the coast of Japan at latitude 36° N and longitude 144° E. Dallas, Texas, lies at latitude 32° N and longitude 96° W. Both of these examples pinpoint exact locations, or absolute locations, on the earth.

Relative Location

Absolute location is not the way people usually think about where a place is. Instead, people tend to think of a place in relation to other places, or by its **relative location**. For example, New Orleans is located near the mouth of the Mississippi River, and St. Louis is located where the Missouri River flows into the Mississippi. Knowing the relative location of people, places, and things helps you to orient yourself in space and to develop an awareness of the geography of the world.

Place

Another important geographic theme is place. Place is concerned with "What is it like there?" Each place on earth has its own physical features. It can be described in terms of its land, water, weather, soil, and plant and animal life.

Each place on the earth also has its own human features. It can be described in terms of the number and kinds of people who live there. Each place can also be described by the activities that take place there. People's activities change the way a place looks. Thus, a place may look quite different depending on whether it is used for hunting and fishing, herding, farming, manufacturing, or shopping. People's religions, languages, and cultural backgrounds also provide distinctive characteristics for places.

Human/ Environment Interaction

An important theme in geography is human and environmental interaction. It answers the question "What is the relationship between people and their environment?" Geographers strive to understand the relationships of places on the earth to people and to other places. All places have some desirable and some undesirable features.

Places attract people for various reasons. People may be attracted to a place by an ocean, a river, or a lake. They may be attracted to a place by the amount of sunshine it receives. Different groups of people may use the

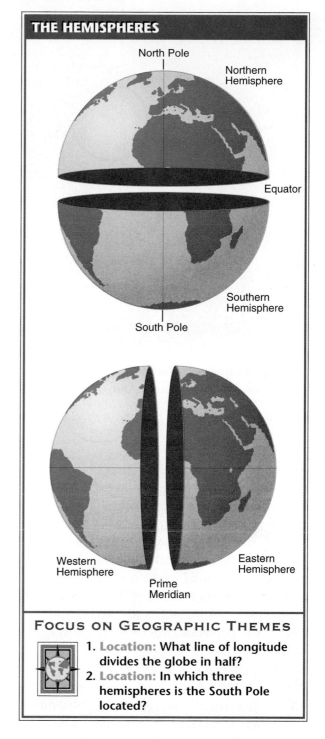

THE HEMISPHERES

North Pole

Northern Hemisphere

Equator

Southern Hemisphere

South Pole

Western Hemisphere

Eastern Hemisphere

Prime Meridian

FOCUS ON GEOGRAPHIC THEMES

1. **Location:** What line of longitude divides the globe in half?
2. **Location:** In which three hemispheres is the South Pole located?

features of a place in different ways. For example, some people are interested in warm, sunny places for growing crops. Other people are interested in the same places for recreational activities.

Geographers are interested in how people adapt to their environment. For example, people wear light clothing in hot places and warm clothing in cold places. Geographers are also

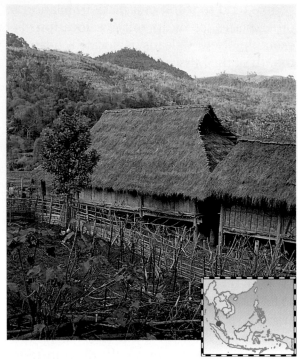

Geographic Themes

Region: Northeastern United States and Southeast Asia
The northeastern United States has cold winters, while Southeast Asia has a year-round tropical climate. *In addition to climate, what other characteristics define regions?*

interested in how people change their environment. For example, at one time deserts were considered by many people to be undesirable places to live. Today people use irrigation to change desert land into farmland.

Geographers are also concerned with how people have created problems with their environment. Among these problems are air pollution, water pollution, and waste material, much of which is hazardous to living things.

Movement

Another important geographic theme is movement. This theme relates to the question "How are people and places connected?" Throughout history, there have been movements of large groups of people from one place to another. Groups have moved for different reasons—better land, religious freedom, a chance to earn a better living. Movement has now become a daily part of our lives. People use automobiles, buses, subways, and commuter trains to move from one place to another.

Geographers are also interested in the movement of goods, information, and ideas. Nearly everywhere, people are **interdependent**, relying on each other for goods, services, and ideas near and far. Geographers help us to understand the importance of these movements as well.

Region

Yet another important theme in geography is region. Geographers often divide the world into regions, or areas, based on physical features, such as land type or plant and animal life. Geographers also divide the world into regions based on human characteristics, such as the way people are governed or the language they speak.

There are two basic types of regions. One is a uniform region, which has boundaries determined by the distribution of some uniform characteristic. A uniform region could be the corn-hog-cattle belt centering on Iowa and Illinois or the irrigated-cotton belt in the Central Valley of California. A second type of region is a functional region, an area that focuses on a central point with surrounding territory linked to that central point by arteries (roads, railroads) or by people's wants and needs (jobs, shopping, entertainment). The metropolitan area surrounding a city is a functional region. Regions make the study of geography more manageable.

Geography and Other Subjects

Geographers study both the physical and human features of the earth and analyze the patterns and relationships of each. In the process, these areas of geographic study are linked to other subjects, including science, history, economics, and sociology.

Science and Technology

Like all scientists, geographers observe, hypothesize, and collect data to prove or disprove their theories. Aiding them in their tasks are advanced technological tools such as satellites, remote sensors, and computers. Satellites orbiting the earth carry remote sensors, or high-tech cameras and/or radar, that collect information and photographs about such topics as the earth's environment, weather, human settlement patterns, and vegetation. This information is sent to computers on the earth. Computer programs known as Geographic Information Systems (GIS) process and organize the satellite images with other data collected through censuses, cartographers, and so on. The GIS technology is already invaluable to urban planners, engineers, and geographers, and it may some day help you plan your vacation!

History and Political Science

Geographers use history to help them understand the way places looked in the past. For example, geographers might want to know how Boston, Massachusetts, looked during colonial times. They might also wish to look at the changes that have occurred in Boston over the past two centuries.

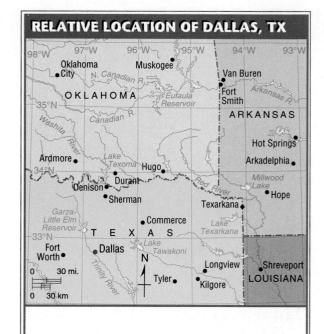

RELATIVE LOCATION OF DALLAS, TX

FOCUS ON GEOGRAPHIC THEMES

1. **Location:** What is the absolute location of Dallas, Texas, in terms of latitude and longitude?
2. **Place:** What body of water lies northwest of Dallas? What river runs through Dallas?

Geographic Themes

Place: Dallas, Texas
The city of Dallas lies on the rolling prairies of northeast Texas. Dallas is a major commercial and financial center. *How can a place like Dallas be described?*

Geographic Themes

Location: Nile River valley, Egypt
This image of Egypt's Nile River valley comes from satellite data. It enables geographers to study population and vegetation patterns. *Why are geographers considered scientists?*

Geographers use political science to help them see how people in different places are governed. They look at how political boundaries have been formed and how they have been changed. Geographers are also interested in how the natural environment has influenced political decisions.

Sociology and Anthropology

Geographers use sociology to help them understand societies throughout the world. They study the relationships between the physical environment and social structure.

Geographers use anthropology to help them gain insights into the **culture**, or way of life, of people in different places. Geographers are interested in how the activities of people affect their physical environment.

Economics

Geographers use economics to help them understand how the location of resources affects the way people make, transport, and use goods. They are also concerned with how and where services are provided.

Geographers are interested in how locations are chosen for various economic activities, such as farming, mining, manufacturing, and selling. They are also interested in the interdependence of people's economic activities throughout the world.

SECTION 1 REVIEW

Checking for Understanding
1. **Define** geography, absolute location, hemisphere, latitude, longitude, grid system, relative location, interdependent, culture.
2. **Locating Places** State the absolute location of Dallas.
3. What are the five themes of geography?
4. Why do geographers use other fields of study?

Critical Thinking
5. **Making Generalizations** What types of uniform regions do you live in?

Geography Skills Handbook

KNOWING HOW to use maps and graphs is an important skill in the study of geography—and in daily life. Maps and graphs are used during the nightly news on television and appear in magazines and newspapers. Maps and graphs are invaluable sources of information that can help you understand the world around you. This Geography Skills Handbook introduces you to the basic kinds of maps and graphs and explains how to use them. It will help you to get the most out of your textbook and will provide you with skills that you can use every day for the rest of your life.

Map Symbols Cartographers, or mapmakers, use symbols to present information on a map. In this way, maps can be read and understood by people throughout the world. Look at the chart of major map symbols on this page and the maps of Mexico City and France on pages 12 and 13. Note the different elements that are shown.

 PARTS OF MAPS

Maps are important tools. They compare places and relate people's activities to the locations where they live. To read a map you must know the elements, or parts, of a map.

Road Map Symbols

Roads and Related Symbols:	
Free limited access highways	
Under construction	
Other four-lane divided highways	
Principal highways	
Other through highways	
Other roads	
Unpaved roads	
Scenic routes	
Interstate highways	85 675
U.S. highways	1
State and provincial highways	11 166 11

Cities and Towns:
National capital; state/provincial capital
Cities and towns; county seats; neighborhoods

Parks, Recreation Areas, Points of Interest:
Parks; recreation areas
Campsites
Points of interest

Other Symbols:
Airport
Mountain peak; highest point in state
Swamp
Ferry
Railroad

Source: *Rand McNally Road Atlas*

Source: 1993 Rand McNally Road Atlas

The Key explains the symbols used on a map. On this map, dots are used to indicate towns. A circle with a star means a capital city.

The Compass Rose is a direction marker that shows the cardinal directions—north, south, east, west. It may show the intermediate directions—northeast, northwest, southeast, and southwest. Sometimes, the compass rose may point in only one direction because the locations of the other directions can be determined in relation to the given direction. On the map above, north is given.

Scale A map can show a small area, such as a city block, or a large area, such as a continent. All maps are drawn to a certain scale. **Scale** means that a certain measurement on a map represents a certain measurement on the earth's surface. The scale bars found on maps give you this relationship. For example, on this map, the scale bar shows that ½ inch on the map represents 3 miles. The scale bar varies from map to map.

MAP SKILLS REVIEW

1. What is the symbol for principal highways?
2. What is the symbol for an airport?
3. What is the purpose of a map key?
4. How far is Toluca from Mexico City?

PARALLELS AND MERIDIANS

There are two sets of lines on a map. One set is called parallels, or lines of latitude. These east-west lines form circles that run in the same direction as the Equator. The other set is called meridians, or lines of longitude. These are north-south lines that form half circles from the North Pole to the South Pole.

FRANCE

5°W UNITED KINGDOM 0° 5°E

50°N

ENGLISH CHANNEL Straits of Dover

BELGIUM

GERMANY

LUX.

•Amiens

Seine River

⊛ PARIS

Nancy•

Rhine River

Loire River

•Nantes F R A N C E

SWITZ.

45°N

Bay of Biscay

•Bordeaux

Garonne River

Rhône River

Lyon•

ITALY

MONACO

•Marseille

SPAIN

ANDORRA

MEDITERRANEAN SEA

N

0   100 mi.
0   100 km

— National boundary
⊛ Capital city
• Other city

Conic Projection

Longitude The vertical lines of longitude measure distances east and west of the Prime Meridian (0° longitude) that passes through Greenwich, England. Lines of longitude to the east of the Prime Meridian are called east longitude. Lines of longitude to the west are called west longitude. On this map, the Prime Meridian is shown along with west longitude line 5° W and east longitude line 5° E.

Latitude The horizontal lines of latitude are used to measure distances north and south of the Equator. Each line of latitude has a measurement in degrees. Lines of latitude north of the Equator (0° latitude) are called lines of north latitude. On this map, they are shown as latitude 45° N and 50° N.

MAP SKILLS REVIEW

1. What line of longitude passes close to Bordeaux?
2. On this map, what city is closest to 50° N?
3. In what body of water is the intersection of 50° N and the Prime Meridian?
4. On this map, what city is located east of 5° E and south of 45° N?

TYPES OF MAPS

GENERAL PURPOSE MAPS

Maps that show a wide range of general information about an area are called **general purpose maps.** Two of the most common are physical and political maps.

Physical maps show landforms and bodies of water, while political maps show national and regional boundaries and cities.

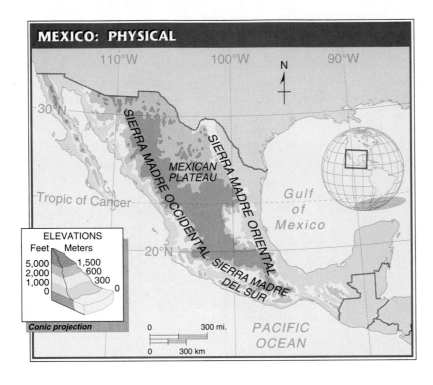

MEXICO: PHYSICAL

110°W   100°W   90°W

N

30°N

SIERRA MADRE OCCIDENTAL

MEXICAN PLATEAU

SIERRA MADRE ORIENTAL

Tropic of Cancer

SIERRA MADRE DEL SUR

20°N

Gulf of Mexico

ELEVATIONS

Feet	Meters
5,000	1,500
2,000	600
1,000	300
0	0

Conic projection

0   300 mi.

0   300 km

PACIFIC OCEAN

Physical Map A general purpose map that shows **topography,** or the shape of physical features of the earth's surface, is usually called a physical map. It presents the earth's **relief,** or the differences in elevation, or height, of landforms in a particular area. It also shows such physical features as rivers and valleys. Some physical maps also have **contour lines** that connect all points of land of equal elevation.

Political Map Another general purpose map is a political map. This map shows the boundaries between countries and often smaller divisions, such as states or counties. Capitals and cities are also frequently shown.

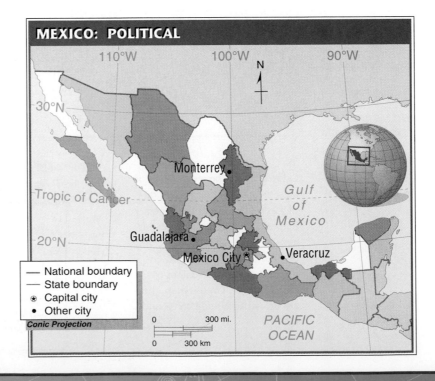

MEXICO: POLITICAL

110°W   100°W   90°W

N

30°N

Tropic of Cancer

Monterrey

Gulf of Mexico

20°N

Guadalajara

Mexico City   Veracruz

— National boundary
— State boundary
⊛ Capital city
• Other city

Conic Projection

0   300 mi.

0   300 km

PACIFIC OCEAN

SPECIAL PURPOSE MAPS

Maps that emphasize a single idea about an area are called **special purpose maps.** There are many kinds of special purpose maps. There are road maps, natural resource maps, economic activity maps, and time zone maps, to name a few. Each map serves a different purpose. For example, a resource map provides the location of natural resources in a country or region, while an economic activity map focuses on different kinds of economic activities in which people participate and where these activities take place.

Special purpose maps often use different colors and symbols to show the location or distribution of a product or resource in a region or in the world. Colors also may indicate how much of a product or resource is grown or manufactured by certain areas.

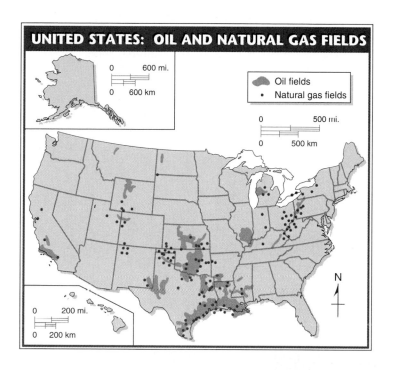

UNITED STATES: OIL AND NATURAL GAS FIELDS

0   600 mi.
0   600 km

Oil fields
• Natural gas fields

0   500 mi.
0   500 km

N

0   200 mi.
0   200 km

Natural Resource Map
One interesting kind of special purpose map is a natural resource map. The map to the left is a natural resource map that shows the distribution of oil and natural gas fields in the United States.

MAP SKILLS REVIEW

1. What areas of Mexico have the lowest elevation?
2. What do the thin lines in the key for the political map of Mexico represent?
3. Compare both physical and political maps. Of the four cities shown on the political map of Mexico, which has the highest elevation?
4. In what parts of the United States is oil a major industry?
5. How many states have both major oil and natural gas industries?

COMPARING MAPS AND GLOBES

A map is a symbolic representation of the earth or a part of the earth on a flat piece of paper. A globe shows the earth's continents and oceans, but it is round in shape. Because it is a scale model of the earth, a globe is a truer representation of the earth than a map is. A map, however, can be folded and easily stored or taken from place to place. A globe cannot be.

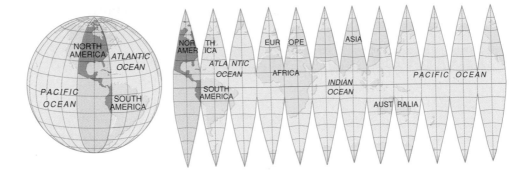

From Globes to Maps With the help of mathematics, mapmakers are able to represent the earth on a flat surface. Size, shape, distance, and/or area, however, are distorted when the curves of a globe become the straight lines of a map.

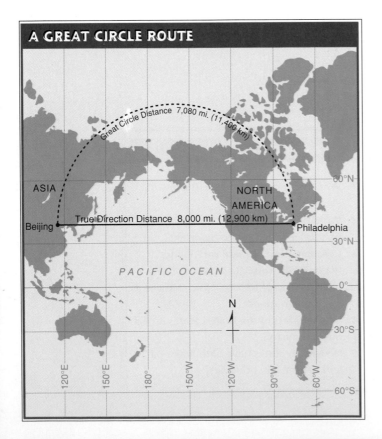

A Great Circle Route Because of their round shapes, globes can accurately show great circle routes. A **great circle** is the shortest possible distance between any two places on the earth's surface. Ships and airplanes often follow the curve of the great circle. By following great circle routes, ships and airplanes use less fuel, and passengers and cargo reach their destinations sooner.

The curved surface of the earth cannot be shown accurately on a map because such a surface must be stretched and/or broken in some places as it is flattened. For this reason, mapmakers use map projections. A **map projection** is a way of representing the round earth on a flat surface. No map projection, however, can show the earth as accurately as a globe does. Each kind of projection—and there are several—has some distortion, or inaccuracy. Typical distortions involve distance, direction, shape, and/or area.

Mercator Projection A Mercator projection is based on the idea of wrapping a piece of paper around a globe to make a cylinder. Such a map shows shapes fairly accurately, but not size or distance. Areas in high latitudes away from the Equator are quite distorted. Thus, Greenland and Alaska appear much larger than they do on a globe. However, because true directions are shown, a Mercator map is very useful for sea travel.

Conic Projection A conic projection comes from the idea of placing a cone over part of a globe. This type of map is accurate for showing small east-west areas in the middle latitudes. Distances and directions on this kind of map are fairly accurate.

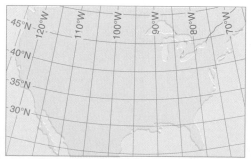

Sinusoidal Projection In a sinusoidal (siy•nyuh•SOYD•uhl) projection, all parallels and the central meridian are straight lines, with the other meridians curved. Shapes are fairly accurate in the center but have increasing distortion toward the edges. This kind of map has no lines of true distance.

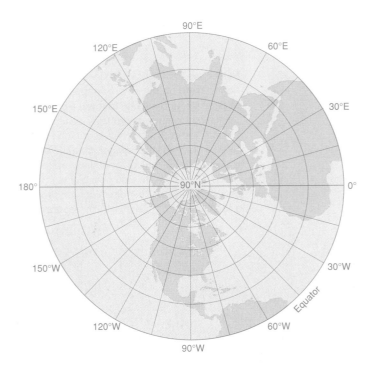

Azimuthal Projection An azimuthal (az•uh•MUHTH•uhl) projection shows the earth centered in such a way that a straight line coming from the center to any other point represents the shortest distance. A common form of azimuthal projection is a polar projection, which uses the North Pole or the South Pole as the center of the map. Although size and shape have distortion, especially toward the edges of the map, distances and directions are accurate when the line of travel passes through the Pole. Therefore, polar maps are often used in air navigation.

Goode's Interrupted Equal-Area Projection The Goode's Interrupted Equal Area projection shows the true size and shape of the earth's landmasses, but distances are generally not accurate.

Robinson Projection A Robinson projection has minor, but not major, distortions. The sizes and shapes near the eastern and western edges of the map are accurate, and the outlines of the continents appear much as they do on a globe. However, the shapes of areas near the poles appear somewhat flat.

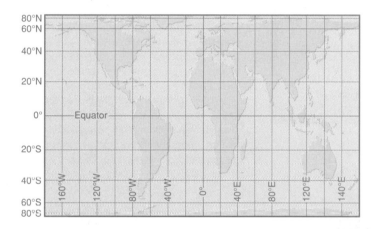

Gall-Peters Projection A Gall-Peters projection has standard parallels of 45 degrees. The sizes of landmasses are accurate. In particular, South America, Africa, and Southeast Asia are shown in their correct size relationship to Europe and North America. Their shapes, however, are greatly distorted. Distances also are inaccurate.

MAP SKILLS REVIEW

1. Why are there different map projections?
2. Why is the Mercator projection useful to navigators?
3. What map projection would best show Antarctica?
4. What projection has shapes that are fairly accurate in the center but have increasing distortion toward the edges?
5. What projection shows true size and shape of landmasses, but inaccurate distances?
6. How does the size of South America on the Gall-Peters projection map compare with its size on the Mercator projection map on page 17?

GRAPHS, CHARTS, AND DIAGRAMS

Graphs, charts, and diagrams are important tools for gaining and interpreting data related to geography. They provide geographers with much valuable information in ways that are well organized and easy to read.

Graphs are convenient ways of presenting information visually. There are many different kinds of graphs.

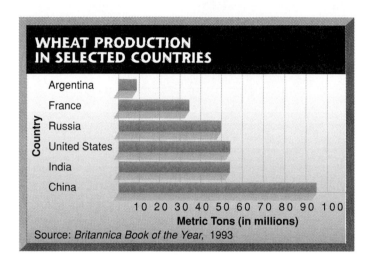

WHEAT PRODUCTION IN SELECTED COUNTRIES

Argentina
France
Russia
United States
India
China

Country

10 20 30 40 50 60 70 80 90 100
Metric Tons (in millions)
Source: *Britannica Book of the Year,* 1993

Bar Graphs show comparisons, making highs and lows stand out clearly.

The bar graph to the left shows wheat production in selected countries of the world. Like all bar graphs, it shows two sets of data, one displayed along the vertical axis and the other displayed along the horizontal axis.

Labels on these axes identify the data and units of measurement. In this case, the vertical axis lists the wheat-producing countries from the smallest producer at the top to the largest producer at the bottom; the horizontal axis shows the amount of production measured in millions of metric tons.

Analyzing data on bar graphs requires noting all changes and relationships, especially differences in quantities. Using such information, geographers and others can make generalizations and draw conclusions based on the data.

Line Graphs show changes in two variables, or changing sets of circumstances. They generally show changes over periods of time. The line graph to the right shows how the population of the United States has changed since 1900. The vertical axis lists population in millions, while the horizontal axis indicates the passage of time at ten-year intervals from 1900 to 1990.

Analyzing data on line graphs involves studying changes and trends and drawing conclusions based on the information.

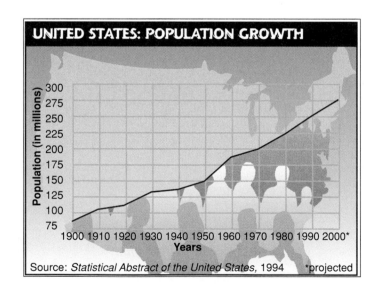

UNITED STATES: POPULATION GROWTH

300
275
250
225
200
175
150
125
100
75

Population (in millions)

1900 1910 1920 1930 1940 1950 1960 1970 1980 1990 2000*
Years
Source: *Statistical Abstract of the United States,* 1994   *projected

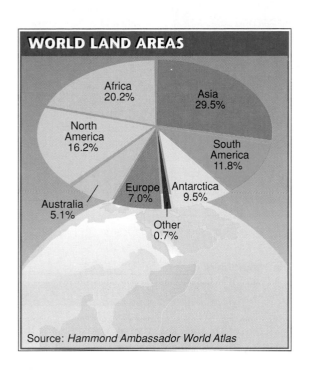

WORLD LAND AREAS

Africa 20.2%
Asia 29.5%
North America 16.2%
South America 11.8%
Europe 7.0%
Antarctica 9.5%
Australia 5.1%
Other 0.7%

Source: *Hammond Ambassador World Atlas*

Circle Graphs use percentages to show how the parts of the whole compare. Because of their shape, circle graphs sometimes are called pie graphs. The circle graph to the left shows the land areas of the world's continents and other landforms. The information indicates the relative sizes of the areas.

Studying data on circle graphs involves noting the relationships of areas to each other and to the whole.

Pictographs are special graphs using a picture of the subject to present important information. Like bar graphs, pictographs show comparisons. The pictograph to the right illustrates wheat production in selected countries of the world. The countries are arranged in order from the smallest producer to the largest producer. Each symbol is a bag of wheat and stands for 10 million metric tons.

As in the case of bar graphs, analyzing the data on pictographs requires analyzing differences in quantities.

WHEAT PRODUCTION IN SELECTED COUNTRIES

= 10,000,000 metric tons

Argentina
France
Russia
United States
India
China

Source: *Britannica Book of the Year,* 1993

THE CONTINENTS OF THE WORLD

Continent	Population*	Land Area
Africa	700,000,000	11,707,000 sq. mi. 44,362,815 sq. km.
Antarctica	——	5,500,000 sq. mi. 14,245,000 sq. km.
Asia	3,392,000,000	17,128,500 sq. mi. 44,362,815 sq. km.
Australia	18,000,000	2,966,136 sq. mi. 7,682,300 sq. km.
Europe	728,000,000	4,057,000 sq. mi. 10,507,630 sq. km.
North America	290,000,000	9,363,000 sq. mi. 24,250,170 sq. km.
South America	470,000,000	6,875,000 sq. mi. 17,806,250 sq. km.

*Estimated to nearest million. Antarctica has no permanent population.
Europe's population includes Russia, Belarus, Moldova, and Ukraine. South America
includes Mexico, Central America, and the Carribean.
Source: 1994 World Population Data Sheet and *Hammond Ambassador World Atlas*

Charts and Tables are useful tools that show facts arranged in columns and rows. They present information in an organized way, providing easy access to data and making comparisons easier to see.

Diagrams are drawings that show what something is or how something is done. Often, diagrams have several parts that show the steps in a process. When you buy an unassembled bicycle, for example, the instructions usually include diagrams to make it easier to assemble the bike.

The diagram below shows how the moon appears to change shape. Note that as the moon revolves around the earth, it goes from the full moon phase—when it appears as a giant orb—to the new moon phase—when it is all but invisible.

MAP SKILLS REVIEW

1. Study the chart above and name the continent that has the largest population.
2. Look at the pictograph on page 21 and the bar graph on page 20 and list the countries that have the largest and smallest wheat production.
3. Study the line graph on page 20. What was the population of the United States in 1900? In 1930?
4. Study the circle graph on page 21. What percentage of the earth's land area is occupied by Africa?
5. Study the diagram on this page. When is the moon not seen from the earth?

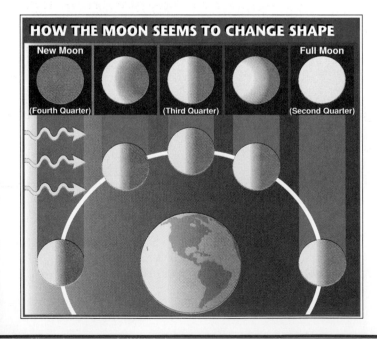

HOW THE MOON SEEMS TO CHANGE SHAPE

New Moon (Fourth Quarter) — (Third Quarter) — Full Moon (Second Quarter)

	SECTION	KEY TERMS	SUMMARY
1	**Themes of Geography**	geography (p. 5) absolute location (p. 5) hemisphere (p. 5) latitude (p. 5) longitude (p. 6) grid system (p. 6) relative location (p. 7) interdependent (p. 8) culture (p. 10) **Dallas, Texas**	• The five themes of location, place, human/environment interaction, movement, and region are important to the study of geography. • Geographers use themes to help them locate places and to understand relationships among places and between people and places. • Geographers also use information from the fields of history, political science, sociology, anthropology, and economics to help them understand the interactions of people with their environments.

GEOGRAPHY SKILLS HANDBOOK	KEY TERMS	SUMMARY
Robinson projection	key (p. 12) compass rose (p. 12) scale (p. 12) general purpose maps (p. 14) topography (p. 14) relief (p. 14) contour lines (p. 14) special purpose maps (p. 15) great circle (p. 16) map projection (p. 17) graph (p. 20) chart (p. 22) table (p. 22) diagram (p. 22)	• Geographers use maps and graphs to gather, interpret, and analyze geographic information. Charts, graphs, and diagrams are also important tools of geographers. • Reading a map requires you to know the elements or parts of a map. Those parts include the key, the compass rose, the scale, and a global grid. • The curved surface of the earth is difficult to represent accurately on a flat map. Different projections show the round earth on flat maps with some distortion.

80°N
60°N Arctic Circle
40°N
20°N Tropic of Cancer
0° Equator
20°S Tropic of Capricorn
40°S
60°S Antarctic Circle
80°S

160°W 120°W 80°W 40°W 0° Prime Meridian 40°E 80°E 120°E 160°E

Reviewing Key Terms

Choose the vocabulary term that best completes each of the sentences below. Write your answers on a separate sheet of paper.

- geography (p. 5)
- absolute location (p. 5)
- hemisphere (p. 5)
- latitude (p. 5)
- longitude (p. 6)
- grid system (p. 6)
- relative location (p. 7)
- interdependent (p. 8)
- culture (p. 10)
- scale (p. 12)
- map projection (p. 17)

SECTION 1

1. A _____ is one of the two halves of the earth divided by the Equator.
2. A global network of horizontal and vertical lines is called a _____ .
3. _____ refers to a place's position on the globe.
4. _____ is the study of the earth and the ways people live and work on it.
5. Telling where a place is in relation to another place is describing its _____ .
6. _____ refers to a people's way of life.
7. Because of improved transportation and communications links, countries in today's world are _____ .
8. Lines of _____ are used to locate places north and south of the Equator.

GEOGRAPHY SKILLS HANDBOOK

9. Lines of _____ are used to locate places east and west of the Prime Meridian.
10. A line or bar on a map that translates distance on the earth to distance on the map is called its _____ .
11. A _____ is a way of showing the round earth on flat paper.

Reviewing Facts

SECTION 1

12. Why are location and place important geographic themes?
13. Why is movement an important part of geography?
14. What are two ways that every place on the earth can be located?

GEOGRAPHY SKILLS HANDBOOK

15. What kind of map would you use to study the boundaries between countries and distance between the capital cities of those countries?
16. What kind of graph would you use to best show the change in the volume of trade between the United States and Japan since 1945? Why would this kind of graph be better than the alternatives available?
17. Which of the map projections available shows the true size and shape of the earth's landmasses?

Critical Thinking

18. **Drawing Conclusions**   Of what value to geographers are the five themes of geography?
19. **Expressing Problems Clearly**   All map projections distort and show the earth inaccurately although some distort less than others. Which map projection is best for general purposes?

Geographic Themes

20. **Place**   What are the physical and human characteristics of your community?
21. **Location**   Which map projection would be best to plan a sea voyage around the world?

Projects

Individual Activity

Collect a variety of maps used in newspapers and newsmagazines. Watch the television news and write descriptions of the maps used to illustrate some features. Organize these into a map scrapbook. Write a definition of a map based on your collection and summarize why maps are useful.

Cooperative Learning Activity

Working in a group of five, describe the geography of your community using the five themes. Each group member should take a theme. Use the following five skills to organize your description. Collect information, present it, analyze it, and draw conclusions to make generalizations.

Writing About Geography

Description

Using the material in your journal, write a two-page letter describing the geography of your community. You may base the organization of your letter on the five geographic themes. It should be so clear that someone who lives in another country would be able to know what it is like to live in your town. Describe where you are, how people in your community make a living, where they came from, how you get to school every day, and other items of interest.

Locating Places

THE WORLD: PHYSICAL GEOGRAPHY

Match the letters on the map with the places and physical features of the earth. Write your answers on a separate sheet of paper.

1. North America
2. South America
3. Africa
4. Asia
5. Europe
6. Australia
7. Antarctica
8. Indian Ocean
9. Atlantic Ocean
10. Pacific Ocean

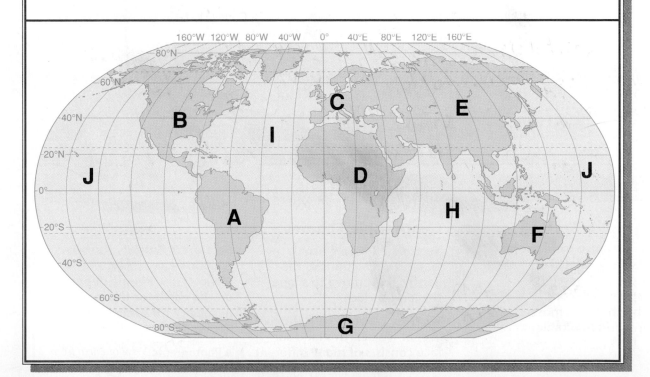

chapter 2

Looking at the Earth

CHAPTER FOCUS

Geographic Setting

Earth's distance from the sun, its daily rotation, slight tilt, and gaseous atmosphere all work together to make most of our world habitable.

Geographic Themes

Section 1 Planet Earth
MOVEMENT Sections of the earth's crust move to shape the land surface.

Section 2 Earth's Features
REGION The earth's land surface consists of many different landforms, such as mountains, hills, plateaus, and plains.

Section 3 Earth's Resources
HUMAN/ENVIRONMENT INTERACTION People depend on the earth for the materials necessary for basic survival.

▲ Photograph: *View of Earth from space*

SETTING THE SCENE

Read to Discover . . .
- the nature and structure of the earth.
- the forces that affect the surface of the earth, the setting for human life.

Key Terms
- atmosphere
- hydrosphere
- lithosphere
- biosphere
- mantle
- fold
- fault
- weathering
- erosion
- glacier

Identify and Locate
Mount Everest, Dead Sea, Mariana Trench, Grand Canyon of the Colorado River

---

The first astronaut to walk on the moon described the earth as looking "like a beautiful jewel in space." The earth's great beauty was seen as a contrast of water and land beneath huge swirls of white clouds. Together these features form the physical environment of the earth.

Earth Viewed From Outer Space

The earth is part of a system of objects that revolve around the sun. The earth's surface is made up of water and land and is surrounded by air. Great contrasts exist in the heights and depths of the earth's surface.

The Solar System

Earth is part of the solar system, which is made up of the sun and all the objects that revolve around it. The sun is a star and the center of the solar system. The sun's great mass—the amount of matter it contains—creates the gravitation that keeps the other objects revolving around it.

The planets are the largest objects that revolve around the sun. Planets are spheres. There are at least 9 planets in our solar system, each with its own orbit around the sun. Planets vary in their distance from the sun. Mercury, Venus, Earth, and Mars are nearest to the sun. Jupiter, Saturn, Uranus, Neptune, and Pluto are farthest away from the sun. The planets vary in size. Jupiter is the largest. Earth ranks fifth in size among the planets. All the planets except Mercury and Venus have moons. The number of moons a planet has also varies. Earth has 1 moon, while Saturn has perhaps as many as 22 moons.

There are thousands of smaller objects that revolve around the sun. Asteroids are planet-like objects. These small, irregularly shaped objects are found mainly between the orbits of Mars and Jupiter. Comets are bodies of dust and frozen gases. They resemble bright balls with long tails. Meteoroids are pieces of rock and iron. Many meteoroids fall into the earth's **atmosphere**—the air that surrounds the earth—but most are burned up by friction before they reach the surface of the earth.

Earth's Measurements

Earth is about 93 million miles (150 million km) from the sun. Earth is the third planet from the sun. Only Mercury and Venus are closer.

The diameter of Earth at the Equator is about 8,000 miles (12,700 km). The distance around Earth is shorter at the poles than at the Equator.

Water, Land, and Air

The surface of the earth is made up of water and land. About 70 percent of the

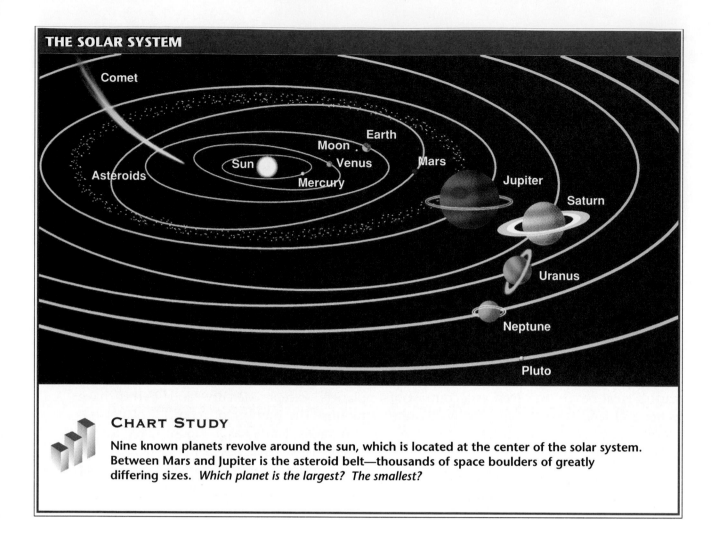

THE SOLAR SYSTEM

Comet
Earth
Moon
Sun Venus
Asteroids Mercury Mars
Jupiter
Saturn
Uranus
Neptune
Pluto

CHART STUDY

Nine known planets revolve around the sun, which is located at the center of the solar system. Between Mars and Jupiter is the asteroid belt—thousands of space boulders of greatly differing sizes. *Which planet is the largest? The smallest?*

surface is water. Oceans, lakes, rivers, and other bodies of water make up a part of the earth called the **hydrosphere.**

About 30 percent of the earth's surface is land. Land makes up a part of the earth called the **lithosphere,** the earth's crust. The largest bodies of land, which are known as continents, and the ocean basins, which are the lands beneath the oceans, are part of the lithosphere.

The atmosphere of the earth extends about 1,000 miles (about 1,600 km) above the earth's surface. About 78 percent of the atmosphere is nitrogen and 21 percent, oxygen. The remaining 1 percent consists of argon and small amounts of other gases.

All people, animals, and plants live on the earth's surface, close to the earth's surface, or in the atmosphere. The part of the earth where life is found is called the **biosphere.**

Earth's Heights and Depths

The average height of the earth's land is about 2,800 feet (850 m) above sea level. The highest point on the earth is the top of Mount Everest in Asia, which is 29,028 feet (about 8,850 m) above sea level. The lowest point on the earth is the shore of the Dead Sea, which is 1,312 feet (400 m) below sea level.

The average depth of the earth's oceans is 12,450 feet (3,975 m). The deepest part of the ocean is the Mariana Trench, a long, narrow depression in the Pacific Ocean, southwest of Guam. The Mariana Trench is about 35,800 feet (10,900 m) deep.

Earth's Structure

The earth's surface is always changing. Internal forces bring about changes in the earth's surface over time. Surface forces, such as wind, flowing water, and ice also change the earth's surface.

Inside the Earth

The inside of the earth is composed of three layers—the core, the **mantle**, and the crust. The inner core makes up the center of the earth. It lies about 4,000 miles (6,400 km) below the surface of the earth. Scientists believe that the inner core is solid and consists of iron and nickel. The other part of the core, the outer core, begins about 1,800 miles (2,900 km) below the surface of the earth. It is made up of melted iron and nickel.

Next to the outer core is a thick layer of dense, hot rock called the mantle. The rock in the mantle consists of silicon, oxygen, aluminum, iron, and magnesium.

Next to the mantle is the earth's crust. This is a relatively thin layer, extending perhaps 3 to 30 miles (5 to 50 km) below the surface. The crust consists of huge platelike sections of rock that rest—or more accurately, float—on a partially melted layer in the upper mantle. The crust includes the continents and ocean basins.

Internal Forces

The surface of the earth has changed greatly over time. These changes have been largely the result of internal forces. These internal forces cause the plates of the earth's crust to move. Generally they move very slowly—only about 4 inches (10 cm) each year. When the plates spread apart, melted rock rises through the gaps and forms ridges. When the plates bump together, one may slide under another, forming a trench.

Shaking or sudden movements in the plates, called earthquakes, change the surface of the land and the floor of the ocean. Volcanoes are mountains formed when lava, or melted rock, rises through the earth's crust. If

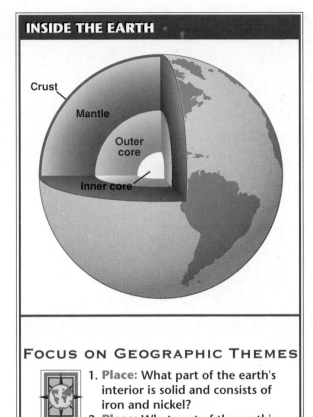

INSIDE THE EARTH

Crust
Mantle
Outer core
Inner core

FOCUS ON GEOGRAPHIC THEMES

1. **Place:** What part of the earth's interior is solid and consists of iron and nickel?
2. **Place:** What part of the earth's interior consists of melted iron and nickel?

the lava is too thick, the flow is blocked and pressure builds. A sudden release may then occur, often with great force.

Internal forces can build or break down mountains in other ways, such as by **folds** or **faults**. Folds are bends in layers of rock. Such bends occur when the moving plates squeeze the earth's surface until it buckles.

Faults, or breaks in the earth's crust, occur when the folded land cannot be bent any further. Then the earth's crust cracks and breaks into huge blocks. Movement occurs along the faults and may be in any direction. Mountains formed by faults, or fault-block mountains, are generally steep on one side and gently sloping on the other.

Earthquakes and volcanoes under the ocean can cause as much damage as those on land. The release of these forces beneath the ocean often causes seismic sea waves, or tsunami. Such a wave may move through the water

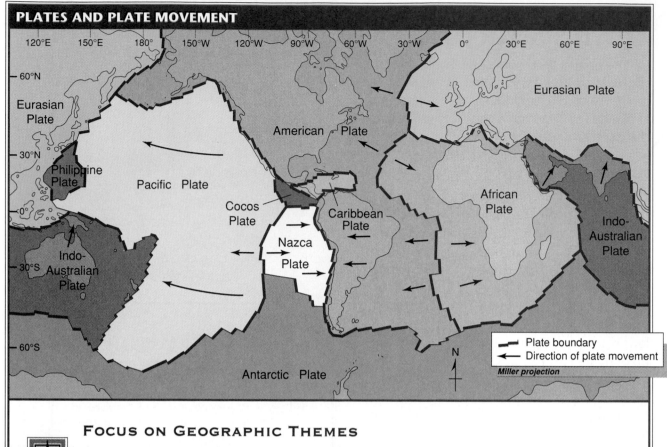

PLATES AND PLATE MOVEMENT

Eurasian Plate

Eurasian Plate

Philippine Plate

American Plate

Pacific Plate

Cocos Plate

Caribbean Plate

Nazca Plate

African Plate

Indo-Australian Plate

Indo-Australian Plate

Antarctic Plate

Plate boundary
Direction of plate movement

Miller projection

N

FOCUS ON GEOGRAPHIC THEMES

1. **Location:** Where is the Nazca Plate located?
2. **Movement:** Which plates are moving toward each other?
3. **Movement:** What plates are moving northward?
4. **Location:** Between which two plates is the Philippine Plate situated?

faster than 400 miles (644 km) per hour. Near the shore, tsunami can pile up and reach a height of more than 100 feet (30 m).

Earthquakes often occur where different plates meet one another. Many major earthquakes and volcanoes occur along the edges of the plates beneath the Pacific Ocean. Geologists call the area of earthquake and volcano activity that rims the Pacific Ocean the Ring of Fire. The Ring of Fire marks the boundary where the plates that cradle the Pacific meet the plates that hold the continents surrounding the Pacific.

Geologists believe that about 240 million years ago all the earth's landmasses were joined together. For example, Africa and South America were next to each other. Over time, the spreading of the ocean floor caused Africa and South America to be located as they are

today, with the Atlantic Ocean between them. The idea that the continents were once joined and then slowly drifted apart is called continental drift.

External Forces

Other forces also change the surface of the earth. Rocks are always breaking into smaller pieces. The process that breaks down rocks is called **weathering**. There are two basic kinds of weathering—chemical weathering and physical weathering.

Chemical weathering results when water dissolves some of the chemicals in rocks, causing them to disintegrate or when parts of iron-bearing rocks rust—just as metal does—and break apart. Physical weathering, by contrast, breaks rocks into large pieces. For example, water seeps into the cracks in a rock and freezes, expanding and causing the rock to split. Physical weathering can also result when tree roots grow through cracks in a rock, forcing it apart.

Another force that changes the surface of the earth is **erosion**—the wearing away of the earth's surface. Erosion occurs by means of wind, flowing water, and glaciers.

Wind erosion involves the movement of dust, sand, and soil from one place to another. Plants help to protect the land from wind erosion; however, in dry places where people have cut down trees and plants, winds pick up large amounts of soil and blow it away. In deserts and on some beaches, windblown sands form hills called dunes. In general, vegetation grows on beach dunes and helps stop drastic erosion. The vegetation also helps protect the shoreline from erosion caused by pounding waves. As humans develop beachfront properties, however, they often destroy the protective dunes and hasten erosion.

Water erosion begins when rainwater flows off the land downhill in streams. As the water flows, it cuts into the land, wearing away the soil and rock. Over a period of time, the eroding action of water works to form first a gully and then a valley. Sometimes valleys are eroded even further to form valleys with high, steep walls called canyons. The Grand Canyon of the Colorado River is a good example of the eroding power of water. Over millions of years, the Colorado River has cut a canyon that is more than 1 mile (1.6 km) deep.

Erosion can also occur as **glaciers**, or large bodies of ice, move across the surface of the earth. As they move, glaciers change the land, destroying forests, carving out valleys, altering the course of rivers, and wearing down mountain tops. Scientists believe that in the last 2 million years glaciers have covered large areas of the earth's surface for long periods of time.

Collectively these periods are called the Ice Ages. The last part of the last one took place during the Pleistocene epoch—long before

CALIFORNIA EARTHQUAKE: JANUARY 17, 1994

1 The earthquake was directly under Northridge

2 ...on a previously unmapped east-west fault.

3 Almost 10 miles under Northridge, rock on one side of the fault surged upward

0 15 miles

Northridge
Santa Monica
Los Angeles
Pacific Ocean

Pacific Ocean
Santa Monica Fault
Northridge
Santa Monica Mountains Thrust Fault
Epicenter
Oakridge Fault
San Fernando Fault
San Andreas Fault

4 ...while the other side plunged downward. Such movement characterizes a "thrust fault."

5 The earthquake was caused by a rock 10 miles long by 2 miles wide that moved upward 1 foot, setting off vibrations that spread out for miles.

Source: USA Today, Columbus Dispatch

FOCUS ON GEOGRAPHIC THEMES

Place: Los Angeles, California

The earthquake that struck the Los Angeles area on January 17, 1994, was caused by a "thrust fault" located about 10 miles (16 km) beneath the town of Northridge. *What kind of underground activity occurs in a "thrust fault" earthquake?*

Geographic Themes

Place: High and Low Points
South Asia's Mount Everest is the world's highest mountain. California's Death Valley contains the lowest point in the Western Hemisphere. *Where is the world's lowest point?*

humans developed civilizations. It ended about 10,000 years ago. Some scientists theorize that as the earth's orbit around the sun changes, the planet will cool and glaciation will take place again.

Even though the last Ice Age ended in the distant past, some glaciation remains on the earth today. Glaciers are of two types—sheet glaciers and mountain glaciers. Sheet glaciers are sheets of ice that cover large areas. Most of Greenland and all of Antarctica are covered by sheet glaciers, generally called ice caps. Mountain glaciers are more common than sheet glaciers. Mountain glaciers form when fallen snow in mountains builds up and turns into ice. Gravity then pulls these glaciers downhill. As they move downward, mountain glaciers pick up rocks and soil in their paths and carve U-shaped valleys. When a glacier melts, it deposits its rock and soil.

SECTION 1 REVIEW

Checking for Understanding
1. **Define** atmosphere, hydrosphere, lithosphere, biosphere, mantle, fold, fault, weathering, erosion, glacier.
2. **Locating Places** Where is Earth located in relation to the sun?
3. **Movement** How have internal forces changed the surface of the earth?
4. **Movement** How does water erosion change the surface of the earth?

Critical Thinking
5. **Predicting Consequences** Imagine that the mantle of the earth ceased to circulate molten rock. What would be the consequences on land formation on the surface of the earth?

2 Earth's Features

SETTING THE SCENE

Read to Discover . . .	Key Terms	Identify and Locate
• the variety of the earth's landforms. • the features of the earth's oceans and seas. • how the earth's water is recycled.	• isthmus • plateau • archipelago • continental shelf • groundwater • water cycle • evaporation	The continents: North America, South America, Europe, Asia, Africa, Australia, Antarctica; Isthmus of Suez; Isthmus of Panama; The oceans: Atlantic, Pacific, Indian, Arctic

Photographs of the earth taken from space show that the surface of the earth is far from uniform. The first section of this chapter discussed the internal and external forces that act on the natural features of the earth. In this section, you will read about the planet's variety of land and water areas.

PLACE

Landforms

The natural features of the earth's land surfaces are called landforms. These features are classified by type in order to describe and define them. The names given to these features help people locate specific places.

Continents

Geographers divide most of the land surface of the earth into seven large landmasses called continents. North America and South America are the continents in the Western Hemisphere. Australia and Asia are in the Eastern Hemisphere. Most of Europe and Africa are in the Eastern Hemisphere, but a small part of their western coastal areas is in the Western Hemisphere. Antarctica, which includes the South Pole, is located in both the Western Hemisphere and the Eastern

Hemisphere. Asia is the largest continent, and Australia is the smallest.

Some continents, like Australia and Antarctica, stand alone, while others are joined in some way. An **isthmus** is a narrow piece of land that connects two large landmasses and separates two bodies of water. The Isthmus of Panama joins North America and South America and separates the Atlantic and Pacific oceans.

Europe and Asia are actually parts of one huge landmass. Some people consider this landmass to be one continent and call it Eurasia. Most geographers, however, use natural or political boundaries to divide the area into two separate continents. The Ural Mountains serve as a natural boundary between Europe and Asia.

Major Landforms

The landforms of the earth vary greatly from place to place. The four major kinds of landforms are mountains, hills, plateaus, and plains. These landforms can be described in terms of their shapes and elevations.

Parts of the land that rise noticeably above the rest of the land are called either mountains or hills. Mountains have steep slopes and some kind of peak or summit. Mountains are

LANDFORMS AND WATER BODIES

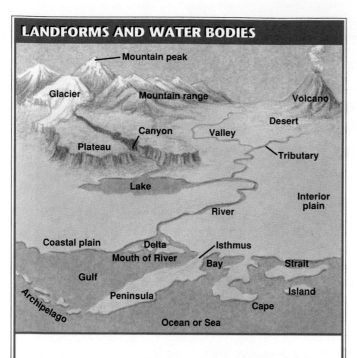

Mountain peak
Glacier
Mountain range
Volcano
Desert
Canyon
Valley
Plateau
Tributary
Lake
Interior plain
River
Coastal plain
Delta
Isthmus
Mouth of River
Bay
Strait
Gulf
Island
Peninsula
Cape
Archipelago
Ocean or Sea

FOCUS ON GEOGRAPHIC THEMES

1. **Place:** What landform connects two large landmasses?
2. **Location:** Where is a delta located?
3. **Place:** What landform is surrounded by water on three sides?
4. **Place:** What is a river branch called?

also called highlands because they are the highest landforms and have the greatest relief. Hills are generally more rounded, lower, and have less relief.

Two large areas of flatland with very little relief are plateaus and plains. A **plateau** is higher than the surrounding land and usually has at least one steep side, called a cliff. A plateau is sometimes called a tableland. Mountains often surround high-altitude plateaus. Plains are flat or gently rolling lands. Plains along the coasts of continents generally have low elevations and are called coastal plains. Interior plains are those that are located away from the coasts of continents. They generally have higher elevations.

Other Landforms

A valley and a canyon are two other kinds of landforms. A piece of land that extends out-

ward from a continent and that is surrounded by water on three sides is called a peninsula. An island is any body of land smaller than a continent that is completely surrounded by water. A group of closely scattered islands is called an **archipelago.**

The earth's oceans also have many kinds of landforms. There are as many different kinds of landforms on the bottoms of the oceans as there are on the continents. The underwater extension of a continent is known as a **continental shelf.** Continental shelves are narrow in some places and wide in others. They slope out from the land for up to 800 miles (about 1,290 km) and descend to a depth of about 600 feet (183 m) before dropping steeply to the ocean floor.

In some places the ocean floor is a flat plain. In other places there are high mountain ranges, great cliffs, valleys, deep trenches, and seamounts. Seamounts are underwater mountains with steep sides that rise above the ocean floor.

PLACE

Water Features

Water covers most of the earth's surface. Water makes up a portion of all living things, and all living things need water in order to live. The amount of water on the earth remains relatively constant as it moves from ocean to air to ground to ocean.

Oceans and Seas

About 70 percent of the earth's surface is water—almost all of it salt water. This large, continuous body of salt water is generally divided into four oceans. The oceans are named the Pacific, the Atlantic, the Indian, and the Arctic. The Pacific, the largest of the oceans, covers more area than all the earth's land combined. The Pacific Ocean is also deep enough in some places to cover the world's highest mountain with more than 1 mile (1.6 km) to spare.

Bodies of salt water that are smaller than oceans are called seas, gulfs, and bays. These bodies of water are often partially enclosed by land. The Mediterranean Sea is one of the earth's largest seas. It is almost entirely encircled by the southern part of Europe, the northern part of Africa, and the southwestern part of Asia. The Gulf of Mexico is nearly encircled by the coasts of the United States and Mexico. The Bay of Bengal borders Southeast Asia and part of southern Asia.

Although 97 percent of the world's water is found in oceans, the water is too salty to be used for drinking, farming, or manufacturing. Today, only a small amount of freshwater can be obtained from the ocean by removing salt. Efficient and low-cost methods of changing seawater into freshwater will need to be developed in order to meet the world's increasing shortage of freshwater.

Lakes, Streams, and Rivers

Other water features of the earth include lakes, streams, and rivers. A lake is a body of water completely surrounded by land. The greatest number of lakes are found in areas where glacial movement has cut deep valleys, and glacial deposits have acted as dams as the ice melted. Northern North America contains thousands of these glacial lakes. Most lakes contain freshwater.

A stream is a body of water flowing through the land. Streams combine to form a river—a stream of water of considerable volume. Most rivers begin high in the mountains and hills. The river's source might be a melting glacier or an overflowing lake. As a river flows along, it picks up additional water from rainfall. Often rivers flow into one another, creating major waterways that flow for thousands of miles before emptying into a gulf, sea, or ocean.

The water in lakes and rivers makes up a small percentage of the earth's water supply. This water, however, is very important to people because it is freshwater. Unlike ocean water, freshwater can be used by people for drinking, farming, or manufacturing. These water sources are so important that most large urban areas began as settlements along the shores of lakes and rivers where people would have a constant supply of water.

Groundwater

Another source of freshwater is **groundwater**, which lies beneath the earth's surface and supplies wells and springs. The main source of groundwater is rain and melted snow that filter through the soil. Water that seeps into the ground from lakes and rivers also contributes to groundwater. People in many rural areas and in some cities depend on groundwater for their needs.

Of the earth's total water supply, only 3 percent is freshwater, and most of this is not available for human consumption. More than 2 percent is locked in glaciers and ice caps. The Antarctic ice cap, for example, contains more freshwater than the rest of the world's regions combined. Another 0.5 percent is groundwater. Rivers and lakes contain far less than 1 percent of the earth's water.

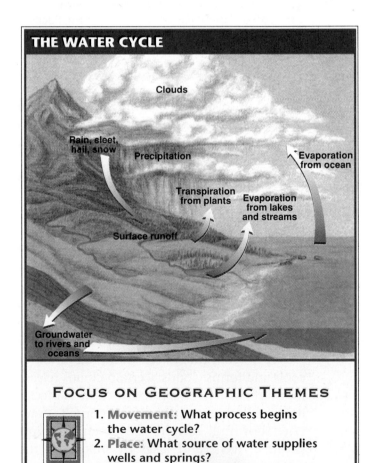

THE WATER CYCLE

Clouds

Rain, sleet, hail, snow

Precipitation

Evaporation from ocean

Transpiration from plants

Evaporation from lakes and streams

Surface runoff

Groundwater to rivers and oceans

FOCUS ON GEOGRAPHIC THEMES

1. **Movement:** What process begins the water cycle?
2. **Place:** What source of water supplies wells and springs?
3. **Movement:** To where does all water return before the cycle repeats?

Geographic Themes

Place: Kayangel Atoll, South Pacific
This ring-shaped low island in the Pacific Ocean surrounds an inner lagoon. *How does the Pacific Ocean compare to the world's other oceans?*

The Water Cycle

The earth today has as much water as there was and as much as there ever will be. This is because all of the water that is used eventually comes back to the oceans. The regular movement of water from ocean to air to ground to ocean is called the **water cycle.**

The cycle begins with **evaporation**—the changing of liquid water into vapor, or gas. The sun's heat causes evaporation. Water vapor rising from the oceans, other bodies of water, and plants is gathered by the air. How much moisture can be carried by the air depends mainly on the temperature. Warmer air carries more moisture than cooler air.

When moisture-filled warm air rises, it cools and forms clouds. Certain clouds release moisture, which returns to the earth as precipitation. Because of gravity, returned water flows downhill toward the ocean. It forms streams, rivers, and lakes. It sinks into the ground and becomes groundwater. Sometimes it forms ice caps and glaciers. Eventually, however, the water returns to the ocean and the cycle repeats.

The amount of water that evaporates is approximately the same amount that falls back to the earth. This amount varies little from year to year. Thus, the total volume of water in the cycle is more or less constant.

SECTION 2 REVIEW

Checking for Understanding
1. **Define** isthmus, plateau, archipelago, continental shelf, groundwater, water cycle, evaporation.
2. **Locating Places** What continents are joined by the Isthmus of Panama?
3. **Region** What are the four basic types of landforms?
4. **Location** Where is freshwater found?

Critical Thinking
5. **Making Comparisons** How are the landforms of the ocean floor similar to the landforms of the continents?

SETTING THE SCENE

Read to Discover . . .
- the importance of natural resources.
- the ways in which the distribution of resources affects people and countries.

Key Terms
- natural resource
- renewable resource
- nonrenewable resource
- imports
- exports

Identify and Locate
Southwest Asia, Japan

Elements from the earth that are not made by people but can be used by them are called **natural resources.** Even though a place might be rich in natural resources, people must develop them. For example, some places have fertile soil, but people must work that soil in order to produce crops and have large supplies of food.

HUMAN/ENVIRONMENT INTERACTION

Importance of Resources

The earth supports human life because it provides what is needed for survival. The basic elements include air, water, soil, plants, and animals. The air that is around the earth contains oxygen, which people and animals breathe. People, animals, and plants depend upon freshwater to live. The earth's soils support the growth of vegetation. Plants and animals form part of the food chain for humans.

Minerals and Fuels

People use the earth's resources to make their lives better. Minerals and fossil fuels are among these resources. Minerals are substances from the earth that are not living or made from living things. Fossil fuels are fuels—including coal, oil, and gas—that formed from the remains of plants and animals that lived millions of years ago.

Value of Resources

Use, supply, and changes over time help determine how important certain natural resources are. People living in separate parts of the world and at different times may not give the same value to the same resource. For example, a resource such as copper can serve as a raw material for making useful things, such as water pipes in houses. On the other hand, an artist may prize copper because of its worth in making works of art, such as wall decorations. Some people think resources such as gold and silver are valuable because of their use in making jewelry or as a form of money. Photographers might assign a different value to silver because of its importance in making and processing film.

Supply, often influenced by location, also affects value. When there is a small supply of something, it is generally given a greater value. For example, Native Americans who lived far from the oceans used shells as a form of money. Those groups who lived near the shore, where there were many shells, did not place as much value on them. Rubber is another example. People once thought of rubber trees as important natural resources because they provided all the world's rubber. Later synthetic, or artificial, rubber was developed. This made it possible for people to produce large amounts of

Geographic Themes

Place: Arabian Peninsula

The Arabian Peninsula of Southwest Asia is rich in oil, a fossil fuel on which modern industrialized countries depend. *What are other examples of fossil fuels?*

a substance that could be used in place of natural rubber. The increased use of synthetic rubber lowered the value of natural rubber.

The value of a resource may change over time. The energy resource uranium is an example. Uranium is needed to split atoms to release nuclear energy. Before the development of nuclear energy, uranium had few uses. Therefore, people did not give it as much value as they do today.

HUMAN/ENVIRONMENT INTERACTION

Managing Resources

Resources are renewable if they replace themselves naturally or if people can grow or raise continuous supplies of them. Some **renewable resources** are forests and animal life.

People are important in determining how resources are used and renewed. For example, lumber companies can carefully choose which trees to cut and how many. They can also plant a harvested area with new trees to help renew forestland resources.

The earth's crust, however, has many **nonrenewable resources**—resources that can never be replaced. Such resources include most minerals and fossil fuels. People may recycle, or reuse, these resources, but natural growth or human skill cannot replace them.

People also affect the quality of the basic elements of air, water, and soil. These resources cannot be replaced but can be conserved, or protected, through proper management. Farmers, for example, can keep soil fertile by changing the crops that are grown on a plot of land from year to year.

Minerals form most of the earth's land resources and are often found naturally in the ores that people mine. Many of the earth's more than 2,000 different minerals help support or improve human life, and so people value them. Certain mineral resources provide important medicines and building materials. Factories often mix minerals to make different kinds of materials. For example, factories blend iron ore with alloys such as manganese to produce steel. Minerals in the form of fertilizers aid in producing greater amounts of food.

Fossil fuels are an especially valued resource today. Because these fuels were formed over thousands of lifetimes, they are considered nonrenewable. Such resources provide heat, light, and the energy necessary to run machines. They are also used in the manufacturing of plastics, fertilizers, and other goods.

HUMAN/ENVIRONMENT INTERACTION

Distribution of Resources

The natural distribution of resources greatly influences how countries relate to one another. Most natural resources are not evenly distributed over the earth. Some places may have large amounts of a certain resource while others may have little or none.

The scarcity of certain resources and goods has led to trade among the world's countries. For example, in order to build jet aircraft, the United States must buy certain resources from other countries. Resources or goods brought into one country from another are known as **imports.** Resources or goods sent from one country to another are known as **exports.**

Because of the scarcity of resources, countries are interdependent, relying on each other for goods and services. Some southwestern Asian countries, for example, depend on the United States for wheat, other food products, and certain manufactured goods. The United States, in turn, depends on these countries for part of its oil supply. In another case, Japan sells steel, automobiles, and other manufactured goods throughout the world. Yet Japan, which is poor in natural resources, must get oil and raw materials from other countries to manufacture the items that it sells.

The uneven distribution of the earth's resources has effects other than promoting

Geographic Themes

Movement: Alaska
The trans-Alaska pipeline carries oil from northern Alaska to the port of Valdez. *Why is oil a nonrenewable resource?*

trade. At many times in the earth's history, it has led to conflict. Many wars have begun because rulers believed that their countries needed the resources or goods that another country possessed.

SECTION 3 REVIEW

Checking for Understanding
1. **Define** natural resource, renewable resource, nonrenewable resource, imports, exports.
2. **Locating Places** What region is a leading oil producer?
3. **Place** What determines the importance of natural resources?
4. **Human/Environment Interaction** How are renewable and nonrenewable resources different?

Critical Thinking
5. **Expressing Problems Clearly** Summarize the relationship between resource use and supply.

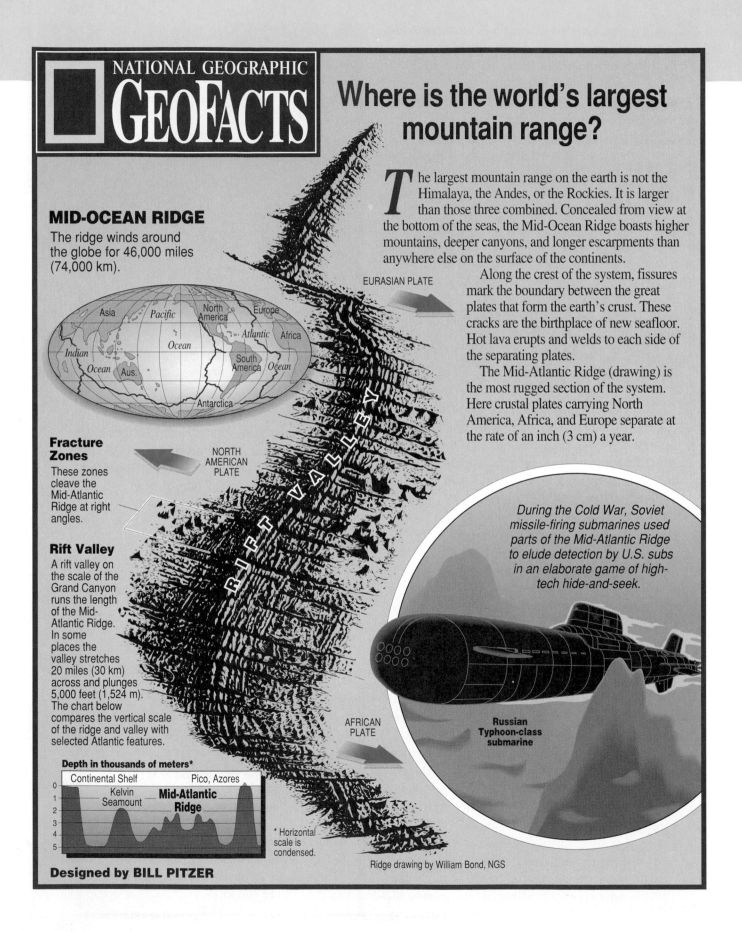

NATIONAL GEOGRAPHIC
GEOFACTS

Where is the world's largest mountain range?

MID-OCEAN RIDGE

The ridge winds around the globe for 46,000 miles (74,000 km).

The globe shows: Asia, Pacific, North America, Europe, Atlantic, Africa, Ocean, Indian Ocean, Aus., South America Ocean, Antarctica

Fracture Zones

These zones cleave the Mid-Atlantic Ridge at right angles.

Rift Valley

A rift valley on the scale of the Grand Canyon runs the length of the Mid-Atlantic Ridge. In some places the valley stretches 20 miles (30 km) across and plunges 5,000 feet (1,524 m). The chart below compares the vertical scale of the ridge and valley with selected Atlantic features.

Depth in thousands of meters*

Continental Shelf		Pico, Azores
	Kelvin Seamount	**Mid-Atlantic Ridge**

0
1
2
3
4
5

* Horizontal scale is condensed.

Designed by BILL PITZER

T he largest mountain range on the earth is not the Himalaya, the Andes, or the Rockies. It is larger than those three combined. Concealed from view at the bottom of the seas, the Mid-Ocean Ridge boasts higher mountains, deeper canyons, and longer escarpments than anywhere else on the surface of the continents.

Along the crest of the system, fissures mark the boundary between the great plates that form the earth's crust. These cracks are the birthplace of new seafloor. Hot lava erupts and welds to each side of the separating plates.

The Mid-Atlantic Ridge (drawing) is the most rugged section of the system. Here crustal plates carrying North America, Africa, and Europe separate at the rate of an inch (3 cm) a year.

EURASIAN PLATE

NORTH AMERICAN PLATE

RIFT VALLEY

AFRICAN PLATE

During the Cold War, Soviet missile-firing submarines used parts of the Mid-Atlantic Ridge to elude detection by U.S. subs in an elaborate game of high-tech hide-and-seek.

Russian Typhoon-class submarine

Ridge drawing by William Bond, NGS

1 SECTION	KEY TERMS	SUMMARY
Planet Earth Mount Everest in the Himalaya range of South Asia	**atmosphere** (p. 27) **hydrosphere** (p. 28) **lithosphere** (p. 28) **biosphere** (p. 28) **mantle** (p. 29) **fold** (p. 29) **fault** (p. 29) **weathering** (p. 30) **erosion** (p. 31) **glacier** (p. 31)	• The earth is made up of water, land, and air. Water makes up the earth's hydrosphere. Land makes up part of the earth's lithosphere, while the air comprises earth's atmosphere. • Sections of the earth's crust float and move on a mantle layer, causing some continents to move apart and some to move together. • External forces, such as water, wind, and gravity, help to shape the earth's surface through erosion, movement, and new landforms.
2 SECTION	KEY TERMS	SUMMARY
Earth's Features Kayangel Atoll in the South Pacific	**isthmus** (p. 33) **plateau** (p. 34) **archipelago** (p. 34) **continental shelf** (p. 34) **groundwater** (p. 35) **water cycle** (p. 36) **evaporation** (p. 36)	• Landforms are the physical features that make up the surface of the earth. Four major types are mountains, hills, plains, and plateaus. • Water is both a physical feature and a resource. Oceans, rivers, lakes, and streams are water features. • Water is a limited resource that is circulated and purified repeatedly through the water cycle.
3 SECTION	KEY TERMS	SUMMARY
Earth's Resources The Arabian Peninsula	**natural resource** (p. 37) **renewable resource** (p. 38) **nonrenewable resource** (p. 38) **imports** (p. 39) **exports** (p. 39)	• The earth's many natural resources are not divided evenly among the countries of the world. Use, supply, and changes over time are factors in deciding how important natural resources are. • Renewable resources replace themselves naturally or can be raised in continuous supply by people. Nonrenewable resources, such as fossil fuels, can never be replaced.

Reviewing Key Terms

Choose the vocabulary term that best completes each of the sentences below. Write your answers on a separate sheet of paper.

hydrosphere (p. 28)   lithosphere (p. 28)
mantle (p. 29)   folds (p. 29)
weathering (p. 30)   glaciers (p. 31)
plateau (p. 34)   archipelago (p. 34)
groundwater (p. 35)   water cycle (p. 36)
natural resources (p. 37)   imports (p. 39)
exports (p. 39)

SECTION 1

1. _____ are bends in layers of rock formed by internal forces in the earth.
2. The mixture of solid and liquid rock around the earth's core is called the _____ .
3. The process that breaks down rocks is called _____ .
4. The earth's _____ consists of oceans, lakes, and other bodies of water.
5. Land makes up part of the earth called the _____ .
6. _____ are large masses of ice that carve out U-shaped valleys.

SECTION 2

7. A group of islands is called a/an _____ .
8. The _____ purifies water and keeps a global water balance.
9. A _____ is a large flatland with one steep side and little relief.
10. The main source of _____ is rain that filters through the soil.

SECTION 3

11. Earth elements used by humans but not made by them are called _____ .
12. Resources sent from one country to another are called _____ .
13. _____ are resources brought into one country from another.

Reviewing Facts

SECTION 1

14. What are comets and meteoroids?
15. How does chemical weathering occur on the earth?

SECTION 2

16. Oceans cover most of the earth's surface. What are some features of the ocean floor?
17. Where are the greatest number of lakes found?

SECTION 3

18. Many of the earth's resources are available in limited quantities and cannot replenish themselves. What fossil fuels are classified as nonrenewable resources?
19. What are the earth's resources that replace themselves naturally called?

Critical Thinking

20. **Determining Cause and Effect**   What forces—both external and internal—shaped the landforms in your immediate region?
21. **Identifying Central Issues**   What are the important factors facing the earth in regard to supplies of freshwater?
22. **Analyzing Information**   Why is the demand for the earth's natural resources increasing?

Geographic Themes

23. **Movement**   Explain how eroded soil and the movement of plates shape landforms.
24. **Place**   Describe the physical features of your community.
25. **Place**   Which of the earth's natural resources do you use on a daily, weekly, and periodic basis?

Projects

Individual Activity

Prepare a chart like the one below with six headings: mountains, hills, plateaus, plains, and two other landforms of your choice. Use an atlas to find at least seven of each feature, one from each continent. What conclusions can you draw about landforms?

Cooperative Learning Activity

Work in teams of three to create an advertising campaign about the wise use of resources in your part of the country. Posters, pamphlets, and informational skits are a few ways to draw attention to issues.

Writing About Geography

Narration

Choose two or three landforms in your community. Describe the relief, slope, and elevation of each and the processes that caused each landform. Then write a descriptive paragraph telling how these landforms have caused people to follow a certain way of life. Use your journal notes as reference.

	Mountains	Hills	Plateaus	Plains		
Africa						
Antarctica						
Asia						
Australia						
Europe						
North America						
South America						

Locating Places

THE WORLD: PHYSICAL GEOGRAPHY

Match the letters on the map with the places and physical features of the earth. Write your answers on a separate sheet of paper.

1. Arctic Ocean
2. Himalayas
3. Gulf of Mexico
4. Isthmus of Panama
5. Pacific Ocean
6. Bay of Bengal
7. Asia
8. Mediterranean Sea
9. Australia
10. Atlantic Ocean
11. North America
12. Africa
13. Indian Ocean
14. Antarctica
15. Ural Mountains

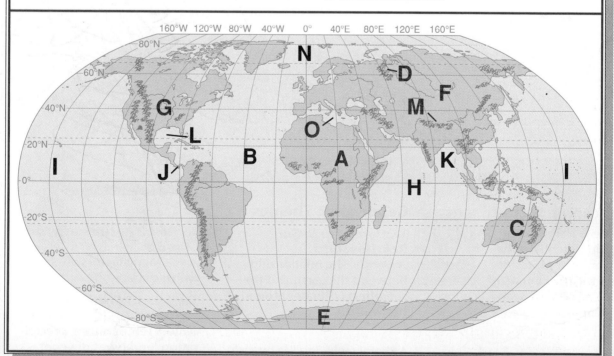

Climates of the Earth

CHAPTER FOCUS

Geographic Setting

Climate is a significant factor in describing the geography of places on the earth. The climate of a place affects the way that people in an area live.

Geographic Themes

Section 1 Earth-Sun Relationships

LOCATION The relationship between the earth and the sun affects climates around the world.

▲ Photograph: *Brazilian research station, King George Island, Antarctica*

Section 2 Factors Affecting Climate

PLACE Many factors affect world climate.

Section 3 World Climate Patterns

REGION Temperature, precipitation, and types of vegetation can be used to define climate regions.

Earth-Sun Relationships

Weather is the condition of the atmosphere in one place during a short period of time. It can be described as cold or hot, windy or calm, wet or dry. **Climate**, on the other hand, is the term for weather patterns that an area typically experiences during a long period of time. Weather and climate are influenced by the amount of direct sunlight a place receives. They are also affected by ocean currents, winds, and the features of the earth's surface.

The relationship between the earth and the sun especially affects climates around the world. The sun provides the earth with heat and light. Different parts of the earth, however, receive different amounts of sunlight at different times.

The Greenhouse Effect

Only a small amount of the sun's radiation reaches the earth's atmosphere. Some of the radiation is reflected back into space by the atmosphere and by the earth's surface. Enough radiation, however, remains to warm the earth's land and water.

The atmosphere also keeps heat from escaping back into space too quickly. In this sense, the earth's atmosphere has been compared to a greenhouse, which traps the sun's warmth for growing plants. Without this greenhouse effect, the earth would be too cold for most living things.

Even inside the "greenhouse" of the atmosphere, not all places on earth get the same amount of heat and light from the sun. Day and night, seasonal change, and differing climates all depend somewhat on the relative positions of the sun and the earth.

Earth's Tilt and Rotation

The earth has an **axis**—an imaginary line that runs through its center between the North Pole and the South Pole. The earth's axis is tilted at a 23½° angle. The axis is always tilted in the same direction.

Because the earth's axis is tilted, not all places on earth receive the same amount of direct sunlight. Therefore, the earth's tilt affects the **temperature** of places. Temperature is a measure of how hot or cold something is. Temperature is generally measured in degrees on a set scale. Air temperature is usually measured in Fahrenheit (F) or Celsius (C).

The earth rotates, or spins, on its axis. The earth makes one complete rotation every 24 hours, turning from west to east. The earth's rotation causes day and night.

The sun shines on the earth all the time. As the earth spins on its axis, the part of the earth that faces the sun has daylight. The part of the earth facing away from the sun has darkness.

Earth's Revolution

As it rotates on its axis, the earth also travels in an orbit, or path, around the sun. The earth's **revolution**, or trip around the sun, takes 1 year, or 365¼ days.

The earth's revolution and tilt cause the changing seasons. They also cause changes in the amount of daylight during the year.

On about March 21, the sun is directly over the equator and the days and nights are equal in length. This day is called an **equinox**. In the Northern Hemisphere, March 21 marks the beginning of spring. In the Southern Hemisphere, the seasons are reversed. The earth gradually moves so that the direct rays of the sun strike the latitude 23½° N, or the Tropic of Cancer, on about June 21. This is the northernmost point on the earth that receives the direct rays of the sun. This day is called a

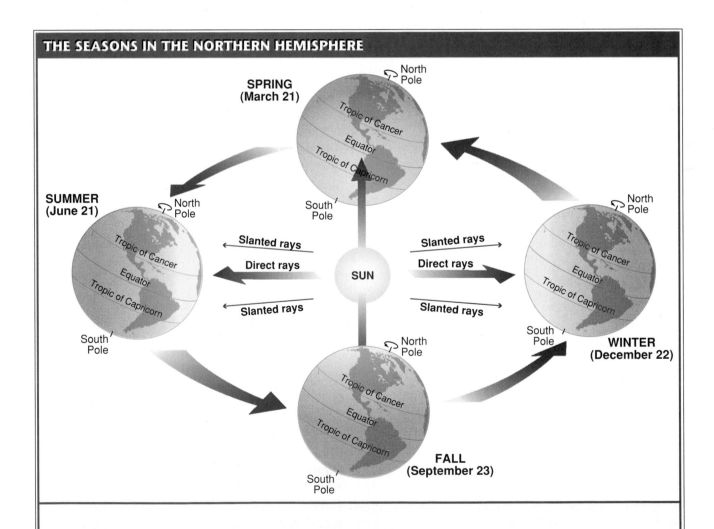

THE SEASONS IN THE NORTHERN HEMISPHERE

SPRING (March 21)

SUMMER (June 21)

SUN

Slanted rays
Direct rays
Slanted rays

Slanted rays
Direct rays
Slanted rays

WINTER (December 22)

FALL (September 23)

FOCUS ON GEOGRAPHIC THEMES

1. Movement: Why are the seasons reversed in the Northern and Southern hemispheres?
2. Movement: What does March 21 mark in the Northern Hemisphere?
3. Place: What is the northernmost point on the earth that receives the direct rays on June 21 (the solstice)?

Geographic Themes

Place: Great Plains, United States
This meeting of two dissimilar air masses over part of the Great Plains is bringing dramatic changes in weather to the region. *What factor distinguishes weather from climate?*

solstice. In the Northern Hemisphere, June 21 marks the beginning of summer. It is the day of longest sunlight there.

The earth moves until on about September 23, the sun is again directly over the Equator. In the Northern Hemisphere, this equinox marks the beginning of fall. The earth gradually moves so that the direct rays of the sun strike 23½° S, or the Tropic of Capricorn, on about December 22. This is the southernmost point that receives the direct rays of the sun. In the Northern Hemisphere, this solstice marks the beginning of winter and is the shortest day of the year. Then the earth's movement causes the direct rays of the sun to move north, and the cycle repeats itself.

The amount of sunlight at the poles varies the most dramatically as the earth's revolution and tilt causes the changing seasons. At the North Pole, the sun never sets from about March 20 to September 23. At the South Pole, it never sets from about September 23 to March 20. The tilting of the earth's axis as it revolves around the sun causes this natural phenomenon, known as the midnight sun. For six months one Pole is slanted toward the sun and receives continuous sunlight, while the other Pole is slanted away from the sun and receives no sunlight at all.

SECTION 1 REVIEW

Checking for Understanding
1. **Define** weather, climate, axis, temperature, revolution, equinox, solstice.
2. **Locating Places** What latitude is the Tropic of Cancer? Tropic of Capricorn?
3. **Movement** How does the revolution of the earth cause seasons?
4. **Movement** How are the temperatures of places affected by the earth's tilt?

Critical Thinking
5. **Analyzing Information** Why does March 21 generally mark the beginning of spring in the Northern Hemisphere?

2 Factors Affecting Climate

SETTING THE SCENE

Read to Discover . . .
- the patterns of wind and ocean currents.
- the role temperature and precipitation play in describing climates.
- the factors that control the locations of climates around the world.

Key Terms
- prevailing wind
- doldrums
- current
- precipitation
- windward
- leeward
- rain shadow

Identify and Locate
High, middle, and low latitudes; Arctic Circle, Antarctic Circle

All places on the earth are not heated or cooled equally. The kind of climate that a place has depends in part on latitude, elevation, wind and ocean currents, and landforms.

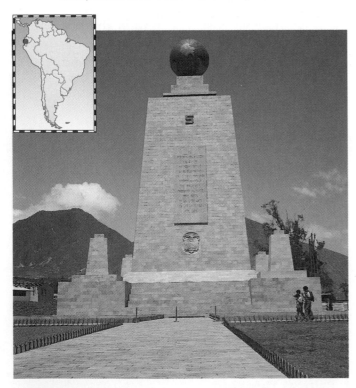

Geographic Themes
Location: Quito, Ecuador
This monument near Quito, Ecuador in South America marks the line of the Equator. *What major lines of latitude define the low latitudes?*

PLACE

Latitude

Bands of latitude can be used to describe climate in a general way according to certain climate zones. The zones indicate how the rays of the sun strike the places within the zones. During the earth's yearly revolution around the sun, the sun's direct rays fall on the earth in a regular pattern.

Low Latitudes

The latitudes between the Tropic of Cancer and the Tropic of Capricorn are known as the low latitudes. The low latitudes receive direct rays of the sun year-round. Places in these latitudes have a very warm to very hot climate and are often said to be in the tropics.

Polar Areas

When either the Northern Hemisphere or the Southern Hemisphere is tilted toward the sun, its polar area receives continuous sunlight. Starting on about June 21, the sun never sets above a line called the Arctic Circle (66½° N). In the Southern Hemisphere, the Antarctic Circle (66½° S) is a line that marks the boundary of endless daylight starting on about December 22. During the times when there is

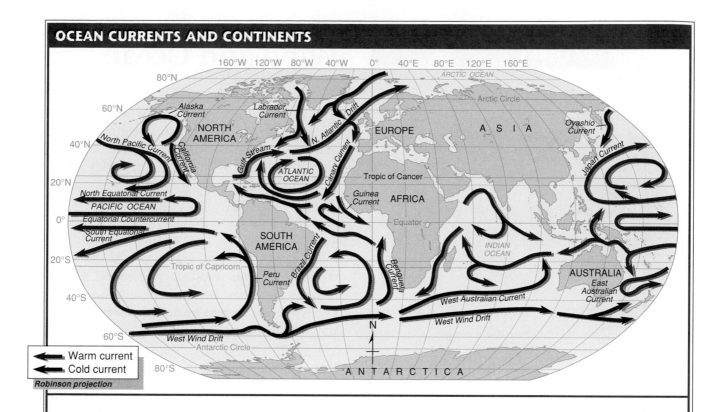

OCEAN CURRENTS AND CONTINENTS

FOCUS ON GEOGRAPHIC THEMES

1. **Region:** What continent is affected by the North Atlantic Current?
2. **Movement:** What current moves along the northwestern coast of Africa?
3. **Movement:** What currents cross the Tropic of Cancer?
4. **Place:** What current brings cooler temperatures to Japan?

endless daylight at the poles, they actually receive very little heat from the sun. This is because the sun's rays that far from the Equator always hit the earth as slanted rays rather than as direct rays.

High and Middle Latitudes

The latitudes between the North Pole and the Arctic Circle and between the South Pole and the Antarctic Circle are known as the high latitudes. Places in the high latitudes receive slanted rays of the sun throughout the year and have a generally cold climate.

The latitudes between the Tropic of Cancer and the Arctic Circle in the Northern Hemisphere and between the Tropic of Capricorn and the Antarctic Circle in the Southern Hemisphere are known as the middle latitudes. The middle latitudes receive warm masses of air from the tropics during summer and cold masses of air from the high latitudes during winter. Thus, many places at these latitudes have a temperate climate—or one that ranges from fairly hot to fairly cold. The weather of most places in the middle latitudes changes dramatically with the seasons.

PLACE

Elevation

The temperature of a place depends on its elevation. The earth's atmosphere gets thinner as altitude increases, so air temperatures decrease with elevation. For every 1,000

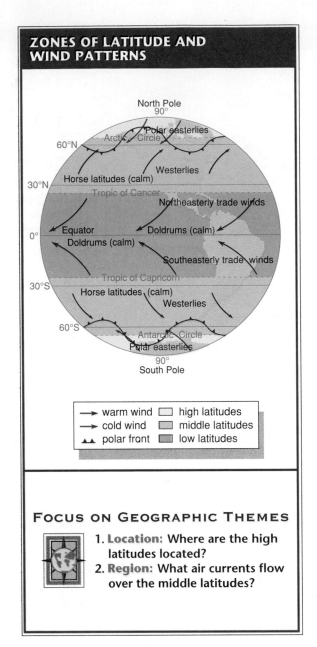

ZONES OF LATITUDE AND WIND PATTERNS

North Pole
90°

Polar easterlies

Arctic Circle

60°N

Westerlies

Horse latitudes (calm)

30°N

Tropic of Cancer

Northeasterly trade winds

0° Equator   Doldrums (calm)

Doldrums (calm)

Southeasterly trade winds

Tropic of Capricorn

30°S

Horse latitudes (calm)

Westerlies

60°S

Antarctic Circle

Polar easterlies

90°
South Pole

→ warm wind   ☐ high latitudes
→ cold wind   middle latitudes
▲▲ polar front   low latitudes

FOCUS ON GEOGRAPHIC THEMES

1. **Location:** Where are the high latitudes located?
2. **Region:** What air currents flow over the middle latitudes?

Wind and Ocean Currents

Wind and water combine with the effects of the sun to create the weather and climates of the earth. Air moving across the surface of the earth is called wind. Winds occur when temperatures create differences in air pressure. The earth's atmosphere is made up of gases. Near sea level, gravity pulls the gases together, increasing the pressure. The atmosphere is heavier near sea level and becomes thinner as the altitude increases. Other changes in the atmospheric pressure are caused by the uneven heating of the earth's atmosphere. These changes create winds.

Wind Patterns

Winds that blow in fairly constant patterns are called **prevailing winds**. The prevailing winds are divided into belts of latitude. Trade winds are the prevailing winds in the low latitudes. They blow toward the Equator from about 30° N latitude and 30° S latitude. The prevailing winds in the belts between 30° N and 60° N latitude and between 30° S and 60° S latitude are called westerlies. These winds generally blow in a west to east direction. The belts of the polar easterlies lie between 60° N latitude and the North Pole and between 60° S latitude and the South Pole. These winds blow somewhat from east to west and push cold polar air toward the middle latitudes. At the Equator is a frequently windless area called the **doldrums**.

Ocean Currents

Cold and warm "rivers" of seawater, known as **currents**, flow in the oceans. Ocean currents generally flow in circular patterns, moving clockwise in the Northern Hemisphere and counterclockwise in the Southern Hemisphere.

Currents are caused by the rotation of the earth, moving air, and differences in water temperature in the ocean itself. Currents may be warm or cold.

feet (305 m) gained, the temperature drops about 3.5°F (1.9°C). For example, Quito, the capital city of Ecuador, lies nearly on the Equator. Nevertheless, Quito's elevation of more than 9,000 feet (2,743 m) causes its average temperature to be about 25°F (14°C) cooler than that of the surrounding lowlands.

Sunlight is very bright on top of mountains because there is less atmosphere to filter out rays of the sun. High mountains, however, are generally cold places covered with ice and snow year-round, even if the mountains are located near the Equator.

Cold water from the polar areas moves slowly toward the Equator. The water warms as it nears the Equator. The warm water, in turn, moves away from the Equator. This water forms the warm ocean currents. As the warm water moves away from the Equator, it becomes colder and forms a cold current.

Ocean currents affect the climates of coastal lands that they flow along. Cold currents cool the lands they pass. Warm currents have a warming effect. For example, the warm water extension of the Gulf Stream current—called the North Atlantic Drift—flows near western Europe. This current gives western Europe a rather mild climate in spite of its northerly latitude.

Water and winds interact with temperature to cause **precipitation**—the falling of moisture to the earth. Precipitation falls in the forms of rain, sleet, hail, or snow.

PLACE

Landforms

The earth's surface features can also affect climates. The climates of places located at the same latitude can be very different depending on whether large bodies of water are nearby. Water is slower to heat and to cool than land. Therefore, water temperatures are more constant and uniform than land temperatures. For the same reason, temperatures of land areas located near oceans do not change as much as temperatures of interior land areas.

Interior land temperatures can change dramatically. The middle of a landmass will generally have much hotter summers and much colder winters than land areas near the ocean, even though these locations may be on the same line of latitude.

Temperatures, precipitation, and surface features interact with wind to affect climate. Winds that blow over an ocean and then meet a mountain range on the **windward** side—the side facing toward the direction from which the wind is blowing—are pushed upward. As the winds rise and cool, they drop moisture gathered through evaporation. Thus the air that descends the other side of the mountains,

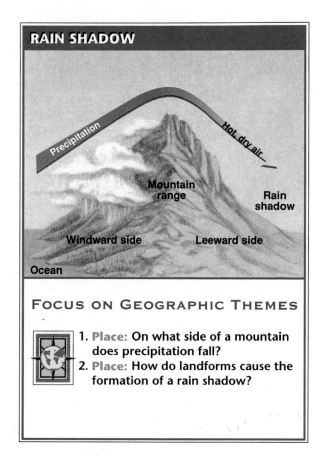

RAIN SHADOW

Precipitation

Hot, dry air

Mountain range

Rain shadow

Windward side   Leeward side

Ocean

FOCUS ON GEOGRAPHIC THEMES

1. **Place:** On what side of a mountain does precipitation fall?
2. **Place:** How do landforms cause the formation of a rain shadow?

the **leeward** side, is dry and becomes warmer as it falls. This hot, dry air results in a dry area called a **rain shadow.**

SECTION 2 REVIEW

Checking for Understanding
1. **Define** prevailing wind, doldrums, current, precipitation, windward, leeward, rain shadow.
2. **Locating Places** What and where are the trade winds, westerlies, and polar easterlies?
3. **Region** Why do the climates of the low latitudes, the high latitudes, and the middle latitudes differ?
4. **Movement** How do winds and ocean currents affect climate?

Critical Thinking
5. **Making Generalizations** What factors affect climate in your region?

SETTING THE SCENE

Read to Discover . . .
- the climate regions of the world.
- ways that climate affects humans and their environment.
- how climates change over time.

Key Terms
- natural vegetation
- oasis
- deciduous
- mixed forest
- chaparral
- prairie
- permafrost
- taiga
- timberline
- hypothesis
- smog

Identify and Locate
Major global climate regions: tropical, dry, mid-latitude, high latitude, highland

C limate affects the soil and **natural vegetation.** Natural vegetation is the plant life that grows in an area if the natural environment has not been changed by people.

Geographers often divide the earth into five major climate regions—tropical, dry, mid-latitude, high latitude, and highland. Because climates vary within these broad regions, geographers further divide the major regions into smaller ones.

REGION

Tropical Climates

T ropical climate regions are found in or near the low latitudes—the tropics. The two kinds of tropical climate regions are tropical rain forest and tropical savanna.

Tropical Rain Forest Climate

Hot and wet throughout the year, tropical rain forest climate regions are found near the Equator. Direct rays of the sun keep the temperatures high, averaging around 80°F (27°C),

year-round. The warm, humid air produces rain almost daily. Yearly rainfall averages about 80 inches (203 cm).

Tropical rain forest vegetation grows thick in layers formed at different heights. Tall teak or mahogany trees form a high canopy over shorter trees and bushes. Vines and shade-loving plants grow on the floor of the rain forest.

The Amazon River basin in South America contains the world's largest tropical rain forest. This same climate is found in other parts of South America, in the Caribbean area, and in parts of Africa and Asia.

Tropical Savanna Climate

Areas that have a dry season in winter and a wet season in summer are called tropical savanna climate regions. Although savannas are located farther from the Equator than tropical rain forest regions, temperatures are high.

In the dry season the tough ground is covered with clumps of coarse grass. Few trees dot the large savannas of Africa and South America.

Dry Climates

Because of vegetation, dry climate regions are also divided into two types, desert and steppe.

Desert Climate

Dry areas with sparse plant life are called deserts. Scattered vegetation such as scrubs and cacti can survive with little rain. Flowering plants that lie dormant during the dry season bloom when the rains come.

Yearly rainfall in deserts seldom is more than 10 inches (about 25 cm). Underground springs, however, may support an **oasis**, an area of lush vegetation. Some deserts have fertile soil in which plants can grow if irrigated. Others have dunes or rocky surfaces.

Deserts can be extremely hot during the day and cold at night. The Gobi in central Asia has hot summers and harsh winters with temperatures as cold as –40°F (–40°C).

Desert climates cover about one-fifth of the earth's land surface. The Sahara extends over nearly the entire northern one-third of Africa.

Steppe Climate

Dry areas, often bordering deserts, are called steppes. Yearly rainfall in steppe zones averages 10 to 20 inches (25.4 to 50.8 cm).

Steppe vegetation consists of bushes and patches of short grasses without many trees. The world's largest steppe stretches across eastern Europe and western and central Asia. Steppes are also found in North America, South America, Africa, and Australia.

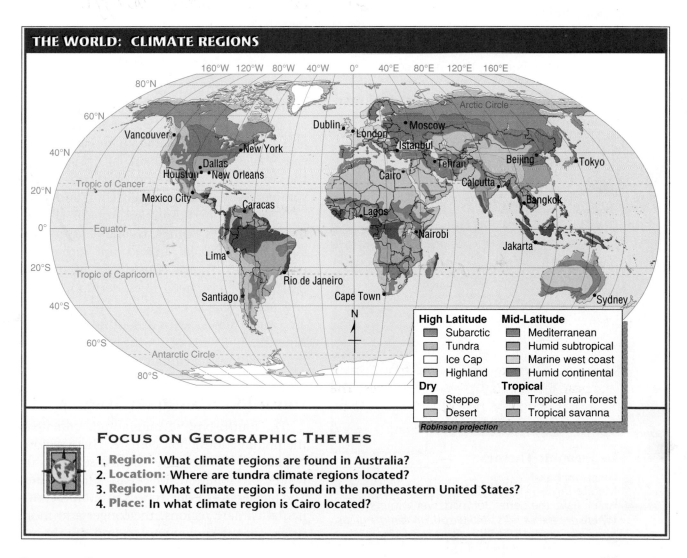

THE WORLD: CLIMATE REGIONS

Robinson projection

High Latitude
- Subarctic
- Tundra
- Ice Cap
- Highland

Dry
- Steppe
- Desert

Mid-Latitude
- Mediterranean
- Humid subtropical
- Marine west coast
- Humid continental

Tropical
- Tropical rain forest
- Tropical savanna

FOCUS ON GEOGRAPHIC THEMES

1. **Region:** What climate regions are found in Australia?
2. **Location:** Where are tundra climate regions located?
3. **Region:** What climate region is found in the northeastern United States?
4. **Place:** In what climate region is Cairo located?

Mid-latitude Climates

The world has four mid-latitude climate regions. They are marine west coast, Mediterranean, humid subtropical, and humid continental.

Marine West Coast Climate

Climate areas generally found along western coastlines between latitudes 30° and 60° north and south are called marine west coast climate regions. Ocean winds produce cool summers and mild but damp winters. Rainfall, quite heavy in places, supports both evergreen and **deciduous** trees.

Deciduous trees lose their leaves in autumn. Most deciduous trees, including oak, maple, and elm, have broad leaves. Evergreens have either needle-shaped or broad leaves. Needle-leaved pine and spruce trees are also called conifers because they have cones.

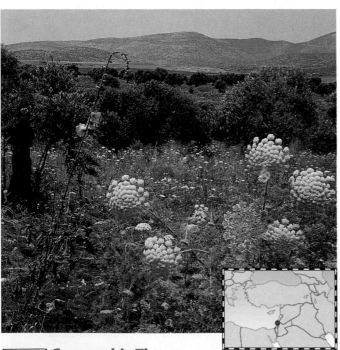

Geographic Themes

Location: Israel
Mediterranean climate areas, such as that in Israel, have the benefit of mild, wet winters. *Where are the world's Mediterranean climate areas generally located?*

Mixed forests are those with both evergreen and deciduous trees. Marine west coast climate regions cover much of western Europe as well as the Pacific coast of North America. South America, Africa, and Australia also have marine west coast climate regions.

Mediterranean Climate

Areas that have weather patterns and vegetation like those near the Mediterranean Sea are called Mediterranean climate regions. These regions are generally found in coastal lands between latitudes 30° and 40° north and south. They have mild rainy winters and hot, sunny summers.

Vegetation in Mediterranean climate regions includes woody bushes and short trees, such as olive and cork oak, which grow in dense forests. This type of vegetation is called **chaparral.** Southern California has a Mediterranean climate.

Humid Subtropical Climate

Humid subtropical climate regions are generally found at mid-latitudes in the southeastern parts of continents. Here a pattern of wind and high pressure related to nearby oceans causes high humidity. Rain falls throughout the year but heavy thunderstorms occur in the summer. Winters are generally short and mild.

Vegetation in humid subtropical climate regions includes both grasslands and forests. Grasslands that lie inland are known as **prairie** lands. Forests consist of a mixture of broad-leaved evergreen trees, deciduous trees, and needle-leaved evergreens. The southeastern United States, areas of southeastern South America, and parts of southeastern Asia have humid subtropical climates.

Humid Continental Climate

The fourth type of mid-latitude climate is the humid continental climate. These regions are more influenced by landmasses than by winds, precipitation, or ocean temperatures. The farther north one travels in humid continental climate regions, the longer and more severe are the snowy winters and the shorter

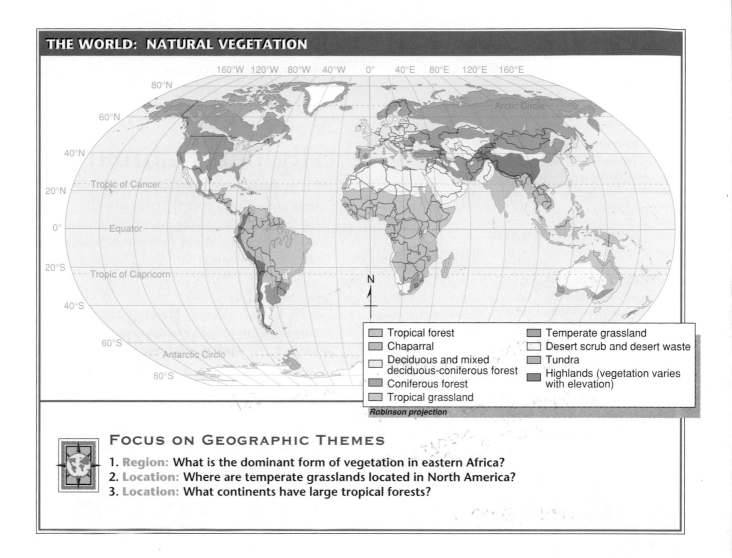

THE WORLD: NATURAL VEGETATION

Tropical forest
Chaparral
Deciduous and mixed deciduous-coniferous forest
Coniferous forest
Tropical grassland
Temperate grassland
Desert scrub and desert waste
Tundra
Highlands (vegetation varies with elevation)

Robinson projection

FOCUS ON GEOGRAPHIC THEMES

1. **Region:** What is the dominant form of vegetation in eastern Africa?
2. **Location:** Where are temperate grasslands located in North America?
3. **Location:** What continents have large tropical forests?

---

and cooler the summers. These regions are located only in the Northern Hemisphere.

<u>REGION</u>

High Latitude Climates

There are three types of high latitude climates—subarctic, tundra, and ice cap. Just south of the Arctic Circle lie the subarctic climate regions. Temperatures average below freezing for half the year. Winters are bitterly cold, and summers are short and cool. In some places only a thin layer of surface soil thaws. The frozen subsoil is known as **permafrost.** Relatively high temperatures may occur for a

few brief summer days. Subarctic climates have the world's greatest range of temperature—as much as 120°F (65°C).

Subarctic Climate

The subarctic's severe conditions limit the variety of plant life. Vegetation consists mainly of needle-leaved evergreen trees. One vast subarctic forest stretches across northern Russia. Geographers often use **taiga,** the Russian word for this forest, to refer to subarctic climate regions in general. Another large subarctic region stretches across Canada.

Tundra Climate

Like the subarctic climate regions, the tundra climate regions have bitterly cold winters with greatly reduced sunlight. In summer the sun's slanted rays bring constant light but little heat.

The tundra region's thin soil above the permafrost supports certain low plants during the short summers. Mosses, bushes, very short grasses, and lichens—plants that grow on rocks—survive on the treeless plain. The world's major tundra climates lie north of the subarctic zones in the Northern Hemisphere.

Ice Cap Climate

Because monthly temperatures average below freezing, ice cap climate regions support no vegetation. The land surface is constantly covered by snow and ice, sometimes more than 2 miles (3 km) thick. Only plants that can live on rocks grow in ice-cap regions. The earth's greatest polar ice cap spreads over almost all of Antarctica. The interior of Greenland also has an ice-cap climate.

Highland Climates

In mountain areas the climate varies with elevation. The higher the altitude, the cooler the air becomes. Some mountains in South America that lie on the Equator remain snow covered year-round.

Elevation also influences vegetation. Near the bases of mountains, deciduous and evergreen forests grow. Higher up are meadows with small trees and shrubs. Above the **timberline**, the elevation above which it is too cold for trees to grow, are scattered tundra plants.

People, Climate, and Environment

Climate affects the kinds of clothing people wear and the kinds of houses they build. It can also affect methods of transportation they use. Changes that people make in the environment also affect climate.

Adaptations

People adapt to the climate. In cold regions they wear clothing made of warm material such as wool. People in warm regions wear light-colored linen and cotton clothing that reflects the sun's rays.

In cold regions people build well-insulated houses with furnaces or other means of heating. In some cold regions, the frozen ground melts in summer so that houses sink. Houses here are built on gravel pads or pilings—heavy poles driven into the permafrost.

Houses in deserts often have light-colored roofs to reflect the sun's heat. Often these houses are made of sun-dried bricks, because in hot weather they stay cool. In wet regions

Geographic Themes

Place: The Alps, Austria
This village in Austria is located in the Alps, a mountain chain that stretches across central Europe. *What geographic factor affects the type of highland climate found in mountainous areas?*

houses may have steep, pointed roofs so that rain or snow run off easily.

Climate affects transportation. For example, in some tropical rain forests, plants and trees grow so quickly that building and maintaining roads is very difficult. Rivers often substitute for roads in these regions. At the other extreme, people in cold, snowy regions may use snowmobiles.

Climatic Changes

Climates change gradually over time. During the last 1 to 2 million years, for example, the earth passed through four eras when large areas were covered with glaciers.

Geographers have developed several possible explanations for what caused glacial eras. One explanation is that variations in the sun's output of energy and in the earth's orbit may have caused our world to absorb less solar energy and cool off.

Another **hypothesis**, or scientific explanation, suggests that volcanic activity, which put massive amounts of dust in the atmosphere, might have had a cooling effect. Volcanic dust reflected sunlight into space, keeping it from warming the earth.

Geographers also believe that human activity causes changes in the world's climates. Particles in smoke from the burning of fossil fuels may stay in the air for years, scattering the sun's rays. This reduces the sunlight reaching the ground, lowering the temperature.

An opposite effect of burning fossil fuels is the release of carbon dioxide. This gas allows sunlight to reach the ground but prevents some surface heat from leaving the atmosphere. This causes temperatures near the earth's surface to rise—a greenhouse effect. Also, gases produced by burning fuels mix with water in the air, forming acids. These damaging acids fall in rain and snow.

The exhaust from automobiles helps create **smog**, a haze caused by the sun's ultraviolet radiation. Smog endangers people's health.

People also affect climate through water projects, such as dams and river diversions. Dams built for industrial water supplies or for irrigation sometimes cause new areas to become dry.

Geographic Themes

Human/Environment Interaction: South Asia
The monsoons, or seasonal winds, bring practically all the rain that falls on South Asia. Fields and villages can be swept away by flooding. *How do people in various parts of the world respond to climate?*

SECTION 3 REVIEW

Checking for Understanding
1. **Define** natural vegetation, oasis, deciduous, mixed forest, chaparral, prairie, permafrost, taiga, timberline, hypothesis, smog.
2. **Locating Places** What and where are the five main climate regions?
3. **Region** Why do tropical climates have high temperatures year-round?
4. **Human/Environment Interaction** How does climate affect human activities?

Critical Thinking
5. **Distinguishing Fact from Opinion** In what ways may the earth's climate change due to human and natural processes?

MAP & GRAPH SKILLS

Understanding Scale

Maps are a visual representation of the earth's surface. A map can show an area as small as a backyard or as large as the world. How can cartographers draw something as large as a continent on a piece of paper?

REVIEWING THE SKILL

Cartographers draw maps to **scale**. On each map, a measured distance will represent a fixed distance on the earth. For example, 1 inch on a map may represent 100 miles; however, on another map, 1 inch might represent 1,000 miles. This relationship, or **scale of distance**, often is shown as a **scale bar**—a line with numbers specifying the unit of measurement and the number of miles or kilometers this unit represents. On some maps, scale appears as a fraction.

To use the scale of distance on a map, apply the following steps:

- Find the scale bar or scale fraction, and identify the unit of measurement and the distance that unit represents.
- Using this unit of measurement, measure the distance between two points on the map.
- Multiply that number by the number of miles or kilometers represented by each unit.

PRACTICING THE SKILL

Use the maps below to answer the following questions about scale:

1. On each map, what unit measures scale?
2. On Map 1, what is the scale of distance?
3. How far is Orlando from Atlanta?
4. Suppose you are traveling through West Palm Beach on I-95. About how far is it from the intersection of Route 702 to the intersection of Route 98?

For additional practice in this skill, see Practicing Skills on page 60 of the Chapter 3 Review.

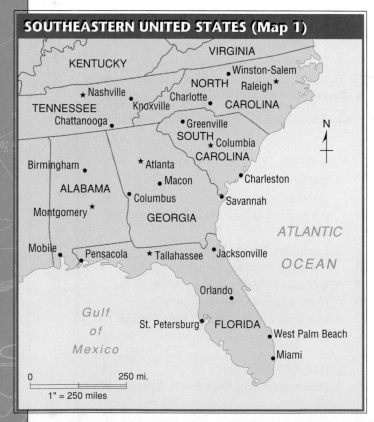

SOUTHEASTERN UNITED STATES (Map 1)

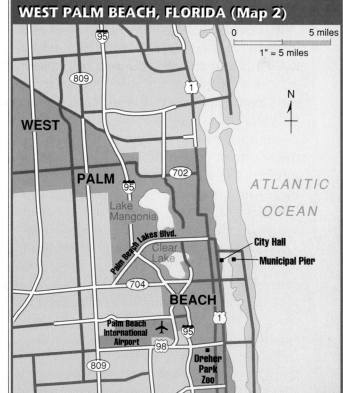

WEST PALM BEACH, FLORIDA (Map 2)

SECTION	KEY TERMS	SUMMARY
1 **Earth-Sun Relationships** **Weather system crossing the Great Plains**	weather (p. 45) climate (p. 45) axis (p. 45) temperature (p. 45) revolution (p. 46) equinox (p. 46) solstice (p. 47)	• The relationship between the earth and the sun affects climates around the world. • The sun provides the earth with heat and light. Different areas of the planet, however, receive different amounts of sunlight at different times.

SECTION	KEY TERMS	SUMMARY
2 **Factors Affecting Climate** **Monument near Quito, Ecuador, marking the line of the Equator**	prevailing wind (p. 50) doldrums (p. 50) current (p. 50) precipitation (p. 51) windward (p. 51) leeward (p. 51) rain shadow (p. 51)	• All places on earth are not heated or cooled equally by the sun. • Latitude, elevation, wind and ocean currents, and landforms also affect climate.

SECTION	KEY TERMS	SUMMARY
3 **World Climate Patterns** 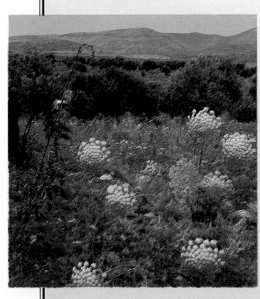 **Mediterranean vegetation in Israel**	natural vegetation (p. 52) oasis (p. 53) deciduous (p. 54) mixed forest (p. 54) chaparral (p. 54) prairie (p. 54) permafrost (p. 55) taiga (p. 55) timberline (p. 56) hypothesis (p. 57) smog (p. 57)	• Geographers often divide the earth into five major climate regions, generally on the basis of latitude. • These regions are tropical, dry, mid-latitude, high latitude, and highland. • Major climate regions are further divided into smaller regions based on such factors as plant life, location, landscape, and temperature. • Climates change over time due to natural and human causes.

Reviewing Key Terms

Choose the vocabulary term that best completes each of the sentences below. Write your answers on a separate sheet of paper.

revolution (p. 46)
equinox (p. 46)
solstice (p. 47)
prevailing wind (p. 50)
leeward (p. 51)
rain shadow (p. 51)
mixed forest (p. 54)
prairie (p. 54)
permafrost (p. 55)
taiga (p. 55)
smog (p. 57)

SECTION 1

1. The day on which the sun is directly over the Equator and the days and nights are equal in length is called an _____ .
2. _____ refers to the earth's trip around the sun.
3. The day on which the direct rays of the sun strike the Tropic of Cancer is called a _____ .

SECTION 2

4. _____ are divided into belts of latitude.
5. A _____ is caused by hot, dry air.
6. _____ refers to the dry side of a mountain.
7. _____ blow in fairly constant patterns.

SECTION 3

8. _____ refers to forested subarctic climate regions.
9. Grasslands that lie inland are _____ areas.
10. Frozen subsoil is known as _____ .
11. The exhaust from automobiles affects climate by causing _____ .
12. Areas with both evergreen and deciduous trees are called _____ .

Reviewing Facts

SECTION 1

13. What causes day and night on the earth?
14. What is the greenhouse effect?

SECTION 2

15. What are the latitudes between the North Pole and the Arctic Circle?
16. What causes ocean currents?

SECTION 3

17. How much of the earth's land surface is covered by desert areas?
18. How does climate affect the way people are clothed and housed?

Critical Thinking

19. **Expressing Problems Clearly** Why is March 21 usually the first day of spring in the Northern Hemisphere?
20. **Making Generalizations** Why do the middle latitudes have a temperate climate?
21. **Analyzing Information** Why do scrubs and cacti grow in desert climates?

Geographic Themes

22. **Movement** How does the earth's tilt affect the temperature of places?
23. **Place** How does the temperature of a place depend on its elevation?
24. **Human/Environment Interaction** Why do people who live in some desert areas wear loose, flowing clothing?

Practicing Skills

Understanding Scale

Refer to the maps on page 58. Suppose you want to travel to the Dreher Park Zoo from City Hall. The most direct route is Route 1. About how many miles would you travel to the zoo? About how many miles would you travel from West Palm Beach to Knoxville, Tennessee?

Projects

Individual Activity

Prepare a chart of climate regions. The first column should describe the climate, the second column should list locations where the climate is found, and the third column should rank the climate according to desirability. Use a world map and the climate map to describe climate in reference to temperature and precipitation. Note at least 4 places on the earth where certain climates occur. Which one would you like to live in? Mark your preference by placing 1 in the third column beside the climate in which you would most like to live, 2 beside your second choice, and so on.

Cooperative Learning Activity

Working in pairs, take climate data from different locations and create a climate graph that shows monthly precipitation and temperature averages. Exchange the climate graphs with other teams of students. Deduce the location of the climate graphs by observing elements such as seasons, precipitation, and temperatures. Let each team prepare clues if help is needed.

Writing About Geography

Cause and Effect

Sections of this chapter review the natural and human causes that may affect climate patterns. Using your journal for reference, write a story that takes place in a future in which the climate has changed in your community. Include details about how this change has affected vegetation, economic activities, and human and animal populations.

Locating Places

THE WORLD: PHYSICAL GEOGRAPHY

Match the letters on the map with the places and physical features of the earth. Write your answers on a separate sheet of paper.

1. Arctic Circle
2. Antarctic Circle
3. Cold Water, Pacific
4. Equator
5. Tropic of Cancer
6. Tropic of Capricorn
7. Warm Water, Atlantic

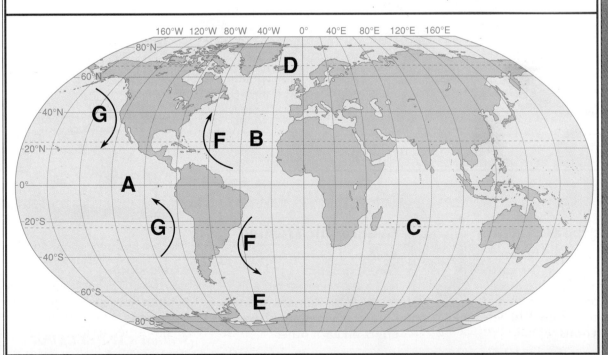

Environments, Peoples, and Cultures

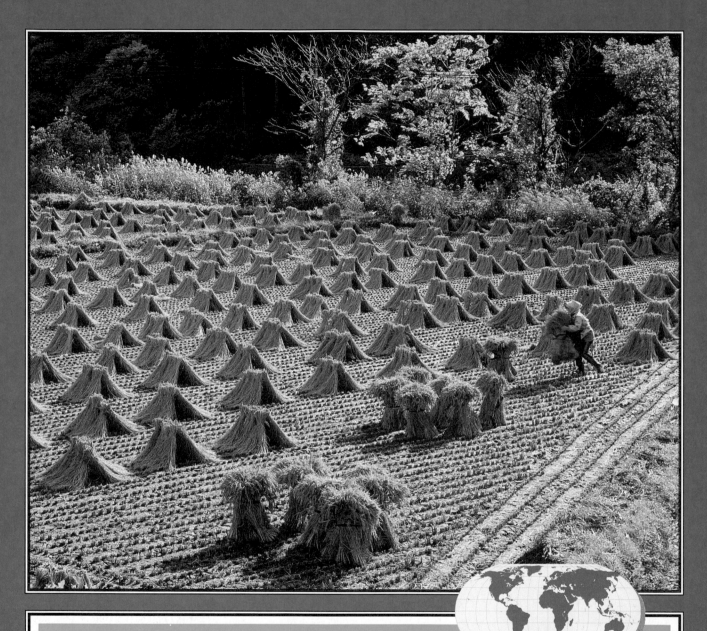

▲ Photograph: *Rice field after a harvest, Japan*

CHAPTER FOCUS

Geographic Setting

More than 5.5 billion people live on the earth. Their ways of life make up a complex pattern of learned customs, beliefs, and actions.

Geographic Themes

Section 1 Limits and Opportunities
HUMAN/ENVIRONMENT INTERACTION Humans and the natural environment have an effect on each other.

Section 2 Cultural Expressions
MOVEMENT Throughout history peoples have exchanged ideas and goods.

Section 3 World Culture Regions Today
REGION Geographers divide the world into culture regions.

Limits and Opportunities

SETTING THE SCENE

Read to Discover . . .
- the differences between developed countries and developing countries.
- the challenges that rapid population growth brings to the planet.
- the impact of environmental hazards on people's lives.

Key Terms
- culture
- subsistence farming
- population distribution
- population density
- tornado
- hurricane
- tsunami
- pollution

Identify and Locate
Canada, Bangladesh, Tornado Alley, Armenia

Culture is the way of life of a group of people with common traditions, interests, and beliefs. A society's culture includes the way in which people meet their needs. The culture of a society also includes its history, government, language, religious beliefs, art, literature, and music.

HUMAN/ENVIRONMENT INTERACTION

Making a Living

Cultures are shaped by the various ways groups of people meet their economic needs. At least 10,000 years ago, agriculture, the earliest form of economic activity, began to develop. Eventually early farmers stopped moving from place to place and began to farm the same land from one season to the next. Successful farmers produced a surplus of food. Because everyone no longer had to raise their own food, some people started to specialize, or do one kind of work, such as weaving or milling grain. They traded their goods and services for the surplus food of farmers. The exchange of goods and services was easier when people gathered in one place. Therefore, villages, towns, and cities often began and grew where trade routes crossed.

Agriculture

Today about half of the world's people still make their living through agriculture. There are two ways to classify agriculture—traditional and commercial. Traditional agriculture, or **subsistence farming**, depends heavily on human labor, animal power, and basic farm

Geographic Themes

Place: Guatemala, Central America
Farmers gather to sell their produce in an outdoor market in the Central American country of Guatemala. *About how many people in the world make their living through agriculture?*

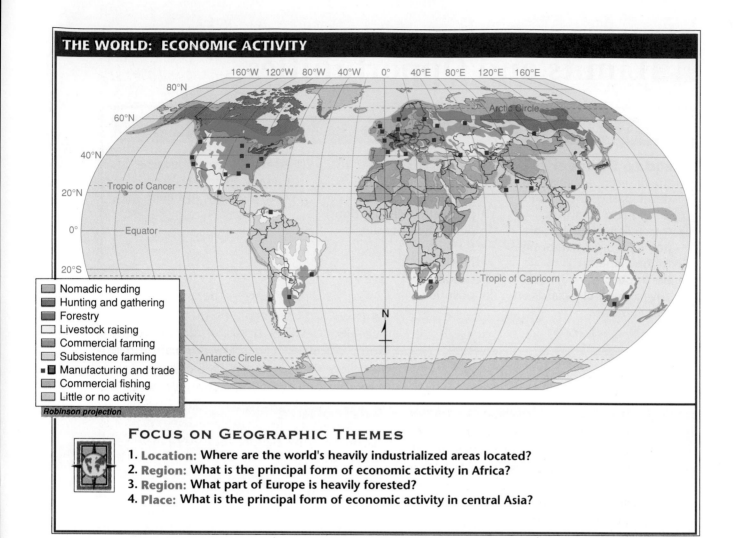

160°W 120°W 80°W 40°W 0° 40°E 80°E 120°E 160°E

80°N
60°N
40°N
20°N
0°
20°S

Arctic Circle
Tropic of Cancer
Equator
Tropic of Capricorn
Antarctic Circle

N

Nomadic herding
Hunting and gathering
Forestry
Livestock raising
Commercial farming
Subsistence farming
Manufacturing and trade
Commercial fishing
Little or no activity

Robinson projection

FOCUS ON GEOGRAPHIC THEMES

1. **Location:** Where are the world's heavily industrialized areas located?
2. **Region:** What is the principal form of economic activity in Africa?
3. **Region:** What part of Europe is heavily forested?
4. **Place:** What is the principal form of economic activity in central Asia?

tools. Traditional farmers usually grow just enough food for themselves. If they are fortunate enough to have a very good crop or have extra livestock, they may sell or trade it; however, most of their efforts involve growing food to eat, not to sell. Most farmers in the world are traditional farmers.

In commercial agriculture, food crops and animals are produced chiefly for sale. Modern fertilizers, pesticides—chemicals used to control pests—and machinery are used to produce crops. Commercial farmers can farm large areas of land using little human labor.

Industry

A business that produces goods or services is called an industry. The number and kinds of industries vary from country to country.

Countries that produce great quantities of goods and services and employ many of their workers in industry are known as developed countries. People in these countries use science to improve their technology and to build well-developed economies. Developed countries generally have adequate food, clothing, and housing as well as good health care and education for their people.

People in many countries in the world meet their needs in much the same way their ancestors did. These countries, known as developing countries, often do not have modern technology and industries. Most lack the money, resources, and skilled workers needed for economic growth. Although populations in their cities have rapidly increased, developing countries are still mainly rural, and the majority of their workers are traditional farmers. Developing countries often have a poor distribution of income, clothing, and housing. Few people get proper health care or attend school, and life expectancy is relatively short.

Population Growth and Distribution

The world's population is more than 5.5 billion and growing rapidly. Scientists estimate that by the year 2000 it will be more than 6.3 billion; and by 2025, more than 8.5 billion.

Growth Rates

The world's population, however, is not growing at the same rate in every country. A country's population growth rate is largely based on the relationship between its birthrate and its death rate. The birthrate is the number of births per year for every 1,000 people. The death rate is the number of deaths per year for every 1,000 people. The difference between those two rates is the natural growth rate.

When the two rates are more or less equal, a country has reached what is called zero population growth. This situation exists in some highly industrialized countries today. In less industrialized countries, however, birthrates are still high, while death rates have fallen because of improved health and living conditions. Population in these countries is growing rapidly compared with the overall world growth rate.

Rapid population growth presents many challenges. As the number of people grows, so does the difficulty of producing enough food to feed them. The birthrates of developing countries are higher than the birthrates of developed countries. Developing countries, however, already have shortages of food, clothing, and housing. Rapidly growing populations in these countries only heighten the problems. Another challenge that faces the world as a result of rapid population growth is the increasing rate at which nonrenewable resources are being used up.

Population Distribution

The **population distribution**, or the population pattern, of the world shows that the continents are not evenly populated. About a third of the earth's surface is land. Mountains, deserts, and climatic extremes, however, make about half of this land nearly uninhabitable. Therefore, almost everyone on earth lives on a relatively small percentage of the earth's surface. Most people live where the soil is fertile, water is available, and the climate is favorable for growing crops and raising animals.

Population Density

Population density—the average number of people in a square mile or square kilometer—varies widely from country to country. Some countries have a low population density; others have many people crowded into a relatively small area. For example, Canada has about 8 people per square mile (3 people per sq. km), while the country of Bangladesh has about 2,320 people per square mile (895 people per sq. km).

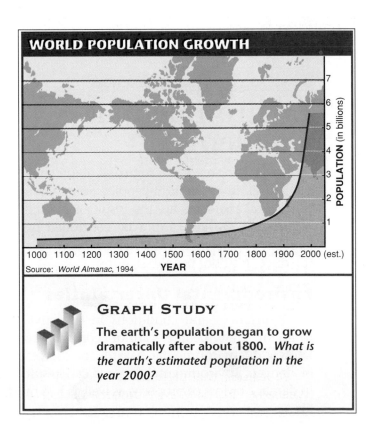

WORLD POPULATION GROWTH

Source: *World Almanac*, 1994   **YEAR**

GRAPH STUDY

The earth's population began to grow dramatically after about 1800. *What is the earth's estimated population in the year 2000?*

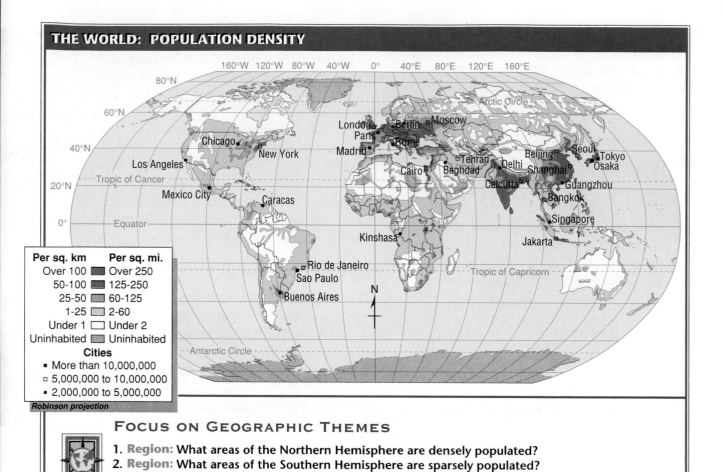

THE WORLD: POPULATION DENSITY

Per sq. km
Over 100
50-100
25-50
1-25
Under 1
Uninhabited

Per sq. mi.
Over 250
125-250
60-125
2-60
Under 2
Uninhabited

Cities
■ More than 10,000,000
□ 5,000,000 to 10,000,000
• 2,000,000 to 5,000,000

Robinson projection

FOCUS ON GEOGRAPHIC THEMES

1. **Region:** What areas of the Northern Hemisphere are densely populated?
2. **Region:** What areas of the Southern Hemisphere are sparsely populated?
3. **Place:** What cities in East Asia have more than 10 million people?
4. **Place:** What city in the United States has more than 10 million people?

HUMAN/ENVIRONMENT INTERACTION

Environmental Challenges

The environment is a source of many challenges to the world's peoples. Some environmental problems are the result of natural occurrences, which cannot be controlled by people. Other environmental problems are the direct result of people's actions.

Environmental Uncertainties

Occurrences and conditions in the environment that people cannot control are known as environmental hazards, or sources of danger. Environmental hazards can result in damage or loss of property, as well as loss of life.

Weather is often the cause of environmental hazards. One type of weather-related hazard is a **tornado**, a powerful, whirling windstorm. The tornado is the most violent of all storms. It may last several hours or just a few minutes and can measure up to 1.5 miles (2.4 km) in diameter. The winds of a tornado, rotating at up to 300 miles (483 km) per hour, destroy almost everything in their path. Only the strongest buildings made of steel and concrete can escape great damage. In the United States, an area of land about 460 miles (740 km) long and 400 miles (644 km) wide extending from northern Texas through Oklahoma, Kansas, and Missouri is known as Tornado Alley. More tornadoes occur annually here than in any other place on the earth.

Another kind of weather-related hazard is a **hurricane**, a powerful, whirling storm that forms over oceans. Unlike a tornado, a hurricane measures several hundred miles (or km) in diameter. The winds and rain of a hurricane combine with the forces of the sea to produce huge waves, called storm surges. The environmental importance of hurricanes lies in the extent of destruction that they can bring to islands and coastal areas.

Earthquakes are another kind of environmental hazard. Most earthquakes are mild and occur beneath the sea. Earthquakes that occur near large cities, however, can result in much damage and loss of life. A disastrous earthquake in Armenia in 1988 resulted in more than 50,000 deaths and 130,000 injuries. Earthquakes occurring primarily under the ocean can result in **tsunami**, or ocean waves. These waves can cause additional damage where they sweep up onto land.

Eruptions of volcanoes and lava flows are severe environmental hazards. Volcanic eruptions have resulted in loss of life and the destruction of towns and cities.

Pollution

A serious environmental problem today is **pollution**—unclean or impure elements in the environment. Pollution affects the air, the water, and the land.

Most air pollution is caused by burning fossil fuels. Burning fuel gives off poisonous gases and tiny particles of solid or liquid matter. Homes, industries, and motor vehicles that burn such fuels are the major sources of air pollution. The burning of garbage and trash also contributes to air pollution.

The most harmful result of air pollution is its effect on people's health. The gases and particles in the air burn people's eyes and irritate their lungs. Air pollution can worsen some respiratory diseases, such as bronchitis and asthma, and cause other diseases, such as cancer. Air pollution can also destroy plants and animals and erode the surfaces of buildings.

There are several causes of water pollution. Tankers and offshore drilling accidents sometimes cause oil spills that pollute the water. Industries dump large amounts of waste products, which include chemicals, into bod-

Geographic Themes

Human/Environment Interaction: Kansas, United States
A whirling tornado sweeps across Sumner County in the state of Kansas. Many tornadoes occur yearly in central parts of the United States. *What effect do tornadoes have on an area?*

ies of water. Untreated sewage, which is made up of people's wastes and garbage, is another major source of water pollution.

Water pollution harms all living things. Plants and animals cannot live in polluted waters. Polluted water is also very harmful to people's health. Higher-level living organisms often store up pollutants obtained by eating lower-level organisms. The pollutants are passed upward in the food chain. Eventually the food eaten by humans may be poisoned to a dangerous level.

Soil pollution involves damage to the thin layer of fertile soil that covers a large portion of the earth's land. Fertilizers and pesticides are the main causes of soil pollution. Soil pollution can damage and contaminate fertile soils that are necessary for growing the world's food.

all too often dumped in streams and ditches, have caused people to get sick and have led to birth defects. They also have contributed to the rise in cancer and other life-shortening diseases.

Attempts at Cleanup

People have developed different ways to control pollution. One way is to use fuels that cause less air pollution. Other ways include removing chemicals from the wastes dumped into water, and improving water treatment facilities. The use of organic farming instead of fertilizers and pesticides helps control soil pollution. Recycling is another step that has been taken to lessen pollution.

Attempts at Regulation

National and local governments in many countries have taken steps to control pollution. Laws have been passed that limit the harmful materials that automobiles and industries can put into the environment. Funds have been established to conduct research into ways of controlling pollution.

Geographic Themes

Place: Hawaiian Islands
Volcanoes formed the Hawaiian Islands. Hawaii, the largest Hawaiian island, has active volcanoes, including Mount Kilauea. *How do volcanoes, such as Mount Kilauea, pose an environmental hazard?*

Solid wastes are a major form of land pollution. People throw out billions of tons of solid wastes each year. Examples of solid wastes are used tires, cans, plastics, and scrap metal. Some of this waste ends up littering roadsides and floating in streams. Many solid wastes end up in open dumps. These dumps provide areas for disease-carrying animals, such as rats, to breed.

Many industrial processes create toxic or hazardous wastes. Nuclear power plants, for example, create radioactive wastes that must be stored properly if they are not to become a threat to society. Poisonous chemical wastes,

---

SECTION 1 REVIEW

Checking for Understanding

1. **Define** culture, subsistence farming, population distribution, population density, tornado, hurricane, tsunami, pollution.
2. **Locating Places** Where is Tornado Alley located?
3. **Region** Why is industry more important in developed countries than it is in developing countries?
4. **Human/Environment Interaction** What factors have contributed to the pollution of air and water?

Critical Thinking

5. **Making Comparisons** How does traditional agriculture compare with commercial farming?

SECTION 2
Cultural Expressions

SETTING THE SCENE

Read to Discover . . .
- how the first civilizations developed.
- the ways in which the movement of people, goods, and ideas has caused cultural change.
- the factors that have contributed to cultural contact and cultural barriers.

Key Terms
- civilization
- history
- prehistory
- culture hearth
- cultural diffusion

Identify and Locate
Egypt, Iraq, Pakistan, China, Greece

A society expresses its culture through such things as language, religion, and the arts. From the beginning of time, people developed different ways of expressing their cultures.

REGION

Cultural Origins

Over the centuries, many cultures have built cities, developed writing systems, and achieved varying kinds of development in the arts, sciences, government, and business. These cultures are often called **civilizations.**

Learning From the Past

Before the rise of civilizations, people focused their attention on meeting basic needs and did not leave many written records. Some of the records they did leave were written in a form that is not understood by people today. Studying the written information about a people's past to learn what, how, and why things happened is called **history.** The time in a people's past before written records were kept is known as **prehistory.**

Geographers have learned about the prehistory of different groups of people with the help of other scientists called archaeologists. Archaeologists study the sites where people once lived, looking for evidence left by these people. Such evidence includes things like buildings and ruins of buildings, bones, and artifacts. Artifacts are objects that were made or used by people, such as weapons, tools, and pottery. Sometimes only bits and pieces of artifacts are found. Archaeologists use artifacts to look for hints about the way people lived before written history. These hints show how cultures developed at certain locations and times.

Culture Hearths

Four ancient civilizations made special contributions to world cultures. These civilizations developed in areas of the world known today as Egypt, Iraq, Pakistan, and China. These areas are known as **culture hearths,** or places where civilizations began.

These culture hearths had certain common geographic features that were helpful for the beginning of early agriculture. Each location was characterized by a mild climate and fertile lands. Each civilization was near a major river. The people discovered ways to make use of these good conditions. For example, they dug canals and ditches in order to use the rivers to irrigate the land. In this way, people were able to grow surplus crops.

Cultural Change

Cultures often are changed by both internal and outside influences. Within a specific culture, discoveries and inventions can promote change. Outside influences come through **cultural diffusion**, or the spread of people, ideas, practices, and goods from one culture to another.

Cultural Contacts

Travel and trade are two age-old activities that have encouraged cultural contacts among different groups of people. As a culture developed better ways of moving over land and water, its trade increased. Inventions like the magnetic compass improved navigation and led to the exploration of new lands. Consequently, contacts were made among many cultures.

Many times people migrated, or made a permanent move to live in another place. Throughout history, migrations have generally occurred as a reaction to natural or political conditions. The Ice Age, for example, caused people to move to warmer climates. People have also migrated to avoid harsh governments, wars, religious persecutions, and famines.

When people migrate, they carry their culture with them. In their new homelands their ideas and ways of doing things generally become mixed with the ideas and ways of the people already living there.

Cultural Barriers

While some factors have encouraged cultural contact, others have created barriers to it. Natural barriers, such as huge deserts, high mountains, dense rain forests, and unknown ocean waters, have sometimes restricted the movement of goods and ideas between cultures.

People have also created cultural barriers. Such barriers generally come about because of

Geographic Themes

Movement: Northern China
The early Chinese built the Great Wall in the northern part of their country to keep out foreign invaders. *What impact did the Great Wall have on Chinese relations with the outside world?*

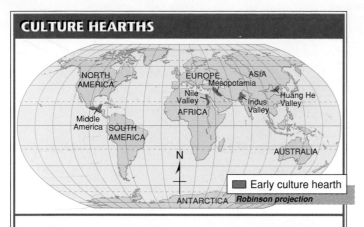

CULTURE HEARTHS

Early culture hearth

Robinson projection

FOCUS ON GEOGRAPHIC THEMES

1. **Region:** What culture hearths emerged in Asia?
2. **Region:** On what continent did the Nile Valley culture hearth develop?

people's beliefs. One culture might not understand or accept another culture's activities or viewpoints. This lack of understanding leads to fear or mistrust. Such feelings encouraged the ancient Chinese to build their Great Wall to keep others from crossing their boundaries.

Today the barriers posed by distance and natural features are gradually disappearing. Technology enables people to speak to others almost anywhere in the world. Satellites broadcast television signals around the globe. As modern communications systems spread more information, cultural exchange will increase.

Far-reaching Changes

Peoples and their cultures change and evolve through time. Historians have labeled periods of time when change has taken place on a large scale and created a great impact. The time when European countries were exploring the world, for example, is called the Age of Discovery. The mobility of this period encouraged cultural diffusion.

The Industrial Revolution was another time of great change. Power-driven machinery and mass production were introduced at a rapid pace. This led to great changes in the economies of many countries, since goods could be produced quickly and cheaply. The Industrial Revolution also led to social changes. Many people moved to large cities in order to get jobs in factories.

Historians also have labeled periods when great ideas are stressed. One such period is known as the Age of Classical Greece. This period is known for its democratic ideas of government and for its great achievements in art. The Renaissance (REN•uh•SAHNTS), meaning rebirth, is the name given to a period that took place hundreds of years after the time of classical Greece. During the Renaissance, many ideas of early civilizations were reintroduced, and there was a great search for knowledge that led to many changes in the arts, the sciences, and education.

At certain times in history, ideas about government have been rethought. People often wanted more freedom from their rulers. Sometimes, the desire for freedom led to revolutions, or complete changes in government in short periods of time. An age of nationalism also developed. Nationalism involves loyalty and devotion to country. Before the development of nationalism, people generally expressed their loyalty to individual rulers. Nationalism includes a people's pride in their heritage, or those things handed on to people from their ancestors. A people's history and culture are a part of their heritage.

SECTION 2 REVIEW

Checking for Understanding
1. **Define** civilization, history, prehistory, culture hearth, cultural diffusion.
2. **Locating Places** Where did the earliest civilizations develop?
3. **Movement** What factors have affected contact between cultures?
4. **Movement** How have cultural changes had far-reaching effects?

Critical Thinking
5. **Identifying Central Issues** Why do people create cultural barriers?

OUT OF OZONE

*T*hough the news keeps breaking, good and bad, the Montreal Protocol is a real achievement. For once, nations worked together to prevent an environmental catastrophe instead of trying haplessly to repair one that has already happened.

The Global Citizen, 1991

In March 1985, British scientists announced that they had recorded a steady loss of ozone in the upper atmosphere during the previous 10 years. NASA confirmed the British report. Later in the year, American scientists added alarming figures of their own: ozone above Antarctica was depleted 40 to 60 percent.

Discovery of the "ozone hole," as the media dubbed it, shocked the world. Scientific teams around the globe began a burst of research and environmental and diplomatic activities to push national governments into action.

In September of 1987, representatives from 46 countries met in Montreal, Canada, to consider the proposal. From this meeting came the Montreal Protocol, the first multinational treaty to curb a global air pollutant.

THE ISSUE

The Montreal Protocol called on the world's nations to cut in half their use of chemicals proven devastating to the ozone layer. Developed nations, accounting for 97 percent of such use, supported the treaty. Many had already begun to search for substitute chemicals.

Developing nations, however, protested the treaty. They pointed out that the chemicals in question were so widely used in their growing industries that to cut their use would stop economic progress in their countries. In addition, they said, their governments could not afford the costs of finding substitutes.

THE BACKGROUND

The ozone layer is a "buffer zone" of pale blue gas between 14 and 15 miles up in the atmosphere. It protects the earth from the sun's deadly ultraviolet rays.

The same studies that exposed the ozone hole also exposed the factor destroying it: *chlorofluorocarbons* (CFCs). CFCs are "wonder" gases that do not rust, explode, burn, or pose immediate dangers to users. They are found in refrigerators, air conditioners, fire extinguishers, plastic foams, aerosol sprays, and many other products. CFCs, however, are very hard to contain. Millions are produced every year, and most find their way to the upper atmosphere. There they devour highly unstable ozone molecules.

> *Most scientists agree, however, that ozone-damaging CFCs will remain in the atmosphere for 75 years.*

THE POINTS OF VIEW

Developing nations, led by China, India, and Brazil, protested that cutting CFC use would considerably hurt their economic progress. In China, for example, refrigerator production is the fastest growing sector of their economy. Besides, developing nations used only a small percentage of CFCs: China, India, and Brazil—the 3 largest—account

HOW CFCs DESTROY OZONE

Ultraviolet light — Chlorofluorocarbon molecule

Free chlorine atom → Ozone molecule

Chlorine monoxide → Oxygen molecule

Carbon, fluorine, and chlorine atoms make up CFC molecules. Ultraviolet rays break chlorine atoms free.

A free chlorine atom "steals" an oxygen atom from an ozone molecule.

Oxygen and the chlorine atoms then form a molecule of chlorine monoxide. The two remaining oxygen atoms form an oxygen molecule.

The chlorine monoxide molecule can break up again and again to "eat" more ozone molecules. A single atom of chlorine can devour 100,000 molecules of ozone!

A computer-generated image shows the "hole" that has appeared in the ozone layer above Antarctica.

for 2 percent of the world's CFC use. A Chinese environmental official stated, "Developed countries are responsible for most of the damage to the ozone layer so they should do the most to clean up the problem."

Without that buffer, more of the sun's ultraviolet rays would reach the earth. Such rays cause skin cancer and eye cataracts, weaken the body's immune system, and harm plants, wildlife, and marine food chains.

THE ISSUE TODAY

By the end of 1989, continuing reports that the ozone layer was disappearing more rapidly than first thought caused another UN-sponsored meeting. In Helsinki, Finland, delegates from 80 nations revised the Montreal Protocol to completely ban CFC use in industrialized nations by the year 2000, and in developing nations by 2010. Developed countries agreed to establish a global fund to help developing nations find substitute chemicals.

In 1992 both the European Union and the United States announced that their industries would stop the use of CFCs by 1995. Most scientists agree, however, that ozone-damaging CFCs will remain in the atmosphere for 75 years. The ozone layer may not return to its full strength until at least 2100.

Reviewing the Case

1. **What was the final main provision of the Montreal Protocol?**
2. **Why did developing nations object to the treaty's demands?**
3. **Human/Environment Interaction** What concerns does the Montreal Protocol address?

SETTING THE SCENE

Read to Discover . . .
- what factors are considered to determine the earth's culture regions.
- how other social sciences help geographers determine culture regions.

Key Terms
- culture region
- government
- standard of living
- economic system
- per capita income
- free enterprise
- capitalism
- socialism
- language family
- religion

Identify and Locate
World culture regions: United States and Canada; Latin America; Europe; Russia and the Eurasian Republics; North Africa and Southwest Asia; Africa South of the Sahara; South Asia; East Asia; Southeast Asia; Australia, Oceania, and Antarctica

G eographers often divide the planet into areas called **culture regions.** These culture regions may not have clear boundaries. For this reason geographers with varying viewpoints may use different ways to decide the number of culture regions and the countries included in each. The authors of this book have divided the world into the 10 culture regions shown on the map. Geographers, as well as political scientists, economists, sociologists, and anthropologists, might divide the world into different culture regions based on government, social groups, economic systems, languages, or religions.

REGION

Governments

P eople who study **governments,** or groups' political systems, are political scientists. The kind of government a society has reflects the values of a culture. Democracy—a form of government in which the people of a country vote for their leaders—shows that the people value individual freedom.

Among some cultures, the power of the government is more important than individual freedom. These governments are called authoritarian governments. A government in which one leader has full power over a country is a dictatorship. Iraq and North Korea are dictatorships.

Some countries combine elements. For example, some countries that have monarchs—kings or queens—also have elected a lawmaking group. This type of government is called a constitutional monarchy.

REGION

Social Groups

T hose who study people's relationships to one another in groups are called sociologists. Sociologists study the structure of a society, people's social institutions, and the quality of life in a society.

Sociologists use certain measures to determine how well a society meets its needs. For example, the infant survival rate—the number of babies that live to be 1 year old out of the number of babies born—is often used. This figure and a group's life expectancy, or the average number of years a person can expect to live, show the level of health care. The number of people in a group who can read and write is the literacy rate. This figure shows how

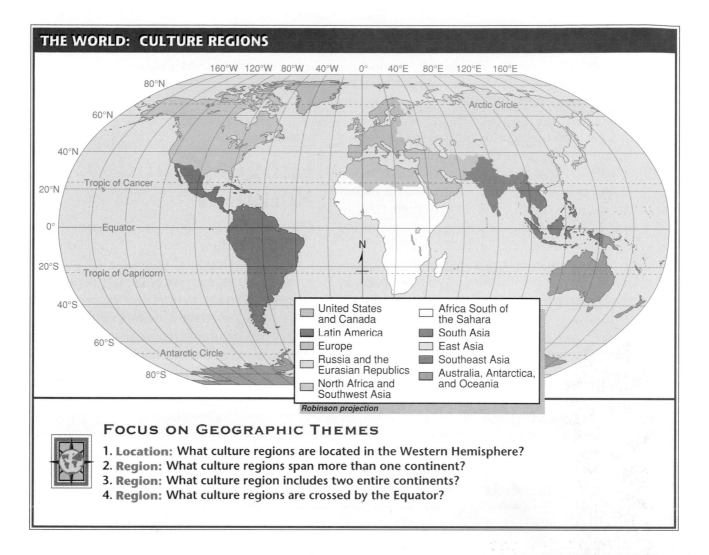

THE WORLD: CULTURE REGIONS

Legend:
- United States and Canada
- Latin America
- Europe
- Russia and the Eurasian Republics
- North Africa and Southwest Asia
- Africa South of the Sahara
- South Asia
- East Asia
- Southeast Asia
- Australia, Antarctica, and Oceania

Robinson projection

FOCUS ON GEOGRAPHIC THEMES

1. **Location:** What culture regions are located in the Western Hemisphere?
2. **Region:** What culture regions span more than one continent?
3. **Region:** What culture region includes two entire continents?
4. **Region:** What culture regions are crossed by the Equator?

widely people are educated. The **standard of living** measures the quality of life based on available material goods.

Sometimes quality of life is affected by urbanization—the growth of large cities. Rapid growth can be a problem if the city cannot provide such things as food and housing.

REGION

Economic Systems

A country's **economic system** is the way in which the people of the country produce, get, and use goods and services. Economists are people who study and describe how economic systems work.

The value of all goods and services produced annually by the citizens, working inside or outside the country, is the gross national

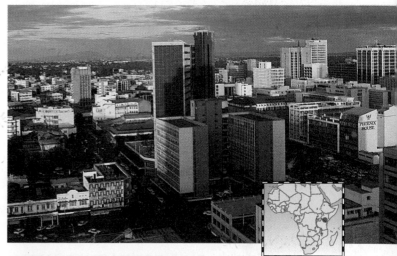

Geographic Themes

Place: Nairobi, Kenya
The African country of Kenya—along with its modern capital, Nairobi—has prospered under a free enterprise economy. *What is the relationship between government and business in a free enterprise economy?*

product (GNP). Many nations prefer the more precise measure of gross domestic product (GDP). GDP covers all annual production *within* a country. It includes output by both foreign and domestic concerns operating in that country.

Per capita income measures how much money per person a country or a region earns. GNP, GDP, and per capita income help classify countries. A developed country has a manufacturing economy and a fairly high GNP or GDP. A developing country has an agricultural economy and a fairly low GNP or GDP.

Governments that value individual freedom often have economic systems based on **free enterprise.** Under free enterprise private businesses operate with little interference from government. An economic system based on free enterprise, as in the United States, is called **capitalism.** Authoritarian governments often use an economic system called **socialism**, in which the government decides how resources will be used and how businesses will be run.

Language and Religion

Scientists who study people's cultures are called anthropologists. These scientists trace the development of people's cultures by considering factors such as language. Languages spoken in a culture region often belong to the same **language family**, or group of languages having similar beginnings. Some major languages are Chinese, English, Hindi, Russian, Spanish, and Arabic.

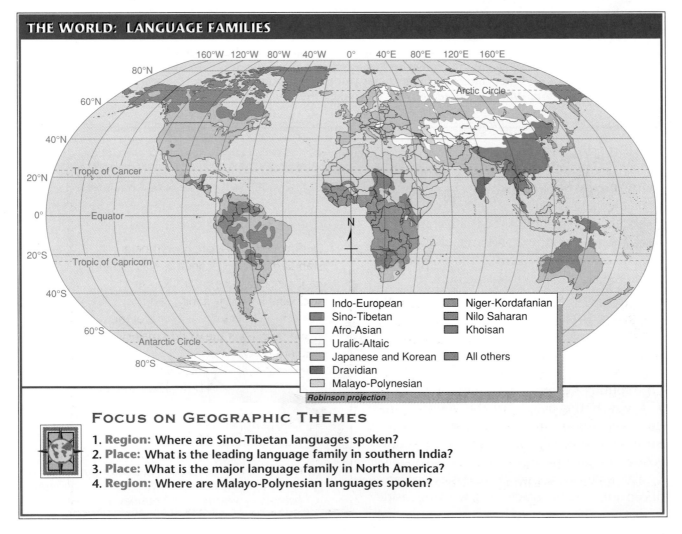

THE WORLD: LANGUAGE FAMILIES

Legend:
- Indo-European
- Sino-Tibetan
- Afro-Asian
- Uralic-Altaic
- Japanese and Korean
- Dravidian
- Malayo-Polynesian
- Niger-Kordafanian
- Nilo Saharan
- Khoisan
- All others

Robinson projection

FOCUS ON GEOGRAPHIC THEMES

1. **Region:** Where are Sino-Tibetan languages spoken?
2. **Place:** What is the leading language family in southern India?
3. **Place:** What is the major language family in North America?
4. **Region:** Where are Malayo-Polynesian languages spoken?

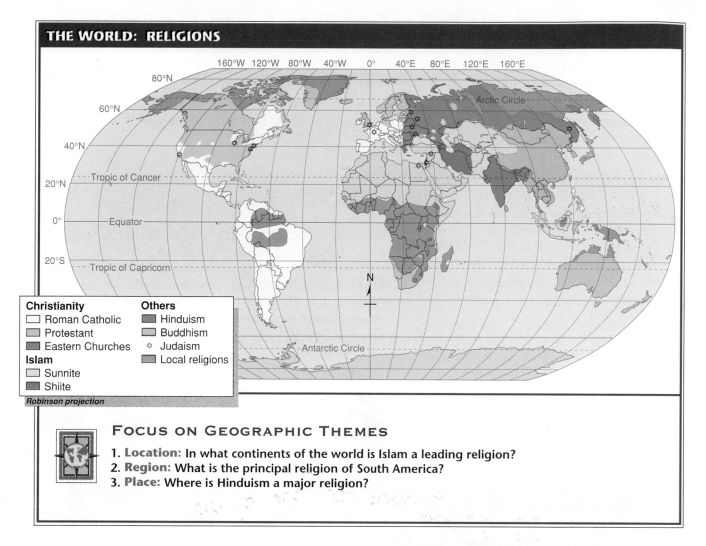

THE WORLD: RELIGIONS

Christianity
- ☐ Roman Catholic
- ☐ Protestant
- ☐ Eastern Churches

Islam
- ☐ Sunnite
- ☐ Shiite

Others
- ☐ Hinduism
- ☐ Buddhism
- ✡ Judaism
- ☐ Local religions

Robinson projection

FOCUS ON GEOGRAPHIC THEMES

1. **Location:** In what continents of the world is Islam a leading religion?
2. **Region:** What is the principal religion of South America?
3. **Place:** Where is Hinduism a major religion?

Language is a powerful tool of communication. It offers a way for people to share information and experiences. Language also permits people to preserve their past and present experiences through history and literature. Through the written word, the people of one generation can pass their knowledge and skills to later generations.

Anthropologists also consider people's **religion** when studying their cultures. Religion is an organized way of worshiping a spiritual being or thinking about life. Anthropologists study which religions are practiced in different parts of the world. Some of the major religions in the world today are Judaism, Christianity, Buddhism, Islam, Hinduism, and Confucianism. Religion and language are part of a society's traditions, or the practices and beliefs passed on to people throughout the ages.

SECTION 3 REVIEW

Checking for Understanding

1. **Define** culture region, government, standard of living, economic system, per capita income, free enterprise, capitalism, socialism, language family, religion.
2. **Locating Places** In what parts of the world do each of the world's major religions predominate?
3. **Region** What factors are considered when describing different culture regions?

Critical Thinking

4. **Analyzing Information** Why do scientists use such measures as GNP, GDP, and literacy rate in studying groups of people?

MAP & GRAPH SKILLS

Interpreting a Climate Graph

Throughout history people have adapted to different climates. The discoveries of fire and clothing allowed humans to live in cold climates. Dams and irrigation systems have reduced damage from floods and droughts. Despite these discoveries, climate is still a major factor in human culture.

REVIEWING THE SKILL

A climate graph shows the annual variation in temperature and precipitation in a given region. In the graphs below, the months of the year are shown on the horizontal axis. Temperature (in °Fahrenheit and °Centigrade) appears on the left vertical axis as a line graph; precipitation (in inches and millimeters) appears on the right vertical axis as a bar graph.

To analyze the graphs, apply these steps:
- Study the values shown for precipitation and temperature to determine the general nature of the climate (hot/cool, wet/dry).
- Determine annual temperature variation by identifying highest and lowest temperatures.
- Determine annual precipitation variation.
- Identify the months with the most extreme temperatures and precipitation.

- Use this information to describe and compare the two climates.

PRACTICING THE SKILL

Use the graphs below to answer the following questions about climate graphs:
1. Which city is warmest year-round?
2. Which city has the wettest climate?
3. Which city has the greatest annual variation in temperature?
4. What are Mogadishu's driest months? Its wettest month?
5. In which months do both cities have about the same average temperature?

For additional practice in this skill, see Practicing Skills on page 80 of the Chapter 4 Review.

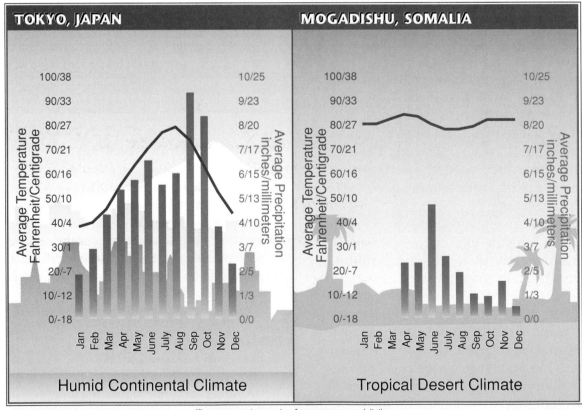

TOKYO, JAPAN — Humid Continental Climate

MOGADISHU, SOMALIA — Tropical Desert Climate

Source: *World Weather Guide*, 1990   *lines measure temperature/bars measure precipitation

1 SECTION	KEY TERMS	SUMMARY
Limits and Opportunities Market scene in Guatemala	culture (p. 63) subsistence farming (p. 63) population distribution (p. 65) population density (p. 65) tornado (p. 66) hurricane (p. 66) tsunami (p. 67) pollution (p. 67)	• Nations can be classified as either developed or developing. Developed countries are highly industrialized, while developing countries are largely agricultural. • The rapidly growing population of the world is creating many challenges, including meeting food needs and conserving resources. • Environmental hazards include weather-related phenomena and pollution.

2 SECTION	KEY TERMS	SUMMARY
Cultural Expressions 	civilization (p. 69) history (p. 69) prehistory (p. 69) culture hearth (p. 69) cultural diffusion (p. 70) Archaeological dig	• Cultures express themselves in different ways. Some important cultural expressions are language, religion, and the arts. • Early civilizations developed near major rivers in areas where the climate was mild and the lands were fertile. • As cultures developed better modes of transportation, trade increased and cultural contacts were made.

3 SECTION	KEY TERMS	SUMMARY
World Culture Regions Today Nairobi, Kenya	culture region (p. 74) government (p. 74) standard of living (p. 75) economic system (p. 75) per capita income (p. 76) free enterprise (p. 76) capitalism (p. 76) socialism (p. 76) language family (p. 76) religion (p. 77)	• To help them describe people and cultures, geographers divide the world into culture regions. • Different factors are used to determine world culture regions. Among the factors considered are environment, history, language, religion, government, social structure, and economy.

Reviewing Key Terms

Choose the vocabulary term that best completes each of the sentences below. Write your answers on a separate sheet of paper.

culture (p. 63)
subsistence farming (p. 63)
tornado (p. 66)
tsunami (p. 67)
civilization (p. 69)
cultural diffusion (p. 70)
capitalism (p. 76)
free enterprise (p. 76)
socialism (p. 76)

SECTION 1

1. A _____ is a powerful, whirling storm that ranks as the most violent of all storms.
2. _____ is the way of life of a group of people having common traditions, interests, and beliefs.
3. Earthquakes under the ocean can result in _____, or ocean waves.
4. Many people in developing countries engage in _____.

SECTION 2

5. The spread of ideas and practices from one part of the world to another is called _____.
6. A culture with a high level of development in the arts and sciences is called a _____.

SECTION 3

7. _____ is an economic system based on free enterprise.
8. The American economy is based on the principles of _____.
9. Under _____, a government decides how resources will be used and how businesses will be run.

Reviewing Facts

SECTION 1

10. What challenges does the world's rapidly growing population present?

SECTION 2

11. What is prehistory? History?

SECTION 3

12. What are some major languages of the world today?

Critical Thinking

13. **Making Comparisons** How do developed and developing countries differ?
14. **Identifying Central Issues** What steps have governments taken to solve environmental problems?
15. **Analyzing Information** Why are countries increasingly preferring gross domestic product (GDP) over gross national product (GNP) as a measure of economic well-being?

Geographic Themes

16. **Human/Environment Interaction** What is the most harmful result of air pollution?
17. **Region** What geographic features did culture hearths have in common?
18. **Movement** Why have cultures changed over the years?

Practicing Skills

Interpreting a Climate Graph

Refer to the climate graph on page 78.

19. Referring to the climate graph for Mogadishu, how would you describe a desert climate?
20. Referring to the climate graph for Tokyo, how would you describe a humid continental climate?
21. What is the total annual precipitation for each city?
22. What are the highest and lowest average monthly temperatures for each city?

Projects

Individual Activity

Make a list of objects that you own or use, such as clothes, radios, and sports gear. Note where each item was manufactured. Locate these places on a world map. What culture regions of the world have contributed most to your way of life?

Cooperative Learning Activity

Working with a partner, use a world almanac and other data sources to create an economic data chart of selected countries of the world. Pick 10 countries from different culture regions. For each country, find information that provides evidence of its level of economic development. Rank the countries by level of development. Compare your findings with those of other groups.

Writing About Geography

Narration

In this chapter, you have read about the characteristics of cultures, such as political systems, economic systems, religions, and languages. Pick a current international event that is significant and write a geographic analysis of the story. Apply the observations recorded in your journal as well as the ideas and concepts that you have learned in this chapter to discuss the event in geographic terms.

Locating Places

THE WORLD: CULTURE REGIONS

Match the letters on the map with the culture regions of the world. Write your answers on a separate sheet of paper.

1. The United States and Canada
2. Latin America
3. Europe
4. Russia and the Eurasian Republics
5. North Africa and Southwest Asia
6. Africa South of the Sahara
7. South Asia
8. East Asia
9. Southeast Asia
10. Australia, Oceania, and Antarctica

GEOGRAPHY CONNECTION

The World and the United States

THE GLOBAL CULTURE

Since the end of World War II, the fads and fashions of the United States have spread across the globe. American television, American businesses and industries, and American products have greatly influenced today's global culture.

ROCK AS WELL AS COUNTRY AND WESTERN MUSIC ▶ are popular from Mozambique to Japan. Rock began as rock 'n roll, getting its start in the 1950s with American musicians Chuck Berry and Elvis Presley. Country and western developed from early American folk tunes. During the mid-1980s, country music began to gain in worldwide popularity. This Japanese teenager is part of a rock band performing before an outdoor audience.

▼ SKYSCRAPERS are found in many countries of the world. These structures first reached skyward in Chicago and New York. Steel-and-concrete buildings now define skylines throughout the world. These modern skyscrapers in Cairo, Egypt, provide living and office space for the city's growing population.

◀ PRODUCTS FROM OTHER NATIONS, such as this German sports car, influence American culture. From Japanese assembly lines come automobiles and electronic products. Silk, batik, and bamboo goods make their way to American malls from Thailand, Turkey, and India. Colorful textiles from Africa modify our fashions.

▲ JEANS AND SNEAKERS, worn by these students in Latin America, are two of the most popular products from the United States ever to reach global markets. Developed in the 1860s by Levi Strauss, jeans took off globally in the 1950s, when jeans-wearing American movie stars Marlon Brando and James Dean roared onto movie screens. United States Rubber introduced rubber-soled Keds in 1917. As other brands of rubber-soled footwear appeared, they became known as sneakers because wearers could "sneak" around almost soundlessly on the rubber soles.

▲ MASS PRODUCTION AND MOVING ASSEMBLY LINES characterize manufacturing in most of the world's nations. The American automobile industry developed assembly lines during the early 1900s. Mass production is now an indispensable part of manufacturing worldwide. These South African workers are assembling transistor radios.

AMERICAN FAST FOODS ▶ are as much a part of global culture as they are of American culture. Shoppers in Moscow and Milan enjoy Kentucky Fried Chicken. Coca-Cola fills glasses in Budapest, Beijing, and Bogotá. This customer is buying a McDonald's hamburger in Tokyo.

Checking for Understanding

1. What are the main features of the global culture?
2. **Movement** In what ways are you a global citizen?

The United States and Canada

GeoJournal Activity

As you study this region of the world, look through newspapers and magazines for articles about the United States and Canada. Cut out any articles you find and place them in the following categories: Geography, Peoples and Cultures, and Economy and Environment.

© Annie Griffiths Belt

NATIONAL GEOGRAPHIC SOCIETY

Picturing the World

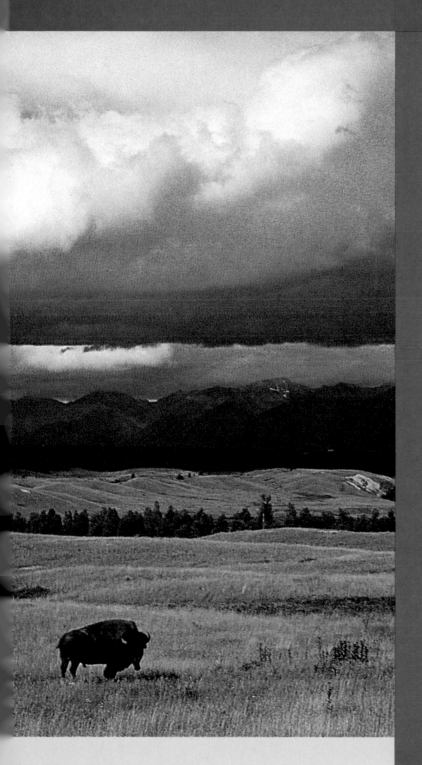

The landscape of the National Bison Range in northwestern Montana still looks much like the shortgrass plains of more than a century ago. Before settlement, the Great Plains consisted of shortgrass plains to the drier west and tallgrass prairies to the wetter east. Settlers converted much of the Great Plains—especially the eastern tallgrass prairie—to fields of corn and wheat. Look at the map on page 88.

1. What large mountain system (visible in the photo) is located to the west of the Great Plains?
2. What is the elevation range of the western short-grass plains?
3. Now look at the map on page 99. What is the climate of the western shortgrass plains?

Picture Atlas CD-ROM Enrichment Corner

Assemble a file of Great Plains information. (See the *Picture Atlas of the World* User's Guide for information on how to use the Collector button.) Include in your file the essays on the United States and Canada and the two photographs of the Great Plains. Then answer the following questions:

1. What percent of the world's corn does the United States produce?
2. The United States leads the world in the export of what grain?
3. What nickname describes the Great Plains?
4. Canada ranks second worldwide in the export of what crop?

EXPLORING CULTURAL DIVERSITY

1. **What areas of this region are the most populated? Least populated?**
2. **Which states of the United States have Spanish roots?**
3. **What countries border the United States?**

French Canadians make up a little more than one-fourth of Canada's population. Most French Canadians live in the province of Quebec.

UNITED STATES AND CANADA: POLITICAL

— National boundary
— State boundary
⊛ National capital

Lambert Equal-Area projection

The border of the **United States** and **Canada** is the longest undefended border in the world.

Hawaii's population includes many citizens of Japanese, Filipino, Chinese, Korean, and Polynesian ancestry.

California, Colorado, Arizona, New Mexico, and **Texas** once belonged to Spain. The area's culture reflects its Spanish roots.

Many people who live in **Miami, Florida,** claim a Cuban heritage. During the 1970s, 1980s, and 1990s, many Cuban refugees risked death to sail to Florida.

About 6 of every 10 Canadians live in **Ontario** or **Quebec**.

UNITED STATES AND CANADA: POPULATION DENSITY

Per sq. km	Per sq. mi.
Over 100	Over 250
50-100	125-250
25-50	60-125
1-25	2-60
Under 1	Under 2
Uninhabited	Uninhabited

Cities
- ■ Over 5,000,000
- ▫ 2,000,000 – 5,000,000
- ◉ 1,000,000 – 2,000,000
- ● 250,000 – 1,000,000
- ○ Under 250,000

Lambert Equal-Area projection

California is the most populous of the 50 American states.

During the 1980s, many Americans moved to the southern and western **Sunbelt** states to take advantage of growing business opportunities and the mild climate.

The deserts of **Arizona** and **New Mexico** are home to many **Native Americans**.

New York City is the largest urban center in the United States and one of the most famous cities in the world.

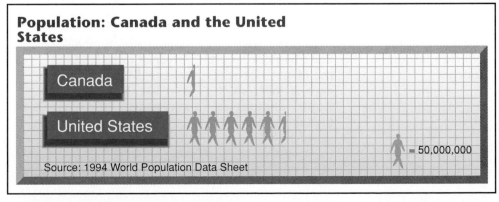

Population: Canada and the United States

Canada

United States

Source: 1994 World Population Data Sheet

🧍 = 50,000,000

The population of the **United States** is almost 10 times that of **Canada**.

CHARTING YOUR COURSE

1. *What ocean borders this region to the east? To the west?*
2. *Name two mountains located in this region.*
3. *What are four of this region's principal natural resources?*
4. *What major waterways are found in the United States and Canada?*

The **Canadian Shield**, which covers almost half of Canada, is a huge area of ancient rock.

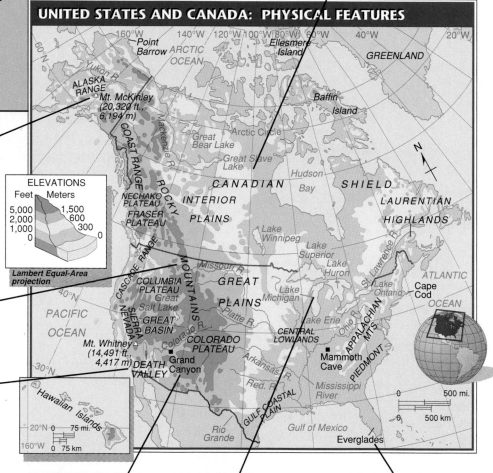

UNITED STATES AND CANADA: PHYSICAL FEATURES

ELEVATIONS
Feet   Meters
5,000   1,500
2,000   600
1,000   300
   0   0

Lambert Equal-Area projection

Mt. McKinley, rising 20,320 feet (6,194 m) in Alaska, is North America's highest mountain.

The Rockies, the region's largest mountain system, stretch more than 3,000 miles (4,827 km) from Alaska to New Mexico.

Death Valley in California, the continent's hottest spot, is the lowest place in the Western Hemisphere—282 feet (89 m) below sea level.

Arizona's **Grand Canyon** is the world's largest gorge.

The **Great Lakes** on the United States-Canadian border are the planet's largest expanse of freshwater—about one-fifth of the planet's supply.

Florida's **Everglades** have been called a "river of grass" 100 miles (161 km) long and 50 miles (81 km) wide.

UNITED STATES AND CANADA: NATURAL RESOURCES

Legend:
- I Iron ore
- Petroleum
- Coal
- Copper
- Zinc
- Gold
- Silver

Lambert Equal-Area projection

The **Canadian Shield** holds rich stores of copper, nickel, zinc, and iron ore.

Forests cover almost half of **Canada.** The country is the world's leading exporter of lumber and producer of newsprint.

The fertile soil of the **Midwest** of the **United States** helps make the country the world's agricultural leader.

The fertile soil of the eastern **Great Plains** produces large quantities of soybeans and corn.

The region's greatest quantities of fish are caught in coastal waters off the **Gulf of Mexico.**

United States: Physical Profile

COAST RANGES · ROCKY MOUNTAINS · GREAT PLAINS · CENTRAL LOWLANDS · APPALACHIAN MOUNTAINS · ATLANTIC COASTAL PLAIN

12000 ft. · 6000 ft. · 3000 ft. · 1200 ft. · Sea level

PACIFIC OCEAN · ATLANTIC OCEAN

West to East at 39°N latitude

Canada: Physical Profile

COAST MOUNTAINS · ROCKY MOUNTAINS · INTERIOR PLAINS · LAKE SUPERIOR · CANADIAN SHIELD · LAURENTIAN HIGHLANDS · GULF OF ST. LAWRENCE

12000 ft. · 6000 ft. · 3000 ft. · 1200 ft. · Sea level

PACIFIC OCEAN · ATLANTIC OCEAN

West to East at 49°N latitude

COUNTRY* AND CAPITAL	FLAG AND LANGUAGES	POPULATION	LANDMASS	PRINCIPAL EXPORT	PRODUCTS IMPORT
Canada Ottawa	English, French	29,100,000 8 per sq. mi. 3 per sq. km	3,849,674 sq. mi. 9,970,610 sq. km	Motor Vehicles	Motor Vehicles
United States Washington, D.C.	English	260,800,000 74 per sq. mi. 28 per sq. km	3,539,230 sq. mi. 9,166,606 sq. km	Machinery	Machinery

*Country maps not drawn to scale.

The United States and Canada both are democracies. The United States Congress meets in the United States Capitol in Washington, D.C. (below). The Canadian Parliament assembles in the Parliament Building in Ottawa (left).

A NEW CANADA?

On October 30, 1995, voters in Quebec faced a decision: Should Quebec remain a province of Canada or should it become independent? By a perilously close 51-49 percent margin, the voters decided against secession. Why would Quebec want to secede from the rest of Canada? And what would happen if, in the future, Quebec is successful in gaining independence?

Quebec At a Glance

• Area: At 594,860 square miles—more than twice the size of Texas—Quebec is Canada's largest province.
• Population: With 7.2 million people, Quebec holds 25 percent of the Canadian population.
• Language: About 82 percent of Quebeckers speak French, the province's official language.
• GDP: Quebec produces $116.9 billion in GDP, 22 percent of Canada's total GDP.

Quebec's desire to secede springs from a desire to preserve its French language and unique culture. Separatists believe that having their own nation is the only way Quebeckers can control their destiny. Quebec's separatists, who lost a 1980 independence referendum by a 60-40 percent vote, narrowed the margin so dramatically in 1995 that another attempt at nationhood is sure to be launched.

If Quebec were to become its own nation, the rest of Canada would suffer. Quebec holds one-fourth of Canada's people and one-sixth of its land. Trade with the United States—about $1 billion a day—would be disrupted as Canada reorganized its economy. And the Maritime Provinces—Nova Scotia, New Brunswick, Newfoundland, and Prince Edward Island—would be cut off from the rest of Canada.

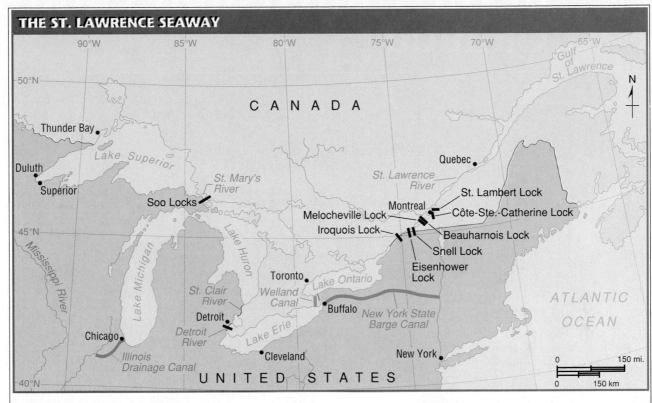

THE ST. LAWRENCE SEAWAY

Thunder Bay
Duluth
Superior
Lake Superior
St. Mary's River
Soo Locks
CANADA
Quebec
St. Lawrence River
St. Lambert Lock
Montreal
Melocheville Lock
Côte-Ste.-Catherine Lock
Iroquois Lock
Beauharnois Lock
Snell Lock
Eisenhower Lock
Mississippi River
Lake Michigan
Lake Huron
Toronto
Lake Ontario
Welland Canal
St. Clair River
Detroit
Detroit River
Buffalo
New York State Barge Canal
ATLANTIC OCEAN
Chicago
Illinois Drainage Canal
Lake Erie
Cleveland
New York
UNITED STATES
Gulf of St. Lawrence

0   150 mi.
0   150 km

Duluth
St. Mary's River
Soo Locks
St. Clair River
Detroit River
Welland Canal
Iroquois Lock
Eisenhower Lock
Snell Lock
St. Lambert Lock
Detroit
Lake Erie
600 ft. (183 m)
579 ft. (176 m)
570 ft. (174 m)
St. Lawrence River
245 ft. (75 m)
Lake Huron
SEA LEVEL
Melocheville Lock
Montreal
Lake Superior
Lake Ontario
Beauharnois Lock
Côte-Ste.-Catherine Lock

FOCUS ON GEOGRAPHIC THEMES

1. **Location:** At about what line of longitude is the Iroquois Lock located?
2. **Place:** Which of the Great Lakes is the deepest?
3. **Place:** Which city is near the St. Lambert Lock?
4. **Movement:** What is the purpose of the St. Lawrence Seaway?

The Physical Geography of the United States and Canada

CHAPTER FOCUS

Geographic Setting

The United States and Canada both are located on the continent of North America. Because they occupy the same landmass, they also share many of the same landforms and kinds of vegetation.

Geographic Themes

Section 1 The Land

PLACE The United States and Canada both have mountains framing eastern and western coasts and a large plains area in the center.

▲ Photograph: *Bass Head, Maine*

Section 2 The Climate and Vegetation

LOCATION The climates of the United States and Canada range from frigid tundra in northern Canada to subtropical areas in the southern United States. Hawaii is the only truly tropical area in the region.

1 The Land

Read to Discover . . .
- the landforms of the United States and Canada.
- the water sources that the environments of the United States and Canada offer.
- the natural resources found in the United States and Canada.

Key Terms
- plateau
- mesa
- continental divide
- headwaters
- tributary
- fishery

Identify and Locate
Pacific Ranges, Rocky Mountains, Great Basin, Great Plains, Canadian Shield, Appalachian Mountains, Mackenzie River, Mississippi River, Great Lakes

Ontario, Canada

Traveling across Canada — from the eastern Atlantic coastline to the western Rocky Mountains — I see many changes in the landscape. As a young Canadian, I feel that Canada's strength lies in its natural resources as the basis for its economic growth and legacy for future generations.

Jasmin Lalonde

Jasmin Lalonde, who comes from the Canadian province of Ontario, refers to her country's diverse landscape, a geographic characteristic shared by Canada's North American neighbor, the United States. Both nations are huge. Together, they cover more than 7 million square miles (18 million sq. km). Their continental land area extends from the Arctic Ocean in the north to the Gulf of Mexico and the Rio Grande in the south; and from the Pacific Ocean in the west to the Atlantic Ocean in the east.

PLACE

Landforms

The United States and Canada generally share the same landforms. Both nations have towering, snowcapped mountains in the west; fertile, rolling plains in the center; and low, smoothly formed mountains in the east.

Western Mountain Ranges

The Pacific Ocean forms the western border of both the United States and Canada. Paralleling the coastline are a series of mountain ranges that were formed by the collision of two tectonic plates millions of years ago. This mountain system includes the Alaska Range, the Coast Range, the Cascade Range, and the Sierra Nevada. Together, these mountains are called the Pacific Ranges.

Another western chain called the Rocky Mountains lies east of the Pacific Ranges. The massive, craggy Rocky Mountains stretch more than 3,000 miles (about 4,800 km) from northern Alaska to northern New Mexico.

Like the Pacific Ranges, the Rockies were formed by tectonic forces millions of years

Comparing Lands

The **continental USA** is a little more than 1 million square miles smaller than Canada.

ago. Many peaks in the Rockies, especially those in the state of Colorado, rise more than 12,000 feet (3,658 m).

The area that lies between the Pacific Ranges and the Rocky Mountains is known as the intermontane basins and plateaus. The northern and southern parts of this dry expanse are **plateaus**, or high, level surfaces. The Columbia Plateau, in the north, was created by lava seeping out of cracks in the earth. The southern plateau, the Colorado Plateau, is heavily eroded. This natural activity has produced unusual landforms, such as the Grand Canyon and various flat-topped natural elevations called **mesas.**

Between the Columbia and Colorado plateaus lies the Great Basin. This broad, low bowl includes the hottest and lowest place in the United States—Death Valley.

Farther north, the distance between the Rockies and the Pacific Ranges narrows. As a result, Canada's Fraser Plateau and Nechako Plateau are smaller than the plateaus of the United States.

Plains Areas

The area east of the Rockies marks the beginning of the Great Plains. The Great Plains is a broad, flat upland extending for about 400 miles (about 644 km) from the Rocky Mountains through the central parts of Canada and the United States. In Canada and parts of the United States, the Great Plains is sometimes called the Interior Plains or High Plains, because of the area's high elevation. This elevation reaches up to 6,000 feet (1,829 m).

The Great Plains area is flat and has no significant change in landforms. Its elevation,

however, descends gradually to the east at a rate of about 10 feet per mile (about 2 m per km). In the United States, this lower elevation signals the beginning of another plains area, the Central Lowlands. In Canada, the Interior Plains area continues to the Canadian Shield.

Eastern Mountains and Lowlands

The Appalachian Mountains lie to the east of the plains. This mountain system is North America's second-longest mountain range. Its 1,500-mile (2,400-km) length extends from the Canadian province of Quebec to Alabama in the United States. The Appalachians also are North America's oldest mountains, and erosion has worn them down and rounded their ancient peaks.

East and south of the Appalachians in the United States lie coastal lowlands. To the east, the Piedmont, a wide area of low, rolling hills, and the Atlantic Coastal Plain lead to the Atlantic Ocean. To the south, the Gulf Coastal Plain fans out and extends westward into Texas. In Canada, the Canadian Shield is bordered by lowlands around Hudson Bay.

MOVEMENT

Water Systems

The United States and Canada have an abundance of water systems. Large rivers and lakes supply freshwater for metropolitan and rural areas in both nations.

Because rivers flow downhill, the pattern of landforms determines the direction in which water systems flow. A **continental divide** is a line that separates rivers that flow toward opposite ends of a continent. In North America, a high ridge of the Rockies known as the Continental Divide, or the Great Divide, separates the waters flowing west to the Pacific Ocean from those flowing east toward the Mississippi River and Atlantic Ocean. In Canada, the Continental Divide joins another divide known as the Height of Land, which separates the waters flowing into the Arctic Ocean.

THE UNITED STATES AND CANADA: PHYSICAL-POLITICAL

RUSSIA

ARCTIC OCEAN

Ellesmere Island

Alaska (U.S.)

ALASKA RANGE △Mt. McKinley (20,320 ft., 6,194 m)

YUKON TERRITORY

Victoria Island

Baffin Island

NORTHWEST TERRITORIES

Mackenzie R.

Arctic Circle

Great Bear Lake

Great Slave Lake

Hudson Bay

Ungava Peninsula

COAST RANGE

British Columbia

INTERIOR PLAINS

CANADIAN

SHIELD

Queen Charlotte Islands

NECHAKO PLATEAU

ROCKY

CANADA

Newfoundland

FRASER PLATEAU

Alberta

Manitoba

Quebec

Vancouver Island

Saskatchewan

Lake Winnipeg

New Brunswick

Prince Edward Is.

ELEVATIONS

Feet	Meters
5,000	1,500
2,000	600
1,000	300
0	0

—— National boundary
—— State boundary
⊛ National capital

Lambert Equal-Area projection

Wash.

COLUMBIA PLATEAU

Ontario

St. Lawrence River

Nova Scotia

Missouri R.

Montana

N. Dak.

Minn.

Lake Superior

Ottawa⊛

Me.

Vt.

N.H.

CASCADE RANGE

Ore.

Idaho

GREAT

S. Dak.

Wis.

L. Michigan

L. Huron

Ontario

N.Y.

Mass.

SIERRA NEVADA

MOUNTAINS

Wyo.

PLAINS

Neb.

Iowa

Mich.

L. Erie

Penn.

R.I.
Conn.

N.J.

ATLANTIC OCEAN

Great Salt Lake

Nevada

UNITED

Ill.

Ind.

Ohio

W.V.

Md.

Del.

PACIFIC OCEAN

Calif.

Utah

DEATH VALLEY

Colo.

STATES

Kansas

Mo.

Ky.

Ohio R.

Va.

Washington, D.C.

Mt. Whitney (14,491 ft., 4,417 m)

COLORADO PLATEAU

Colorado R.

Arkansas R.

APPALACHIAN MTS.

PIEDMONT

N.C.

Arizona

N. Mex.

Okla.

Ark.

Tenn.

S.C.

Red R.

Miss.

Ala.

Ga.

ATLANTIC COASTAL PLAIN

Texas

La.

Mississippi R.

GULF COASTAL PLAIN

Rio Grande

Fla.

N

0 500 mi.
0 500 km

Hawaii

20°N

0 100 mi.
0 100 km

160°W

Tropic of Cancer

MEXICO

Gulf of Mexico

FOCUS ON GEOGRAPHIC THEMES

1. **Location:** Death Valley is one of the lowest points on the North American continent. Where is Death Valley located?

2. **Region:** Canada is made up of provinces and territories. What Canadian territory borders the American state of Alaska?

Geographic Themes

Human/Environment Interaction: The Great Flood of 1993
After eight months of rain, the Mississippi River reached record flood levels in the summer of 1993. *What other kinds of severe weather affect parts of the United States?*

Rivers in the United States whose **headwaters,** or water sources, are found in the Rocky Mountains include the Colorado River, which flows toward the west. The headwaters of the Rio Grande, the MacKenzie River, and the Missouri River are also in the Rockies. Each of these rivers has many **tributaries,** or brooks, rivers, and streams that feed their waters into one river.

The Mississippi is the largest river in the United States and Canada in both water volume and drainage area. It runs 2,340 miles (3,765 km) from its source near the border of the United States and Canada to its outlet in the Gulf of Mexico.

The United States and Canada also include many lakes formed as a result of the Ice Age. As the great frozen ice sheets advanced and retreated, the land over which they moved changed. As the ice moved relentlessly south, it formed dams on river systems and forced the waters to follow the glaciers' boundaries. It was this action that established the courses of the Missouri and Ohio rivers.

Some of this water blocked by glacial dams became lakes. In northern Canada, two major lakes—Great Bear Lake and Great Slave Lake—were formed in this way. They mark the ancient boundary of the glaciers.

As the glaciers moved over the land, they also gouged out and scoured hollows in the rocks they passed. As the glaciers receded, these hollows filled with water. The Great Lakes are examples of glacial lakes.

The Great Lakes—Lake Superior, Lake Huron, Lake Erie, Lake Ontario, and Lake Michigan—connect with one another and with the St. Lawrence River, whose mouth opens to the Atlantic Ocean. Glacial lakes, too numerous to count, also dot the Canadian Shield.

HUMAN/ENVIRONMENT INTERACTION

Resources

The United States and Canada have many important natural resources. The rivers and lakes of both nations supply plentiful amounts of freshwater. The waters of the shallow continental shelf along the Atlantic Ocean and the Gulf of Mexico teem with fish

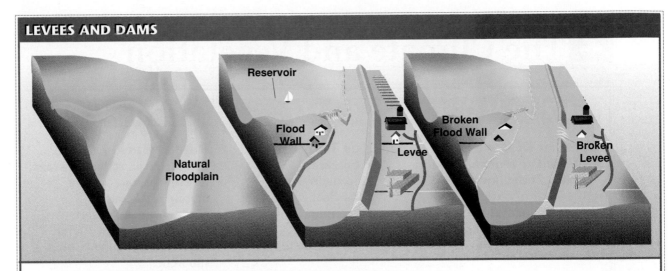

LEVEES AND DAMS

Reservoir

Natural Floodplain

Flood Wall

Broken Flood Wall

Levee

Broken Levee

FOCUS ON GEOGRAPHIC THEMES

Human/Environment Interaction: How Levees Work

People build levees to prevent flooding and to use the natural floodplain. Levees prevent rivers from widening during heavy rains. Therefore, the water level rises, and the river flows faster. As the river's pressure increases, levees may break or the river may overflow the levee. *Why is flood damage from a broken levee more severe than damage from a river overflowing its natural banks?*

and shellfish as do the waters along the Pacific coastline. The major freshwater **fisheries** of the United States include the inland waters of the southern states and the Great Lakes. Fisheries are places for catching fish and other sea animals. The Great Lakes are the center of the freshwater fishing industry in Canada.

Mineral resources of the United States and Canada include gold, silver, nickel, iron, copper, uranium, and zinc. The Rocky Mountains contain a great wealth of gold, silver, and copper. Parts of the Canadian Shield have deposits of iron and nickel. Canadian officials estimate that the mostly unexplored northern areas of Canada may hold as much as 40 percent of the country's mineral riches. Important energy resources, such as oil, natural gas, and coal, are found throughout both nations. Rich coal deposits are found in the Appalachian Mountains and in the central and western parts of the United States and Canada.

Timber reserves include the huge forests that cover about one-third of each nation. More than 1,000 animal species thrive in these woodland areas.

Parts of the United States and Canada have excellent conditions for agriculture. The Great

Plains and the Central Lowlands in the United States have some of the world's most fertile soil. Fertile farmlands also cover the vast Interior Plains of Canada.

SECTION 1 REVIEW

Checking for Understanding

1. **Define** plateau, mesa, continental divide, headwaters, tributary, fishery.
2. **Locating Places** What two mountain systems dominate the western portion of the United States and Canada?
3. **Region** What landform claims much of the land in the central portion of the United States and Canada?
4. **Region** What mineral resources can be found in the United States and Canada?

Critical Thinking

5. **Making Generalizations** How do the Rocky Mountains affect the rivers of this region?

2 The Climate and Vegetation

SETTING THE SCENE

Read to Discover . . .
- the climate regions of the United States and Canada.
- the kinds of natural vegetation found in the United States and Canada.

Key Terms
- blizzard
- tornado
- hurricane
- typhoon
- chinook
- timberline

Identify and Locate
Climate regions: tropical rain forest, tropical savanna, marine west coast, Mediterranean, desert, humid continental, humid subtropical, highland, tundra, subarctic.

The locations and vast sizes of landforms in the United States and Canada influence the climate regions and vegetation in these nations. Many types of climate regions can be found in the United States and Canada.

REGION

Climates

In the United States and Canada, most of the earth's climate types are represented. Even a tropical rain forest climate can be found 2,400 miles (3,862 km) away from the United States mainland, on the islands of Hawaii.

Climate Regions

Winds, ocean currents, and protective mountains along the Pacific coast help create a marine west coast climate from northern California through British Columbia to the southern border of Alaska.

As they blow eastward, the Pacific winds encounter the Pacific Ranges. As the winds are forced over the mountains, the air cools and moisture is released. This means that the west coast enjoys tremendous rainfall, and some parts of the area receive more than 100 inches (254 cm) of rain each year.

The Pacific Ranges also create a rain shadow, which limits the amount of rainfall east of the mountains. This place of plateaus and basins, bordered in the east by the Rocky Mountains, is known for its hot, dry air. The only deserts in the northern part of North America are found here. These deserts include the Great Salt Lake Desert, the Blackrock Desert, and Death Valley.

The higher parts of the Rocky Mountains and Pacific Ranges have highland climates. Even in Hawaii, with its tropical rain forest climate, some mountains have snowy peaks.

Large parts of Canada and Alaska lie in a subarctic climate zone with very cold winters. Two-thirds of Canada has January tempera-

Geographic Themes

Region: Great Plains
The Great Plains that stretch through the central part of the United States and Canada include vast wheat fields. *What kind of climate dominates the Great Plains region?*

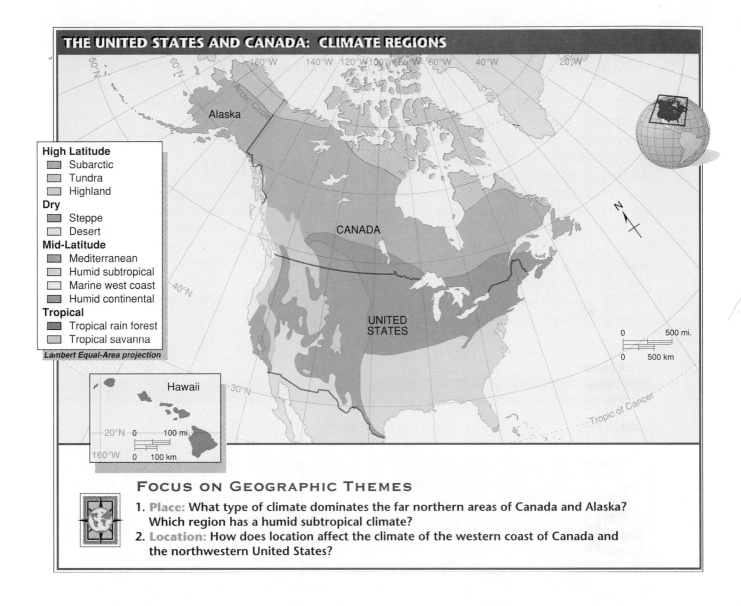

High Latitude
- Subarctic
- Tundra
- Highland

Dry
- Steppe
- Desert

Mid-Latitude
- Mediterranean
- Humid subtropical
- Marine west coast
- Humid continental

Tropical
- Tropical rain forest
- Tropical savanna

Lambert Equal-Area projection

Hawaii

FOCUS ON GEOGRAPHIC THEMES

1. **Place:** What type of climate dominates the far northern areas of Canada and Alaska? Which region has a humid subtropical climate?
2. **Location:** How does location affect the climate of the western coast of Canada and the northwestern United States?

tures that average below 0°F (−18°C). Winter temperatures of −70°F (−57°C) have been recorded in some places. A persistent high pressure cell in this area spawns the cold winds that chill much of the central United States during the winter.

Farther north, lands across the Arctic coastlines lie in a tundra climate zone. These areas experience bitter winters and cool summers. This vast expanse of land is still a wilderness, inhabited by few people.

The Great Plains are far from oceans or other large bodies of water that moderate climate. Although western mountains block moisture-bearing Pacific winds, the Great Plains are not completely dry because mois-

ture travels with winds that blow north along the Rockies from the Gulf of Mexico and south from the Arctic region. The region is classified as a humid continental climate region with bitter winters and hot summers.

The humid continental climate region continues east to the Atlantic. Most of the southern states, however, are in a humid subtropical climate region. Only the tip of Florida is far enough south to have a tropical savanna climate.

Seasonal Weather Conditions

Canada and the United States are affected by seasonal weather conditions. In winter, much of northern North America experiences blizzards. **Blizzards** are snowstorms with winds in excess of 35 miles (56 km) per hour, temperatures below freezing, and visibility of less than 500 feet (152 m) for 3 hours or more.

Summer **tornadoes**, swirling columns of air whose winds can reach 300 miles (483 km) per hour, plague the Great Plains and the eastern portion of the United States. During summer and autumn, **hurricanes**—ocean storms hundreds of miles wide with winds of 74 miles (119 km) per hour or more—threaten the Atlantic and Gulf of Mexico coastlines. **Typhoons**, or Pacific hurricanes, threaten Hawaii and other Pacific islands each year.

Some seasonal weather conditions are improvements over the normal patterns for a climate zone. For example, a warm wind called the **chinook** blows down the slopes of the Rockies in winter and early spring. This wind melts the snow at the base of the mountains, exposing grass for grazing cattle.

HUMAN/ENVIRONMENT INTERACTION

Vegetation

B efore the arrival of settlers, almost half of present-day United States and Canada—an estimated 3 million square miles (7,770,000 sq. km)—was covered with forests. Over the past 2 centuries, humans, however, have permanently cleared over one-half million square miles (1,295,000 sq. km) of original forestland.

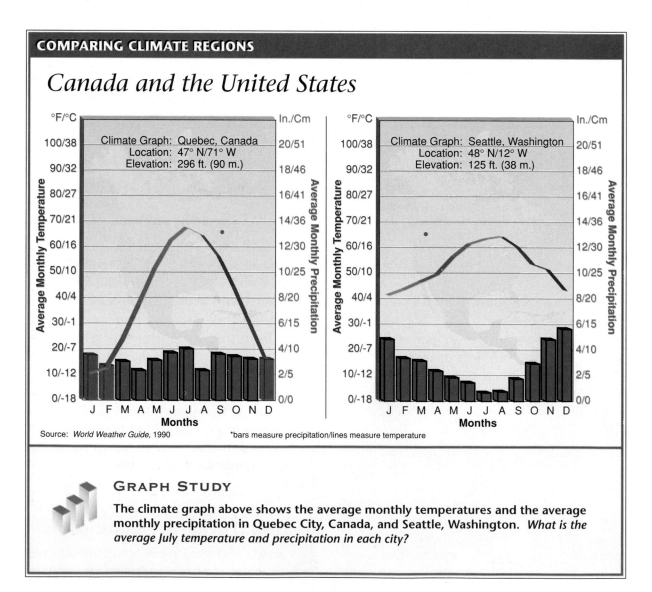

COMPARING CLIMATE REGIONS

Canada and the United States

Climate Graph: Quebec, Canada
Location: 47° N/71° W
Elevation: 296 ft. (90 m.)

Climate Graph: Seattle, Washington
Location: 48° N/12° W
Elevation: 125 ft. (38 m.)

Source: *World Weather Guide*, 1990   *bars measure precipitation/lines measure temperature

GRAPH STUDY

The climate graph above shows the average monthly temperatures and the average monthly precipitation in Quebec City, Canada, and Seattle, Washington. *What is the average July temperature and precipitation in each city?*

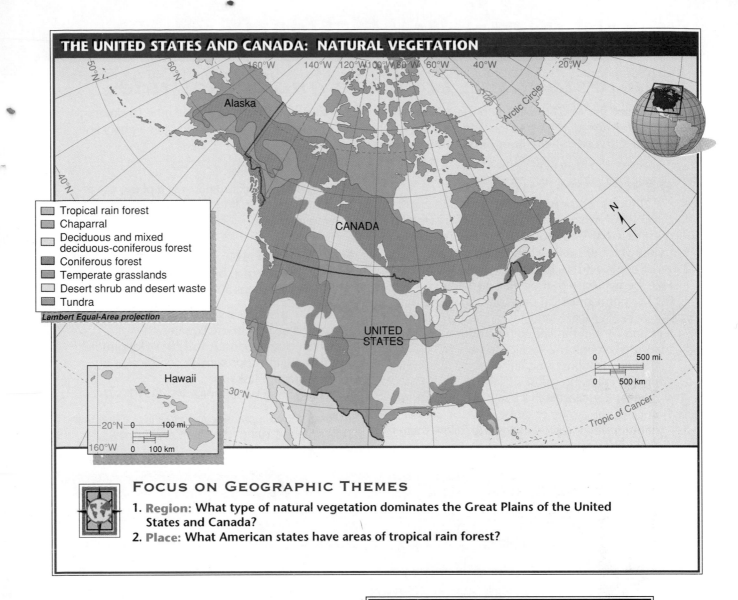

THE UNITED STATES AND CANADA: NATURAL VEGETATION

Legend:
- Tropical rain forest
- Chaparral
- Deciduous and mixed deciduous-coniferous forest
- Coniferous forest
- Temperate grasslands
- Desert shrub and desert waste
- Tundra

Lambert Equal-Area projection

Alaska

CANADA

UNITED STATES

Hawaii

FOCUS ON GEOGRAPHIC THEMES

1. **Region:** What type of natural vegetation dominates the Great Plains of the United States and Canada?
2. **Place:** What American states have areas of tropical rain forest?

Despite human pressures on the land's resources, a vast forest area still spans subarctic Canada. Forests also cover the sides of the western mountain ranges until they reach the **timberline**, or the elevation above which trees cannot grow.

The Great Plains of the United States and Canada were once a prairie region, a treeless expanse of grasses whose tangled roots formed dense layers of vegetation called sod. Settlers, however, soon populated the plains, broke up the sod, and used it to build homes. These changes led to dust bowl conditions in the 1930s. Since then, scientific farming methods have improved conditions on the Great Plains, and the region now supplies most of North America's wheat.

SECTION 2 REVIEW

Checking for Understanding
1. **Define** blizzard, tornado, hurricane, typhoon, chinook, timberline.
2. **Locating Places** What deserts lie in the rain shadow of the Pacific Ranges?
3. **Region** Through what two climate regions does the Mississippi River flow?
4. **Region** In what climate region can most of Canada's forest area be found?

Critical Thinking
5. **Making Comparisons** How do the Pacific winds and the Arctic winds differ in their impact on climate?

Understanding Latitude and Longitude

Imagine that you are sailing on the open ocean and must find a particular island. With no landmarks, how can you find it? Early sailors and navigators solved this problem by creating a grid of imaginary lines encircling the earth—**the lines of latitude and longitude.**

REVIEWING THE SKILL

Latitude lines, or *parallels,* run east and west like the Equator, which is at 0°. Parallels increase in number, north and south, as they approach the poles, which are at 90°. Longitude lines, or *meridians,* run from the North Pole to the South Pole, beginning with the *prime meridian,* which is 0°. The prime meridian runs through western Africa and Europe. Meridians increase in number east and west of this line to the 180th meridian that runs through the Pacific Ocean.

To find locations using latitude and longitude, apply the following steps:

• If you have coordinates of a place and want to locate it on a map or globe, find the correct latitude and longitude lines and follow them to their intersection.

• To identify the coordinates of a place, use a map or globe to find the nearest latitude and longitude lines.

PRACTICING THE SKILL

Use the map below to answer the following questions about latitude and longitude:

1. Identify the three mainland cities on this map located nearest to the Equator.
2. Which cities lie closest to 120° W longitude?
3. What are the approximate coordinates of Anchorage, Alaska?
4. Which city is located near 45° N, 90° W?

For additional practice in this skill, see Practicing Skills on page 104 of the Chapter 5 Review.

THE UNITED STATES AND CANADA: POLITICAL

1 SECTION	KEY TERMS	SUMMARY
The Land **The Mississippi River**	**plateau** (p. 94) **mesa** (p. 94) **continental divide** (p. 94) **headwaters** (p. 96) **tributary** (p. 96) **fishery** (p. 97)	• The nations of the United States and Canada form a region that makes up most of the North American continent. • Two mountain ranges dominate the landforms to the west, with plateaus and basins lying between the ranges. • Western mountain ranges, and another major range in the east, border the vast interior plains that mark the central portion of this region. • Several major rivers help drain the land's water into the oceans that border the region. • This region is rich in many renewable and nonrenewable natural resources.

2 SECTION	KEY TERMS	SUMMARY
The Climate and Vegetation **Harvesting grain in the Great Plains**	**blizzard** (p. 100) **tornado** (p. 100) **hurricane** (p. 100) **typhoon** (p. 100) **chinook** (p. 100) **timberline** (p. 101)	• Although Canada and the United States share some climate regions, others are particular to each nation. • The winds from the Pacific Ocean, the Arctic Ocean, and the Gulf of Mexico exert tremendous influence on the region's climates. • Most climate regions—from desert to tundra—are represented in this region. • Humans have had an enormous impact on the natural vegetation of the region.

Reviewing Key Terms

Choose the vocabulary term that best completes each of the sentences below. Write your answers on a separate sheet of paper.

mesa (p. 94)   hurricanes (p. 100)
continental   blizzard (p. 100)
  divide (p. 94)   typhoons (p. 100)
tributaries (p. 96)   timberline (p. 101)

SECTION 1

1. The brooks, rivers, and streams that feed a river are called its _____ .
2. _____ is the name given flat-topped natural elevations of the southwest.
3. The Great Divide is a _____ .

SECTION 2

4. During a _____ , snow-filled, frigid winds buffet an area.
5. Hurricanes that occur in the Pacific Ocean are called _____ .
6. In high mountains, the _____ indicates the point above which trees cannot grow.
7. _____ are swirling ocean storms with sustained high winds that plague the Atlantic and Gulf of Mexico coasts during summer and fall.

Reviewing Facts

SECTION 1

8. What landform includes the Piedmont, the Atlantic Coastal Plain, and the Gulf Coastal Plain?
9. In what mountain range is North America's Continental Divide located?
10. What river forms part of the border between the United States and Mexico?

SECTION 2

11. What kind of climate does Hawaii have?
12. What mountain systems are separated by desert areas?

13. The states of the southeast lie in what kind of climate region?

Critical Thinking

14. **Analyzing Information**   Compare the map of oil and natural gas resources in the United States on page 15 of the Geography Skills Handbook with the physical features map of the United States and Canada on page 88. What kind of landform seems to support deposits of these resources?
15. **Determining Cause and Effect**   How did settlers' farming techniques lead to the tremendous loss of soil in the Great Plains of the United States?

 ## Geographic Themes

16. **Human/Environment Interaction** How did human settlement alter the forests of this region?
17. **Region**   What kind of vegetation grew in the Great Plains before human settlement?

 ## Practicing Skills

Understanding Latitude and Longitude
Using the map on page 102, find the cities located nearest to these coordinates:
18. 30° N, 95° W   20. 52° N, 96° W
19. 33° N, 84° W   21. 40° N, 75° W

Using the Unit Atlas

Refer to the physical geography section of the Unit Atlas on pages 88–89.
22. In what mountain range is Mt. McKinley located?
23. What part of Canada and the United States is a major grain-producing area?

Projects

Individual Activity

In this chapter you have learned about the landforms that cross the United States and Canada. Choose one of these landforms. Create a collage illustrating the landform you have chosen. Use pictures from magazines, newspapers, or your own drawings. Present your collage to the class, explaining what each illustration represents.

Cooperative Learning Activity

In a group of six, assign each member one of the climate regions of Canada. Each member is to research and prepare a report on the animal life in the assigned climate zone. When the reports are finished, share the information with the group. Then determine whether some climate regions share species of animals, and report what you have learned to the class.

Writing About Geography

Description

Select a place described in your journal under the heading Geography. Write a letter in which you describe how this area differs from your home in landforms, water, climate, and vegetation. Use the information and photographs presented in the text as well as the information in the journal. You may wish to use an encyclopedia or other resource book to obtain additional details.

Locating Places

THE UNITED STATES AND CANADA: PHYSICAL GEOGRAPHY

Match the letters on the map with the physical features of the United States and Canada. Write your answers on a separate sheet of paper.

1. Pacific Ranges
2. Rocky Mountains
3. Appalachian Mountains
4. Mississippi River
5. Mackenzie River
6. Río Grande
7. Great Bear Lake
8. Great Slave Lake
9. Great Lakes
10. Hudson Bay
11. Great Plains
12. Canadian Shield

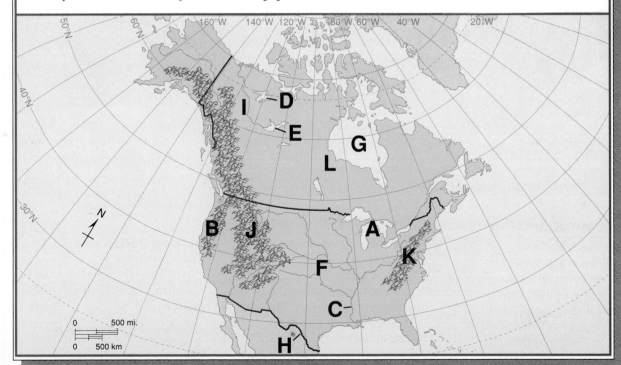

chapter 6
The Cultural Geography of the United States and Canada

CHAPTER FOCUS

Geographic Setting

Most Americans and Canadians trace their ancestral roots to other parts of the world. Some came voluntarily; others were forced to come either as enslaved labor or as exiles.

▲ Photograph: *Street fair in New York City, New York*

Geographic Themes

Section 1 Population Patterns

REGION Canada's population is concentrated in relatively small areas near the United States-Canadian border. Population in the United States tends to be concentrated along the coasts or in the Great Lakes region.

Section 2 History and Government

PLACE The United States and Canada share a British political heritage.

Section 3 Cultures and Lifestyles

MOVEMENT The United States and Canada have culturally diverse societies.

SETTING THE SCENE

Read to Discover . . .
- the human characteristics of the United States and Canada.
- how population is distributed across the United States and Canada.
- how advances in transportation led to the development of large cities.

Key Terms
- immigrant
- Sunbelt
- suburbs
- metropolitan area
- megalopolis

Identify and Locate
New York City, Chicago, Detroit, Pittsburgh, Boston, Philadelphia, Washington, D.C., St. Louis, Los Angeles, Atlanta, Denver, San Francisco, Houston, Dallas, New Orleans, Toronto, Montreal, Winnipeg, Calgary, Vancouver, Ottawa

Toronto, Canada

The Ojibway people believe that in order to function in a positive manner, a balance of Mind, Body and Spirit must be part of daily life. This whole way of thinking and living has been an essential part of native life long before European contact and is very much alive today.

Jeffrey M. Lee

Jeffrey Lee belongs to the Ojibway nation, one of the many Native American peoples who were the first to settle the area that is today the United States and Canada. The region was later settled by people from other areas of the world. Today the region's culture comes from the Europeans, Africans, and Asians who arrived after A.D. 1500. This mixing of different peoples and cultures has given the United States and Canada unique identities.

These huge countries, however, are largely populated by many groups of **immigrants**—people who leave their home countries to settle permanently in others—and their descendants. A large number of these immigrants came from Europe. Many others came from various Asian, African, and Latin American countries.

PLACE

Human Characteristics

Both Canada and the United States are home to various groups of native peoples.

MOVEMENT

Population Distribution and Density

More than 285 million people—about 5 percent of the world's population—live in the United States and Canada. Of these,

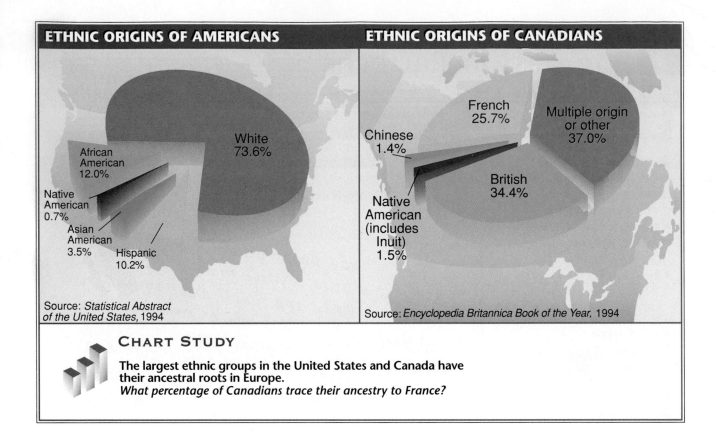

ETHNIC ORIGINS OF AMERICANS

White 73.6%

African American 12.0%

Native American 0.7%

Asian American 3.5%

Hispanic 10.2%

Source: *Statistical Abstract of the United States,* 1994

ETHNIC ORIGINS OF CANADIANS

French 25.7%

Multiple origin or other 37.0%

Chinese 1.4%

British 34.4%

Native American (includes Inuit) 1.5%

Source: *Encyclopedia Britannica Book of the Year,* 1994

CHART STUDY

The largest ethnic groups in the United States and Canada have their ancestral roots in Europe.
What percentage of Canadians trace their ancestry to France?

about 261 million live in the United States. The average population density of the United States is about 74 people per square mile (28 people per sq. km). The United States population is growing slowly. The average yearly population growth rate in the United States is about 1 percent. Canada, with a population of about 29 million people, averages only 8 people per square mile (3 people per sq. km) of land. The Canadian population is increasing at a rate slightly less than 1 percent per year.

Canada and the United States differ noticeably in population distribution as well as in population size. The population of the United States is largely concentrated in certain areas. The northeastern part of the United States is the most densely populated part of the country. A large part of the American population is concentrated in the Great Lakes region. These two areas are located near transportation routes and manufacturing centers. Parts of the western coast of the United States are also heavily populated. An abundance of natural resources, available land, and economic opportunities have helped the western coast of the United States

grow in population. Since the 1970s, the fastest-growing areas in the United States have been the South and the Southwest, including California. Industrial growth and an appealing climate have encouraged migration to the southern United States. Because of its mild climate, the southern United States is often called the **Sunbelt.**

Other areas of the United States are sparsely populated. Few people, for example, live in the subarctic climate of Alaska or in the dry climate of the Great Basin. In addition, thinly populated areas exist in parts of the interior plains.

Most Canadians live in the Great Lakes region and along the St. Lawrence River. These areas extend along the southern parts of Canada's two major industrial provinces: Quebec and Ontario. Pockets of population are also found in southern sections of the Prairie Provinces farther west, and along the Pacific coast of the province of British Columbia. All of these areas have relatively mild climates and are close to the United States, Canada's main trading partner. The remaining two-thirds of Canada, however, remains sparsely inhabited.

Urbanization

Both the United States and Canada have large urban populations. About three-fourths of the people live in or near cities and small towns.

Many of the urban areas in the United States and Canada consist of a central city, nearby neighborhoods, and outlying communities called **suburbs.** A central city and its surrounding suburbs are often called a **metropolitan area.** Because of the use of automobiles and mass-transit systems, more people live in suburbs than in central cities.

Coastal Cities

There are more than 70 urban areas in the United States and Canada with populations of more than 500,000 people. Several major cities lie along the northern Atlantic coast of the United States. The largest are Boston, New York, Philadelphia, Baltimore, and Washington, D.C. These cities are so close to one another that their surrounding areas overlap to form a single urban area. This type of urban pattern is called a **megalopolis.** The megalopolis formed by the cities between Boston and Washington, D.C., is sometimes called Boswash. Cities within Boswash have benefited from their coastal location. New York City, the culture region's largest city, is one of the world's leading centers for overseas trade.

Large port cities in the southern part of the United States include Miami, New Orleans, and Houston. Miami is on the Atlantic Ocean and is a major connection between the United States and the islands in the Caribbean Sea. New Orleans and Houston are busy transportation centers on the Gulf of Mexico.

Major port cities on the Pacific Ocean are Los Angeles, San Diego, San Francisco, Seattle, and Vancouver. In Los Angeles and Seattle, an important industry is the production of airplanes. An area near San Francisco called Silicon Valley is important for producing electronic equipment. Vancouver in the Canadian province of British Columbia is an important shipping center for western Canada.

Inland Cities

Many cities in the United States and Canada are located near inland waterways. In Canada Toronto, Montreal, Quebec City, and Ottawa are near the Great Lakes, the St. Lawrence River, or the Ottawa River.

In the United States, the cities of Chicago, Detroit, Milwaukee, and Cleveland are located on the Great Lakes. These cities grew partly because industries were able to use the Great Lakes to transport natural resources and manufactured goods. Pittsburgh's location on the Ohio River has been important for the shipment of goods related to western Pennsylvania's steel industry. St. Louis is situated near the confluence of the Missouri River and the Mississippi River. St. Louis's location made it a gateway to the settlements of the West during the 1800s.

Other major cities in the interior parts of the United States and Canada include Dallas, San Antonio, Atlanta, Memphis, Minneapolis, Kansas City, Denver, Salt Lake City, Winnipeg, Calgary, and Edmonton. These cities serve as transportation and business centers for their surrounding areas.

SECTION 1 REVIEW

Checking for Understanding

1. **Define** immigrant, Sunbelt, suburbs, metropolitan area, megalopolis.
2. **Locating Places** Where is North America's biggest megalopolis located?
3. **Place** What major ethnic groups make up the population of the United States? The population of Canada?
4. **Location** Where in Canada do most people live?

Critical Thinking

5. **Making Comparisons** Compare population patterns of the United States and Canada.

NATIONAL GEOGRAPHIC
GEOFACTS

What is the tallest living thing on earth?

Survivors of ice ages and chain saws, California's coast redwoods are the tallest living things on the earth. The largest of these giant trees towers 367.8 feet (112 m) —higher than the Statue of Liberty.

Sprouting from seeds no larger than the head of a pin, coast redwoods grow at a rate of 2 feet (more than 0.5 m) a year, finally maturing in 400 years. With few natural enemies, the redwoods can live for 2,000 years. Thick bark shields them from insects and fires. Even disease and floods don't often kill them.

But redwoods do need a lot of moisture, a fact that limits their range to rainy, foggy stretches of southern Oregon and northern California. Their durable wood is prized by loggers. Only about 10 percent of the virgin redwood forest remains. Today 260,000 acres (104,000 ha) of redwood forests are protected in state and in national parks.

Another California redwood, the giant sequoia, is shorter and fatter than the coast redwood. With a 35-foot (10.7-m) diameter, the giant sequoia is wider than many city streets.

Designed by BILL PITZER

AREA SHOWN

CALIFORNIA

REDWOOD NATIONAL PARK

Six Rivers National Forest

OREGON
CALIFORNIA

Eureka

Klamath National Forest

Humboldt Woods State Park

Trinity National Forest

PACIFIC

COAST REDWOODS

Mendocino National Forest

OCEAN

Clear Lake

Point Reyes National Seashore

Sacramento

Muir Woods National Monument

San Francisco

SILICON VALLEY

San Jose

N

Coast Redwood

Sequoia sempervirens

Cone

Needles

0   50 km
0   50 mi

Monterey

Los Padres National Forest

Camper

SECTION 2
History and Government

The first people to come to what is now the United States and Canada migrated from Asia. These people developed cultures that were influenced in part by the various environments in which they settled. After A.D. 1500 most of the region's settlers came from Europe. The Europeans used the land and its resources very differently from the region's first settlers.

MOVEMENT

History

The northwestern part of North America is separated from the northeastern part of Asia by a **strait**—a narrow passageway connecting two large bodies of water. The Bering Strait connects the Arctic Ocean and the Pacific Ocean. It is believed that during the last Ice Age the level of the water in the Pacific Ocean lowered, exposing a land bridge across the Bering Strait.

Many archaeologists believe that 25,000 or more years ago people from Asia used the land bridge to migrate to the nearby lands of North America. The cold northern climate encouraged many of these people to migrate throughout the continent in search of better living conditions. By 10,000 years ago, people were living in almost every part of the present-day United States and Canada. The early people became known as Native Americans. The kinds of cultures formed by these early groups of people varied and were influenced by their location.

Early Americans

The Inuit lived in the cold tundra lands of the Arctic. The harsh polar climate there made them rely upon such animals as caribou for fur and food because other resources were scarce and farming was impossible. The Native Americans of the Far North, who lived in the subarctic, also relied on the animals they hunted to help fill their needs for food and clothing.

The Native Americans along the Pacific Coast lived where the climate was mild and the natural resources, especially fish, were abundant. Large trees and a variety of plants covered the land. With stone and copper woodworking tools these Native Americans split cedar, fir, and redwood trees into planks to make elaborate houses and large canoes. They also developed ways to harvest salmon with fiber nets, spears, and wooden traps.

Native Americans who settled in the high desert regions of present-day Arizona, New Mexico, Colorado, and Utah had fewer resources than those who settled in other areas. Nevertheless, the Native Americans of the

Geographic Themes

Human/Environment Interaction: Mesa Verde National Park, Colorado
Mesa Verde is a huge plateau covered with pine forests where Native Americans built cliff dwellings hundreds of years ago. *How did Native Americans in other parts of the Southwest make use of their environment?*

Southwest adapted to their environment. For example, they invented techniques of irrigation to farm the land. One community in southern Arizona dug an irrigation canal 3 miles (4.8 km) long to draw the river's waters onto fields planted with corn, beans, and squash.

Native Americans living on the grasslands of the Great Plains found farming very difficult because the thick plains sod was hard to plow. Although some farming was done along streams, most Plains Native Americans depended on the great herds of buffalo that roamed the plains. From earliest times, they followed the herds from one grazing ground to another. They used every part of the buffalo for their food, clothing, shelter, and tools.

Native Americans of the woodlands east of the Mississippi River hunted a variety of animals. Deer, turkeys, geese, and squirrels were common in eastern forests. Like the Plains people, Woodlands Native Americans made use of every part of the animals they killed—eating deer meat, wearing deerskin clothing,

and making tools out of animal bones and antlers. Because summers were warm, rainfall abundant, and soil fertile throughout most of the Eastern Woodlands, the people of this region lived in farming villages and grew crops such as corn, squash, beans, and tobacco.

European Colonization

European migration to the United States and Canada had begun by the late 1500s. Europeans came to the region in search of land to farm, valuable minerals, and political and religious freedom.

Most early European settlers came from Spain, France, and England. People from these nations established colonies in different parts of the present-day United States and Canada. By the 1700s, England had colonies or controlled land along much of the Atlantic Coast and around Hudson Bay.

The settlers in the northern English colonies were not able to farm very well because of the thin, rocky soil and the short growing season. The area, however, had excellent harbors, good timber, many types of fish, and cheap waterpower. As a result, the settlers generally made their living by fishing, shipbuilding, trade, and manufacturing.

The English colonies just south of the northern colonies had wide river valleys, level land, and rich soil. They also had mild winters; warm, long summers; and a long growing season. Many of the settlers were farmers who raised **cash crops**, or crops that are raised to be sold.

The English colonies farthest south produced surpluses for export because the mild climate, rich soils, and open land encouraged large-scale plantation agriculture. Most plantation owners used enslaved Africans to provide the labor such large-scale farming required.

The French came to North America primarily for economic reasons, especially the fur trade. French trappers, traveling such major rivers as the St. Lawrence and the Mississippi, settled at places along waterways where beaver pelts and other furs could be collected and shipped to Europe. Most did not plan to settle, wanting to make money and then return to France. Those who did settle lived primarily near the St. Lawrence River, where they founded Quebec. Other French settlements thrived along the Mississippi River and the Gulf of Mexico, especially the port city of New Orleans.

The Spanish ruled large areas of the present-day United States west of the Mississippi River. These lands were part of the vast Spanish Empire that included much of South America and all of Central America and Mexico. In 1565 Spain set up the first European settlement in the present-day United States at St. Augustine, Florida. Most Spanish settlements made during the colonial era, however, were in the Southwest—Texas, New Mexico, Arizona, and California. Many of these communities were founded as barriers to block

Geographic Themes

Movement: Quebec City, Canada
This street in Quebec City reveals the French character of the Canadian province of Quebec. *What other areas of North America were settled by the French?*

Geographic Themes

Movement: Loyalist Historic Site, New Brunswick, Canada
Loyalists from the 13 American colonies also settled in Nova Scotia, New Brunswick, and Prince Edward Island. *How did the Loyalists receive their name?*

potential expansion by such colonial powers as France and Great Britain. They served two purposes—as military outposts and as missions, or religious settlements to convert Native Americans to Christianity. Although the population of the Spanish colonies remained small, Spanish settlers in time started farms and huge cattle ranches, based largely on practices brought from their European homelands.

Two Nations

In 1763 France was forced to give up a great part of its empire in North America to the British. Conflicts soon arose between the Native Americans and the settlers in the British colonies. The settlers' methods of cutting down forests and clearing fields in order to farm destroyed the Native Americans' hunting grounds. Conflict also affected the fur trade. Some Native Americans began to resent the number of traders entering their lands.

During the 1760s relations between the American colonies and Great Britain began to worsen. The British government gradually extended its control over the colonies by passing laws that taxed the colonists and limited their freedoms. The colonists had become accustomed to governing themselves, and had developed a sense of unity and independence. As a result they deeply resented what they viewed as British interference in their affairs.

Another development in the American colonies at this time was growing opposition to monarchy as a form of government. Along with independence, some colonists favored the creation of a **republic**, a form of government in which people elect their own officials, including their head of state. Beginning in 1775, 13 of the British colonies along the Atlantic coast fought a war to gain independence. As a result of the War for Independence, a new republic—the United States of America—was formed.

A number of colonists, however, did not want to sever ties with Great Britain. During the war, more than 40,000 American colonists who remained loyal to the British monarch moved north to Canada, which had a large French population. Known as United Empire Loyalists, they settled mainly in sparsely inhabited areas of the present-day Canadian provinces of Quebec, Ontario, Nova Scotia, and New Brunswick.

Unlike its southern neighbor, Canada united slowly, and without the violence of war. The American War for Independence, however, did have a great impact on Canada. The arrival of the United Empire Loyalists meant that the French Canadians in Quebec no longer enjoyed a comfortable majority. Great Britain divided Quebec into Lower Canada and Upper Canada in an attempt to give representation to both the French Canadians and the Loyalist settlers. The colony of Lower Canada was situated along the eastern part of the St. Lawrence River, where mostly French Canadians lived. English-speaking Canadians occupied the colony of Upper Canada, which included the area above the Great Lakes and around the western part of the St. Lawrence River.

Upper and Lower Canada became united in 1841, and self-government was approved by Great Britain in 1849. In 1867 the Dominion of Canada was established and the four provinces of Quebec, Ontario, Nova Scotia, and New Brunswick were united. Between 1869 and 1873, Canada established the provinces of Manitoba, British Columbia, and Prince Edward Island. Saskatchewan, Alberta, and Newfoundland were added in the 1900s.

Industry and Expansion

The growth of industry changed the development of the United States and Canada. The northeastern United States has many waterfalls that could be harnessed to produce power to run machines. Partly for this reason, the first water-powered cotton mill was built in Rhode Island in 1793. Other factories soon sprang up where waterpower was available. **Industrialization**—the setting up of manufacturing that uses machinery—spread. Because waterpower was limited to a few places, people in industry searched for a new source of power. In the 1800s, steam became the domi-

nant source of power. The large supplies of coal in Pennsylvania and Ohio, which were used to power steam engines, made steam power cheap and manufacturing very profitable. Soon the Midwest became a leading center of industry and business. The many rivers in the Midwest, improved by the building of canals, were used to transport goods from factories to port cities.

A growing demand for cotton by the textile industry in the Northeast made cotton production highly profitable. Cotton became the South's major cash crop. Swamps were drained and pine forests cleared for more cotton plantations. The labor of enslaved Africans became more important than ever before.

During this period of great economic development, the West became a source of raw materials for the markets of the East. In 1803 the United States bought nearly all the land between the Mississippi River and the Rocky Mountains from France. This agreement, known as the Louisiana Purchase, gave the United States control of the Mississippi River and access to the port of New Orleans. The purchase also nearly doubled the land size of the United States and gave the United States fertile farmland and access to the Far West.

The territories of the West were rich in natural resources. The discovery of gold and silver deposits encouraged settlement in parts of the Far West, the Southwest, and the Far North. Texas, a former Mexican territory that became an independent republic in 1836 and joined the United States in 1845, was valued for cotton production and cattle ranching. The land in parts of present-day California, Arizona, and New Mexico belonged to Mexico. The United States wanted to build a railroad through this land to the Pacific coast. In the 1840s, as a result of a war with Mexico, the Treaty of Guadalupe Hidalgo gave the United States all of the present-day states of California, Utah, and Nevada, and parts of Colorado, Wyoming, Arizona, and New Mexico. This agreement between the United States and Mexico also established the southern border of Texas at the Rio Grande.

The good climate and the rich soil for farming in the northwestern United States

Geographic Themes

Movement: Craigallachie, British Columbia
The Canadian Pacific Railway was completed in 1885 with the nailing of the last spike.
What impact did transcontinental railroads have on the United States and Canada?

and southwestern Canada began to attract settlers in the 1840s. This part of the region was known as the Oregon Country. Both the United States and Great Britain claimed the Oregon Country. In 1846 the two countries agreed to divide Oregon's territory between them, extending the United States-Canadian border along the 49th parallel from the Rocky Mountains to the Pacific Ocean.

During the late 1800s, settlement of the Great Plains was encouraged by both the United States and Canada. The governments wanted to ease the crowding in eastern cities, caused by people coming to these cities from Europe. They also wanted people to farm the region, thus providing more food for city populations. Thousands of people from the crowded lands in the eastern parts of the region, as well as European immigrants, started farms on the Great Plains of Canada and the United States.

In 1867 the United States bought Alaska from Russia. Alaska was rich in fur-bearing animals and in fish. Alaska later proved to be important for its deposits of gold, oil, and other valuable resources.

Technology and Growth

Settlers on the dry Great Plains used a special farming method, called **dry farming**, to ease the shortage of water there. Dry farming is a way of saving water in the soil by plowing land so that it holds rainwater.

Advances in farm machinery also helped the farmers. Steel plows replaced iron plows. Stronger than iron plows, steel plows were better able to cut through the prairie sod. During the late 1880s, steam tractors and planting and harvesting machines made it possible to farm large areas of land faster and easier.

The completion of transcontinental railroads in the United States and Canada made it possible to transport goods from the East to the West and to transport food products and beef cattle from the West to the East. Chinese, Irish, Mexicans, and other groups of people were recruited to come to the region to help build the railroads.

By the early 1900s, the Industrial Revolution led to the development of new and better methods of mass production. These new industrial developments greatly changed the lives of many people in the United States and Canada. Now, more people lived in cities rather than in rural areas. The use of standard parts and assembly lines in automobile factories cut the time and cost needed to build an automobile. Because more people could afford automobiles, more roads had to be built. The automobile made it possible for great numbers of people to move out of the central cities by enabling them to commute to their jobs.

In the 1900s industries grew dramatically during the two world wars. The vast resources of the United States and Canada were used to supply the manufacture of military equipment needed for their armed forces and for their allies around the world. Agricultural products, such as cattle and grains, were also in great demand. Because the United States and Canada were separated from the war zones by the Atlantic and Pacific oceans, the countries' resources were vital to their European and Asian allies.

United States Government

In 1787 a group of leaders of the United States drafted a plan of government for the United States, called the **Constitution.** Over the years changes in the Constitution, called **amendments**, have been made to meet the changing needs of the people. The first 10 amendments to the Constitution are called the Bill of Rights. These amendments guarantee the basic rights of citizens, such as freedom of speech, freedom of religion, and freedom of the press.

The Constitution created a national government and gave it certain powers over

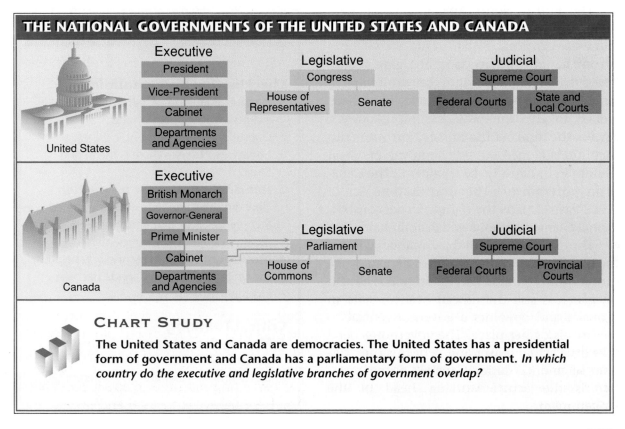

THE NATIONAL GOVERNMENTS OF THE UNITED STATES AND CANADA

United States

Executive
- President
- Vice-President
- Cabinet
- Departments and Agencies

Legislative
- Congress
  - House of Representatives
  - Senate

Judicial
- Supreme Court
  - Federal Courts
  - State and Local Courts

Canada

Executive
- British Monarch
- Governor-General
- Prime Minister
- Cabinet
- Departments and Agencies

Legislative
- Parliament
  - House of Commons
  - Senate

Judicial
- Supreme Court
  - Federal Courts
  - Provincial Courts

CHART STUDY

The United States and Canada are democracies. The United States has a presidential form of government and Canada has a parliamentary form of government. *In which country do the executive and legislative branches of government overlap?*

things that affected the entire country, such as defense and foreign affairs. Each of the former colonies of Great Britain became a state, and was also given certain powers, such as control over education. The national government and the state governments, along with various forms of local government, share the governing of the country. The government of the United States is a representative democracy in which people elect those who govern them.

The national government of the United States has three branches: executive, legislative, and judicial. The executive branch includes the President, the Vice President, and the executive departments that administer various divisions of the national government. The heads of these departments are members of the President's **cabinet**—a group of special advisers. The legislative branch consists of Congress, made up of the Senate and the House of Representatives. The judicial branch of the United States government is made up of the Supreme Court and other courts throughout the country.

Canada's Government

The British North America Act of 1867 made Canada a self-governing nation with close ties to Great Britain. This act set up a strong national government and gave the individual Canadian provinces only minor powers. Over the years amendments have been added to give the provinces more powers. Under the terms of the British North America Act, Canada needed the approval of Great Britain in order to make changes in the Canadian government. The Constitution Act of 1982 gave Canada the right to make constitutional changes without British approval.

The executive part of the Canadian government includes the governor-general, the prime minister, and the cabinet. The British monarch is still the official head of state in Canada and appoints a governor-general to act in his or her place. The governor-general has little actual power and performs only certain ceremonial duties. Canada's prime minister is the actual working head of the government.

The national legislature of Canada is called the Parliament and is made up of the Senate and the House of Commons. The Supreme Court of Canada, which is the highest court in the country, has nine judges. There are also other lower courts.

States, Provinces, and Territories

The United States is made up of 50 states and several territories. United States territories include the Commonwealth of Puerto Rico and the Virgin Islands of the United States in the Caribbean Sea. American Samoa, Guam, and several other Pacific islands and island groups are also territories of the United States.

Canada is made up of 10 provinces and 2 territories. The territories, located in the extreme northern part of the country, are the Yukon Territory and the Northwest Territories. In 1999 a third territory—Nunavut—will be carved out of part of the Northwest Territories. Nunavut will have a largely Inuit population.

SECTION 2 REVIEW

Checking for Understanding
1. **Define** strait, cash crop, republic, industrialization, dry farming, Constitution, amendment, cabinet.
2. **Locating Places** Where is the Bering Strait?
3. **Human/Environment Interaction** How did the early peoples of the United States and Canada interact with the region's different environments?
4. **Movement** How has technology helped the United States and Canada become industrial leaders?

Critical Thinking
5. **Making Comparisons** How are the governments of Canada and the United States similar? How are they different?

Geography *and* History

CANADA'S TWO LANGUAGES

As you read, examine how Canada became a bilingual country.

Loyalists Move to Canada

The Treaty of Paris opened to British settlement a huge area of land in the north. Known as Quebec, the British-ruled territory later provided a perfect refuge for residents of the 13 American colonies who opposed the American Revolution. Known as Loyalists, these immigrants left the unpleasant situation in the 13 colonies to resettle in Canada. With them, they brought the English language, as well as British law and customs.

French Culture Recognized

Quebec, however, was home to thousands of French Canadians. Although the British Parliament guaranteed them political and religious rights, the French Canadians felt at a disadvantage with their British rulers and the English-speaking Loyalists.

The British tried to solve the problem by dividing Quebec into two colonies in the Constitutional Act of 1791. Lower Canada, along the lower St. Lawrence River, remained largely French in population and law. Upper Canada, along the Great Lakes, was British in population and law.

MAJOR LANGUAGES OF CANADA

- English
- French
- English and Native Languages

Arctic Circle

0   500 mi.
0   500 km

N

Two Languages Recognized

When the modern nation of Canada was formed in 1867, both French and English were recognized as Canada's official languages. In many places, however, English continued to be used almost exclusively.

Finally, in 1969, the Canadian Parliament passed the Official Languages Act. This law guarantees all Canadians the right to communicate with the Canadian federal government in English or French.

In 1974 the Quebec legislature strengthened the position of the French language in the province by making French the sole official language for the provincial government. In 1977 it adopted the Charter of the French Language, making French the language of business and communications.

Checking for Understanding

1. How did the relocation of the Loyalists lead to Canada's present-day system of two languages?

2. **Location** Study the map at the top of the page. Why was Canada "the perfect place" for British Loyalists?

The cultures and lifestyles of the people of the United States and Canada are rooted in the rich diversity of the Native Americans and of the later immigrants who settled in the region. The religions, languages, and arts of the United States and Canada reflect various aspects of many world cultures.

REGION

A Region's Cultures

Because of their diversity, the United States and Canada are considered **multicultural** societies—that is, societies having more than one culture. One Canadian refers to his country in the following way:

---◆---

. . . Canadians believe . . . in a mosaic [an elaborate design] of separate pieces with each chunk becoming part of the whole physically but retaining its own separate color and identity.

---◆---

Whether described as a mosaic or some other term, these cultures offer a bounty of beliefs and traditions that help define the region of the United States and Canada.

Religious Freedom

Freedom of religion has always been valued in the United States and Canada. This is true because many of the people who migrated to the region did so to worship freely. As early as 1774 a law recognizing French Canadian religious rights was passed by the British Parliament. After the United States became an independent country, citizens were guaranteed religious freedom under the Constitution.

Most people who are members of an organized religion in the United States and Canada today are Christians. In the United States more than one-half of all religious people are Protestants, while another one-third are Roman Catholics. In Canada, Roman Catholics make up almost one-half of all religious people. Judaism, Islam, and Buddhism are among other religions in the United States and Canada. Religion and where people live today often reflect earlier settlement patterns.

Languages

Like religion, language in the United States and Canada also reflects the identities of early settlers. People from Great Britain brought English to the United States as the primary language. In some areas of the United States that were first colonized by Spain or France, however, many people speak Spanish or French. Many Spanish-speaking people live in the Southwest and many French-speaking people live in southern Louisiana.

Many recent Spanish-speaking immigrants to the United States have come from Latin America. These immigrants have generally settled in the Southwest, in Florida, and in such major cities as New York and Chicago. Therefore, in many of these places, information in public places is often printed in English and Spanish. In New Mexico, which is officially a **bilingual** state, any communications with the state government or with local governments may be in Spanish or English. *Bilingual* means "having two languages." Canada is a bilingual nation, with English and French as the two official languages. In California the presence of Asian cultures is evident in the signs written in Korean, Japanese, and Chinese.

The Arts

Early people in the region used objects from their environment to make artwork. Native Americans who settled in the Ohio and Mississippi river valleys made detailed carvings of shell or stone. Native Americans living in the Southwest used clay from their area to make pottery, and wove baskets, sandals, and mats from native plants.

After European settlement, the arts of the region were greatly influenced by European styles. By the mid-1800s, however, the region's artists began to create art that showed the beauty of the land and life in their own countries.

In the early 1900s, a group of American artists painted scenes that reflected the reality of city life. This group of artists became known as the Ashcan school. Later in the 1900s, American and Canadian artists began to use the new European **abstract** style of art. In abstract art, the artist tries to show his or her own attitudes and emotions.

Like art, architecture in colonial times in the United States and Canada was greatly influenced by European styles. Later the region developed its own approach to architecture. The skyscraper, which can house many people or businesses over a small land area, was developed in the United States.

Literature in the United States and Canada at first dealt mainly with history and religion and reflected European themes. Later, writers such as James Fenimore Cooper, Thomas Chandler Haliburton, and Edgar Allan Poe wrote about life in North America. Since the late 1800s some American and Canadian authors have written about different regions of the country. Mark Twain wrote about life on the Mississippi River, Margaret Laurence focused on the prairies of Manitoba, and a later writer, Willa Cather, described life on the Great Plains. More recently, African American writers, such as Richard Wright, and Jewish writers, such as Isaac Bashevis Singer, have explored the experiences of their people.

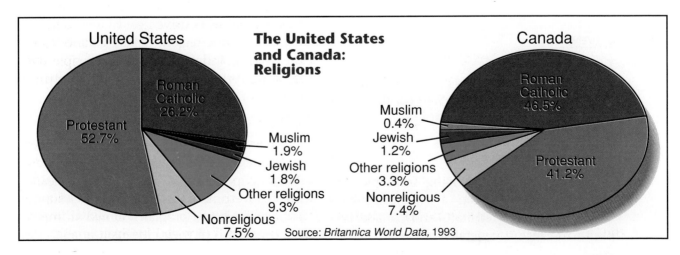

The United States and Canada: Religions

United States
- Protestant 52.7%
- Roman Catholic 26.2%
- Muslim 1.9%
- Jewish 1.8%
- Other religions 9.3%
- Nonreligious 7.5%

Canada
- Roman Catholic 46.5%
- Protestant 41.2%
- Muslim 0.4%
- Jewish 1.2%
- Other religions 3.3%
- Nonreligious 7.4%

Source: *Britannica World Data,* 1993

Geographic Themes

Region: The American Southwest
Georgia O'Keeffe's paintings reflect her interest in the landscape of the American Southwest. *What group of Americans painted urban life?*

Native Americans developed their own music, while Europeans brought European folk and religious music to the region. At the beginning of the 20th century, a distinctive form of music known as **jazz** developed in the United States. Jazz blends African rhythms with the harmony of European music. In the 1950s another unique form of music—rock 'n' roll—became an instant success.

MOVEMENT

Lifestyles

Throughout the United States and Canada, various lifestyles can be found.

A Mobile Society

Being **mobile**, or moving from place to place, has always been a characteristic of lifestyles in the United States and Canada. People in the region generally move to increase their business opportunities, to get better housing, or to get a better education. Widespread use of the automobile has given people a greater choice of where to work and live.

Standard of Living

The United States and Canada are among the richest countries in the world. Because the region has an agricultural surplus, foods are relatively inexpensive and are available throughout the region. Housing varies to suit the needs of individuals and families, whether it be high-rise apartments, multifamily row houses, or ranch-style suburban houses.

Health Care

People in both the United States and Canada can expect to live long, generally healthy lives. Governments in both countries support public clinics and programs aimed at improving the health of their citizens. Canada, however, spends more money ensuring the health of its citizens than does the United States.

Many people in the United States have health insurance, but the cost of this insurance, as well as of medical costs, is skyrocketing. Although the United States government does offer public insurance—Medicare and Medicaid—for older and disabled citizens, no national health insurance plan now exists. In the early 1990s, the government offered hotly debated proposals for a national health-care system.

Education

These nations have similar educational systems. Each has public and private schools. Both countries require a minimum number of years be spent in school. In the United States, school systems have 12 grades. In Canada, most provinces also have 12 grades. In addition, every province and every state has colleges and universities.

The literacy rates of the countries reflect this concern for education. The United States has a **literacy rate** of 97 percent. This means that 97 of every 100 residents can read and write. Canada's literacy rate is 96 percent.

Sports and Recreation

Citizens of both nations have plenty of leisure time. Many use this time to play and watch sports. In the United States, baseball, football, and basketball are very popular.

Ice hockey tops the list of popular Canadian sports. Other winter sports, such as skiing, snowshoeing, and ice skating, are popular as well.

The United States and Canada offer their citizens a grand series of national parks in which to play. Since the establishment of Yellowstone National Park in 1872, the United States has created 330 national parks that together offer 124,000 square miles (321,000 sq. km) of parkland.

In Canada, every province and territory boasts at least one national park. Some of these parks are huge. The Wood Buffalo Park, lying partly in Alberta and partly in the North-

Geographic Themes

Region: The Sunbelt
The Sunbelt region of the United States is a popular recreation area that draws tourists from other parts of the country. *What natural areas are popular recreation spots for Americans and Canadians?*

west Territories, encompasses 17,296 square miles (44,807 sq. km).

Celebrations

The United States and Canada share several holidays. For example, some religious holidays are observed in both countries. Other celebrations pay tribute to certain people or patriotic holidays, such as Independence Day in the United States and Canada Day in Canada.

SECTION 3 REVIEW

Checking for Understanding

1. **Define** multicultural, bilingual, abstract, jazz, mobile, literacy rate.
2. **Locating Places** What Canadian provinces lie west of Ontario?
3. **Region** Why has religious freedom been valued in the United States and Canada?
4. **Place** How do people in the United States and Canada spend their leisure time?

Critical Thinking

5. **Analyzing Information** Why did early art in the United States and Canada reflect a European influence?

STUDY AND WRITING SKILLS

Outlining

In studying for exams or writing reports, two common problems arise: 1) identifying the most important information, and 2) keeping related information together. Outlining is an excellent tool for organizing information in a clear, logical order.

REVIEWING THE SKILL

In an outline, related ideas and facts are grouped together. Each group begins with a broad idea, followed by increasingly specific information. For example, an outline begins with two or more main ideas. Under each main idea two or more subtopics, or parts of main ideas, can be listed. Finally, supporting details follow each subtopic.

Letters and numbers identify and separate the different categories of information in an outline. Roman numerals usually identify main ideas. Capital letters mark subtopics, while Arabic numerals and lowercase letters identify supporting facts.

Outlines can be used in several ways. First, creating an outline is a good way to study textbook material for exams. Use the main headings in the chapter as main ideas in your outline. Then, read the material under each main heading and identify subtopics and supporting details. Second, when researching and writing essays or reports, use an outline to help clarify and organize your thoughts. Decide what main ideas to include and flesh out each main idea with subtopics and supporting details.

To use the technique of outlining, apply these steps:

- Identify the general topic of the outline and write the topic as a question.
- Write the main ideas that answer this question. Label these with Roman numerals.
- Write subtopics under each main idea. Label these with capital letters.
- Write supporting details for each subtopic. Label these with Arabic numerals and lowercase letters.

PRACTICING THE SKILL

Study the incomplete outline of Chapter 6. The main ideas in the outline correspond to the section headings in the chapter. On a separate sheet of paper, copy this outline and fill in the missing information for Section 1.

General topic: Cultural Geography of the United States and Canada

Topic as question: _____
_____

I. Population Patterns
    A.
        1.
            a. Most are of European descent
            b.
        2. Ethnic composition of Canada
            a.
            b. Others—Asian, Inuit, or Native American descent
    B. Population Distribution and Density
        1. Population Size
            a. United States: 261 million, about 74 people/sq. mile (28 per sq. km)
            b.
        2. Low growth rate
        3. Population Spread
            a.
            b. Most Canadians live within 200 miles of the U.S. border
    C. Urbanization
        1.
            a.
            b. Southern port cities
            c.
        2. Inland cities
            a. Near inland waterways
            b.

II. History and Government
III. Culture and Lifestyles

For additional practice in this skill, see Practicing Skills on page 126 of the Chapter 6 Review.

HIGHLIGHTS

1 | SECTION | KEY TERMS | SUMMARY

Population Patterns

immigrant (p. 107)
Sunbelt (p. 108)
suburbs (p. 109)
metropolitan area (p. 109)
megalopolis (p. 109)

- Most immigrants to the United States and Canada were of European descent, with Great Britain supplying the greatest number.
- Other ethnic groups include French, African American, Hispanic, and those of Asian ancestry.
- Climate limits the population of Canada's northern two-thirds, and most people live along Canada's border with the United States.
- Most of the people of the region live in urban areas.

Skyline of Chicago

2 | SECTION | KEY TERMS | SUMMARY

History and Government

strait (p. 111)
cash crop (p. 113)
republic (p. 114)
industrialization (p. 115)
dry farming (p. 116)
Constitution (p. 117)
amendment (p. 117)
cabinet (p. 118)

St. Louis Street in old Quebec City

- Scientists believe that the first humans to settle in the region crossed a land bridge between Asia and North America.
- Colonists fought the War of Independence to free themselves from Great Britain.
- The British North America Act of 1867 made Canada a self-governing nation with ties to Great Britain.

3 | SECTION | KEY TERMS | SUMMARY

Cultures and Lifestyles

multicultural (p. 120)
bilingual (p. 121)
abstract (p. 121)
jazz (p. 122)
mobile (p. 122)
literacy rate (p. 123)

Golfers in southern Florida

- Freedom of religion has always been valued in the region.
- The United States has a largely English-speaking population, although many Americans speak Spanish and other languages. Canada recognizes both English and French as its official languages.
- Citizens of both countries enjoy a variety of cultures and a high standard of living.

Reviewing Key Terms

Choose the vocabulary term that best completes each of the sentences below. Write your answers on a separate sheet of paper.

immigrants (p. 107)
Sunbelt (p. 108)
strait (p. 111)
cash crops (p. 113)
republic (p. 114)
amendments (p. 117)
cabinet (p. 118)
bilingual (p. 121)
abstract (p. 121)
jazz (p. 122)
mobile (p. 122)

SECTION 1

1. Those who leave their homes to settle in another country are _____ .
2. The _____ includes southern and southwestern states with temperate climates.

SECTION 2

3. Middle Colonies produced _____ for sale.
4. A narrow body of water called a _____ often separates two larger seas.
5. The first 10 _____ to the United States Constitution are known as the Bill of Rights.
6. The heads of executive departments in the United States government are members of the President's _____ .
7. A _____ is a form of government in which citizens elect their own officials.

SECTION 3

8. Because Canada has two official languages, it is considered _____ .
9. In _____ art, the artist tries to show his or her own emotions and attitudes.
10. _____ means moving from place to place.
11. A musical blend of African rhythms and European harmony is called _____ .

Reviewing Facts

SECTION 1

12. What are the population densities for the United States and Canada?
13. Where is Canada's least populated area?

SECTION 2

14. How was the land of the United States and Canada changed by European settlers?
15. What were the first four provinces to join the Dominion of Canada?

SECTION 3

16. How has immigration affected language in the United States and Canada?
17. What are Medicare and Medicaid?

Critical Thinking

18. **Analyzing Information** Why do most Canadians live near the United States?
19. **Determining Cause and Effect** How do archaeological finds suggest when people first came to North America?
20. **Predicting Consequences** How would things be different if the United States were officially bilingual?

Geographic Themes

21. **Human/Environment Interaction** Why was Pittsburgh's location favorable for the development of the steel industry?
22. **Human/Environment Interaction** How did early art reflect the environment?
23. **Movement** Why do most people in the United States and Canada generally move?

Practicing Skills

Outlining

Create a detailed outline of Chapter 6, Section 2, similar to the one you completed for Section 1 in the skill lesson on page 124.

Using the Unit Atlas

Refer to the cultural geography section of the Unit Atlas on pages 86–87.

24. What are the two most densely populated provinces of Canada?
25. What five states once belonged to Spain?

Projects

Individual Activity

Use an encyclopedia to help you select a United States territorial acquisition, such as the Louisiana Purchase. Write a report on the area's importance today.

Cooperative Learning Activity

Working in groups of four, imagine your class is immigrating to the region. Use your text's physical and climatic maps to select a location. Present a speech explaining your choice. After all speeches are heard, take a class vote on your future home.

Writing About Geography
Description

Using your journal as well as reference works in your library, find out what major group or groups of immigrants settled in your local area. Write an essay about the cultural influences these people have had.

Locating Places

THE UNITED STATES AND CANADA: PHYSICAL/POLITICAL

Match the letters on the map with the places and physical features of the United States and Canada. Write your answers on a separate sheet of paper.

1. Yukon Territory
2. Great Salt Lake
3. Nova Scotia
4. Quebec
5. Alberta
6. Saskatchewan
7. Prince Edward Island
8. Manitoba
9. Ontario
10. British Columbia

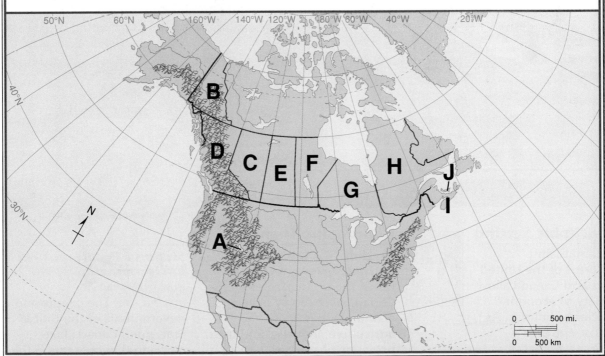

chapter 7

The United States and Canada Today

▲ Photograph: *Skyline of Toronto, Ontario, Canada*

CHAPTER FOCUS

Geographic Setting

The climate and landforms of the United States and Canada allow a variety of economic activities to flourish. As they use the area's resources, however, people drastically alter the region's environment.

Geographic Themes

Section 1 Living in the United States and Canada
PLACE The United States and Canada have highly developed economies based on agriculture, industry, and the provision of services.

▲ Photograph: *Skyline of Toronto, Ontario, Canada*

Section 2 People and Their Environment
HUMAN/ENVIRONMENT INTERACTION The people and governments of the United States and Canada face challenges in conserving the resources on which they depend.

1 Living in the United States and Canada

SETTING THE SCENE

Read to Discover . . .
- how agriculture and industry affect the economies of the United States and Canada.
- how a nation's surplus leads to trade.
- what methods of transportation and communication are most important to the United States and Canada.

Key Terms
- free enterprise
- truck farm
- contour plowing
- crop rotation
- service industry
- interdependent
- North American Free Trade Agreement (NAFTA)

Identify and Locate
Midwest, Wheat Belt, Corn Belt, California, Utah, New York, Toronto, St. Lawrence River, Ohio River

Toronto, Ontario

In my spare time I play baseball and softball. I usually attend a baseball game at the Skydome once a week. I also spend a lot of time at my computer, either playing games or running a Bulletin Board Service.

Colin Lee

Colin Lee, an outstanding mathematics student, is preparing for a career in Canada's diverse economy. The United States and Canada both have highly developed economies and are among the world's top 10 economic powers. Their economies are based on **free enterprise**, or capitalism, which allows individuals to own, operate, and profit from their own businesses. Canada, however, also has a number of government-owned corporations that carry out public services.

The many natural resources available combined with the use of advanced technology have boosted the economic growth of the United States and Canada. With its small population, Canada is a major exporter of mineral products, largely to the United States. The United States, a major producer, imports many goods for several reasons: because of the depletion of United States resources such as petroleum; because of improvements in foreign products; and because of the enormous demands of the United States economy.

HUMAN/ENVIRONMENT INTERACTION

Agriculture

Farmers in the United States and Canada produce a wide variety of agricultural goods. Different parts of the region support different products.

Many Climates, Many Products

One-fourth of the land in the United States is pastureland. Huge western ranches and ranches in the South and Midwest support 100 million head of cattle. Beef is one of the most important agricultural products in the United States.

Cattle also provide the most important agricultural products in Canada. Beef cattle ranches prosper in the drier, western parts of the Prairie Provinces—Alberta, Saskatchewan, and Manitoba. In addition, the north central part of the United States and the Canadian provinces of Quebec and Ontario support dairy farming and raise hogs and chickens.

The three most important grains in the world—wheat, corn, and rice—are grown in the United States and Canada. The region is a world leader in the production of both wheat and corn.

In the United States, the Great Plains has been called the Wheat Belt because so much wheat is grown there. The Prairie Provinces of Canada also are great wheat producers.

In the short growing season of the northern United States, spring wheat, which is planted in early spring and harvested in the fall, is grown. The southern parts of the Wheat Belt produce winter wheat. Winter wheat is planted in the fall so that the roots can grow before the soil freezes. The winter's snow

THE UNITED STATES AND CANADA: ECONOMIC ACTIVITY

Alaska

CANADA

UNITED STATES

Hawaii

Lambert Equal-Area projection

- Nomadic herding
- Hunting and gathering
- Forestry
- Livestock raising
- Commercial farming
- Subsistence farming
- Manufacturing and trade
- Commercial fishing
- Little or no activity

Tropic of Cancer

FOCUS ON GEOGRAPHIC THEMES

1. **Location:** Where are the most highly industrialized areas of Canada?
2. **Region:** What is the main economic activity in the southeastern United States?
3. **Region:** What part of the United States has little or no economic activity?
4. **Region:** What economic activity dominates most of northern Canada?

covering protects the young plants and provides spring watering as it melts. Winter wheat is harvested during the summer.

Corn, grown by Native Americans long before the arrival of Europeans, also thrives in the United States and Canada. The United States alone grows more than 40 percent of the world's corn. The nation's Corn Belt extends through the northern Great Plains in a rough band from Ohio to Nebraska. The Canadian provinces of Ontario, Quebec, and Manitoba also count corn as a major crop. About 96 percent of the corn crop is used for animal feed; only about 4 percent is eaten by humans.

The United States and Canada also grow many other products. In the United States, soybeans, tobacco, and peanuts grow well in the South, while cotton thrives in the South and on irrigated land in the Southwest. Midwest farmers bring oats, sorghum, and barley to market. In Canada, barley, flaxseed, oats, and rye thrive in a belt north of Canada's wheat-growing areas. Southern Ontario's warm summers and relatively long growing season produce a variety of specialty crops, such as soybeans and tobacco.

The United States and Canada also grow vegetables. Potatoes are an important crop in the Canadian provinces of Prince Edward Island and New Brunswick. **Truck farms** in the northeastern United States produce vegetables such as tomatoes, cabbages, and string beans. Located near large cities, truck farms can ship vegetables quickly to market. In the southeastern United States, vegetables such as tomatoes, cabbages, and celery are grown to ship north during the winter. Parts of the Pacific Coast region also produce vegetables. California ranks first among the states in the production of tomatoes, lettuce, and dozens of specialty vegetables, such as peas, asparagus, okra, and avocados.

The United States and Canada also grow many kinds of fruit. Apples, peaches, and cherries flourish in the Great Lakes region. California produces a great diversity of fruits, especially grapes and strawberries. Citrus fruits are grown in central and southern Florida, in the lower Rio Grande Valley of Texas, and in

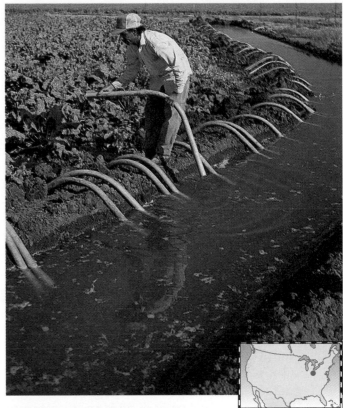

Geographic Themes

Human/Environment Interaction: American Midwest
Irrigation systems help crops survive during periods when there is too little rainfall. *What other techniques do American and Canadian farmers use?*

southern California. In Canada, southeastern British Columbia, the St. Lawrence River valley, and areas of Quebec and Ontario are important fruit-growing areas.

Agriculture and Technology

Technology boosts agricultural production in the United States and Canada. Modern methods of irrigation, for example, improve the harvest on more than 40 million acres (16 million ha) in both countries. Farmers also try to conserve precious soil by **contour plowing**, or plowing along the natural curves of the land to keep topsoil from washing away with rainwater runoff. **Crop rotation**, in which farmers grow different crops in succession on the same land, helps preserve the soil's nutrients. Farmers also allow some land to lie fallow—plowed but not seeded—during a growing season. In addition, farmers often rotate regular crops, such as soybeans which nourish the soil, with fallow fields.

Scientific developments aid the growth and productivity of farming. Advances in pesticides—substances that kill crop-eating pests—and chemical fertilizers—mixtures that make soil more fertile—increase crop yields. Scientific developments in the breeding of both plants and animals improve output. Hybrid seeds, or seeds from two different types of plants that are crossbred, has led to the production of stronger plants and higher yields.

Inventions of farm machinery such as the tractor, the reaper, the thresher, and eventually the combine—a combination of reaper and thresher—have made farmers more efficient. In the last 60 years, new farming methods have quadrupled the yield in the Midwest alone.

Owners of smaller farms, however, often cannot afford this new equipment. In addition, combines and other machines are best suited for very large farms. These factors make it harder for owners of small farms to compete with the owners of large farms.

As a result, the size of the region's farms has increased, while the number of farmers has decreased. In the last 70 years, the average farm in the United States has more than tripled in size from about 143 acres (58 ha) to about 462 acres (187 ha). Less than 2.5 percent of the United States population now works in farm occupations compared to more than 70 percent in the early 1800s. Only about 4.5 percent of all Canadians still make their living through farming.

New technologies have enabled farmers to grow surplus crops. Farmers export their surpluses to international markets. This enriches the economies of their nations.

Manufacturing and Service Industries

About one in five workers in the United States and Canada makes a living in manufacturing. The region is a world leader in manufactured goods largely because of tech-

nologies such as robotics and computerized automation.

Transportation equipment, which includes airplanes, cars, and their parts, ranks near the top of both nations' manufacturing industries. Transportation equipment and machinery is the United States' largest export. The United States manufactures about 18 percent of the world's motor vehicles and ranks second, after Japan, in production.

Food processing is big business in both the United States and Canada. Everything from canned fruits to soft drinks is manufactured in the region. Canada's manufacture of wood pulp, paper, and newsprint makes it a world leader in wood-related industries. Other goods manufactured in this region include clothing, iron, steel, and petroleum products.

Economies produce both goods and services. **Service industries** provide services rather than produce goods. Some services provided by service industries include financial help (banks and insurance), distribution and sale of goods (shipping companies and retail stores), credit cards, financial investment, education, health care, and tourism.

In the United States and Canada, service industries employ more people than any other kind of industry. More than two-thirds of all workers—including doctors, lawyers, teachers, secretaries, and government employees—offer services to others. Service industries account for most of the gross domestic product in both nations as well.

In contrast to manufacturing industries, service industries are growing at a fast rate. Some of the fastest-growing service occupations include computer technicians, analysts, operators, health care, insurance, advertising, and legal services.

Trade and Interdependence

In any modern economy, surpluses produced by agriculture and industry can be traded with others. Sometimes this trade takes place inside a nation's boundaries. At other times trade occurs between two different countries.

Foreign Trade

Trade makes up an important part of the economies of the United States and Canada. Thousands of jobs are connected to exporting, sending goods to other countries, and importing, bringing goods into the country.

The United States leads the world in trade, supplying one-tenth of all goods exported worldwide and importing an even higher percentage. American farmers export more than one-fourth of their crops, including cotton, soybeans, tobacco, and wheat. Many manufactured goods, especially aircraft and spacecraft, computers, and electrical equipment, are exported as well.

The United States imports goods either that it cannot provide or that are cheaper from other countries. Important imports include large amounts of raw materials, such as copper, nickel, and petroleum.

Canada also depends on foreign trade to bolster its economy. The nation exports transportation equipment, wood and wood products, ores, petroleum, and grain. Three-fourths of the fish caught and processed by Canadians enter the export market as well. Among Canada's most important imports are cars and car parts, industrial machinery, computers, and textiles.

The United States and Canada are major trading partners. The United States trades more with the Canadian province of Ontario than with the entire nation of Japan, the United States's second-largest trading partner. In the early 1960s, President John F. Kennedy expressed American-Canadian trade ties when he told a Canadian audience:

---✦---

Geography made us neighbors. History made us friends. And economics has made us partners.

---✦---

This trading partnership, however, is not equal. Imports from and exports to Canada ac-count for about 20 percent of the United States's total trade. In contrast, trade with the United States accounts for 70 percent of Canada's exports and imports. These huge trade revenues—totaling billions of dollars for each nation—lead to an interdependence between nations.

Interdependence

The economies of the United States and Canada, and many other nations as well, have become increasingly **interdependent**, or reliant on each other, during the last few decades. For example, the United States and Saudi Arabia, a country in southwestern Asia, have become interdependent. The United States produces a surplus of food, but it cannot produce enough oil to meet its large energy needs. On the other hand, Saudi Arabia produces much more oil than it uses, but its farmers cannot feed all the Saudi people. The United States depends on Saudi Arabia for part of its oil imports, and Saudi Arabia depends on exports of food, machinery, and other finished

Geographic Themes
Movement: Los Angeles, California
An extensive freeway system links cities in the United States. *What freeway system links eastern and western Canada?*

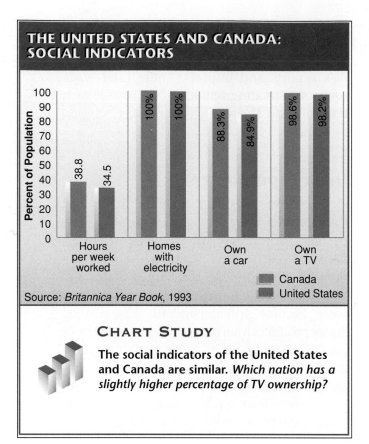

THE UNITED STATES AND CANADA: SOCIAL INDICATORS

Percent of Population

| Hours per week worked | Homes with electricity | Own a car | Own a TV |

Canada: 38.8, 100%, 88.3%, 98.6%
United States: 34.5, 100%, 84.9%, 98.2%

Canada
United States

Source: *Britannica Year Book*, 1993

CHART STUDY

The social indicators of the United States and Canada are similar. *Which nation has a slightly higher percentage of TV ownership?*

---

goods from the United States. Similarly, Japan depends on Canada's raw materials, while Canada depends on Japan's manufactured products.

Countries often worry about increased interdependence, especially when their imports exceed their exports. They sometimes restrict trade, hoping to become more self-reliant by supporting domestic production. At times Canada has passed legislation trying to restore balance to its trading relationship with the United States.

Recently, however, the United States and Canada have signed trade agreements that ensure their continued interdependence. The early 1990s saw significant steps taken toward the elimination of remaining trade barriers and the creation of a free trade pact called the **North American Free Trade Agreement (NAFTA)**. The new trading area includes Canada, the United States, and Mexico. NAFTA has created one of the world's most productive economic blocs, rivaled only by the European Union and Japan.

Transportation and Communications

The United States and Canada lead the world in transportation and communications systems. The many methods of moving people and goods and of exchanging information are very efficient and depend on the latest technology.

An Economy on the Move

The United States and Canada have excellent roadway systems. In the United States, about 190 million motor vehicles travel the 4 million miles (6.4 million km) of streets, roads, and highways that crisscross the nation. Canada's smaller, more concentrated population relies on about 14.5 million motor vehicles and 550,000 miles (885,000 km) of roads. Most of the roadways in the region have paved surfaces.

The Federal Interstate Highway System in the United States is a 42,500-mile (68,383 km) network of freeways designed to link 90 percent of the country's cities that have populations greater than 50,000. The interstate system is scheduled to be finished during the 1990s. In Canada, the freeway system includes the Trans-Canada Highway. This two-lane highway, completed in 1962, extends almost 5,000 miles (8,045 km) across the nation, from British Columbia to Newfoundland.

All these roads are used by millions of cars and trucks each day. The trucking industry carries almost 25 percent of the total freight hauled in the United States. In Canada, the trucking industry transports a smaller share of the country's total freight—partly because Canada's severe winters can create poor conditions for shipping freight by road. Still, more than 110 million short tons (100 million t) of freight are transported over Canada's road system each year.

Automobiles account for more than four-fifths of the passenger traffic in the cities of the United States and Canada. Therefore, automobile manufacturing and sales are important businesses in both countries. The automobile's great popularity and the development of freeway systems have also encouraged the rise of other businesses, including motels, shopping malls, and drive-in banks and restaurants.

The railroad changed the face of the region forever. The tracks created a link between East and West, ending the West's isolation and opening it for settlement. On May 10, 1869, two rail lines in the United States connected in Utah, creating the world's first transcontinental railroad. One observer for the *New York Times* described its effect on the country's unity:

---◆---

The inhabitants of the Atlantic seaboard and the dwellers on the Pacific slopes are henceforth emphatically one people.

---◆---

In 1885, Canada also opened its western lands when it pounded the last spike into its own transcontinental railroad.

Industry in the United States and Canada has always relied heavily on the railroads. United States railroad lines carry about 35 percent of the freight transported each year. About 30 percent of Canada's freight moves over that nation's rails.

Although passenger use has declined on the regular rail lines, commuter trains—trains that carry workers between the outlying communities and central cities such as New York, San Francisco, and Toronto—are important passenger carriers. One commuter train can carry as many commuters as 1,000 cars. Underground rail systems and elevated rail systems also transport people from one part of a city to another.

The natural waterways of the region were the most important means of transportation for early settlers. The French used the St. Lawrence River, the Great Lakes, and the Mississippi River as their routes to the interior of the continent. To the south, pioneers depended on the Ohio River to guide them westward.

Geographic Themes

Place: Niagara Falls, New York
Power plants harness the waterpower of the Niagara River to generate electricity. *What Great Lakes waterway is also important to the economies of the United States and Canada?*

Today, about 15 percent of all United States freight travels the nation's inland waterways—canals, rivers, and lakes that can be used by boats, mainly barges. Half of this amount is shipped on the Mississippi River, which together with the Ohio and its tributaries is the United States' busiest inland waterway.

Canada's most important waterways are the Great Lakes and the St. Lawrence Seaway. A joint project between the United States and Canada that was completed in 1959, the St. Lawrence Seaway is a system of canals and locks that opened a shipping lane from the Great Lakes to the Atlantic Ocean.

This new seaway made ocean ports out of inland cities like Montreal and Toronto. Although closed by ice from December to April, the St. Lawrence Seaway is used heavily during the rest of the year. Canadian barges carry most of the 50 million short tons (45 million t) of freight shipped each year on this inland waterway.

Pipelines are another important means of freight transportation in the United States and Canada. Pipelines carry such cargo as natural gas, oil, gasoline, and kerosene. About one-fourth of the total freight shipped within the United States is carried by pipeline. The Trans-Alaska Pipeline carries oil 800 miles (1,287 km) from the northern tundra lands of Alaska southward to the port of Valdez, where warmer waters make pickup by oil tankers possible. In Canada the 2,500-mile-long (4,022-km-long) Interprovincial Pipeline and the slightly shorter Trans-Canada Pipeline transport petroleum and natural gas from Alberta to Montreal.

Dependable Communications Networks

Advanced communications systems help provide this region with ways to share information and exchange ideas. One of the basic, government-supported communications systems found in both nations is the postal systems. The postal systems help people and businesses stay in communication with one another.

Telephones also provide networks for exchanging information. The United States and Canada have about 200 million telephones—more than 1 telephone for every 2 people. The United States alone uses about two-fifths of all the telephones in the world.

The use of computers and other advanced technologies, such as microwave relays and communications satellites, have advanced the telecommunications systems in this region. Telecommunications systems send and receive messages over long distances.

Some telecommunications systems not only cover long distances but also reach large audiences. Television and radio are examples of this kind of mass communication. In the United States, 98 percent of all households have at least 1 television, and most of the televisions are color. In both the United States and Canada, there is more than 1 television for every 2 people—as many televisions as there are telephones. Radios, however, are the most popular form of communication. In Canada the number of radios almost equals the number of people, and in the United States, there are 2 radios for every person.

In the United States, most telecommunications systems used for mass communication,

like television and radio stations, are owned privately. The government, however, does regulate their use to some extent. The Federal Communications Commission (FCC) licenses stations, decides which broadcast channels should be used, and requires each station to offer public service programs. Canada's government exerts greater control over mass communications industries than does the United States'. For example, a government agency called the Canadian Radio-television and Telecommunications Commission regulates and licenses all electronic communications systems in Canada. It also requires that 30 percent of all musical radio programs and 60 percent of all television programs involve Canadian writers or performers.

Written materials are another vital form of mass communications in this region. In both countries, thousands of private publishers produce newspapers, books, and magazines. The United States has more than 1,500 daily newspapers. Canada has more than 100 daily newspapers printed in English and about 10 printed in French. In addition, the United States publishes about 45,000 book titles each year, while Canada publishes about 20,000. Several thousand magazine titles also are produced in this region.

SECTION 1 REVIEW

Checking for Understanding
1. **Define** free enterprise, truck farm, contour plowing, crop rotation, service industry, interdependent, North American Free Trade Agreement.
2. **Locating Places** Where is the United States Corn Belt?
3. **Movement** Why does the United States import goods?
4. **Place** What is the St. Lawrence Seaway?

Critical Thinking
5. **Determining Cause and Effect** How have advances in farm machinery affected the owners of small farms?

SETTING THE SCENE

Read to Discover . . .
- how pollution can cause international problems.
- how the overuse of natural resources is affecting the economies of the region.

Key Terms
- acid rain
- smog
- eutrophication
- bycatch

Identify and Locate
Adirondack Mountains, Los Angeles, Cleveland, Pacific Northwest, Grand Banks

As the people of the United States and Canada look to the future, they confront many challenges. Over the past two centuries, the United States and Canada have created mighty economies. Sometimes, however, people have lost sight of the importance of preserving resources as well as utilizing them. As a result, they have harmed the land that gives them both life and livelihoods. Some of this harm comes in the form of human-made pollutants. At other times, overuse of natural resources is the problem.

HUMAN/ENVIRONMENT INTERACTION

Pollution

To thrive, plants and animals need clean air, uncontaminated water, and wholesome nutrients. Pollution, however, is threatening the natural environment. Pollution—the introduction of harmful materials into the environment—damages the quality of air, water, and land. Some of this pollution has natural causes. For example, active volcanoes toss millions of tons of ash into the atmosphere every year.

Now, however, human-made pollution is interfering with nature's ability to adjust. One ecologist expressed the change pollution has brought to each person in this way:

As the tide of chemicals born of the Industrial Age has arisen to engulf our environment, a drastic change has come about. . . . For the first time in the history of the world, every human being is now subject to contact with dangerous chemicals, from the moment of conception until death.

Acid Rain

One kind of pollution that affects plants and fish is **acid rain**—precipitation that carries abnormally high amounts of acidic material. This acidic material is created when the chemicals emitted by cars, factories, and power plants react with the water vapor in the air. For example, fumes belching out of industrial smokestacks may carry high amounts of sulfur dioxide—which becomes sulfuric acid—while car exhaust includes nitrogen oxide—which becomes nitric acid. Scientists estimate that about 60 percent of the nitrogen oxide in the whole region comes from cars and trucks.

Sulfuric acid and nitric acid are found in acid rain. As acid rain falls to the ground, it corrodes stone and metal buildings and bridges, damages crops, and pollutes the soil.

Acid rain also takes a terrible toll on the waters of the region. Fish and other marine life cannot live in waters with high acid levels.

ACID RAIN

Acid rain (kilograms per hectare)
- 15 – 20
- 20 – 25
- 25 – 30
- 30 – 35
- Over 35

Lambert Equal-Area projection

FOCUS ON GEOGRAPHIC THEMES

1. **Location:** Where are the highest levels of acid rain concentrated?
2. **Place:** What level of acid rain is found in Detroit?
3. **Place:** What Canadian city has the highest level of acid rain?

Acid rain is held responsible for the deaths of at least 15,000 Canadian lakes, as well as 8 percent of the lakes found in New York's Adirondack Mountains. An additional 150,000 North American lakes have been damaged by this form of pollution.

Because the emissions that help create acid rain are carried by the wind, the source of these chemicals often is far from where the rain finally falls. This results in emissions from United States industries accounting for much of Canada's acid rain. Nearly one-half of the acid rain that falls on eastern Canada comes from emissions in the midwestern and northeastern sections of the United States.

As a result of acid rain crossing country borders, these 2 nations have spent the last 15 years working together to solve this problem. In the 1980s, they worked to identify causes of acid rain. Then, in 1991, the governments signed a pact to reduce by half the 1980 level of emissions that contribute to acid rain by the end of the century.

Smog

The nitrogen oxides that help create acid rain also are a major ingredient in **smog**, a haze caused by the sun's interaction with exhaust gases. Smog kills plants and also harms the human population, burning people's eyes and irritating their throats and lungs.

The California city of Los Angeles is plagued by smog. In Los Angeles, the 8 million cars and trucks on the road produce between 70 and 80 percent of all smog-causing emissions. Smog is measured daily in Los Angeles. On days when the smog's yellow haze is too thick, smog alerts are issued. During these alerts people with respiratory diseases are asked to stay inside, and everyone is told to drive only if necessary.

To deal with this problem of smog, many governments have passed laws regulating car emissions. California and several other states are requiring that, by 1998, 2 percent of all cars sold in the state create no emissions. By the year 2003, that figure jumps to 10 percent. In response, Chrysler recently introduced a "zero-emission" minivan that runs on electricity instead of nitrogen-producing gasoline. In addition a Massachusetts company has a solar-powered car on the drawing board. It is estimated that by the turn of the century 200,000 cars that run on alternate fuel sources will be on California's roads.

Pollution and the Great Lakes

Water systems in the United States and Canada are polluted not only by acid rain but also by sewage and industrial and agricultural wastes dumped by humans into the water supplies. The Great Lakes have been polluted in this way. Once considered an inexhaustible resource, these waters have been used as dumping sites. This problem grew as industries and cities began to spring up along the shores and dump their wastes into the lakes. In 1976, one writer described one of the sources of Lake Erie's pollution like this:

One can stand, for example, at the top of a Cleveland skyscraper and see the Cuyahoga River running out into Erie as a thick, chocolate-brown stream carrying the washings of a dozen steel works.

Surrounding industries also expose the Great Lakes to the effects of thermal pollution, caused by the release of heated industrial water into the cooler lake water. Runoff from farms using chemical fertilizers and pesticides also damages life in the lakes.

All this pollution has had a profound effect on the marine life of the Great Lakes. In recent years the amount of fish provided by Great Lake fisheries has decreased by millions of pounds. Pollution has had a particularly severe impact on some fish species such as the valuable lake herring.

Another result of all this pollution is the speedup of eutrophication (yu•TROH•fuh•KAY•shuhn). **Eutrophication** is the process in which a lake, or other body of water, becomes rich in dissolved nutrients. These nutrients nourish many small plants, especially algae. In extreme cases, these masses of plants—in their growing, dying, and decomposing—can use up all the oxygen in a body of water, leaving none for the fish. The algae also can choke the lake, eventually turning it first into a marsh, and finally into dry land. Normally, eutrophication takes thousands of years. The minerals spilled into the waters as humans pollute, however, speeds up this process. Scientists fear that this pollution is causing eutrophication to occur in sections of Lake Erie.

Today the governments of Canada and the United States have passed legislation designed to decrease the pollution in the Great Lakes region and other waters. In addition, the United States offers financial aid to state and local governments to encourage construction of sewage treatment and water treatment facilities. These facilities work to remove contami-

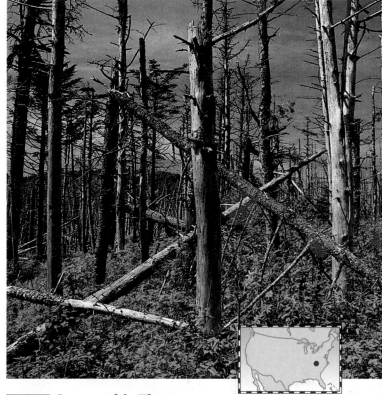

Geographic Themes

Human/Environment Interaction: North Carolina
This forest near the Great Smoky Mountains of North Carolina was damaged by acid rain. *How have American and Canadian governments responded to the dangers of pollution?*

nated particles before the waste reaches water sources. As a result of the efforts of federal, state or provincial, and local governments, some progress has been made in bringing the waters of the Great Lakes and other bodies of water to their natural state.

HUMAN/ENVIRONMENT INTERACTION

Overuse of Resources

As pioneers struggled to settle this region, they slashed, hacked, and burned their way through the forests that stood before them. At the same time, fishing fleets from many European nations discovered the wealth of marine life in the North American coastal waters and began filling their holds with fish. These activities, begun and often continued without regard to conservation, have seriously depleted two resources on which the economies of the United States and Canada depend.

Logging

Wood and wood products are important economic contributors to this region. The United States leads all other nations, producing 15 percent of the world's wood. Canada, to which lumber represents an even more important export, supplies more than 5 percent. All this lumber production requires more than 1.5 million workers and 45,000 manufacturing facilities. These huge numbers indicate the importance of the lumber industry to employment in the region.

In the United States, logging companies are allowed to harvest logs from public lands. The United States Forest Service is charged with monitoring this harvesting. The Forest Service's job is to balance timber harvests with other uses of public forestland, including recreation and preservation of wildlife habitats. Some conservation leaders claim that the Forest Service is putting lumber profits above other concerns, because its budget is partly based on money earned from lumber sales.

Another concern is the Forest Service's approval of clearcutting. When a forest is clearcut, all trees are cut down. In addition, roads must be built into the forests so that the lumber can be brought out. The Forest Service has constructed 365,000 miles (587,000 km) of roads for logging companies—more than eight times the lengths of roads comprising the Federal Interstate Highway System. Conservationists argue that the combination of road-building and clearcutting destroys the natural ecosystem of the area.

Clearcutting also threatens the remaining old-growth forests of the Pacific Northwest. A common definition for old-growth forests is forests "containing at least 8 big trees per acre and exceeding 300 years in age or measuring more than 40 inches (102 cm) in diameter at breast height." Between 1986 and 1988, more than 100,000 acres (40,500 ha) of old-growth forest were cleared each year. If this rate continues, all old-growth forests will disappear from the Pacific Northwest by the end of the 20th century.

This clearcutting of old-growth trees also endangers the wildlife of a region. For example, the northern spotted owl, whose home is the old-growth forests of the Pacific Northwest, was placed on the endangered species list in 1990. Experts say that to save the bird from extinction, logging in this area will have to be cut back drastically. This has pitted the fate of a species against the jobs of a region. Clearcutting deprives humans of other benefits of old growth as well. For example, a potential treatment for cancer was discovered using the bark of the yew tree. Yew trees thrive in old-growth forests and were traditionally viewed by loggers as trash trees, burned during the clearcutting process. Some scientists worry about what valuable discoveries will be gone with the lost old-growth forests.

Geographic Themes

Region: Pacific Northwest
The United States Forest Service has sought to balance timber harvests with forest conservation. *What practice allowed by the Forest Service has been opposed by many conservationists?*

One alternative to clearcutting is called sustainable forestry. When this method is used, certain trees in a forest are targeted for harvesting while other trees are left untouched. In addition, trees harvested in this way can be taken from the forest by mule or horse, which means extensive roads would not have to be built. Sustainable forestry would protect the area's natural ecosystem and preserve old growth.

The confrontation between the lumber industry and conservationists is far from over. In response to the concern about lost lumber jobs, one environmentalist said:

---◆---

*T*he question in the Pacific Northwest is not whether the logging of old growth should stop, but when. The supply of ancient trees is limited.

---◆---

Fishing

The abundance of fish in the oceans along the Atlantic Coast was in part responsible for original European settlement of this region. As early as 1497, explorer John Cabot reported bountiful fishing in the Grand Banks area. The Grand Banks consists of a 139,000-square-mile (360,010-sq.-km) area off the southeast coast of Newfoundland. Fishing fleets from England, France, and Spain came to reap the fishing site's economic benefits. Immigrants, mostly from Ireland, England, and France, settled the coasts of Newfoundland and became actively involved in catching and preparing fish for regional and foreign markets.

By the mid-1900s, fishing by ships from many nations had depleted the fish population. As a result, Canada imposed a fishery conservation zone covering a 200-nautical-mile (370-km) band around its coast. This zone, however, was not wide enough to include the Grand Banks. Fishing off the eastern coast, especially by foreign fleets, has continued even as the number of fish decline.

In 1992, the Canadian government, concerned about dwindling populations of cod in the waters, lowered cod-fishing quotas by 35 percent and announced the temporary closing of Newfoundland's east coast cod fishery. These actions caused the largest layoff in Canadian history, putting 20,000 people out of work. Newfoundlanders, so reliant on fishing, are still trying to recover from these economic blows.

A combination of pollution and overfishing also has damaged the fishing industry in the United States. In one recent seven-year period, the total United States catch declined by more than 25 percent.

Waste in the fishing industry also is partly responsible for the depletion of fish populations. High-tech trawlers sweep the oceans for fish, often catching unwanted fish species, marine mammals, and birds. This dead **bycatch**, as it is called, is simply tossed overboard. Scientists estimate that more than 10 percent of the fish caught worldwide are bycatch, thrown away by commercial fishers. It is believed this amount easily equals the amount of fish caught in all United States waters every year. Conservationists urge increased government funding to develop fishing gear that will cut down on the amount of bycatch netted by fishing ships.

SECTION **2** REVIEW

Checking for Understanding
1. **Define** acid rain, smog, eutrophication, bycatch.
2. **Locating Places** Where are this region's old-growth forests located?
3. **Human/Environment Interaction** How has pollution affected the Great Lakes?
4. **Human/Environment Interaction** What caused the largest layoff in Canadian history?

Critical Thinking
5. **Drawing Conclusions** Why has acid rain made it necessary for the governments of the United States and Canada to work together?

CASE STUDY

NOT IN MY BACKYARD!

As the landfills close, America is finally admitting that there's no 'away' to throw things to. . . . But human beings are above all creative creatures, and ingenious solutions to waste problems are popping up all over. . . . If there was ever a solvable problem, this is it.

The Global Citizen, 1991

In 1987 the town of Islip, New York, ran out of room for its garbage. The city appealed to the state to expand its dump. The state, however, refused. An Alabama businessman offered to sail a load of garbage to North Carolina. The town loaded more than three thousand tons of stinking refuse onto a barge, and it set out.

North Carolina, however, refused to let the barge drop off its cargo. So began the barge's spring search along the coast of the southern United States and beyond. It stopped at Florida, Alabama, Mississippi, Louisiana, Texas, Mexico, Belize, and the Bahamas. There were no "trash takers."

THE ISSUE

In a very graphic way, the Islip garbage barge focused attention on America's growing problem of too much garbage and nowhere to take it.

The smelly boat did for the environmental cause what environmentalists had been trying to do for several decades: shock the American public into an awareness of the seriousness of the landfill situation.

Barge loaded with garbage from Islip, New York

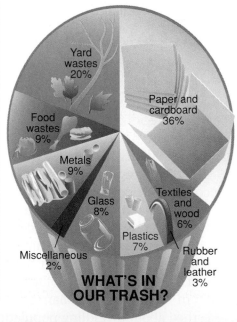

Yard wastes 20%

Paper and cardboard 36%

Food wastes 9%

Metals 9%

Glass 8%

Textiles and wood 6%

Plastics 7%

Miscellaneous 2%

Rubber and leather 3%

WHAT'S IN OUR TRASH?

THE BACKGROUND

In the mid-1950s, *Life* magazine reported on a popular trend called "throw-away living." The report pointed to an American buying binge of disposables: disposable plates, eating utensils, razors, ballpoint pens, diapers—anything that promised to cut down on the tedium of everyday tasks. Most disposable items were made of paper or plastic. Both were light, inexpensive, and, in the case of plastic, extremely durable.

> *"Suddenly," Goeller said, "there was this wonderfully awful symbol of the problem—a huge plate of garbage that no one wanted to take a bite out of."*

When *Life* magazine published its report, very few Americans were concerned about the explosive growth of trash. By the early 1960s, environmentalists were sounding the alarm for eventual landfill overflow and calling for recycling programs.

During the next 30 years, environmental concerns grew as studies showed the reason that the dumps were filling so rapidly. Very little of the material was disintegrating. Dumps covered each day's garbage with dirt to keep out rats, flies, and other scavenging animals as well as minimize the odor. The dirt, however, also kept out the natural "ingredients" of decomposition: bacteria and sunlight. Garbage in landfills was being preserved, not decomposing.

When the Islip barge appeared, most states and communities were aware of the problems of overflow and pollution from which America's landfill system suffered.

THE POINTS OF VIEW

Transporting garbage to another place seemed reasonable to Islip. Angry North Carolina environmentalists, however, were having none of somebody else's garbage. Dave Goeller of Environmental Action, a Washington-based group, recalled that environmentalists had tried to spark interest in the landfill crisis for years, and no one cared. "Suddenly," Goeller said, "there was this wonderfully awful symbol of the problem—a huge plate of garbage that no one wanted to take a bite out of."

THE ISSUE TODAY

After 57 days at sea, the barge was allowed to return to Islip. The garbage was finally burned in Brooklyn.

Since that embarrassing spring, Islip has gotten rid of 75 percent of its landfill with a vigorous recycling program. It has also built a mass fill incinerator to handle 50 percent of its garbage intake.

Many communities around the country followed Islip's lead. Recycling programs are in place in many cities; plans for more than a thousand huge incinerators to be built during the 1990s are in the works.

Environmentalists, however, continue to be concerned. Each American generates about 4 pounds (1.8 kg) of trash and garbage a day, some of which, particularly the plastic, will never decompose. Landfills are closing, incinerators are highly controversial, and fewer communities want either in their backyards. So, to their call for recycling programs, environmentalists have added the need to reduce the use of throwaway items. They maintain that recycling is better than disposal, reuse is better than recycling, and reduction is best of all.

Reviewing the Case

1. What is the landfill crisis?
2. How do environmentalists think the landfill problem can be solved?
3. **Human/Environment** **Interaction** What effects have landfills had on the environment?

MAP AND GRAPH SKILLS

Reading a Cartogram

On most maps, land areas are drawn in proportion to the actual surface areas on the earth. In a **cartogram**, country size is based on some value *other* than land area, such as population, or gross national product.

REVIEWING THE SKILL

A cartogram provides clear visual comparisons of whatever value it measures.

To read a cartogram, apply the following steps:

- Read the map title and key to identify the kind of information presented on the cartogram.
- Look for relationships among the countries. Determine which countries are largest and smallest.
- Compare the cartogram with a conventional land-area map to determine the degree of distortion of particular countries.

PRACTICING THE SKILL

Use the cartogram below to answer the following questions:

1. What value determines the relative sizes of countries on this cartogram?
2. Compare the cartogram with the conventional land-area map on pages A2–A3. How has the relative size of Canada been changed on the cartogram? How would you explain this change?

For additional practice in this skill, see Practicing Skills on page 146 of the Chapter 7 Review.

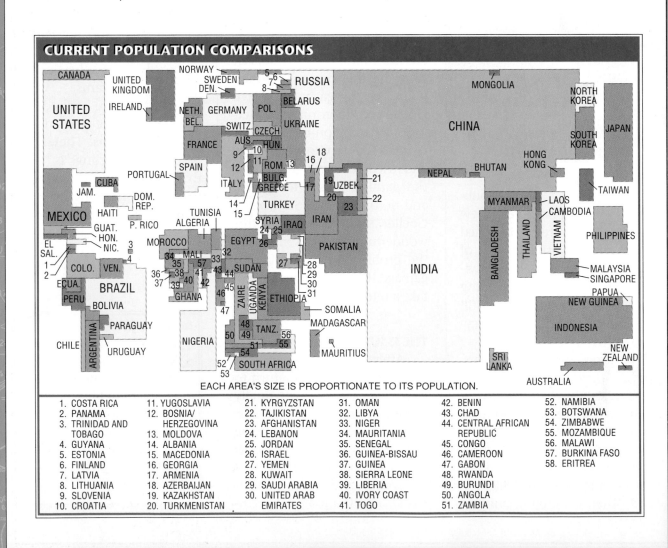

CURRENT POPULATION COMPARISONS

EACH AREA'S SIZE IS PROPORTIONATE TO ITS POPULATION.

1. COSTA RICA	11. YUGOSLAVIA	21. KYRGYZSTAN	31. OMAN	42. BENIN	52. NAMIBIA
2. PANAMA	12. BOSNIA/	22. TAJIKISTAN	32. LIBYA	43. CHAD	53. BOTSWANA
3. TRINIDAD AND	HERZEGOVINA	23. AFGHANISTAN	33. NIGER	44. CENTRAL AFRICAN	54. ZIMBABWE
TOBAGO	13. MOLDOVA	24. LEBANON	34. MAURITANIA	REPUBLIC	55. MOZAMBIQUE
4. GUYANA	14. ALBANIA	25. JORDAN	35. SENEGAL	45. CONGO	56. MALAWI
5. ESTONIA	15. MACEDONIA	26. ISRAEL	36. GUINEA-BISSAU	46. CAMEROON	57. BURKINA FASO
6. FINLAND	16. GEORGIA	27. YEMEN	37. GUINEA	47. GABON	58. ERITREA
7. LATVIA	17. ARMENIA	28. KUWAIT	38. SIERRA LEONE	48. RWANDA	
8. LITHUANIA	18. AZERBAIJAN	29. SAUDI ARABIA	39. LIBERIA	49. BURUNDI	
9. SLOVENIA	19. KAZAKHSTAN	30. UNITED ARAB	40. IVORY COAST	50. ANGOLA	
10. CROATIA	20. TURKMENISTAN	EMIRATES	41. TOGO	51. ZAMBIA	

SECTION	KEY TERMS	SUMMARY

1 Living in the United States and Canada

free enterprise (p. 129)
truck farm (p. 131)
contour plowing (p. 131)
crop rotation (p. 131)
service industry (p. 132)
interdependent (p. 133)
North American Free Trade Agreement (p. 134)

- The rich soils, plentiful waters, and varied climates of farms in the United States and Canada encourage the production of a wide variety of meats, grains, vegetables, and fruits.
- Advanced farming technologies have increased crop yield and farm size but decreased the number of farm workers.
- The culture region of the United States and Canada is a world leader in the production of manufactured goods, but its service industries employ more people than its factories.
- The many agricultural and manufactured products of the United States and Canada help the region lead the world in trade.
- Complex networks for transportation and communications support the peoples and economies of the region.

Irrigation on a farm in the Midwest

SECTION	KEY TERMS	SUMMARY

2 People and Their Environment

acid rain (p. 137)
smog (p. 138)
eutrophication (p. 139)
bycatch (p. 141)

- Pollutants include acid rain and smog, both caused by emissions from factories and cars.
- The water supply in the United States and Canada is polluted by industry wastes, agricultural chemicals, and sewage.
- Pollution of the waters severely impacts the fish population and also speeds up eutrophication.
- Logging, especially of public lands, is endangering the old-growth forests of the Pacific Northwest.
- Overfishing and waste in the fishing industry have seriously depleted the fish population, resulting in economic hardship for areas dependent on the sea.

Forest in North Carolina damaged by acid rain

Reviewing Key Terms

Choose the vocabulary term that best completes each of the sentences below. Write your answers on a separate sheet of paper.

free enterprise (p. 129)
truck farms (p. 131)
contour plowing (p. 131)
crop rotation (p. 131)
service industries (p. 132)
interdependent (p. 133)
North American Free Trade Agreement (p. 134)
acid rain (p. 137)
smog (p. 138)
eutrophication (p. 139)
bycatch (p. 141)

SECTION 1

1. _____ are located near large cities so that vegetables grown on them can be shipped to urban markets.
2. Education, health care, and tourism are examples of _____ .
3. To preserve nutrients, farmers practice _____ by growing different crops in succession, or they let land lie fallow.
4. In recent decades, the economies of the United States and Canada have become increasingly _____ .
5. _____ keeps topsoil from washing away.
6. _____ refers to an economic system that allows individuals to own, operate, and profit from their own businesses.
7. The _____ was developed to eliminate trade barriers.

SECTION 2

8. Pollution partly created by car emissions includes _____ and _____ .
9. The _____ snared by trawlers' nets is thrown overboard.
10. _____ can eventually turn a body of water into dry land.

Reviewing Facts

SECTION 1

11. Where in the United States and Canada are most beef cattle raised?
12. What is the United States's leading export?
13. What country is Canada's chief trade partner?

SECTION 2

14. How has acid rain affected lakes in the United States and Canada?
15. What is the United States Forest Service and what are its responsibilities?
16. What is the Grand Banks?

Critical Thinking

17. **Analyzing Information**   How has agricultural surplus added to the economies of the United States and Canada?
18. **Identifying Central Issues**   How does NAFTA reflect interdependence between the United States and Canada?

Geographic Themes

19. **Movement**   In what ways is the St. Lawrence Seaway important to the movement of freight in the United States and Canada?
20. **Human/Environment Interaction** Why do conservationists prefer sustainable forestry to clearcutting?

Practicing Skills

Reading a Cartogram

21. Refer to the cartogram on page 144. How have the relative sizes of Japan and Australia been changed on the cartogram? What do the sizes of these countries on the cartogram tell us about them?

Using the Unit Atlas

Refer to the physical geography section of the Unit Atlas on pages 88–89.

22. What mineral resources are found in the Canadian Shield?
23. Where are the Everglades located?

Projects

Individual Activity

In this chapter, you learned about the many agricultural products grown in the United States and Canada. Research the agriculture of either country. Use your research, as well as the material in this chapter, to create an agricultural map of your chosen nation.

Cooperative Learning Activity

Divide your group of four into two. Have two students imagine they are loggers dependent on the harvesting of old-growth forests. The other two students are environmentalists concerned with preserving the old-growth forests. Prepare and present a debate on the use of old-growth forests on public lands.

Writing About Geography

Cause and Effect

Imagine you are a reporter researching environmental issues in the United States and Canada. Use your journal, the text, and other resources to decide which issues you will address. Write a newspaper story in which you discuss how you think these issues will continue to affect these nations.

Locating Places

THE UNITED STATES AND CANADA: PHYSICAL/POLITICAL

Match the letters on the map with the places and physical features of the United States and Canada. Write your answers on a separate sheet of paper.

1. Midwest
2. Prairie Provinces
3. California
4. New York
5. Toronto
6. St. Lawrence River
7. Ohio River
8. Alaska
9. Texas
10. Pacific Northwest

ICE HOCKEY

One day in the mid-1860s, at the frozen harbor of Kingston, Ontario, a group of bored Canadian soldiers cleared the snow from the ice. Then they strapped on their skates, and using their field hockey sticks and balls, proceeded to "invent" Canadian ice hockey. By 1900 hockey had become Canada's national pastime. During the 20th century, millions of Americans have developed the same passionate interest in this fast, entertaining sport.

◀ **THE SPREAD OF HOCKEY** from Canada to the United States began in the 1880s and 1890s when Canadians sparked interest in the game among their American relatives, friends, or business contacts. By the end of the 1890s, Americans along the East Coast and in the Midwest had developed a keen interest in Canadian players and teams.

THE AMERICAN HOCKEY TEAM ▶ at the 1980 Olympics at Lake Placid, New York, went into the final playoffs a heavy underdog, having lost to the Soviets 11-3. Then, in an unexpected upset, the Americans plowed to victory over the Soviet team in the final match. Not only did the American team bring home an Olympic gold medal, they gave the world a new respect for American hockey skills.

◀ THE FIRST PRO HOCKEY CIRCUIT was formed during the first decade of the 20th century. Dr. J. L. Gibson, a retired Canadian hockey player who later became a dentist, hired a team of Canadian hockey professionals. For three years Gibson's team played teams in the American Midwest.

▲ ENTHUSIASTIC FANS still are attracted to hockey in the 1990s. Hockey teams play in almost every American state. The Kid hockey system has divisions for boys and girls, men and women. Significantly, at the boys' "Bantam" level (13 and 14 years old), promising youngsters are scouted, and at the Junior level (17 to 19 years old) the most talented American players are prepared for the National Hockey League.

CANADIAN AND AMERICAN HOCKEY GREAT WAYNE GRETZKY ▶

owned the ice in the 1980s. In 1989 he became the National Hockey League's all-time leading scorer with 1,851 points. Hockey stars packed crowds into arenas throughout North America beginning in the 1920s. The stars included Howie Morenz, dubbed Lightning Legs, for his grace and speed. Morenz and other players made hockey a major league attraction on both sides of the border.

Checking for Understanding
1. How did ice hockey spread from Canada to the United States?
2. **Place** What role does ice hockey play in your community?

Latin America

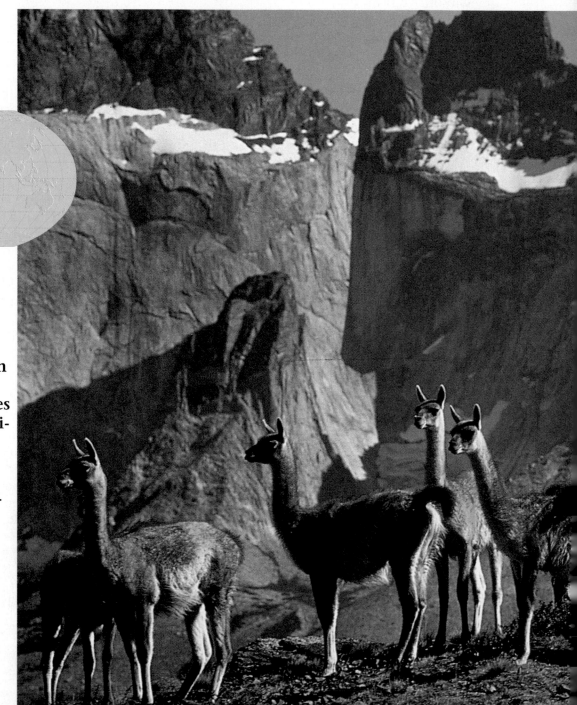

GeoJournal Activity

While studying Latin America, keep a record of news stories on the region's physical geography, its cultures and lifestyles, its economies and environments. Write short summaries of each news story.

NATIONAL GEOGRAPHIC SOCIETY

Picturing the World

These guanacos, relatives of llamas and alpacas, thrive in Chile's Torres del Paine National Park located high in the Andes. Extending some 4,500 miles from the Caribbean to Cape Horn, the Andes are the world's longest mountain range.

They also contain numerous peaks over 20,000 feet (6,960 m), making the Andes the second highest mountain range in the world.

1. Using the map on page A11, jot down the name and elevation of the highest peak in the Andes.
2. What country is it in?

Picture Atlas CD-ROM Enrichment Corner

Put together a cultural reference file on the Andes. (See the *Picture Atlas of the World* User's Guide on how to use the Collector button.) Collect the items on the CD-ROM for the following three countries: Ecuador—photographs of crafts and Canari peoples; Peru—photographs of Native Americans near Cuzco, boys kicking a ball, Native Americans in hats, video of Lake Titicaca, and Inca music; Bolivia—photographs of market day in Sucre, young Bolivians, and guitar music. Read the photo captions and answer the following questions:

1. Crafts of the Andes enjoy an international reputation. Name a popular product tourists often buy in the villages of the Andes.
2. Name a major textile product of Peru.
3. What instrument did the ancient Incas play?
4. What is a sampoña?

LATIN AMERICA
Cultural Geography

1. **What areas of Latin America are the most heavily populated? Most sparsely populated?**
2. **What nations make up Latin America?**
3. **What cities in Latin America have more than 5 million people?**
4. **What countries border Brazil?**

Brazil is the only South American country in which Portuguese is the official language.

The great majority of **Mexico's** people are of mixed European and Native American ancestry.

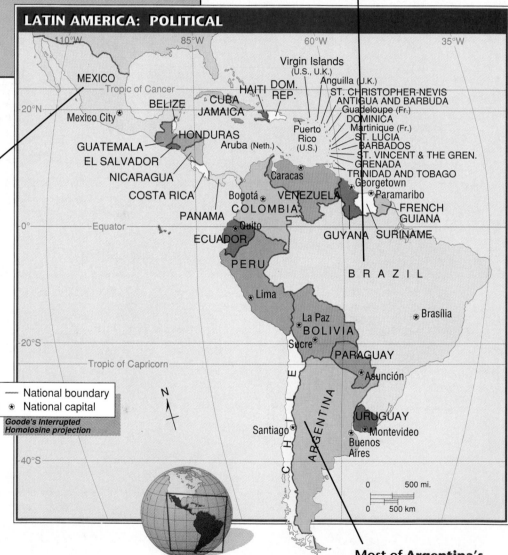

LATIN AMERICA: POLITICAL

110°W   85°W   60°W   35°W

MEXICO
Tropic of Cancer
20°N
Mexico City
BELIZE
GUATEMALA
EL SALVADOR
NICARAGUA
COSTA RICA
PANAMA
HONDURAS
CUBA
JAMAICA
HAITI
DOM. REP.
Aruba (Neth.)
Puerto Rico (U.S.)
Virgin Islands (U.S., U.K.)
Anguilla (U.K.)
ST. CHRISTOPHER-NEVIS
ANTIGUA AND BARBUDA
Guadeloupe (Fr.)
DOMINICA
Martinique (Fr.)
ST. LUCIA
BARBADOS
ST. VINCENT & THE GREN.
GRENADA
TRINIDAD AND TOBAGO
Caracas
Bogotá
VENEZUELA
COLOMBIA
Georgetown
Paramaribo
FRENCH GUIANA
GUYANA SURINAME
Equator
Quito
ECUADOR
PERU
Lima
BRAZIL
Brasília
La Paz
BOLIVIA
Sucre
PARAGUAY
Asunción
20°S
Tropic of Capricorn
CHILE
ARGENTINA
URUGUAY
Santiago
Montevideo
Buenos Aires
40°S

— National boundary
⊛ National capital
Goode's Interrupted Homolosine projection

N

0   500 mi.
0   500 km

Most of **Argentina's** people are of Spanish or Italian ancestry. Native Americans—the original inhabitants—make up only a small part of the country's population.

Spanish is the official language of all the countries of **Central America**, except Belize. English is the official language of Belize.

Mexico City is Latin America's largest city. It has the world's second-largest population.

Caracas is Venezuela's capital and largest city. About four-fifths of Venezuela's population lives in cities and towns.

Brazil is one of the largest, most populated of the world's countries. About half of South America's population lives here.

The growing population of **La Paz**, in Bolivia, is nearly one-half Native American.

Argentina's capital, **Buenos Aires**, is home to one-third of Argentina's people.

LATIN AMERICA: POPULATION DENSITY

Monterrey
Guadalajara
Mexico City
Havana
Santo Domingo
Kingston
Port-au-Prince
San Juan
Guatemala
Tegucigalpa
San Salvador
Maracaibo
Caracas
Medellín
Cali
Bogotá
Guayaquil
Quito
Belém
Fortaleza
Lima
Recife
Salvador
Brasília
La Paz
Belo Horizonte
Rio de Janeiro
Asunción
Curitiba
São Paulo
Pôrto Alegre
Valparaíso
Santiago
Rosario
Montevideo
Buenos Aires

Tropic of Cancer
Equator
Tropic of Capricorn

Per sq. km	Per sq. mi.
Over 100	Over 250
50-100	125-250
25-50	60-125
1-25	2-60
Under 1	Under 2
Uninhabited	Uninhabited

Cities
- ■ Over 10,000,000
- □ 5,000,000 – 10,000,000
- ⊙ 2,000,000 – 5,000,000
- • 1,000,000 – 2,000,000
- ○ 250,000 – 1,000,000

Goode's Interrupted Homolosine projection

0   500 mi.
0   500 km

Latin America has almost twice as many people as the United States.

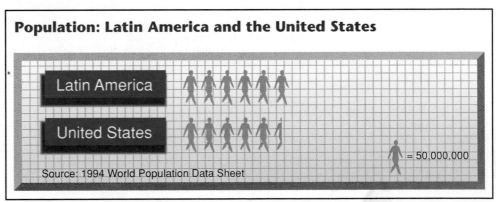

Population: Latin America and the United States

Latin America

United States

= 50,000,000

Source: 1994 World Population Data Sheet

LATIN AMERICA
Physical Geography

CHARTING YOUR COURSE

1. *What large lake is found in the Andes?*
2. *Name two highland regions in South America.*
3. *What are three major natural resources of Latin America?*
4. *What islands are located in the West Indies?*

The Amazon is the second-longest river in the world. It winds about 4,000 miles (6,438 km) from its source in the Peruvian Andes to its mouth in Brazil.

The West Indies separate the Caribbean Sea from the Atlantic Ocean. They are part of an underwater mountain chain.

Many of the mountains in **Central America** contain active volcanoes.

The Andes are the world's longest mountain range above sea level. They stretch 4,500 miles (7,240 km) along the entire west coast of South America.

The Pampas is a fertile plain that makes up about one-fifth of Argentina's total area.

LATIN AMERICA: PHYSICAL FEATURES

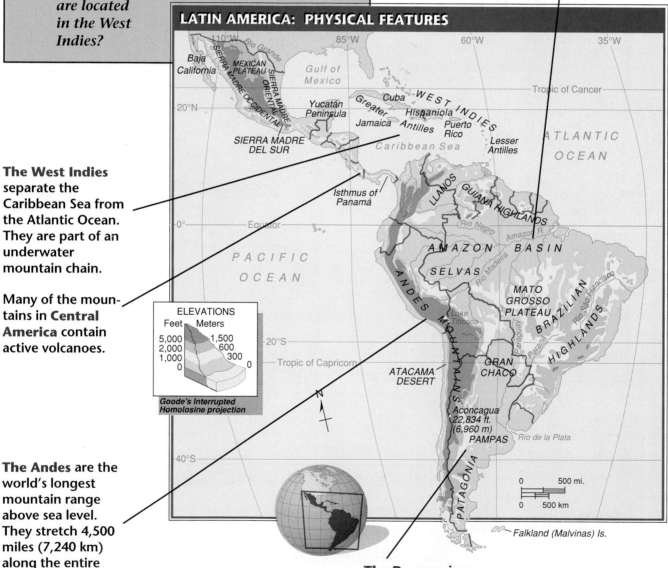

ELEVATIONS

Feet	Meters
5,000	1,500
2,000	600
1,000	300
0	0

Goode's Interrupted Homolosine projection

0   500 mi.
0   500 km

Falkland (Malvinas) Is.

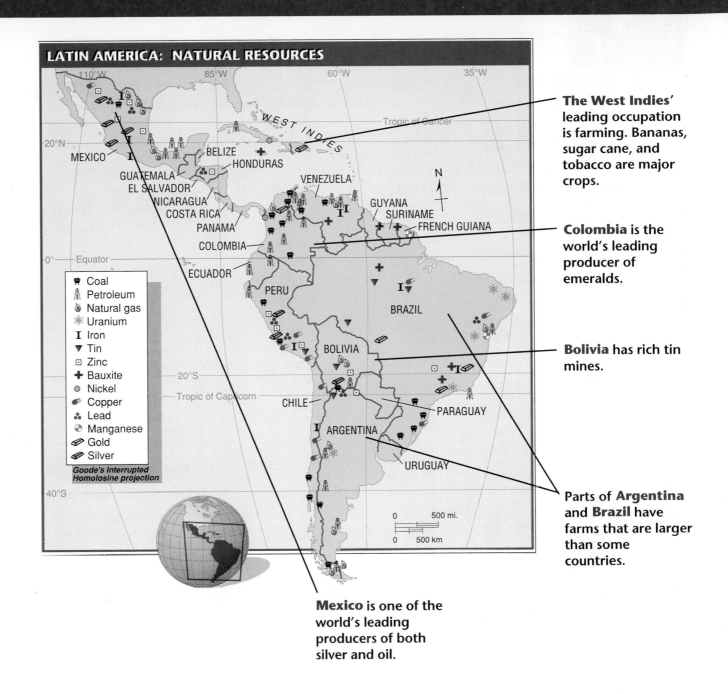

LATIN AMERICA: NATURAL RESOURCES

WEST INDIES

Tropic of Cancer

MEXICO
BELIZE
GUATEMALA
EL SALVADOR
HONDURAS
NICARAGUA
COSTA RICA
PANAMA
VENEZUELA
GUYANA
SURINAME
FRENCH GUIANA
COLOMBIA
ECUADOR
PERU
BRAZIL
BOLIVIA
CHILE
PARAGUAY
ARGENTINA
URUGUAY

Equator

Tropic of Capricorn

Legend
- 🪨 Coal
- ⛏ Petroleum
- 💧 Natural gas
- ☢ Uranium
- I Iron
- ▼ Tin
- ▣ Zinc
- ✚ Bauxite
- ● Nickel
- ◤ Copper
- ♣ Lead
- ◉ Manganese
- ◢ Gold
- ◿ Silver

Goode's Interrupted Homolosine projection

N

0   500 mi.
0   500 km

The West Indies' leading occupation is farming. Bananas, sugar cane, and tobacco are major crops.

Colombia is the world's leading producer of emeralds.

Bolivia has rich tin mines.

Parts of **Argentina** and **Brazil** have farms that are larger than some countries.

Mexico is one of the world's leading producers of both silver and oil.

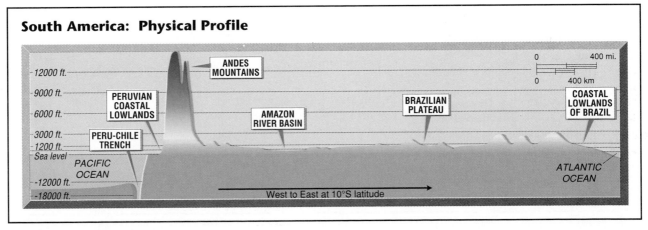

South America: Physical Profile

- 12000 ft.
- 9000 ft.
- 6000 ft.
- 3000 ft.
- 1200 ft.
- Sea level
- -12000 ft.
- -18000 ft.

0   400 mi.
0   400 km

ANDES MOUNTAINS

PERUVIAN COASTAL LOWLANDS

AMAZON RIVER BASIN

BRAZILIAN PLATEAU

COASTAL LOWLANDS OF BRAZIL

PERU-CHILE TRENCH

PACIFIC OCEAN

ATLANTIC OCEAN

West to East at 10°S latitude

COUNTRY* AND CAPITAL	FLAG AND LANGUAGES	POPULATION	LANDMASS	PRINCIPAL PRODUCTS EXPORT	IMPORT
Antigua and Barbuda — St. Johns	English	100,000 / 588 per sq. mi. / 227 per sq. km	170 sq. mi. / 440 sq. km	Petroleum	Food and Live Animals
Argentina — Buenos Aires	Spanish	33,900,000 / 32 per sq. mi. / 12 per sq. km	1,056,640 sq. mi. / 2,736,698 sq. km	Food and Live Animals	Machinery
Bahamas — Nassau	English	300,000 / 78 per sq. mi. / 30 per sq. km	3,860 sq. mi. / 9,997 sq. km	Petroleum	Crude Oil
Barbados — Bridgetown	English	300,000 / 1,765 per sq. mi. / 682 per sq. km	170 sq. mi. / 440 sq. km	Sugar	Machinery
Belize — Belmopan	English, Spanish	200,000 / 23 per sq. mi. / 9 per sq. km	8,800 sq. mi. / 22,792 sq. km	Sugar	Machinery
Bolivia — La Paz, Sucre	Spanish, Aymara, Quechua	8,200,000 / 19 per sq. mi. / 7 per sq. km	418,680 sq. mi. / 1,084,381 sq. km	Zinc	Raw Materials
Brazil — Brasília	Portuguese	155,300,000 / 48 per sq. mi. / 18 per sq. km	3,265,060 sq. mi. / 8,456,505 sq. km	Machinery	Petroleum
Chile — Santiago	Spanish	14,000,000 / 47 per sq. mi. / 18 per sq. km	289,110 sq. mi. / 748,795 sq. km	Paper Products	Intermediate Goods
Colombia — Bogotá	Spanish	35,600,000 / 89 per sq. mi. / 34 per sq. km	401,040 sq. mi. / 1,038,694 sq. km	Petroleum	Machinery
Costa Rica — San José	Spanish	3,200,000 / 167 per sq. mi. / 65 per sq. km	19,710 sq. mi. / 51,049 sq. km	Garments	Petroleum
Cuba — Havana	Spanish	11,100,000 / 259 per sq. mi. / 100 per sq. km	42,400 sq. mi. / 109,816 sq. km	Sugar	Crude Oil
Dominica — Roseau	English, French, Creole	100,000 / 345 per sq. mi. / 133 per sq. km	290 sq. mi. / 751 sq. km	Bananas	Machinery

*Country maps not drawn to scale.

COUNTRY* AND CAPITAL	FLAG AND LANGUAGES	POPULATION	LANDMASS	PRINCIPAL EXPORT	PRODUCTS IMPORT
Dominican Republic Santo Domingo	Spanish	7,800,000 407 per sq. mi. 157 per sq. km	18,680 sq. mi. 48,381 sq. km	Ferro nickel	Petroleum
Ecuador Quito	Spanish	10,600,000 96 per sq. mi. 37 per sq. km	106,890 sq. mi. 276,845 sq. km	Petroleum	Raw Materials
El Salvador San Salvador	Spanish	5,200,000 650 per sq. mi. 251 per sq. km	8,000 sq. mi. 20,720 sq. km	Coffee	Chemicals
French Guiana Territory of France Cayenne	French	127,505 4 per sq. mi. 1 per sq. km	35,126 sq. mi. 91,000 sq. km	Shrimp	Food
Grenada St. George's	English, French patois	100,000 769 per sq. mi. 297 per sq. km	130 sq. mi. 337 sq. km	Bananas	Machinery
Guatemala Guatemala City	Spanish, Mayan languages	10,300,000 239 per sq. mi. 92 per sq. km	41,860 sq. mi. 108,417 sq. km	Coffee	Petroleum
Guyana Georgetown	English, Amerindian dialects	800,000 11 per sq. mi. 4 per sq. km	76,000 sq. mi. 196,840 sq. km	Sugar	Fuels
Haiti Port-au-Prince	French, Haitian Creole	7,000,000 611 per sq. mi. 236 per sq. km	10,640 sq. mi. 27,558 sq. km	Textiles	Food
Honduras Tegucigalpa	Spanish	5,300,000 130 per sq. mi. 50 per sq. km	43,200 sq. mi. 111,888 sq. km	Bananas	Machinery
Jamaica Kingston	English, Creole	2,500,000 585 per sq. mi. 226 per sq. km	4,180 sq. mi. 10,826 sq. km	Alumina	Fuels
Mexico Mexico City	Spanish	91,800,000 125 per sq. mi. 48 per sq. km	736,950 sq. mi. 1,908,701 sq. km	Machinery	Machinery
Nicaragua Managua	Spanish	4,300,000 90 per sq. mi. 35 per sq. km	45,850 sq. mi. 118,752 sq. km	Coffee	Petroleum

*Country maps not drawn to scale.

COUNTRY* AND CAPITAL	FLAG AND LANGUAGES	POPULATION	LANDMASS	PRINCIPAL EXPORT	PRODUCTS IMPORT
Panama Panamá	Spanish, English	2,500,000 86 per sq. mi. 33 per sq. km	29,340 sq. mi. 75,991 sq. km	Bananas	Fuels
Paraguay Asunción	Spanish, Guaraní	4,800,000 31 per sq. mi. 12 per sq. km	153,400 sq. mi. 397,306 sq. km	Cotton	Machinery
Peru Lima	Spanish, Quechua	22,900,000 46 per sq. mi. 18 per sq. km	494,210 sq. mi. 1,280,004 sq. km	Copper	Machinery
Puerto Rico San Juan	Spanish	3,600,000 1,047 per sq. mi. 404 per sq. km	3,420 sq. mi. 8,858 sq. km	Chemicals	Chemicals
Saint Kitts and Nevis Basseterre	English	40,000 286 per sq. mi. 110 per sq km	140 sq. mi. 363 sq. km	Sugar	Food
St. Lucia Castries	English, French patois	100,000 417 per sq. mi. 161 per sq. km	240 sq. mi. 622 sq. km	Bananas	Machinery
Saint Vincent & the Grenadines Kingstown	English	100,000 667 per sq. mi. 257 per sq. km	150 sq. mi. 389 sq. km	Bananas	Food
Suriname Paramaribo	Dutch, English	400,000 7 per sq. mi. 3 per sq. km	60,230 sq. mi. 155,996 sq. km	Alumina	Machinery
Trinidad & Tobago Port of Spain	English	1,300,000 657 per sq. mi. 257 per sq. km	1,980 sq. mi. 5,128 sq. km	Petroleum	Food
Uruguay Montevideo	Spanish	3,200,000 47 per sq. mi. 18 per sq. km	67,490 sq. mi. 174,799 sq. km	Textiles	Machinery
Venezuela Caracas	Spanish	21,300,000 63 per sq. mi. 24 per sq. km	340,560 sq. mi. 882,050 sq. km	Petroleum	Machinery
Virgin Islands (U.S.) Charlotte Amalie	English	101,809 771 per sq. mi. 298 per sq. km	132 sq. mi. 342 sq. km	Sugar	Food

*Country maps not drawn to scale.

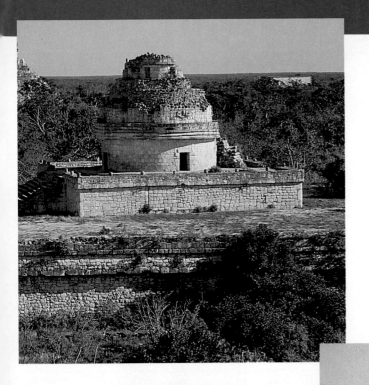

Ruins of the Maya civilization are seen today in the steamy lowland forests of southern Mexico and Guatemala.

Native Americans form a large part of the population in the Andes region of South America.

The Congress Building is one of many modern structures in Brasília, the capital of Brazil.

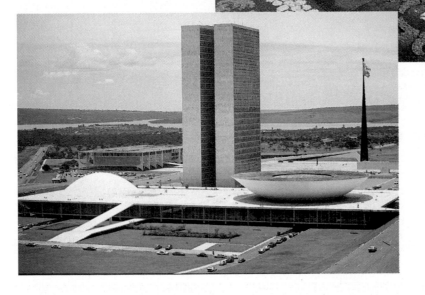

Religious festivals and processions are an important part of life for the largely Roman Catholic population of Latin America.

chapter 8

The Physical Geography of Latin America

CHAPTER FOCUS

Geographic Setting

Latin America is made up of Mexico, Central America, South America, and the island-countries in the Caribbean Sea.

Geographic Themes

Section 1 The Land

PLACE Towering mountain ranges, broad plateaus, and rolling plains are the dominant landforms of Latin America.

Section 2 The Climate and Vegetation

LOCATION Latin America's vast territorial expanse—from 33°N latitude to 56°S latitude—makes its climate and vegetation diverse.

▲ Photograph: *Iguaçu Falls, Brazil*

The Land

Read to Discover . . .
- the diverse landforms of Latin America.
- the abundant natural resources of Latin America.

Key Terms
- escarpment
- *llanos*
- *Pampas*
- hydroelectric power

Identify and Locate
Middle America, Central America, South America, Sierra Madre Occidental, Sierra Madre Oriental, Sierra Madre del Sur, Andes, *Altiplano*, Amazon River basin, Río de la Plata, Amazon River, Rio Grande, Lake Maracaibo

Margarita Island, Venezuela

¡Hola! ¿Cómo estás?
From the time we landed, the white sand beaches, warm ocean air, and blue water of Margarita welcomed us. This island off the coast of Venezuela has many small fishing villages along its coastline. Palm trees are everywhere. From most any high spot, there is a wonderful view of the nearby islands of Coche and Cubagua. Wish you were here!
Carla Martinez

VENEZUELA Bs.50
CADAFE
Sistema de Transmisión Eléctrico del Sur

arla Martinez describes the tropical beauty of the Caribbean coastline of Venezuela, one of the many countries of Latin America. Most of the region was settled by people from Spain or Portugal. To this day, Spanish and Portuguese are the official languages of most countries. Because these languages are based on Latin, the region became known as Latin America.

narrow land link between North and South America. The islands of the Caribbean, also known as the West Indies, fall into three groups—the Bahamas, the Greater Antilles, and the Lesser Antilles.

The continent of South America is by far the largest land area of Latin America. Among South America's 13 countries, Brazil is the largest. More than half of all South American land and people are Brazilian.

REGION

The Americas and the Caribbean

Geographers often divide Latin America into three areas—Middle America, the Caribbean, and South America. Middle America consists of Mexico and the seven countries of Central America. Central America is the

PLACE

Mountains, Plateaus, and Hills

The physical geography of Latin America is diverse. Dominating all other physical features, however, are the vast rain forests of

Region: The Mexican Plateau
Mexico, the largest part of Middle America, consists of a large central plateau and surrounding mountains. *What plateaus are located in South America?*

the Amazon River basin and the towering mountain chain of the Andes.

Mountains

High mountain ranges cover much of Latin America. Many of the Caribbean islands are actually the exposed peaks of an underwater mountain range. In Central America, mountains thread through much of the interior. Two prominent mountain ranges in Mexico—the Sierra Madre Occidental and the Sierra Madre Oriental—meet near Mexico City to form the sharp-peaked Sierra Madre del Sur.

In South America mountains interrupt the Guiana Highlands—in the northeast—and the Brazilian Highlands of eastern Brazil. The eastern edge of the Brazilian Highlands drops sharply to the Atlantic Ocean, forming an **escarpment**, a slope or long cliff between a higher and lower surface.

None of Latin America's mountains, however, compare with the 4,500-mile (7,250-km) stretch of the Andes, the world's longest mountain chain. Some peaks in the Andes rise more than 20,000 feet (6,096 m) above sea level, making the Andes the second-highest range in the world. Only the Himalayas of South Asia are higher.

Many people have settled in valleys near the mountains of Latin America because these areas are rich in mineral and soil resources. Mountain ranges often block communications, however, thus isolating regions and peoples.

Plateaus and Hills

Latin America is also a region of large plateaus, high flatlands often used for grazing and farming. For example, in Mexico, lodged between the Sierra Madre Oriental and Sierra Madre Occidental, is Anáhuac (uh•NAH•WAHK), the densely populated Mexican Plateau.

In Bolivia and Peru, nestled among the Andes, is the *Altiplano* (AHL•tih•PLAH•NOH)—

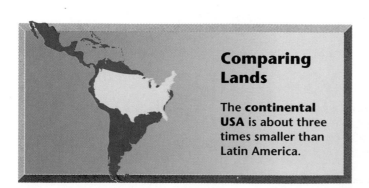

Comparing Lands

The **continental USA** is about three times smaller than Latin America.

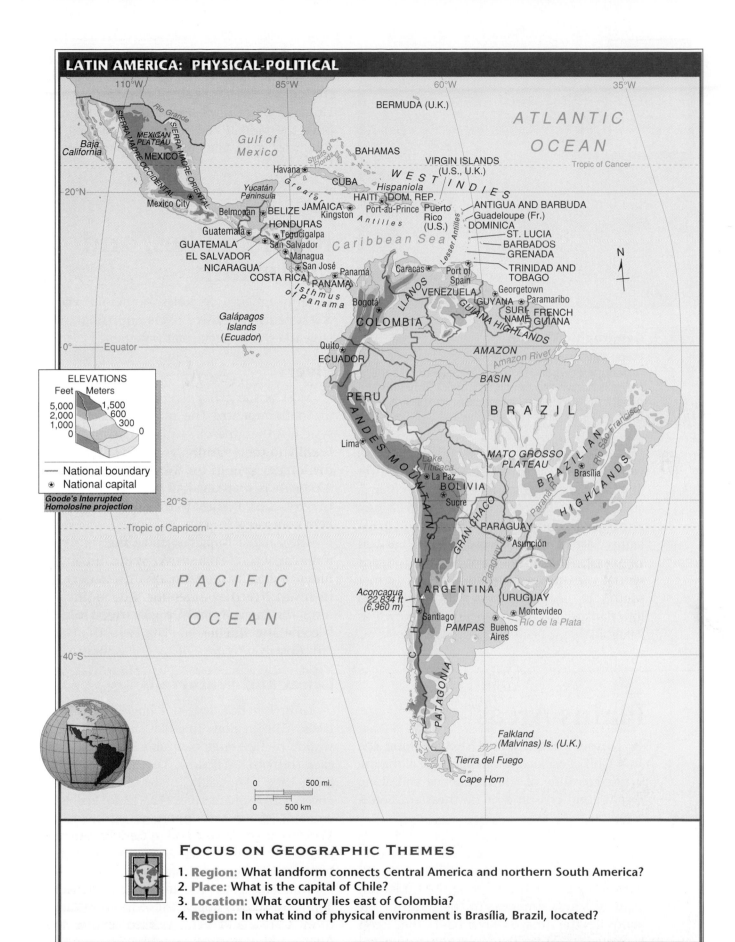

LATIN AMERICA: PHYSICAL-POLITICAL

ATLANTIC OCEAN

BERMUDA (U.K.)

Tropic of Cancer

Gulf of Mexico

BAHAMAS

Havana

CUBA

Hispaniola

VIRGIN ISLANDS (U.S., U.K.)

W E S T I N D I E S

Baja California

MEXICAN PLATEAU

SIERRA MADRE ORIENTAL

Rio Grande

SIERRA MADRE OCCIDENTAL

MEXICO

Mexico City

Yucatán Peninsula

Belmopan

BELIZE

JAMAICA

Kingston

HAITI

Port-au-Prince

DOM. REP.

Puerto Rico (U.S.)

ANTIGUA AND BARBUDA

Guadeloupe (Fr.)

DOMINICA

ST. LUCIA

BARBADOS

GRENADA

TRINIDAD AND TOBAGO

Guatemala

GUATEMALA

HONDURAS

Tegucigalpa

San Salvador

EL SALVADOR

Managua

NICARAGUA

San José

COSTA RICA

PANAMA

Panamá

Isthmus of Panama

Caribbean Sea

Antilles

Lesser Antilles

Caracas

Port of Spain

Galápagos Islands (Ecuador)

Bogotá

COLOMBIA

LLANOS

VENEZUELA

GUYANA

Georgetown

Paramaribo

SURI-NAME

FRENCH GUIANA

GUIANA HIGHLANDS

Equator

Quito

ECUADOR

AMAZON BASIN

Amazon River

PERU

BRAZIL

Lima

MATO GROSSO PLATEAU

Rio São Francisco

BRAZILIAN HIGHLANDS

Lake Titicaca

La Paz

BOLIVIA

Brasília

Sucre

GRAN CHACO

PARAGUAY

Paraná R.

Asunción

Paraguay R.

Aconcagua 22,834 ft (6,960 m)

ARGENTINA

URUGUAY

Montevideo

Santiago

CHILE

PAMPAS

Buenos Aires

Río de la Plata

PACIFIC OCEAN

PATAGONIA

Tropic of Capricorn

Falkland (Malvinas) Is. (U.K.)

Tierra del Fuego

Cape Horn

N

ELEVATIONS

Feet	Meters
5,000	1,500
2,000	600
1,000	300
0	0

—— National boundary

✳ National capital

Goode's Interrupted Homolosine projection

0   500 mi.

0   500 km

110°W   85°W   60°W   35°W

20°N   0°   20°S   40°S

FOCUS ON GEOGRAPHIC THEMES

1. **Region:** What landform connects Central America and northern South America?
2. **Place:** What is the capital of Chile?
3. **Location:** What country lies east of Colombia?
4. **Region:** In what kind of physical environment is Brasília, Brazil, located?

Geographic Themes

Place: The Pampas, Argentina
Argentine cowhands known as *gauchos* ride the Pampas herding livestock, the major agricultural product of Argentina. *What prominent plains area is located in northern South America?*

which means "high plain." Spreading over much of Brazil, across the southwest to Bolivia and Peru, is yet another plateau, Mato Grosso, a sparsely populated area of forests and grasslands. East of Mato Grosso lie the Brazilian Highlands, a plateau so vast that it spans several climate and vegetation zones. Farther south, in southern Argentina, hills and low flatlands form a plateau area known as Patagonia.

PLACE

Plains Areas

Narrow coastal plains stretch along the Gulf of Mexico. More plains lie along the Pacific coastline of South America and along the Atlantic coastline of northeastern South America.

People of Venezuela and Colombia have been raising cattle for hundreds of years on the large, fertile plains areas called *llanos* (LAH•nohz), which run along the Caribbean coast of South America. To the south of the llanos lies the Amazon River basin, the largest lowland area of South America. Just south of the Amazon River basin is the Gran Chaco, a heavily forested lowland. In direct contrast are the grassy, treeless plains of Argentina and Uruguay, known as *Pampas*. The Pampas have the rainfall and fertile soils needed for producing grain and grazing cattle and sheep.

MOVEMENT

Rivers, Lakes, and Waterfalls

Latin America includes numerous water systems—extensive rivers and tributaries, large lakes, and spectacular waterfalls.

Rivers

Most of the major rivers of the region are in South America. The most extensive river system is the Amazon, which drains much of Brazil and other nearby lands. The Amazon is the longest river in the Western Hemisphere. A little more than one-half of its length—from the east coast of Brazil to the city of Iquitos in Peru—is navigable.

The Paraná, Paraguay, and Uruguay rivers form the second-largest river system in South America and its most important commercial highway. Near the Argentine city of Buenos Aires, the Paraguay and Uruguay rivers join to become the Río de la Plata, which means "river of silver."

Lakes and Waterfalls

Latin America does not have many large lakes. The region includes, however, the world's highest large navigable lake, Lake Titicaca (TIHT•ih•KAHK•uh). The region's largest lake—Lake Maracaibo (MAR•uh•KY•BOH)—covers 5,217 square miles (13,512 sq. km) and contains the most important oil fields in Venezuela. The largest lake in Central America is Lake Nicaragua, which lies on the border between Nicaragua and Costa Rica.

Waterfalls grace the region, especially in South America. Angel Falls, in Venezuela, drops 3,212 feet (979 m), making it the world's highest uninterrupted waterfall.

Geographic Themes

Place: Atacama Desert, Chile
Chile's Atacama Desert, formed by dry westerly winds, is one of the driest and most barren spots on the earth. *What mineral resource is found in the Atacama Desert?*

REGION

Natural Resources

L atin America has significant natural resources, some not yet utilized.

Energy Resources

Latin American countries are among the world's leading producers of oil and natural gas. The oil fields along the Gulf of Mexico, for example, have helped make Mexico the world's fifth-largest oil producer. Venezuela also produces large quantities of oil.

Natural gas is extracted in many of the same areas that produce oil. Coal is found in varying quantities in Colombia, Mexico, Brazil, Chile, Ecuador, and Honduras. Deposits of uranium are located in Brazil and Argentina. Rivers and waterfalls give many countries the capacity for **hydroelectric power**, the energy of water generating electricity.

Mineral Resources

In addition to energy resources, Latin America is rich in a number of mineral re-

sources. Bauxite, used to make aluminum, is mined in Jamaica and Guyana. The Atacama Desert in Chile contains deposits of copper. Bolivia and Brazil have reserves of tin. Peru and Mexico are known for silver.

SECTION 1 REVIEW

Checking for Understanding

1. **Define** escarpment, *llanos, Pampas,* hydroelectric power.
2. **Locating Places** What are the three geographic areas of Latin America?
3. **Region** What is the largest mountain range in Latin America?
4. **Region** What are two major river systems of Latin America?

Critical Thinking

5. **Drawing Conclusions** Why does much of Latin America have the potential to produce hydroelectric power?

---

2 The Climate and Vegetation

SETTING THE SCENE

Read to Discover . . .
- the climate regions of Latin America.
- the kinds of vegetation found in Latin America.

Key Terms
- *tierra caliente*
- *tierra templada*
- *tierra fría*
- canopy

Identify and Locate
Atacama Desert, Climate regions: Mediterranean, marine west coast, tropical rain forest, tropical savanna, humid subtropical, desert, steppe, highland.

Latin America has a wide range of climates and vegetation, the two being closely linked. Traveling the region, a person can go from desert to tropical rain forest, from subtropical plain to grassy plateau to barren, cold steppe. Other smaller climate regions, such as in central Chile where the climate is Mediterranean, or on the lower slopes of the Chilean Andes, where a marine west coast climate brings constant rain and winds, exist throughout the region.

REGION

Climate Regions

Much of Latin America lies in the low latitudes—between the Tropic of Cancer and the Tropic of Capricorn. As a result, most of the region has some form of tropical climate.

Tropical Climates

Southern Mexico, eastern Central America, the eastern shores of some Caribbean Islands, and large parts of South America—especially the Amazon River basin—have a tropical rain forest climate. In these areas, hot temperatures and abundant rainfall occur year-round.

Most of Central America and the Caribbean Islands, however, have a tropical savanna climate. These areas are hot and very wet, but not all year round. During certain times of the year, they tend to be cooler and drier than the tropical rain forest regions. Parts of Colombia, Venezuela, Brazil, Bolivia, and Paraguay also have a tropical savanna climate.

Humid Subtropical Climate

A humid subtropical climate prevails in much of southeastern South America, stretching from the Brazilian city of Rio de Janeiro to the Pampas of northern Argentina. In these places winters are short and mild, and summers are long and humid. Sometimes the summer brings a short dry period, but at other times there is no dry period at all.

Desert Climate

Climatic conditions are almost the opposite in parts of northern Mexico and southern and northwestern Argentina. In these areas a hot and dry climate prevails most of the time. Here, as in Pacific coastal areas of Peru and Chile, a desert climate affects large areas. The Atacama Desert, which runs south from Chile's northern border with Peru, is one of the driest places in the world. In some parts of this desert area, no rainfall has ever been recorded.

Steppe Climate

Some parts of Latin America receive little rainfall but do not have a desert climate. Instead, they have a steppe climate—hot summers, cold winters, light rainfall. Areas with this kind of climate include northern Mexico, highland areas in South America near the Andes, and coastal areas of South America along the Caribbean Sea and the Pacific Ocean.

Highland Climates

In Mexico along the Sierra Mountains and along the Andes in Colombia, Ecuador, Peru, Bolivia, Argentina, and Chile, highland climates dominate. How warm, cool, or cold an area is depends on latitude and elevation. The farther from the Equator and the higher the elevation, the colder it is.

Highland climates are commonly arranged vertically by altitude into three major zones. Lands at the lowest altitudes—sea level to 3,000 feet (914 m) above sea level at or near the Equator—fall in the zone called *tierra caliente,* which means "hot country." Lands from 3,000 to 6,000 feet (914 to 1,829 m) above sea level are considered *tierra templada,* which means "temperate country." Lands at the highest altitudes—6,000 to 10,000 feet (1,829 to 3,048 m)—are said to be *tierra fría,* meaning "cold country." Although frost may occur in some areas of *tierra fría,* average temperatures usually do not fall much below 45° F (7.2° C), because most of the lands lie in the tropics.

REGION

Vegetation

The natural vegetation of Latin America mainly consists of rain forests and grasslands. Like the climate, the vegetation varies from one place to another throughout the region.

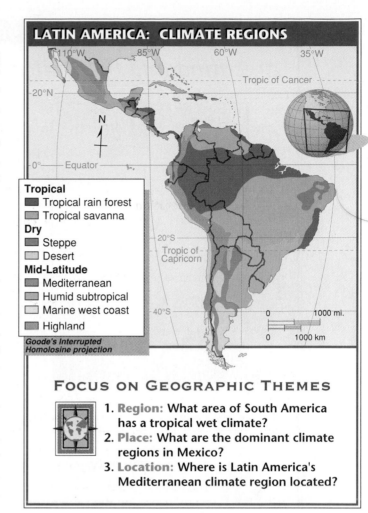

LATIN AMERICA: CLIMATE REGIONS

Tropical
- Tropical rain forest
- Tropical savanna

Dry
- Steppe
- Desert

Mid-Latitude
- Mediterranean
- Humid subtropical
- Marine west coast
- Highland

Goode's Interrupted Homolosine projection

FOCUS ON GEOGRAPHIC THEMES

1. **Region:** What area of South America has a tropical wet climate?
2. **Place:** What are the dominant climate regions in Mexico?
3. **Location:** Where is Latin America's Mediterranean climate region located?

Tropical Rain Forests

A number of tropical rain forests are scattered across Latin America, mostly in the warm, humid regions near the Equator. The countries of Belize, Guatemala, Honduras, El Salvador, Nicaragua, Costa Rica, Panama, Puerto Rico, Colombia, Venezuela, Guyana, Suriname, French Guiana, Peru, and Brazil contain rain forests. The largest rain forest is in Brazil in the Amazon River basin. This rain forest covers about one-third of the South American continent.

In Latin America's tropical rain forests, broad-leaved and needle-leaved evergreen trees grow tall and lush. Their tops come together to form a dense **canopy,** or covering, that keeps the sun from reaching the forest floor. As a result not many small ground plants survive. More kinds of trees and more species of animals live in these forests than in

Argentina and the United States

°F/°C
100/38
90/32
80/27
70/21
60/16
50/10
40/4
30/-1
20/-7
10/-12
0/-18

In./Cm
20/51
18/46
16/41
14/36
12/30
10/25
8/20
6/15
4/10
2/5
0/0

Average Monthly Temperature

Average Monthly Precipitation

Climate Graph: Buenos Aires, Argentina
Location: 34° S/58° W
Elevation: 89 ft. (27 m.)

J F M A M J J A S O N D
Months

°F/°C
100/38
90/32
80/27
70/21
60/16
50/10
40/4
30/-1
20/-7
10/-12
0/-18

In./Cm
20/51
18/46
16/41
14/36
12/30
10/25
8/20
6/15
4/10
2/5
0/0

Average Monthly Temperature

Average Monthly Precipitation

Climate Graph: Dallas, Texas
Location: 33° N/97° W
Elevation: 512 ft. (156 m.)

J F M A M J J A S O N D
Months

Source: *World Weather Guide*, 1990   *lines measure temperature/bars measure precipitation

GRAPH STUDY

The climate graphs above show the average monthly temperature and the average monthly precipitation in Buenos Aires, Argentina, and Dallas, Texas. *What is the average September temperature and precipitation in each city?*

Geographic Themes

Place: Puerto Rico's Highlands
A tropical climate characterizes this village in the foothills of Puerto Rico's interior mountains. *What kind of vegetation thrives at this elevation?*

any other area of the world. A writer painted this picture of rain forest activity:

With imperious gaze, an endangered Guiana crested eagle searches for prey. A harpy eagle, also endangered, homes in for a landing. The [bird of prey's] perch wins in the incessant competition for sunlight. Poking above the dense canopy of its neighbors, the tree gets a boost in its propagation when winds scatter its seeds. Birds such as the lemon-throated barbet and the channel-billed toucan help other trees by dispersing seeds . . . as they fly.

Grasslands and Deserts

In areas with a humid subtropical climate, such as parts of Paraguay and Uruguay and parts of the Pampas of northern Argentina, prairie-like grasses grow. The grasses tend to be short and to grow in clumps that leave the soil between them exposed.

Because of their rainy seasons, some of these grassland areas, such as the llanos of northern South America, are covered with scattered trees. As a result, geographers often consider them as transition regions between grasslands and forests. In the Pampas of Argentina and the grasslands of Paraguay, the cooler climate enables only short grasses to thrive, depending on the amount of rainfall.

In desert areas such as those of northern Mexico, southern Chile, and the coasts of Peru, very few plants grow. The plant life that does thrive usually consists of prickly cacti and small bushes with thick leaves that store water. In some of the deserts, seeds lying within the soil may sprout and suddenly burst into bloom after a heavy rain, only to die and disappear quickly.

Vertical Climate Zones

In tropical highland and mountain areas, the vegetation, like the climate, varies with elevation. Because air cools as it rises in altitude, a variety of vegetation thrives on Latin America's mountainsides. Thus, the foot of a mountain may be dry and have scattered grasses, while farther up the mountain, abundant rainfall produces many different trees and plants. In the hot, wet *tierra caliente,* the lush vegetation of the tropical rain forest flourishes. Crops such as rice, sugar cane, and cacao (which has seeds used in making chocolate) are grown in this area. A little higher, in the *tierra templada,* where most people have chosen to settle, coffee is the chief crop. Sugar cane, fruits, and vegetables are also cultivated. The broad-leaved evergreen trees that grow at the lower levels of this zone, where it is moister and hotter, give way to needle-leaved cone-bearing evergreens as the elevation rises. Higher still, in the *tierra fría,* hardy crops such as potatoes and barley are grown.

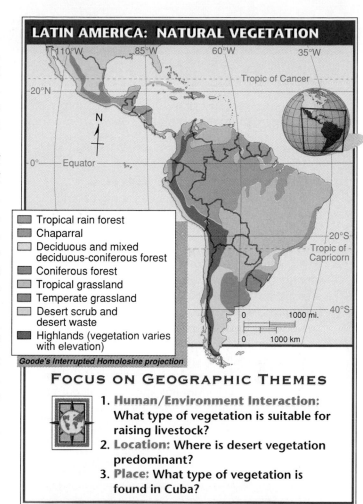

LATIN AMERICA: NATURAL VEGETATION

- Tropical rain forest
- Chaparral
- Deciduous and mixed deciduous-coniferous forest
- Coniferous forest
- Tropical grassland
- Temperate grassland
- Desert scrub and desert waste
- Highlands (vegetation varies with elevation)

Goode's Interrupted Homolosine projection

FOCUS ON GEOGRAPHIC THEMES

1. **Human/Environment Interaction:** What type of vegetation is suitable for raising livestock?
2. **Location:** Where is desert vegetation predominant?
3. **Place:** What type of vegetation is found in Cuba?

SECTION 2 REVIEW

Checking for Understanding
1. **Define** tierra caliente, tierra templada, tierra fría, canopy.
2. **Locating Places** What kind of climate does Cuba have?
3. **Place** What areas in Latin America have a humid subtropical climate?
4. **Place** Why is it difficult for small ground plants to survive in Latin America's tropical rain forests?

Critical Thinking
5. **Determining Cause and Effect** How are climate and vegetation in Latin America affected by elevation above sea level?

Reading a Relief Map

Suppose you must draw a map of a country. The country you are mapping is not flat. It contains hills, valleys, perhaps even mountains. How can you show these three-dimensional features on a two-dimensional piece of paper?

REVIEWING THE SKILL

Variation in the height, or elevation, of land areas is called *relief*. In a relief map, colors or shadings identify areas of different elevation. Green often indicates the lowest elevations (closest to sea level), while yellows, oranges, browns, and reds identify higher elevations. Sometimes the highest areas, such as mountain peaks, are white. Specialized relief maps, called contour maps, use curved lines to show the shapes of land features.

Elevation determines many factors of an area's physical and cultural geography. Elevation directly affects climate. Higher elevations are cooler than lower elevations. Mountains affect rainfall patterns by creating wet and dry sides. By determining climate, elevation affects vegetation and agriculture. In tropical Latin America, for example, climates are arranged into zones by altitude. This arrangement results from the cooling of the air as it rises in elevation. Air temperature decreases with altitude at a rate of about 3.6°F (1.7°C) per 1,000 feet (304.8 m) of height. The three major vertical climatic zones found in the tropics of Latin America are the *tierra caliente* (hot country), the *tierra templada* (cool country), and the *tierra fría* (cold country).

Elevation also influences land use and settlement patterns. Both farming and transportation are easier in low-lying, relatively flat regions than in mountainous areas. Elevation also affects the cultural and political development of a region. Although mountains provide natural defenses against enemies, they may also hamper trade and communication.

Because elevation affects many aspects of geography, relief maps are an important source of geographic information. To read a relief map, apply the following steps:

- Read the map title to identify the land area shown on the map.
- Use the map key to determine what elevations are shown in the map.
- Identify the areas of highest and lowest elevation on the map.

PERU

ECUADOR
COLOMBIA
PERU
BRAZIL
N

0   150 mi.
0   150 km

ELEVATIONS
Feet   Meters
10,000   3,000
5,000   1,500
2,000   600
1,000   300
0   0

Sinusoidal projection

PRACTICING THE SKILL

Use the relief map to answer the following questions:

1. What country is highlighted on the map?
2. What is the elevation of the green areas on the map?
3. What elevation on the map does the color orange represent?
4. What color is used to show the highest elevations on the map? How many feet high are these areas? How many meters?

For additional practice in this skill, see Practicing Skills on page 172 of the Chapter 8 Review.

1	SECTION	KEY TERMS	SUMMARY

The Land

escarpment (p. 162)
llanos (p. 164)
Pampas (p. 164)
hydroelectric power (p. 165)

- Latin America is made up of Mexico, Central America, South America, and the Caribbean Islands.
- Huge mountain ranges, the largest of which is the Andes, dominate much of Latin America, often blocking communications.
- Large plateaus, used for grazing and farming, dot the Latin American landscape.
- Plains areas of Latin America have provided significant land areas for pastureland, farmland, and forestland.
- Most of the major river systems of Latin America, including the Amazon and the Río de la Plata, are in South America.

Gaucho riding the Pampas of Argentina

2	SECTION	KEY TERMS	SUMMARY

The Climate and Vegetation

tierra caliente (p. 167)
tierra templada (p. 167)
tierra fría (p. 167)
canopy (p. 167)

- Tropical climates such as tropical rain forest and tropical savanna are the most common climates in Latin America.
- While a subtropical climate brings mild winters, hot summers, and a short dry season to grassland areas, other areas have a desert climate or a steppe climate.
- One of the most significant features of Latin America's climate and vegetation are three highland zones based on elevation.
- The natural vegetation of Latin America varies according to climate and ranges from lush tropical rain forest evergreens to desert cacti.
- Among the major natural resources of Latin America are oil, natural gas, bauxite, tin, copper, gold, silver, and valuable gems.

Village in the central highlands of Puerto Rico

Reviewing Key Terms

Choose the vocabulary term that best completes each of the sentences below. Write your answers on a separate sheet of paper.

escarpment (p. 162)
llanos (p. 164)
Pampas (p. 164)
hydroelectric power (p. 165)
tierra caliente (p. 167)
tierra templada (p. 167)
tierra fría (p. 167)
canopy (p. 167)

SECTION 1

1. The fertile plains in Argentina and Uruguay are called _____ .
2. _____ results from the use of water to produce electricity.
3. The fertile plains in Colombia and Venezuela are called _____ .
4. In the Brazilian Highlands, low mountain ranges drop sharply to the sea to form an _____ .

SECTION 2

5. Lands from 3,000 to 6,000 feet (914 to 1,829 m) above sea level are in the zone called _____ .
6. Lands at sea level to 3,000 feet (914 m) above sea level at or near the Equator fall in the zone called _____ .
7. The tops of the trees in a rain forest form a _____ .
8. Lands at 6,000 to 10,000 feet (1,829 to 3,048 m) above sea level are in the zone called _____ .

Reviewing Facts

SECTION 1

9. Into what three groups is the West Indies divided?
10. Why are settlers attracted to the mountain areas of Latin America?

11. What is the largest lowland area of South America?

SECTION 2

12. What are the eight climate regions of Latin America?
13. Where are the rain forests of Latin America found?
14. What kind of vegetation and crops grow in the *tierra caliente*?

Critical Thinking

15. **Drawing Conclusions** Why is the Amazon River an important water system to Latin America?
16. **Making Generalizations** What generalization can be made about the types of climate and vegetation found in Latin America?

Geographic Themes

17. **Place** What two Latin American nations are leading producers of oil and natural gas?
18. **Region** Why is a tropical climate dominant in much of Latin America?

Practicing Skills

Reading a Relief Map
Refer to the relief map on page 170.
19. In what direction do Peru's mountains run?
20. How might Peru's elevation affect its trade patterns?

Using the Unit Atlas

Refer to the physical geography section of the Unit Atlas on pages 154–155.
21. What river makes up two-thirds of the boundary between Mexico and the United States?

22. How can the landscape of the Pampas be described?

Projects

Individual Activity

You have learned about the different types of physical features in various parts of Latin America. Select one to research, such as the Andes or the Amazon River basin, and write a brief report explaining why the feature is significant to the region.

Cooperative Learning Activity

Work in a group of eight to learn more about the climates and vegetation of Latin America. Each group member will select a different type of climate and research it using encyclopedias, atlases, and other resources.

Determine what causes the particular type of climate, in what areas of Latin America it is found, and what vegetation grows in each climate area. Relate vegetation and soils with animal life and human activity. As a group, prepare a written report, poster, or map that will illustrate the group's findings.

Writing About Geography

Description

Imagine that you are visiting the rain forest of the Amazon River basin. Use your journal, textbook, travel books and magazines, and videos to learn about the area's physical features, climate, and peoples. Then write a poem describing the forest environment and the lifestyles of its inhabitants.

Locating Places

LATIN AMERICA: PHYSICAL GEOGRAPHY

Match the letters on the map with the places and physical features of Latin America. Write your answers on a separate sheet of paper.

1. Gulf of Mexico
2. Pampas
3. Lake Maracaibo
4. Rio Grande
5. Mexican Plateau
6. Orinoco River
7. Lake Titicaca
8. Hispaniola
9. Caribbean Sea
10. Amazon River

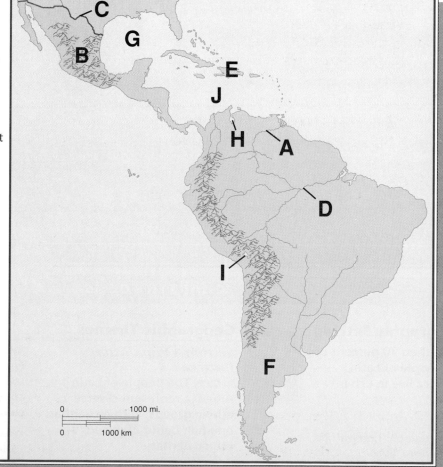

The Cultural Geography of Latin America

CHAPTER FOCUS

Geographic Setting

More than 70 percent of the people of Latin America live in urban areas.

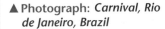

▲ Photograph: *Carnival, Rio de Janeiro, Brazil*

Geographic Themes

Section 1 Population Patterns

REGION The people of Latin America represent diverse ethnic groups, with more than one-half being of mixed ethnic heritage.

Section 2 History and Government

MOVEMENT Latin American countries were once European colonies.

Section 3 Cultures and Lifestyles

PLACE Roman Catholicism has influenced Latin American culture.

Population Patterns

SETTING THE SCENE

Read to Discover . . .
- the ethnic diversity of Latin America.
- the population density and distribution in Latin America.
- the urbanization of Latin America.

Key Terms
- *mestizos*
- *mulatto*
- *dialect*
- *primate city*

Identify and Locate
Mexico, Guatemala, Ecuador, Peru, Bolivia, Argentina, Brazil, Cuba, Honduras, El Salvador, Dominican Republic, Caracas, Santiago, Patagonia, Mexican Plateau, Barbados, Bahamas, Suriname, Mexico City, São Paulo, Rio de Janeiro, Buenos Aires, Montevideo

> Acapulco, Mexico
>
> ¡Hola! ¿Como están?
> I am 15 years old and I live in Mexico City with my family, but every Christmas we drive to my uncle's house in Acapulco. The beaches are beautiful. On Christmas morning Santa brings toys for the younger children, but I look forward to January 5 when the Three Kings bring us clothes. For Christmas dinner, we usually eat Mexican specialties such as romeritos or red snapper a la Veracruzana. I hope you visit someday.
>
> Lorena Lopez

L orena Lopez comments on two of the many holiday celebrations enjoyed by people in Latin America. Each of these festivals reflects the diverse backgrounds of the region's population. In spite of this diversity, there are common threads binding the people into a single culture region.

MOVEMENT

Human Characteristics

A bout 470 million people live in Latin America—about 8 percent of the world's population. Latin Americans come from many different backgrounds and are members of various ethnic groups. There are Native Americans, Europeans, Africans, Asians, and mixtures of these groups.

Ethnic Diversity

Native Americans were the first to settle present-day Latin America. They built great civilizations long before the Europeans even knew of their region's existence. Chief among them were the Aztec of Mexico, the Maya of the Yucatán Peninsula and surrounding areas of Central America, and the Inca of the highlands of Peru. Over the centuries, the Native American cultures blended with the cultures of the other groups that later conquered and settled the region. Many Native American cultural characteristics, however, still remain. Today most Native Americans in Latin America live in Mexico, Central America, and the

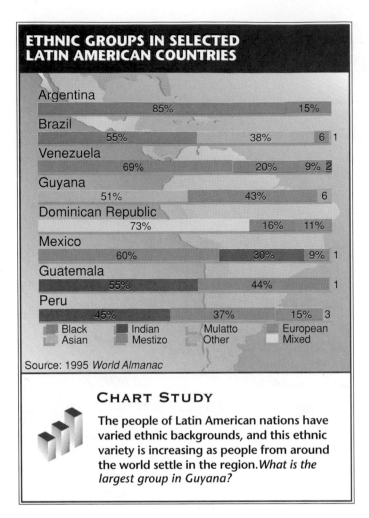

ETHNIC GROUPS IN SELECTED LATIN AMERICAN COUNTRIES

Country			
Argentina	85%		15%
Brazil	55%	38%	6 1
Venezuela	69%	20%	9% 2
Guyana	51%	43%	6
Dominican Republic	73%	16%	11%
Mexico	60%	30%	9% 1
Guatemala	55%	44%	1
Peru	45%	37%	15% 3

Black Indian Mulatto European
Asian Mestizo Other Mixed

Source: 1995 *World Almanac*

CHART STUDY

The people of Latin American nations have varied ethnic backgrounds, and this ethnic variety is increasing as people from around the world settle in the region. What is the largest group in Guyana?

Andes area of Ecuador, Peru, and Bolivia. Many Native Americans live in isolated villages and continue to practice the traditional ways of their ancestors. In areas where they are a large part of the population, Native American peoples have worked to preserve their own cultures.

Europeans first arrived in present-day Latin America in the late 1400s. Since that time, millions of immigrants have come to the region. Most of the early European settlers were Spanish and Portuguese. Until the 1800s, about 2,000 Spaniards and Portuguese came each year. Over the years, however, many other groups came as well—Italians, British, French, and Germans. In modern times, so many Europeans settled in Argentina and Uruguay that these countries became known as immigrant nations. Descendants of the Europeans continue to follow many of the ways of life their ancestors brought with them.

Africans first came to Latin America in the 1500s. They arrived as enslaved people, forcibly brought by the Europeans to work the plantations in Brazil and the Caribbean Islands. Their labor helped build the economy, and their culture remains a vital part of the Latin American way of life.

Asians first settled Latin America during the 1800s. They, too, worked on plantations. Unlike the Africans, however, the Asians came voluntarily. Today the Caribbean Islands and some countries of South America have large Asian populations. In Guyana, about one-half of the population is of Asian descent. Many Chinese make their homes in Peru, Mexico, and Cuba, and many Japanese live in Brazil.

A Blending of Peoples

More than 50 years ago, a Latin American author, Germán Arciniegas, wrote these words about her fellow Latin Americans:

For four hundred years [immigrants] from the four corners of the earth . . . have been mixing with the [Native Americans] of these lands. It is the most amazing experiment in the intermingling of [peoples] that history has ever witnessed. . . .

The writer's words continue to ring true today. The blending of peoples can be seen throughout Latin America. In some countries, such as Mexico, Honduras, and El Salvador, *mestizos*—people of mixed Native American and European descent—make up the biggest part of the population. In other countries, such as Cuba and the Dominican Republic, **mulattoes**—people of mixed African and European descent—form a large percentage of the population.

Language

Germán Arciniegas, who spoke about the blending of races and cultures in Latin America, also said this about the languages of the region:

. . . Ours has been a dual world, one part of which speaks Portuguese—Brazil—and the other . . . Spanish—Spanish America. But inland, in the heart of the [region], other accents are heard.

Most of the countries of Latin America adopted the languages of the countries that colonized them. The official language of Brazil, for example, became Portuguese; of Haiti and Martinique, French; and of Jamaica and Guyana, English.

Today Spanish is the official language of most of the countries of Latin America. In most cases, however, the Spanish spoken is no longer that of Spain. Over the years, it has been changed by the addition of certain Native American words. The word *chicle* (CHIK•uhl), for example, which means "chewing gum," comes from a Native American language. Each nation also has its own **dialects**, forms of a language peculiar to a particular place or group. Meanings of words and the words themselves often differ from one place to another.

Millions of Latin Americans speak Native American languages such as Quechua (KECH•wuh), Guaraní, and Mayan. Some Latin Americans speak only a Native American language. Many others speak both a Native American language and their country's official European language. Peru, for example, has two official languages—Spanish and Quechua.

REGION

Population Density and Distribution

About 470 million people live in Latin America. As in other regions of the world, they are not evenly distributed across the region. Some parts of the region are more populated than others. The same holds true in individual countries.

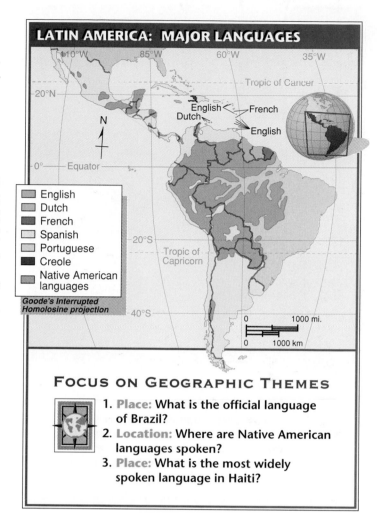

LATIN AMERICA: MAJOR LANGUAGES

English
French
Dutch
English

N

Tropic of Cancer

Equator

Tropic of Capricorn

- English
- Dutch
- French
- Spanish
- Portuguese
- Creole
- Native American languages

Goode's Interrupted Homolosine projection

0   1000 mi.
0   1000 km

FOCUS ON GEOGRAPHIC THEMES

1. **Place:** What is the official language of Brazil?
2. **Location:** Where are Native American languages spoken?
3. **Place:** What is the most widely spoken language in Haiti?

Population Distribution

Much of the land of Latin America is not densely populated. Most Latin Americans live on only about one-third of its land. A significant number of people are clustered in two general areas—around the coasts of South America or in a broad strip of land that reaches south from central Mexico into Central America.

More than 66 percent of Latin Americans—311 million—live in South America. Most of them live in or around cities on or near the coast in what one geographer calls "the populated rim of South America."

Geographers often divide this rim into two major parts. The larger of the two parts in size and number of people stretches along the eastern edge of South America—from the mouth of the Amazon River in Brazil to the grasslands around Buenos Aires, Argentina. The smaller

Geographic Themes

Region: Patagonia, South America
A shepherd tends his flock in the sparsely populated region of Patagonia in southern South America. *What two areas of Latin America are heavily populated?*

part includes land along the coast and in the Andes. It stretches along the western side of South America from Caracas, Venezuela, to Santiago, Chile.

The populated rim of South America is often interrupted. For example, the eastern coast between the mouth of the Amazon River and Caracas, an area that has hot and rainy weather most of the time, is sparsely populated. Another sparsely populated area is in the far south in the Andes and Patagonia, where the climate and the land are harsh.

The next largest number of Latin Americans—123 million—live in Middle America, most of them in the Mexican Plateau and along the Pacific coast of Central America, largely in the highlands. In these areas, the land is fertile and the climate is relatively mild.

Population Density

Population density varies greatly in Latin America. About 92 million people live in Mex-

ico—more than 3 times as many as in all of Central America. Mexico is the most populated Spanish-speaking nation in the world. It is also the second most heavily populated country in Latin America after Brazil. The land area of Brazil, however, is more than 3 million square miles (7.8 million sq. km), while that of Mexico is about 700,000 square miles (1.8 million sq. km). Thus, population density is much greater in Mexico. In Mexico there are 125 people per square mile (48 per sq. km). In Brazil there are 48 people per square mile (18 per sq. km). In contrast, the most sparsely populated country is Suriname, with only 7 people per square mile (3 per sq. km).

Caribbean countries are small, and have areas not suitable for settlement or for farming. In addition, most Caribbean countries have a high birthrate. The combination of a small land area and a growing number of people creates high population density. Barbados, with 1,765 people per square mile (682 per sq. km), has the highest density in the area. The Bahamas, in contrast, contain only 78 people per square mile (30 per sq. km).

In South America, population densities are relatively low. Even Ecuador, with the highest population density of the continent, has only about 96 people per square mile (37 per sq. km). Suriname has the lowest density—7 people per square mile (fewer than 3 per sq. km).

In most Latin American countries, population density varies by region. Few people live where a harsh climate, poor soil, or the physical landscape make life difficult. About four-fifths of all Mexicans, for example, live in the southern half of the Mexican Plateau. Three-fourths of the people of Argentina live in Buenos Aires or the nearby Pampas. In most of the island countries of the Caribbean, however, people tend to be more evenly distributed.

MOVEMENT

Urbanization

I n the past most Latin Americans lived in the countryside and worked the land. Now most live in urban areas.

One-Way Migration

Living conditions are poor in many rural areas of Latin America. As a result, each year thousands of Latin Americans migrate to the cities. There they hope to find a new life—a better education, higher-paying jobs, broader markets, and decent health care. Most people do not find what they seek, largely because they cannot read or write or do not have the skills needed to qualify for the available jobs. Nevertheless, they stay.

The resulting urban population explosion has brought problems. Latin American urban areas lack the resources to meet the needs of their people. Most migrants are now living under the very conditions they wanted to escape. They cannot get a decent job—if they can get any job at all. They have little or no money and are forced to live in slums and shantytowns, often without water or sanitary facilities.

The Cities

As a result of people moving to the cities, today most Latin American nations are urbanized. More than 20 Latin American cities have populations of more than 1 million. Four cities rank among the 10 largest urban areas in the world—Mexico City, Mexico; São Paulo and Rio de Janeiro, Brazil; and Buenos Aires, Argentina.

Many Latin American cities have become what some geographic experts call **primate cities**, cities with a concentrated urban population that dominate the economy, culture, and government. Caracas, Venezuela; Montevideo, Uruguay; and Santiago, Chile, all are primate cities. So are Mexico City, Buenos Aires, and Havana.

Many of the cities of Latin America were founded in the 1500s and 1600s by the Spanish. Each city, large and small, is unique and offers benefits people could not find in the countryside. At the same time, however, the cities are crushed by rapid population growth.

Some of the fastest-growing cities in the world are in Latin America. For example, some experts predict that by 2000, Mexico City will have a population of 30 million. The city is the nation's capital and functions as Mexico's

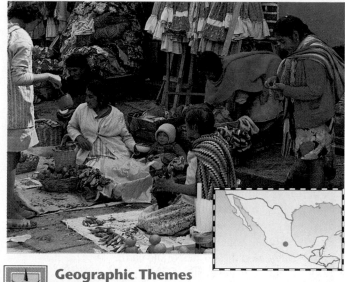

Geographic Themes

Movement: Mexico City, Mexico
Like most Latin American cities, Mexico City has seen a tremendous population increase that has strained local resources. *From what area do most of Latin America's new city dwellers come?*

leading business, industrial, and cultural center. It has broad avenues, a skyline dominated by modern, high-rise office towers, and a fairly new and efficient subway system. Yet Mexico City also is one of the most polluted cities in the world. It, too, shares the other urban problems of most rapidly growing cities—poverty, slums, and crime.

SECTION 1 REVIEW

Checking for Understanding
1. **Define** *mestizos,* mulatto, dialect, primate city.
2. **Locating Places** In what two general areas do most Latin Americans live?
3. **Place** What are the two most densely populated countries of Latin America?
4. **Place** What 4 Latin American cities are among the world's 10 largest urban areas?

Critical Thinking
5. **Analyzing Information** Latin America has been called the "melting pot of the Western Hemisphere." What reasons can you give for this?

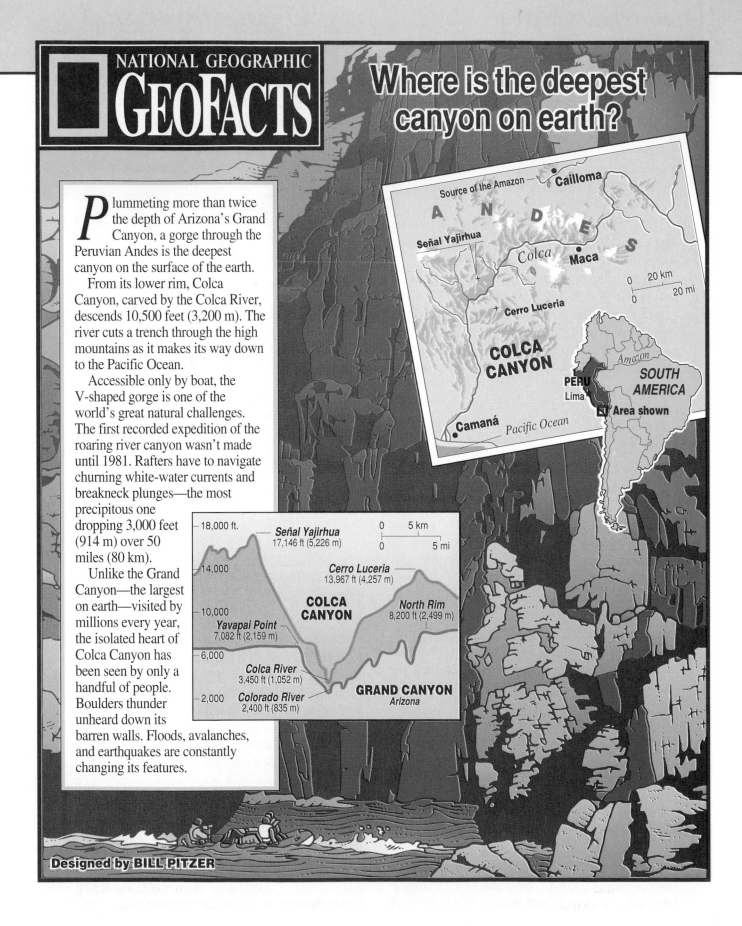

NATIONAL GEOGRAPHIC GEOFACTS

Where is the deepest canyon on earth?

*P*lummeting more than twice the depth of Arizona's Grand Canyon, a gorge through the Peruvian Andes is the deepest canyon on the surface of the earth.

From its lower rim, Colca Canyon, carved by the Colca River, descends 10,500 feet (3,200 m). The river cuts a trench through the high mountains as it makes its way down to the Pacific Ocean.

Accessible only by boat, the V-shaped gorge is one of the world's great natural challenges. The first recorded expedition of the roaring river canyon wasn't made until 1981. Rafters have to navigate churning white-water currents and breakneck plunges—the most precipitous one dropping 3,000 feet (914 m) over 50 miles (80 km).

Unlike the Grand Canyon—the largest on earth—visited by millions every year, the isolated heart of Colca Canyon has been seen by only a handful of people. Boulders thunder unheard down its barren walls. Floods, avalanches, and earthquakes are constantly changing its features.

Source of the Amazon — Cailloma

A N D E S

Señal Yajirhua

Colca

Maca

0   20 km
0   20 mi

Cerro Luceria

COLCA CANYON

Amazon

PERU
Lima

SOUTH AMERICA

Area shown

Camaná   *Pacific Ocean*

—18,000 ft.

Señal Yajirhua
17,146 ft (5,226 m)

0   5 km
0   5 mi

—14,000

Cerro Luceria
13,967 ft (4,257 m)

COLCA CANYON

North Rim
8,200 ft (2,499 m)

—10,000

Yavapai Point
7,082 ft (2,159 m)

—6,000

Colca River
3,450 ft (1,052 m)

GRAND CANYON
Arizona

—2,000

Colorado River
2,400 ft (835 m)

Designed by BILL PITZER

SETTING THE SCENE

Read to Discover . . .
- the Native American civilizations of Latin America.
- the European empires of Latin America.
- the status of modern government in Latin America.

Key Terms
- *chinampas*
- *quipu*
- *conquistador*
- *viceroy*
- *fazenda*
- *caudillo*

Identify and Locate
Yucatán Peninsula, Lake Texcoco, Tenochtitlán, Cuzco, Ecuador, Chile, Lima, Brazil, Haiti, Mexico, Cuba

Latin America has a long and often violent history. Its past includes Native American civilizations, European colonial empires, and struggles for independence.

REGION

Native American Empires

Native Americans came to the Western Hemisphere thousands of years ago, probably across the Bering Strait that now separates Alaska and Siberia. Years before Christopher Columbus arrived in the Americas in 1492, three Native American civilizations—the Maya, the Aztec, and the Inca—emerged.

The Maya

The Maya created an empire in Central America and southern Mexico. They built many cities, the greatest of which was Tikal, located in present-day Guatemala. Pyramid-shaped temples, terraces, and courts stood in these cities. Priests and nobles ruled the cities and surrounding areas. The Maya based their economy on trade and agriculture.

Skilled in mathematics, the Maya used a number system based on 20 and developed a symbol for the mathematical concept of zero. Basing their calculations on the orbit of the earth around the sun, they created a calendar of a little more than 365 days.

The Aztec

The Aztec were originally wanderers. In the 1300s they finally built a permanent capital city called Tenochtitlán on an island in the center of a large lake. Farmers grew crops of beans and maize on *chinampas*, floating artificial islands. They made the islands by building large rafts and covering them with mud from the bottom of the lake.

The Aztec developed a complex political system headed by an emperor. They worshiped many gods and goddesses and held ceremonies to win the deities' favor and guarantee good harvests.

The Inca

At about the same time the Aztec were building their empire, the Inca were establishing a civilization. The Inca empire stretched along the Andes from Ecuador to Chile. The Inca built their capital, Cuzco, in Peru and ruled their lands through a central government headed by an emperor.

Incan farmers cut terraces into the slopes of the Andes to keep the soil from washing away, and built irrigation systems to bring water to desert areas along the coast. They also domesticated the alpaca and the llama, which they used both for food and for wool.

The Inca, known for their building skills, constructed stone temples and fortresses. Inca

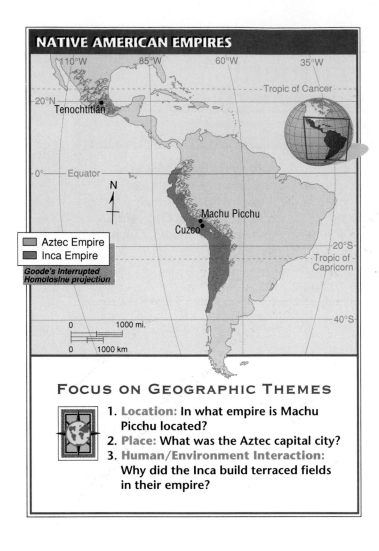

NATIVE AMERICAN EMPIRES

- Aztec Empire
- Inca Empire

Goode's Interrupted
Homolosine projection

Tropic of Cancer

Tenochtitlán

Equator

Machu Picchu
Cuzco

Tropic of
Capricorn

0   1000 mi.
0   1000 km

FOCUS ON GEOGRAPHIC THEMES

1. **Location:** In what empire is Machu Picchu located?
2. **Place:** What was the Aztec capital city?
3. **Human/Environment Interaction:** Why did the Inca build terraced fields in their empire?

buildings often were adorned with gold and silver. The Inca had no written language. They kept records and sent messages using a *quipu* (KEE•poo), a rope with knotted cords of various lengths and colors.

<u>MOVEMENT</u>

European Empires

In the late 1400s, European explorers set out to find new trade routes to Asia. In the process, the explorers reached the Americas. Spain and Portugal vied for land in the Americas. To avoid conflicts, the Pope drew an imaginary line—the Line of Demarcation—that ran from the North Pole to the South Pole. All lands east of the line were to belong to Portu-gal, all those to the west of the line to Spain. Thus, Portugal claimed present-day Brazil, and Spain claimed Central America and the rest of South America.

Spanish Conquests

The European search for trade routes eventually turned into a search for riches—and for opportunities to convert Native Americans to Christianity. Spanish *conquistadors,* or conquerors, overpowered the Aztec and Inca empires, seizing their wealth for Spain.

Spain soon established colonies from Mexico to Bolivia and set out to mine gold and silver in its new lands. To provide bases for exploration and for mining, the Spaniards built cities and towns, many of them on the sites of Native American cities.

In the tropics, the Spaniards set up plantations. In the highlands, where it was cooler, they established farms and huge cattle ranches. The Spaniards at first used Native Americans to work the plantations. When hundreds of thousands of Native Americans died from being forced to work in the hot tropical climate and from European diseases, the Spaniards brought in enslaved Africans to replace the Native Americans.

The Spanish monarch appointed **viceroys** from distant Spain to govern the colonies and make sure that Spanish law was enforced. A strict social structure emerged in the Spanish colonies. Europeans were at the top of society, and Native Americans and Africans were at the bottom.

The Portuguese and Brazil

The Portuguese, meanwhile, had claimed Brazil as early as 1500. Although the land seemed to contain no precious metals, it did have brazilwood, a tree from which red dyes could be made. The land also was good for raising livestock. On the coastal lowlands, which were well-suited for raising sugarcane, the Portuguese built sugar plantations called *fazendas.* Like the Spaniards, the Portuguese relied on enslaved peoples to work the plantations, first Native Americans and then Africans.

Independence

Beginning in the late 1700s, many people in Latin America began to resent European rule. Upper-class Latin Americans born in the Americas resented the strict social structure, which limited their rights. Native Americans and Africans also wanted their freedom. Feelings of patriotism were strengthened by revolutions in the United States and France.

The first Latin American country to rid itself of European rule—Haiti—was ruled by the French. Unrest first erupted there in 1794 when enslaved Africans led by a former slave named Francois Toussaint L'Ouverture (TOO•SAN LOO•vuhr•TYUHR) revolted. In 1804, Haiti finally became independent.

Mexico was the first Spanish-ruled nation in Latin America to gain freedom. The struggle for independence went on for many years, and in 1824, Mexico became an independent republic.

Other countries of Latin America sought to gain independence. By the mid-1800s most of them had achieved their goal under such leaders as Simón Bolívar of Venezuela and José de San Martín of Argentina. Only one nation—Brazil—became independent without revolution. In 1822 it became the only independent South American country to choose monarchy—rule by a king or queen—as its form of government.

With the exception of Haiti, independence was longer in coming to the islands of the Caribbean. Cuba, for example, did not win its independence from Spain until 1898, and many of the other islands did not gain their independence until well into the 1900s.

Dictatorships and Democracies

Wars of independence created political and economic confusion in the countries of Latin America. Leaders of the newly independent countries wanted to build stable governments and prosperous economies. In

EUROPEAN COLONIAL EMPIRES

Spanish
Portuguese
Dutch
French
British

Goode's Interrupted Homolosine projection

0   1000 mi.

0   1000 km

FOCUS ON GEOGRAPHIC THEMES

1. **Place:** What European nation ruled the Viceroyalty of New Granada?
2. **Location:** In which territory was Mexico City located?
3. **Place:** What was the largest Caribbean island under Spanish rule?

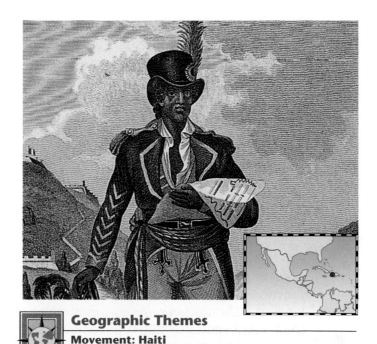

Geographic Themes

Movement: Haiti
Toussaint L'Ouverture led an independence movement to bring colonial rule in Haiti to an end. *What foreign events inspired his efforts?*

Geographic Themes

Place: Panama Canal
As a result of a 1977 treaty, the Panama Canal will pass from American to Panamanian control by the year 2000. *What has been the dominant political trend in Latin America since the 1970s?*

most countries, however, political control was still in the hands of a small group of wealthy landowners, army officers, and clergy. The huge size of many of the new countries and such physical barriers as mountains and dense rain forests made communications and trade difficult.

Power of the Strong

New leaders, known as *caudillos*, or "strong men," promised to solve Latin America's problems. Almost all caudillos were military rulers supported by wealthy landowners eager to protect their interests.

In the later 1800s and early 1900s, caudillos ruled as dictators in many Latin American countries.

Desire for Change

Rapid industrialization between 1940 and 1970 brought social changes to Latin America. Much of the region's newfound wealth simply enriched the upper classes. The growing gap between rich and poor spread unrest among farmers and workers. Military governments resisted demands for reform and fought political unrest with terror. Nonetheless, democracy was a political goal in most nations, the great-

est exception being the Communist rule of Fidel Castro in Cuba.

Military leaders were unable to solve the rising political and economic problems of the 1970s, and their tactics inspired calls for democratic reform. By the early 1990s, new democratic governments began to replace the old, harsh political systems.

SECTION 2 REVIEW

Checking for Understanding
1. **Define** *chinampas, quipu, conquistador, viceroy, fazenda, caudillo.*
2. **Locating Places** Where were the Maya, Aztec, and Inca civilizations located?
3. **Movement** How did the Line of Demarcation affect Spanish and Portuguese colonization in the Americas?
4. **Region** What changes took place in Latin America under Spanish and Portuguese rule?

Critical Thinking
5. **Determining Cause and Effect** Why did Latin Americans seek independence in the late 1700s and early 1800s?

Geography and History

BUENOS AIRES, ARGENTINA'S GATEWAY

As you read, examine how Buenos Aires became a leading Latin American metropolis.

The metropolitan area of Buenos Aires spreads over 1,421 square miles (3,680 sq. km). The city is a leading Latin American banking, business, and cultural center. Around the central business district, residential neighborhoods called barrios fan out to the northwest, west, and southern city limits. City residents number more than 11.5 million: More than one-third of all Argentinians are *porteños,* or "port dwellers."

Few skyscrapers dominate the skyline of Buenos Aires, but the city has broad avenues and many parks and plazas. As a result, Buenos Aires has a sense of openness and peace. The Avenida 9 de Julio, the widest street in the world, runs north and south through the city's central business district. It links the president's residence with the Congress Building, site of the national legislature.

Location

Buenos Aires is located at the mouth of Argentina's widest river, on the edge of Argentina's fertile Pampas. For nearly two centuries, however, Buenos Aires's broad harbor remained little more than a backwater smuggling port and slave market. As a Spanish colony, *la grand aldea,* "the big village," could not engage in trade with any country except Spain.

In the early 1800s, with the onset of independence movements in Latin America, Buenos Aires set up its own government. By mid-century, Argentina was an independent nation; Buenos Aires became its capital in 1880.

Between 1880 and 1940, Buenos Aires enjoyed a Golden Age. Beef, lamb, wool, and wheat were brought from the fertile Pampas to markets in Buenos Aires, and from there shipped to markets around the world. Ships docked in the harbor, and goods and produce were unloaded and routed to marketplaces in Argentina's interior. Building and construction changed *la grand aldea* into a gracious metropolis of broad avenues and European-like architecture. Immigrants swelled the city's population.

Contemporary Buenos Aires handles more than 80 percent of Argentina's trade. Meat packing, food processing, and textile, rubber, and electrical manufacturing employ hundreds of thousands of workers.

Like most huge urban areas, Buenos Aires struggles with overpopulation and poverty. Although immigration has dwindled, thousands of rural migrants come annually seeking work. Even though the city is prosperous, it is struggling to create jobs for its poor.

Checking for Understanding

1. Why is Buenos Aires called Argentina's Gateway?
2. **Location** How did Buenos Aires's location help it to become a center of commerce?

Cultures and Lifestyles

The culture of Latin America is rooted in its history. Beginning with the Native Americans, each group that settled the region had an impact on cultural development. As the peoples intermingled, so did their cultures.

MOVEMENT

Religion

When the Spaniards and the Portuguese came to Latin America, they brought with them Roman Catholicism. Since then the Roman Catholic Church has had a strong influence in the region.

Roman Catholicism

During colonial times, Roman Catholicism was the official religion of the Spanish colonies and Brazil. Priests had come to the Americas with the conquistadors. Priests worked to convert Native Americans to Christianity, and when European settlers came, the priests saw to their spiritual needs as well.

Before long, church leaders were playing an important part in political affairs, and the Roman Catholic Church had become wealthy. When the fight for independence came, church leaders backed the European powers. This led some Latin Americans to question the

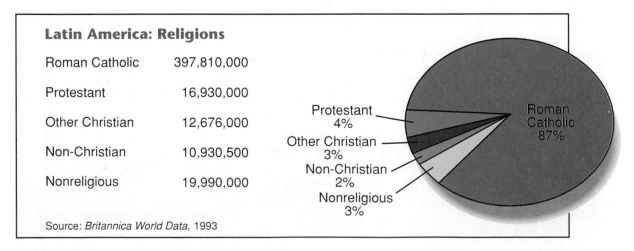

Latin America: Religions

Roman Catholic	397,810,000
Protestant	16,930,000
Other Christian	12,676,000
Non-Christian	10,930,500
Nonreligious	19,990,000

Source: *Britannica World Data*, 1993

Protestant 4%
Other Christian 3%
Non-Christian 2%
Nonreligious 3%
Roman Catholic 87%

Geographic Themes

Place: Guadalajara, Mexico
Nicknamed the "Pearl of the West," Guadalajara's modern buildings and colorful shops convey a sense of excitement and progress. *What are two areas of concern for the people of Latin America?*

Church's privileges and to work to reduce its power.

The Roman Catholic Church remains strong in Latin America today, but it does not have the influence it once did. Church leaders have shifted their support from the wealthy and powerful to the poor and oppressed. In recent years, the church has been active in movements for land reform and for improvements in education and health care.

Growth of Protestantism

Some of the Europeans who came to Latin America in the 1800s were Protestant. In time Protestant missionaries, primarily from the United States, came and built hospitals, schools, and colleges. After years of being a minority religion, in the 1960s Protestantism began to attract large numbers of Latin Americans. If Protestantism keeps growing at its current rate, many Latin Americans will be Protestants by the year 2000.

PLACE

Health Care and Education

Health care and education are two major areas of concern in Latin America. While advances have been made over the years, much remains to be done.

Health Care

Because of medical advances, better health care services, improved diets, and better sanitation, more Latin Americans are living longer. In addition more infants are surviving, and there are fewer epidemic diseases. Health care, however, is still poor in many rural and urban areas. In some places, **malnutrition**, poor nutrition because of badly balanced diet or not enough food, is a major problem. Many people do not have enough money to spend on the right kind of foods.

Educational Opportunities

Education in Latin America remains a challenge. The literacy rate is low in many countries, and there are too few schools and teachers. More than half the teachers, especially in rural areas, do not have teaching degrees. In addition, many children cannot go to school because their families need the money the children earn by working.

Latin American education, however, has improved in recent years. In the past, only the children of the wealthy went to school. Today all children can go for free for 12 years, and there are private schools for those who can afford them. Also, more children than ever before can read and write. In some countries the literacy rate has risen to more than 90 percent.

Students who pass special examinations can go on to colleges or universities. Institutions like the University of Santo Domingo and the Central University of Caracas provide higher education at little or no cost. Some students attend vocational and agricultural schools. Latin American leaders have encouraged students—as well as adults—to attend these schools.

Geographic Themes

Place: Mexico City, Mexico
Diego Rivera and other 20th-century Mexican artists painted murals that showed key events in Mexico's history. *What themes have been popular among modern Latin American artists and writers?*

The Arts and Literature

For hundreds of years, the arts and literature of Latin America were dominated by European standards. Today's Latin American artists have developed unique styles, many of which reflect their diverse ethnic heritages.

Traditional Arts and Literature

Native Americans produced the earliest Latin American art forms. They left a legacy of weavings, wood carvings, pottery, and metalwork. They built temples decorated with colored murals and **mosaics**—pictures or designs made by setting small bits of colored stone, glass, or tile in mortar. Native Americans also created the region's earliest music and dance.

During colonial times, almost all arts were European-inspired. During this time, however, Africans brought to the region the rhythms, songs, and dances out of which calypso, reggae, and samba evolved.

Most colonial-era paintings had religious themes. Murals mixed the brightly colored abstract designs of the Native Americans with realistic European styles. Churches built in Spanish and Portuguese designs often were enlivened by the ethnic details added by Native American and African artists.

After independence, Latin American painters and composers began mixing European and Native American themes. In the late 1800s a literary movement known as **modernism** developed, in which writers and poets focused on artistic expression for its own sake.

Art and Literature

In the 1900s Mexican artists, such as Diego Rivera, began using art to educate. They created huge murals that combined modern forms with traditional Native American designs to present the daily life and history of their countries. Latin American writers also began to show more interest in social and political subjects.

During the last 50 years, Latin American artists and writers have become recognized internationally. The Brazilian architect Oscar Niemeyer, who designed many of the buildings in the Brazilian capital of Brasília, is known worldwide for his curved sculptures and his use of Native American designs in mosaics. Audiences in many countries have applauded the skillful footwork of dance companies like the Ballet Folklórico of Mexico, which performs traditional Native American and Spanish dances. Writers like Gabriela Mistral and Pablo Neruda of Chile, Octavio Paz of Mexico, Miguel Angel Asturias of Guatemala, and Gabriel García Márquez of Colombia have all won Nobel Prizes for Literature.

Life and Leisure

Latin Americans place great emphasis on social status and family life. They also cherish values, such as personal honor and individual freedom.

Way of Life

Latin Americans have a strong sense of family. Each person is part of an **extended family** that includes aunts, uncles, and other relatives besides parents and children. Life and most social events are often centered in the family and home. In Latin America a person's quality of life depends on his or her social class, nationality, and place of residence. A large gap exists between the lower class and the middle and upper classes, however.

Leisure Time and Celebrations

Latin Americans enjoy sports, especially *fútbol*, or soccer. In many South American countries, it is the national sport and a way of life. Latin Americans also appreciate baseball, basketball, and volleyball. A traditional favorite among many Mexicans and Cubans is **jai alai** (HY•LY), a fast-paced game much like handball that is played with a ball and a long curved basket that is strapped to a player's wrist.

Other Latin American pastimes are musical events, dances, the theater, movies, and parties. Most Latin Americans celebrate their in-

Geographic Themes
Place: Rio de Janeiro, Brazil
In Latin America, every village has some kind of soccer field, and the larger cities have stadiums. In Rio de Janeiro, the stadium can seat 220,000 fans. *What other competitive sports are popular in Latin America?*

dependence days and religious holidays. The festival known as Carnival, for example, is celebrated just before the beginning of Lent, the Christian holy season that comes before Easter. The biggest Carnival is held each year in Rio de Janeiro, Brazil.

SECTION 3 REVIEW

Checking for Understanding
1. **Define** malnutrition, mosaic, modernism, extended family, *fútbol*, jai alai.
2. **Locating Places** In what country did artists begin using art to educate?
3. **Region** What was the official religion of the Spanish colonies and Brazil?
4. **Place** Why is the literacy rate improving in some Latin American countries?

Critical Thinking
5. **Drawing Conclusions** How have medical advances affected population growth?

MAP & GRAPH SKILLS

Interpreting a Population Pyramid

Demography is the study of population. Demographers measure population density (how many people live in a given area), distribution (where people live), and migration patterns (who is moving where). Demographers also illustrate age distribution by a **population pyramid.**

REVIEWING THE SKILL

A population pyramid is a bar graph that shows the percentages of males and females by age group. Its shape indicates whether the population is increasing or decreasing. If a population is growing, the pyramid is wider at the base because children will be more numerous than adults. If the graph appears almost rectangular, it indicates a stable population.

To interpret a population pyramid:
- Identify the age groups and percentages shown on the graph.
- Look for differences among males and females, and compare the various age groups.
- Use the data to draw conclusions about age distribution in the given countries.

PRACTICING THE SKILL

Use the graphs to answer the following questions:

1. What countries are shown in the graphs?
2. What percentage of Uruguay's male population is between the ages of 20–29?
3. What percentage of Cuba's total population is between the ages of 40–59?
4. Which country has a declining population?
5. In which country is there a greater percentage of older women than men?
6. Which country has the most even distribution of men and women?

For additional practice in this skill, see Practicing Skills on page 192 of the Chapter 9 Review.

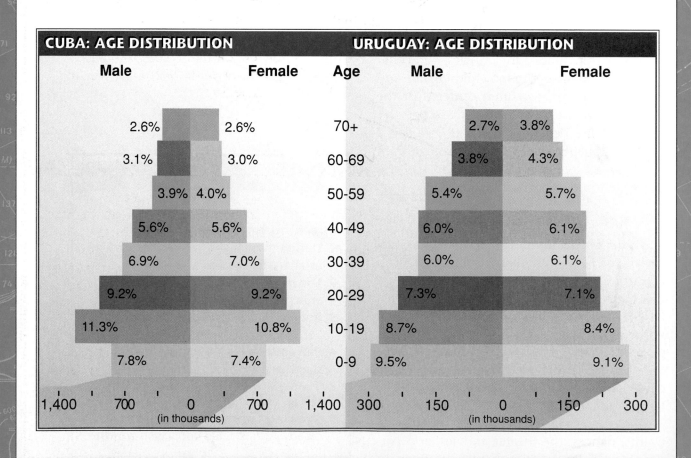

CUBA: AGE DISTRIBUTION

Male	Female	Age
2.6%	2.6%	70+
3.1%	3.0%	60-69
3.9%	4.0%	50-59
5.6%	5.6%	40-49
6.9%	7.0%	30-39
9.2%	9.2%	20-29
11.3%	10.8%	10-19
7.8%	7.4%	0-9

1,400   700   0   700   1,400
(in thousands)

URUGUAY: AGE DISTRIBUTION

Male	Female	Age
2.7%	3.8%	70+
3.8%	4.3%	60-69
5.4%	5.7%	50-59
6.0%	6.1%	40-49
6.0%	6.1%	30-39
7.3%	7.1%	20-29
8.7%	8.4%	10-19
9.5%	9.1%	0-9

300   150   0   150   300
(in thousands)

1 Population Patterns

Outdoor market in Mexico City

KEY TERMS

mestizos (p. 176)
mulatto (p. 176)
dialect (p. 177)
primate city (p. 179)

SUMMARY

- Latin America's ethnically diverse population includes Native Americans, Europeans, Africans, Asians, *mestizos,* and mulattoes.
- The Latin American population is not evenly distributed.
- Latin America's urban population has increased rapidly as people have moved from rural to urban areas.

2 History and Government

Toussaint L'Ouverture, Latin American independence leader

KEY TERMS

chinampas (p. 181)
quipu (p. 182)
conquistador (p. 182)
viceroy (p. 182)
fazenda (p. 182)
caudillo (p. 184)

SUMMARY

- Maya, Aztec, and Inca built highly developed civilizations long before Europeans arrived in the Americas.
- Spain and Portugal controlled most of Latin America for more than 300 years.
- Most present-day leaders want a stable government and an improved quality of life for Latin Americans.

3 Cultures and Lifestyles

Soccer fans in Rio de Janeiro's Marcana Stadium

KEY TERMS

malnutrition (p. 187)
mosaic (p. 188)
modernism (p. 188)
extended family (p. 189)
fútbol (p. 189)
jai alai (p. 189)

SUMMARY

- The major religion of Latin America, Roman Catholicism, was brought to the region by the Spaniards and the Portuguese.
- Many advances have been made in Latin America in health care and education.
- Arts and literature have become less European and more uniquely Latin American.
- Although social class, way of life, and leisure activities may differ, all Latin Americans have a strong sense of family.

REVIEW

Reviewing Key Terms

Choose the vocabulary term that best completes each of the sentences below. Write your answers on a separate sheet of paper.

mestizos (p. 176)
mulattoes (p. 176)
primate city (p. 179)
quipu (p. 182)
conquistadors (p. 182)
caudillos (p. 184)
mosaics (p. 188)
extended family (p. 189)
jai alai (p. 189)

SECTION 1

1. People of mixed African and European ancestry are known as _____ .
2. A _____ dominates a country's economy, culture, and government.
3. People of mixed Native American and European ancestry are known as _____ .

SECTION 2

4. The Inca used a rope with knotted cords called a _____ .
5. The Aztec and Inca empires were conquered by Spanish _____ .
6. In the 1800s many Latin Americans were ruled by dictators called _____ .

SECTION 3

7. _____ is a game like handball enjoyed by Cubans and Mexicans.
8. An _____ includes relatives other than a husband, wife, and children.
9. Pictures made from small bits of colored glass set in mortar are called _____ .

Reviewing Facts

SECTION 1

10. What is the official language of more than one-half of Latin America?
11. Why are most Caribbean countries so densely populated?

SECTION 2

12. What was the Aztec capital?
13. What was the only independent South American country to choose monarchy?

SECTION 3

14. What are some problems associated with education in Latin America?
15. Who created the earliest dance and music of Latin America?

Critical Thinking

16. **Expressing Problems Clearly** What has been the effect of the migration to cities of large numbers of rural people?
17. **Determining Cause and Effect** What problems did the leaders of the newly independent Latin Americans encounter?
18. **Predicting Consequences** How might the Catholic Church in Latin America be affected if Protestantism continues to grow rapidly?

Geographic Themes

19. **Movement** From where did most of the early settlers of Latin America come?
20. **Region** What European nation controlled most of Latin America?
21. **Place** Where and when is the largest Carnival celebration of Latin America?

Practicing Skills

Interpreting a Population Pyramid

Refer to the population pyramids on page 190.

22. In Uruguay, at what age do women begin to outnumber men by at least 0.3 percent? What is the difference in percentage at age 70+?
23. In each country, what is the largest age group?

Using the Unit Atlas

Refer to the cultural geography section of the Unit Atlas on pages 152–153.

24. Where are the uninhabited areas of Latin America?
25. What is the official language of Brazil? Of Belize?

Projects

Individual Activity

Select a Latin American writer, painter, architect, or some other type of artist. Research several of his or her best known works. Write a two-paragraph overview of the most important features of his or her work.

Cooperative Learning Activity

Working in groups of three, research one of the major early civilizations of Latin America.

Find information about the following: the area in which the civilization developed; how government and society were organized; and why the civilization declined. Working as a group, prepare a chart comparing the three civilizations.

Writing About Geography

Description

Select one Latin American city, and imagine that you are a member of a committee organized to attract tourists to that city. Be sure to check your journal for notes or comments about the city you select. Write a travel brochure or visitor's guide for the city that will accomplish the committee's goal.

Locating Places

LATIN AMERICA: POLITICAL GEOGRAPHY

Match the letters on the map with the places and physical features of Latin America. Write your answers on a separate sheet of paper.

1. Mexico City
2. Lima
3. Port-au-Prince
4. Montevideo
5. Havana
6. La Paz, Sucre
7. Quito
8. Brasília
9. Buenos Aires
10. Bogota
11. Santiago
12. Caracas

0   1000 mi.

0   1000 km

chapter 10

Latin America Today

CHAPTER FOCUS

Geographic Setting

In many areas of Latin America, vegetation and landforms, such as tropical rain forests and steep mountains, create natural barriers to the movement of people and goods.

Geographic Themes

Section 1 Living in Latin America

REGION Most nations of Latin America are increasing their efforts to modernize and industrialize.

▲ Photograph: *Skyline of Caracus, Venezuela*

Section 2 People and Their Environment

HUMAN/ENVIRONMENT INTERACTION The development of resources in the Amazon River basin has seriously affected the environment of the area.

1 Living in Latin America

SETTING THE SCENE

Read to Discover . . .
- the status of agriculture and industry in Latin America.
- the role of trade and interdependence in Latin America.
- the transportation and communications systems of Latin America.

Key Terms
- developing country
- export
- cash crop
- *campesinos*
- *latifundia*
- *minifundia*
- service industry
- *maquiladoras*

Identify and Locate
Brazil, Mexico, Costa Rica, Argentina, Chile, Ciudad Juárez, Rio Grande, Manaus, Isthmus of Panama, Bogotá, Lima, Santiago

Kingston, Jamaica

I live in Jamaica, where tourism plays a big part in the economy. The Jamaican dollar is very weak against the American dollar. While this is good for tourists, it isn't so good for people who live here.

Christine Bennett

JAMAICA $5

Strombus gallus
Rooster Tail Conch

Christine Bennett from the Caribbean island of Jamaica describes one of the many problems of economic development. Latin America consists largely of **developing countries**, countries in the process of becoming industrialized. Most Latin American countries, however, are moving slowly toward this goal.

HUMAN/ENVIRONMENT INTERACTION

Agriculture

The economies of many Latin American countries are based on agriculture. Most of what Latin Americans **export**, or send to other countries for sale or trade, comes from the land.

Cash Crops and Livestock

Coffee is an example of a **cash crop**, a crop produced to sell or trade. Brazil, Colombia, Mexico, and El Salvador rank among the world's leading coffee producers. This is largely because they have the fertile volcanic slopes and warm moist climate in which coffee trees thrive.

Because tropical coastal areas are well-suited for growing bananas, Central America, along with Cuba, Jamaica, Brazil, and Ecuador, produce much of the world's bananas. Cuba and Brazil also are among the world's leaders in the production of sugarcane, the most

Geographic Themes

Human/Environment Interaction: Andes, Colombia
Many farmers in the foothills of the Andes of western Colombia grow coffee, Colombia's major crop. *Why is coffee a major crop in countries such as Colombia, Brazil, Mexico, and El Salvador?*

important agricultural product in the Caribbean.

Some Latin American countries have based their entire economy on a single crop. Honduras, for example, relies on bananas. Cuba depends largely on sugarcane. Specializing in one crop often puts the national economy at risk. For example, if drought or disease seriously damages the crop, the country's entire economy can be severely affected. In addition, if a country uses most of its farmland to grow just one cash crop, little land is left to grow the food crops needed to feed the population.

Some Latin American countries have much grazing land on which to raise livestock. Argentina, Mexico, and Brazil are among the world's leaders in cattle production. Beef is

also a major export of Costa Rica, Paraguay, and Uruguay.

Latifundia and Minifundia

In the past many Latin Americans lived and worked in the countryside. Now only about one-third of the people are *campesinos,* people who live and work in rural areas.

The farms on which these people work often are divided into two classes. One is *latifundia,* large estates owned by families or corporations. The other class of farm is *minifundia,* small farms that produce food chiefly for family use and the local market.

Whether campesinos own or work small plots of land or labor on the large landholdings of the wealthy, almost all are poor. Among the poorest are the Native Americans who live in places like the *Altiplano* where the soil is poor and the climate unfavorable. Their crops generally are staples like beans, corn, potatoes, and cassavas, plants whose large root supplies the starch used to make tapioca.

HUMAN/ENVIRONMENT INTERACTION

Industry

Most Latin American countries recognize the need to modernize and industrialize. Some, however, are moving faster than others. In many countries, **service industries**, enterprises such as banking that provide services rather than goods, have grown sharply in the last 25 years.

Industrial Progress

One Latin American country that has made great progress in recent years is Mexico. Among the goods produced in Mexico are motor vehicles, electrical goods, and processed foods. Over the last 50 years, American and other foreign firms have set up manufacturing plants in Mexican cities close to the Mexican-American border to take advantage of low-cost labor.

One such city is Ciudad Juárez, which lies across the Rio Grande from El Paso, Texas. Together these cities' factories, known as *maquiladoras,* employ a large number of Mexicans. Unlike many other Latin American countries, Mexico has a large workforce, well-developed power sources and transportation networks, and abundant natural resources. These advantages, combined with a stable government, an involved business community, and foreign investors, have made industrial expansion possible.

Brazil, like Mexico, has increased its industrial production in recent years. It is a major producer of iron and steel, automobiles, textiles, cement, paper, machinery, chemicals, airplanes, processed food, and electrical goods. Also like Mexico, Brazil has profited from plentiful natural resources, a large workforce, well-developed power sources, and a government that has worked to promote industrial growth.

Both Mexico and Brazil produce handicrafts—jewelry, baskets, rugs. Other leading manufacturers of such items are Venezuela and Argentina. Argentina processes and packages meat and other foods and produces textiles, electrical equipment, automobiles, and railroad cars. Chile, Costa Rica, Nicaragua, and Bolivia all produce foods and textiles. Bolivia also mines and refines tin. For most Caribbean nations, sugar refining is a leading industry.

Industrial Development

Latin American countries have not been able to industrialize more rapidly for a variety of reasons. Factories and machinery cost money—money that many Latin American countries do not have. Some countries, like Mexico, have been able to attract foreign investment. Foreign investors, however, are reluctant to provide funds to a country whose government appears unstable or that has political problems. Investors are afraid that if something happens to the government, they will lose their investment.

Industry requires skilled workers—engineers, scientists, technicians. Industry also requires certain kinds of raw materials and natural resources, including energy resources. Many countries of Latin America do not have

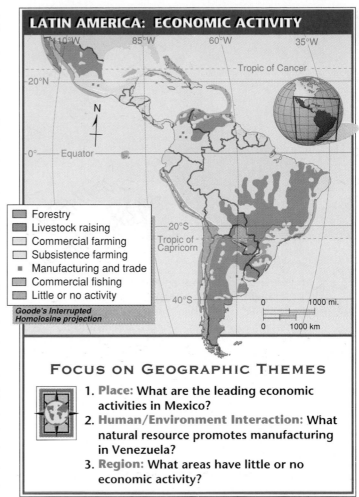

LATIN AMERICA: ECONOMIC ACTIVITY

Legend:
- Forestry
- Livestock raising
- Commercial farming
- Subsistence farming
- Manufacturing and trade
- Commercial fishing
- Little or no activity

Goode's Interrupted Homolosine projection

FOCUS ON GEOGRAPHIC THEMES

1. **Place:** What are the leading economic activities in Mexico?
2. **Human/Environment Interaction:** What natural resource promotes manufacturing in Venezuela?
3. **Region:** What areas have little or no economic activity?

the necessary trained workers, materials, or resources.

MOVEMENT

Trade and Interdependence

Few Latin American countries manufacture enough goods or grow enough food to satisfy all the needs of their people. As a result, they must trade with other countries—many of which are outside of the region.

Much of the interdependence that exists between Latin American countries and nations outside the region is a result of Latin America's desire to industrialize. Industrialization has made much of the region dependent on imported goods, raw materials, technology,

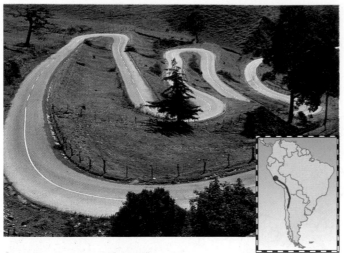

Movement: Trans-Andean Highway, Peru
The Trans-Andean Highway connects Lima, the capital of Peru, to Chile through the Andes. *What major highway in Latin America extends from Mexico to Chile?*

and foreign capital. This dependence has created large foreign debts.

MOVEMENT

Transportation and Communications

Transportation and communications systems in Latin America are not highly developed outside of urban areas. This is largely because of cost and physical barriers—rugged terrain, dense vegetation, and mountains.

Roads and Railroads

In Latin America the building of good roads and railroads has been difficult and slow. In South America, for example, the Andes are a formidable barrier. In Central America, because of dense vegetation near the Caribbean coast and highland areas in the interior, very few roads run east and west.

Some nations have networks of modern highways. Argentina, for example, has one of the better-developed highway systems in South America. Mexico also has a large number of modern highways known as *autopistas*. Most other countries, however, do not have roads like these. In Brazil, for example, less

than 10 percent of the roads are paved. A new series of roads known as the Trans-Amazonian Highway, however, is under construction in Brazil. One of the main purposes of the project is to stimulate the development of the Amazon River basin.

The major road system of Latin America is the Pan-American Highway. This network of roadways stretches from northern Mexico to southern Chile, linking the capitals of 17 Latin American nations.

In some Latin American countries, excellent railway networks compensate in part for poor roads. Mexico, Guatemala, Argentina, Panama, and Brazil have well-developed railroad networks. In most of the Caribbean countries, however, railway systems are inadequate for the needs of local economies and populations.

Inland Waterways

In some parts of Latin America, inland waterways provide the only means of transportation. The Plata river system formed by the Paraná, Paraguay, and Uruguay rivers, for example, helps link Buenos Aires and northeastern Argentina with Paraguay, Uruguay, and Brazil.

A major natural waterway exists in the Amazon River basin. Thick vegetation and swamps in the basin often make overland travel difficult. The Amazon River and its tributaries, however, provide a natural waterway on which people and goods can be transported.

The Panama Canal is another important waterway, but it is not a natural one. Built in the early 1900s, it crosses the Isthmus of Panama, making it possible for ships to travel between the Atlantic Ocean and Pacific Ocean without having to go around the southern tip of South America.

Air Travel

In recent years, airplanes and air travel have become increasingly important in Latin America. Airplanes can go where roads and railroads often cannot. Airplanes provide a fast and efficient means of travel over rough terrain, dense vegetation, and mountains that cover many areas of the region.

Brazil, Argentina, and Mexico are among the world's leading countries in numbers of airports. Bogotá, Lima, Santiago, Buenos Aires, São Paulo, and Rio de Janeiro all have major airports that serve both domestic and international airlines. The busiest airport in the entire region, however, is Mexico City's International Airport. More than 10 million passengers pass through it each year.

Communications

The same dense vegetation and rough terrain that have made it so difficult to build roads and railroads in much of Latin America have also slowed the development of communications networks.

Millions of people in Latin America use telephones to communicate with others. Yet many countries in the region do not have the funds to buy the equipment needed to build modern telephone systems. Even in wealthier countries like Brazil, Mexico, Argentina, and Venezuela, many people do not own telephones. In fact, for every 100 people, there are only about 5 to 10 telephones. In some poorer nations, such as Haiti, there may be only one telephone for every 79 persons.

Many countries are trying to improve their communications systems by building more and better radio and television stations and making greater use of international telecommunications satellites. Every country in Latin America has at least one radio station. However, not every nation has its own television station. And not every household or family owns a television set. Currently, there is approximately 1 television for every 10 people in Latin America.

Newspapers are a major means of communication. About one-seventh of the world's daily newspapers are published in Latin America. Most of these are printed in Brazil, Mexico, and Argentina. Latin America also publishes about 5 percent of the world's books each year, mostly in the Spanish or Portuguese language.

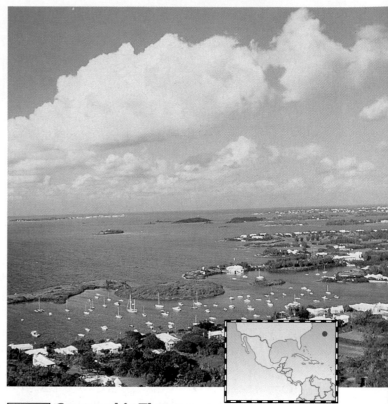

Geographic Themes

Movement: Bermuda
Millions of tourists visit Bermuda and the Caribbean countries each year to enjoy the pleasant climate and the beautiful beaches. *How has transportation aided tourism?*

SECTION 1 REVIEW

Checking for Understanding
1. **Define** developing country, export, cash crop, *campesinos, latifundia, minifundia,* service industry, *maquiladoras.*
2. **Locating Places** What Latin American countries rank among the world's leading coffee producers?
3. **Human/Environment Interaction** What factors have made industrial expansion possible in Mexico?
4. **Movement** What is the major road system of Latin America? Where is it located?

Critical Thinking
5. **Making Comparisons** What do *latifundia* and *minifundia* have in common?

CASE STUDY

RAIN FORESTS FOR FARMLANDS

I think the whole planet is caught in this problem. If we want to make it to the 21st century, we need to find the other frontier—efficiency and sustainable development.

Alvaro Ugalde, former head of the Costa Rican Park Service

In the late 1970s, the tiny Latin American country of Costa Rica suddenly found itself faced with disaster. Studies showed that the country's three major industries—cattle ranching, lumbering, and farming—had depleted the nation's rain forests by almost half.

THE ISSUE

To feed its people, create industries, and raise money to repay foreign debts, Costa Rica sold parcels of land to cattle ranchers and farmers. The ranchers and farmers cleared thousands of acres of land, selling the felled trees for lumber.

"Clearing the land" in Costa Rica, however, meant chopping down the lush evergreens that are the mainstay of the country's rain forests.

THE BACKGROUND

In 1940, evergreen rain forests covered between 65 and 80 percent of Costa Rica. In the early 1960s, however, a growing population began cutting into the forests to clear land for cattle ranches. Also in the late 1960s, the Costa Rican government began to sell small lots of rain forest land. People who wanted to farm could buy the lots at low prices. For the most part, the country's forestry laws allowed the new land owners to cut down any tree on their property.

The logging industry also expanded, buying and towing the felled trees to sawmills. They sold the cut lumber to builders and exported it.

By the early 1980s, Costa Rica had lost almost half of its rain forests and was rapidly losing its soil.

Without the trees' root systems to hold the soil in place, or the trees' canopy overhead, the soil was eroding or being baked hard by the sun.

THE POINTS OF VIEW

Conservationists demanded that the remaining forests receive government protection as parks and preserves. They pointed out that more than 600 tons of soil per acre (about

FORESTED REGIONS IN COSTA RICA

NICARAGUA

Caribbean Sea

PACIFIC OCEAN

SOUTH AMERICA

COSTA RICA

San José

Caribbean Sea

PACIFIC OCEAN

PANAMA

N

□ Forested areas

0   50 mi.

0   50 km

300 tons per ha) was being lost every year. Just as serious, they maintained, was the loss of plant and animal species that lived in the rain forest. Such species are essential for making improved foods, new environmentally safe pesticides, and more effective medicines.

> By the early 1980s, Costa Rica had lost almost half of its rain forests and was rapidly losing its soil.

After deforestation had eliminated about 80 percent of Costa Rica's forests, the government established parks and conservation areas to protect the forests that remained.

The lumber industry claimed that *deforestation*, or the removal of large areas of forest, was due mostly to the way the farmers and ranchers cleared the land. Said one trucker, "We only haul trees 12 to 15 inches (30 cm to 38 cm) across or bigger. The owners of the farms cut everything down because it's easier to plant that way."

Cattle ranchers and farmers spoke of their need to make a living. In the words of one farmer, who had been a day laborer, "I had nothing, no future, no life." His neighbor added proudly, "I used to have to work for a *patron* (landowner), but now the patron is me."

THE ISSUES TODAY

In the late 1970s, the Costa Rican government began conservation efforts. Parks and forest preserves now protect almost all of what is left of Costa Rica's rain forests—about 20 percent of the country's territory. The government tightened forestry laws and established a permit system. The Forestry Department provides ranchers and farmers with fast-growing, debranched laurel trees. Planted as "living fences," the trees slow the wind and hold the thinning topsoil in place. Some communities have started tourist businesses built around the rich plant and animal life of the rain forest. Conservationists warn that much still needs to be done. Almost 30,000 acres (about 57,000 ha) of rain forest are still lost annually.

Land also must be provided for Costa Rica's ever-increasing population. Costa Rica has a rising birthrate, and the country has received thousands of people fleeing civil wars in El Salvador and Nicaragua.

Conservationists feel that the government must maintain an ongoing educational program. Such a program is the only way to convince the people that it is in their long-term interest to preserve their environments. These environments themselves can provide the nation with future economic prosperity.

Reviewing the Case

1. **What groups are involved with Costa Rica's rain forests?**
2. **What problems does Costa Rica face?**
3. **Human/Environment** **Interaction What problems occur when the rain forest is cleared away?**

People and Their Environment

SETTING THE SCENE

Read to Discover . . .
- how human development of the Amazon River basin has affected the environment.
- the major challenges that have accompanied rapid urban growth in Latin America and possible solutions for them.

Key Terms
- ecosystem
- deforestation
- slash-and-burn farming
- reforestation

Identify and Locate
Amazon River basin, Brazil, Mexico City, São Paulo

An **ecosystem** is a complex variety of life in a delicately balanced environment. Humans acting within an ecosystem probably upset the balance more than any other organism. In Latin America, environmental disruption has been occurring in several different places, including the tropical rain forest of the Amazon River basin and many urban areas across the region.

HUMAN/ENVIRONMENT INTERACTION

The Amazon River Basin

The Amazon River basin covers about 2.7 million square miles (7 million sq. km), an area about the size of the United States east of the Rocky Mountains. The basin contains the world's largest tropical rain forest. About two-thirds of this forest is in Brazil. The rest covers parts of Bolivia, Peru, Ecuador, Colombia, Venezuela, Guyana, Suriname, and French Guiana.

Deforestation

In recent years many people have become concerned about the **deforestation**—the cutting down and clearing away of trees in the rain forest. According to recent estimates, about 10 percent of Amazon rain forest has already been destroyed.

Several activities have contributed to the deforestation. One is construction of the Trans-Amazonian Highway and of access roads into the forest. A great deal of forest land, especially in the Brazilian Amazon rain forest, had to be cleared to make way for these roads.

Another of the most widespread activities is the clearing of forest land along new access routes so that migrant families might permanently farm the land. Traditionally migrant farmers use what is often called **slash-and-burn farming.** They cut down all the plants and strip any trees of bark. After the plants and trees have dried out, they are set on fire. The ash from the fire puts nutrients into the soil. Within two or three years, however, the soil begins to lose its fertility and crop yields decline. When this happens, the farmers move on to a new piece of land and start the same process over again. The cycle is repeated, and each time more forest is destroyed.

Attempts to develop commercial cattle ranches have also caused much deforestation. Cattle need a large amount of pastureland for grazing. To support large-scale ranching, huge amounts of forest land must be cleared, and

Geographic Themes

Human/Environment Interaction: Amazon River Basin
The Amazon River basin contains more than 50,000 species of plants—about 20 percent of all plant species on the earth. *How is human activity threatening the basin's vegetation?*

slash-and-burn techniques are used. Grasses at first grow well in the charred soil. After four or five years, however, fewer grasses grow, and the land cannot support as many cattle as it once did. In time, the growth of weeds takes over the production of grasses, and the cattle ranches are abandoned.

Still another activity that has contributed to deforestation is the commercial exploitation of trees for lumber and other products. Profits are made from the export of these products. In the view of some scientists, however, deforestation may have serious long-term negative effects that may be difficult or even impossible to overcome. These scientists point out that some of the damage could be corrected if lumber companies would practice **reforestation**, the planting of young trees or the seeds of trees, on the lands they have stripped.

Yet in many cases, replanting has not happened. The environmental impact of logging has been growing steadily, partly because of an increasing demand to develop the resources of the Amazon River basin.

Major Concerns

Scientists and other experts do not always agree on the nature, significance, or possible harmful effects of deforestation. Several years ago, it was thought that widespread deforestation would upset the oxygen balance of the entire world. This occurrence is no longer thought to be likely. Now the concern is that deforestation may upset the world's heat balance, causing a dangerous warming effect. Some scientists also believe that major deforestation might produce an imbalance in the world's water cycle, affecting rainfall in certain areas.

Another concern is that deforestation eventually will cause many plants and animals to become extinct. Certain species of plants have extracts that are valuable to humans as medicine and for commercial and industrial uses. The value of other species found in the rain forest has not yet been determined. Scientists fear that these species might become extinct before their value can be known.

Many people believe that the huge Amazon rain forest can regenerate itself over time. Others, however, point out that such a secondary forest is almost always less healthy and less productive than the original one.

Toward the Future

No one knows how extensive the consequences of deforestation will become. Many Latin Americans, as well as others around the world, are hopeful that better methods of utilizing the resources in the Amazon River basin can be developed.

Many people believe that the Amazon River basin is important to the world as an abundant supply of natural resources and that controlled fishing, mining, and logging can be done without doing serious harm to the environment. Many also think that the Amazon basin holds the promise for a better future for thousands of people. Many people agree that new and more flexible methods must be found to settle families in the area engaged in small-scale farming so that they do not move from one part of the forest to another.

Most experts see a need for stronger governmental regulation and more national parks and Native American reserves throughout the area for the groups who will have to move from their traditional land. To keep migrant families and commercial developers from misusing parks and reserves, tough measures and strict enforcement are needed.

Geographic Themes

Human/Environment Interaction: Amazon Basin
This brilliant tree frog is one of about 4,000 species of frogs living in the rain forests whose habitats are threatened. *What do the world's scientists believe about the effects of deforestation?*

PLACE

Population Growth

Latin American cities have experienced tremendous population growth in recent years. Mexico City, for example, has become home to about one-fourth of the people of Mexico and has the second-greatest population of any city in the world. São Paulo has become the largest city of South America and the second-largest metropolitan area of Latin America after Mexico City. The challenges facing these two cities because of their rapid growth are also confronting other Latin American cities.

Urban Challenges

One of the most serious challenges facing Latin American cities is poverty. Many people who left their rural homes expected to find jobs in the city. Many of the cities, however, were already overcrowded, and jobs often proved scarce, especially for the unskilled. As a result, as many as one-half of the people of working age in an overcrowded city like São Paulo or Mexico City might be unemployed.

Housing is another challenge. The number of people living in urban areas often exceeds the number of houses or apartments. Even if more good housing were available, many city dwellers could not afford it. Consequently, every major city has its slum areas, called by a different name from one city to another—*favelas* in São Paulo, *barriadas* in Bogotá, *villas miserias* in Buenos Aires. In these places people often live in shacks made of cardboard, asbestos panels, or sheets of metal, often without electricity, running water, underground sewer systems, or sanitary facilities.

In many urban areas, air pollution has also become a serious problem. Millions of automobiles, trucks, buses, and other vehicles clog city streets, creating serious traffic jams and congestion, and sending massive amounts of exhaust fumes into the air. Along with the pollutants from industrial smokestacks, these fumes badly pollute the air. In Mexico City the air pollution is so serious that people with breathing problems cannot always go outside, and the use of automobiles must be restricted.

Poorer urban residents also have difficulty getting enough food to eat. Many cannot afford to buy food, and in the city they do not have a place to grow their own.

Solutions for One City

Latin American political leaders are aware of the problems of their cities and are trying to solve them. The Mexican government, for example, has carried out several efforts to improve the quality of life in Mexico City.

The government is encouraging businesses to relocate outside the city and is promoting tourism so that more jobs will be created. Mexico is also working to improve agriculture so that many former farm workers will be encouraged to leave the city and return to the countryside.

In an effort to cut down on the number of automobiles in Mexico City, a new subway system is being built. A new water system is being constructed to help overcome the city's water problems. The city has planted millions of trees, not only to help beautify urban areas but also to help purify the air.

Geographic Themes

Place: Havana, Cuba

Cuba's Communist policies led to shortages of goods for many people living in Havana and other Cuban cities. *What challenges have faced other Latin American cities?*

| SECTION | 2 | REVIEW |

Checking for Understanding
1. **Define** ecosystem, deforestation, slash-and-burn farming, reforestation.
2. **Locating Places** Where is the second-largest city in the world located?
3. **Human/Environment Interaction** What activities have contributed to deforestation in the Amazon River basin?
4. **Region** What are four challenges faced by many Latin American cities?

Critical Thinking
5. **Making Comparisons** In what ways are the challenges facing the major cities in your country the same as those facing major cities in Latin America?

Reading a Vegetation Map

Suppose you are traveling by car in the eastern United States. Beginning in northern Maine, you see vast stretches of evergreen trees such as pine, fir, and spruce. Farther south, the evergreen trees will mix with broad-leaved trees such as oak, hickory, maple, and aspen. At the southernmost tip of Florida, you will see palm trees and other tropical plants. Traveling from north to south, you have passed through several different vegetation zones, which can be shown on a **vegetation map.**

REVIEWING THE SKILL

Vegetation maps illustrate the kinds of plants that naturally grow in a given area. Because climate largely determines the vegetation of an area, there are many similarities between climate and vegetation maps. For example, evergreen trees, such as firs and spruces, grow in cool climates because their needle-like leaves can withstand cold temperatures. In the year-round warmth of the tropics, evergreens with broad leaves, such as palm trees, banana trees, and rubber trees, can grow. Between these two extremes, broad-leaved deciduous trees predominate. Like tropical species, these trees have broad leaves, but they shed them in autumn to endure cold winters. In dry climates, grasses and shrubs predominate because there is insufficient water to support tree growth.

Extremely cold or dry climates may have little or no vegetation at all.

When reading a vegetation map, study the map key carefully to determine what kinds of plants predominate in each area. Boundaries between vegetation zones are approximate because plants merge gradually with border areas usually having plants from both zones. To read a vegetation map, apply the following steps:

- Study the map key to identify the vegetation zones included on the map.
- Find examples of each vegetation zone on the map.
- Look at other aspects of the area's geography such as landforms, latitude, oceans, and climate zones to explain the vegetation patterns.

PRACTICING THE SKILL

Use the vegetation map to answer the following questions:

1. What vegetation zones are shown on this map?
2. What kind of vegetation grows nearest to the Equator in South America?
3. What vegetation zone is represented by the color yellow?
4. What color represents the areas of temperate grasslands?
5. Which vegetation zone(s) would be well suited for grazing livestock? Why?
6. How do you explain the lack of vegetation on the west coast of South America?

For additional practice in this skill, see Practicing Skills on page 208 of the Chapter 10 Review.

LATIN AMERICA: NATURAL VEGETATION

- Tropical rain forest
- Chaparral
- Deciduous and mixed deciduous-coniferous forest
- Coniferous forest
- Tropical grassland
- Temperate grassland
- Desert scrub and desert waste
- Highlands (vegetation varies with elevation)

Goode's Interrupted Homolosine projection

SECTION	KEY TERMS	SUMMARY
1 Living in Latin America	**developing country** (p. 195) **export** (p. 195) **cash crop** (p. 195) *campesinos* (p. 196) *latifundia* (p. 196) *minifundia* (p. 196) **service industry** (p. 196) *maquiladoras* (p. 197)	• The economies of many Latin American countries are based on agriculture. • There are two major classes of farms in Latin America—*latifundia* and *minifundia*. • Most Latin American countries have been slow to industrialize because of lack of funds, a skilled workforce, and raw materials and energy sources. • Latin America and some nations outside the region are interdependent due to Latin America's desire to industrialize. • The development of transportation and communication networks in Latin America has been slowed because of cost and physical barriers.

Coffee farm in Colombia

SECTION	KEY TERMS	SUMMARY
2 People and Their Environment	**ecosystem** (p. 202) **deforestation** (p. 202) **slash-and-burn farming** (p. 202) **reforestation** (p. 203)	• Large areas of the Amazon River basin are suffering from deforestation. • Road construction, small-scale farming, large-scale ranching, and the commercial exploitation of trees have all contributed to the deforestation of the Amazon rain forest. • There is need for new methods, better planning, and stronger government regulation to help solve the problems of the Amazon rain forest and develop the resources without seriously harming the environment. • The rapid growth of some Latin American cities has led to environmental and social problems. • Latin American governments are aware of the problems facing large cities and are working to solve them.

Logging in the Amazon basin

Reviewing Key Terms

Choose the vocabulary term that best completes each of the sentences below. Write your answers on a separate sheet of paper.

developing countries (p. 195)
export (p. 195)
cash crop (p. 195)
campesinos (p. 196)
latifundia (p. 196)
service industries (p. 196)
deforestation (p. 202)
slash-and-burn farming (p. 202)
reforestation (p. 203)

SECTION 1

1. Bananas produced to sell or trade with someone else are a _____ .
2. Large estates owned by families or corporations are known as _____ .
3. Countries in the process of becoming industrialized are called _____ .
4. People who live in the countryside are known as _____ .
5. To send a product to other countries for sale or trade is to _____ .
6. Industries that provide personal services for others are _____ .

SECTION 2

7. _____ is the practice of planting young trees or the seeds of trees where the forest land has been stripped.
8. The cutting down and clearing of forest land is known as _____ .
9. The process of cutting down plants and stripping trees of bark and then burning it all is known as _____ .

Reviewing Facts

SECTION 1

10. On what is the economy of many Latin American countries based?
11. What has slowed the development of communication networks in Latin America?

SECTION 2

12. What are some concerns people have about the deforestation of the Amazon River basin?
13. What is one of the most serious challenges facing Latin American cities?

Critical Thinking

14. **Drawing Conclusions**   Why is the Panama Canal important?
15. **Predicting Consequences**   What do you think will be the future of the Amazon River basin? Give reasons for your answer.

Geographic Themes

16. **Human/Environment Interaction** Why are Latin American transportation and communications systems not more highly developed?
17. **Human/Environment Interaction** How has rapid urban growth caused environmental problems?

Practicing Skills

Reading a Vegetation Map

Refer to the vegetation map on page 206.

18. Compare the vegetation in the northern and southern parts of South America.
19. How does the vegetation change farther inland from the southeastern coastline?

Using the Unit Atlas

Refer to the physical geography section of the Unit Atlas on pages 154–155.

20. What South American country is a leader in emerald mining?
21. Where is the source of the Amazon River?

Projects

Individual Activity

Select one of Latin America's overcrowded cities, and imagine that you are a city planner for that city. Write a plan for the mayor, who has asked you to help resolve some of the city's problems.

Cooperative Learning Activity

The Pan-American Highway connects the east and west coasts of Latin America and provides a route through much of the region. Working in a group of six, divide the route among group members. Each group member should find four or five interesting facts about the places through which his or her section of the route passes. Group members should share the facts with each other. Then, as a group, prepare a poster that shows the route with the most interesting facts written next to the appropriate places on the map.

Writing About Geography

Narration

Words can have different meanings to different people. Write four definitions of the concept of deforestation as each of these people might define it: a Native American who has grown up and still lives in the Amazon rain forest; a logger; a small-scale migrant farmer; a Brazilian government official. Then, write a paragraph discussing how the definitions are similar and how they are different. Use your journal, text, and library resources for help.

Locating Places

LATIN AMERICA: POLITICAL GEOGRAPHY

Match the letters on the map with the places of Latin America. Write your answers on a separate sheet of paper.

1. Brazil
2. Mexico
3. Costa Rica
4. Belém
5. Isthmus of Panamá
6. Bogotá
7. Lima
8. Santiago
9. Mexico City
10. São Paulo

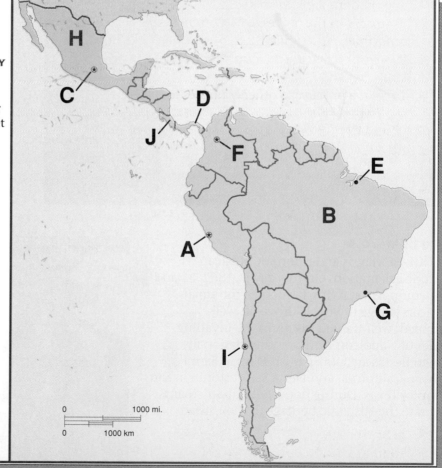

0   1000 mi.

0   1000 km

LATIN AMERICAN CELEBRATIONS

Mexican Americans are the largest Hispanic group living in the United States today. They are the third-largest ethnic group in the United States. Many other people of Hispanic cultural heritage also live in the United States. Two of the largest groups are Puerto Rican Americans and Cuban Americans.

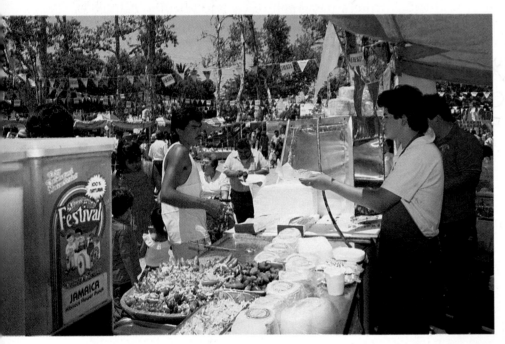

◄ **MEXICAN AMERICAN FIESTAS** are woven into the fabric of life in the American Southwest. Filled with food, dancing and singing, colorful costumes, and decorations, a fiesta is a joyous time. Parades, processions, and fireworks also are often part of fiestas.

CINCO DE MAYO, ►

the Fifth of May, is an important Mexican patriotic celebration. On this day in 1862, a band of ill-equipped, starving farmers in the small Mexican village of Puebla drove off well-equipped, well-trained troops of the invading armies of Napoleon III. Two other nationally known fiestas are Old Spanish Days in Santa Barbara, California, and Fiesta San Antonio in San Antonio, Texas. During both fiestas, participants celebrate the Hispanic heritage of the United States.

▲ **CUBAN AMERICAN FESTIVITIES** bring family and friends together to sing and toast with *sidra espa ola*, a type of apple cider.

▲ **PUERTO RICAN AMERICAN FESTIVALS** celebrate saints' days and other special occasions. Like Mexican American ficstas, Puerto Rican festivals feature plenty of food and drink, music, fireworks, and parades.

A PIÑATA ▶ is the centerpiece of any fiesta for Mexican American children. Filled with small gifts and candy, the brightly colored *piñata* is suspended in the air. Children, sometimes blindfolded, take turns trying to break it. Everyone wins when the treats finally shower down.

Checking for Understanding

1. **What group celebrates Cinco de Mayo? What does the fiesta commemorate?**
2. **Place** What evidences of Hispanic culture do you find in your community?

Europe

GeoJournal Activity

While studying Europe, collect current information about the physical geography, economy, cultures, and human-environment interactions of the region. Clip related newspaper or magazine articles; as you read, highlight or underline the information you find interesting.

David Doubilet

NATIONAL GEOGRAPHIC SOCIETY

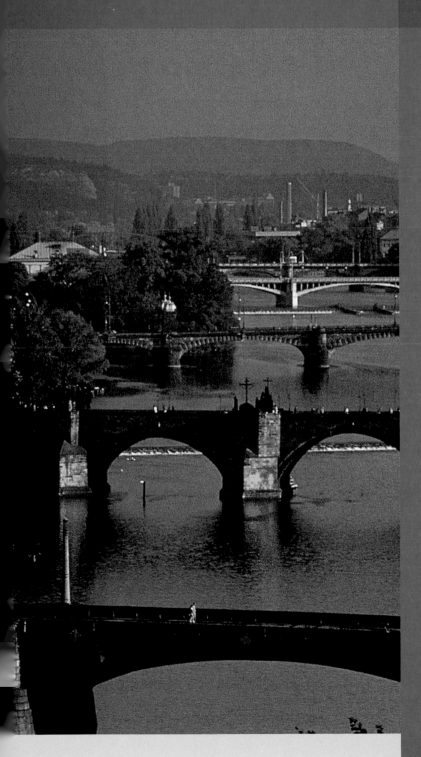

Picturing the World

Sunlight strikes the Charles Bridge and the curving roof of the National Theater in Prague, the capital of the newly-formed Czech Republic. Like other major European cities, Prague, located on the Vltava River in central Europe, has served as a political, academic, and cultural center for hundreds of years. Today's European city manages to combine Old World charm with modern conveniences. Look on the map on page 225.

1. What other capital cities are located on rivers?

2. Why did cities develop along rivers?

Picture Atlas CD-ROM Enrichment Corner

Many interesting bridges and buildings have been built over and along rivers in major European cities. Gather the following seven photographs for a Handbook of Architectural Styles: the Tower Bridge and the Houses of Parliament in London; the Louvre and Notre Dame in Paris; the Vltava River in Prague; the "old bridge" in Florence, Italy; and the Danube River in Budapest, Hungary. Read the photo captions and then answer the following questions:

1. How many bridges span the Thames River in London?

2. The Louvre is located on the north bank of which river?

3. What is the architectural style of the Cathedral of Notre Dame?

EXPLORING CULTURAL DIVERSITY

1. **What nations make up the European continent?**
2. **What areas of Europe are the most heavily populated? Most sparsely populated?**
3. **What is the approximate population of Europe?**

From the 1200s to the early 1900s, **Austria** was the center of a huge empire that included much of central and eastern Europe. Today it is a small landlocked country.

Iceland has the oldest legislature in the world, the *Althing*.

Switzerland has three official languages: German, French, and Italian.

The Olympic Games began in **Greece** about 776 B.C. as part of religious festivals.

EUROPE: POLITICAL

30°W 20°W 10°W 0° 10°E 20°E 30°E 40°E

Arctic Circle

Prime Meridian

— National boundary
⊛ Capital city

Lambert Conformal Conic projection

ICELAND
⊛ Reykjavík

60°N

SWEDEN   FINLAND

NORWAY   Helsinki ⊛

Oslo ⊛   Stockholm ⊛   ⊛ Tallinn
                          ESTONIA
                          N

                          Riga ⊛ LATVIA

UNITED   DENMARK   LITHUANIA
KINGDOM   Copenhagen ⊛   Vilnius ⊛

Dublin ⊛
IRELAND

50°N   NETH.   Berlin ⊛   Warsaw ⊛
     London ⊛ Amsterdam ⊛ GERMANY   P O L A N D
                  ⊛ Brussels
               BELGIUM   Prague ⊛
     Paris ⊛ ⊛ Luxembourg CZECH   SLOVAKIA
                  LUX.   REPUBLIC ⊛ Bratislava
0   300 mi.   LIECHT.   Vienna ⊛ ⊛ Budapest
                           AUSTRIA HUNGARY   ROMANIA
0   300 km F R A N C E SWITZ. Ljubljana ⊛   Bucharest ⊛
                          Bern ⊛   SLOVENIA Zagreb ⊛ Belgrade ⊛
                     SAN   CROATIA BOSNIA-   SERBIA
             MONACO MARINO   HERZ.   BULGARIA
40°N   ITALY Sarajevo ⊛ YUGO. ⊛ Sofia
PORTUGAL   ANDORRA   MONTENEGRO   ⊛ Skopje
         ⊛ Madrid   ⊛ Rome Tiranë ⊛ MAC.
   ⊛ Lisbon   ALBANIA
       S P A I N   GREECE
                                              ⊛ Athens

EUROPE: POPULATION DENSITY

London, the capital of the **United Kingdom**, is the largest city in Europe. It has a population of 9.1 million.

Per sq. km	Per sq. mi.
Over 100	Over 250
50–100	125–250
25–50	60–125
1–25	2–60
Under 1	Under 2
Uninhabited	Uninhabited

Cities
- ■ More than 5,000,000
- □ 2,000,000 to 5,000,000
- ● 1,000,000 to 2,000,000
- ○ 250,000 to 1 million

Lambert Conformal Conic projection

The Netherlands is one of the most densely populated countries in Europe, with an average of more than 1,000 people per square mile.

Germany has experienced a rapid flight from farms into towns and cities; the rural population dropped from about 23 percent in 1950 to about 15 percent in 1993.

Vatican City, located within the city of Rome, is the center of the Roman Catholic Church and is the world's smallest populated nation. Only about 1,000 people live there.

Population: Europe and the United States

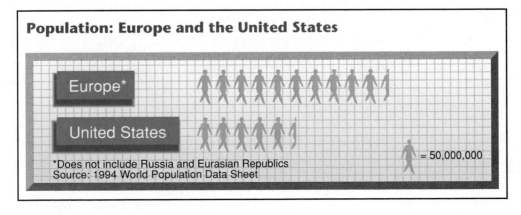

Europe*

United States

*Does not include Russia and Eurasian Republics
Source: 1994 World Population Data Sheet

= 50,000,000

Europe has twice as many people as the United States.

EUROPE
Physical Geography

CHARTING YOUR COURSE

1. *Is Europe's coastline long or short, jagged or straight?*
2. *What major mountain ranges are located in Europe?*
3. *What are three of Europe's principal natural resources?*

Frequent rainfall in the **British Isles** helps to make much of the rolling countryside lush green.

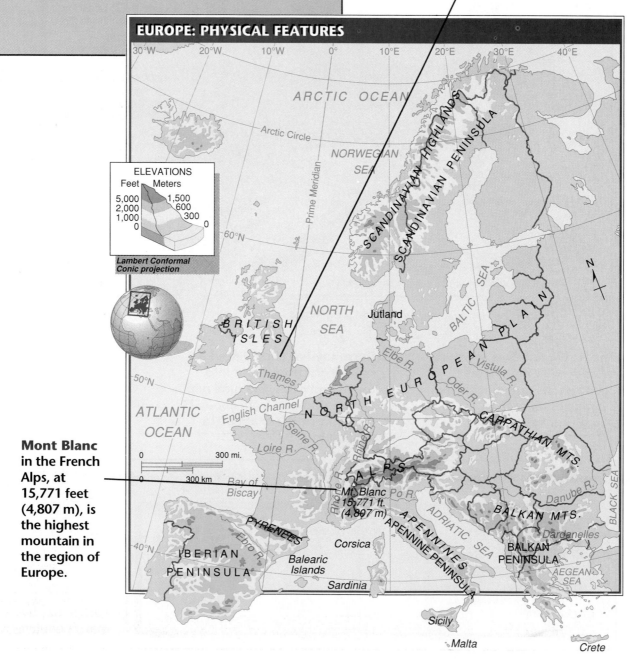

EUROPE: PHYSICAL FEATURES

ELEVATIONS

Feet	Meters
5,000	1,500
2,000	600
1,000	300
0	0

Lambert Conformal Conic projection

ARCTIC OCEAN

Arctic Circle

NORWEGIAN SEA

SCANDINAVIAN HIGHLANDS

SCANDINAVIAN PENINSULA

Prime Meridian

60°N

BALTIC SEA

NORTH SEA

Jutland

NORTH EUROPEAN PLAIN

BRITISH ISLES

Elbe R.

Vistula R.

Oder R.

CARPATHIAN MTS.

Thames

50°N

ATLANTIC OCEAN

English Channel

Seine R.

Loire R.

Rhine R.

0   300 mi.
0   300 km

Bay of Biscay

A L P S

Mt. Blanc 15,771 ft. (4,807 m)

Po R.

Danube R.

BLACK SEA

BALKAN MTS.

PYRENEES

Ebro R.

Rhône R.

Corsica

APENNINES

ADRIATIC SEA

Dardanelles

BALKAN PENINSULA

40°N

IBERIAN PENINSULA

Balearic Islands

APENNINE PENINSULA

AEGEAN SEA

Sardinia

Sicily

Malta

Crete

N

Mont Blanc in the French Alps, at 15,771 feet (4,807 m), is the highest mountain in the region of Europe.

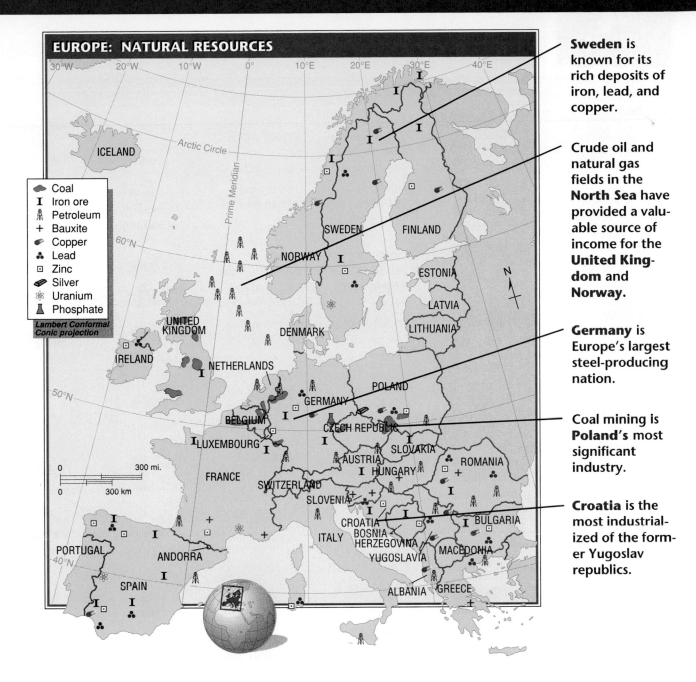

EUROPE: NATURAL RESOURCES

Legend:
- Coal
- I Iron ore
- Petroleum
- + Bauxite
- Copper
- Lead
- Zinc
- Silver
- Uranium
- Phosphate

Lambert Conformal Conic projection

0 — 300 mi.
0 — 300 km

Sweden is known for its rich deposits of iron, lead, and copper.

Crude oil and natural gas fields in the **North Sea** have provided a valuable source of income for the **United Kingdom** and **Norway.**

Germany is Europe's largest steel-producing nation.

Coal mining is **Poland's** most significant industry.

Croatia is the most industrialized of the former Yugoslav republics.

Map labels: ICELAND, SWEDEN, FINLAND, NORWAY, ESTONIA, LATVIA, LITHUANIA, UNITED KINGDOM, DENMARK, IRELAND, NETHERLANDS, POLAND, GERMANY, BELGIUM, CZECH REPUBLIC, LUXEMBOURG, SLOVAKIA, FRANCE, AUSTRIA, HUNGARY, ROMANIA, SWITZERLAND, SLOVENIA, CROATIA, BOSNIA HERZEGOVINA, ITALY, YUGOSLAVIA, MACEDONIA, BULGARIA, PORTUGAL, ANDORRA, SPAIN, ALBANIA, GREECE

Arctic Circle, Prime Meridian, 30°W, 20°W, 10°W, 0°, 10°E, 20°E, 30°E, 40°E, 60°N, 50°N, 40°N

Europe: Physical Profile

MESETA (Spain)
PYRENEES
ALPS (Switzerland)
MASSIF CENTRAL (France)
GERMAN HIGHLANDS
MORAVIAN HILLS (Czech Rep.)
COASTAL LOWLANDS (Portugal)
NORTH EUROPEAN PLAIN (Poland)
ATLANTIC OCEAN

6000 ft.
3000 ft.
1200 ft.
Sea level

Lisbon
Warsaw

0 — 400 mi.
0 — 400 km

Southwest to Northeast from 39°N, 9°W to 52°N, 21°E

COUNTRY* AND CAPITAL	FLAG AND LANGUAGES	POPULATION	LANDMASS	PRINCIPAL PRODUCTS	
				EXPORT	IMPORT
Albania Tiranë	Albanian, Greek	3,400,000 321 per sq. mi. 124 per sq. km	10,580 sq. mi. 27,402 sq. km	Fuels	Machinery
Andorra Andorra la Vella	Catalan	54,000 291 per sq. mi. 113 per sq. km	185 sq. mi. 479 sq. km	Clothing	Electronics
Austria Vienna	German	8,000,000 250 per sq. mi. 97 per sq. km	31,940 sq. mi. 82,725 sq. km	Machinery	Machinery
Belgium Brussels	Flemish, French, German, Italian	10,100,000 850 per sq. mi. 328 per sq. km	11,750 sq. mi. 30,433 sq. km	Machinery	Machinery
Bosnia and Herzegovina Sarajevo	Serbo-Croatian	4,600,000 223 per sq. mi. 86 per sq. km	19,740 sq. mi. 51,127 sq. km	Machinery	Fuels
Bulgaria Sofia	Bulgarian, Turkish	8,400,000 197 per sq. mi. 76 per sq. km	42,680 sq. mi. 110,541 sq. km	Machinery	Machinery
Croatia Zagreb	Croatian	4,800,000 220 per sq. mi. 85 per sq. km	21,830 sq. mi. 56,540 sq. km	Machinery	Machinery
Czech Republic Prague	Czech	10,300,000 337 per sq. mi. 130 per sq. km	30,590 sq. mi. 79,228 sq. km	Chemicals	Chemicals
Denmark Copenhagen	Danish	5,200,000 311 per sq. mi. 120 per sq. km	16,630 sq. mi. 42,372 sq. km	Machinery	Machinery
Estonia Tallinn	Estonian, Russian	1,500,000 91 per sq. mi. 35 per sq. km	17,410 sq. mi. 45,092 sq. km	Textiles	Textiles
Finland Helsinki	Finnish, Swedish	5,100,000 43 per sq. mi. 17 per sq. km	117,610 sq. mi. 304,610 sq. km	Metals	Fuels

*Country maps not drawn to scale.

COUNTRY* AND CAPITAL	FLAG AND LANGUAGES	POPULATION	LANDMASS	PRINCIPAL EXPORT	PRODUCTS IMPORT
France · Paris	French	58,000,000 273 per sq. mi. 105 per sq. km	212,390 sq. mi. 550,090 sq. km	Machinery	Machinery
Germany · Berlin	German	81,200,000 602 per sq. mi. 232 per sq. km	134,930 sq. mi. 349,469 sq. km	Machinery	Machinery
Greece · Athens	Greek	10,400,000 206 per sq. mi. 79 per sq. km	50,520 sq. mi. 130,847 sq. km	Food	Machinery
Hungary · Budapest	Hungarian	10,300,000 287 per sq. mi. 111 per sq. km	35,650 sq. mi. 92,334 sq. km	Food	Machinery
Iceland · Reykjavík	Icelandic	300,000 8 per sq. mi. 3 per sq. km	38,710 sq. mi. 100,259 sq. km	Fish	Ships
Ireland · Dublin	English, Irish (Gaelic)	3,600,000 135 per sq. mi. 52 per sq. km	26,600 sq. mi. 68,894 sq. km	Machinery	Machinery
Italy · Rome	Italian	57,200,000 504 per sq. mi. 195 per sq. km	113,540 sq. mi. 294,069 sq. km	Machinery	Machinery
Latvia · Riga	Latvian	2,500,000 108 per sq. mi. 42 per sq. km	24,980 sq. mi. 64,491 sq. km	Machinery	Textiles
Liechtenstein · Vaduz	German, Alemannic dialect	30,000 500 per sq. mi. 194 per sq. km	60 sq. mi. 155 sq. km	Machinery	Machinery
Lithuania · Vilnius	Lithuanian	3,700,000 147 per sq. mi. 57 per sq. km	25,210 sq. mi. 65,294 sq. km	Machinery	Petroleum
Luxembourg · Luxembourg	French, German, Luxembourgisch	400,000 404 per sq. mi. 156 per sq. km	990 sq. mi. 2,564 sq. km	Metals	Metals
Macedonia · Skopje	Macedonian	2,100,000 211 per sq. mi. 82 per sq. km	9,930 sq. mi. 25,719 sq. km	Clothing	Food

*Country maps not drawn to scale.

COUNTRY* AND CAPITAL	FLAG AND LANGUAGES	POPULATION	LANDMASS	PRINCIPAL EXPORT	PRODUCTS IMPORT
Malta Valletta	Maltese, English	400,000 3,125 per sq. mi. 1,286 per sq. km	120 sq. mi. 311 sq. km	Machinery	Machinery
Monaco Monaco	French	29,712 49,520 per sq. mi. 14,856 per sq. km	.6 sq. mi. 1.6 sq. km		
Netherlands Amsterdam	Dutch	15,400,000 1,175 per sq. mi. 454 per sq. km	13,100 sq. mi. 33,929 sq. km	Machinery	Machinery
Norway Oslo	Norwegian	4,300,000 36 per sq. mi. 14 per sq. km	118,470 sq. mi. 306,837 sq. km	Fuels	Machinery
Poland Warsaw	Polish	38,600,000 328 per sq. mi. 127 per sq. km	117,550 sq. mi. 304,455 sq. km	Machinery	Machinery
Portugal Lisbon	Portuguese	9,900,000 279 per sq. mi. 108 per sq. km	35,500 sq. mi. 91,945 sq. km	Textiles	Motor Vehicles
Romania Bucharest	Romanian, Hungarian, German	22,700,000 254 per sq. mi. 98 per sq. km	88,930 sq. mi. 230,329 sq. km	Fuels	Raw Materials
San Marino San Marino	Italian	20,000 1,000 per sq. mi. 384 per sq. km	20 sq. mi. 52 sq. km	Wine	Crude Oil
Slovakia Bratislava	Slovak	5,300,000 282 per sq. mi. 109 per sq. km	18,790 sq. mi. 48,667 sq. km	Machinery	Petroleum
Slovenia Ljubljana	Slovenian, Serbo-Croatian	2,000,000 254 per sq. mi. 98 per sq. km	7,820 sq. mi. 20,256 sq. km	Machinery	Machinery
Spain Madrid	Spanish, Catalan, Basque, Galician	39,200,000 203 per sq. mi. 78 per sq. km	192,830 sq. mi. 499,430 sq. km	Transport Equipment	Machinery
Sweden Stockholm	Swedish	8,800,000 55 per sq. mi. 21 per sq. km	158,930 sq. mi. 411,629 sq. km	Machinery	Machinery

*Country maps not drawn to scale.

COUNTRY* AND CAPITAL	FLAG AND LANGUAGES	POPULATION	LANDMASS	PRINCIPAL EXPORT	PRODUCTS IMPORT
Switzerland Bern	German, French, Italian	7,000,000 456 per sq. mi. 176 per sq. km	15,360 sq. mi. 39,782 sq. km	Chemicals	Electronics
United Kingdom London	English, Welsh, Gaelic	58,400,000 626 per sq. mi. 242 per sq. km	93,280 sq. mi. 241,595 sq. km	Machinery	Machinery
Vatican City Vatican City	Italian, Latin	802	.17 sq. mi. .44 sq. km		
Yugoslavia Belgrade	Serbo-Croatian	10,500,000 390 per sq. mi. 150 per sq. km	26,940 sq. mi. 69,775 sq. km	Clothing	Machinery

*Country maps not drawn to scale.

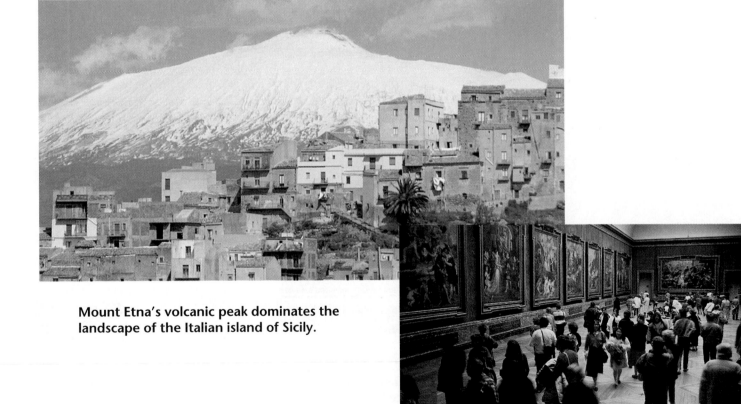

Mount Etna's volcanic peak dominates the landscape of the Italian island of Sicily.

The Louvre, in Paris, France, is considered one of the greatest art museums in the world.

The Physical Geography of Europe

CHAPTER FOCUS

Geographic Setting

The continent of Europe is a large peninsula with a long, irregular coastline. Europe's northern location and closeness to the sea result in a diversity of climates and kinds of vegetation.

Geographic Themes

Section 1 The Land
PLACE The continent of Europe consists of fertile plains interrupted by mountains.

Section 2 The Climate and Vegetation
LOCATION Europe's latitude and location relative to the sea affect its climate regions.

▲ Photograph: *Rolling meadows in southern England*

SETTING THE SCENE

Read to Discover . . .
- the features of Europe's coastline.
- the characteristics of Europe's mountains and plains.
- the kinds of natural resources found in Europe.

Key Terms
- fjord
- polder
- peat

Identify and Locate
Eurasia, Scandinavian Peninsula, Iberian Peninsula, Balkan Peninsula, British Isles, Sicily, Alpine mountain system, North European Plain, Rhine River, Danube River, North Sea, English Channel

Gijón, Spain

¡Hola, amigos!
My family and I are spending our summer vacation in Gijón, a beautiful seaport in the northern region of Spain called Asturias. This region is known as the Switzerland of Spain because of its green valleys and tall snowy peaks.   ¡Hasta pronto!
José María González

Europe's varied mountains, islands, and unusually long, irregular coastline offer many vacation sites like the ones described in José's postcard. Most of Europe lies within 300 miles (483 km) of a seacoast. This closeness to the sea has helped to fashion the history of its nations and the cultures of its peoples.

PLACE

Peninsulas and Islands

The continent of Europe is a giant peninsula that extends westward from northwestern Asia. Some geographers refer to this large landmass as Eurasia. The European continent curves in and out in a series of large and small peninsulas. For this reason, Europe often has been called "a peninsula of peninsulas."

The Northern Peninsulas

Norway and Sweden make up the Scandinavian Peninsula in northern Europe. During the Ice Ages, glaciers along the Norwegian coastline cut deep valleys to the ocean. When the ice sheets retreated, the sea filled in the valleys, called **fjords** (fee•YORDZ). The deep waters of the fjords provide fine harbors surrounded by rocky cliffs topped with thick forests.

Jutland, the northern peninsula opposite the Scandinavian Peninsula, is the major geographic feature of Denmark. Great sandy beaches extend along the western coast of Jutland. The marshes in the southwest result from the tides of the North Sea. Jutland's eastern coast consists of rolling hills indented by narrow inlets.

The Southern Peninsulas

Spain and Portugal are located on southern Europe's Iberian Peninsula. Most of the Iberian Peninsula is a large, semiarid plateau. Sun-drenched plains stretch along the peninsula's western and southern coasts. The forested Pyrenees Mountains rise sharply along the northern coast and follow the border with France.

The Apennine Peninsula, which forms Italy, extends like a giant boot into the Mediterranean Sea. The interior of the southern part of the peninsula consists of mountains. The northern part is largely plains. Cliffs line the coast.

The former Yugoslav republics, Albania, Bulgaria, Greece, Romania, and the European part of Turkey occupy most of the Balkan Peninsula in southeastern Europe. The Black Sea, the Bosphorus, the Sea of Marmara, the Dardanelles Strait, and the Aegean Sea border the peninsula on the east. Like the Apennine Peninsula, the Balkan Peninsula is mountainous and is sometimes subject to earthquakes and volcanic activity.

Atlantic Islands

The island country of Iceland lies just south of the Arctic Circle in the North Atlantic Ocean. Grassy lowlands stretch along Iceland's coast, but the land rises sharply to form a large plateau that covers most of the island. Lying

Geographic Themes

Region: Scandinavian Peninsula
Long narrow inlets called fjords are common along the mountainous Norwegian coast of the Scandinavian Peninsula. *How were fjords formed?*

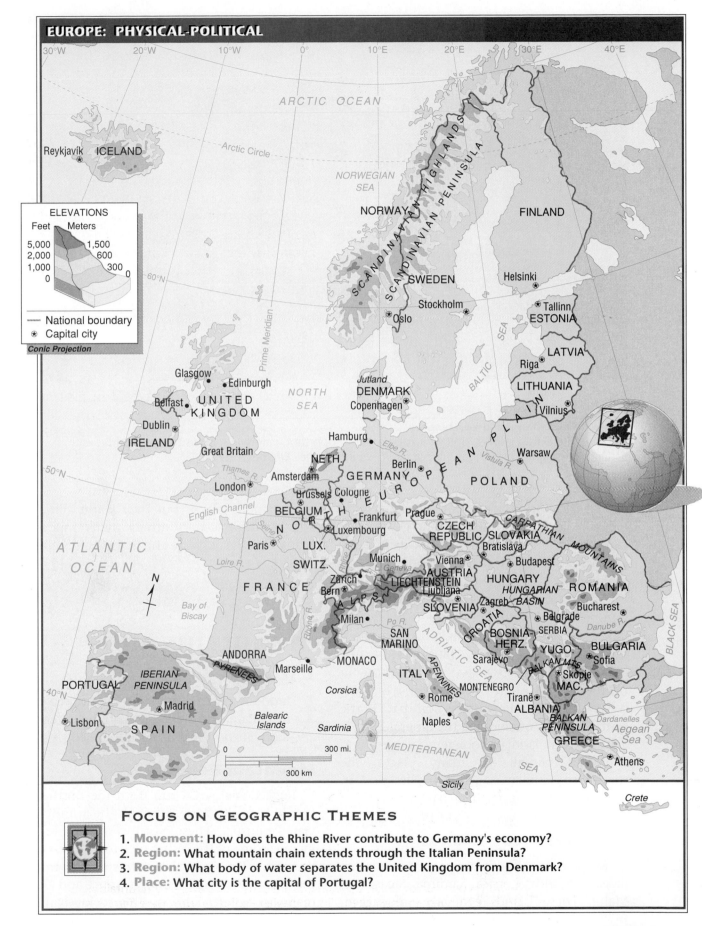

EUROPE: PHYSICAL-POLITICAL

30°W 20°W 10°W 0° 10°E 20°E 30°E 40°E

ARCTIC OCEAN

Arctic Circle

Reykjavík ICELAND

NORWEGIAN SEA

ELEVATIONS

Feet	Meters
5,000	1,500
2,000	600
1,000	300
0	0

— National boundary
⊛ Capital city

Conic Projection

NORWAY

SCANDINAVIAN HIGHLANDS

SCANDINAVIAN PENINSULA

FINLAND

SWEDEN

Helsinki

Stockholm

Oslo

Tallinn ESTONIA

BALTIC SEA

LATVIA

Riga

LITHUANIA

Vilnius

60°N

Prime Meridian

Glasgow •Edinburgh

Belfast

UNITED KINGDOM

Dublin

IRELAND

Great Britain

NORTH SEA

Jutland

DENMARK

Copenhagen

Hamburg

Elbe R.

Vistula R.

Warsaw

50°N

Thames R.

NETH.

Berlin

EUROPEAN PLAIN

POLAND

Amsterdam

London

GERMANY

Brussels Cologne

BELGIUM

Frankfurt

Prague

CZECH REPUBLIC

SLOVAKIA

CARPATHIAN MOUNTAINS

English Channel

Seine R.

Luxembourg

LUX.

Bratislava

ATLANTIC OCEAN

Paris

Loire R.

SWITZ.

Munich

Vienna

Budapest

Zürich

L. Geneva

AUSTRIA

HUNGARY

ROMANIA

N

FRANCE

Bern

LIECHTENSTEIN

Ljubljana

HUNGARIAN BASIN

Rhône R.

ALPS

SLOVENIA

Zagreb

Bucharest

Bay of Biscay

Milan

Po R.

CROATIA

Belgrade

Danube R.

BLACK SEA

SAN MARINO

ADRIATIC SEA

BOSNIA-HERZ.

SERBIA

BULGARIA

ANDORRA

PYRENEES

Marseille

MONACO

ITALY

APENNINES

Sarajevo

YUGO.

Sofia

MONTENEGRO

BALKAN MTS.

Skopje

MAC.

IBERIAN PENINSULA

Corsica

Rome

Tiranë

PORTUGAL

40°N

•Madrid

Balearic Islands

Naples

ALBANIA

BALKAN PENINSULA

Dardanelles

Aegean Sea

Lisbon

SPAIN

Sardinia

GREECE

0 300 mi.

MEDITERRANEAN SEA

0 300 km

Sicily

Athens

Crete

FOCUS ON GEOGRAPHIC THEMES

1. **Movement:** How does the Rhine River contribute to Germany's economy?
2. **Region:** What mountain chain extends through the Italian Peninsula?
3. **Region:** What body of water separates the United Kingdom from Denmark?
4. **Place:** What city is the capital of Portugal?

Geographic Themes

Place: Danube River, Hungary
The Danube River, one of Europe's most important waterways, flows through Budapest, the capital of Hungary. *What plains area does the Danube cross?*

astride the Mid-Atlantic Ridge, Iceland is an area of volcanoes, hot springs, and geysers. Because of Iceland's far-northern location, large glaciers are found next to volcanoes and hot springs.

The British Isles, which lie northwest of the European mainland, consist of two large islands, Great Britain and Ireland, and thousands of smaller islands. Mountain ranges, plateaus, and deep valleys cover most of northern and eastern Great Britain, while low hills and gently rolling plains dominate in the south. Ireland, often called the Emerald Isle, is a lush green land of cool temperatures and abundant rainfall. In many places, the rugged coastline of the British Isles rises in rocky cliffs that drop to deep bays.

Mediterranean Islands

Major islands south of Europe include the Balearic Islands, Corsica, Sardinia, Sicily, and Malta. These islands generally are rugged,

mountainous places, but their warm climate and beautiful scenery attract many tourists. Many Greek islands are chiefly hills and fertile valleys.

PLACE

Mountains and Plains

Europe is essentially plains interrupted by mountains running through its interior and along its northern and southern edges.

Mountain Regions

Rugged highlands run from the northern part of the British Isles through the Scandinavian Peninsula. These Northwest Mountains include some of the oldest rock formations on the earth. The Central Uplands extend from the Iberian Peninsula through France and Germany to eastern Europe. This rocky, barren

Geographic Themes

Place: Mont Blanc, French Alps
Mont Blanc rises 15,771 feet (4,807 m) and is the highest mountain in the Alps. Its peak is always snow-covered. *Where is the Alpine mountain system located?*

region includes low mountains and high plateaus with scattered forests.

The Alpine mountain system extends across southern Europe from Spain to the Balkan Peninsula. It branches into Russia and some of the Eurasian republics in the region of the Caspian Sea. The Alpine mountain system is higher and younger than those of the Northwest Mountains region and the Central Uplands. Several mountain ranges, including the Alps and the Carpathians, make up the Alpine system. The Alps, however, make up the largest part. These world-famous peaks cover most of Switzerland and Austria and parts of Italy and France. The snowcapped Alps provide some of the world's most spectacular scenery as well as uncounted challenges for expert skiers and accomplished mountain climbers. A British mountain climber offers this description:

The Alps stretch in a tight-drawn bow for five hundred miles [805 km], from the Mediterranean to the Adriatic; a mountainspine which has helped to determine the history of Europe throughout the ages and which today provides the most developed playground in the world. It was also the birthplace of both mountaineering and skiing as sports.

Plains Regions

Europe's broad, fertile plains curve around the highlands. The vast North European Plain stretches from the southeastern United Kingdom and western France more than 1,800 miles (2,896 km) eastward to Poland. An extension of the plain reaches into Ukraine, Belarus, and Russia.

Geographic Themes

Human/Environment Interaction: North Sea Oil and Gas Fields
Europe's richest oil and natural gas fields are found in the North Sea between Scotland and Norway. *What other area of Europe has oil and natural gas resources?*

Most of the North European Plain is rolling land with isolated hills or low mountains. In the Netherlands, people pumped out the water to reclaim land that once was covered by the sea. The **polders**, or drained areas, became rich farmland like many other parts of the North European Plain.

Other plains regions are located in parts of Italy and the Iberian Peninsula and among the mountain ranges of eastern Europe. The Hungarian Basin is a treeless stretch of land noted for agriculture and horse-raising. In general, fertile soils and ease of movement have made the plains regions the most populated areas in Europe.

MOVEMENT

Rivers and Lakes

Many of Europe's rivers flow from interior mountain and highland areas to the coasts. They provide water to irrigate farmland and to produce electricity. Today, as in the past, Europe's rivers play an important role as transportation links between the interior and the coast. Europe does not have many large lakes similar to the Great Lakes in North America. A large number of lakes, however, are located in Sweden and Finland.

Rivers

Europe's rivers have differing characteristics. The rivers in Scandinavia are short and do not provide easy connections between cities. In the heartland of western and eastern Europe, however, relatively long rivers provide links between inland areas as well as to the sea. The Rhine is the most important river in western Europe. It flows from Switzerland, along the border of France and then north through Germany and the Netherlands, connecting many industrial cities to the busy port of Rotterdam on the North Sea. The Danube, which flows 1,776 miles (2,858 km) from Germany's Black Forest to the Black Sea, is eastern Europe's most important waterway. Each year, ships and barges carry millions of tons of cargo on the Danube. The major rivers of the Iberian Peninsula are too narrow and shallow for large ships. Britain's Thames River, on the other hand, allows oceangoing ships to reach the port of London.

Lakes

Many lakes formed in the Scandinavian countries and Finland when melting glaciers retreated after the last Ice Age. Lakes cover about one-twelfth of Sweden, and Finland's interior plateau is called the Lake Plateau. Some of western and eastern Europe's most popular recreation areas center around lakes famous for their natural beauty. Located on the border between France and Switzerland, the clear blue waters of Lake Geneva mirror the Alpine peaks that surround it. The shores of Lake Como in northern Italy are lined with fertile vineyards and fine gardens. Hungary's Lake Balaton provides a scenic attraction among gently rolling hills and low mountains.

Natural Resources

Minerals rank among Europe's most important natural resources. Many mineral deposits are found in the plains and mountain areas of the European mainland. Others are located in the highlands of the British Isles and in the countries of southwestern Europe.

Iron and Coal

Europe, the birthplace of modern industry, has considerable amounts of coal and iron ore. These resources are considered the traditional necessities of an industrial society because they are used together to make steel. The major iron ore deposits are found in northeastern France, western Germany, northern Sweden, and the Balkan Peninsula. The major coal deposits are in the British Isles, the Ruhr district in western Germany, northern France, Belgium, the Czech Republic, and Poland.

Other Energy Sources

Resources that provide fuel for homes and factories in Europe vary widely. **Peat,** a kind of vegetable matter usually composed of mosses, was traditionally burned as fuel in some western European homes. Today Europeans largely rely on such energy sources as coal, oil, gas, and nuclear and hydroelectric power. The discovery and development of vast oil and natural gas reserves under the North Sea in the 1960s and 1970s greatly increased western Europe's energy sources. Eastern Europe also has oil and natural gas resources, especially in Bulgaria and Romania. Fast-flowing streams and rivers throughout the continent provide good sources of power for electricity. The world's first tidal power plant began operating in France in the 1960s. This plant uses the power of incoming and outgoing tides to provide electricity.

Other Mineral Resources

Two of Europe's major resources are bauxite, a source of aluminum, and potash, an element used in fertilizer. Bauxite deposits are found in southern France, Hungary, and the former Yugoslav republics, while potash is located in France, Germany, and Spain. Other minerals mined in Europe include copper, lead, zinc, uranium, gold, and silver. Many of Europe's industrial and transportation centers developed near mineral deposits.

SECTION 1 REVIEW

Checking for Understanding
1. **Define** fjord, polder, peat.
2. **Locating Places** Where are Europe's major mountain regions located?
3. **Region** What are three characteristics of Europe's coastline?
4. **Human/Environment Interaction** What are Europe's major energy sources?

Critical Thinking
5. **Drawing Conclusions** How did Europe's rivers contribute to the development of its industries?

2 The Climate and Vegetation

SETTING THE SCENE

Read to Discover . . .
- how latitude and water bodies affect Europe's climate regions.
- why Europe's natural vegetation has changed over the centuries.

Key Terms
- mistral
- sirocco
- permafrost
- foehn
- avalanche
- chaparral

Identify and Locate
Gulf Stream, North Atlantic Drift, Climate regions: marine west coast, Mediterranean, humid continental, humid subtropical, steppe, subarctic, tundra, highland

Europe's climates vary from the tundra and subarctic regions of Iceland, Scandinavia, and Finland to the Mediterranean coasts of Italy, Spain, and Greece. Its diverse vegetation includes the dark fir and spruce trees of Germany's Black Forest as well as the short grasses and scattered shrubs of Spain's dry, central plateau, the Meseta. In Europe, as in other parts of the world, climate and vegetation patterns are closely linked. Europe's northern latitude and its location near large bodies of water are major factors in determining the diversity of its climates and vegetation.

REGION

Europe's Climate Regions

In spite of Europe's northern location, most of the continent has a mild climate. The climate in many parts of Europe is milder than that of other places in the world at about the same latitude. For example, January temperatures in Frankfurt, Germany, are warmer than those in Winnipeg, Canada, or in Irkutsk in the Asian part of Russia. Yet all three cities are about the same distance from the Equator. Europe's peninsular location in relation to the sea helps explain its relatively mild climate.

Major Climate Regions

A large part of western Europe has a marine west coast climate. This climate region extends from the Arctic Circle to the Alps and from Ireland to the western parts of Poland, the Czech Republic, and Hungary. Places in this climate region enjoy moderate tempera-

Geographic Themes

Place: Po River Valley, Italy
The Po River valley of northern Italy is an area of productive farms and factories. *What two major factors help shape the diversity of Europe's climate and vegetation?*

tures in both summer and winter, and they receive between 20 and 40 inches (51 and 102 cm) of precipitation each year.

Northwest Europe's temperate, moist climate is caused by winds that blow across the continent from the Atlantic Ocean. The Gulf Stream and the North Atlantic Drift are powerful ocean currents that bring warm water from the Gulf of Mexico and the middle part of the Atlantic Ocean near the Equator to the west coast of Europe. Prevailing westerly winds, blowing over these currents, carry warm air across the continent. Even the Norwegian coast, which lies in northern Europe, remains ice-free in winter as a result of this climate pattern.

Most of southern Europe has a Mediterranean climate. Places in this part of the continent have hot, dry summers and mild, rainy winters. Southern Europe receives less yearly precipitation than northwestern Europe, because the Alpine mountain system and shifting air pressure belts during summer block the moist Atlantic winds. In winter, however, winds from the Mediterranean bring moderate rainfall. Local winds in this region sometimes cause changes in the normal weather pattern. The **mistral**, a strong, northerly wind from the Alps, may bring very cold air to southern France. **Siroccos**, hot winds from the North African deserts of Libya, can bring desert air and dust.

Most of eastern and northern Europe has a humid continental climate. This climate region includes the eastern parts of Poland, Hungary, the Czech Republic, Slovakia, Romania, and Bulgaria. The southern parts of Sweden and Finland also have a humid continental climate. Warm ocean currents have little influence on the climate because of the distance from the North Atlantic. Therefore, places in the humid continental climate region have greater differences between summer and winter temperatures than places in western and southern Europe.

Other Climates

Several other climates are found in small areas of Europe. A humid subtropical region

EUROPE: CLIMATE REGIONS

Steppe
Mediterranean
Humid subtropical
Marine west coast
Humid continental
Subarctic
Highland

Lambert Conformal Conic projection

FOCUS ON GEOGRAPHIC THEMES

1. **Region:** What climate regions are found in Scandinavia?
2. **Movement:** Why does northwestern Europe have a milder climate than eastern Europe?
3. **Region:** What climate region includes eastern Switzerland and western Austria?
4. **Place:** What kind of climate region is found in central Italy?

stretches from northern Italy to the central part of the Balkan Peninsula. Parts of Spain's Meseta have a steppe, or partly dry, climate.

Most of Iceland and the northern parts of Scandinavia and Finland have subarctic and tundra climates. Places in these climate regions have long, bitterly cold winters and short, cool summers. Tundra and subarctic regions have **permafrost**, soil that is often permanently frozen below the surface.

The Alps have a highland climate with generally colder temperatures and more pre-

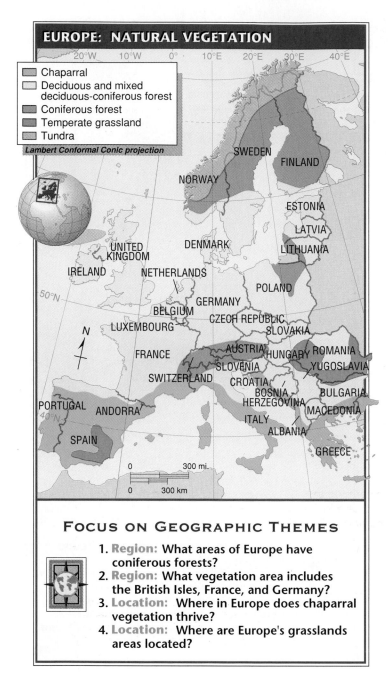

FOCUS ON GEOGRAPHIC THEMES

1. **Region:** What areas of Europe have coniferous forests?
2. **Region:** What vegetation area includes the British Isles, France, and Germany?
3. **Location:** Where in Europe does chaparral vegetation thrive?
4. **Location:** Where are Europe's grasslands areas located?

cipitation than nearby lowland areas. Sudden changes can occur, however, when dry winds called **foehns** (FUHNZ) blow down from the mountains. Foehns can cause an **avalanche**, a mass of ice, snow, or rock sliding down a mountainside.

HUMAN/ENVIRONMENT INTERACTION

Europe's Vegetation

The natural vegetation of Europe consists of forests, grasslands, and tundra plants.

These types of vegetation are closely linked to the climate regions. Over the centuries, changing climate patterns have affected vegetation, but people have caused even greater changes.

Natural Vegetation Patterns

Deciduous forests, trees that lose their leaves, are the natural vegetation of Europe's marine west coast climate region. These forests include ash, beech, elm, maple, and oak trees that provide spectacular autumn color. Coniferous forests, needle-leaf evergreen trees consisting of fir, larch, pine, and spruce, are common in northern Europe and in mountain areas. Mediterranean climates support broad-leaved evergreens, such as the cork oak tree and the olive tree. Such trees are well suited to the dry summers of this climate region. Their tough, waxy leaves conserve moisture. Unlike other broad-leaved trees, they do not lose their leaves in autumn.

Parts of the North European Plain consist of grasslands. The height of the grasses is related to the amount of rainfall in the region. Fertile areas with tall grasses cover most of the western plain. Dry areas where only short grasses grow are found in Hungary and parts of the Iberian Peninsula. The hot, dry summers of the Mediterranean area produce **chaparral**, or shrubs and short trees. The tundra region near Europe's Arctic coast supports little vegetation. Mosses, small shrubs, and colorful wildflowers cover the tundra during the brief summer, however. The upper slopes of the Alps resemble tundra and support similar kinds of vegetation.

Human Interaction

Europeans cut down most of the natural forests that once covered large parts of the continent. They cleared the land for agriculture and industry and used the timber for fuel and building materials. Today, much of the once-forested land is occupied by urban areas and farms. Farmers also use parts of the tundra and high mountains as grazing land.

Great pine and spruce forests still cover parts of Scandinavia and Finland. Forests also cover parts of Poland, Slovakia, and the Czech

Europe and the United States

Climate Graph: Paris, France
Location: 49° N/2° E
Elevation: 246 ft. (75 m.)

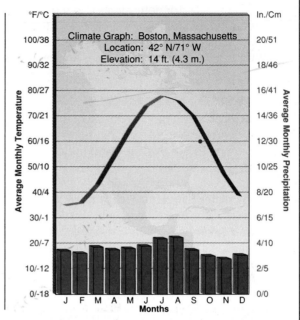

Climate Graph: Boston, Massachusetts
Location: 42° N/71° W
Elevation: 14 ft. (4.3 m.)

Source: *World Weather Guide*, 1990   *lines measure temperature/bars measure precipitation

GRAPH STUDY

The climate graphs above show the average monthly temperatures and the average monthly precipitation in Paris, France, and in Boston, Massachusetts. *What is the average January temperature and precipitation in each city?*

Republic. Lumbering is an important industry in these European forest regions.

Some European governments regulate the cutting of trees to protect forests. In Germany's Black Forest, for example, new trees are planted to replace trees that are cut for timber.

Air pollution from Europe's industries and automobiles, however, poses a serious threat to forests as well as to other natural vegetation. In many industrialized countries, such as Germany, Belgium, Poland, and the Czech Republic, auto and factory pollution has brought widespread disaster to many woodlands. For example, scientists estimate that more than 20 percent of forests in the Czech Republic have been either killed or irreversibly damaged as a result of unregulated pollution.

SECTION 2 REVIEW

Checking for Understanding
1. **Define** mistral, sirocco, permafrost, foehn, avalanche, chaparral.
2. **Locating Places** In which country is the Black Forest located?
3. **Region** What type of climate is found in northwestern Europe?

Critical Thinking
4. **Determining Cause and Effect** How has human interaction with the environment changed vegetation patterns in Europe?

Reading a Climate Map

Climate is a main factor determining how people dress, live, work, and play in a particular region. People on different continents may share similar climates. For example, people living in Wyoming or Montana must survive the same harsh, dry climate as people in western China. By reading a climate map, you can discover these similarities and differences among regions.

REVIEWING THE SKILL

Several factors determine the climate of a region: latitude, temperature, precipitation, altitude, proximity to oceans, and wind patterns. Regions in the low latitudes have tropical climates, which are warm year-round. Variation in precipitation creates different types of tropical climates such as **rain forest** (very wet), **desert** (very dry), and **savanna** (wet and dry seasons).

Middle-latitude climates have seasonal variations in temperature. On the west coast of continents between the latitudes of 30° and 60°, ocean breezes produce **marine west coast** climates with cool summers and mild damp winters. Near the tropics, ocean winds create **humid subtropical** climates with hot rainy summers and mild winters. Other coastal areas in these latitudes have **Mediterranean** climates with mild damp winters and hot dry summers. Regions lying farther north and inland have **humid continental** climates with cold snowy winters and warmer summers. Polar regions have **subarctic** and **tundra** climates with bitterly cold winters and short cool summers.

Steppe (or semidesert) climates are dry but have more rainfall than deserts; these occur all over the globe. **Highland,** or mountain, climates vary with elevation.

On a climate map, different colors represent various climate regions. The map key explains the color code. To read a climate map, apply the following steps:

- Identify the area covered in the map.
- Study the key to identify the climate regions on the map.
- Locate the regions in each climate zone.
- Draw conclusions about the climate similarities and differences among regions.

EUROPE: CLIMATE REGIONS

Steppe
Mediterranean
Humid subtropical
Marine west coast
Humid continental
Subarctic
Highland

Lambert Conformal Conic projection

PRACTICING THE SKILL

Use the map to answer the following questions about climate maps:

1. What geographic area does this map cover?
2. Name two European cities that share a Mediterranean climate.
3. What kind of climate is shared by most of the countries in northwestern Europe?
4. Which region has the coolest climate?
5. Describe the climate in Sofia and Riga.

For additional practice in this skill, see Practicing Skills on page 236 of the Chapter 11 Review.

1 SECTION	KEY TERMS	SUMMARY

The Land

fjord (p. 223)
polder (p. 228)
peat (p. 229)

**The Danube River at
Budapest, Hungary**

- The continent of Europe is a huge peninsula that extends westward from the landmass of Eurasia.
- Europe has a long, irregular coastline with many peninsulas and islands surrounded by different seas.
- Europe consists of plains surrounded by mountains along its northern and southern edges.
- Rivers play an important role as transportation routes linking the interior of Europe with coastal ports.
- Europe has major coal, iron ore, oil, and natural gas deposits.

2 SECTION	KEY TERMS	SUMMARY

The Climate and Vegetation

mistral (p. 231)
sirocco (p. 231)
permafrost (p. 231)
foehn (p. 232)
avalanche (p. 232)
chaparral (p. 232)

**Po River valley in
northern Italy**

- Because of warm ocean currents, much of Europe has milder climates than other parts of the world at similar northern latitudes.
- Northwestern Europe has a marine west coast climate, with moderate temperatures in both summer and winter.
- Most of southern Europe has a Mediterranean climate with mild, rainy winters and hot, dry summers.
- The interior of Europe experiences more extreme seasonal temperatures than other parts of the continent.
- Europe's natural vegetation is influenced by climate and human interaction.

Reviewing Key Terms

Choose the vocabulary term that best completes each of the sentences below. Write your answers on a separate sheet of paper.

fjord (p. 223)
polder (p. 228)
peat (p. 229)
mistral (p. 231)
sirocco (p. 231)
permafrost (p. 231)
foehns (p. 232)
avalanche (p. 232)
chaparral (p. 232)

SECTION 1

1. Some homes in western Europe burn ___ for fuel.
2. Along Norway's coast, a deep water-filled valley called a ___ may be used as a harbor.
3. A ___ is land that people in the Netherlands have reclaimed from the sea.

SECTION 2

4. The word ___ refers to ice, snow, or rock sliding down a mountainside.
5. A wind called the ___ brings desert air to the Mediterranean coast of western Europe.
6. A ___ is a warm, dry wind in Alpine areas.
7. Cold air is brought from the Alps to southeastern France by the ___.
8. ___ is soil that often is permanently frozen below the surface.
9. The hot, dry summers of the Mediterranean area produce shrubs and short trees known as ___.

Reviewing Facts

SECTION 1

10. Why is Europe called "a peninsula of peninsulas"?

11. Which mountains form the largest part of the Alpine system?
12. Where are Europe's major iron ore deposits located?

SECTION 2

13. How do the Gulf Stream and the North Atlantic Drift affect Europe's climate?
14. How has northwestern Europe's natural vegetation changed over time?

Critical Thinking

15. **Drawing Conclusions** Europe has a diversity of peoples and cultures. How might geographical factors have shaped this diversity?
16. **Expressing Problems Clearly** How has human interaction affected Europe's environment?

Geographic Themes

17. **Movement** How have rivers aided Europe's economic development?
18. **Region** What vegetation is found in the Mediterranean climate region?

Practicing Skills

Reading a Climate Map
Refer to the climate map on page 234.
19. Which climate regions do not occur in Europe? Explain why.
20. Compare climates in northern Europe and southern Europe.

Using the Unit Atlas

Refer to the physical geography section of the Unit Atlas on pages 216–217.

21. What body of water affects the climate of northwestern Europe?
22. What points in Europe are higher than 5,000 feet (1,500 m) above sea level?

Projects

Individual Activity

Choose a city in Europe and prepare typical January and July weather forecasts for the location you choose. Present your forecasts to the class. You may use weather maps, charts, or graphs in your presentation.

Cooperative Learning Activity

Work in groups of four to do additional research on one of the regions of Europe described in this chapter and that you have described in your journal. Examples include the Iberian Peninsula, the Scandinavian Peninsula, the Alpine mountain system, or the North European Plain. Each member of the group should be responsible for reporting about one of the following topics: land features, water bodies, plants and animals, or human/environment interaction. Combine the reports to make a booklet or a display about the region.

Writing About Geography

Description

Imagine that you are in charge of an advertising campaign to attract tourists to Europe. Choose an area that you have learned about in this chapter and have described in your journal records. Write a 30-second television commercial that will encourage American tourists to visit that place. If possible, videotape your commercial.

Locating Places

EUROPE: PHYSICAL GEOGRAPHY

Match the letters on the map with the places and physical features of Europe. Write your answers on a separate sheet of paper.

1. British Isles
2. Rhine River
3. Sicily
4. Apennine Mountains
5. Danube River
6. Mediterranean Sea
7. Scandinavian Peninsula
8. Crete
9. Iberian Peninsula
10. Balkan Peninsula

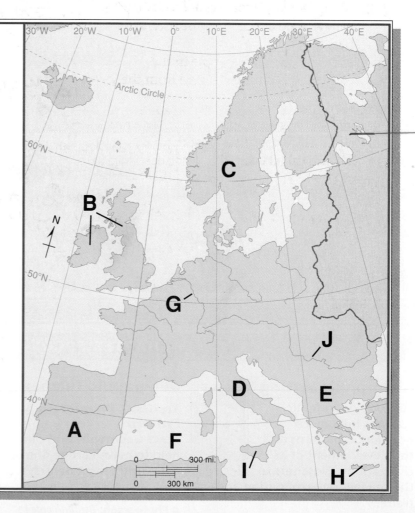

chapter 12

The Cultural Geography of Europe

CHAPTER FOCUS

Geographic Setting

Europe's geographic features influenced population patterns and the development of its civilizations. Closeness to the sea favored exploration and trade.

Geographic Themes

Section 1 Population Patterns
PLACE Geography and climate help to make Europe one of the world's most densely populated areas.

▲ **Photograph:** *Bustling cafe in Kraków, Poland*

Section 2 History and Government
MOVEMENT European culture has spread around the world.

Section 3 Cultures and Lifestyles
PLACE European lifestyles reflect many cultural differences.

Population Patterns

1

SETTING THE SCENE

Read to Discover . . .
- the differences and similarities among Europeans.
- how Europe's physical geography influences population distribution.
- why population patterns in Europe have changed.

Key Terms
- multicultural
- refugee

Identify and Locate
Spain, France, United Kingdom, Sweden, Belgium, Germany, Bosnia-Herzegovina, Vatican City, San Marino, Paris, London, Brussels

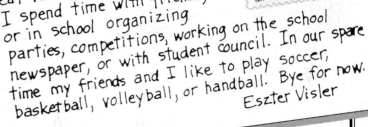

Balassagyarmat, Hungary

Szia! I live in Balassagyarmat, a town in Hungary. After school is finished for the day, I eat lunch. In the afternoon I spend time with friends, or in school organizing parties, competitions, working on the school newspaper, or with student council. In our spare time my friends and I like to play soccer, basketball, volleyball, or handball. Bye for now.

Eszter Visler

Eszter Visler's postcard reflects the typical lifestyle of a present-day European teenager. She comes from Hungary, a European nation that recently became a democracy after years of Communist rule. Hungary consists mainly of one ethnic group. Almost 95 percent of Hungarians are descended from the Magyars who settled the area in the late A.D. 800s. Other European nations, however, think of themselves as **multicultural**—having more than one culture. Europe is home to more than 30 countries, whose peoples speak some 50 different languages. In recent years, Europeans have been working toward unity. For centuries, however, conflict and competition have been far more characteristic. One of the challenges facing Europe today is dealing with the differences among its peoples.

Human Characteristics

Europe's diverse population reflects a long history of migrations throughout the continent. Most Europeans are descended from various Indo-European and Mediterranean peoples who settled the Continent centuries ago. Europe's population also includes more recent immigrants from Asia, Africa, and the Caribbean who arrived during this century.

European Differences

In some European countries, most people belong to the same ethnic group. For example, more than 90 percent of the people in Sweden are Swedes, descendants of Germanic and other groups that settled the Scandinavian Peninsula centuries ago. They share a common cultural background, the Swedish language, and the Lutheran religion. In other countries, the population consists of a few or a variety of different ethnic groups. Belgium, for example, has two leading ethnic groups—the Flemings and the Walloons. The Flemings make up about 55 percent of Belgium's population, and the Walloons make up about 30 percent. The Flemings are descendants of Germanic groups who invaded present-day Belgium during the A.D. 400s. The Walloons trace their ancestry to the Celts who lived in the area during the Germanic invasion. Flemings and Walloons share a common faith in Roman Catholicism, but language differences have led to bitter relations between them. Both groups, however, have managed to keep their disputes from endangering Belgium's national unity.

In other cases, however, tensions among European ethnic groups have led to violent conflict. In the early 1990s, the Balkan Peninsula became a battleground between ethnic groups in former Yugoslavia. Religious and ethnic differences among Serbs, Croats (KRO•atz), and Bosnian Muslims erupted in brutal warfare in newly independent Bosnia-Herzegovina. The Serbs, and to a lesser extent the Croats, carried out a policy they referred to as "ethnic cleansing" in which residents considered to be enemies were driven from their homes in captured areas. As a result, more than a million people became **refugees**—people who flee to a foreign country for safety.

Since the 1960s, large numbers of immigrants have arrived in western Europe. Some come from former European colonies; others come from less prosperous parts of the Continent. North Africans from the former French colonies of Morocco, Algeria, and Tunisia have migrated to France. Immigrants from former French colonies in Southeast Asia have also come to live and work in France. Germany and other countries in Central Europe have admitted large numbers of people from Turkey and Greece, as well as from former Yugoslavia. These immigrants were welcomed at first because western Europe had a labor shortage. In recent years, however, economic and cultural differences have led to increased tensions between "old" and "new" Europeans. As a result of attacks on Turks by extremist groups, Germany, in 1993, decided to place limits on the flow of immigrants.

Geographic Themes

Place: Sarajevo, Bosnia-Herzegovina
In the early 1990s, fighting among various ethnic groups reduced Sarajevo to a war zone. *What problems have the Bosnian people faced since independence?*

European Similarities

In spite of division and conflict, Europeans share several common attitudes and values. Most Europeans regard the family as the center of their social and economic lives. They also value the importance of the past and take pride in the cultural achievements of their ancestors. Most Europeans expect government to play an important role in running the economy of their nation and in providing for their welfare. These similarities make it increasingly possible for people to think of themselves as Europeans as well as members of ethnic or national groups.

PLACE

Population Distribution

Europe is smaller than any continent except Australia. Only Asia, however, has a larger population and is more densely populated than Europe. In the mid-1990s, Europe's population was about 514 million. Germany, with more than 81 million people, ranked as Europe's most heavily populated country. Vatican City, with about 1,000 people, had the smallest population of any country in the world.

If Europe's population were distributed evenly throughout the Continent, the average population density would be 264 people per square mile (102 people per sq. km). In Europe, of course, as in all other continents, the population is not distributed evenly. Most of Europe has far less than the average population density. Some parts of the Continent, however, are among the world's most densely populated areas.

Sparsely Populated Areas

Population distribution is closely related to physical geography. Compare the population density map on page 215 with the physical features map on page 216. Notice that mountainous regions are less populated than plains regions. For example, the population density in much of the Alpine mountain system is less than 60 persons per square mile (25 persons per sq. km). The rugged highlands of northern Scotland are another sparsely populated area.

Climate also plays a role in determining population density. Compare the population density map with the climate map on page 231. Notice that the dry, barren regions of the Iberian Peninsula have a sparse population. The most sparsely populated areas of Europe include parts of the Scandinavian Peninsula and Iceland. Subarctic and tundra climates make these regions nearly uninhabited.

Densely Populated Areas

Some European countries have a high population density because of their small sizes. For example, San Marino, a small country that is surrounded by Italy, covers only 20 square miles (52 sq. km). With a population of more than 20,000 people, San Marino has a population density of about 1,000 people per square mile (384 people per sq. km).

In general, the areas of Europe with average or higher than average population density share one or more of the following characteristics: favorable climate, plains, fertile soil, mineral resources, and inland waterways. One of the most densely populated parts of Europe extends from the United Kingdom into France and across the North European Plain into the Czech Republic and Poland. Another densely populated area extends from southeastern France into the Apennine Peninsula.

These regions contain some of the world's richest farmland. Although Europe's total agricultural area is less than half as large as that of North America, the total yearly production of European farms about equals that of North American farms. Europe's high crop yields, however, result from advanced farming techniques rather than a large number of farmers. Farming areas generally have fewer people than other parts of Europe's densely populated regions.

Industrialization and the location of mineral resources influenced population distribution in Europe. Urbanization is linked closely to industrialization. As a result of these two factors, the greatest concentration of Europe's people today live in and near its major cities.

Urbanization

Beginning in the late 1700s, the Industrial Revolution transformed Europe from an agricultural society to an industrial society. Between 1750 and 1900, many countries in western Europe became industrialized. Industrialization in eastern Europe increased rapidly after World War II but still lags behind western Europe.

By the early 1990s, about three-fourths of Europe's population lived in urban areas. According to the U. S. Bureau of the Census esti-

mates, 2 European cities—Paris and London —ranked among the world's 20 largest urban areas in 1994. Other European cities with large populations include Milan and Rome, Italy; Madrid and Barcelona, Spain; Essen and Berlin, Germany; Budapest, Hungary; and Athens, Greece.

Europe's large cities, like cities everywhere, face the challenges of overcrowding and pollution. In spite of these problems, European cities provide a unique combination of old and new ways of life. Landmarks that date back hundreds of years stand near fast-food restaurants and shopping malls.

Many Europeans oppose the modernization of their historic cities. In the early 1990s, massive development projects were undertaken in Brussels, Belgium. One reporter summarized public opinion about the changes:

---✦---

Brussels . . . is a pleasant city in which to live, even though much of its charm has been mauled by the new, modern, nondescript office buildings that have sprouted everywhere and are crowding out much that is Old World in a city that built its first, fortified walls in the 13th century.

---✦---

GeoFacts

What is the smallest country on earth?

MONACO

FRANCE

N

0 1/2 km
0 1/2 mi

Monte Carlo

Mediterranean Sea

0.6 SQ MI

SAN MARINO

0 2 km
0 2 mi

ITALY

San Marino

N

ITALY

20 SQ MI

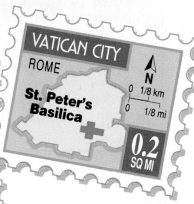

VATICAN CITY

ROME

N

0 1/8 km
0 1/8 mi

St. Peter's Basilica

0.2 SQ MI

MALTA

GOZO

COMINO

Mediterranean Sea

N

0 5 km
0 5 mi

Valleta

MALTA

120 SQ MI

LIECHTENSTEIN

AUSTRIA

0 2 km
0 2 mi

Vaduz

SWITZ.

N

60 SQ MI

Vatican City, at only 0.2 square miles (0.4 sq. km), is the world's tiniest country. It could fit within the U. S. Capitol grounds. Vatican City is one of Europe's "postage stamp" countries, so called because of their small size and their special stamps.

Though tiny dots on the map, some of these countries have a global reach. Vatican City is the center of the world's largest religious body, the Roman Catholic Church. Liechtenstein counts more companies than citizens; its banks have outlets from New York to Hong Kong. Andorra is a kind of Hong Kong of the Pyrenees, with duty-free shops attracting about 10 million tourists a year.

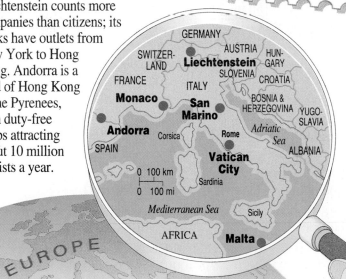

GERMANY

SWITZER-LAND

AUSTRIA

HUN-GARY

FRANCE

Liechtenstein

SLOVENIA

CROATIA

ITALY

Monaco

San Marino

BOSNIA & HERZEGOVINA

YUGO-SLAVIA

Andorra

Corsica

Adriatic Sea

SPAIN

Rome

ALBANIA

Vatican City

Sardinia

0 100 km
0 100 mi

Mediterranean Sea

Sicily

AFRICA

Malta

EUROPE

ANDORRA

FRANCE

N

Andorra La Vella

0 5 km
0 5 mi

SPAIN

185 SQ MI

Designed by BILL PITZER

SETTING THE SCENE

Read to Discover . . .
- how early civilizations developed in Europe.
- why European cultures had worldwide influence.
- what events led to the creation of the New Europe.

Key Terms
- city-state
- feudalism
- Crusades
- Renaissance
- Reformation
- communism
- Holocaust
- cold war

Identify and Locate
Greece, Roman Empire, Byzantine Empire, European Union

T hrough colonization, immigration, and trade, European civilization has had a powerful influence on world history. Europeans made great advances in learning and the arts as well as in science and technology.

MOVEMENT

The Development of European Civilizations

S cientific evidence suggests that early humans lived in Europe more than a million years ago. Prehistoric hunters, who lived in groups of 25 to 30 people, wandered from place to place in search of food. By about 6000 B.C., people in southeastern Europe had begun farming. Between the 300s B.C. and the A.D. 500s, great empires flourished in Europe. During the Middle Ages, major religions greatly influenced the development of European civilizations.

Early Peoples

A huge chinless jawbone with large teeth, discovered in Germany in 1907, led scientists to conclude that prehistoric people lived in that area about 650,000 years ago. A painting on a wall in a cave in Lascaux in southwestern France provides a record of prehistoric life in that area around 30,000 B.C. Clues such as these have helped anthropologists determine how and when civilizations began in Europe.

With the development of farming, early Europeans no longer had to move in search of food. Europe's first cities developed from some of these early farming villages. Between 6000 B.C. and 3000 B.C., farming spread from Southwest Asia to southeastern Europe and then to all but the dense northern forest regions of the Continent.

The first European civilization began on the Aegean Islands east of present-day Greece. Between 3000 B.C. and 1400 B.C., peoples in this region developed a system of writing. They became skilled craftworkers and traders who spread their way of life along the southern and western coasts of Europe.

The Classical World

Two later Mediterranean civilizations developed as models for the western world. The first was ancient Greece, which reached its peak during the 400s and 300s B.C. The Romans borrowed Greek ideas and added many contributions of their own to European civilization. The Roman Empire reached the height of its power between 27 B.C. and A.D. 180.

Geography played an important role in the development of Greek civilization. The mountainous landscape separated ancient Greeks in independent communities called **city-states**. Each city-state had its own way of life, but the Greeks were united by a common language and culture. Greek city-states established the first democratic governments. Except for women and enslaved persons, who could not vote, more people had a voice in these governments than in any earlier civilization. Greek art, literature, drama, and philosophy as well as mathematics and medicine spread across the Mediterranean world.

People called Etruscans (i•TRUHS•kuhnz) built a trading empire in Italy during the 800s B.C. Around 500 B.C., Rome, a city under Etruscan control, revolted and established a republic. By A.D. 117, Roman conquerors expanded their empire into half of Europe, much of the Middle East, and the north coast of Africa.

The Romans imitated Greek art and literature. They borrowed Greek science and architecture. Roman government, however, influenced many cultures. Roman engineers built a vast network of roads, aqueducts, and bridges throughout the empire.

Christianity became the official religion of the Roman Empire in A.D. 380. By the end of that century, the empire split into two parts—the West Roman Empire and the East Roman, or Byzantine, Empire. During the A.D. 400s, Germanic tribes from north of the West Roman Empire overthrew Roman rule in present-day Spain, Italy, France, and the United Kingdom. About a century later, Slavic peoples migrated from Ukraine into eastern and central Europe and the Balkan Peninsula. The Slavs lived in peace with the eastern Romans, or Byzantines. Over the next few centuries, the Slavs and Germans accepted Christianity and adopted aspects of Greek-Roman culture.

The Middle Ages

With the collapse of the West Roman Empire's government, western Europe entered the Middle Ages. During this period, from about A.D. 500 to 1500, **feudalism**—a system in which powerful lords gave land to nobles in

THE ROMAN EMPIRE, A.D. 117

Roman Empire
Conic projection

FOCUS ON GEOGRAPHIC THEMES

1. **Place:** What body of water did most of the Roman Empire's territory border?
2. **Location:** On what peninsula was the city of Rome located?
3. **Movement:** About how many miles separate Rome from Byzantium?

return for pledges of loyalty—replaced centralized government. The Roman Catholic Church, the western branch of Christianity, became the most powerful force in Europe. The Church introduced Roman government and justice to the Germanic peoples who had settled much of western Europe. Cathedrals and monasteries became the only centers of learning. Monks copied ancient Greek and Roman manuscripts.

The Byzantine Empire influenced the cultures of southeastern Europe and the Middle East spreading to Italy, Spain, and the north coast of Africa. The Byzantines preserved ancient Greek and Roman cultures. Eastern Orthodoxy, the Byzantine form of Christianity, spread as missionaries converted the Slavs in eastern Europe. In the 1000s, the Christian Church split into two separate bodies: the Roman Catholic Church and Eastern Orthodox Church.

Islam, a religion based on belief in one God, was preached by the prophet Muhammad in Arabia during the early A.D. 600s. The followers of Islam, known as Muslims, spread their religion through Southwest Asia, North

Geographic Themes

Place: France and Romania
France's Chartres Cathedral (left) and Romania's Moldovita monastery (right) reflect the Christian heritage of the Middle Ages. *What were the two major branches of Christianity during this time?*

Africa, and Spain, contributing much to the culture of Europe. Muslims spread the Chinese inventions of paper and gunpowder and the Hindu system of numerals and expanded mathematics, medicine, and astronomy. They developed distinctive Islamic arts and founded many universities.

MOVEMENT

The Spread of European Civilizations

Beginning in the 1000s, western European forces carried out the **Crusades**—a series of religious wars to win Palestine from Muslim rule. Europeans failed to win permanent control of the area but did extend trade routes to the eastern Mediterranean. The increased trade renewed European interest in other parts of the world. Beginning in the early 1300s, the **Renaissance**—a 300-year period of learning and the arts—brought about great advancements in European civilization.

Renaissance

During the Middle Ages, European culture centered around the powerful Roman Catholic Church. During the Renaissance, scholars and artists were influenced by the cultures of ancient Greece and Rome. They stressed the importance of people and their lives in the present world. Writers described human feelings, artists created lifelike paintings and sculptures, and architects designed nonreligious buildings.

A religious movement called the **Reformation** lessened the power of the Roman

Catholic Church and led to the beginnings of Protestantism. By the mid-1500s, separate Protestant churches were dominant in much of Europe.

The Renaissance and Reformation encouraged scientific advancements and world exploration. The invention of movable type in printing spread new ideas faster and easier.

Exploration

During the Middle Ages, Europe lagged behind China and the Islamic Empire in economic development. In the 1400s the Portuguese searched for new trade routes to Asia around Africa. Financed by Spain, the Italian explorer Christopher Columbus reached the Americas in the late 1400s. During the 1500s and 1600s, many European nations sent out exploration expeditions. They set up colonies in lands discovered by their explorers, often destroying the cultures already thriving there.

Trade with colonies in the Americas, Australia, Asia, and Africa brought great wealth and power to European nations. Trade also increased Europe's global influence.

A Changing Europe

By the early 1700s, wars and the building of empires had developed powerful European nations. During the next 200 years, however, economic and political revolutions swept the Continent. World wars changed the map of Europe as well as the balance of power in the world. By the 1990s, a new Europe had emerged.

Revolutions

The Industrial Revolution began in Great Britain in the 1700s and rapidly spread. Power-driven machinery and new methods of production transformed life in Europe. Industrial cities and improved transportation and communication developed. The Industrial Revolution also caused the growth of a prosperous middle class of merchants and factory owners. Factory workers, however, were poorly paid and lived under crowded, unhealthy conditions. These social problems in 1848 led to the birth of **communism**—an economic

Geographic Themes
Location: Venice, Italy
Venice was a major port and cultural center during the Middle Ages and the Renaissance. Today it is still an important city of Italy. *On what body of water is Venice located?*

Conflict and Division

In the first half of the 1900s, two major wars resulted in great changes in Europe. European competition for colonies and economic power, the desire for independence, and secret military alliances led to World War I. As a result of that war, from 1914 to 1918, several central and eastern European nations won independence.

Unresolved problems from World War I and a worldwide economic depression enabled dictators Adolf Hitler and Benito Mussolini to gain control of Germany and Italy. Following aggressive territorial expansion by these two nations, World War II broke out in 1939. After it ended in 1945, most of Europe and all but a few of the world's nations had been involved. One of the horrors of World War II was the **Holocaust**, the mass killing of 6 million European Jews and others by Germany's Nazi leaders.

World War II brought the downfall of Western Europe as the center of world power. Most Eastern European governments came under Communist control, creating the **cold war**— a power struggle between the Communist world, led by the Soviet Union, and the non-Communist world, led by the United States. A divided Germany became a symbol of the cold war conflict because of Communist East Germany and non-Communist West Germany.

During the cold war, governments in Eastern Europe and Western Europe differed significantly. Western Europe had a commitment to democracy and private ownership of the economy. In Eastern Europe, the Communist party allowed people little voice in government, the society, or the economy.

Cooperation and Unity

In the 1980s, reform movements swept Eastern Europe. People in Poland, Hungary, Czechoslovakia, East Germany, Romania, and Bulgaria demanded more freedom. In 1989 and 1990, free elections in many countries ended Communist control. In 1990, East and West Germany were united into a single, non-Communist nation.

Geographic Themes

Place: Buchenwald, Germany
Holocaust concentration camps, such as Buchenwald, were liberated by Allied armies at the end of World War II. The condition of the survivors shocked the liberators. *Who planned and carried out the Holocaust?*

and political system designed to establish classless societies in which workers would control industrial production.

People wanting a voice in the government began political revolutions in Europe. In the 1600s the English Parliament passed a Bill of Rights that limited the powers of the monarch. The French Revolution in 1789 made France a republic and spread the ideals of democracy. During the 1800s, uprisings took place in Spain, Italy, Greece, Belgium, and Poland. By 1900, most European nations had democratic constitutions that guaranteed some human rights.

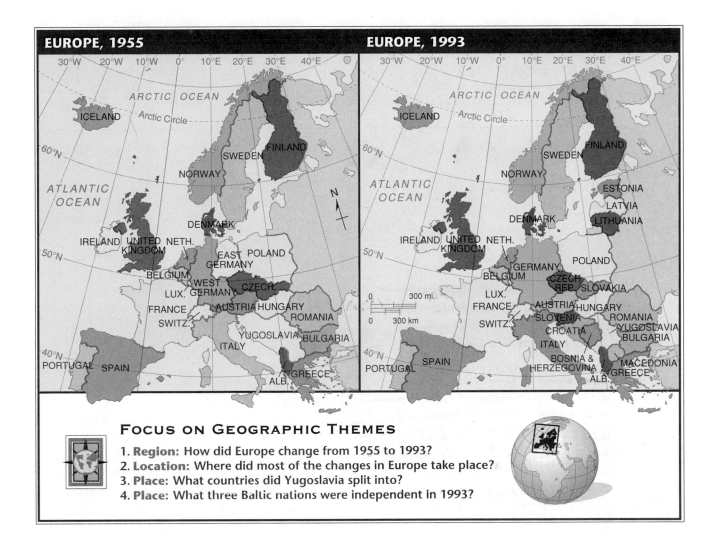

EUROPE, 1955

EUROPE, 1993

FOCUS ON GEOGRAPHIC THEMES

1. **Region:** How did Europe change from 1955 to 1993?
2. **Location:** Where did most of the changes in Europe take place?
3. **Place:** What countries did Yugoslavia split into?
4. **Place:** What three Baltic nations were independent in 1993?

Changes also occurred in Western Europe. Belgium, France, Italy, Luxembourg, the Netherlands, and West Germany in 1958 banded closer together in the European Community (EC)—an economic unit forming a single market for their resources. By 1990, Denmark, Ireland, the United Kingdom, Greece, Portugal, Spain, and the new united Germany had joined the others in the European Union. Turkey, Malta, and Cyprus were associate members.

The European Union worked to create a new Europe in which goods, services, workers, and money could move freely among countries. As a result, nations have increased their national incomes, total value of goods and services produced, and volume of trade. The opposition of some nations to a central all-European government, however, has blocked greater political and social unity.

SECTION 2 REVIEW

Checking for Understanding

1. **Define** city-state, feudalism, Crusades, Renaissance, Reformation, communism, Holocaust, cold war.
2. **Locating Places** What area had the Romans conquered by A.D. 117?
3. **Movement** How did Renaissance art differ from that of the Middle Ages?
4. **Movement** How did European cultures spread to other parts of the world?

Critical Thinking

5. **Expressing Problems Clearly** Why did the nations of Europe lack unity during the cold war era?

CHUNNEL VISION

As you read, examine how the Chunnel is expected to change Europe.

Chunnel
Major highways
Major railroads

Ramsgate
Deal
Cheriton
Dover
Folkestone
Strait of Dover
Calais
Boulogne

N

0   10 mi.
0   10 km

A Dream Come True

In 1993, the United Kingdom and France, separated for thousands of years by the English Channel, were once again "joined." Linking the island country to mainland Europe was the Channel Tunnel, nicknamed the Chunnel.

For many Europeans, the Chunnel represents a dream come true. The French in particular have worked for an under-the-seabed tunnel to the United Kingdom. On one occasion, the British actually began to dig. However, fear of military attack from the Continent halted construction.

In 1984, however, both the French and British governments agreed to connect the two nations. Eurotunnel, a private Anglo-French corporation, proposed the winning plan and raised money for construction.

In 1987, huge laser-guided, computerized boring machines called "moles" began digging, one from the French side, the other from the English side of the Channel. Digging was finished by mid-1991, and the three tunnels were open in 1993.

British and French workers celebrated completion of the Chunnel. It is hoped that the new Chunnel can offer a crucial economic link between the United Kingdom and the rest of Europe.

Far-Reaching Changes

The most obvious change the Chunnel brought is the length of time to travel between London and Paris. The trip took 6 hours by boat and train; now trains will speed through the Chunnel, covering the distance in half the time.

By the year 2003, the Chunnel is expected to carry more than 120,000 people between the United Kingdom and France each day. At night, tons of freight will move through it. The continental nations expect the Chunnel to allow the United Kingdom to fully join Europe.

Checking for Understanding

1. How does the Chunnel affect the geography of Europe?

2. **Human/Environment Interaction** What changes is the Chunnel expected to cause?

SETTING THE SCENE

Read to Discover . . .
- the differences and similarities among European languages, religions, and art forms.
- the quality of life in European countries.
- how European lifestyles reflect cultural traditions.

Key Terms
- dialect
- language family
- romanticism
- realism
- impressionism
- welfare state

Identify and Locate
Athens, Rome, Venice, Vienna, Language groups: Balto-Slavic, Germanic, Romance, Greek, Albanian, Celtic, Uralic

Differences in European ways of life were influenced by culture and tradition, economic development, and political systems. Rural people followed more traditional ways of life than urban people did. Industrialization and urbanization increased the gap between northern and southern Europe. Political factors produced different lifestyles in Eastern and Western Europe. People in Western Europe did not experience the limits placed on the artistic, economic, political, and social freedoms of people by Communist-controlled governments in Eastern European countries.

PLACE

Cultural Expressions

Language, religion, and art are culture traits—characteristics of a culture. Through these traits, people express their ideas and values. A study of European languages, religions, and art forms reveals some similarities and some differences.

Languages

In Europe there are about 50 different languages and more than a hundred **dialects**, or local forms of languages. Almost all these languages belong to the Indo-European language family. A **language family** is a group of related languages that developed from an earlier language.

The Indo-European family has three major branches in Europe. Most people in eastern Europe speak Balto-Slavic languages, which include Bulgarian, Czech, Polish, Slovak, and Serbo-Croatian. Most northern Europeans speak Germanic languages, such as Danish, English, German, Dutch, Norwegian, and Swedish. The Romance languages, spoken mostly in southern Europe, include French, Italian, Spanish, Portuguese, and Romanian. Other Indo-European branches are Greek, Albanian, and Celtic, which includes Irish Gaelic, Scots Gaelic, Welsh, and Breton. Basque, Finnish, and Hungarian are European languages that belong to the Uralic family.

Many European countries have one or more official languages, those recognized by the government, and other minority languages. Romanian is the official language in Romania, but Hungarian or German is also spoken. Switzerland has three official languages—German, French, and Italian. Almost 70 percent of the Swiss people, however, speak Swiss-German; and people in some eastern mountain valleys speak Romansch.

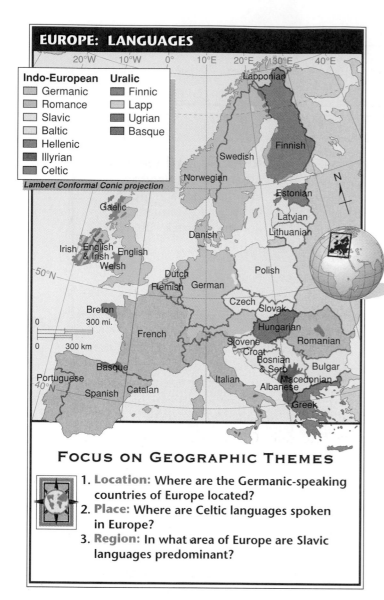

EUROPE: LANGUAGES

Indo-European
- Germanic
- Romance
- Slavic
- Baltic
- Hellenic
- Illyrian
- Celtic

Uralic
- Finnic
- Lapp
- Ugrian
- Basque

Lambert Conformal Conic projection

FOCUS ON GEOGRAPHIC THEMES

1. **Location:** Where are the Germanic-speaking countries of Europe located?
2. **Place:** Where are Celtic languages spoken in Europe?
3. **Region:** In what area of Europe are Slavic languages predominant?

Religions

Today some European countries are almost totally Christian (Roman Catholic, Protestant, or Eastern Orthodox) or Muslim. Others have a diversity of Christian and non-Christian faiths.

Most of Europe's Christians are Roman Catholics who live primarily in the southern areas of western Europe and the northern areas of eastern Europe. Protestantism is dominant in northern Europe, while Eastern Orthodoxy is strongest in the southern part of eastern Europe. Many Muslims live in Albania, Bosnia-Herzegovina, and Bulgaria; and Jews live in most European countries.

With the collapse of communism, religious freedom has been restored to many east European people.

Religious differences in Europe sometimes have resulted in violence. Recently, bitterness between Catholics and Protestants has caused conflict in Northern Ireland. Conflict between Christians and Muslims has played a role in the violent warfare in Croatia and Bosnia-Herzegovina.

Many historians believe that Christian ideas and values encouraged economic, political, and scientific developments and art forms in Europe.

The Arts

The art of Europe reflects its history as well as the ideas and values of its people and cultures, which have spread around the world. Europe's churches and temples show the development of architecture and major religions. The Parthenon in Athens and the Pantheon in Rome are examples of temples built by ancient Europeans. The cathedral in Cordoba, Spain, shows the influence of the Moors who spread Islam to Spain. The Basilica of St. Mark in Venice, Italy, and the Church of the Holy Apostles in Salonika, Greece, are examples of Byzantine art that reflect the spread of Eastern Orthodox beliefs. Notre Dame Cathedral in Paris is an example of Gothic architecture, which flourished from the mid-1100s to the 1400s. This style of construction enabled builders to substitute stained-glass windows for large portions of the walls.

During the Renaissance, European artists began to deal with everyday subjects as well as religious themes. The works of Leonardo da Vinci and Michelangelo Buonarotti influenced generations of artists.

After the Renaissance new art forms emerged. Opera and symphony developed in Europe during the 1600s and 1700s. **Romanticism** developed in Europe in the late 1700s and early 1800s. This artistic style tried to show feelings and emotions. **Realism**—an artistic style that tried to portray life as it really was—developed during the mid-1800s. It was followed later in the century by French **Impressionism**—a style that showed the natural appearance of objects and light using dabs or strokes of primary colors.

Artists in the 1900s searched for new forms and styles. Sculptures and paintings became more abstract. A European artist who influenced modern art was the Spanish painter Pablo Picasso. In architecture, the Bauhaus school of design in Germany was influential worldwide.

REGION

Quality of Life

In general, Europeans who live in urban areas or in northern and western regions have a higher standard of living than those who live in rural areas or in southern and eastern regions. Literacy rate, life expectancy, and health care also indicate a region's quality of life.

Education

Respect for education is a traditional European value. The quality of education in Europe, whose people are among the world's best educated, is linked to the economy. Nations with a high standard of living can afford to improve schools and provide specialized training for students. Very few European nations have literacy rates below 90 percent.

The number of years of compulsory, or required, school attendance varies from country to country. In Portugal children must attend school for only 6 years. The United Kingdom requires 12 years of schooling. Some European school systems provide preparation for college or vocational training.

Europe has some of the world's finest universities, several of which date from the Middle Ages. Europe's famous schools include Cambridge and Oxford in England; the University of Bologna in Italy; the University of Heidelberg in Germany; the University of Vi-

enna in Austria; Jagiellonian University in Kraków, Poland; and the Sorbonne, or the University of Paris, in France.

Health Care

Good nutrition and health care have given Europeans high life expectancies. The 1993 average life expectancy for all Europeans was 69.3 years for men and 76.9 years for women, the highest of any continent. Western European countries have a high average infant survival rate of 992 per 1,000, with eastern Europe's rate slightly lower.

One measure of health care is the ratio of population to doctors in a nation. In the world, the ratio is 740 people per doctor. In Europe, the average is 300 people per doctor.

Almost all European governments subsidize, or help pay for, health-care services. Some countries have a national health insurance that provides complete tax-supported medical care. Other countries provide more limited low-cost medical care through taxes.

The Role of Government

European governments generally play a major role in their nations' economies. They may operate airlines, railroads, electric companies, telephone companies, and other public services.

Most European governments provide some social welfare programs. In **welfare states**, such as the United Kingdom, Norway, and Sweden, the government assumes major responsibility for the welfare of its people. In the United Kingdom, for example, a child's elementary, high school, and often, university education is paid for by the government. In Norway, the government guarantees all employed people an annual four-week paid vacation and rent aid if they have more than one child. In Sweden, every family receives an allowance for each child under 16 and for secondary school or university students. Newlyweds can obtain government loans for home furnishings. Single parents with low incomes receive allowances for family vacations.

Europe: Religions

Roman Catholic	262,026,000
Protestant	73,766,000
Orthodox	36,080,000
Other Christian*	40,918,000
Jewish	1,466,000
Muslim	12,545,000
Nonreligious	69,825,000
Other religions	1,466,000

*mainly Anglican (Church of England)
Source: *World Almanac,* 1993

Orthodox 7.2%
Protestant 14.8%
Other Christian* 8.2%
Roman Catholic 52.4%
Muslim 2.5%
Nonreligious 14.0%
Jewish 0.3%
Other religions 0.6%

PLACE

Lifestyles

Cultural and economic differences have produced a wide variety of lifestyles in Europe. But these differences have diminished as industrialization has brought a more common culture to many places. Many Hungarian farm families live in small stucco houses with tile roofs. The Lapps, a nomadic people in northern Scandinavia, for six months of the year live in cone-shaped tents and move frequently in search of food for their reindeer herds.

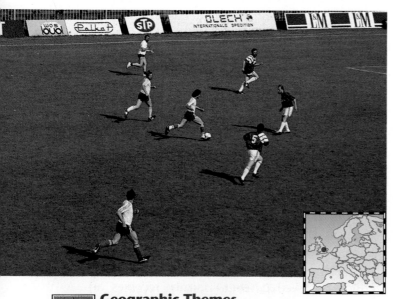

Geographic Themes

Place: London, United Kingdom
Athletic events, especially soccer matches, draw large crowds in Europe, and fans passionately root for their local teams. *What other recreational activities do Europeans enjoy?*

Home Life

In most European cultures, life centers around the extended family. Even when young people move away from home, they often maintain close family ties.

By the 1980s, many European women had begun to work outside the home. In the early 1990s, 42 percent of the workforce in Europe consisted of women. According to a survey in 1991, more than half of Europeans took a vacation at least once a year. July and August were the most popular vacation months, and seaside resorts were popular destinations.

Sports and Recreation

Soccer is the national sport in Europe, and many countries have professional soccer leagues. Rugby football also is a popular team sport, especially in the United Kingdom, France, and Ireland. Many Europeans play tennis for recreation, and the British tournament at Wimbledon is a major championship.

Communist governments in Eastern Europe required schoolchildren to play sports. Those with special talent were enrolled in rigorous sports training programs which produced many Olympic champions.

Many Europeans enjoy outdoor activities. Skiing and other winter sports are popular in the Alpine regions. Swimming, rowing, and hiking are favorite pastimes in many parts of Europe. Many young people take bicycling or hiking trips throughout Europe and spend the nights at inexpensive inns called youth hostels.

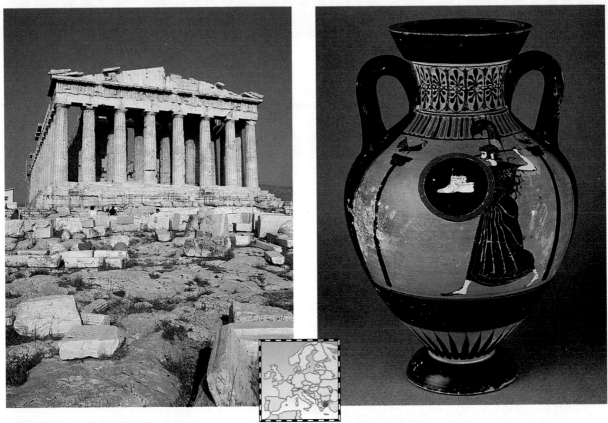

The ancient Greeks built the Parthenon and fashioned beautiful pottery. *What other ancient people set standards of cultural excellence in the Mediterranean region of Europe?*

Celebrations

European celebrations include family gatherings for special occasions. Traditional celebrations include eating special foods, wearing national costumes, and performing folk dances. Greeks celebrate Easter with a lamb feast. On Swedish St. Lucia Day, December 13, young girls dressed in white awaken their families with hot coffee and buns. In Poland, the Christmas celebration includes breaking and eating an *oplatek*—a thin wafer made of wheat flour and water.

Most European countries celebrate festivals to honor historical events. For example, Bastille Day, celebrated in France on July 14, commemorates the storming of Bastille prison in 1789 and the start of the French Revolution. A military parade, street dancing, and fireworks mark the occasion throughout the country.

SECTION 3 REVIEW

Checking for Understanding

1. **Define** dialect, language family, romanticism, realism, impressionism, welfare state.
2. **Locating Places** What are three European countries that are welfare states?
3. **Region** In what ways has religion both unified and divided Europe?
4. **Place** How do European festivals reflect cultural traditions?

Critical Thinking

5. **Predicting Consequences** Are recent political and economic developments in Europe likely to produce greater similarities or differences in ways of life? Why do you think so?

STUDY AND WRITING SKILLS

Writing a Topic Sentence

Writing is a basic survival skill in today's society. In school, you must write reports and answer essay questions. Some college applications require an essay about your goals and background. As adults, you may have to write letters for a wide range of business problems, such as applying for jobs and complaining about faulty products or poor services. Although typewriters and computers can simplify the mechanics of writing, you still must master the art of writing clear, readable prose.

REVIEWING THE SKILL

Most prose writing is divided into paragraphs. A *paragraph* is a group of sentences that develop a single main idea. In most paragraphs, a *topic sentence* states the main idea.

Although the topic sentence often appears at the beginning of a paragraph, it may appear at the end or within the paragraph. Sometimes, a paragraph has no topic sentence directly stating its main idea. Instead, the main idea is implied by the material in the other sentences.

To write a topic sentence, apply the following steps:

- Read the paragraph to identify its main idea.
- Reread the paragraph sentence by sentence. For each sentence, ask yourself: "Would the other sentences tie together and make sense without this sentence?" If the answer to the question is no, then you have probably identified the topic sentence stating the main idea.
- If the paragraph has no topic sentence, write a sentence stating the paragraph's main idea.
- Reread the entire paragraph. Be sure that each sentence directly relates to and supports the main idea stated in the topic sentence.

PRACTICING THE SKILL

Read the following paragraphs. Write a topic sentence for each paragraph. Topic sentences may or may not appear in the paragraphs.

1. Europeans share several common values. Most Europeans regard the family as the center of their social and economic lives. They also value the past and take pride in the achievements of their ancestors. Most Europeans expect government to play an important role in providing for their welfare.

2. For centuries, scientific ideas and principles had been held to be true because the Greek philosopher Aristotle had said they were true. At first Renaissance thinkers substituted the Greek physician Galen's authority for Aristotle's. But in pitting one authority against another, they opened a door to freedom. As the 1500s progressed, people began to base scientific truths on observation and experimentation.

3. My eyes delighted in the architecture of Prague. The city has been beautifully restored. Prague is a rich city, not merely in relics of the Habsburg monarchs, but in a contemporary prosperity. The Czech economy is a little shaky nowadays, but it does not show in the cafés stocked with pastries and cakes.

For additional practice in this skill, see Practicing Skills on page 259 of the Chapter 12 Review.

SECTION	KEY TERMS	SUMMARY
1 Population Patterns	multicultural (p. 239) refugee (p. 240)	• The diversity of Europe's population reflects a history of migrations throughout the Continent. • Europe's physical features, climate, and resources influenced population distribution. • As a result of industrialization, nearly three-fourths of Europe's population lives in urban areas.

War-ravaged Sarajevo, Bosnia-Herzegovina

SECTION	KEY TERMS	SUMMARY
2 History and Government	city-state (p. 245) feudalism (p. 245) Crusades (p. 246) Renaissance (p. 246) Reformation (p. 246) communism (p. 247) Holocaust (p. 248) cold war (p. 248)	• Greek and Roman civilizations served as models for the western world. • Scientific advancements during the Renaissance made it possible for Europeans to explore distant parts of the world. • European civilization spread to other continents through trade, colonization, and immigration. • After World War II, Europe became the center of the cold war, which divided Communist-controlled Eastern Europe from non-Communist Western Europe. • The European Union promotes economic unity among the nations of Europe.

Grand Canal in Venice, Italy

SECTION	KEY TERMS	SUMMARY
3 Cultures and Lifestyles	dialect (p. 251) language family (p. 251) romanticism (p. 252) realism (p. 252) impressionism (p. 253) welfare state (p. 253)	• Differences in European ways of life reflect culture and tradition, economic development, and political systems. • Most European governments play a major role in providing for the welfare of their citizens. • Industrialization and urbanization have diminished differences in European lifestyles.

Reviewing Key Terms

Choose the vocabulary term that best completes each of the sentences below. Write your answers on a separate sheet of paper.

- refugees (p. 240)
- city-states (p. 245)
- feudalism (p. 245)
- Renaissance (p. 246)
- communism (p. 247)
- Holocaust (p. 248)
- cold war (p. 248)
- dialect (p. 251)
- romanticism (p. 252)
- impressionism (p. 253)
- welfare states (p. 253)

SECTION 1

1. _____ are people who flee to a foreign country for safety.

SECTION 2

2. The mass killing of 6 million European Jews in World War II is known as the _____ .
3. After World War II, _____ became the dominant political movement in Eastern Europe.
4. Ancient Greeks settled in independent communities called _____ .
5. The _____ was a period of renewed interest in learning that brought advancements in European arts.
6. The _____ refers to the power struggle between the Soviet Union and the United States.
7. A system in which powerful lords gave land to nobles in return for pledges of loyalty was known as _____ .

SECTION 3

8. The term _____ refers to a local form of a language.
9. Artists influenced by _____ tried to show emotions in their work.

10. In _____ , governments assume major responsibility for education and health care.
11. _____ emphasized the natural appearance of objects and light.

Reviewing Facts

SECTION 1
12. Which parts of Europe are most densely populated?

SECTION 2
13. What were some accomplishments of ancient Greek civilization?

SECTION 3
14. How do European governments provide for the welfare of their people?

Critical Thinking

15. **Drawing Conclusions**   What similarities create the strongest connections among Europeans?
16. **Analyzing Information**   How did religion influence the development of Europe during the Middle Ages?
17. **Making Generalizations**   How has urbanization diminished differences among European lifestyles?

Geographic Themes

18. **Movement**   How did the Industrial Revolution change population patterns in Europe?
19. **Movement**   How did the Crusades and the Renaissance encourage the spread of European civilization?
20. **Region**   How does the quality of life differ in urban/rural, northern/southern, eastern/western regions of Europe?

▼ Practicing Skills

Writing a Topic Sentence

Refer to the skills activity on page 256. What is the topic sentence in the first paragraph of the skills activity?

Using the Unit Atlas

Refer to the cultural geography section of the Unit Atlas on pages 214–215.

21. What nation divided after World War II was reunited in 1990?

22. When and where were the first Olympics held?

Projects

Individual Activity

Make a chart of some simple words common to many languages such as days of the week or numbers. Refer to a dictionary to find the origin of language for each. Write a generalization about European languages.

Cooperative Learning

Form small groups. Choose one era in European history such as Classical Civilizations, Renaissance, or 20th Century. Each group member should research three events related to the topic. Plot all the events on a time line to create an overview of European history.

Writing About Geography

Cause and Effect

Using your journal record and other references, write an essay explaining the factors that helped spread European civilization to other parts of the world. Include the role of geography and be as specific as possible.

Locating Places

**EUROPE:
EUROPEAN UNION**

Match the letters on the map with the names of members of the European Union. Write your answers on a separate sheet of paper.

1. Belgium
2. France
3. Italy
4. Luxembourg
5. Netherlands
6. Denmark
7. Ireland
8. United Kingdom
9. Greece
10. Portugal
11. Spain
12. Germany

European Union Members

chapter 13

Europe Today

CHAPTER FOCUS

Geographic Setting

The physical closeness of European nations creates shared responsibility for the causes of pollution and the problems involved in cleanup.

Geographic Themes

Section 1 Living in Europe
REGION The European Union and the nations of eastern Europe adjusted to changing economies in the early 1990s.

▲ Photograph: *Port at Barcelona, Spain*

Section 2 People and Their Environment
HUMAN/ENVIRONMENT INTERACTION Acid rain, air pollution, and water pollution affect Europe's environment and economy.

Munich, Germany

Golt mitnander. I'm excited because today my sister and I will go for a train trip on the new ICE (Intercity Express Train) to visit our uncle in Esslingen. We'll also look around in Stuttgart, but we'll use underground transportation in order to avoid heavy city traffic. On Monday, Uncle Hans will show us around in the Mercedes-Benz plant where he works as a technical engineer.

Tschüs

Rebekka Prapler

Rebekka Prapler describes the ease of travel in Germany, Europe's most economically powerful country. Since World War II, most Europeans have experienced rising standards of living and have had greater opportunity to travel at home and abroad. Meanwhile, Europe's diverse nationalities and ethnic groups have taken steps toward greater continental unity. In spite of this progress, national antagonisms still remain to trouble Europe's political life.

The economies of Europe, like its populations, are diverse and changing. More than half the land in Europe is used for farming. Europe also has 5 of the world's top 10 manufacturing nations. The European Union (EU) is a major economic unit with a greater volume of trade than any one country in the world. Eastern European economies are undergoing major changes as their governments adapt to growing democracy and economic reform.

REGION

Changing Economies

While the 12 nations of the European Union took steps toward economic unity in the early 1990s, eastern European nations struggled to adjust to free enterprise. Both regions experienced the realization that change is difficult. Their peoples looked to the dawning of the 21st century in a mood of hope mixed with concern.

European Union

In 1950 France proposed closer links among Europe's coal and steel industries. The move was seen as a first step toward a united Europe. Over the years more steps were taken toward that goal, but not until the 1990s did most Europeans agree that such a goal could be reached.

Different traditions and points of view, however, made unity within the European Union difficult to achieve. Members defeated the proposal for a single European currency, but most of the proposed single-market measures were adopted into law. Results, however, failed to meet expectations. Forecasters had predicted overall economic growth, but Europe—along with the rest of the industrialized world—plunged into a recession.

In an effort to make their products competitive in a world market, many European companies cut costs by cutting jobs. Some economists proposed that governments also reduce or eliminate costly social welfare programs. Many Europeans oppose such measures, which they think would only increase hardships during a time of rising unemployment. The European Union continues to work toward the goal of a stronger single economy in spite of the difficulties brought on by change.

Eastern Europe

For more than 40 years, Communist governments closely tied to the Soviet Union controlled Eastern European industries. Central planners made all decisions about what goods to produce and how to produce them. Industries generally employed many more workers and managers than they needed. Many factories lacked modern technology, such as automation, pollution controls, and energy conservation equipment.

To compete in a free market economy, eastern European industries must overcome the obstacles of outdated equipment and inefficient methods. Many workers must be laid off or retrained. Industries need to build new facilities with modern technology and adopt energy conservation methods to reduce pollution. The new democratic governments are seeking investments and financial aid from western Europe as well as from other parts of the world. Eastern Europeans have realized that change is costly as well as difficult.

THE EUROPEAN UNION

Members of the European Union, 1993

Lambert Conformal Conic projection

DENMARK
IRELAND
UNITED KINGDOM
NETH.
GERMANY
BELGIUM
LUX.
FRANCE
PORTUGAL
SPAIN
ITALY
GREECE

300 mi.
300 km

FOCUS ON GEOGRAPHIC THEMES

1. **Region:** What countries are members of the European Union?
2. **Location:** Where are most of the Union's member countries located?
3. **Place:** What two European Union members are island nations?

REGION

Agriculture and Industry

Europe has some of the world's most fertile and productive farmland. Many European farmers use advanced scientific methods and farming equipment. They annually add fertilizers to the soil and plant a variety of crops to maintain the land's fertility.

More Europeans earn a living from farming than from any other single economic activity. The percentages of workers engaged in farming varies dramatically from one country to another, however. In highly industrialized countries, such as the United Kingdom and Belgium, less than 2 percent of the labor force works in agriculture. In Poland and Greece, almost 30 percent of the labor force is engaged in farming.

Economic Expansion

Europe is the birthplace of modern industry. Beginning in the late 1700s, the Industrial Revolution helped lay the foundation of Europe's economic growth and global influence. The increased productivity and lower costs brought by the use of machines slowly raised European living standards. Meanwhile, as markets at home and abroad expanded, several European countries became leading industrial centers of the world.

The development of industry is often linked to the availability of raw materials. In the 1800s and early 1900s, the largest coal and iron-ore deposits in Europe provided bases for the growth of **heavy industry**—the manufacture of machinery and equipment needed for factories and mines. Today, a series of large-scale industrial areas now stretch from the United Kingdom to Poland. These industrial centers include the Ruhr and Middle Rhine districts in Germany, the Lorraine-Saar district in France, the Po Basin in Italy, and the Upper Silesia-Moravia district in Poland and the Czech Republic. Vast deposits of mineral wealth have helped to make such nations as France and Germany leaders in manufacturing.

Nations lacking industrial raw materials, such as the Netherlands and Denmark, specialize in **light industry**, such as textiles or food processing. Service industries employ a large percentage of the workforce in most European nations. Switzerland, for example, has prospered from banking and finance.

Geographic Themes

Place: Stuttgart, Germany
Coal, iron, and steel have made Germany's Ruhr and Middle Rhine districts leading industrial centers. *Where are most of Europe's industrial centers located?*

Food Production

Europe leads the world in the production of barley, oats, potatoes, rye, and sugar beets. Wheat, the major grain crop, grows in most European nations. Citrus fruits, dates, and figs grow in the Mediterranean region. Nations in that region also produce most of the world's olives. Grapes grown in southern Europe are used to make much of the world's wine. Dairy farming is important in Denmark, the United Kingdom, and the Netherlands. Some of the world's finest breeds of cattle and sheep are raised in western Europe.

Europeans generally produce most of their own food supply. Imports consist mostly of tropical foods, such as cocoa and coffee. Nations that specialize in a few farm products trade among themselves for the foods they need. In addition to farming, the European fishing industry provides an important part of the Continent's food. Denmark and Norway rank among the world's leading fishing nations.

Farming Techniques

Soil and climate play a major role in determining the kinds and amounts of crops produced in a region. European farmers also have found ways to make the best use of their limited agricultural area. Farmers rely on **organic farming**—the use of natural substances to enrich the soil—as well as chemical fertilizers to increase crop yields. **Mixed farming**—raising several kinds of crops and livestock on the same farm—is common practice in parts of western Europe. Most farmers in western Europe own their land, and the average farm covers about 30 acres (12.2 ha). In Belgium and the United Kingdom, many farmers rent their land from private land owners. **Farm cooperatives**—organizations in which farmers share in growing and selling farm products—help farmers reduce their costs and increase profits.

Farming, like other aspects of life in eastern Europe, has undergone change in recent times. Under Communist control, all farms were owned by the government. On **collective farms**, the farmers received wages plus a share of products and profits. **State farms** were managed by government officials, and farmers did not share in the profits. Outdated farm machinery and methods, combined with a lack of incentive, resulted in poor crop yields. With the growth of democracy in the region, countries have begun to encourage private control of agricultural production and private ownership of the land.

Manufacturing

France, the United Kingdom, Italy, Poland, and Germany rank among the world's leaders in manufacturing. These nations are among the leading steel producers and automobile manufacturers in the world. Switzerland is noted for the high quality of its watches and other precision instruments. The Czech Republic and Poland are major manufacturers of machinery and chemicals.

In western Europe, most industries are privately owned. In eastern Europe, however, state-owned industries under the former Communist governments, emphasized heavy industry. As a result, few factories in Communist countries produced **consumer goods**—household goods, shoes, and clothing that individuals buy. In recent years, factories have switched to private ownership. Foreign companies have begun to buy or start new businesses in this region. Changing conditions have resulted in high prices and unemployment as eastern European governments struggle to stabilize their economies.

Services and Trade

Service industries employ nearly 60 percent of the labor force in western European countries. International banking and insurance rank among Europe's top service industries. Switzerland and the United Kingdom are leaders in these fields. Belgium serves as the headquarters for hundreds of international companies.

Tourism is another large service industry in Europe. The United Kingdom, France, Spain, Germany, Switzerland, Italy, and Austria are among the world's leading tourist nations. Barriers to travel among European nations

THE EUROPEAN UNION'S SHARE IN WORLD TRADE

Exports: 20.7% 12.1% 13.3% 53.9%

Imports: 19.7% 7.5% 20.3% 52.5%

- European Union
- Japan
- United States
- All Other Countries

CHART STUDY

The European Union commands large shares of the world's trade. *What is the European Union's share of exports? Of imports?*

generally have been eliminated. People living in the European Union can travel freely among member nations. The collapse of communism in eastern Europe resulted in the removal of travel barriers in that region as well.

European Union members no longer pay a **tariff**, or tax, on goods traded among themselves. This policy encouraged bargain hunters to seek the best buys on consumer goods in neighboring countries. The single-market economy of the EU has made it the world's largest importer and exporter.

Before 1989, most Eastern European countries belonged to the Council for Mutual Economic Assistance (COMECON). Members of COMECON traded primarily among themselves for needed goods. For example, Romania traded coal to Czechoslovakia in exchange for manufactured goods. Since eastern European nations have switched to market economies, trade with other nations has increased.

EUROPE: ECONOMIC ACTIVITY

Legend:
- Nomadic herding
- Forestry
- Commercial farming
- Subsistence farming
- Manufacturing and trade
- Commercial fishing

Lambert Conformal Conic projection

FOCUS ON GEOGRAPHIC THEMES

1. **Location:** Where does most of Europe's manufacturing and trade occur?
2. **Place:** What is the major form of economic activity in Portugal?
3. **Region:** In what area of Europe is forestry a major industry?

Communication and Transportation

Almost all of Europe's communication and transportation systems are government-owned. Although the quality varies from one region to another, these systems are among the best in the world. Modern communications systems link most parts of Europe with each other and with other parts of the world. Networks of highways, railways, waterways, and airline routes crisscross the Continent.

Communication Links

Many European nations belong to the International Telecommunications Satellite Organization (Intelsat). This international system uses communications satellites for the worldwide broadcast and reception of television programs. A television network called *Eurovision* links most western European countries, and a similar network called *Intervision* operates in eastern Europe. These net- works sometimes exchange television programs.

Telephone service varies throughout the Continent. France, for example, has one telephone for every two people. The Czech Republic has one telephone for every four people, and in Poland the ratio is one telephone for every eight people. Within the European Union, rates generally are high and vary greatly from one government-owned telephone company to another. A call from Spain to Denmark, for example, costs twice as much as a call from Denmark to Spain.

Books, magazines, and newspapers are published throughout Europe. The growth of democracy has reduced or eliminated government censorship of printed materials in eastern European countries. Many Europeans read daily newspapers. Sweden, with about 570 copies sold daily for every 1,000 people, leads the world in newspaper readership. Some European newspapers, such as *The Times* of London and *Le Monde* of Paris, are read by people in many parts of the world.

Highways and Railways

A well-developed system of highways and roads links all major cities in Europe. Germany's four-lane superhighways, called *autobahnen*, are among Europe's best roads. Bridges and tunnels carry traffic over or through the barriers posed by physical features. For example, the St. Gotthard Road Tunnel cuts through the Alps in central Switzerland. It is 10.14 miles (16.32 km) long, which makes it one of the world's longest road tunnels.

There are more automobile owners in Europe than in any other part of the world except the United States. The percentage of car owners is greater in western Europe than in eastern Europe. Bicycles and motorcycles provide popular forms of transportation for many Europeans.

Trucks carry much of the freight in many western European countries. France, the United Kingdom, Germany, Spain, Italy, and Belgium rely on trucks for transporting goods. Road signs make use of pictures and symbols instead of words so that travelers from any country can understand traffic instructions.

Europe has about one-fourth of the total railroad trackage in the world. Railroads are a major means of freight and passenger transportation throughout the Continent. In eastern Europe, railroads provide the link between areas rich in natural resources and major industrial centers. Rail lines connect almost all the Continent's major cities. Railroad stations provide easy access to downtown and suburban areas. Tunnels carry rail traffic through Europe's mountains.

France's *trains á grande vitesse* (TGVs), which means "very fast trains," are the fastest in the world. TGVs travel at an average speed of 170 miles (270 km) per hour, but they can reach a top speed of 235 miles (380 km) per hour. Powered by smokeless, silent electricity, TGVs are much less harmful to the environment than are most other forms of transportation. Relatively low fares make TGVs more economical as well as more efficient than airline travel.

Major Transportation Centers

Most of Europe's major cities are railroad centers. Many of them have major airports as well. Airports in London, Frankfurt, Paris, Rome, Amsterdam, Stockholm, Zurich, Copenhagen, and Munich rank among the busiest in the world. European airlines fly throughout the Continent, but much of Europe's air traffic consists of international flights.

Europe handles more than half the world's international shipping. The Continent's long coastline influenced the seafaring tradition of many countries. Most of the world's largest merchant fleets belong to European countries. Europe also has many bustling ports. These include London; Rotterdam, in the Netherlands; Antwerp, Belgium; Genoa, Italy; Le Havre and Marseilles, France; and Gdansk, Poland.

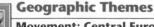

Geographic Themes

Movement: Central European Superhighways
Germany has about 3,900 miles (6,500 km) of four-lane superhighways. *What major physical obstacle has been overcome in building highways in central Europe?*

Waterways

Europe's rivers and canals form an important transportation system. Waterways carry passenger traffic, but they are more important for transporting freight. The Rhine River and its tributaries carry a greater volume of freight than any other river system in Europe. The Rhine River provides access to the North Sea for industrial centers in Switzerland, France, Belgium, Germany, and the Netherlands.

Canals link Europe's major waterways. For example, the Kiel Canal cuts across the part of Germany that occupies the Jutland Peninsula and shortens the route between the North Sea and the Baltic Sea. Canals also connect the Oder and the Vistula rivers in Poland and provide links between the Oder River and rivers in western Europe. The Main-Danube Canal in Germany links hundreds of inland ports from the North Sea to the Black Sea. The ambitious project, completed in 1992, sparked much controversy. Some people think that the amount of trade on the canal will not meet expectations. They consider the Main-Danube Canal an "extravagant folly." Environmentalists argue that construction of the canal upset the balance of nature in Bavaria's Altmuhl Valley. Reinhard Grebe, landscape architect for the canal, defends his plan to preserve the natural beauty of the region:

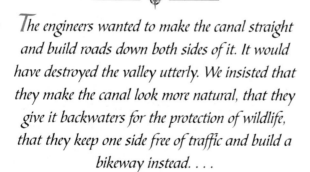

The engineers wanted to make the canal straight and build roads down both sides of it. It would have destroyed the valley utterly. We insisted that they make the canal look more natural, that they give it backwaters for the protection of wildlife, that they keep one side free of traffic and build a bikeway instead. . . .

The long-range economic impact of the Main-Danube Canal remains unknown. The extraordinary effort to make the canal fit the landscape, however, expresses Europeans' growing concern for their environment.

Geographic Themes

Movement: France's Rail System
The French rail network, including the famous TGV lines, forms a cobweb pattern with Paris as the hub. *Why are the TGVs much less harmful to the environment than other trains?*

SECTION 1 REVIEW

Checking for Understanding
1. **Define** heavy industry, light industry, organic farming, mixed farming, farm cooperative, collective farm, state farm, consumer goods, tariff.
2. **Locating Places** What two major bodies of water does the Main-Danube Canal link?
3. **Region** From what economic activity do most Europeans earn a living?
4. **Movement** Why are railroads a major means of transportation in Europe?

Critical Thinking
5. **Making Comparisons** How do the problems of forming a single-market economy in the European Union differ from those of adjusting to free enterprise in eastern Europe?

PROTECTING THE NETHERLANDS

I was here about 18 years ago, going through this new land, and I couldn't believe my eyes. I realized what had been accomplished, but seeing all this virgin country with the soil very bumpy and the steam actually coming out of it like primeval land was like witnessing the dawn of creation. Just incredible. . . . To see it now in its final form is a miracle, really. Nowhere else in the world can you see something like this.

Hank Fisher in *Sea Frontiers* May-June 1989

On the night of February 1, 1953, a raging Atlantic sea storm roared toward the European coastline, pushing a storm surge before it. Hitting the English Channel, the surge had nowhere to go. It coupled with the heavy spring tide of the North Sea, forming a 15-foot-high (4.6 m) wall of water. The frothing waves crashed over and through the dikes and dams of Zeeland Province in the southwest corner of the Netherlands. Engulfing the entire area, the surge killed nearly 2,000 people and thousands of animals and livestock, washed away some 50,000 homes, and destroyed thousands of acres of farmland.

To protect Holland "once and for all" from other such tragedies, the Dutch set up the Delta Works Project. The project called for building barriers to seal off and protect the inlets of Holland's southwestern coast.

THE ISSUE

The Dutch planned to seal off three of the four Rhine-Maas tributaries that empty into the sea through Holland's southwestern corner. The fourth tributary would remain open, so that the shipping port of Antwerp would not be disrupted.

As construction progressed during the 1960s and 1970s, however, conservationists increasingly raised objections to closing off the third tributary. Its unique environment is a rich breeding ground for fish as well as an abundant source of mussels and oysters. In addition, this area is one of Europe's most important havens for migratory birds.

THE BACKGROUND

For centuries, the Dutch have waged war against the seas that batter the land and erode the country's coastlines. Early Dutch settlers reclaimed the delta land by building mounds of clay and peat. Then they built simple crude dams to protect the land from the rivers' flow, and dikes to keep out the sea.

Over the centuries, the Dutch worked continuously to improve and perfect their dam-and-dike system. By the mid-1900s, more than 1,800 miles (2,896 km) of dams and dikes protected the country.

> To protect Holland "once and for all" from other such tragedies, the Dutch set up the Delta Works Project. The project called for building barriers to seal off and protect the inlets of Holland's southwestern coast.

The tragedy of 1953, however, proved to many how inade-

Since the 1950s, the Netherlands has used the latest modern technology to reclaim and protect land from the sea.

quate the system was. The Delta Project offered the protection many thought necessary. By 1972, two of the major southwestern inlets had been closed. Work had started on the third and widest tributary. Environmentalists and oyster farmers, however, were opposed to the plan and had enough support to halt the barrier's construction.

THE POINTS OF VIEW

Environmentalists pointed out that the abundant plant and animal life for which the third tributary is famous was at risk. Should this particular inlet be blocked, ecologists warned, it would turn into a stagnant, brackish lake, and the wildlife would eventually die. Oyster farmers protested that a barrier would also destroy the rich seabeds that provided them with their income.

Supporters of the barrier believed that to leave the third tributary open defeated the very purpose of the barrier. The area through which it flowed

was the most vulnerable to devastating storms.

THE ISSUE TODAY

The Dutch parliament called a halt to the barrier's construction in the mid-1970s and ordered studies. In 1978, after two years of research, parliament ordered a seemingly impossible compromise: Build a barrier that will usually stay open, but can be closed in as little as an hour.

Today, an open barrier guards the third tributary's inlet. More than 2 miles long, it consists of 65 gigantic concrete pillars. Hanging like curtains between the pillars are 62 steel gates. Each gate measures as much as 138 feet (42 m) wide, 18 feet (5.5 m) thick, and 39 feet (11.9 m) high and weighs nearly 500 tons (453.5 metric tons). Each supporting pillar is about 12 stories high and weighs almost 18,000 tons (16,326 metric tons).

The gates remain open except for once or twice a year when high tides threaten the

land. Thus, the barrier does not threaten the ecological balance or the tidal movement that supports it. Each gate is tested every month to ensure the entire system's workability.

The Netherlands appears safe from the sea for some years to come. In the meantime, the Dutch are "exporting" their skills to developing nations of Latin America, Africa, and Asia. They are also keeping in mind the future of their own country. They hope to be ready with bigger dikes and pumps if global warming causes the seas to rise, as some scientists predict.

Reviewing the Case

1. Why was the Delta Project undertaken?
2. Who had concerns about the barrier at the third tributary?
3. **Human/Environment** **Interaction** How were the concerns of the conservationists handled?

2 People and Their Environment

SETTING THE SCENE

Read to Discover . . .
- the causes and effects of environmental pollution in Europe.
- why cleanup and reduction of pollution requires cooperation among European governments.
- what steps Europeans are taking to protect the environment.

Key Terms
- acid rain
- meltwater
- acid deposition
- environmentalist
- biologist

Identify and Locate
Black Forest, Mediterranean Sea, Strait of Gibraltar, Lake Balaton

---

In spite of social, political, and economic differences, all Europeans have one thing in common—the environment. Environmental problems affect all Europeans regardless of their traditions, the country they live in, or their standard of living. Europeans, like people everywhere, face the challenge of resolving these growing problems.

HUMAN/ENVIRONMENT INTERACTION

Environmental Pollution

As in North America, **acid rain**, or precipitation carrying large amounts of pollutants, has damaged millions of acres of Europe's forests, destroyed wildlife, and hastened the erosion of historic buildings. Air pollution covers the land with soot, poisons the crops, and endangers the health of many Europeans. Water pollution threatens not only the beauty of the seas, rivers, and lakes but also the wildlife that these bodies of water support. Poor farming practices and lack of proper sewage treatment threaten Europe's drinking water as well.

Acid Rain

In the 1960s, industrial firms in several European countries built high smokestacks to carry pollution away from industrial sites. The method worked, but the pollution directed away from factories drifted into other countries. These kinds of pollutants combine with water vapor in the atmosphere and fall to the earth in what has been termed acid rain. In the 1970s, scientists began to observe the effects of acid rain on Europe's forests. Needles or leaves turned yellow and fell. As trees sickened, insects and disease took over.

The problems caused by acid rain are widespread. In western Germany, acid rain has damaged about one-third, or more than 5 million acres (2 million ha) of the Black Forest. Forests in Austria, Switzerland, and France also have been damaged. Acid rain has drifted north from the industrial belt of Europe to Scandinavia. Forests in Norway and Sweden show the withering effects of high-sulfur-content rain.

In winter, snow carries the industrial pollution to the earth. In spring, the **meltwater**—the result of melting snow and ice—flows into rivers and lakes. The high concentration of acid in the meltwater destroys fish. Almost all fish are gone from lakes in the southern part of Norway. Scientists estimate that nearly one-fifth of Sweden's lakes are mostly or entirely without fish. The damage is costly. In Germany alone, scientists estimate the acid-rain damage to trees, lakes, and rivers at more than $1 billion each year.

Automobile exhaust also adds acid-forming compounds to the atmosphere. Scientists believe that **acid deposition**—wet or dry acid pollution that falls to the earth—damages more than the natural environment. Europe's historic buildings, such as the Acropolis in Greece, the Tower of London, and Cologne Cathedral in Germany, are among the buildings that have been affected by the corrosive effects of this acid. A Danish architect described the effects of acid deposition: "These buildings are melting away like sugar candy." Statues, bridges, and stained-glass windows also are showing the harmful effects of this kind of pollution.

Air Pollution

The nations of eastern Europe are paying the price for the inefficient factories once run by their Communist governments. Most plants derived their power from burning soft brown coal. This kind of coal is plentiful in the region, but it pollutes the air heavily. Smokestacks belched soot, sulfur, and carbon dioxide into the air by the hundreds of tons. As a result, Poland, Romania, and the Czech Republic are among the most polluted nations on the earth. Industrial pollution has ruined much of the food grown in that region of Europe. Houses, trees, grass, and even animals turn black from the soot. The poor quality of the air endangers the health of the people living there. Children in the northern part of the Czech Republic are sent away from home for one month each year for health reasons.

The problems of air pollution also affect industrial nations in western Europe. The people of the Netherlands drive the most cars per square mile (sq. km) and burn the most fossil fuel per person in Europe. As a result, levels of air pollution in the Netherlands cause concern for human health.

Global Warming

Air pollution, like other environmental concerns, has far-reaching effects. Some **environmentalists**—people concerned with the quality of the environment—believe that old factories, such as those in eastern Europe, are one of the many causes of the greenhouse effect. These factories burn coal, which releases carbon dioxide into the atmosphere. The carbon dioxide traps the sun's heat near the earth's surface. Over a period of time, this greenhouse effect could result in an increase in the earth's average temperature.

The long-range effects of possible global warming remain unknown. Many environmentalists believe that a rise in the earth's temperature would melt parts of the icy regions at the North and South Poles. As a result, the level of the oceans would rise. Among the possible consequences for Europe would be the flooding of some coastal lands. As a result,

Geographic Themes

Human/Environment Interaction: The Czech Republic
Heavy industrialization of the Czech Republic during the Communist era has led to the destruction of many forests by acid rain. *What other countries have had forests damaged by acid rain?*

millions of people from low-lying areas would crowd into other regions of the Continent.

Water Pollution

Every European country that borders the Mediterranean Sea uses it for recreation and transportation. These countries also use it for waste disposal. Coastal cities dump millions of tons of raw and partially treated sewage into the Mediterranean. Floating garbage, blown from landfills or thrown directly into the sea, creates an unsightly mess.

In the past, bacteria in the Mediterranean Sea were able to break down most of the wastes that the sea received. In recent times, however, growing populations and tourism along the coast have increased the environmental problems of the Mediterranean. Small tides and weak currents tend to keep pollution where people discharge it. The Mediterranean Sea, open to the Atlantic only through the narrow Strait of Gibraltar, takes almost a century to renew itself completely.

Coastal cities are not the only sources of water pollution in the Mediterranean region. Hundreds of rivers flow into the Mediterranean Sea. These rivers carry into the sea pesticides from Greek farms, detergents from Spanish homes, and industrial pollutants from French factories. These forms of pollution contaminate marine and animal life and create health hazards for people.

Oil and floating garbage pollute beaches, greatly decreasing tourism. Most of the countries that border the Mediterranean depend on tourists' money. A decrease in tourism would hurt the economies of France, Spain, Italy, and Greece. All European countries that border the Mediterranean Sea share responsibility for cleanup and protection of this vital resource.

Water pollution affects Europe's rivers and lakes as well as its coastal waters. Hungary's Lake Balaton, one of the largest freshwater

Geographic Themes
Human/Environment Interaction: Kraków, Poland
This huge steel mill near Kraków is the largest industrial plant—and the greatest polluter—in Poland. *How do factories such as this one contribute to the greenhouse effect?*

UNIT 4

lakes in Europe, has been threatened by industrial pollution. Industries in western Europe dump wastes into rivers, such as the Meuse and the Rhine. These rivers, in turn, carry the pollutants into the North Sea. Pollution levels in the coastal region from the Netherlands to Denmark have doubled over the past few decades.

Pollution from agricultural sources has affected the drinking water in many parts of Europe. Chemical and organic fertilizers seep into the groundwater, making it unfit for humans to drink. Lack of proper sewage treatment adds to the problem. Nearly 25 percent of Hungary's towns and cities do not have safe supplies of drinking water.

HUMAN/ENVIRONMENT INTERACTION

Efforts to Reduce Pollution

European citizens and government leaders share concern over growing environmental problems. They recognize their responsibility to preserve the environment for future generations. They also understand the economic impact of pollution—on the one hand, the loss of tourists; and on the other, the high cost of cleanup.

Concern for the Environment

Europeans share a long history of concern for the environment. Efforts to control air pollution date back to the Middle Ages. The English Parliament placed bans on burning coal in 1253. During the nineteenth century, Great Britain developed laws to control air pollution, health, and safety.

A sense of national heritage makes Europeans feel responsible for protecting and preserving the environment for future generations. This concern for the future makes many Europeans willing to take action to reduce pollution. At the United Nations Conference on Environment and Development in June 1992, European policy makers pushed for strong measures to reduce greenhouse gases.

Geographic Themes

Human/Environment Interaction: London
Throughout Europe, restorers must repair many historic buildings and monuments damaged by air pollution. *How are Europeans affected by industrial pollution?*

Other nations were less willing to act because the outcome of global climate change is uncertain.

Europeans also share a respect for nature. People who live in densely populated areas value an opportunity to get away from urban areas and enjoy the natural landscape. Those who live in sparsely populated areas often depend on the natural environment to support their way of life.

Europeans' idea of a natural environment differs somewhat from that concept in other parts of the world. Europe has few, if any, areas that have not been changed by human interaction. Over the centuries, people cleared the forests for farms, then paved over the farms to build factories and cities. They dug canals to connect rivers and tunneled through mountains to connect roads and rail lines. Although their environment has been modified greatly by humans, Europeans want to preserve their landscapes for future generations.

Geographic Themes

Place: Lake Balaton, Hungary
Lake Balaton, the largest lake in central Europe, is one of Hungary's most popular recreation areas. *How has Lake Balaton been affected by pollution?*

Cleanup Efforts

In recent decades, Europeans have enacted several programs to counteract acid rain. Germany has passed laws to ensure that all cars built after 1986 have smog-control devices. Environmentalists have promoted lower speed limits to reduce harmful emissions from automobiles. Many western European cities have protected buildings and works of art with acid-resistant coatings. Lime has been used to lower the acid level in Scandinavian lakes. **Biologists**—scientists who study plant and animal life—are trying to raise fish that can tolerate higher acid levels.

Denmark has become a leader in attempts to control environmental pollution. Wastewater treatment plants have reduced pollution levels in some cities by 60 percent. Denmark also identified more than 3,000 hazardous waste sites and has begun to clean up these areas. Hungary's efforts to improve water quality has reduced pollution levels in Lake Balaton by half. The Netherlands accomplished its goal of reducing air pollution by 50 percent from 1980 to 1995.

Since 1975, European governments have joined forces to tackle the pollution of the Mediterranean Sea. The United Nations' Mediterranean Action Plan (MAP) involved 17 nations in developing strict laws against pollution. As a result, the waters off some Mediterranean beaches have been made suitable again for swimming. The success of MAP made the program a model for other cooperative efforts. In 1992, many European nations signed a pledge to combat global warming by reducing greenhouse gases.

Plans for the Future

Local governments are taking steps to reduce pollution. For example, Naples, Marseille, and Athens are among several cities in the Mediterranean area that are planning major new sewage systems. Portugal is planning to construct a new system to properly handle toxic waste.

The task of cleaning up the environment and reducing pollution requires continued cooperation among all levels of European gov-

Geographic Themes

Place: Brussels, Belgium
Brussels, an important EU center, often hosts meetings dealing with Europe's environmental concerns. *What environmental decision was made in Brussels by the EU in 1993?*

ernments. Citizens must be made aware of the problems, and policy makers must enact legislation to provide solutions. The enormous cost of cleanup makes progress slow. The estimated cost of cleaning up air pollution in eastern Europe, for example, ranges from $200 billion to $500 billion. The cost of providing adequate sewage treatment for cities in the Mediterranean region could be from $25 billion to $100 billion.

The highly industrialized nations of the European Union cause about 70 percent of the Mediterranean's problems. EU members have pledged funds to help developing nations reduce pollution. Their plan calls for the Mediterranean to be cleaned by 2025.

In 1992, European Union representatives at a United Nations environmental conference in Dublin, Ireland, set goals for improving the quality of Europe's stream, river, and lake waters. That same year, European environment ministers agreed in Brussels to limit cross-border shipments of hazardous industrial wastes within the European Union.

Eastern Europeans are seeking financial aid to control pollution. They look to the EU for help because the air pollution from eastern factories threatens western Europe as well.

American companies have offered technology, expertise, and investment to help modernize eastern European factories. Such efforts point out not only the economic impact but also the global aspects of Europe's environmental concerns.

SECTION 2 REVIEW

Checking for Understanding
1. **Define** acid rain, meltwater, acid deposition, environmentalist, biologist.
2. **Locating Places** Which European nations border the Mediterranean Sea?
3. **Human/Environment Interaction** What are the effects of acid rain in Europe?
4. **Human/Environment Interaction** What are the causes of pollution of the Mediterranean Sea?

Critical Thinking
5. **Identifying Central Issues** Why does cleanup and preservation of the environment require the cooperation of European nations?

CRITICAL THINKING SKILLS

Analyzing Information

In modern society, television, radio, computer networks, newspapers, magazines, and advertisements constantly bombard us with information. Amid this clamor for our attention, how can we learn to analyze information to determine what is truly useful and accurate?

REVIEWING THE SKILL

There are two basic types of information sources: primary sources and secondary sources. *Primary sources* are those created by eyewitnesses to events. For example, interviews or letters written by survivors of an earthquake are primary sources. Other examples of primary sources include diaries, speeches, and photographs. *Secondary sources*, on the other hand, are accounts generally created by scholars and writers after a period of time has elapsed following the event. Secondary sources often synthesize information from several sources. For example, a book about earthquakes all over the world would be a secondary source.

After determining the nature of the source, try to answer the following questions about it: Who created it? When was it created? Who and what is it about? Where does it take place? Why was it created? What is its purpose? Answering these questions will help you to understand the content of the information, and determine how accurate it is. Finally, always look for footnotes and references that identify information sources used to create the document.

To analyze information, apply the following steps:
- Determine whether the information is a primary or secondary source.
- Identify who created the document and when it was created.

- Examine the content of the document to answer these questions: Who and what is it about? Where does it take place? Why was it created, or what is its purpose? What are the main ideas?
- Look for references explaining the sources used to produce the document or information.

PRACTICING THE SKILL

Read the following excerpt on European efforts to improve the environment. Then answer the questions below:

On the waste management front, Denmark has emerged as a model by banning throwaway beverage containers, thus sharply reducing garbage generation. By forcing a shift to refillable containers, it has cut the energy invested in beverage containers by two-thirds or more and lowered air and water pollution accordingly. Employment, meanwhile, may have increased, because reusing beverage containers is more labor-intensive than manufacturing new ones.

Among the industrial countries, the Netherlands has pioneered the use of bicycles for personal transportation. With a bicycle fleet of 12 million for a population of 15 million, this compact country has more than twice as many bicycles as cars. In Groningen, the largest city in northern Netherlands, bicycles already account for half of all trips. . . . Using a combination of grants and taxes, the goal is to get more people out of their cars and onto bicycles for shorter trips and into trains for longer ones.

1. Is this a primary or secondary source of information?
2. What is the topic of this document?
3. According to this document, what are some European countries doing to improve the quality of the environment?
4. What European country has pioneered the use of bicycles for personal transportation?

For additional practice in this skill, see Practicing Skills on page 278 of the Chapter 13 Review.

SECTION	KEY TERMS	SUMMARY
1 Living in Europe	heavy industry (p. 263) light industry (p. 263) organic farming (p. 264) mixed farming (p. 264) farm cooperative (p. 264) collective farm (p. 264) state farm (p. 264) consumer goods (p. 264) tariff (p. 265)	• The 12 nations of the European Union worked toward economic unity in spite of difficulties brought on by change. • Eastern European countries struggled to adjust to a free market economy after more than 40 years of Communist control. • Europe has diverse economies based on agriculture, manufacturing, and services. • Europe's communication and transportation systems are among the best in the world. • Railroads are a major means of freight and passenger transportation throughout Europe.

Assembly line in Germany

SECTION	KEY TERMS	SUMMARY
2 People and Their Environment	acid rain (p. 270) meltwater (p. 271) acid deposition (p. 271) environmentalist (p. 271) biologist (p. 274)	• Acid rain has damaged forests, wildlife, and buildings in many parts of Europe. • Air pollution from factories in various parts of Europe endangers health and contributes to the greenhouse effect. • Pollution from industrial wastes, sewage, garbage, and oil threatens the Mediterranean Sea and the wildlife the sea supports. • Europeans share a concern for the environment and a sense of responsibility for future generations. • European nations have taken steps to reduce pollution and clean up the environment.

Czech forest damaged by acid rain

Reviewing Key Terms

Choose the vocabulary term that best completes each of the sentences below. Write your answers on a separate sheet of paper.

heavy industry (p. 263)
light industry (p. 263)
organic farming (p. 264)
mixed farming (p. 264)
consumer goods (p. 264)
acid rain (p. 270)
meltwater (p. 271)
acid deposition (p. 271)

SECTION 1

1. Communist governments in Eastern Europe emphasized ____ , or the manufacture of machinery for factories and mines.
2. Farmers who rely on ____ use natural substances to enrich the soil.
3. Household goods, shoes, and clothing that individuals buy are called ____ .
4. ____ is the raising of several kinds of crops and livestock on the same farm.
5. ____ involves the production of consumer goods.

SECTION 2

6. The result of melting snow and ice is called ____ .
7. Scientists believe that ____ damages buildings as well as the natural environment.
8. Precipitation containing pollutants is called ____ .

Reviewing Facts

SECTION 1

9. What is the single most important occupation in Europe?
10. How did Europeans overcome the barriers to transportation posed by physical geography?

SECTION 2

11. Why are the problems caused by acid rain so widespread?
12. Why does pollution tend to remain in the Mediterranean Sea?

Critical Thinking

13. **Drawing Conclusions** Why did changing economies in both eastern and western Europe result in unemployment?
14. **Making Predictions** What might happen to Europe as a result of global warming?

Geographic Themes

15. **Movement** Why are France's TGVs more economical and more efficient than other forms of transportation?
16. **Human/Environment Interaction** What steps have been taken to reduce water pollution in European countries?

Practicing Skills

Analyzing Information

Refer to the excerpt in the Analyzing Information skill on page 276.

17. What is the purpose of this document?
18. Do you think this information is factually correct? What leads you to this conclusion?

Using the Unit Atlas

Refer to the physical geography section of the Unit Atlas on pages 216–217.

19. What recently-discovered natural resources have helped the economies of the United Kingdom and Norway?
20. What country is Europe's largest steel producer?

Projects

Individual Activity

Create a diagram or a flow chart illustrating the effects of pollution in Europe. Find or draw pictures showing how acid deposition, air pollution, and water pollution affect the European environment.

Cooperative Learning Activity

Organize into groups of three. Plan a European trip that includes travel through three countries. Have one member of the group determine the approximate cost of traveling by automobile. Have another member determine the cost of the trip by train. Have the third member of your group determine the cost of traveling by bicycle and staying in youth hostels. Use maps and travel guides. Compare the results of your research.

Writing About Geography

Argumentation

Imagine that you are a member of Europe's environmental policy community. You must convince other members to enact policies based on your views about global warming. Choose the role of someone who favors immediate action or of someone who prefers to take a "wait-and-see" approach. Write an argument that will convince others to accept your views. Use your journal and other references as you develop your argument.

Locating Places

MEDITERRANEAN REGION

Match the letters on the map with the places of the Mediterranean Region. Write your answers on a separate sheet of paper.

1. Mediterranean Sea
2. Italy
3. Greece
4. Strait of Gibraltar
5. Spain
6. France
7. Adriatic Sea
8. Sicily
9. Corsica
10. Sardinia

BEETHOVEN, THE BEATLES, AND BEYOND

European instruments, composers, and performers have long appealed to a wide variety of American musical tastes. Our European musical heritage began with simple instruments and tunes brought by the first colonists to these shores. Europe's influence continues to be felt in music today.

▲ **THE FIDDLE** has long been a basic instrument of American country music. Also called the violin, the instrument as we know it today originated near Venice in the mid-1500s. Italian master craftsman Antonio Stradivari perfected the violin in the 1600s and 1700s; one of his instruments is nearly priceless today.

◀ **ANTONÍN DVOŘÁK,** a Czech composer, first became popular among Americans in the late 1800s. The success of his music in the United States brought him to New York City in the 1890s to become director of the National Conservatory of Music. His American experiences inspired him to compose his most famous symphony, which he titled *From the New World.*

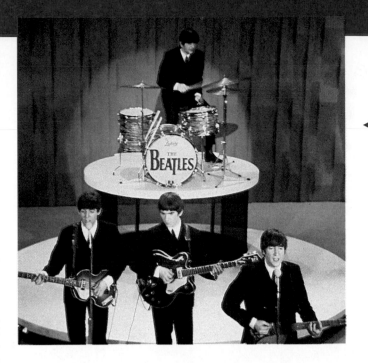

THE BEATLES, a band from Liverpool, England, gave a new direction to rock and roll during the 1960s. Previous rock and roll had been based on a strong beat. The Beatles' music, however, emphasized highly imaginative and memorable melodies and lyrics. Their fantastic success changed American music. Although the group broke up in 1970, lead singer Paul McCartney continues to be a strong influence on music as a composer and a performer.

LUDWIG VAN BEETHOVEN, the 18th-century German composer, is practically an American household name. "He will give the world something worth listening to," said Mozart when he first heard Beethoven perform. Beethoven fulfilled Mozart's prophecy, creating grand musical works filled with passionate emotion. In recent times, American composers have used some of Beethoven's most famous passages as themes in rock and roll.

◄ THE GUITAR comes from Spain and probably was introduced to America by the Spanish in the 1500s. Today's guitar-playing methods also were developed by a Spanish musician in the late 1800s. The acoustic guitar was important in early American rock and roll. The electric guitar, an American refinement, is now popular with rock musicians around the world.

▲ U2, an Irish rock group, has been popular with American audiences. Rock/country/western music has its roots in European folk music. Rock music was also influenced by the spirituals and blues style of African Americans, whose musical traditions have become well known in Europe.

Checking for Understanding

1. How has European music influenced the United States?

2. **Movement** Which European musical contribution has had the greatest effect on your life?

Russia and the Eurasian Republics

GeoJournal Activity

While studying Russia and the Eurasian republics, clip newspaper and magazine articles related to the physical features, cultures, politics, economy, and human-environment interactions of the region. Jot down recent changes occurring in any of the above categories.

NATIONAL GEOGRAPHIC SOCIETY

Picturing the World

Lavish mosaics grace the Church of the Resurrection, located in the Russian city of St. Petersburg. Founded by Russian tsar Peter the Great in 1703, St. Petersburg was built as a gateway to the West. Most Russians are members of the Russian Orthodox Church, a branch of the Eastern Orthodox Church. Many political changes have occurred in Russia since the founding of St. Petersburg. Power shifted in 1917 from the tsars to the Communists, who ruled until the breakup of the Soviet Union in 1991.

1. (a.) What is an icon? (b.) Do you see any in the picture on pages 282-83?
2. Now look at the picture on page 317. What was the Communist view toward religion?
3. How has that view changed?

Picture Atlas CD-ROM Enrichment Corner

Explore the Eurasian republics. Divide into five groups and choose one of the following republics: Ukraine, Belarus, Kazakhstan, Armenia, or Georgia. Read the essays and browse the photographs and captions, vital statistics, maps, and other features on the CD-ROM for information. As a group, present a comprehensive electronic report on one of the republics to the class.

RUSSIA AND THE
Cultural Geography

EXPLORING CULTURAL DIVERSITY

1. *What areas of Russia and the Eurasian republics are most sparsely populated? Most heavily populated?*
2. *What nations border the Black Sea?*
3. *What cities in the region have more than 2 million people?*

Siberia covers 75 percent of Russia. However, only 22 percent of the Russian people live there. The weather is too harsh for most people.

RUSSIA AND THE EURASIAN REPUBLICS: POLITICAL

— National boundary
⊛ National capital

Lambert Equal-Area projection

ARCTIC OCEAN

BELARUS
⊛ Minsk
Chisinau
⊛ Kiev
UKRAINE
MOLDOVA
⊛ Moscow

RUSSIA

Arctic Circle

GEORGIA
Black Sea
Tbilisi ⊛
Yerevan ⊛
AZERBAIJAN
ARMENIA ⊛ Baku
Caspian Sea
Ashkhabad ⊛
TURKMENISTAN
Dushanbe ⊛

KAZAKHSTAN
Aral Sea
UZBEKISTAN
Bishkek ⊛ Almaty
Tashkent ⊛
KYRGYZSTAN
TAJIKISTAN

N

0   500 mi.
0   500 km

The **Armenians** are among Europe's oldest ethnic groups. They have inhabited the area east and south of the Black Sea since the 600s B.C.

During ancient times, the cities of Tashkent, Samarkand, and Khiva in **Uzbekistan** were crossroads where the cultures and products of Europe, Southwest Asia, China, and India met.

The **Kazakhs** and the **Kyrgyz** are descendants of the nomadic Mongol herders who first settled the area.

About half of the region's population is **Russian**, and **Ukrainians** make up another 15 percent. The remaining 35 percent is composed of people from more than 100 ethnic groups.

Belarus has one of the fastest growing urban populations.

About 33 percent of the **Ukrainian** people live in rural areas.

RUSSIA AND THE EURASIAN REPUBLICS: POPULATION DENSITY

Per sq. km		Per sq. mi.		Cities
Over 100		Over 250		▪ 5,000,000 to 10,000,000
50-100		125-250		▫ 2,000,000 to 5,000,000
25-50		60-125		• 1,000,000 to 2,000,000
1-25		2-60		○ 250,000 to 1,000,000
Under 1		Under 2		
Uninhabited		Uninhabited		

Lambert Equal-Area projection

Azerbaijan is almost 50 percent urbanized.

Turkic peoples, including the Azeris, Uzbeks, Kazakhs, Kyrgyz, and Turks, live in central Asia.

The combined population of **Russia and the Eurasian Republics** is just slightly greater than that of the United States.

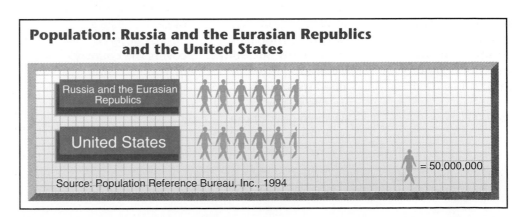

Population: Russia and the Eurasian Republics and the United States

Russia and the Eurasian Republics

United States

= 50,000,000

Source: Population Reference Bureau, Inc., 1994

RUSSIA AND THE
Physical Geography

CHARTING YOUR COURSE

1. *Use the map to determine which of the republics are landlocked.*
2. *What two major landforms are found in Russia and the Eurasian republics?*
3. *What are four of the principal natural resources found in the republics?*

The **Ural Mountains** run north to south, separating Russia into a European section and an Asian section.

RUSSIA AND THE EURASIAN REPUBLICS: PHYSICAL FEATURES

The **Caspian Sea,** the world's largest inland lake, covers 143,630 square miles (372,000 sq. km).

Armenia lies in a seismic region where earthquakes often occur. In 1988 a violent quake killed thousands of people in the western part of the country.

The **Kara Kum,** one of central Asia's largest deserts, covers the country of Turkmenistan.

RUSSIA AND THE EURASIAN REPUBLICS: NATURAL RESOURCES

EUROPE

BELARUS

UKRAINE
MOLDOVA

GEORGIA

ARMENIA
AZERBAIJAN

TURKMENISTAN

RUSSIA

Arctic Circle

KAZAKHSTAN

UZBEKISTAN

KYRGYZSTAN

TAJIKISTAN

ASIA

0   500 mi.

0   500 km   60°E   80°E

Lambert Equal-Area projection

🐚 Coal	I Iron ore	◉ Manganese	◗ Copper
Lignite	● Nickel	◪ Tungsten	♣ Lead
Petroleum	▲ Chromium	◆ Platinum	⊡ Zinc
Natural gas	+ Bauxite	⬦ Gold	▼ Tin

The West Siberian Plain is the world's largest flat region. Covered with swamps and marshes, the area is too flat to drain well.

The region's richest soils lie in the **Black Earth Belt**, which extends from western Ukraine to southwestern Siberia.

Russia is the world's largest country, covering almost a third of the continent of Europe and almost half of the continent of Asia.

Azerbaijan's capital, **Baku**, lies in one of the world's major oil-producing areas.

Russia's famous caviar comes from sturgeon caught in the **Caspian Sea.** Caviar is salted sturgeon eggs.

The rugged, barren **Pamirs** in Tajikistan are called *Bam i Dunya*, meaning "roof of the world." The area is the meeting place of four major Asian mountain ranges.

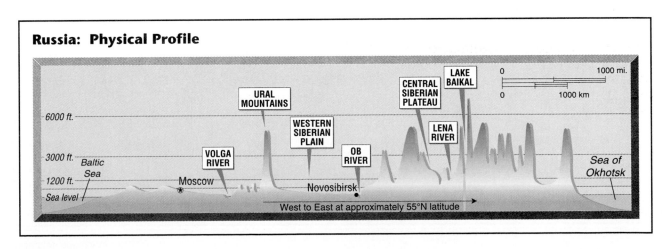

Russia: Physical Profile

LAKE BAIKAL

URAL MOUNTAINS

CENTRAL SIBERIAN PLATEAU

0   1000 mi.

0   1000 km

6000 ft.

WESTERN SIBERIAN PLAIN

LENA RIVER

VOLGA RIVER

OB RIVER

3000 ft.   Baltic Sea

Sea of Okhotsk

1200 ft.

Moscow

Novosibirsk

Sea level

West to East at approximately 55°N latitude

COUNTRY PROFILE

COUNTRY* AND CAPITAL	FLAG AND LANGUAGES	POPULATION	LANDMASS	PRINCIPAL PRODUCTS EXPORT	PRINCIPAL PRODUCTS IMPORT
Armenia — Yerevan	Armenian	3,700,000 322 per sq. mi. 124 per sq. km	11,500 sq. mi. 29,785 sq. km	Machinery	Machinery
Azerbaijan — Baku	Azeri, Turkish	7,400,000 222 per sq. mi. 86 per sq. km	33,400 sq. mi. 86,506 sq. km	Food	Food
Belarus — Minsk	Belorussian, Russian	10,300,000 129 per sq. mi. 50 per sq. km	80,200 sq. mi. 207,718 sq. km	Machinery	Machinery
Georgia — Tbilisi	Georgian, Russian	5,500,000 204 per sq. mi. 79 per sq. km	26,900 sq. mi. 69,671 sq. km	Food	Machinery
Kazakhstan — Almaty	Kazakh, Russian	17,100,000 16 per sq. mi. 6 per sq. km	1,049,200 sq. mi. 2,717,428 sq. km	Raw Materials	Raw Materials
Kyrgyzstan — Bishkek	Kyrgyz	4,500,000 59 per sq. mi. 23 per sq. km	76,600 sq. mi. 198,394 sq. km	Machinery	Light Industrial Products
Moldova — Chisinau	Romanian, Ukranian	4,400,000 311 per sq. mi. 120 per sq. km	14,170 sq. mi. 36,700 sq. km	Food	Machinery
Russia — Moscow	Russian	147,800,000 23 per sq. mi. 9 per sq. km	6,592,800 sq. mi. 17,075,352 sq. km	Fuels	Machinery
Tajikistan — Dushanbe	Tadzhik, Russian	5,900,000 107 per sq. mi. 41 per sq. km	55,300 sq. mi. 143,227 sq. km	Aluminum	Chemicals
Turkmenistan — Ashkhabad	Turkmen, Russian	4,100,000 21 per sq. mi. 8 per sq. km	188,500 sq. mi. 488,215 sq. km	Natural Gas	Machinery
Ukraine — Kiev	Ukrainian	51,500,000 221 per sq. mi. 85 per sq. km	233,100 sq. mi. 603,729 sq. km	Machinery	Machinery
Uzbekistan — Tashkent	Uzbek	22,100,000 128 per sq. mi. 49 per sq. km	172,700 sq. mi. 447,293 sq. km	Cotton	Food

*Country maps not drawn to scale.

Winters in Moscow, Russia's capital, are severe—with plenty of snow and bitterly cold temperatures.

Vast areas of tundra stretch across the northern part of Russia.

The ideas of Russian revolutionary leader Vladimir Lenin shaped the political and cultural life of Russia and the Eurasian republics from 1917 until the early 1990s.

Russian czars and czarinas built beautiful palaces in St. Petersburg during the period of the Russian Empire.

chapter 14

The Physical Geography of Russia and the Eurasian Republics

CHAPTER FOCUS

Geographic Setting

Together Russia and the Eurasian republics stretch almost halfway around the world. Diverse climate and vegetation zones extend across the broad expanse.

Geographic Themes

Section 1 The Land
PLACE Three interconnected plains and numerous mountain ranges form the major landscapes of Russia and the Eurasian republics.

▲ Photograph: *Towering Caucasus Mountains, Georgia*

Section 2 The Climate and Vegetation
LOCATION The climates and vegetation of Russia and the Eurasian republics are affected by their northern location and their distance from the sea.

1 The Land

Read to Discover . . .
- the major landforms in Russia and the Eurasian republics.

Key Terms
- chernozem
- *kums*

Identify and Locate
North European Plain, West Siberian Plain, Caucasus Mountains, Black Sea, Caspian Sea, Aral Sea, Volga River, Dnieper River

Siberia, Russia

Zdravstvuy!
I was born in the Altai Mountains in the southwestern part of Siberia. I often come back here to spend my summer vacation. I enjoy hiking in the mountains where you can see glaciers on the distant mountaintops, drink crystal-clear and ice-cold water from rapid streams, and breathe the sweet air of Alpine meadows. Come and see for yourself!
Best wishes, Vladimir Marchenkov

Vladimir Marchenkov comes from Siberia, the eastern part of Russia. Russia and the Eurasian republics together cover 8,534,370 square miles (22,104,018 sq. km) of territory. They are more than the size of Canada, the United States, and Mexico combined. Territorial size and a diversity of landforms have affected the development of these countries.

PLACE

Plains Areas

Three plains connect Europe and Asia. The North European Plain, the West Siberian Plain, and the Turan Lowland stretch eastward from Poland to the Yenisey (yeh•nuh•SAY) River.

The North European Plain

The North European Plain is the center of economic life for almost three-fourths of the people of Russia and the Eurasian republics. The region's rich black topsoil called **chernozem** (cher•nuh•ZYAWM) makes Ukraine one of Europe's best farming areas. Three large cities—Moscow and St. Petersburg in Russia and Kiev in Ukraine—are located in the region. Its major rivers are the Volga, the Dniester (NEES•tuhr), the Dnieper (NEE•puhr), and the Don.

The West Siberian Plain

East of the Ural Mountains lies the world's largest area of flat land. Most of its one million square miles (2.6 million sq. km) is swamps, marshes, and frozen land unsuitable for farming. The northern two-thirds is evergreen forest and swamp.

The Turan Lowland

Between the Caspian Sea and the Tian Shan (tee•AHN SHAHN) mountain range, the Turan Lowland has a few areas irrigated for agriculture. The rest is dune-covered *kums,* or deserts. The Kara Kum, or black sand desert, occupies most of Turkmenistan. The Kyzylkum (ky•zuhl•KUHM), or red sand desert, covers half of Uzbekistan.

Comparing Lands

The **continental USA** is a little less than three and a half times smaller than Russia and the Eurasian republics.

Mountains and Plateaus

Mountain ranges and plateaus punctuate the landscape of Russia and the Eurasian republics. The Carpathian Mountains bordering Ukraine and the Caucasus (KAW•kuh•suhs) in the southwest are extensions of the Alpine mountain system of Europe. Thickly covered with pines and other trees, the Caucasus form the Russian frontier with Azerbaijan and Georgia.

Mount Elbrus, in the Caucasus, rises 18,510 feet (5,642 m). Communism Peak, in the Pamirs on the eastern border of Tajikistan, at 24,590 feet (7,495 m) is the region's highest elevation. The Tian Shan, meaning "heavenly mountains" in Chinese, is a towering system covering much of Kyrgyzstan. It includes some of the world's largest glaciers.

The mineral-rich Ural Mountains, worn down by streams and wind erosion, rise only a few thousand feet. Stretching 1,500 miles

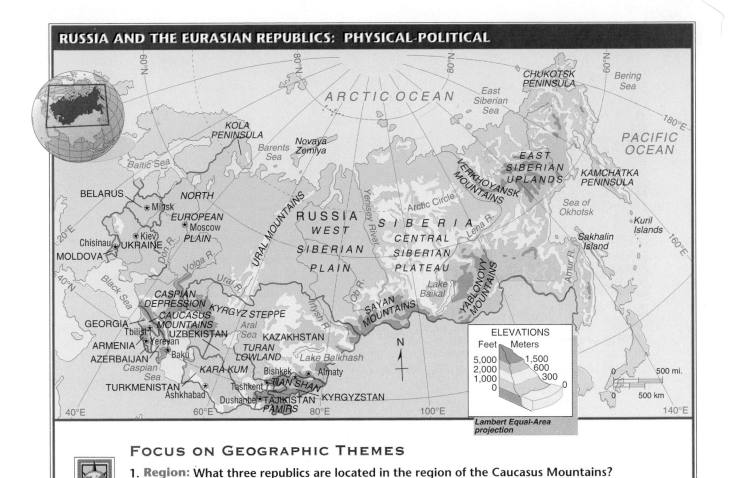

RUSSIA AND THE EURASIAN REPUBLICS: PHYSICAL-POLITICAL

ELEVATIONS

Feet	Meters
5,000	1,500
2,000	600
1,000	300
0	0

Lambert Equal-Area projection

0 500 mi.

0 500 km

FOCUS ON GEOGRAPHIC THEMES

1. **Region:** What three republics are located in the region of the Caucasus Mountains?
2. **Place:** What city is the capital of the Ukraine?
3. **Movement:** What sea lies south of Russia and Ukraine?
4. **Place:** What desert area lies in Turkmenistan?

(2,414 km) from the Arctic Ocean to near the Aral Sea, the Urals divide European Russia and Siberia.

The East Siberian Uplands form the largest region of Siberia. This wilderness of forests, mountains, and plateaus extends to the Pacific Ocean. To the west, the Central Siberian Plateau slopes upward as you move from the Arctic Ocean to the Sayan and Baikal mountains. Fast-running streams have cut deep canyons in these plateaus.

REGION

Seas and Lakes

Russia and the Eurasian republics contain many seas and lakes. Ice-covered most of the year, the White, the Barents, the Kara, the Laptev, the East Siberian, and the Chukchi seas all border northern Russia. The Sea of Okhotsk (oh•KAHTSK) and the Bering Sea border on the northeast. The Black Sea—a warm water sea—touches Russia, Georgia, and Ukraine and flows south into the Mediterranean.

Nestled among the republics of Azerbaijan, Russia, Kazakhstan, and Turkmenistan is the Caspian Sea. The largest inland body of water in the world is really a saltwater lake. Although four rivers flow into it, the Caspian Sea is shrinking from evaporation. The Aral Sea is also shrinking because Soviet policies allowed its waters to be overused for irrigation.

Lake Baikal (by•KAHL) in Siberia is the oldest and deepest lake in the world. Called in Russian folk songs a "glorious and sacred sea," it holds one-fifth of the earth's total freshwater supply.

HUMAN/ENVIRONMENT INTERACTION

Rivers

Long navigable rivers, connected to seas and other rivers by canals, have played a major role in Russian and Eurasian trade and development. Some flow eastward, like the Amur, which forms part of Russia's border with China. Others, like the Ural and the Volga, flow southward. Many that flow north-ward, such as the Lena, Ob, and Yenisey, are frozen much of the year.

The Dnieper, the Western Dvina, the Dniester, the Don, and the Volga cross the plains. Called *Matushka Volga,* or "Mother Volga," the longest river in European Russia flows 2,193 miles (3,528.5 km) from Russia's Valdai Hills to the Caspian Sea. Although frozen for four to six months each year, this river provides hydroelectric power, municipal water supplies, and water for industries and irrigation. For centuries the Volga has been a major highway for trade and communications.

The only large river of Siberia that does not flow northward is the Amur. Its river valley is the only major food-producing area in eastern Siberia. Four Siberian rivers are among the 12 largest in the world—the Lena, the Ob, the Yenisey, and the Irtysh (ihr•TISH).

REGION

Natural Resources

Russia and the Eurasian republics are rich in natural resources. Russia is the world's largest producer of <u>manganese</u> and <u>chromium</u>

and the second-largest producer of gold. Together Russia, Kazakhstan, and Ukraine contain almost 20 percent of the world's known coal and lignite reserves. The Tyumen field in the West Siberian Plain produces more oil in a day than any country except the United States and Saudi Arabia. Russia is the world's leading exporter of natural gas.

Minerals and Energy

Almost every mineral used by industry is found in Russia and the Eurasian republics. The region leads in coal, copper, and silver production and ranks second in production of gold, lead, salt, tin, tungsten, and zinc. Iron ore, nickel, asbestos, chromium, bauxite, antimony, manganese, and precious stones are in abundance. Turkmenistan has the world's largest deposits of sulfur and sodium sulfate.

Nearly all the republics have natural gas and oil. The main oil-producing areas are the Tyumen and Volga-Urals fields in Russia and the Baku field in Azerbaijan. Russia is a leading producer of hydroelectric power. A series of power stations along the Volga and at Bratsk on the Angara River are among the world's largest.

Soils, Forests, Wildlife, and Fish

The Black Earth Belt stretches from western Ukraine to southwestern Siberia. Its rich black chernozem makes the region a leading producer of wheat, rye, oats, barley, and sugar beets. Fertile soil made Ukraine the former Soviet Union's breadbasket for years.

About one-third of Russia and the Eurasian republics is forestland. Hardwood forests cover about one-fourth of the republic of Belarus. The region's vast forests with larch, pine, fir, linden, elm, and other trees account for about one-fifth of the world's timber.

Eastern Siberia is home to the majestic Siberian tiger, an endangered species. Other wildlife in the region include bear, fox, reindeer, elk, lynx, deer, wolf, wildcat, sable, and boar.

Fish are a key regional resource—salmon from the Pacific coast area; herring, cod, and halibut from the Barents Sea; and carp and sturgeon from the Caspian Sea.

 Geographic Themes

Human/Environment Interaction: Baku, Azerbaijan
The major source of wealth for the economy of Azerbaijan is oil. The Caspian Sea near Baku has many oil refineries. *What are the two major oil-producing areas in Russia?*

SECTION 1 REVIEW

Checking for Understanding
1. **Define** chernozem, *kums.*
2. **Locating Places** What are the three major plains areas of Russia and the Eurasian republics?
3. **Region** What are two common characteristics of most rivers in Russia and the Eurasian republics?
4. **Region** What are five natural resources found in Russia and the Eurasian republics?

Critical Thinking
5. **Making Comparisons** In what ways are Lake Baikal and the Caspian Sea the same? How are they different? What does the future hold for these two lakes and the people who rely on them for a living?

2 The Climate and Vegetation

SETTING THE SCENE

Read to Discover . . .
- the major climates found in Russia and the Eurasian republics.
- the kinds of natural vegetation in different climate regions of Russia and the Eurasian republics.

Key Terms
- permafrost
- tundra
- taiga
- steppe

Identify and Locate
Arctic Circle, Odessa, Siberia, Kara Kum, Climate regions: humid continental, subarctic, steppe, desert, humid subtropical, Mediterranean

The vast size of Russia and the Eurasian republics has an important impact on their climate. Within their borders is a diversity of natural vegetation, including tundra, forest, grassland, and desert.

Geographic Themes

Place: Kara Kum, Central Asia
In the Kara Kum, the temperature has been known to rise above 120°F (48.9°C). *How does much of the vegetation of the Kara Kum compare with other desert areas?*

REGION

Climate Regions of Russia and the Eurasian Republics

The lack of mountains near lowlands and a northern location influence the climate of Russia and the Eurasian republics. About 75 percent of the region is located farther north than the United States, excluding Alaska. Like parts of Canada, the far northern part of Russia is within the Arctic Circle.

Most of the republics lie well within the continent, far from the moderating influences of the sea. This leads to a wide range of annual temperatures. Verkhoyansk, located at about 68°N latitude, has been called the "cold pole of the world" because of its bitter winter temperatures. Without mountains to shelter them, lowland areas receive the full impact of sultry summer winds and frigid winter storms.

Kinds of Climate

Two major climates—humid continental and subarctic—are found in most of Russia and the Eurasian republics. The range between temperature highs and lows is the widest in the world. While summers may be hot or warm, they are always short, and winters are

EUROPE

BELARUS

RUSSIA

Arctic Circle

MOLDOVA

UKRAINE

GEORGIA

KAZAKHSTAN

AZERBAIJAN

UZBEKISTAN

ARMENIA

TURKMENISTAN

KYRGYZSTAN

N

ASIA

TAJIKISTAN

0   800 mi.

0   800 km

60°E   80°E   100°E

120°E   140°E

Dry
- Steppe
- Desert

Mid-Latitude
- Humid subtropical
- Humid continental
- Mediterranean

High Latitude
- Tundra
- Subarctic
- Highland

Lambert Equal-Area projection

FOCUS ON GEOGRAPHIC THEMES

1. **Region:** What climate region is found in the far north of Russia?
2. **Place:** In what climate region is Belarus located?
3. **Region:** What climate region extends around the north coast of the Black Sea?
4. **Location:** Where are highland areas found?

always long and cold. More than half of the land is covered with snow six months a year. About half has **permafrost**, a permanently frozen layer of soil beneath the ground. In the words of one writer, "Indeed, so cold does it get that almost all of the . . . northern coast is never entirely free of ice, and even the southern port of Odessa on the Black Sea is frozen in for six weeks or so each winter."

Range of Climates

In the far north, the landscape is dominated by the vast treeless plains called **tundra**. In winter, when the northern part of the earth is tipped away from the sun, the sky stays dark for long periods. In summer there is daylight for weeks. The cold is the fiercest in northeastern Siberia. Temperatures there have been known to drop as low as −90°F (−68°C).

In the subarctic **taiga**, the vast woodland that begins where the tundra ends, summers are reasonably warm. Yet a deep blanket of snow often cloaks the land for as long as eight months of the year.

In contrast, the desert regions of central Asia have cold winters and long, hot summers. In July, for example, daytime temperatures average about 90°F (32°C) and have been known to rise above 120°F (49°C) in the shade.

In the North European Plain, summers are warm. Winters are cold, but not so painfully cold as farther north. More precipitation falls in summer than in winter, giving rise to conditions favorable for agriculture.

Russia and the United States

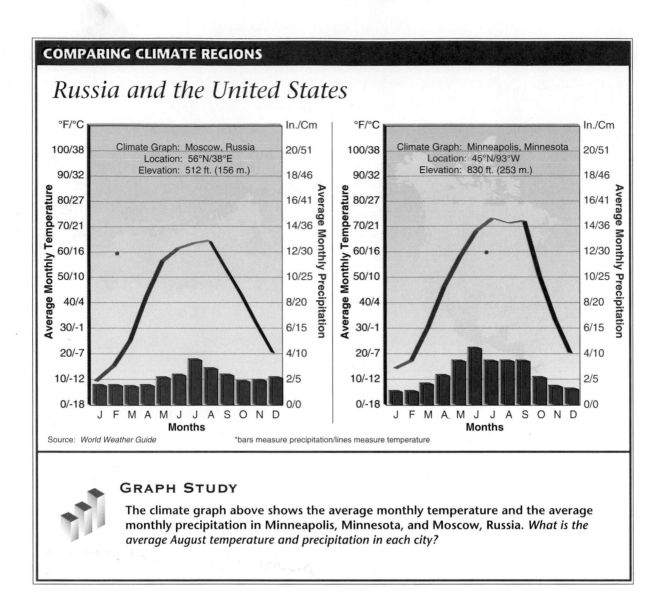

°F/°C — Average Monthly Temperature

Climate Graph: Moscow, Russia
Location: 56°N/38°E
Elevation: 512 ft. (156 m.)

In./Cm — Average Monthly Precipitation

100/38 — 20/51
90/32 — 18/46
80/27 — 16/41
70/21 — 14/36
60/16 — 12/30
50/10 — 10/25
40/4 — 8/20
30/-1 — 6/15
20/-7 — 4/10
10/-12 — 2/5
0/-18 — 0/0

J F M A M J J A S O N D
Months

°F/°C — Average Monthly Temperature

Climate Graph: Minneapolis, Minnesota
Location: 45°N/93°W
Elevation: 830 ft. (253 m.)

In./Cm — Average Monthly Precipitation

100/38 — 20/51
90/32 — 18/46
80/27 — 16/41
70/21 — 14/36
60/16 — 12/30
50/10 — 10/25
40/4 — 8/20
30/-1 — 6/15
20/-7 — 4/10
10/-12 — 2/5
0/-18 — 0/0

J F M A M J J A S O N D
Months

Source: *World Weather Guide*   *bars measure precipitation/lines measure temperature

GRAPH STUDY

The climate graph above shows the average monthly temperature and the average monthly precipitation in Minneapolis, Minnesota, and Moscow, Russia. *What is the average August temperature and precipitation in each city?*

In the wide grassy plains known as **steppes** that stretch from the western shores of the Black Sea to the Altai Mountains, winter is a time when frosty northern winds pile the snow in drifts across the frozen earth. In summer, rainfall is uncertain and, as one writer explains:

---✧---

The sun of the steppelands is like a boiling kettle, pouring yellow boiling water over your back.

---✧---

Other climates prevail in scattered parts of Russia and the Eurasian republics. The Black

Sea coast of Georgia has a humid subtropical climate suitable for growing cotton, tea, citrus fruits, and tobacco. The Crimean Peninsula has a Mediterranean climate in which citrus fruits, winter grains, and vegetables thrive.

PLACE

Vegetation

M any kinds of vegetation can be found in this region. In western Georgia, Azerbaijan, and Turkmenistan, for example, a person can see subtropical vegetation such as citrus fruits. At the far eastern end of the Black

Sea, there are rich tea plantations and a sub-tropical rain forest. Seven natural vegetation zones run roughly from west to east across the vast territory. These zones are tundra, taiga, mixed forest, wooded steppe, steppe, semi-desert, and desert.

Tundra

Tundra is the northernmost vegetation zone. The soil beneath the tundra is always frozen, but different kinds of low grasses, reeds, and mosses still grow.

Taiga and Mixed Forest

South of the tundra is the taiga—the coniferous forest belt. The largest forest region in the world, it stretches from Finland to the Sea of Okhotsk. One writer refers to these large forests as "one of the mightiest features of our planet."

In past decades, many furbearing animals lived in the forests. Mink and Russian sable pelts sold for a great deal of money—a source of wealth for many generations. Today the animals are fewer in number, and the wealth rests more in timber. In some places the forest has been cleared, and farmers have cultivated crops. The soil, however, is not very good, and the growing season is short.

To the south of the taiga is a mixed forest with both coniferous trees and deciduous trees. It encompasses much of Belarus and eventually joins with forests of central Europe.

Steppe Areas

The northern areas of the steppes border the southern edge of the mixed forest. This strip of steppes alternates thick clumps of trees with wide open spaces. The rest of the steppe is largely grassland.

Semidesert and Desert

The semidesert and desert south of the steppes have little vegetation. The hot, dry climate makes much of the area barren. Large stretches of bare rock and sandy dunes dominate drought-resistant shrubs and cacti. In the Kara Kum, however, vegetation supports nomadic herds of sheep, goats, and camels. The

 Geographic Themes

Place: Irkutsk, Siberia
Warmly dressed pedestrians are on their way to work on a typical winter morning in Siberia. *How does the cold climate affect the soil in Siberia and other parts of Russia?*

valleys of the Syr and Amu Darya rivers in Uzbekistan have been irrigated. In these regions melons, rice, and cotton grow.

SECTION 2 REVIEW

Checking for Understanding
1. **Define** permafrost, tundra, taiga, steppe.
2. **Locating Places** In what part of Russia and the Eurasian republics are the steppes located?
3. **Region** What two general kinds of climate prevail in most of Russia and the Eurasian republics?
4. **Place** How does the vegetation of the tundra compare with that of the taiga?

Critical Thinking
5. **Making Generalizations** What generalization can you make about climate and vegetation in Russia and the Eurasian republics? Relate this generalization to human activity, particularly agriculture.

Interpreting a Political Map

As you travel, you may see signs indicating that you have left one town, county, or state and entered the next. Lines drawn to separate towns, counties, states, and nations are called *political boundaries* because they divide areas controlled by different governments. A **political map** illustrates these divisions and relationships.

REVIEWING THE SKILL

On political maps of large areas, lines indicate boundaries between countries, or *international boundaries*. Political maps often also include cities and selected natural features, such as large bodies of water and major rivers.

Unlike physical maps, which remain fairly constant over time, political maps change as political relationships evolve. By comparing political maps from different periods of history, you can see changes in political relationships over time.

To interpret a political map, apply the following steps:

• Read the map title to find out what geographic area it covers and what time period the map reflects.

• Identify the countries or other political units named on the map.
• Identify capitals and major cities.

PRACTICING THE SKILL

Use the map below to answer the following questions about political maps:

1. Which countries separate Russia from the rest of Europe?
2. What is the capital of Kazakhstan? Of Ukraine?
3. Which countries border the Black Sea?
4. Which two cities lie farthest east on this map?

For additional practice in this skill, see Practicing Skills on page 302 of the Chapter 14 Review.

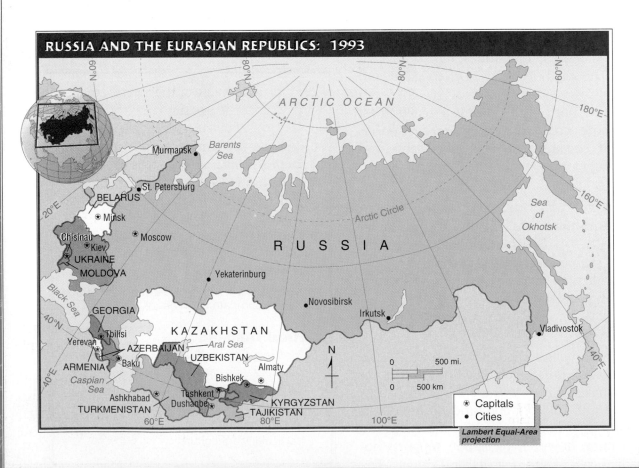

RUSSIA AND THE EURASIAN REPUBLICS: 1993

ARCTIC OCEAN

Barents Sea

Murmansk

St. Petersburg

BELARUS

Minsk

Chisinau
Kiev
UKRAINE
MOLDOVA

Moscow

Yekaterinburg

R U S S I A

Arctic Circle

Sea of Okhotsk

Novosibirsk

Irkutsk

Vladivostok

Black Sea

GEORGIA

Tbilisi

Yerevan

AZERBAIJAN

ARMENIA

Baku

Caspian Sea

KAZAKHSTAN

Aral Sea

UZBEKISTAN

Bishkek

Almaty

N

KYRGYZSTAN

Ashkhabad
Dushanbe
TURKMENISTAN

Tashkent

TAJIKISTAN

0   500 mi.
0   500 km

⊛ Capitals
• Cities

Lambert Equal-Area projection

SECTION	**KEY TERMS**	**SUMMARY**

1

The Land

chernozem (p. 291)
kums (p. 292)

The Ural Mountains—the divide between Europe and Asia

- The land occupied by Russia and the Eurasian republics spans two continents—Europe and Asia.
- Plains areas cover the greatest part of Russia and the Eurasian republics.
- Numerous mountain ranges, uplands, plateaus, and inland bodies of water are scattered throughout Russia and the Eurasian republics.
- All of the republics except Russia, Georgia, and Ukraine are landlocked.
- Most of the rivers of the region flow northward and are frozen for much of the year.
- Minerals, energy resources, fertile soils, forests, wildlife, and fish are abundant in Russia and the Eurasian republics.

SECTION	**KEY TERMS**	**SUMMARY**

2

The Climate and Vegetation

permafrost (p. 297)
tundra (p. 297)
taiga (p. 297)
steppe (p. 298)

A winter morning in Siberia, the eastern half of Russia

- Because of their northern location, distance from large bodies of water, and lack of mountains near lowland areas, most areas of Russia and the Eurasian republics have a humid continental or subarctic climate.
- More than half the land of Russia and the Eurasian republics is covered with snow for much of the year. Permafrost (permanently frozen subsoil) is found beneath about 40 percent of the area of Russia and the Eurasian republics.
- Throughout the region summers are short, and winters are very long and very cold.
- Natural vegetation varies, ranging from treeless tundra in the north to densely wooded taiga in the center to barren desert in the south.

Reviewing Key Terms

Choose the vocabulary term that best completes each of the sentences below. Write your answers on a separate sheet of paper.

chernozem (p. 291)　tundra (p. 297)
kums (p. 292)　　taiga (p. 297)
permafrost (p. 297)　steppes (p. 298)

SECTION 1

1. The rich black topsoil of the North European Plain is called _____ .
2. A few areas of the Turan Lowland are agriculturally productive, but most of the plain is _____ .

SECTION 2

3. Wide grassy plains called _____ cover southern Russia and Ukraine.
4. _____ is the permanently frozen layer of soil that lies beneath the ground.
5. A deep blanket of snow often cloaks the _____ for many months of the year.
6. Vast treeless plains called _____ dominate the landscape of the far northern regions of Russia.

Reviewing Facts

SECTION 1

7. Which mountains form a natural dividing line between European Russia and Siberia?
8. Which republics have direct access to the seas?
9. What functions does the Volga River fulfill for the people of Russia? Where is the Volga River located?

SECTION 2

10. How much of a range is there between temperature highs and lows in Russia and the Eurasian republics?
11. What are the seven vegetation zones found in Russia and the Eurasian republics?

12. What two vegetation zones are south of the steppe?

Critical Thinking

13. **Drawing Conclusions**　Most of the people of Russia and the Eurasian republics make their homes on a Russian extension of the North European Plain. What reasons can you give for this?
14. **Determining Cause and Effect**　Why are the climates of Russia and the Eurasian republics so harsh?

 ## Geographic Themes

15. **Region**　What kinds of natural resources are abundant in Russia and the Eurasian republics?
16. **Place**　What vegetation is found in the tundra?

 ## Practicing Skills

Interpreting a Political Map
Refer to the political map on page 300.
17. What is the capital of Georgia?
18. What seas border Kazakhstan?

Using the Unit Atlas

Refer to the physical geography section of the Unit Atlas on pages 286–287.
19. What mountains in Tajikistan are called the "roof of the world"?
20. What natural resource is found in Baku?

Projects

Individual Activity
Rivers have always played an important role in Russia and the Eurasian republics. Re-

search a major river of the region. Then imagine that you are on a ship traveling from one end of the river to the other and write a poem describing the physical features, environment, climate, vegetation, and human activity in the areas through which you journey.

Cooperative Learning Activity

Work in a group of seven. Each group member will research a different vegetation zone of Russia and the Eurasian republics and present to the other group members what he or she learned. Then group members will work together to construct a poster that will illustrate what it might be like to live in each of the region's vegetation zones.

Writing About Geography

Proposal

Suppose you are a Russian. A foreign automobile manufacturer plans to open a plant in Russia or in one of the Eurasian republics and has asked you to recommend one or two areas in which to build the plant. Write a letter to the company president that includes your recommendations and an argument to support those recommendations. Use your journal, text, and magazine and newspaper articles as references in writing your letter.

Locating Places

THE PHYSICAL GEOGRAPHY OF RUSSIA AND THE EURASIAN REPUBLICS

Match the letters on the map with the places and physical features of Russia and the Eurasian republics. Write your answers on a separate sheet of paper.

1. Ural Mountains
2. Caucasus Mountains
3. Kazakhstan
4. Tian Shan
5. Siberia
6. East Siberian Uplands
7. Arctic Ocean
8. Bering Sea
9. Caspian Sea
10. Volga River

chapter 15

The Cultural Geography of Russia and the Eurasian Republics

CHAPTER FOCUS

Geographic Setting

In the early 1990s, a number of independent republics arose in the area once occupied by the Russian Empire and later, the Soviet Union.

▲ Photograph: *Busy shoppers in St. Petersburg, Russia*

Geographic Themes

Section 1 Population Patterns

PLACE Russia and the Eurasian republics once made up the world's third most populous nation.

Section 2 History and Government

REGIONS From the 1200s through much of the 1900s, autocratic rulers expanded first Russian and then Soviet territory in all directions.

Section 3 Cultures and Lifestyles

HUMAN/ENVIRONMENT INTERACTION Since the fall of communism, culture in Russia and the Eurasian republics has been changing.

Population Patterns

Read to Discover . . .
- the diverse peoples who live in Russia and the Eurasian republics.
- where most people of Russia and the Eurasian republics live and why.

Key Terms
- ethnic group
- nationalities

Identify and Locate
Russia, Ukraine, Belarus, Moldova, Azerbaijan, Kazakhstan, Uzbekistan, Tajikistan, Caucasus, Armenia, Georgia, Turkmenistan, Ural Mountains, Moscow, St. Petersburg, Kiev, Tashkent

> Moscow, Russia
> My name is Anton Alexeev and I live in an apartment in Moscow. The school that I attend is really small. We have a total of about 1,000 students and we have all grades — from first grade through eleventh grade. We have just 11 years in school. In my free time I hang out with my friends, ride bikes, and go to the park and to parties.
> Anton Alexeev

Anton Alexeev is Russian and lives in Russia, the largest of the republics in a culture region known as Russia and the Eurasian republics. The vast lands of Russia and the Eurasian republics are home to diverse peoples.

PLACE

Ethnic Diversity

Each people, or **ethnic group**, has its own unique heritage, customs, beliefs, and language. When Russia and the Eurasian republics were all part of the Soviet Union, boundaries were based on one of the country's major ethnic groups, or **nationalities.**

Language

During the Soviet era, Russian was the official language and was taught in all Soviet schools. It was the native language, however, of only about one-half of the people. Today Russian is still spoken and read in most of the republics, but now each republic has its own official language. The more than 100 nationalities who live in the region speak many hundreds of different languages.

Many people in Russia and the Eurasian republics are of Slavic background and speak languages that belong to the Indo-European family. Others are of Turkic background and speak one of the Turkic languages, which are part of the Ural-Altaic (YOR•uh•lal•TAY•ik) family. Still others speak either an Indo-European or Turkic language like Caucasian.

Russians, Ukrainians, and Belarusians, for example, are Slavs. Uzbeks, Kazakhs, Turkmenis, and most other peoples of the republics in central Asia are in the Turkic group. Georgians and Armenians, on the other hand, are Caucasian peoples and speak distinctive languages.

The Slavs

Of all the ethnic groups in Russia and the Eurasian republics, the Slavs are most numerous. During their early history, all Slavs in the region shared a common cultural identity. In time, the different types of Slavs in different places developed customs and languages distinct from the others. The Slavs living in the south near the city of Kiev became known as Ukrainians. Those inhabiting the west near present-day Poland were called Belarusians. Another group of Slavs living in the north near the city of Moscow became known as Russians.

Together the Slavs now make up the greater part of the population of three of the European republics—Russia, Ukraine, and Belarus. The greatest number live in Russia, where 83 percent of the population are actually ethnic Russians, people who follow Russian customs and speak Russian as their first language.

There is only one Eurasian republic in which the Slavs are not the majority—Moldova. Sixty-four percent of the people are Moldovans, most of them Romanians who came originally from the Bessarabia region of Romania. They speak Romanian and follow Romanian customs.

Turkic Peoples

With the exception of the Azeri, whose land—now the Republic of Azerbaijan—was for several centuries part of the Persian Empire, most Turkic peoples live in the republics of central Asia. They are Uzbeks, Kazakhs, Kyrgyz, Tatars, and Turks, and each is different from the other in a number of ways. But they all have one thing in common—language. All speak some form of a Turkic language. Almost all are Muslim, followers of the religion of Islam.

The Uzbeks are the largest group of Turkic people in the republics and the second-largest in the world. Only the Turks of Turkey form a larger group. Of all the Turkic peoples of the republics, only one—the Kazakhs—are a minority in their own country. For many years, more Russians than Kazakhs have lived in Kazakhstan. Since the end of the Soviet era,

Geographic Themes
Place: Ukraine
Ukrainians shop for goods and produce in a Kiev department store. Nearly 52 million people live in the republic of Ukraine. *What Slavic republics border Ukraine?*

Geographic Themes

Human/Environment Interaction: Russia
For centuries, the Slavic peoples of Russia, Ukraine, and Belarus have used timber from the forests to build *izbas*, or cottages. *What Eurasian republic in the region is not Slavic?*

however, thousands of Russians have returned to Russia.

Another large non-Turkic group in the central Asian republics is the Tajiks, who make up most of the population of Tajikistan. They are descendants of Iranian-speaking people who entered central Asia many centuries ago. The Tajiks speak a language much like Farsi, the major language of Iran.

Caucasian Peoples

One large group of diverse peoples are classified as Caucasian. "The Caucasus presents a living museum of languages and peoples who have lived there since pre-history," says a leading regional writer. Most of these peoples, though, are relatively few in number except for the Armenians, Georgians, and Azeris.

The Armenians, who migrated to the Caucasus many centuries ago, once had a king-dom that stretched from the Mediterranean to the Caucasus. Today the Armenians make up more than 90 percent of the population of Armenia, the smallest of the republics. The Armenians speak their own language and have had their own alphabet and literature for more than 15 centuries.

The Armenian language is very different from the one spoken by Georgians. The Georgian language, also with its own alphabet, is considered a Caucasian language, which means that the Georgians probably originally came from the Caucasus. Language is one of the things in which Georgians take great pride. "Three divine gifts have been bestowed on us by our ancestors: language, homeland, faith," said one Georgian poet.

Like the Armenians, most Georgians are Christians and have their own church. Both are proud that their lands are among the world's oldest Christian countries. Armenia converted to Christianity around A.D. 300. Georgia did the same about 30 years later.

Population Density and Distribution

More than 285 million people live in Russia and the Eurasian republics. Armenia, with about 3.7 million people, and Turkmenistan, with about 4.1 million, have the smallest populations of all the republics. Russia, still the largest country in the world in area, also has the region's largest population—148 million.

Density

More than 285 million people translates into a population density of about 33 persons per square mile (about 13 persons per sq. km). There are not many people in the region compared to the number living in a square mile or kilometer in other parts of the world.

Take the United States, for example. Together Russia and the Eurasian republics are about two and one-half times its size. Yet the population of the United States is only about 26 million less than that of Russia and the other republics. This means that the population of the United States is a little more than twice as dense, with 74 persons per square mile (about 28 persons per sq. km).

Distribution and the Environment

The population of Russia and the Eurasian republics is far from evenly distributed. Many people live in some areas, while hardly any live in others.

Environment has much to do with where people have chosen to live or not live. East of the Ural Mountains, for example, where the climate is harsh and much of the land is mountains or deserts, the population density is low.

However, this is not the case west of the Ural Mountains, between the Baltic and Black seas. Here is where most people of the region

Geographic Themes

Location: Kiev, Ukraine
Kiev, the capital of Ukraine, is located on the banks of the Dnieper River, the major waterway of the republic. *How does environment affect where people live?*

Geographic Themes

Place: Armenia
Armenians gather at a monument to remember the millions of their people who perished in the 1915 Holocaust at the hands of the Ottoman Turks. *What is the capital of the republic of Armenia?*

live, and where the population is most dense. The majority of the large cities and major industrial centers are located in this area, including the three largest cities of the region—Moscow, St. Petersburg, and Kiev. The climate of this western part is the most moderate and cooperative, and here the richest and most fertile farmland lies.

A great many cities dot Russia and the Eurasian republics, especially in the western part. Many cities originally grew up along major rivers because even during the coldest part of the year people and goods could move along them. Even today, all three of the largest cities are linked to major waterways through rivers and canals. In the Caucasus region, the Armenian capital of Yerevan is located on the banks of the Razdan River in the Ararat Valley.

SECTION 1 REVIEW

Checking for Understanding
1. **Define** ethnic group, nationalities.
2. **Locating Places** In what part of the region is population the most dense?
3. **Region** What are three major ethnic groups of Russia and the Eurasian republics?
4. **Place** What are the three largest cities in Russia and the Eurasian republics?

Critical Thinking
5. **Drawing Conclusions** Why are some areas of Russia and the Eurasian republics more densely populated than others?

NATIONAL GEOGRAPHIC
GEOFACTS

Where is the most polluted place on earth?

The shore of a small lake in Russia's heavily industrialized Ural Mountains is considered the most contaminated spot in the world. "No place else on earth can you just stand, and get a lethal dose in an hour," says American physicist Thomas B. Cochran of the Natural Resources Defense Council. A dose of radiation from Lake Karachay would kill a person within weeks.

In the early 1950s, the lake became the repository for radioactive wastes from the nearby nuclear-weapons production complex at Chelyabinsk. When the lake shrank in a 1967 drought, thousands were exposed to wind-borne radioactive dust.

The world's second most polluted place is also found in Russia, at Tomsk. Russian scientists recently disclosed that the former Soviet Union and now Russia have been pumping billions of gallons of radioactive liquid waste directly into the ground at three widely dispersed sites near rivers. The earth around the Tomsk and Krasnoyarsk sites probably contains more nuclear waste than the Karachay area, but is not as accessible or exposed.

▲ Soviet inter-continental ballistic missile.

Barents Sea
Novaya Zemlya
Kara Sea

St. Petersburg
UKRAINE
Moscow
Dimitrovgrad
Black Sea
GEORGIA
Caspian Sea
Aral Sea
KAZAKHSTAN

R U S S I A
URAL MOUNTAINS
Volga
Techa
Tobol
Irtysh
Ob
Ob
Yenisey

Chelyabinsk
Tomsk
Krasnoyarsk

Lake Karachay

Semipalatinsk (Semey)

MONGOLIA
CHINA

0   250 km
0   250 mi.

AREA SHOWN

Legend:
- Nuclear test site
- Plutonium/uranium production
- Nuclear submarine base
- Nuclear weapons production

Designed by BILL PITZER

2 History and Government

SETTING THE SCENE

Read to Discover . . .
- the peoples who populated and created early Russia.
- the rule and power of the czars.
- the rise and fall of the Soviet Union.
- the new independence of Russia and the Eurasian republics.

Key Terms
- czar
- serf
- socialism
- russification
- communism
- *perestroika*
- *glasnost*

Identify and Locate
Dnieper River, Baltic Sea, Volga River, Caspian Sea, Kiev, Moskva River, Moscow, Siberia, St. Petersburg

Russia and the Eurasian republics have a long history as rich and diverse as the land and the peoples who occupy it. Over thousands of years, different peoples have come and gone. Each has left its mark on the land, and each, in turn, was influenced by the land, the climate, and the environment.

MOVEMENT

Early Peoples and States

In ancient times, people were living in and farming much of the land that is now Russia and the Eurasian republics. Over time, different groups came and went. Some were hunters and gatherers, others were nomads, and still others were farmers. Said one Russian expert:

———— ◈ ————

The picture we obtain from the written sources is that of a bewildering procession of tribes and nations which every few centuries succeed each other on the steppes, only to sweep each other off the map.

———— ◈ ————

River Settlers and Towns

Among the many groups who over the centuries cut through the mountain passes and crossed the valleys and plains of the region were Slavs, who came from the northernmost part of eastern Europe. Over time they spread throughout the western part of the region. Some settled near the Dnieper River, which was part of a chain of waterways that led to the Baltic Sea. Others settled near the Volga River, which was a trade route to the Caspian Sea. Before long the Slavs built trading towns along the rivers. These towns became links in a trade route that joined the Slavs with peoples in the Mediterranean, western Europe, and Scandinavia.

In the 800s, fierce warrior-traders from Scandinavia, called Varangians, settled near the Dnieper and the Volga. The area they settled became known as Kievan Rus. In time one of their leaders set up the first state in the region at Kiev, a trading town on the Dnieper.

By the 900s the Varangians had adopted the Slavs' language and many of their customs and had organized the trading towns into city-states. Before long the Slavs organized into a loose union in which each city-state was ruled by a prince. Kiev became the capital and its ruler the Grand Prince.

Geographic Themes

Place: Red Square, Moscow
Early Russian rulers built a huge fortress called the Kremlin in the heart of Moscow. It later became the seat of government and a religious center. *Who was the first Russian czar?*

Mongols

In the early 1200s warriors known as Mongols invaded from central Asia and destroyed Kiev. Ultimately they conquered much of the Slav territories and made them part of their vast empire. Although they allowed the Slavs self-rule, they continued to control the area for more than 200 years, cutting many of the Slavs off from European civilization.

When the Mongols first overran Kiev, many Slavs living there had fled into nearby forests. Later some of those people settled along the Moskva River. In time their settlement grew into the city of Moscow, known then as Muscovy (muh•SKOH•vee). For nearly two centuries, its princes kept peace with the Mongol rulers. Finally, in the 1400s, a Grand Prince of Muscovy named Ivan conquered other Slavic princes, set up a Russian state, and drove out the Mongols.

The Rule of the Czars

Ivan became Ivan III, later known as Ivan the Great, the first **czar,** or supreme ruler, of all Russia. Moscow became the religious and political center of Russia.

In the late 1500s, Russia began to expand its territory and kept on expanding for the next several hundred years. With the new territories came new non-Russian peoples.

A Window to the West

Europeans had made many achievements. They moved forward and left Russia far behind, especially in scientific knowledge and technology. Then, in the late 1600s, Czar Peter I came to power determined to modernize Russia and make it into a European nation.

Peter made war to get some of the things he wanted. From Sweden, for example, he won the seaports he needed along the Baltic Sea to give his country access to major sea routes and increase its trade with northwest and Mediterranean Europe. His hard-won seaports could be used year-round.

Under Peter, who came to be known as Peter the Great, Russia's territory expanded, its naval strength increased, its trade multiplied, and a new capital city—St. Petersburg—was carved out of the wilderness. Built on land along the Gulf of Finland, St. Petersburg was Peter's "window to the West."

Seeds of Discontent

By the late 1800s, the Russian people were tired of war and resentful of the iron rule of the czars and their secret police. Peasants and **serfs,** laborers owned by nobles and bound to the land, lived in poverty and were treated like enslaved persons. The life of factory workers in the cities was not much better. Many thinkers were unhappy as well. They favored **socialism,** a philosophy that called for ownership of all land and factories by peasants and workers.

Geographic Themes

Place: St. Petersburg, Russia

During the 1700s and 1800s, Russian czars built beautiful palaces on the outskirts of St. Petersburg. *Why did Peter the Great move the capital from Moscow to St. Petersburg?*

Frustrated and discontented, many Russians took to heart the writings of a German philosopher, Karl Marx. He believed that in time the conflict between landowners and the working class would lead to a workers' revolution that would spread all over the world. Out of this revolution, he said, would arise a new, classless society.

The few reforms the czars made—freeing the serfs and promoting education—were not enough. To unify the people, the government began a program of **russification** that required everyone in the empire to speak Russian and to become Eastern Orthodox Christians. The policy only made matters worse.

World War I brought more hardship—and more protests. Food, clothing, fuel, weapons, and ammunition all were in short supply. Thousands of striking factory workers demanding "bread and freedom" overran the streets of Petrograd, previously St. Petersburg. After a few days, the government called in the army to end the demonstrations. Most of the soldiers, though, ended up joining the demonstrators. Finally, in March 1917, the czar abdicated, and the rule of the czars came to an end.

PLACE

The Soviet Era

The new government did not last. In November 1917, a group of revolutionaries known as Bolsheviks (BOHL•shuh•viks) took over the city of Petrograd and proclaimed a socialist revolution.

Birth of a New Nation

The Bolsheviks set up a new government headed by a revolutionary named Vladimir Ilyich Lenin. Lenin, whose political ideas were based on the teachings of Karl Marx, promised the Russian people "peace, land, and bread." His government withdrew from World War I, moved the capital back to Moscow, took control of industry and church property, and promised workers an eight-hour workday.

Not all Russians agreed with **communism**, the teachings of Marx and Lenin, and war soon broke out between the Bolsheviks—Reds—and anti-Bolsheviks—Whites. In 1921 the Bolsheviks, now known as Communists, won the war. The next year they established a new nation—the Union of Soviet Socialist Re-

RUSSIAN AND SOVIET EXPANSION

Kievan Territory
1360-1524
1524-1689
1689-1917
1917-1945
Boundary of
Soviet Union in 1945

Lambert Equal-Area projection

FOCUS ON GEOGRAPHIC THEMES

1. **Location:** What effect did location have on the economic development of the earliest Slavic territories?
2. **Region:** When did the lands of central Asia come under Russian rule?
3. **Movement:** Why did Russian and Soviet leaders expand into new territories?

publics (USSR), or Soviet Union. Made up of Russia, Ukraine, Byelorussia, and the Transcaucasus, its capital was Moscow.

Building and Expanding the Communist State

In the late 1920s a new leader, Joseph Stalin, came to power and set about making the Soviet Union one of the world's greatest industrial powers. To accomplish this goal, his government took control of industrial and farm production. Millions of people, however, died or were sent to labor camps as Stalin ruthlessly strengthened his hold over the country.

By the end of 1940, the Soviet Union was a nation of 15 republics. By the middle of the next year, the Soviets found themselves under attack by the Germans, caught in another world war. The war took more than 30 million Soviet lives, but the nation came out of it stronger than ever. The Soviets had expanded their territory and spread communism to eastern Europe.

Now a superpower in competition with the United States, the Soviet Union became involved in a cold war with non-Communist countries, a war in which it sought world influence by any means short of total war. The cold war continued well into the 1980s.

In 1985 a new leader, Mikhail Gorbachev, took power. He thought that the country could not survive without "restructuring," which he called *perestroika* (pehr•ehs•TROY•kah), and a new openness, or *glasnost.* Gorbachev's reforms were not enough.

New Republics

By 1990 many people were dissatisfied with the way communism was working. By the end of the year, the Baltic republics of Latvia, Lithuania, and Estonia had declared their independence, and all the other republics had declared some freedoms.

In the summer of 1991, the Soviet republic of Russia held its first democratic election for president. The new president, Boris Yeltsin, backed Gorbachev when some others turned against him and tried to strengthen the government, but it was too late to save the Soviet Union. By mid-December, all the republics had declared their independence.

Russia's Yeltsin met with the leaders of Ukraine and Belarus, and they announced that they had united to form a new community—the Commonwealth of Independent States (CIS)—in which each member republic was independent and had its own government and constitution. They invited all the other republics to join. By late December all the former Soviet republics except Latvia, Lithuania, Estonia, and Georgia had done so, making the CIS the largest federation of separate republics in the world. In 1992 Azerbaijan left the CIS, but later rejoined. Georgia also became a member. Today the Soviet Union and the cold war belong to the past, and the "new" republics are trying to come to terms with the changes brought by their independence.

In Russia, Yeltsin introduced economic reforms to move the economy toward free enterprise. A better future was promised to the Russian people; but in the short term, the reforms brought increased hardships. Taking advantage of widespread dissatisfaction, extreme nationalists and Communists tried to undermine Yeltsin, while Yeltsin sought to increase his powers.

In 1993 Yeltsin succeeded in blocking a Communist attempt to seize control of the government. A few months later, however, voters gave only partial support to Yeltsin. They approved a new constitution granting him sweeping powers, but many of them

Geographic Themes

Place: Moscow, Russia
After the collapse of the Soviet Union, Boris Yeltsin emerged as the leader of Russia. *What organization replaced the Soviet Union?*

protested against reforms by electing anti-Yeltsin candidates—mostly extreme nationalists and Communists—to the Russian parliament. Analysts predicted continued political instability as Yeltsin and his parliamentary opponents competed for control of Russia.

SECTION 2 REVIEW

Checking for Understanding
1. **Define** czar, serf, socialism, russification, communism, *perestroika, glasnost.*
2. **Locating Places** Where did the Slavs and Varangians settle?
3. **Movement** Why did Peter the Great want to acquire land along the Baltic Sea?
4. **Place** What did the Soviets gain from World War II?

Critical Thinking
5. **Expressing Problems Clearly** Why were most Russians discontented under czarist rule?

THE UNCONQUERABLE RUSSIAN WINTER

As you read, examine how natural forces affected Napoleon's efforts to conquer Russia.

In the spring of 1812, French ruler Napoleon Bonaparte began an assault on Russia. Napoleon had signed an alliance with Russia's czar, Alexander I, in 1807. Alexander, however, had not stopped trade with Great Britain, as the pact demanded. Napoleon decided that Alexander needed to be taught a lesson.

To Moscow

Leading an army of more than 600,000, Napoleon crossed into Russia from Poland, over the Nieman River. The Russians, outnumbered 3 to 1, fought fiercely and retreated slowly, destroying anything that Napoleon might have used as supplies for his troops. Led deeper and deeper into Russia, Napoleon found his supply lines getting longer, thinner, and less reliable. It was also getting later in the year: winter was approaching.

Napoleon and his forces pursued the Russians all the way to Moscow. When he arrived, however, Napoleon found himself the conqueror of a burning, deserted ruin. The Russians had set fire to Moscow and relocated to St. Petersburg. It took the French

Napoleon and his troops retreat from Moscow to face the long and bitter Russian winter.

army a month to stop the flames.

The Russian Winter Wins

During that month, Napoleon offered Czar Alexander a truce. However, the Russian winter had set in. Knowing the Russian winter as Napoleon did not, the czar refused.

The days grew colder; supplies dwindled. When Napoleon learned that thousands of his soldiers were suffering from frostbite and freezing to death, he ordered his troops to abandon Moscow.

During the retreat, the horrendous cold and blinding snowstorms of Russia's winter killed more than 90,000 of the 100,000 troops that left Moscow. A scant 9,000 straggled into Poland during the winter months. The Russian winter accomplished what Europe's leaders could not: Napoleon's defeat.

Checking for Understanding

1. How did the Russians use the size of their country to defeat Napoleon?

2. **Location** How did Russia's location help defeat Napoleon?

Cultures and Lifestyles

For the more than 70 years that the Soviets were in power, they tried to convince the peoples of Russia and the Eurasian republics to abandon their religious beliefs. They made Russian the language of all the schools and worked to glorify communism. They influenced everything from the holidays celebrated to the quality of life. Now everything is different.

REGION

Religion

The Soviets thought that the peoples of the republics should be **atheists**, or nonbelievers, and closed down or destroyed many houses of worship. In 1988, when Mikhail Gorbachev allowed more religious freedom, people of all ages flocked to religious services. The religious revival has continued in the post-Communist era.

Christianity

Many people who practice a religion in Russia and the Eurasian republics practice some form of Christianity. Although some Christians are Protestant or Roman Catholic, most belong to the Eastern Orthodox Church, which is made up of separate, self-governing churches. Most Russians, for example, are members of the Russian Orthodox Church, and most Ukrainians belong to the Ukrainian Orthodox Church. A cornerstone of both is the use of **icons**, or intricate religious images, many of which are hundreds of years old.

Geographic Themes

Place: Moscow, Russia
Russian Orthodox worshippers pray in one of Moscow's newly restored churches. *What art form plays an important role in Russian and Ukrainian Orthodox worship?*

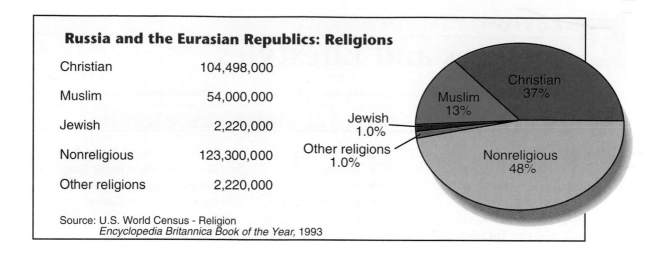

Russia and the Eurasian Republics: Religions

Christian	104,498,000
Muslim	54,000,000
Jewish	2,220,000
Nonreligious	123,300,000
Other religions	2,220,000

Christian 37%
Muslim 13%
Jewish 1.0%
Other religions 1.0%
Nonreligious 48%

Source: U.S. World Census - Religion
Encyclopedia Britannica Book of the Year, 1993

Two other republics, Georgia and Armenia, have strong national churches whose membership grew even under Soviet rule. The center of Georgian Orthodoxy is Sveti Tskhoveli, the Pillar of Life church in Mtskheta, still in use today. Most Armenians, both in Armenia and in neighboring Azerbaijan, belong to the Armenian Apostolic Church. Although its rites are similar to Eastern Orthodox rites, the Armenian Church was founded in the 300s. Like Eastern Orthodox churches, it has a leader called a **patriarch.** The patriarch lives in a monastery not far from the Armenian capital of Yerevan.

Islam

Islam has the second-largest number of followers in the region. Most Muslims live in the central Asian republics of Tajikistan, Uzbekistan, Turkmenistan, and Kyrgyzstan. Together the republics of the region have a Muslim population of 54 million. Most Kazakhs and Azeris also are Muslims. So are most people in the area of Ukraine called the Crimea.

Most Muslims in Russia and the Eurasian republics belong to a sect of Islam known as Sunni, the same sect as those of Saudi Arabia, Turkey, and Afghanistan. An exception is the Azeris. They are Shiite, the same sect as the Muslims of Iran.

Judaism

Over many centuries the Jews in the region suffered from prejudice and discrimination. In czarist Russia Jews were allowed to settle only certain areas, and they were often the target of organized persecution and massacres known as **pogroms.** This persecution continued under the Soviets and became particularly brutal when the invading Nazis shipped hundreds of thousands of Jews to death camps.

In recent years large numbers of Jews have been emigrating, often to Israel or the United States. Some, however, have fought hard to keep their religious and cultural identity and want to stay where they are.

PLACE

Education

The region's literacy rate is extremely high. This high rate is largely the result of the former Soviet rulers' emphasis on free education from grade school through college and the requirement that all children go to school for at least 10 years.

The Soviet Legacy

After independence the republics faced some education-related problems that they have been working to resolve. Most textbooks, for example, must be replaced because they are outdated and were written from the Soviet Communist point of view. Some of the schools need repairs. Others do not have plumbing or running water. Many are short of supplies, especially modern equipment like computers.

As under the Soviets, there are several different kinds of schools students can attend. Vocational schools teach skills such as plumbing or carpentry; technical schools prepare students for jobs in areas like medicine or teaching; and some schools offer courses in farming or language skills. Which kind of high school a student goes to depends on how well he or she does on a national exam that every student must take at the end of ninth grade.

Local and Regional Needs

Since becoming independent, most republics have been making changes that reflect their own local and regional needs. Ukraine, for example, revised the courses taught and made Ukrainian—instead of Russian—the language of the classroom. Children now start school when they are 6 years old and cannot quit until they have finished the ninth grade. High school graduates may go on to a vocational school, an institute, or a university.

Moldova, where most of the people are of Romanian heritage, has taken steps to reverse Soviet efforts to stifle Romanian culture. The Soviets, for example, did not allow the Romanian language to be used in the schools, and gave Russian and Ukrainian students in Moldova first choice of institutions of higher education. Now Romanian is the language of the schools, and the Moldovan educational system has close ties with the Romanian one.

Armenia's leaders also have been reforming their educational system. In Armenia most children start school when they are 6 years old. The government has opened many elementary schools, but there is still a shortage of high schools. Students do not have to pay for their university education, but there is not enough space for every student. Only those who pass difficult exams are admitted.

In Azerbaijan, where there are thousands of elementary and high schools and more than a dozen institutions of higher learning, religion has been returned to the schools. Copies of the Quran, the holy text of Islam, have been provided by some countries in Southwest Asia. Iran is even sending Islamic teachers to provide religious instruction.

The Arts

Russia and the Eurasian republics have a strong cultural tradition that dates back to times long past. The modern governments are attempting to encourage the arts as symbols of national pride.

The Golden Years

The truly golden age of culture—a time when Russian painters, musicians, composers, and writers created works recognized and admired all over the world—was the 1800s and early 1900s.

During this period, Russian painters like Ilya Repin and Isaak Levitan used their talents not only to portray historical and contemporary scenes but also the beauty of the Russian countryside. In the early 1900s, Kasimir Malevich, Wasily Kandinsky, and other artists contributed to the rise of modern art. Meanwhile, Russian composers produced outstanding

Geographic Themes

Human/Environment Interaction: Fabergé Egg
Russia's most famous jeweler, Carl Fabergé, crafted a series of these elaborate eggs from gold, silver, enamel, and precious stones. *When was Russia's golden age of culture?*

Geographic Themes

Region: Central Asia
The people of Uzbekistan in central Asia enliven their festivities with traditional folk dancing. *Why do modern governments encourage the arts?*

musical works. Peter Tchaikovsky composed the dramatic *1812 Overture,* the light and playful *Nutcracker Suite,* and the romantic *Swan Lake* and *Sleeping Beauty;* Nikolay Rimsky-Korsakov wrote many of his symphonies and ballets; and Modest Mussorgsky composed the opera *Boris Godunov.*

Above all, this was an age of great Russian and Ukrainian writers who rank among the best in the history of world literature—Leo Tolstoy, Fyodor Dostoyevsky, Anton Chekhov, Ivan Turgenev, Alexander Pushkin, Nikolay Gogol, Maxim Gorky. Most wrote about the society, politics, and events of their times, mirroring both the extravagant life led by the rich and the sufferings of the poor.

Contemporary Times

The people kept their passion for culture in Soviet times, and artists of all kinds continued to contribute. The Soviet government, however, severely limited artistic freedom.

The government believed that a work of art had to agree with and praise everything Soviet and ignore any Soviet faults. Writers, painters, and other artists who did not go along with this type of art, known as **socialist realism**, were punished in a number of different ways. Alexander Solzhenitsyn, for example, was forced to leave the country because his books criticized the government.

When the Soviet Union ceased to exist, so did most of the restrictions on artists. Now artists in Russia and the Eurasian republics have the freedom to be artistic, to freely express, exhibit, and publish their ideas and beliefs.

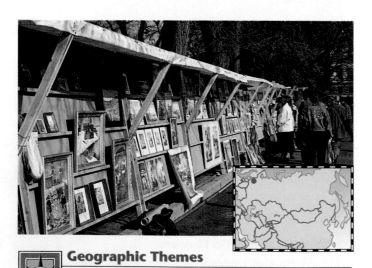

Geographic Themes

Place: Outdoor Art Exhibit, St. Petersburg
Today Russian artists can freely paint and exhibit their works. *What was the artistic policy of Russia's former Communist leaders?*

Life and Leisure

During Soviet rule, the people of the region knew with some certainty what they could and could not do and what to expect or not expect. Whether they lived in the city or the countryside, lifestyle was controlled by the Soviet government.

Way of Life

Under the new regimes, many people in the rural areas still cling to traditional ways. Uzbeks, for example, use the same farming methods that their ancestors used hundreds of years ago.

In the cities, most people live in high-rise apartments, often under crowded conditions. Even though the Soviets built huge numbers of new apartments over the years, there still are not enough to go around, especially in the large cities.

Leisure-time Activities

The people of Russia and the Eurasian republics enjoy many different activities during their free time, from watching television to playing chess in the park to going to a concert, a lecture, a seminar, the theater, or a movie. Almost everyone enjoys reading, especially now that they can buy books, magazines, and newspapers that the Soviets once banned.

Many people enjoy outdoor activities such as skiing, ice skating, hiking, camping, mountain climbing, and hunting. They also relish sports like soccer, ice hockey, and tennis.

Holidays and Celebrations

In most republics, families and friends enjoy celebrating holidays and other special occasions. During these festivities, they enjoy generous amounts of food and drink.

Holidays and celebrations are characterized by the blending of old folk practices with newer traditions. Most ethnic groups have their own traditional dances, costumes, and folk music, which are part of the festivities.

On May 1—May Day—when many nations traditionally celebrated the arrival of spring, people in the former Soviet Union celebrated the Communists and their achievements. Since independence, though, fireworks are set off, and people celebrate both the worker and the arrival of spring.

Geographic Themes

Location: Urban Russia
Many people in Russia and the Eurasian republics still have to cope with housing shortages. *In what kind of dwellings do most urban residents live?*

SECTION 3 REVIEW

Checking for Understanding

1. **Define** atheist, icon, patriarch, pogrom, socialist realism.
2. **Locating Places** What are the major religions of Russia and the Eurasian republics?
3. **Place** In what ways did the Soviets restrict religious freedom?
4. **Place** What education-related problems do the Eurasian republics face?

Critical Thinking

5. **Making Generalizations** What generalization might you make about the role of the arts in Russia and the Eurasian republics?

MAP & GRAPH SKILLS

Reading a Bar Graph

Graphs illustrate numerical data and relationships in a clear visual format. One of the most common ways to show statistical information is the **bar graph.**

REVIEWING THE SKILL

In a bar graph, bars of various lengths represent different quantities. The bars can be drawn vertically or horizontally. In either arrangement, labels on the two axes of the graph identify what the bars represent.

Some bar graphs illustrate changes over time. Other bar graphs compare measurements occurring at the same time, but in different locations.

To read a bar graph, apply the following steps:

• Read the graph title to identify the subject of the graph.

• Study the information presented on the horizontal and vertical axes and the use of colors on the graph.

• Compare the lengths of the bars and look for relationships among the data.

PRACTICING THE SKILL

Use the graphs below to answer the following questions:

1. In what year were the populations of Moldova and Tajikistan about equal?
2. In 1991, which country had a larger population?
3. According to Graph A, which country is growing more quickly?
4. Of the countries shown in Graph B, which country is growing most slowly? Which is growing most quickly?
5. In which countries does population grow at a rate of less than 1 percent each year?

For additional practice in this skill, see Practicing Skills on page 324 of the Chapter 15 Review.

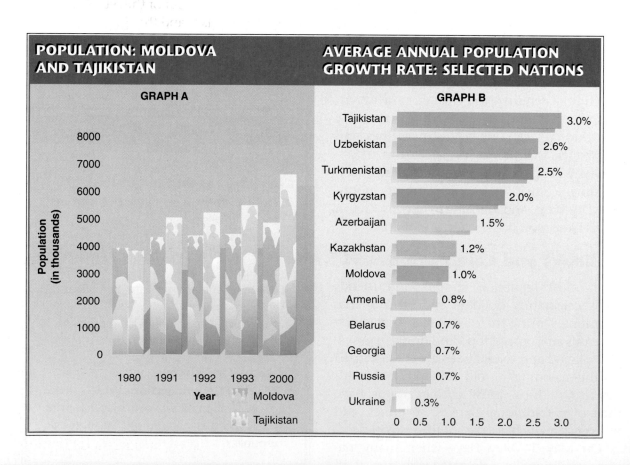

POPULATION: MOLDOVA AND TAJIKISTAN

GRAPH A

Population (in thousands)

8000
7000
6000
5000
4000
3000
2000
1000
0

1980 1991 1992 1993 2000
Year   Moldova   Tajikistan

AVERAGE ANNUAL POPULATION GROWTH RATE: SELECTED NATIONS

GRAPH B

Tajikistan	3.0%
Uzbekistan	2.6%
Turkmenistan	2.5%
Kyrgyzstan	2.0%
Azerbaijan	1.5%
Kazakhstan	1.2%
Moldova	1.0%
Armenia	0.8%
Belarus	0.7%
Georgia	0.7%
Russia	0.7%
Ukraine	0.3%

0   0.5   1.0   1.5   2.0   2.5   3.0

SECTION	KEY TERMS	SUMMARY
1 Population Patterns	ethnic group (p. 305) nationalities (p. 305)	• Both Russia and each of the Eurasian republics has its own official language. • Three major ethnic groups—Slavs, Turkic peoples, and Caucasian peoples—live in Russia and the Eurasian republics. • Population is not evenly distributed across Russia and the Eurasian republics. • In the past most of the people of Russia and the Eurasian republics lived in the countryside; today they live in the city.

Panoramic view of Kiev, Ukraine

SECTION	KEY TERMS	SUMMARY
2 History and Government	czar (p. 312) serf (p. 312) socialism (p. 312) russification (p. 313) communism (p. 313) *perestroika* (p. 314) *glasnost* (p. 314)	• The first Slavic state in the region grew out of the settlements of the Slavs and the Varangians. • Under the czars, Russia became one of the largest empires in the world. • In the early 1900s the Russian Empire became a new nation called the Union of Soviet Socialist Republics, which for more than 70 years was under Communist rule. • All of the former republics of the Soviet Union, which ceased to exist in the early 1990s, are now independent states.

Moscow's Red Square and Kremlin

SECTION	KEY TERMS	SUMMARY
3 Cultures and Lifestyles	atheist (p. 317) icon (p. 317) patriarch (p. 318) pogrom (p. 318) socialist realism (p. 320)	• The three major religions of Christianity, Islam, and Judaism, as well as a number of other faiths, are now practiced openly in Russia and the Eurasian republics. • The people of Russia and the Eurasian republics have strong cultural traditions and are devoted to the arts. They have diverse lifestyles and enjoy a variety of different celebrations.

Folk dancers in central Asia

Reviewing Key Terms

Choose the vocabulary term that best completes each of the sentences below. Write your answers on a separate sheet of paper.

ethnic group (p. 305)
nationalities (p. 305)
czar (p. 312)
socialism (p. 312)
glasnost (p. 314)
patriarch (p. 318)
pogroms (p. 318)

SECTION 1

1. Under the Soviets, republics were based on _____ .
2. Slavs make up the largest _____ in Russia and the Eurasian republics.

SECTION 2

3. For more than 400 years the supreme ruler of all Russia was the _____ .
4. The Bolsheviks believed in the philosophy of _____ .
5. The new "openness" in the Soviet Union in the late 1980s was known as _____ .

SECTION 3

6. The world leader of the Armenian Apostolic Church is called a _____ .
7. The organized persecution and massacres suffered by Jews in czarist Russia are known as _____ .

Reviewing Facts

SECTION 1

8. In which European republic are Slavs in the minority?
9. Where do most Turkic peoples of Russia and the Eurasian republics live?

SECTION 2

10. Who was Russia's first democratically elected president?

11. Which former Soviet republic did not become a member of the CIS?

SECTION 3

12. To what church do most Christians in the former Soviet Union belong?
13. To what does the phrase "Russia's golden age of culture" refer?

Critical Thinking

14. **Making Comparisons**   What do Armenians and Georgians have in common? In what ways are they different?
15. **Analyzing Information**   Explain why you agree or disagree with this statement: "The Soviet experience was 70 years on the road to nowhere."
16. **Making Comparisons**   In what ways is education in Russia and the Eurasian republics like that in your town? In what ways is it different?

Geographic Themes

17. **Human/Environment Interaction** Where did many of the cities of Russia and the Eurasian republics originally develop?
18. **Place**   How did the city of Moscow come into existence?
19. **Movement**   What invasion disrupted Slavic links to Europe?

Practicing Skills

Reading a Bar Graph

Refer to the bar graphs on page 322. How does Graph B support the information presented in Graph A? In which sections of Russia and the Eurasian republics is the population growing most rapidly?

Using the Unit Atlas

Refer to the cultural geography section of the Unit Atlas on pages 284–285.

20. Why do so few people live in Siberia?
21. What central Asian cities were ancient crossroads of trade?
22. What is the second-largest group of people in Russia and the Eurasian republics?

Projects

Individual Activity

Select one of the writers named in the chapter. Research the writer's life and then read one of his works. Then write a brief review of the work.

Cooperative Learning Activity

Working in a group of five, have each member do research to determine what territory Russia acquired during one of these periods: 1400–1500, 1500–1600, 1600–1700, 1800–1900, 1900–1945. Then, as a group, using a different color to represent each period, construct a map showing Russian expansion.

Writing About Geography

Comparison

Select two capital cities, one in a republic west of the Ural Mountains and the other in a republic east of the Ural Mountains. Using your journal record and resources available in your school or public library, research both cities. Then write a one-page comparison of the two cities.

Locating Places

THE PHYSICAL GEOGRAPHY OF RUSSIA AND THE EURASIAN REPUBLICS

Match the letters on the map with the places and physical features of Russia and the Eurasian republics. Write your answers on a separate sheet of paper.

1. Black Sea
2. Moldova
3. Moscow
4. St. Petersburg
5. Kiev
6. Dnieper River
7. Baltic Sea
8. Yerevan
9. Yenisey River
10. Volga River

chapter 16

Russia and the Eurasian Republics Today

CHAPTER FOCUS

Geographic Setting

Most of the heavy industry of Russia and the Eurasian republics is located north of the Black Sea and in the Ural Mountains, where energy resources and raw materials are readily available.

Geographic Themes

Section 1 Living in Russia and the Eurasian Republics

PLACE Russia and the Eurasian republics are trying to move away from the single, centrally controlled economy to various free enterprise economies.

Section 2 People and Their Environment

HUMAN/ENVIRONMENT INTERACTION The badly damaged and heavily polluted environment is a matter of great concern throughout Russia and the Eurasian republics.

▲ **Photograph:** *Street vendors in Bukhara, Uzbekistan*

Living in Russia and the Eurasian Republics

SETTING THE SCENE

Read to Discover . . .
- how the economies of Russia and the Eurasian republics changed after independence.
- how agriculture and industry in Russia and the Eurasian republics changed after independence.
- how the communication and transportation systems of Russia and the Eurasian republics work.
- what economic ties bind Russia and the Eurasian republics.

Key Terms
- command economy
- consumer goods
- black market
- market economy
- *sovkhozes*
- *kolkhozes*

Identify and Locate
Kazakhstan, Baku, Baltic Sea, White Sea, Don River, Black Sea, Vladivostok, Lake Baikal, Amur River, Polotsk, Mozyr, Tbilisi

УЗБЕКИСТОН
1993 UZBEKISTAN

5·00

Remiz pendulinus

Fergana, Uzbekistan
Dobry dyen, I am writing to you from my summer house in the mountains. It is cool up here, even when it is hot down in the valley. Yesterday we had a picnic by a beautiful waterfall. The water comes from a large glacier on the mountain and flows down into the valley. Please come visit me sometime.
Your friend,
Tatyana Yeremenko

Tatyana Yeremenko writes from Uzbekistan, a Eurasian republic that relies on irrigation for its productive agriculture. For many decades, the economies of Russia, Uzbekistan, Ukraine, and the other Eurasian republics were in the hands of the Soviets. The Soviets ran their vast nation as a single economy, one of the largest centrally planned economies in the world. Today, however, each republic is moving at its own rate, trying to make its own way, and struggling to develop its own separate economic path.

REGION

Changing Economies

As Russia and the Eurasian republics make the transition to generally free enterprise economies, they must meet the challenges of providing sufficient food and jobs for their citizens. They must also compete successfully in world markets by producing goods efficiently and cost-effectively.

Geographic Themes

Place: Minsk, Belarus
Belarusian shoppers make purchases in a Minsk department store. *During the Soviet period, what problems did shoppers face in finding food or clothing?*

The Soviet Command Economy

Under the Soviets, Russia and the Eurasian republics had what is known as a **command economy**, an economy in which some central authority makes economic decisions. The Soviet government owned most of the banks, factories, land, mines, and transportation systems. It decided what and how much to produce, how to go about producing, and who would benefit. It also planned and controlled the distribution and pricing of most goods.

Most people worked for the state. While there was no unemployment, no one was paid very much. The government's main concern was heavy industry, the manufacture of such goods as machinery, electric generators, tanks, and military hardware. It was not particularly interested in services or **consumer goods** such as bicycles, shoes, and toys.

This attitude helped make the Soviet Union a leading industrial giant. At the same time, it meant that very often people had to do without many things. Often people could find some items on the **black market,** the ille-

gal market where goods were sold at much higher prices than those set by the government. Very few Soviet citizens, however, could afford to pay the inflated prices.

When Mikhail Gorbachev came to power in the mid-1980s, he admitted what most people had known for some time—the strictly state-controlled system was not working. Gorbachev wanted to move toward a **market economy** like the one in the United States, a free enterprise economy in which businesses are privately owned and what people buy or do not buy determines what and how much is produced.

So, as part of his policy of perestroika, or restructuring, Gorbachev began cutting back the central government's rigid economic controls and allowing local leaders to make more decisions. He also allowed Soviet citizens to start small- and medium-sized businesses and encouraged investment from the West. Even though other reforms followed, they could not save the Soviet system.

The New Economies

When Russia and the other republics became independent, each moved to take charge of its own economy. For each, this has meant a certain amount of burden and pain.

Of all the republics, Russia has probably moved the fastest to create a market economy and private enterprise. State-set prices for most goods were lifted the first week of January 1992. The effect was startling. In no time at all prices skyrocketed by as much as 350 percent. By the end of the month, however, more goods had begun to appear in stores, and prices had started to come down a little. The same year, a plan to turn over state businesses to private owners was initiated.

Although this and other economic reforms represented progress, they have caused hardship for many Russians. The salaries of most Russian workers have not kept pace with rising prices. Food and clothing are still not as plentiful as they should be. Workers are no longer guaranteed employment, and some businesses have had to close their doors. Other republics face many of the same problems.

Agriculture and Industry

Under the Soviets, the government controlled agriculture and industry. In its efforts to make the Soviet Union one of the leading industrial countries of the world, the government pushed steadily forward, ignoring the wants and needs of its people.

The Soviet System

Under the Soviets, most farmers worked on huge state-owned-and-run farms called *sovkhozes* or on large collective farms called *kolkhozes*. The state paid sovkhoz workers wages for the number of items they produced, all of which they turned over to the government. Peasant families worked the kolkhoz. Each family had its own home, household goods, a few animals, and a small plot of land. Everything else, from livestock to buildings to machinery, belonged to the government, which for a set price bought a specific amount of everything the workers produced.

Government control was as strong—or stronger—when it came to industry. Government was the only employer. People worked where the government told them and accepted the wages the government was willing to pay. Government agencies ran the factories. In

RUSSIA AND THE EURASIAN REPUBLICS: ECONOMIC ACTIVITY

Legend:
- Nomadic herding
- Hunting and gathering
- Forestry
- Livestock raising
- Commercial farming
- Subsistence farming
- Manufacturing and trade
- Commercial fishing
- Little or no activity

Lambert Equal-Area projection

FOCUS ON GEOGRAPHIC THEMES

1. **Region:** What are the leading economic activities in Ukraine and central Russia?
2. **Human/Environment Interaction:** How does climate affect the types of economic activity in the northern parts of Russia?
3. **Location:** Where are manufacturing centers in the region concentrated?

most cases workers were paid not for the number of hours they worked but for the number of "pieces" they produced.

Both agriculture and industry suffered because workers were not motivated. They had no reason to be because all decisions were made for them, including exactly how much they had to produce within a given time. For many years, factory managers were not even allowed to buy raw materials on their own.

Change came first under perestroika. Factory managers were given much greater freedom to decide what and how much to produce. Farmers were encouraged to leave the state-run farms and lease land, equipment, buildings, and other property from the government.

Changing Farms and Factories

Reform and change continued after independence. Because each republic was different, however, problems, reactions, and solutions have been different as well.

Take Ukraine and Russia, for example. Ukraine was the Soviet Union's most productive farm area, and its industry was vital to the Soviet economy. Russia too had much fertile land, but it had to import most of its grain be-

Geographic Themes

Region: Ukrainian Steppes
Ukraine is a rich agricultural area that provides grain to Russia and the other Eurasian republics. *How much of Ukraine's land is being farmed or used as pasture?*

cause its farms did not produce well. At the same time, though, Russia had some of the world's largest steel mills, automobile and truck factories, and chemical plants.

Today both Ukraine and Russia want people to have their own farms and are encouraging foreign investment in industry. About one-third of Ukraine's land is being farmed or used as pasture, and Ukrainian coal and iron-ore mines supply raw materials to plants in several major industrial centers. Meanwhile, Russian farms still are not producing well, and most Russian factories have been finding it hard to compete with the better-equipped, more up-to-date, and more progressive Asian and European firms.

Belarus has many of the same goals as Russia and Ukraine but a slightly different set of circumstances and problems. Until a few years ago, more than one-third of its land was being farmed. Then, in 1986, radiation from the damaged Chernobyl nuclear plant located in Ukraine contaminated almost 20 percent of the fertile soil, forcing some areas to stop growing crops entirely. Manufacturing provides more than half of its income. The republic, however, has to import most of the raw materials its industry uses, and most factories are finding it very hard, if not impossible, to get the parts they need to make finished goods. The government has been trying to help industry, but the process is a slow one.

The histories of Azerbaijan and Kazakhstan are very different from those of Russia, Ukraine, or Belarus. The Soviets forced the Azeris to put aside traditional crops to raise specialized crops like peaches and melons, threatened them with prison or death if they refused to combine their farms into huge estates to grow cotton for Soviet textile mills, and took over all the Azeri industries, including the valuable oil industry. They made Kazakhstan part of the Virgin Lands project, sent thousands of Russian and Ukrainian farmers there to plow up and plant millions of acres of steppes, and changed for all times not only the land itself but the makeup of the people who lived on it.

Today Azerbaijan earns a fair amount of export income from agriculture, especially from cotton, and Kazakhstan is an important grain-producing area. Azerbaijan has developed a large-scale petrochemical industry, and the port city of Baku is fast becoming an important shipbuilding hub. The government of Kazakhstan, meanwhile, is pressing hard and fast to put industry in the hands of private owners. The government also has opened the border with China in the hope that Chinese businesspeople will consider doing business in Kazakhstan.

MOVEMENT

Communications and Transportation

There is a saying that a nation is only as strong as its systems of communications and transportation. In Russia and the Eurasian republics, the communications systems are not as highly developed as the governments would like, and railroads are still the major means of transportation.

Communications

Under the Soviets, the government owned and controlled all the mass-communication networks from newspapers and magazines to postal, telegraph, and telephone services. Censorship committees reviewed everything and made sure that there was no criticism of the government. The media was a way to manipulate the news and put forth Communist views and beliefs. The people and news reporters from other countries got their information from a special Soviet news agency called Tass that dispensed official government statements and commentary.

With independence came greater freedom of expression. For the most part, now there is little or no government censorship. People can read books, newspapers, and magazines that once were banned because of their content, because the author was not in favor with the Communists, or simply because they were "foreign" or the wrong kind of influence.

 Geographic Themes

Movement: Moldova's Economy and Trade
These garment workers are manufacturing clothing in a factory in Chisinau, the capital of Moldova. *What major challenge do factories in the former Soviet Union face from abroad?*

Rivers and Canals

Russia and the Eurasian republics have many waterways—both natural and artificial. For many centuries, these waterways were the chief transportation system.

Ships loaded and unloaded their cargoes at Georgian and Ukrainian ports along the Black Sea. With most northern ports closed for almost half the year because of ice, the Black Sea was a major and vital Soviet shipping route. The Ukrainian docks alone handled a tenth of the Soviet Union's ocean freight.

Rivers and canals were—and still are—important links in the system. Belarus and Ukraine are just two of the republics that still depend on a network of canals and rivers for transportation of raw materials and goods. The Volga River, for example, is connected to other rivers by a seemingly endless system of inland waterways.

Geographic Themes
Movement: Trans-Siberian Railroad
The Trans-Siberian, built during the 1890s and early 1900s, is the longest railroad in the world. *How has the Trans-Siberian helped in the development of Russia?*

Roads and Rails

Roads provide vital transportation links in the region today. In some areas, such as the Caucasus, roads provide the only access to the outside world. Because of the mountains, most freight is carried by road in Armenia. Azerbaijan and Georgia have rail networks on which they tend to depend, but they too have many places reachable only by road.

Even so, in many republics, including Russia, good roads, especially paved ones, are still scarce. A major highway system does link Moscow with some of the other major cities, but there are not all that many cars and much of the system is used for trucking. In reality, the trucks do not move much freight, less than 10 percent of the total. Most of what they do carry is farm products or manufactured goods that are not going very far. In winter, the trucks often use frozen rivers as roadways, especially in Siberia.

Railroads are the major means of transportation, one that the republics are commit-

ted to maintaining. One-tenth of the world's railway tracks crisscross the region. The area has the longest railroad in the world—the Trans-Siberian—that stretches from Vladivostok across China and Siberia to the Ural Mountains and north of China from Khabarovsk to Kuenga.

Planes and Pipelines

The Soviet Union was the first country to use jet airplanes for passenger traffic, although the Communists discouraged or regulated travel for most Soviet citizens. Since the republics became independent, travel restrictions have been lifted, and the network of air routes are heavily used. Moldova, for example, has direct flights from its capital city of Chisinau to Bucharest, Romania, making it easier for Moldovan companies to move their exports to foreign markets. Aeroflot, the national airline of Russia and the republics, carries both passengers and cargo to most major cities in the republics and to many countries outside the region, including the United States.

Pipelines have also become much more important as a means of transporting oil and natural gas. The Soviets laid thousands of miles of pipeline, some to carry oil to countries in eastern Europe and some to transport natural gas within their own country. Many of these pipelines are in independent republics. Belarus, for example, controls an important pipeline through which Russia pumps its oil westward to central Europe. Along this pipeline Belarusian refineries at Polotsk and Mozyr process the crude oil for fuel. In Azerbaijan, Soviet-built pipelines carry refined oil from Baku to Batumi and transport natural gas from Karadag to Akstafa and to Tbilisi in Georgia.

Interdependence

Shortly before the Soviet Union collapsed, one reporter offered this information to her readers:

Both Soviet and Western economists warn that a total break now from the giant, if tottering, Soviet economy would only leave individual republics scrambling for survival. Decades of Moscow's central planning have ensured that the republics are interdependent in every economic sphere: energy, food, consumer goods, light and heavy industry.

Russia and the Eurasian republics soon discovered the truth of the economists' warning. They knew that they had inherited a flawed economic system that could not produce enough goods to satisfy the needs of all their people. They soon found out that it also was a system in which no single republic was totally independent. For example, one republic might have industries but no raw materials or parts, while another republic had the raw materials or parts but no industries. One by one, the republics concluded that interdependence was necessary for survival.

Belarus, for example, does not have enough oil and natural gas fuels, but Russia has an abundance of these resources. As a result, much of Belarus's economy hinges on exchanging goods with Russia and Belarus's other neighbor–Ukraine.

Moldova's economy also depends on trade with Ukraine and Russia. When the Soviet Union fell apart, its currency—the ruble—became far less valuable. Rubles were also the currency of Moldova. Because the rubles are worth so little, factory managers in Moldova can no longer buy the raw materials they need with them. So they have had to depend on bartering with other republics.

Other republics have similar dependence on their neighbors. Ukraine, for example, must import oil. Armenia needs petroleum and natural gas, as well as metals, farm machinery, and some consumer goods. Kazakhstan depends on Russia for the chemicals and other products its factories need.

SECTION 1 REVIEW

Checking for Understanding
1. **Define** command economy, consumer goods, black market, market economy, *sovkhozes, kolkhozes.*
2. **Locating Places** What were two of the early changes in industry and agriculture under the Soviets?
3. **Movement** What is the major means of transportation in Russia and the Eurasian republics?
4. **Region** For what does Ukraine have to depend on the other republics?

Critical Thinking
5. **Making Comparisons** In what ways is the market economy preferred by the independent republics different from the Soviet economy?

THE DYING ARAL SEA

*W*e need water not only for the population and farms but also for industrial development. The intellectuals sitting at desks understand the ecological slogans, but they fail to understand the needs of the people working on the farms.

Viktor Dukhovnyi, Director of the Central Asian Scientific Research Institute for Irrigation,
National Geographic, February 1990

The Aral Sea lies in central Asia in the republics of Kazakhstan and Uzbekistan. In 1960 the Aral covered 25,660 square miles (66,459 sq. km) and had a fragile, but rich environment. The huge, inland saltwater lake provided a healthy living for the fishing communities around its shores.

By the 1980s, when the Soviet Union (now the Commonwealth of Independent States) opened its doors under the policy of *glasnost,* or openness, the Aral Sea had shrunk to a third of its former size. The delicate environment had disappeared, every marine plant and animal replaced with salt-coated sand. The fishing industry was a shadow of what it had once been, and people living near the lake were suffering from severe health problems.

THE ISSUE

Scientists claimed that water from the Amu Darya River, the sea's source, had been diverted for irrigating cotton and rice farms. For 30 years, very little water had been flowing into the Aral. To restore the sea, they said, the water must be allowed to flow along its original course back into the Aral Sea.

Government officials said that it was impossible to return the full flow of the Amu Darya to the Aral Sea. They pointed to the 3 million acres (about 1.2 million hectares) of irrigated land on either side of the canal. The irrigation, they said, had made once-arid land productive, growing about half of the former Soviet Union's cotton crop. In addition, the diverted water had increased the acres planted with rice and fruits.

THE BACKGROUND

The Aral is an inland saltwater sea with no outlet. It is fed by two rivers, the Amu Darya and Syr Darya. The freshwater from these two rivers held the Aral's water and salt levels in perfect balance.

In the early 1960s, the Soviet central government decided to make the Soviet Union self-sufficient in cotton and increase rice production. Government officials ordered the

A stranded ship lies beached on the shrinking coastline of the Aral Sea.

Over the past few decades, the Aral Sea has experienced a severe drop in water level, its shoreline receded, and its salt content increased.

additional amount of needed water to be taken from the two rivers that feed the Aral Sea.

> *Raushan Tuliagakov, a member of the Committee to Save the Aral Sea, said, "We knew the problem as far back as 1960, but we were not allowed to speak out."*

Large dams were built across both rivers, and an 850-mile (1,368-km) central canal with a far-reaching system of feeder canals was created. When the irrigation system was completed, millions of acres along both sides of the main canal were flooded.

During the next 30 years, the Aral Sea experienced a severe drop in water level, its shoreline receded, and its salt content increased. The marine environment became hostile to the sea life in it, killing the plants and animals. As the marine life died, the fishing industry suffered.

THE POINTS OF VIEW

Since the mid-1980s, scientists have spoken out more strongly for saving the Aral Sea. Agricultural officials, however, say that it is impossible to demolish the canal system. Too many farmers depend on the income from cotton. Argues an official, "We could [reduce by half the amount of land being irrigated]. But we have to think of the people who depend on the irrigation for work. What will they do then? What will they eat?"

THE ISSUE TODAY

Government leaders have said that the amount of land for cotton will be reduced and large amounts of water will be pumped back into the Aral Sea until the year 2005. The government, however, has also indicated that the welfare of the cotton farmers must come first. Exported cotton is a major source of income.

Most scientists believe that the Aral Sea cannot ever be as it was before. The best they hope for is some sort of stabilization of the sea and the survival of the rivers' two deltas. Saving the deltas could lead to new commercial fishing activity.

Reviewing the Case

1. **Who is involved in the concern over the Aral Sea?**
2. **Human/Environment Interaction** How did governmental policy damage the Aral Sea?

People and Their Environment

SETTING THE SCENE

Read to Discover . . .
- how nuclear disaster and other concerns have affected Russia and the Eurasian republics.
- how environmental problems affect some bodies of water in Russia and the Eurasian republics.
- about the effects of industrial and pesticide

pollution in Russia and the Eurasian republics.

Key Terms
- industrialize
- polluted
- pesticide

Identify and Locate
Tian Shan Mountains, Chernobyl, Kiev, Belarus, Ust-Kamenogorsk, Metsamov, Nayirit, Semipalatinsk, Caspian Sea, Lake Sevan, Radzan River, Lake Baikal, Central Siberian Plateau, Dniester River, Bishkek, Yerevan

---

Almost from the time they took over, the Soviets pushed to **industrialize**, or develop industry, and to make their nation a world power. In the process they neglected and abused the environment. Rivers and lakes, urban areas and rural areas, even the air people breathe—all have been very badly damaged, in some cases permanently. This pollution, most of it caused by the long-term Soviet emphasis on heavy industry, has put millions of people in the republics at risk and made public health a matter of great concern.

HUMAN/ENVIRONMENT INTERACTION

Nuclear Energy

Under the Soviets, a number of different kinds of energy were used as sources of fuel. One of these was nuclear energy, which the government championed as an economical source of fuel. The uranium the Soviets needed to power any nuclear plants they might build lay in their own country, much of it in the area northwest of the Black Sea and in the Tian Shan range.

Committed to nuclear energy as a major source of electric power, in 1986 the Soviets were building 18 new nuclear power stations. They already had other nuclear power stations and two nuclear heat supply stations, each intended to generate enough heat for a city of about 400,000. All that came to a halt—some of it permanently—because of an accident at a nuclear power station in a small Ukrainian town called Chernobyl.

Disaster at Chernobyl

In 1986 Chernobyl was a small, quiet town in northern Ukraine about 60 miles (96 km) from Kiev. It was also the site of one of the Soviet Union's nuclear power stations. On April 26, at a little before 1:30 A.M., an explosion ripped apart a nuclear reactor at the station. The blast started more than 30 fires and released tons of radioactive particles into the atmosphere.

Two days later, scientists in Sweden discovered increased amounts of radiation in the air over their country and began asking questions. It turned out that the Soviet government already knew about the explosion but had not told the public about it or warned them of the dangers it had brought. Because people were not evacuated at once, about 100,000 people in the vicinity were exposed to deadly levels of radiation. Most of those people probably will die prematurely from radioactivity-related diseases.

Aftermath of Chernobyl

The great cloud of radioactive dust released at Chernobyl poisoned a vast area of northwestern Europe. Thousands of people, many of them children, suffer from cancer, blood diseases, and stomach disorders because of the increased radiation in the area. Each year some young Ukrainians are sent to northern Europe and to the United States for a few months to lower the levels of radiation in their bodies.

Chernobyl no longer exists as a populated town. It was evacuated and its houses and trees bulldozed and buried beneath its contaminated soil. The destroyed reactor was put in a special steel and cement building. It is unlikely that anyone will ever be able to live in Chernobyl again, even in the very distant future.

It is estimated that there were 2 million victims of Chernobyl. Many of them live in Belarus, where the wind carried 70 percent of the fallout. Here too much of the soil was contaminated and many people infected with cancer, stomach diseases, breathing ailments, and other serious illnesses. Thousands of acres of rich farmland cannot be used and hundreds of villages cannot be inhabited. Farmers have been told that it is no longer safe to grow crops in some of the soil on their farms. Because the demand for food keeps growing, however, they keep on raising vegetables, fruits, and livestock in soil they know is not safe. Villagers still eat food from their gardens, and many still live in homes and villages they have been told were poisoned by radiation.

After Belarus became independent, the government started to monitor radiation levels. When they found villages where the levels were high enough to indicate contamination, the government made people leave. Experts calculate that the accident at Chernobyl caused radiation ailments in 2 million Belarusians, 500,000 of them children. To help treat all these people, the government also built new clinics that specialize in treating radiation poisoning.

Nuclear Concerns

What happened at Chernobyl made people stop and think about the dangers of nuclear power and led Belarusians, Ukrainians,

Geographic Themes

Place: Chernobyl, Ukraine
The atomic explosion at the Chernobyl nuclear plant killed scores of people and released a radioactive cloud that contaminated surrounding farmland. *What will be the long-term effects of Chernobyl?*

and others to hold protests against nuclear plants and weapons. It was because of these efforts that some reactors completed by the Soviets never opened, and some still in the planning stages were never built. In 1990, when an explosion at the Ulba nuclear fuel processing plant at Ust-Kamenogorsk released beryllium gas into the air, 60,000 people demanded that the plant be closed.

Many Russians are now speaking out against some of the older nuclear power stations in their republic. They say that because the reactors were not well designed in the first place and lack needed spare parts, the reactor plants could become dangerous to operate. Armenians are also expressing their views about two nuclear power plants in their republic, one at Metsamov and one at Nayirit. Even though some of the Metsamov reactors have been shut down, many people still doubt the wisdom of having nuclear power stations in a nation known to have earthquakes.

For some, nuclear weapons and testing are also a cause for concern. For many years the Soviets developed and stocked up on nuclear weapons. When the Soviet Union broke up, what would happen to those weapons became a major—and a controversial—issue. The four republics that now have nuclear weapons— Russia, Ukraine, Belarus, and Kazakhstan— agreed that before any one republic could use the weapons it had to have the consent of the other three.

This, however, has not changed the damage that past nuclear testing has already done in certain areas. One is the Semipalatinsk area of Kazakhstan, where the Soviets once had nuclear bases. Kazakhstan is believed to still have several thousand nuclear warheads within its borders. The Soviet army tested its nuclear weapons in the Semipalatinsk area and its chemical and biological weapons in other places in the republic. In 1989 a Semipalatinsk Oblast Peace Committee announced that there had been radiation leaks in the area as a result of nuclear weapons testing. It will be years before all traces of contamination will be gone.

HUMAN/ENVIRONMENT INTERACTION

Water Problems

The Soviet emphasis on heavy industry and desire to grow certain crops where there was not enough water for them took its toll on some of the rivers, lakes, and seas of Russia and the Eurasian republics. In some cases, water levels have shrunk drastically, endangering the plant, fish, and animal life and changing the nearby landscape. In other cases, the water is being **polluted**, contaminated by harmful substances.

The many industries and farms in the Volga River basin, for example, use huge amounts of river water. Much of that water ends up back in the Volga with different kinds of pollutants discharged by the industries and farms. A fast-flowing river can purify itself. Because so many dams slow the Volga's flow, however, the river remains polluted.

Shrinking of the Caspian Sea and Lake Sevan

The Caspian Sea lies on the border between Europe and Asia, bounded on the west by Rus-

Geographic Themes

Human/Environment Interaction: Caspian Sea
The Caspian Sea, the largest inland body of water in the world, is an important source of a fish called sturgeon. *How has human activity contributed to the shrinking of the Caspian Sea?*

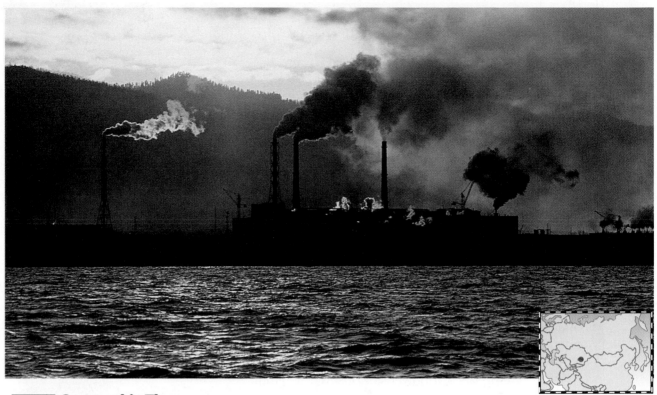

Geographic Themes

Human/Environment Interaction: Lake Baikal
Lake Baikal, the world's deepest lake, is more than 5,315 feet (1,620 m) at its deepest point. *What are the major causes of the pollution problems affecting Lake Baikal?*

sia and Azerbaijan, on the north by Russia and Kazakhstan, and on the east by Kazakhstan and Turkmenistan. Lake Sevan, one of the highest lakes in the world, lies in northeastern Armenia and is surrounded by the Caucasus Mountains. The two bodies of water share a common problem—they have been shrinking.

Kazakhstan and the other central Asian republics do not get much rain. So their land had to be irrigated to grow the cotton and other crops the Soviets demanded of them and to yield the hay and fodder they needed to feed their animals during the winter. Much of the water used for irrigation was diverted from the Caspian Sea. From 1960 to the mid-1970s, the water level of the Caspian dropped 8 feet (2.4 m). Although since then it has risen a little, several thousand square miles have dried up.

Lake Sevan also suffered because its waters were steadily drained over a long period of time. The lake feeds the Radzan River. For more than 60 years, Armenians have drawn water from the river to power hydroelectric stations and to irrigate their farms. In the 1970s concern about the loss of water in the lake led the Soviets to build a tunnel to reroute water to the lake from the Arpa River in Azerbaijan. Even with the tunnel, the water level kept going down. At the same time, organic waste from nearby cities and towns polluted the lake. In the late 1980s, plans were made to build a pipeline to keep the wastes out of the Radzan River. Although the pipeline will help keep the water clean, it will not solve the problem of water level, which by the early 1990s had dropped almost 20 feet (6 m).

Pollution of Lake Baikal

Lake Baikal lies on the southern edge of the Central Siberian Plateau. It holds a huge volume of water that influences the weather around it, making the area nearest the lake warmer in winter and cooler in summer than areas farther away from the lake.

About 40 years ago, a huge paper and pulp mill that had grown up along the southwestern shore of the lake began to spill toxic chemicals into its waters. On top of this, rivers flowing into the lake were depositing farm fertilizers and other poisonous chemicals. All this pollution upset the chemical balance of the lake, posing a real threat to plants and animals.

In the late 1980s, Soviet writers and scientists urged the government to stop pollution. They wanted equipment installed to reduce the amount of waste the paper and pulp factory was emptying in the lake. In 1987 the pulp plant was ordered to stop polluting the lake. Not long after, plans to build other factories along the shores of the lake were halted. The next step, to be taken by the Russian government in the 1990s, is to make the factories already on the shores of the lake convert to cleaner production processes—or to tear them down completely.

HUMAN/ENVIRONMENT INTERACTION

Pollution

Pollution affects more than just the rivers, lakes, and other bodies of water of Russia and the Eurasian republics. It affects the land and the air as well. Just about every feature of the physical and natural environment of the region has suffered because of the Soviet passion to industrialize and to grow more, different, bigger, and better crops.

Under the Soviets, factories dumped toxic wastes into almost every river of Russia and the Eurasian republics. In 1983, for example, when a dam on a tributary of the Dniester River in Ukraine collapsed, hazardous wastes from a fertilizer plant poured into the river. The wastes poisoned the waters that ran downstream through Moldova to the Black Sea, killing fish and putting at risk Moldovans who had to get their water from the Dniester.

Because soft brown coal was plentiful in the region, most Soviet factories burned it even though they knew it polluted the air. Because most factory smokestacks did not have pollution-preventing equipment or devices, they released incredible amounts of soot, sulfur, and carbon dioxide. The wind carried the pollution to other areas. Emissions from smokestacks in Ukrainian and Romanian factories, for example, drifted over Moldova, adding to the pollutants already released into the air by Moldovan factories.

Soviet industries dumped wastes wherever they wanted—even after the Soviets passed laws that were supposed to keep such things from happening. Republics like Moldova that accepted toxic wastes for landfills that did not meet international sanitary regulations only made an already-bad problem worse.

No republic has escaped the effects of the different kinds of pollution associated with industry. People in Kazakhstan, for example, suffer from health problems linked to toxic chemicals in the atmosphere. The chemicals are there because planners in Moscow insisted on building up heavy industry in Kazakhstan. The increase in infant mortality in Kazakhstan has been linked directly to the pollution problem as well. In Kyrgyzstan, too, the development of heavy industry has polluted the air. In Bishkek, for example, the concentration of benzopyrene in the atmosphere is more than 10 times greater than what it should be.

One of the most polluted of all the cities of Russia and the Eurasian republics, though, is Yerevan, the capital of Armenia. Three-fifths of Armenia's industries are located in and around the city, and most are devoted to kinds of heavy industry that produce significant pollution—synthetic rubber, fertilizers, chemicals, nonferrous metals, and equipment.

Not all of the pollution comes from factories. In some areas, much of it is from **pesticides**, chemicals used to kill insects, rodents, and other pests. To rid cotton, vegetables, and fruits of insects and other pests that were destroying them, Soviet farmers began spraying and dumping huge quantities of pesticides on their fields. This went on for more than 30 years. By the 1990s most farmers all across the

Geographic Themes

Region: Central Asia
The growing of cotton is an important agricultural activity in central Asia. *What major source of pollution affects farmers in Russia and the Eurasian republics?*

region were doing it. Banning certain pesticides did not stop some farmers from using them. DDT, one of the most deadly pesticides, was officially banned by the Soviet Union—as well as most other countries—more than two decades ago. But Azeri farmers, who produce more cotton than anyone else in the Caucasus, still spray strong doses of it on their crops.

SECTION 2 REVIEW

Checking for Understanding
1. **Define** industrialize, polluted, pesticide.
2. **Locating Places** What happened at Chernobyl in 1986?
3. **Movement** Why were so many people in Belarus affected by the accident at Chernobyl?
4. **Human/Environment Interaction** What caused the water levels of the Caspian Sea and Lake Sevan to drop?

Critical Thinking
5. **Determining Cause and Effect** What was the major cause of the environmental problems of Russia and the Eurasian republics?

Distinguishing Fact From Opinion

Suppose you overhear the following conversation between two girls who are eating ice cream cones.

Tanya: This is absolutely the best chocolate ice cream in the city!

Lisa: Is that a fact? Well, yesterday I had another kind of chocolate ice cream, and it was much better. It was creamier and richer. This isn't even in the same league.

Tanya: But this chocolate is so dark. This is definitely the best. It's a fact.

Is it? Although Tanya and Lisa claim to know the facts about chocolate ice cream, they are actually expressing opinions. It's important to know the differences between them.

REVIEWING THE SKILL

Facts are statements that can be checked for accuracy. They explain what happened, when and where it happened, who was involved, and so on. However, not all factual statements are true or correct. For example, read the following statement: "In 1989 Russia produced almost 50 million metric tons of iron ore." Because you can check the accuracy of this statement in government reports, almanacs, and other sources, it is a fact. In this case, however, the statement is incorrect. Russia produced almost 96 million metric tons in that year.

Opinions, on the other hand, are statements of feelings, emotions, and beliefs. It is impossible to check their accuracy. For example, suppose someone says, "The breakup of the Soviet Union is the most exciting political change of the 1990s."

Although this statement expresses the speaker's beliefs, no one can prove or disprove it. Therefore, it is an opinion, not a fact. Opinions often begin with phrases such as, *I believe, probably, it seems,* or *in my view.* They often contain qualifying words such as *may, might, could, should, ought,* and superlatives such as *best, worst, greatest, outstanding,* and *extraordinary.*

To distinguish facts from opinions, apply the following steps:

- Identify facts by looking for verifiable statements such as names, dates, places, numbers, and specific actions. Often facts answer the questions *who? what? where?* and *when.*
- Identify opinions by looking for statements expressing beliefs or feelings. Often, they contain phrases such as *I believe* or *In my view,* or qualifiers and superlatives.

PRACTICING THE SKILL

For each statement below, write **F** if it is a fact, or **O** if it is an opinion. Explain each answer.

1. By mid-1991, Russian oil production was down to 7.8 million barrels a day, 17 percent below the rate in 1988.
2. In all likelihood, Soviet carbon emissions will continue to fall in the next few years.
3. The accident at the Chernobyl nuclear reactor could result in hundreds of thousands more cancer deaths.
4. Nuclear power is the most dangerous environmental threat in the world today.
5. In 1967, a hot, windy summer dried up Lake Karachay, a dumping site for Soviet nuclear waste in the 1950s; radioactive dust spread contamination to 41,000 people.

For additional practice in this skill, see Practicing Skills on page 344 of the Chapter 16 Review.

1 SECTION

Living in Russia and the Eurasian Republics

Farmers harvesting wheat in Kazakhstan

KEY TERMS

command economy (p. 328)
consumer goods (p. 328)
black market (p. 328)
market economy (p. 328)
sovkhozes (p. 329)
kolkhozes (p. 329)

SUMMARY

- For many decades, Russia and the Eurasian republics constituted a single economy controlled by the Soviet government.
- Upon becoming independent, each republic took charge of its own economy and is trying to move toward a market economy.
- Russia and the other republics all are taking steps to privatize agriculture and industry.
- Independence brought greater freedom of expression to the communications systems and most forms of media.
- Although waterways, roads, and railways remain vital methods of transportation for freight and passengers, airlines and pipelines are growing in importance.
- Because they were parts of the Soviet system for so long, Russia and the Eurasian republics today are not totally independent of one another.

2 SECTION

People and Their Environment

Fishing in the Caspian Sea

KEY TERMS

industrialize (p. 336)
polluted (p. 338)
pesticide (p. 341)

SUMMARY

- In their push to industrialize, the Soviets neglected and abused the environment.
- Committed to nuclear power as an economical source of electric power, the Soviets built numerous nuclear power stations in various parts of the nation.
- The Chernobyl disaster led to doubts and protests about nuclear energy and weapons.
- Pollution caused by heavy industry and the use of pesticides presents a major problem for Russia and the Eurasian republics.

Reviewing Key Terms

Choose the vocabulary term that best completes each of the sentences below. Write your answers on a separate sheet of paper.

    consumer goods (p. 328)
    black market (p. 328)
    kolkhozes (p. 329)
    industrialize (p. 336)
    polluted (p. 338)
    pesticides (p. 341)

SECTION 1
1. Most Soviet citizens could not afford to buy goods on the _____ .
2. In the Soviet Union large collective farms were called _____ .
3. People in Russia and the Eurasian republics still suffer from a shortage of _____ .

SECTION 2
4. Heavy industry has _____ many rivers in Russia and the Eurasian republics by dumping toxic wastes in their waters.
5. To kill insects destroying their crops, farmers in Russia and the Eurasian republics use _____ .
6. In their drive to _____ , the Soviets severely damaged the environment.

Reviewing Facts

SECTION 1
7. What was the role of the Soviet government in the economy?
8. Which republic has moved the fastest to create a market economy?
9. In what ways have communications changed since independence?

SECTION 2
10. What concerns some Russians and Armenians about nuclear power plants?
11. What four independent republics now have nuclear weapons?

12. How did Lake Baikal, on the Central Siberian Plateau, become polluted?

Critical Thinking
13. **Analyzing Information**   Do you think it is important for the independent republics to cooperate with one another? Explain your answer.
14. **Expressing Problems Clearly**   How have factories contributed to pollution in Russia and the other republics?

Geographic Themes

15. **Movement**   How have railroads aided economic development in the region?
16. **Human/Environment Interaction** How has industrialization affected the environment of Russia and the Eurasian republics?

Practicing Skills

Distinguishing Fact From Opinion

For each statement below, write **F** if it is a fact, or write **O** if it is an opinion. Explain each answer.
17. The collapse of the centrally controlled economies in Russia and the Eurasian republics is a plus for the global environment.
18. The nuclear physicist appointed to supervise the cleanup at Chernobyl estimates that this process has already claimed between 5,000 and 7,000 lives.

Using the Unit Atlas
Refer to the physical geography section of the Unit Atlas on pages 286–287.
19. What Asiatic part of Russia is rich in mineral deposits?

20. What body of water is the center of the sturgeon fishing industry?

Projects

Individual Activity

Imagine that you are an American entrepreneur interested in investing in a business in Russia or one of the other republics. Write a letter to your banker that indicates in which republic the business is located, what kind of business it is, and why you think it would be a good investment.

Cooperative Learning Activity

Working in a group of six, two people will research the history and routes of the Trans-Siberian Railroad, while two others research the history and routes of the Baikal-Amur Mainline (BAM). For each railroad, one person should be prepared to take the role of a construction worker and the other that of a passenger. The remaining two students will take the roles of news reporters and interview the others for a television documentary titled *Adventures in Railroading.*

Writing About Geography

Cause and Effect

Imagine that you are captain of a barge that carries freight along a waterway in one of the republics. Research the waterway and what has happened to it and to the surrounding area over the last 50 years. Then write a letter to the president of the republic explaining how industrialization and/or agriculture have changed the waterway for better or for worse.

Locating Places

THE PHYSICAL GEOGRAPHY OF RUSSIA AND THE EURASIAN REPUBLICS

Match the letters on the map with the places and physical features of Russia and the Eurasian republics. Write your answers on a separate sheet of paper.

1. Baku
2. Don River
3. Vladivostok
4. Lake Baikal
5. Kiev
6. Amur River
7. Kazakhstan
8. Yerevan
9. Chernobyl
10. Caspian Sea

GEOGRAPHY CONNECTION

Russia and the Eurasian Republics and the United States

THE FINE ARTS

Russian artists have influenced many areas of the fine arts in the United States—music, ballet, modern dance, literature, poetry, film, painting, sculpture. Russians have applied their deep love of the lyrical and the beautiful to create works of enduring significance.

▲ **DR. ZHIVAGO** is a timeless novel of the spirit's need for freedom, written by Nobel prize-winning author Boris Pasternak. The hauntingly poetic tale became an Oscar-winning, modern-day American film classic starring Omar Sharif and Julie Christie (1965).

◄ **INNOVATIVE SCULPTURES** called *assemblages* have been created by Louise Nevelson. Nevelson creates in wood scraps, boards, leftovers from Victorian houses, steel, lucite, and aluminum. She often uses paint to unify the parts of her works. Nevelson Square in New York City is named after her, and contains seven mammoth steel sculptures.

MIKHAIL BARYSHNIKOV, a Russian ballet dancer who settled in the United States, delighted his audiences with his flying leaps into the air. Famous for this dynamic style, Baryshnikov executed his moves with great brilliance and daring. He defected to the West in 1974, discontented with the lack of freedom and the limits that the Soviet Union placed on his dancing. Joining the American Ballet Theater, Baryshnikov gave his imagination and style full rein.

RUSSIAN COMPOSER PETER TCHAIKOVSKY produced works that have become classical standards. Instantly recognizable to most Americans are his orchestral composition, *Nutcracker Suite,* and his three ballets, *Swan Lake, Sleeping Beauty,* and *The Nutcracker.*

MODERN ART movements were led by Wassily Kandinsky and Marc Chagall. Kandinsky's clear, pure colors and free-form shapes and lines earned him recognition as the first abstract expressionist. Chagall transformed the "shattered" techniques of the cubists to create graceful, dreamlike surrealist art.

GEORGE BALANCHINE aroused affection and loyalty from every dancer he developed and the millions of fans who loved his ballets. Just a year after arriving in the United States, he cofounded the School of American Ballet, guiding and nurturing it until it became the famed New York City Ballet. Balanchine remained with the ballet from its cofounding in 1934 to his death in 1983, creating more than 200 ballets.

Checking for Understanding

1. Who are two Russian dancers who have influenced American ballet?
2. **Movement** Who are three artists who influenced modern American art?

North Africa and Southwest Asia

GeoJournal Activity

In your study of North Africa and Southwest Asia, read newspapers and magazines, and listen to television and radio broadcasts about events affecting the environment, politics, cultures, and daily life of the region. Make a brief list of the items in your journal.

Mehmet Biber/Ajans Biber

NATIONAL GEOGRAPHIC SOCIETY

Picturing the World

Pilgrims crowd the sacred mosque at Makkah (Mecca) in Saudi Arabia, birthplace of the Prophet Muhammad. The draped Kaaba, in the center of the mosque, is the most sacred shrine of Islam. The vast majority of the people of North Africa and Southwest Asia are followers of Islam. Muslims are divided into two main groups: Sunni Muslims and Shiite Muslims. Look at the graph on page 382.

1. Muslims form what percentage of the region's population?
2. What are the only two countries in the region that do not follow Islam?

Picture Atlas CD-ROM Enrichment Corner

Research the populations of the following countries: Egypt, Iraq, Kuwait, Libya, Morocco, Saudi Arabia, and Tunisia. Look at the population projection graph and figure out how many millions of people are projected to be added to each of these countries by the year 2025. (Round off your answers to the nearest million.) Make a bar graph of your findings. (See page 20 for more information on graphs.) Based on your graph, answer the following questions:

1. Which country will add the most people?
2. Which country will add the fewest?
3. Which country is projected to triple its population?

NORTH AFRICA AND
Cultural Geography

Aleppo, **Syria**, has been an important trading center since the 1500s BC.

NORTH AFRICA AND SOUTHWEST ASIA: POLITICAL

Because of its strategic location, **Egypt** is important in world transportation.

In 1950, **Israel** passed the Law of the Return allowing any Jew to settle in the country. Since then, Jews from all over the world have relocated to Israel.

Bahrain has one of the highest standards of living in the Persian Gulf area.

Many bedouins, Arab nomads who live in **Southwest Asia,** are giving up their traditional nomadic lifestyle to move to the city.

People have lived in present-day **Algeria** for at least 40,000 years.

The **Sahara** is very sparsely populated.

Egypt's **Nile River Valley** is one of the world's most heavily populated areas.

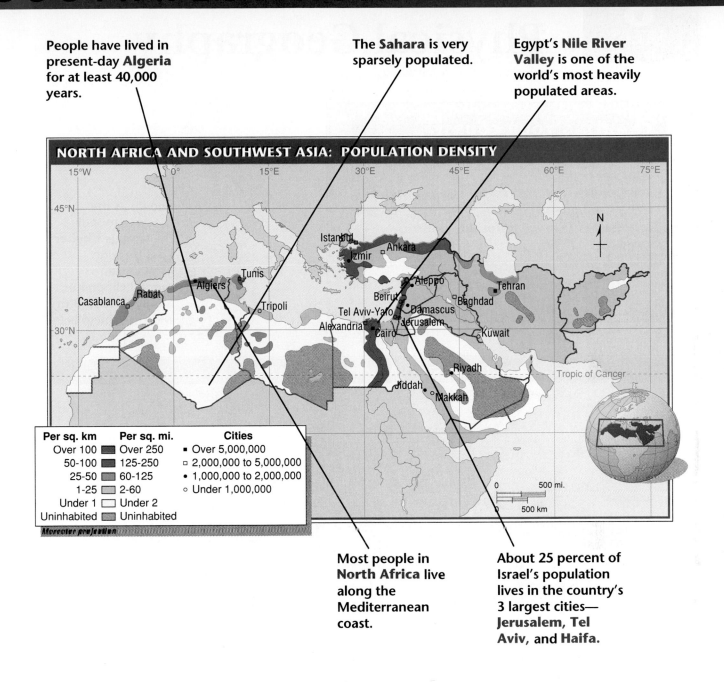

NORTH AFRICA AND SOUTHWEST ASIA: POPULATION DENSITY

Per sq. km	Per sq. mi.	Cities
Over 100	Over 250	■ Over 5,000,000
50-100	125-250	□ 2,000,000 to 5,000,000
25-50	60-125	• 1,000,000 to 2,000,000
1-25	2-60	○ Under 1,000,000
Under 1	Under 2	
Uninhabited	Uninhabited	

Mercator projection

Most people in **North Africa** live along the Mediterranean coast.

About 25 percent of Israel's population lives in the country's 3 largest cities—**Jerusalem, Tel Aviv, and Haifa.**

North Africa and Southwest Asia have about 70 million more people than the United States.

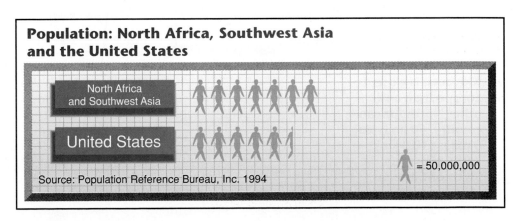

Population: North Africa, Southwest Asia and the United States

North Africa and Southwest Asia

United States

Source: Population Reference Bureau, Inc. 1994

= 50,000,000

NORTH AFRICA AND
Physical Geography

CHARTING YOUR COURSE

1. *What bodies of water provide coastlines for the region?*
2. *What two natural resources are found in the Persian Gulf area?*
3. *What is the most abundant natural resource of the region?*
4. *What mountain ranges are located in North Africa and Southwest Asia?*

Known as the gateway to India, the famous **Khyber Pass** through Afghanistan's rugged Hindu Kush is only 10 feet (3 m) wide in some places.

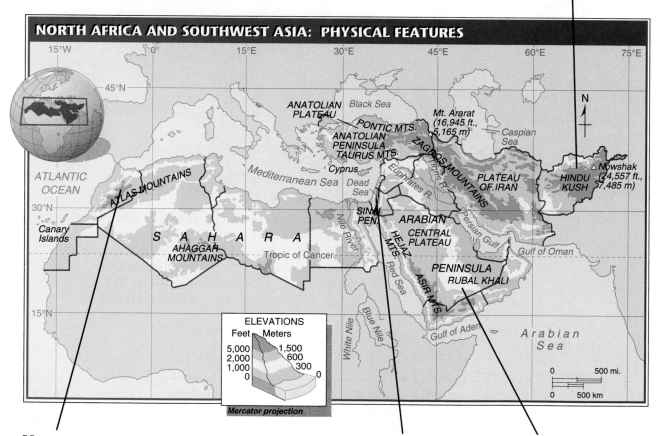

NORTH AFRICA AND SOUTHWEST ASIA: PHYSICAL FEATURES

ANATOLIAN PLATEAU
Black Sea
PONTIC MTS.
Mt. Ararat (16,945 ft., 5,165 m)
Caspian Sea
ANATOLIAN PENINSULA
TAURUS MTS.
ZAGROS MOUNTAINS
PLATEAU OF IRAN
Nowshak (24,557 ft., 7,485 m)
HINDU KUSH
Cyprus
ATLANTIC OCEAN
Mediterranean Sea
Dead Sea
Euphrates R.
Tigris R.
ATLAS MOUNTAINS
Canary Islands
SINAI PEN.
ARABIAN CENTRAL PLATEAU
Persian Gulf
Gulf of Oman
S A H A R A
AHAGGAR MOUNTAINS
Tropic of Cancer
Nile River
HEJAZ MTS.
Red Sea
PENINSULA RUBAL KHALI
ASIR MTS.
White Nile
Blue Nile
Gulf of Aden
Arabian Sea
N

ELEVATIONS
Feet / Meters
5,000 / 1,500
2,000 / 600
1,000 / 300
0 / 0

0   500 mi.
0   500 km

Mercator projection

Morocco is closer to Europe than any other North African country. Spain is just 8 miles (12.9 km) away, across the Strait of Gibraltar.

The **Dead Sea** is the earth's saltiest body of water—about nine times saltier than the oceans.

Some of the sandy areas of the **Arabian Peninsula** are so large they are called "sand seas."

Morocco has about two-thirds of the world's known phosphate reserves.

Cotton is **Egypt's** most important crop.

Oman is one of the world's hottest countries.

NORTH AFRICA AND SOUTHWEST ASIA: NATURAL RESOURCES

15°W 0° 15°E 30°E 45°E 60°E 75°E

EUROPE ASIA

45°N

TURKEY

MOROCCO
ALGERIA
WESTERN SAHARA
TUNISIA
LIBYA
EGYPT

LEBANON
ISRAEL
SYRIA
IRAQ
JORDAN
IRAN
AFGHANISTAN
KUWAIT
UNITED ARAB EMIRATES
BAHRAIN
QATAR
SAUDI ARABIA
OMAN
YEMEN

30°N

AFRICA

15°N

Tropic of Cancer

Legend
- ⚒ Petroleum
- ◊ Natural gas
- I Iron ore
- ✂ Copper
- ⚬ Lead
- ⊡ Zinc
- ⊘ Manganese
- ⚏ Phosphate

0 ___ 500 mi.
0 ___ 500 km

Lambert Equal-Area projection

A variety of crops grow in the **Fertile Crescent**, a region of rich, fertile soil between the Tigris and Euphrates rivers.

The **Arabian Peninsula** supplies the world with one-fourth to one-third of all oil produced.

North Africa and Southwest Asia: Physical Profile

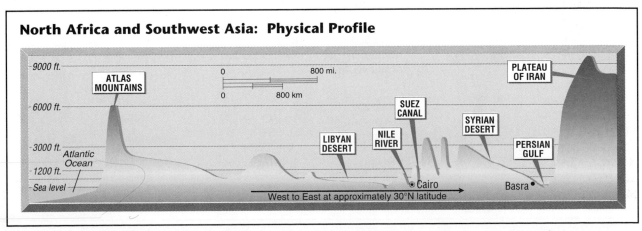

- 9000 ft.
- 6000 ft.
- 3000 ft.
- 1200 ft.
- Sea level

ATLAS MOUNTAINS

Atlantic Ocean

0 ___ 800 mi.
0 ___ 800 km

LIBYAN DESERT
NILE RIVER
SUEZ CANAL
SYRIAN DESERT
PLATEAU OF IRAN
PERSIAN GULF

★Cairo
Basra •

West to East at approximately 30°N latitude

COUNTRY* AND CAPITAL	FLAG AND LANGUAGES	POPULATION	LANDMASS	PRINCIPAL PRODUCTS EXPORT	PRINCIPAL PRODUCTS IMPORT
Afghanistan Kabul	Pushtu, Dari Persian	17,800,000 71 per sq. mi. 27 per sq. km	251,770 sq. mi. 652,084 sq. km	Fruits & Nuts	Machinery
Algeria Algiers	Arabic, Berber	27,900,000 30 per sq. mi. 11 per sq. km	919,590 sq. mi. 2,381,738 sq. km	Petroleum	Machinery
Bahrain Manama	Arabic, Farsi, Urdu	600,000 2,308 per sq. mi. 892 per sq. km	260 sq. mi. 673 sq. km	Petroleum	Petroleum
Cyprus Nicosia	Greek, Turkish, English	756,000 212 per sq. mi. 82 per sq. km	3,570 sq. mi. 9,246 sq. km	Citrus Fruits	Machinery
Egypt Cairo	Arabic, English	58,900,000 152 per sq. mi. 59 per sq. km	384,340 sq. mi. 995,440 sq. km	Petroleum	Machinery
Iran Tehran	Farsi, Turkish, Kurdish, Arabic	61,200,000 97 per sq. mi. 38 per sq. km	631,660 sq. mi. 1,635,999 sq. km	Petroleum	Motor Vehicles
Iraq Baghdad	Arabic, Kurdish	19,900,000 118 per sq. mi. 45 per sq. km	168,870 sq. mi. 437,373 sq. km	Fuels	Machinery
Israel Jerusalem	Hebrew, Arabic	5,400,000 688 per sq. mi. 266 per sq. km	7,850 sq. mi. 20,332 sq. km	Machinery	Diamonds
Jordan Amman	Arabic	4,200,000 122 per sq. mi. 47 per sq. km	34,340 sq. mi. 88,941 sq. km	Phosphates	Food
Kuwait Kuwait	Arabic	1,300,000 189 per sq. mi. 73 per sq. km	6,880 sq. mi. 17,819 sq. km	Petroleum	Machinery
Lebanon Beirut	Arabic, French	3,600,000 911 per sq. mi. 352 per sq. km	3,950 sq. mi. 10,231 sq. km	Jewelery	Machinery
Libya Tripoli	Arabic	5,100,000 7 per sq. mi. 3 per sq. km	679,360 sq. mi. 1,759,542 sq. km	Petroleum	Food

*Country maps not drawn to scale.

COUNTRY* AND CAPITAL	FLAG AND LANGUAGES	POPULATION	LANDMASS	PRINCIPAL PRODUCTS EXPORT	PRINCIPAL PRODUCTS IMPORT
Morocco** Rabat	Arabic, Berber	28,600,000 166 per sq. mi. 64 per sq. km	172,320 sq. mi. 446,309 sq. km	Food	Crude Oil
Oman Muscat	Arabic	1,900,000 23 per sq. mi. 9 per sq. km	82,030 sq. mi. 212,458 sq. km	Petroleum	Machinery
Qatar Doha	Arabic, English	500,000 122 per sq. mi. 47 per sq. km	4,250 sq. mi. 11,008 sq. km	Petroleum	Machinery
Saudi Arabia Riyadh	Arabic	18,000,000 21 per sq. mi. 8 per sq. km	830,000 sq. mi. 2,149,700 sq. km	Petroleum	Machinery
Syria Damascus	Arabic, Kurdish, Armenian, Turkish	14,000,000 197 per sq. mi. 76 per sq. km	71,070 sq. mi. 184,071 sq. km	Petroleum	Food
Tunisia Tunis	Arabic, French	8,700,000 143 per sq. mi. 55 per sq. km	59,980 sq. mi. 155,348 sq. km	Clothing	Textiles
Turkey Ankara	Turkish, Kurdish	61,800,000 208 per sq. mi. 80 per sq. km	297,150 sq. mi. 769,619 sq. km	Textiles	Machinery
United Arab Emirates Abu Dhabi	Arabic	1,700,000 53 per sq. mi. 20 per sq. km	32,280 sq. mi. 83,605 sq. km	Petroleum	Machinery
Yemen San'a	Arabic	12,900,000 63 per sq. mi. 24 per sq. km	203,850 sq. mi. 527,972 sq. km	Coffee	Food

**Morocco claims the Western Sahara area but other countries do not accept this claim.

*Country maps not drawn to scale.

The rulers of the ancient Persian Empire built a magnificent capital at Persepolis.

The Physical Geography of North Africa and Southwest Asia

CHAPTER FOCUS

Geographic Setting

The region of North Africa and Southwest Asia spans a vast area from Morocco to Afghanistan and from the Mediterranean Sea to the Sahara. Its heartland consists of the lands of Southwest Asia that stretch from Turkey to Saudi Arabia.

Geographic Themes

Section 1 The Land
PLACE The region of North Africa and Southwest Asia is at least three-fourths desert and semiarid lands. Mountains are found in North Africa, Turkey, and northern Iraq and Iran.

Section 2 The Climate and Vegetation
LOCATION Coastal areas, western Turkey, and northern Iran receive enough rainfall for agriculture.

▲ Photograph: *Farmland reclaimed from the desert, Israel*

SETTING THE SCENE

Read to Discover . . .
- the seas and coastal areas of North Africa and Southwest Asia.
- the mountains and plateaus in North Africa and Southwest Asia.
- the kinds of natural resources found in North Africa and Southwest Asia.

Key Terms
- seismic
- alluvial-soil deposit
- delta
- wadi
- phosphate

Identify and Locate
Arabian Peninsula, Sinai Peninsula, Anatolian Peninsula, Sahara, Hindu Kush Mountains, Atlas Mountains, Nile River, Tigris River, Euphrates River

Nazareth, Israel

I was born in Nazareth, a small Israeli city with a lot of history. Many of our streets, houses, and churches are very old. A half-hour from Nazareth is the city of Haifa, located by the Mediterranean Sea at the foot of Mt. Carmel. I have lived here for most of my life.

Bishara Baransi

Bishara Baransi describes the historical heritage of his home city in Israel, one of the many countries in the culture region of North Africa and Southwest Asia. Although this region has some of the oldest cities in the world, many people may imagine North Africa and Southwest Asia as expanses of sand dunes stretching to the horizon. This vast and complex part of the world, however, contains relatively few extended areas of sand dunes; much of the deserts consist of gravelly surfaces. River lowlands and the coasts of the Mediterranean Sea, the Caspian Sea, and the Persian Gulf contain plains that can be farmed if rainfall is adequate or irrigation is used.

From Morocco and the Atlantic Ocean on the west to Afghanistan in the east and from the Mediterranean Sea on the north across the Sahara to the south, the region covers about 5.5 million square miles (14.2 million sq. km)—more than 10 percent of the earth's total land surface. In this area are found the world's largest desert as well as the world's longest river, in addition to the sites of two of the world's earliest civilizations. Due to its location around the southern and eastern coasts of the Mediterranean Sea, the region has served as the crossroads of Europe, Africa, and Asia for centuries.

PLACE

Peninsulas and Seas

Two peninsulas and three bodies of water make up the central area of North Africa and Southwest Asia. The largest peninsula is the Arabian Peninsula in Southwest Asia. The Red Sea borders this peninsula on the west. The Persian Gulf lies on the east. The peninsula's southern borders are the Gulf of Aden and the Arabian Sea.

Stretching into the Red Sea is the smaller Sinai Peninsula. To the north lies the Anatolian Peninsula bordered by the Black Sea, the Aegean Sea, and the Mediterranean Sea.

The Dead Sea, located at the mouth of the Jordan River, forms part of the border between Israel and Jordan. The Dead Sea is actually a landlocked, saltwater lake. Its shore, which lies about 1,312 feet (400 m) below sea level, is the lowest place on the earth's surface. The Dead Sea is the saltiest body of water in the world—about 9 times as salty as the ocean.

PLACE

Coasts, Mountains, and Plateaus

Fertile coastal plains are found along the Mediterranean coasts of North Africa and Southwest Asia. Other fertile areas are found along the coasts of the Caspian Sea and the Persian Gulf.

The Mountains of Southwest Asia

Mountains cover much of North Africa and Southwest Asia. Along the west coast of the Arabian Peninsula they divide into two groups. In the north are the Hejaz and to the south are the Asir Mountains, which have taller peaks. Rainfall averaging more than 19 inches (50 cm) a year in the Asir region makes it the most suitable area for agriculture on the

Arabian Peninsula. East of the Asir mountain range lies the Central Plateau where the average annual rainfall ranges from 0 to 4 inches (0 to 10 cm).

The eastern shore of the Mediterranean Sea includes mountain chains. On the Anatolian Peninsula, along the Black Sea are the Pontic Mountains. The Taurus Mountains lie along the Mediterranean or Turkey's southern border. Between these ranges lies the Anatolian Plateau with an elevation that ranges from 2,000 to 5,000 feet (610 to 1,524 m) above sea level. In eastern Turkey, Ararat, an isolated mountain with two peaks, rises 16,945 feet (5,165 m) above sea level.

East of the Anatolian Peninsula, the Zagros Mountains form the western border of the Plateau of Iran, a large desert plateau that stands about 3,000 feet (914 m) above sea level. North of the plateau and directly south of the Caspian Sea lie the Elburz Mountains.

The Zagros and the Taurus Mountains are along a belt of frequent and often severe **seismic**, or earthquake, activity. Earthquakes also occur in North Africa. Perhaps the area of greatest hazard is Iran, which has experienced numerous earthquakes in the last 40 years.

At the easternmost part of the region, in Afghanistan, lies the Hindu Kush mountain range. Some of these mountains rise to heights of 23,000 feet (7,010 m) or more.

The Mountains of North Africa

Along the Mediterranean coast in Morocco and Algeria lies Africa's longest mountain range, the Atlas Mountains. The Atlas Mountains cause greater rainfall on their northern flanks, making the coastal areas of western North Africa more suitable for human settlement. A smaller, isolated mountain range known as the Ahaggar (uh•HAGH•uhr) crosses southern Algeria.

HUMAN/ENVIRONMENT INTERACTION

Rivers

Rivers provide water and deposit rich soil in the otherwise dry desert regions of North Africa and Southwest Asia. The largest

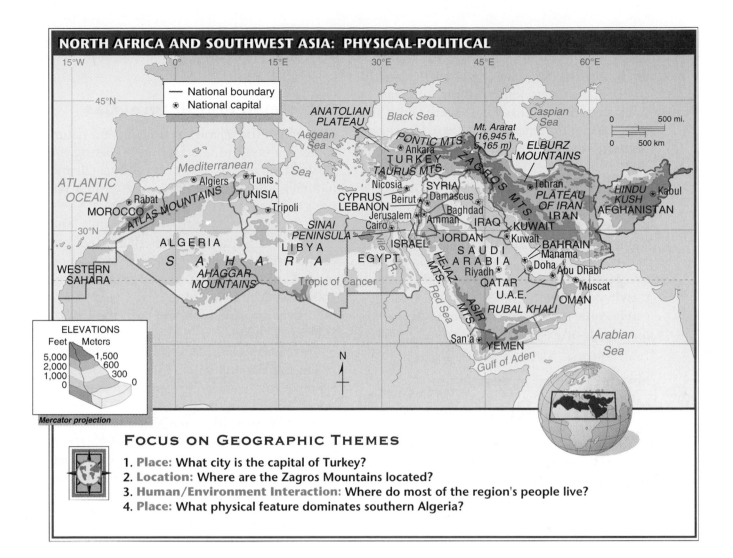

NORTH AFRICA AND SOUTHWEST ASIA: PHYSICAL-POLITICAL

— National boundary
⊛ National capital

ELEVATIONS
Feet   Meters
5,000   1,500
2,000   600
1,000   300
   0   0

Mercator projection

FOCUS ON GEOGRAPHIC THEMES

1. **Place:** What city is the capital of Turkey?
2. **Location:** Where are the Zagros Mountains located?
3. **Human/Environment Interaction:** Where do most of the region's people live?
4. **Place:** What physical feature dominates southern Algeria?

of these rivers are the Nile in northern Africa and the Tigris and Euphrates (yu•FRAT•EEZ) rivers of Southwest Asia.

The Nile

The Nile River, which flows 4,160 miles (6,693 km), is the longest river in the world. Beginning near the Equator, the Nile flows through Egypt to the Mediterranean Sea.

For thousands of years, the Nile River has benefited Egypt. The fertile strip of land along its banks was the site of one of the world's earliest civilizations. Today, the Nile River valley, which makes up 3 percent of the land area of Egypt, is home to more than 90 percent of the Egyptian people.

In ancient times the predictable annual floods allowed farmers to plant their crops in the rich soil deposited by the Nile. These **allu-**

vial-soil deposits—sand and mud deposited by the flowing water—formed a **delta**. A delta is a section of land at a river's mouth that looks like the Greek letter *delta* (∆). Modern dams, such as the Aswan High Dam, now control the river's flow, reducing the deposits of alluvial soil. The dams, however, extend irrigation and allow planting of more than one crop a year.

The Tigris and Euphrates Rivers

Several thousand years ago, a series of civilizations developed in Mesopotamia, which means "land between two rivers." These civilizations thrived in the fertile valley between the Tigris and the Euphrates.

Both rivers originate in the mountains of eastern Turkey and flow southeast through

Syria and Iraq. The Euphrates, the longer river, flows 1,700 miles (2,735 km). The Tigris extends about 1,180 miles (1,899 km). In southern Iraq the rivers join to form the Shatt al Arab that flows into the Persian Gulf. The Tigris and Euphrates rivers help to irrigate farms in otherwise dry Southwest Asia.

Streambeds

Many streams in North Africa and Southwest Asia are not permanent. In the desert, water runoff from infrequent rainstorms creates **wadis**, which are streambeds that are dry except during a heavy rain. Wadis become so heavily laden with eroded material that they can become mud flows. Water in these flows is quickly absorbed by the land surface.

HUMAN/ENVIRONMENT INTERACTION

Natural Resources

The most important natural resources in North Africa and Southwest Asia are petroleum and natural gas. Current estimates are that the region contains more than 60 percent of the world's known petroleum reserves.

Petroleum and Natural Gas

Much of the region's petroleum and natural gas is found in the countries bordering the Persian Gulf and in Algeria and Libya. Oil and natural gas, for the present time, give these nations the appearance of being wealthy.

Before World War II, North Africa and Southwest Asia produced less than 5 percent of the world's oil. Since 1945, oil production in the region has increased dramatically. Today Saudi Arabia is one of the world's top producers of crude oil along with the United States and Russia.

Increased wealth came to the region's oil-producing nations when the global demand for oil in the 1970s led to rapid increases in oil prices. Since then, prices have fallen as industrialized nations have reduced consumption and searched for other energy sources. The result has been a slowdown in economic development among some nations in the region.

Geographic Themes

Place: Nile River Valley, Egypt
The Nile River cuts a lush, green valley through Egypt's vast desert landscape. *How has the Nile River benefited the people of Egypt?*

Geographic Themes

Location: Atlas Mountains
Phosphate rock, iron ore, and manganese are mined in the Atlas Mountains, Africa's longest mountain range. *Where are the Atlas Mountains located?*

Other Minerals

In addition to petroleum and natural gas, North Africa and Southwest Asia have mineral resources. Iron ore, copper, lead, manganese, and zinc are found from Morocco to Afghanistan. For many years most deposits in the area were thought to be modest by world standards. Recent discoveries of iron ore and copper deposits in North Africa and Southwest Asia indicate that the region may have up to 10 percent of the world's iron ore reserves.

In addition to other mineral deposits in the region, **phosphate**—a chemical compound often used in fertilizers—is present in some areas. Phosphate is important to many nations, such as Morocco, which ranks third in world phosphate production.

Although exports of the region's resources, particularly oil, have added prosperity to the region, farming and raising livestock remain the major occupations of most people. These activities are directly affected by the region's climates and vegetation.

SECTION 1 REVIEW

Checking for Understanding

1. **Define** seismic, alluvial-soil deposit, delta, wadi, phosphate.
2. **Locating Places** Through what countries does the Atlas mountain range extend?
3. **Region** What are the three land features characteristic of North Africa and Southwest Asia?
4. **Human/Environment Interaction** How do the major rivers of North Africa and Southwest Asia benefit the people in the region?
5. **Region** What is the most important natural resource in the region?

Critical Thinking

6. **Predicting Consequences** How might economic development in the nations of North Africa and Southwest Asia change in the future? Support your answer.

The Climate and Vegetation

A characteristic common to most of North Africa and Southwest Asia is the scarcity of water. Most parts of the region average 10 inches (25 cm) of precipitation or less each year. The area north of the Elburz Mountains in Iran, however, receives an abundant annual rainfall. Another well-watered area is the southern edge of the Caspian Sea, which receives more than 78 inches (198 cm) of rainfall per year.

These differences in climatic conditions affect the nature of the region's vegetation as well as the economic way of life of most of the population.

REGION

Climate Regions of North Africa and Southwest Asia

In many parts of North Africa and Southwest Asia precipitation averages 10 inches (25 cm) or less each year. Deserts are widespread throughout the region. Three other types of climate regions also are present. These are the Mediterranean, steppe, and highland climates.

Desert Climate

Deserts cover about 50 percent of North Africa and Southwest Asia. Lebanon, Cyprus, and Turkey are the only countries with no desert areas. The Sahara, the largest desert in the world, covers most of North Africa—about 3.5 million square miles (9 million sq. km).

The Sahara and other deserts in the region have sparse vegetation. Farming, however, occurs where water for irrigation is found. **Oases**—places in the desert where water is present—make small-scale agriculture possible in the Sahara. A traveler, arriving at an oasis in North Africa, made the following observation:

---◆---

We wandered . . . through lush groves of palms. There are about a quarter of a million palms in the oasis, but unlike most Saharan oases there is a wide variety of other crops. . . . As one goes through the groves every so often one comes upon one of the two hundred and eighty springs. . . . Young . . . boys play by the springs, diving off the walls sending sluggish ripples across the thick surface of the water. It seems a happy place.

---◆---

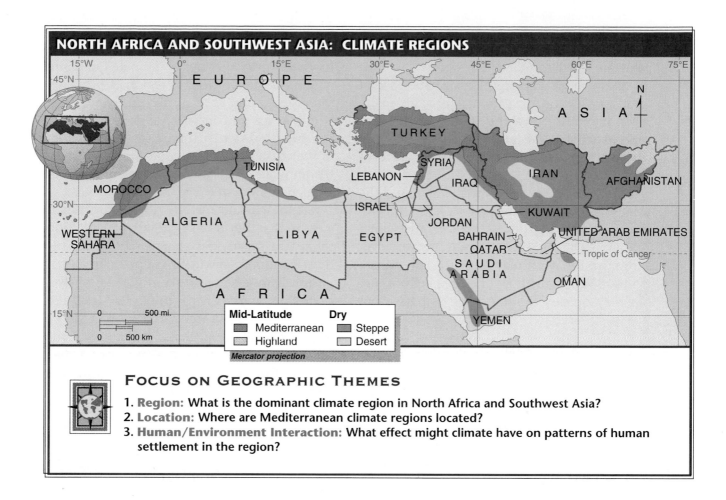

NORTH AFRICA AND SOUTHWEST ASIA: CLIMATE REGIONS

FOCUS ON GEOGRAPHIC THEMES

1. **Region:** What is the dominant climate region in North Africa and Southwest Asia?
2. **Location:** Where are Mediterranean climate regions located?
3. **Human/Environment Interaction:** What effect might climate have on patterns of human settlement in the region?

Some oases scattered across the Sahara are quite large and serve as sites for villages, towns, and in some instances, cities.

The deserts of North Africa and Southwest Asia have limited areas of dunes. More extensive are rocky gravel areas called "desert pavement." For example, less than 10 percent of the Sahara is sand; the rest consists of desert pavement, mountains, and exposed barren rock.

The desert with the largest area of sand in the region is the Rubal Khali, or Empty Quarter, in the southern part of the Arabian Peninsula. The Rubal Khali is one of several deserts and covers about 250,000 square miles (650,000 sq. km) or about one-quarter of the total land area of the Arabian Peninsula.

Mediterranean and Highland Climates

The Mediterranean climate is a variably wet and dry climate found in upland areas of the region as well as on the coastal plains of the Mediterranean Sea, the Black Sea, the Caspian Sea, and in the Tigris-Euphrates Valley. A Mediterranean climate region consists of hot, dry summers and cool, rainy winters. At times during the winter months, it can become relatively cold, particularly at higher elevations.

Coastal and highland areas near mountain ranges usually receive the most rainfall. This rainfall is the result of moist, warm air driven off the sea by prevailing westerly winds during the winter months. As the moist air reaches the mountains, it rises, cools, and the moisture condenses and falls to the earth as rain. The coastal area in North Africa near the Atlas Mountains, for example, averages more than 30 inches (76 cm) of rain each year. The southern coast of the Caspian Sea often has an average annual rainfall of more than twice that amount.

Areas receiving more than 14 inches (35 cm) of rainfall a year can grow certain crops without irrigation. Many farmers grow **cereals**—grains, such as barley, oats, or wheat, that are used for food. In Morocco, cereals make up about 40 percent of the nation's total crop production. Irrigation is used in many parts of North Africa and Southwest Asia, but it is practiced most extensively in the Nile River valley and along the Tigris and Euphrates rivers.

The winds off the Atlantic Ocean and the Mediterranean Sea are major factors in producing the heavy precipitation in the winter months. During the arid summer months, however, the wind may flow from the Sahara to the south. This flow of extremely hot, dry air may quickly destroy crops that have not yet been harvested.

Steppe Climate

As distance from the region's coastal areas increases, the average yearly amount of rainfall decreases. Land suitable for farming gives way to grassy areas used for grazing livestock. In these areas the steppe climate predominates. The steppe climate region is primarily found in upland areas north of the deserts in North Africa and in the interior of parts of Southwest Asia where there is less rainfall than in the coastal areas. In steppe climate regions, the annual rainfall usually averages less than 14 inches (35.6 cm).

Steppe climate regions differ from desert areas in that they receive enough precipitation to sustain substantial grasses. Therefore, the most common activity in steppe climates is **pastoralism**—the raising and grazing of livestock. In many instances in North Africa and Southwest Asia, the most common herds of livestock are of sheep, goats, and camels. Some current estimates place the number of livestock in the region at more than 300 million animals.

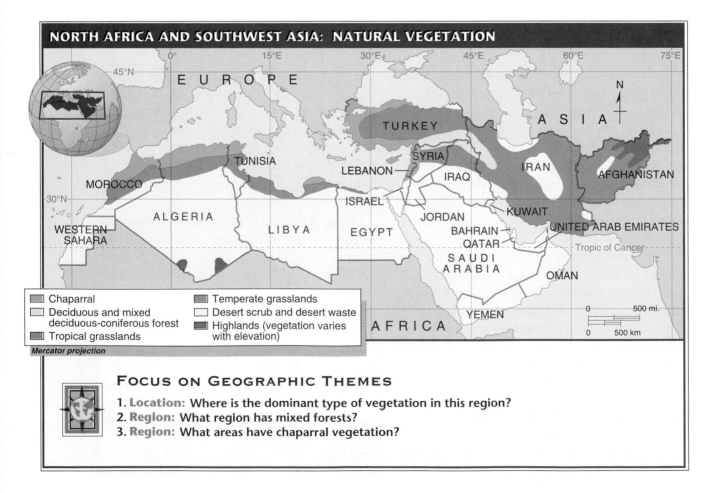

NORTH AFRICA AND SOUTHWEST ASIA: NATURAL VEGETATION

Chaparral
Deciduous and mixed deciduous-coniferous forest
Tropical grasslands
Temperate grasslands
Desert scrub and desert waste
Highlands (vegetation varies with elevation)

Mercator projection

FOCUS ON GEOGRAPHIC THEMES

1. **Location:** Where is the dominant type of vegetation in this region?
2. **Region:** What region has mixed forests?
3. **Region:** What areas have chaparral vegetation?

Geographic Themes

Region: Mediterranean Coast of Turkey
Coastal areas of North Africa and Southwest Asia receive more rainfall than many interior areas of the region. *What type of climate is found along the region's coasts?*

HUMAN/ENVIRONMENT INTERACTION

Natural Vegetation

Natural vegetation in North Africa and Southwest Asia varies according to soil conditions and climate. The region's natural vegetation ranges from forests to grasses and shrubs to sparse desert vegetation.

Forest areas usually are found in higher elevations that have more abundant rainfall, as in the Atlas Mountains in North Africa and the highland areas of Turkey. In desert areas, on the other hand, vegetation is rare and in most cases nonexistent except around oases.

In recent years, natural vegetation in North Africa and Southwest Asia has declined. The needs of growing populations have led to an increase in the demand for agricultural and animal food products. To meet these demands, forests have been cleared for cultivation, and grasses and shrubs in steppe regions have suffered from overgrazing.

SECTION 2 REVIEW

Checking for Understanding
1. **Define** oasis, cereal, pastoralism.
2. **Locating Places** Which North African nations contain parts of the Sahara?
3. **Region** What are four climates found in North Africa and Southwest Asia?
4. **Region** How do mountain ranges along coastal areas in North Africa and Southwest Asia affect the climate?
5. **Human/Environment Interaction** Why is pastoralism common in the steppe areas of North Africa and Southwest Asia?

Critical Thinking
6. **Making Comparisons** Why do the farming techniques in some of the region's coastal areas differ from what is practiced in the Nile River valley?

STUDY AND WRITING SKILLS

Writing a Paragraph

Imagine reading a chapter in this textbook that has not been divided into paragraphs. Most readers would give up after a few pages as the print blurred before their eyes and the ideas blurred in their minds. By visually marking the beginning and end of each idea, paragraphs help readers follow the writer's thoughts.

REVIEWING THE SKILL

The paragraph is the basic unit of prose writing. The American Heritage Dictionary defines a paragraph as, "a distinct division of a written work or composition that expresses a thought or point relevant to the whole but is complete in itself; it may consist of a single sentence or several sentences." Notice the main points of the definition: 1) a paragraph must express a complete thought; 2) that thought must relate to the composition as a whole; and 3) paragraphs can be any length.

A well-written paragraph displays four characteristics. First, it expresses only one main idea, which is usually (though not always) stated in a topic sentence. Second, the other sentences support and develop the main idea. Third, the sentences advance the main idea step-by-step, so the reader can easily follow the writer's thoughts. Fourth, transitional words and phrases clarify relationships among sentences in the paragraph, and between each paragraph and the paragraphs that precede and follow it. Examples of transitional words and phrases include: *first, next, finally, also, therefore, because, however,* and *instead.*

Writing clear, well-organized paragraphs enables you to express your ideas so that any reader can share and understand your thoughts.

To help you write effective paragraphs, apply the following steps:
- State the main idea of the paragraph as a topic sentence.
- Choose details that support or explain the main idea.
- Arrange the sentences in a logical sequence to help the reader follow your thoughts.
- Use transitional words and phrases to clarify relationships within the paragraph and within the composition as a whole.

PRACTICING THE SKILL

A. The sentences below discuss the relationship between landforms, wind patterns, and climate in North Africa. After reading the sentences, arrange them into a paragraph with a topic sentence, supporting details, a logical sequence, and transitional words as needed.

1. This moisture-laden air rises as it crosses the coastal mountain ranges.
2. The largest desert in the world, the Sahara, has been formed by these natural forces.
3. As the air rises, it cools off, dropping most of its moisture on the windward side of the mountains.
4. In North Africa, landforms and wind patterns strongly affect climate.
5. On one side of the mountains, little or no rain falls, creating a desert climate.
6. The rainfall produces a Mediterranean climate with warm, dry summers and cool, wet winters.
7. As the prevailing winds sweep eastward across the Mediterranean Sea, the air picks up moisture.

B. Choose a main idea that is related to the material in Chapter 17. Write a paragraph about this main idea, using a topic sentence, supporting details, and transitional words as needed.

For additional practice in this skill, see Practicing Skills on page 368 of the Chapter 17 Review.

SECTION	**KEY TERMS**	**SUMMARY**

1 The Land

seismic (p. 358)
alluvial-soil deposit (p. 359)
delta (p. 359)
wadi (p. 360)
phosphate (p. 361)

Atlas Mountains of
North Africa

- The region of North Africa and Southwest Asia stretches from Morocco in the west to Afghanistan in the east and covers more than 10 percent of the earth's total land surface.
- North Africa and Southwest Asia have a number of peninsulas and several seas.
- Rainfall in North Africa and Southwest Asia varies widely, ranging from less than 4 inches (10 cm) on some plateaus to far heavier amounts in some highland areas.
- The fertile Nile River valley and the area near the Tigris and Euphrates rivers provide land where agriculture flourishes.
- Petroleum and natural gas, two of the most important natural resources of North Africa and Southwest Asia, provide substantial revenues to some nations in the region.

SECTION	**KEY TERMS**	**SUMMARY**

2 The Climate and Vegetation

oasis (p. 362)
cereal (p. 364)
pastoralism (p. 364)

Mediterranean coast of
Turkey

- The four climate regions in North Africa and Southwest Asia are the desert, the Mediterranean, the steppe, and the highland.
- Much of the farming in North Africa and Southwest Asia occurs along the coastal areas where rainfall is more prevalent than in other areas of the region.
- In recent years the clearing of land for farming and the overgrazing of steppe areas have taken their toll on natural vegetation except in a few areas where there is more abundant rainfall.

Reviewing Key Terms

Choose the vocabulary term that best completes each of the sentences below. Write your answers on a separate sheet of paper.

seismic (p. 358)
alluvial-soil deposits (p. 359)
delta (p. 359)
wadi (p. 360)
oases (p. 362)
cereal (p. 364)
pastoralism (p. 364)

SECTION 1

1. The _____ is the area at the mouth of the Nile River.
2. Some mountain areas in parts of North Africa and Southwest Asia are centers of _____ activity.
3. Before modern dams, the Nile River left _____ along its banks as it flowed to the Mediterranean Sea.
4. A _____ is a dry streambed in the desert that carries water only for a short time during infrequent rainstorms.

SECTION 2

5. In steppe regions a common economic activity is _____ .
6. The growing of _____ is most common in coastal areas of the region where rainfall is heavier.
7. Across the dry Sahara, scattered _____ provide water and shade.

Reviewing Facts

SECTION 1

8. What is the largest peninsula in the region of North Africa and Southwest Asia?
9. Where is the world's longest river?
10. What rivers provide a fertile farming area in Iraq?

SECTION 2

11. Where is the world's largest desert?
12. What are the characteristics of the Mediterranean climate in North Africa and Southwest Asia?
13. What natural vegetation is usually found in the steppe areas?

Critical Thinking

14. **Drawing Conclusions**   How do the region's resources affect North Africa and Southwest Asia's position in the world?
15. **Determining Cause and Effect**   How are increased cultivation and over-grazing linked to population growth in North Africa and Southwest Asia?

Geographic Themes

16. **Movement**   What natural land features affect the movement of people in North Africa?
17. **Human/Environment Interaction** What technology has contributed to the concentration of people in the Nile River valley?

Practicing Skills

Writing a Paragraph

Refer to the Writing a Paragraph skill activity on page 366. Find a paragraph in Chapter 17 that contains all the elements of an effective paragraph. On a separate sheet of paper, rewrite this paragraph. Then, write the paragraph's topic sentence. If it has no topic sentence, write your own. Next, list the supporting details in the paragraph. Finally, write any transitional words and phrases found in the paragraph.

Using the Unit Atlas

Refer to the physical geography section of the Unit Atlas on pages 352–353.

18. What is the region's highest point?

Projects

Individual Activity

An oil crisis faced the United States and other industrialized nations during the 1970s. Research the events and the outcome of this crisis and write a brief report on its effects in the United States.

Cooperative Learning Activity

Working together in a group of four or five students, research and plan an imaginary trip across the Sahara. Each student should take responsibility for one important factor in-volved in the trip. For example, plan the transportation to be used, the number of helpers needed, the supplies, and the best route to take.

When individual planning is complete, each group may discuss the arrangements and present a final report to the class.

Writing About Geography

Description

Imagine that you are traveling along the Nile River. Write a letter to your best friend describing your journey from Khartoum north to the delta. Use your text, journal, and travel books to describe what you see. In your letter, discuss the climate and physical features of the river valley.

Locating Places

THE PHYSICAL GEOGRAPHY OF NORTH AFRICA AND SOUTHWEST ASIA

Match the letters on the map with the places and physical features of North Africa and Southwest Asia. Write your answers on a separate sheet of paper.

1. Persian Gulf
2. Nile River
3. Mediterranean Sea
4. Arabian Peninsula
5. Caspian Sea
6. Red Sea
7. Black Sea
8. Atlas Mountains
9. Gulf of Aden
10. Sahara

The Cultural Geography of North Africa and Southwest Asia

CHAPTER FOCUS

Geographic Setting

The culture region of North Africa and Southwest Asia has been the crossroads for people from Asia, Africa, and Europe who have adopted ways of life necessary for survival in a harsh environment.

Geographic Themes

Section 1 Population Patterns
MOVEMENT The movement and interaction of people in the region have led to ethnic diversity.

Section 2 History and Government
REGION The region's people have settled near water sources.

Section 3 Cultures and Lifestyles
PLACE Southwest Asia is the birthplace of Judaism, Christianity, and Islam.

▲ Photograph: *Cairo, Egypt*

Population Patterns

SETTING THE SCENE

Read to Discover . . .
- the different ethnic groups that inhabit North Africa and Southwest Asia.
- the areas in the region where most of the people live.
- the recent trend toward urbanization.

Key Term
- ethnic diversity

Identify and Locate
Maghreb, Cairo, Bahrain, Israel, Libya, Iran, Iraq, Tehran, Damascus, Baghdad, Kuwait, Riyadh, Istanbul, Jerusalem

Tehran, Iran
I would like to tell you about one of our holidays, called Norose. It was established by an ancient empire, and it begins on the first day of each new year. On this day we visit relatives and neighbors. Children receive gifts of money and candy. We also have 15 days of vacation beginning on the first day of the new year. This is one of my favorite holidays.

Your friend,
Sorush Firouzmandi

Sorush Firouzmandi, who lives in Iran, describes one of the many festivals celebrated by the peoples of North Africa and Southwest Asia. North Africa and Southwest Asia is a complex culture region with a mixture of racial and ethnic groups, languages, religions, cultures, and lifestyles.

<u>PLACE</u>

Human Characteristics

For centuries, North Africa and Southwest Asia has served as the crossroads for the people of Africa, Europe, and Asia. As a result, the region has much **ethnic diversity**—a difference in peoples based on their origins, languages, customs, or beliefs.

Arabs

The vast majority of the people of North Africa and Southwest Asia are Arabs. Most Arabs are Muslims who practice Islam. Their culture, especially the Arabic language, has had a profound impact on the entire region.

Before the spread of Islam in the 600s, Arabic-speaking peoples lived in the Arabian Peninsula and some areas north of the peninsula. Not all Arabic-speaking people, however, trace their roots to the Arabian Peninsula. Many are descendants of such ancient groups as the Canaanites, the Babylonians, and the Egyptians, all of whom became Arab by learning Arabic. Today Arabs live in 21 countries in the region, including the Maghreb—the area of North Africa now comprised of Tunisia, Algeria, and Morocco.

Israelis

About 5 million people of the region are Israelis, citizens of the country of Israel. Of these, about 4.1 million are Jewish and 0.9 million are Arab.

Israeli Jews trace their ancestral roots to the Hebrews, who settled the region in ancient times and believed that God had given them the land as a permanent home. Over the centuries, wars and persecution drove many of the Jews, as the descendants of the Hebrews were called, to settle in other countries. Their religious identity, however, kept alive their links to their ancient homeland until Israel was founded as a Jewish homeland in 1948.

The Arabs of the region, however, did not want a Jewish state on territory that had been their homeland for centuries. As a result, conflict broke out between Arabs and Jews. It brought severe hardship to all the people, including the Palestinians, or the Arabs living in territory on which Israel was established. Today, however, peace agreements between Is-

Geographic Themes

Place: Israel
In October 1995 Israeli Prime Minister Yitzhak Rabin (left) and Palestinian leader Yasser Arafat (right) signed the West Bank Accord, which handed over most Arab-populated areas of Israel to Palestinian control. Several weeks later, on November 4, 1995, Rabin was assassinated by an Israeli Jew who wanted to stop the peace process.
How many countries of the region are predominantly Arab?

Geographic Themes

Place: Western Wall, Jerusalem
Devout Jews from all over the world pray before the Western Wall, which was part of the Jews' holy temple during ancient times.
What two kingdoms formed the ancient homeland of the Hebrews?

rael and Palestinian leaders have led to greater self-rule for Palestinians in the area.

Turks

The people of Turkey are a blend of the many people who have lived for centuries in Southwest Asia. The most notable of these were the Ottoman Turks, whose empire ruled much of the eastern Mediterranean world for more than 600 years.

The Turks are not Arab, but like the Arabs, most practice Islam. They also speak their own Turkish language and have developed a culture that blends Turkish, Islamic, and Western elements.

Iranians and Afghanis

Today more than 60 million people live in Iran, once called Persia. The term *Iran* means "land of the Aryans," and many Iranians believe they are descendants of the Aryans, Indo-Europeans who migrated into the region from southern Russia about 1000 B.C. Iranians today speak Farsi, an Indo-European language that is distantly related to English. Most Iranians practice a form of Islam known as Shiism.

On the eastern border of Iran is Afghanistan, another of the non-Arab countries in the region. Afghanistan is a country of many ethnic groups that reflect the centuries of migrations and invasions of different peoples. A common adherence to Islam is the thread that helps hold the country together.

Cypriots

Another non-Arab nation in North Africa and Southwest Asia is the island nation of Cyprus. The people of Cyprus include a Greek majority and a significant Turkish minority. After the island gained independence from the United Kingdom, a violent civil war erupted between the two groups. Today Cyprus remains a divided nation of Greeks and Turks.

Armenians and Kurds

The region also includes two large ethnic groups—the Armenians and the Kurds. For many years, both groups have struggled to form their own countries.

Before World War I, most Armenians lived in Turkey. During the Greek-Turkish conflict, an estimated 1 million Armenians were massacred, deported, or died of illness at the hands of the Turks. The survivors fled, many settling in other parts of Southwest Asia as well as Europe and the United States. Recently, Armenians have celebrated the independence of the Armenian republic in the former Soviet Union.

The Kurds live in the border region separating Turkey, Iraq, Iran, Syria, and the former Soviet Union. They call their land Kurdistan, but their efforts to win self-rule have been repeatedly crushed.

HUMAN/ENVIRONMENT INTERACTION

Water and Population

Most of the people of North Africa and Southwest Asia live near water. People live along seacoasts, rivers, or near highlands, and near oases. For example, most Egyptians live along the Nile River or near the Suez Canal. In Iraq, many people live in the Tigris-Euphrates Valley.

The environment in these areas makes it possible to grow crops and raise animals. Drinking water is also readily available in these locations. Farming, mining, fishing, and trading are the major economic activities.

The desert areas of North Africa and Southwest Asia are largely unpopulated except for the cities, where oil-related industries provide jobs. Nomadic herders live in or near the desert oases.

PLACE

Population Densities and Growth

The most populous countries in the region are Turkey, Egypt, and Iran. Each of these countries has a population of more than 50 million. Morocco, Algeria, Iraq, Saudi Arabia, and Afghanistan have populations ranging between about 17 million and 28 million. The

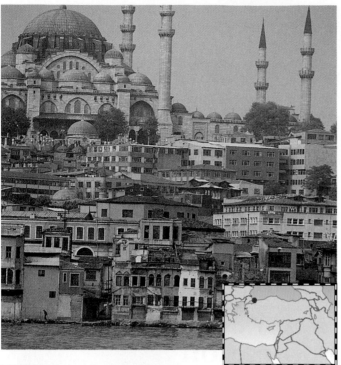

Geographic Themes

Location: Istanbul, Turkey
Istanbul's location near the point where the Black Sea meets the Mediterranean Sea has made it an important trading city. *What religion do most Turks practice?*

remaining countries have populations of roughly 13.5 million or fewer. Tiny Bahrain on the Persian Gulf is the most densely populated, with about 2,000 people per square mile (772 per sq. km).

Overall the populations of the countries of the region currently total about 350 million and are growing at a rapid rate. The result is that citizens in a number of countries already are finding it hard to find jobs and are migrating to other nations to work. This migration serves as a safety valve for some nations, but changing conditions, such as a reduction in oil production, could lead to a decline in the need for foreign workers and become a source of unrest.

PLACE

Urbanization

Many great cities once existed in North Africa and the Middle East. For centuries, however, the region's population was rural rather than urban. Since World War II, most of the major oil-and-gas-producing countries, however, have rapidly become urbanized.

Urban growth has been due, in part, to rural villagers moving to the cities in search of a better life. This population shift, however, has caused problems because the cities have grown faster than have the means of supplying food and housing. As a result, food and housing shortages have become problems in some cities.

Cairo is one of the region's largest cities with more than 10 million people. Located on the Nile River, Cairo is the capital as well as the cultural and economic center of Egypt. Alexandria, Egypt's other major city, is a seaport on the Mediterranean Sea.

The other major cities in North Africa are all located on the coast. They include Tripoli, the capital of Libya; Tunis, the capital of Tunisia; Algiers, the capital of Algeria; and Casablanca in Morocco.

The major cities in the eastern part of the region are Tehran, the capital of Iran; Baghdad, the capital of Iraq; and Istanbul in Turkey. This area also includes two cities that originally developed around oases—Syria's capital, Damascus, and Saudi Arabia's capital, Riyadh (ree•AHD).

SECTION 1 REVIEW

Checking for Understanding
1. **Define** ethnic diversity.
2. **Locating Places** Where in the region are the largest concentrations of people?
3. **Place** What different peoples make up the region?
4. **Movement** What has been the trend in the distribution of population in North Africa and Southwest Asia since World War II?

Critical Thinking
5. **Analyzing Information** What challenges does a growing population bring to the region?

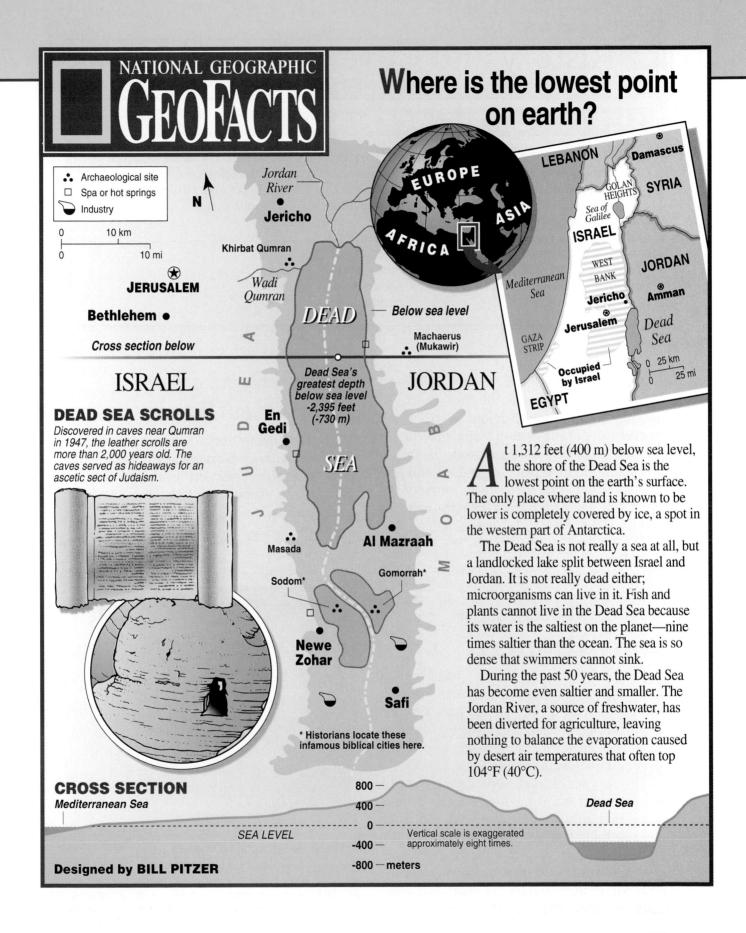

NATIONAL GEOGRAPHIC
GEOFACTS

Where is the lowest point on earth?

Legend:
- .•. Archaeological site
- ☐ Spa or hot springs
- 🥄 Industry

N

0 ────── 10 km
0 ────── 10 mi

Jordan River

● Jericho

Khirbat Qumran .•.

⊛ JERUSALEM

Wadi Qumran

Bethlehem ●

Cross section below

DEAD

— Below sea level

Machaerus (Mukawir) .•.

ISRAEL

JORDAN

Dead Sea's greatest depth below sea level -2,395 feet (-730 m)

DEAD SEA SCROLLS

Discovered in caves near Qumran in 1947, the leather scrolls are more than 2,000 years old. The caves served as hideaways for an ascetic sect of Judaism.

En Gedi ●

SEA

Al Mazraah ●

.•. Masada

Gomorrah*

Sodom*

Newe Zohar ●

Safi ●

* Historians locate these infamous biblical cities here.

At 1,312 feet (400 m) below sea level, the shore of the Dead Sea is the lowest point on the earth's surface. The only place where land is known to be lower is completely covered by ice, a spot in the western part of Antarctica.

The Dead Sea is not really a sea at all, but a landlocked lake split between Israel and Jordan. It is not really dead either; microorganisms can live in it. Fish and plants cannot live in the Dead Sea because its water is the saltiest on the planet—nine times saltier than the ocean. The sea is so dense that swimmers cannot sink.

During the past 50 years, the Dead Sea has become even saltier and smaller. The Jordan River, a source of freshwater, has been diverted for agriculture, leaving nothing to balance the evaporation caused by desert air temperatures that often top 104°F (40°C).

**Inset map labels:**
LEBANON — Damascus ⊗
GOLAN HEIGHTS
Sea of Galilee — SYRIA
ISRAEL
WEST BANK
Mediterranean Sea
JORDAN
Jericho ⊗ — Amman ⊗
Jerusalem ⊗ — Dead Sea
GAZA STRIP
Occupied by Israel
EGYPT
0 ── 25 km
0 ── 25 mi

EUROPE / ASIA / AFRICA

CROSS SECTION
Mediterranean Sea

800 —
400 —
0 —
SEA LEVEL
-400 —
-800 — meters

Dead Sea

Vertical scale is exaggerated approximately eight times.

Designed by BILL PITZER

History and Government

The culture region of North Africa and Southwest Asia saw the rise of some of the world's greatest civilizations as well as the birth of three of the world's major religions. In addition, farmers of the region were the first to raise many of the cereals, vegetables, and animals still used as staple foods in much of the world. The region also has a long history of intense conflicts over land and resources.

HUMAN/ENVIRONMENT INTERACTION

Early Civilizations

Even though most of the region is semiarid, important civilizations developed and prospered here. These civilizations began to grow in the region's most fertile areas about 6,000 years ago.

HUMAN/ENVIRONMENT INTERACTION

Early Peoples

Hunters and gatherers had settled throughout North Africa and Southwest Asia by the end of the last Ice Age. By 6000 B.C., about 4,000 years later, farming communities had spread to the area along the Nile River and the Mediterranean Sea.

The region's farmers were among the first people in the world to **domesticate**, or take plants and animals from the wild and make them useful to people. These early farmers also captured and herded cattle, sheep, goats, pigs, and camels. Some of these animals were used for food. Farmers used the hides of some other animals to make clothes and shelters.

Geographic Themes

Place: Abu Simbel Monument, Egypt
The ancient Egyptians built monuments and pyramid tombs for their rulers. *What were other achievements of ancient Egyptian civilization?*

Mesopotamia

The Sumerian civilization was one early society that developed in Mesopotamia, the area between the Tigris and Euphrates rivers. Mesopotamia's warm climate allowed the Sumerians to raise crops year-round. Irrigation canals and flood-control dikes were used to bring the nearby river water to the land. Efforts to improve water distribution led to progress in the study of mathematics, engineering, and soil science. The Sumerians kept records by carving wedge-shaped symbols on wet clay tablets. These tablets were then baked and hardened. This writing system is called **cuneiform.**

Egypt

Egyptian civilization grew along the Nile River. Because of sophisticated irrigation methods and the alluvial-soil deposits resulting from the annual flooding of the Nile, farmers could grow 2 or 3 crops each year. The Egyptians' cultural achievements included building pyramids as tombs for their rulers and developing a calendar with a 365-day year. In addition, the Egyptians developed a form of picture writing called **hieroglyphics.**

Later Civilizations

The Phoenician civilization arose along the Mediterranean coast of present-day Israel and Lebanon. The Phoenicians' most important achievement was the development of an alphabet in which letters stood for sounds. This alphabet formed the basis for the alphabet used throughout much of the Western world today.

During the 500s B.C., the Persian Empire developed. The Persian Empire extended from beyond the eastern border of the region to the Nile River and the Aegean Sea. Realizing that irrigation water for their settlements would evaporate if carried across the desert in surface canals, the Persians constructed a system of **qanats,** or underground canals, to carry water from the mountains across the desert to farmlands.

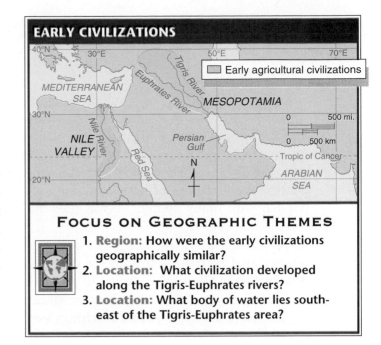

EARLY CIVILIZATIONS

Early agricultural civilizations

FOCUS ON GEOGRAPHIC THEMES

1. **Region:** How were the early civilizations geographically similar?
2. **Location:** What civilization developed along the Tigris-Euphrates rivers?
3. **Location:** What body of water lies southeast of the Tigris-Euphrates area?

The Sumerians, Egyptians, Phoenicians, Persians, and other empires to the west and to the east had many cultural and economic exchanges. Because of these exchanges, North Africa and Southwest Asia became known as the crossroads of civilization.

<u>REGION</u>

The Birthplace of Three Major Religions

Three of the world's major religions began in Southwest Asia. One of the earliest, Judaism, developed as the religion of the Hebrews.

Judaism

Once a nomadic people, the Hebrews established the kingdoms of Israel and Judah along the eastern coast of the Mediterranean Sea. There they made the city of Jerusalem their capital and religious center. The followers of Judaism, called Jews, based their religion on **monotheism**—the belief in one God. In addition, Judaism taught the importance of obedience to God's laws and the creation of a just society. Books based on these laws and on the history of the Jews make up the Hebrew Bible.

Christianity

Another of the region's major religions, Christianity, began in Southwest Asia in the area known as Palestine. Christianity is based on the teachings of Jesus, a Jew who traveled and spread his beliefs throughout Palestine. Because the teachings of Jesus made him unpopular with many people, he was tried and crucified.

After the death of Jesus, his followers claimed that he had risen from the dead and was the Son of God. Those Jews and non-Jews who followed Jesus's teachings became known as Christians. Many Christian teachings were detailed in books about Jesus and the early churches, which Christians added to the Hebrew Bible. The new books are called the New Testament.

Islam

Another major religion that emerged in Southwest Asia, and the religion followed by the vast majority of the people in North Africa and Southwest Asia today, was Islam. This religion began in the Arabian Peninsula about A.D. 600 with Muhammad, a merchant of the city of Makkah (Mecca). Believing that he was God's **prophet**, or messenger, Muhammad proclaimed that people should change their ways of living and believe in the one true God. It is estimated that today as many as one-fifth of the world's people are Muslims—a term from an Arabic word meaning "those who submit to the will of God." Muslims pay close attention to the rules of their faith that are set down in the Islamic holy book, the Quran. They pray in **mosques**—houses of public worship.

By the A.D. 800s, Islam had spread to North Africa, South Asia, Southwest Asia, and parts

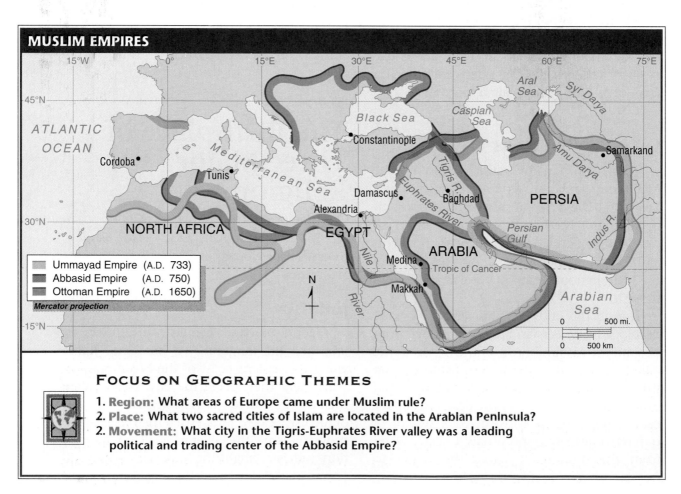

MUSLIM EMPIRES

Ummayad Empire (A.D. 733)
Abbasid Empire (A.D. 750)
Ottoman Empire (A.D. 1650)
Mercator projection

FOCUS ON GEOGRAPHIC THEMES

1. **Region:** What areas of Europe came under Muslim rule?
2. **Place:** What two sacred cities of Islam are located in the Arabian Peninsula?
2. **Movement:** What city in the Tigris-Euphrates River valley was a leading political and trading center of the Abbasid Empire?

of Europe. Islamic scholars, particularly those in the Muslim empires of North Africa and Southwest Asia, made important contributions in the natural sciences, medicine, astronomy, and mathematics. They introduced the Arabic number system, based on the numerals 0 to 9, into the region. The scholars also translated Greek writings into Arabic.

REGION

The Modern Era

Over the years, the Muslim empires of North Africa and Southwest Asia began to decline. By the late 1800s, the region was largely under the control of Europeans. The region's decline was due in part to the many wars fought on its lands. Some major conflicts included the Crusades and the Mongol invasions.

Another reason for the decline was the lack of resources, such as minerals, wood, and coal. The region lacked many of the raw materials needed to fuel an industrial revolution such as the one that took place in Europe.

The peoples of the region chafed under European control. During the 1800s a well-educated urban middle class developed. Trained in European ways, the new middle class accepted European ideas about **nationalism**, or the right of each people to have its own independent nation. This development stirred nationalistic feelings that provided the basis for the modern nations that have been carved out of the region.

Independence

The continuing rise of nationalism after World Wars I and II gradually brought an end to direct European rule. By the 1960s most of the Arab countries in North Africa and Southwest Asia had achieved independence. European nations, however, often controlled the newly independent countries' economies. To counter the European presence, some countries seized European property. Iran, Iraq, and Libya, for example, **nationalized**, or placed

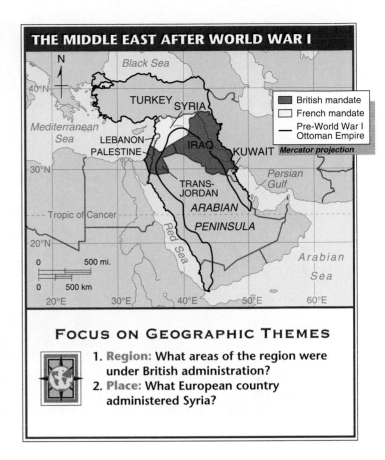

THE MIDDLE EAST AFTER WORLD WAR I

- British mandate
- French mandate
- Pre-World War I Ottoman Empire

Mercator projection

FOCUS ON GEOGRAPHIC THEMES

1. **Region:** What areas of the region were under British administration?
2. **Place:** What European country administered Syria?

under government control, the foreign-owned oil companies in their countries.

Not all the newly independent nations in the region were Arab or Muslim. Many Jews had returned to Palestine since World War I, and in 1948 the United Nations agreed to create the state of Israel. Arab opposition to Israel's existence and Israel's concerns for its security led to a series of wars. An ongoing issue in the Arab-Israeli dispute is the status of the Palestinians, who want a separate homeland in areas occupied by Israeli forces in the 1967 Arab-Israeli war. In 1993, a considerable move toward peace in the region was taken when Israel and the Palestinians agreed to a peace settlement. The agreement called for eventual Palestinian self-rule in return for Arab recognition of Israel's right to nationhood.

Other trouble spots in the region also have led to armed conflicts. In Lebanon there have been continuing struggles between Christians and Muslims over control of the government.

Geographic Themes

Place: Tel Aviv, Israel
Israelis celebrate their country's independence day. *What development in the 20th century led to the emergence of independent countries in the region?*

In addition, border conflicts, such as the conflict between Iraq and Iran that led to years of warfare, still exist.

The most recent dispute arose in 1990 after Iraq invaded its oil-rich neighbor Kuwait. Iraq's invasion and occupation of Kuwait ended only after a coalition of nations led by the United States expelled the Iraqi forces and forced Saddam Hussein, Iraq's president, to withdraw his army.

Today's Governments

The independent nations of North Africa and Southwest Asia have several different types of governments. Monarchs rule eight of the nations in the region. Other types of government include Israel's parliamentary democracy, Egypt's republic with a strong national government and a president, Libya's military dictatorship, and Iran's government based on Islamic laws.

SECTION 2 REVIEW

Checking for Understanding

1. **Define** domesticate, cuneiform, hieroglyphics, qanat, monotheism, prophet, mosque, nationalism, nationalize.
2. **Locating Places** What rivers were the bases for the Mesopotamian and Egyptian civilizations?
3. **Movement** Why was North Africa and Southwest Asia called the crossroads of civilization?
4. **Region** How are the governments of North Africa and Southwest Asia organized?

Critical Thinking

5. **Drawing Conclusions** Why was the domestication of plants and animals so important to the founding of permanent settlements?

THE SAHARA: GROWING OR SHIFTING?

As you read, examine how the Sahara has changed and may change in the future.

Region

The vast, dry Sahara covers about 3.5 million square miles (9 million sq. km)—an area roughly equal to the size of the continental United States. At the Sahara's center are volcanic mountains. Plains broken by plateaus and boulders surround the mountains; at the very edge of the Sahara are seas of sand dunes.

Farmers living in grasslands bordering the Sahara have built shelter belts to prevent soil from being blown away and to control the movement of sand into their fields. Efforts to control the effects of desertification, however, have not always met with success.

A Glorious Green Past

The Sahara as it is today gives no hint that in the past grasslands and forests covered the region. Geologists have determined that the Sahara's climate slowly began to change about 10,000 years ago. By about 4000 B.C., an arid region had appeared at the center of the once fertile area.

The climate continued to slowly dry out through the centuries. People living in the area also contributed to the desert's growth by practicing *shifting cultivation*. They cut down trees in an area, uprooted the shrubs for firewood and building materials, and let their herds overgraze. When they had depleted the resources of an area, the people moved on to another place. With no ground cover

to protect the soil in the abandoned area, the desert took over, increasing its size.

Population Overload

Desertification of the Sahara continues today at an even more alarming rate than in the past. Beginning in the 1940s, foreign aid and enhanced technology increased the population living on the edges of the Sahara. The human activities that contribute to desertification have increased: uprooting bushes and grass, cutting down trees, overgrazing. In the late 1970s, scientists reported that the Sahara was "growing" in a southward direction of 2 to 6 miles (3 to 10 km) a year.

Important new studies in the early 1990s suggested that the Sahara's southward move-

ment might be more like a sea tide, shifting back and forth within a 145-mile (269-km) zone, rather than a permanent increase. Scientists cautioned, however, that whatever natural activity may be taking place, it does not alter the need to change the human behavior in the region.

Checking for Understanding

1. Study the illustration at the top of the page. How has the Sahara region changed since the end of the Ice Age?

2. **Human/Environment Interaction** How have humans contributed to the Sahara's growth?

SECTION 3
Cultures and Lifestyles

SETTING THE SCENE

Read to Discover . . .
- the impact of religion on the cultural and political development of North Africa and Southwest Asia.
- three different ways of life for most people in North Africa and Southwest Asia.
- the geographic factors that have contributed to the region's standard of living.

Key Terms
- ziggurat
- bedouin
- *sūq*

Identify and Locate
Lebanon, Cyprus, United Arab Emirates

R eligion is an important unifying element within each of the cultures of North Africa and Southwest Asia. These cultures have also been enriched by contact with the peoples of the three continents for which this region has been a crossroads.

REGION

Religion

The great majority of people in the region follow Islam. The religion influences the language, arts, government, and lifestyles of its followers. Islam is the major religion of all the countries in the region with the exception of Israel and Cyprus.

Even though Judaism and Christianity have their roots in the region, only a small percentage of the current population is either Jewish or Christian. Although Algeria and Morocco have some Jewish residents, the overwhelming majority of Jews in the region live in Israel.

The countries of Lebanon and Cyprus have large Christian populations. The majority of the Lebanese Christians are Maronites, which is a branch of Roman Catholicism. In contrast, most Cypriot Christians follow the Eastern Orthodox faith.

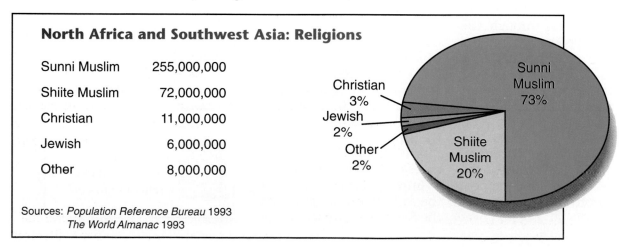

North Africa and Southwest Asia: Religions

Sunni Muslim	255,000,000
Shiite Muslim	72,000,000
Christian	11,000,000
Jewish	6,000,000
Other	8,000,000

Sunni Muslim 73%
Christian 3%
Jewish 2%
Other 2%
Shiite Muslim 20%

Sources: *Population Reference Bureau* 1993
The World Almanac 1993

Location: Grand Mosque, Saudi Arabia
The Grand Mosque, the center of worship for all Muslims, stands in the heart of Makkah, the holiest city of Islam. *What art forms do Muslim artists use in mosques and other public buildings?*

REGION

Languages

B ecause the Quran was originally written in Arabic, non-Arab Muslims often learned Arabic in order to read the Quran. Thus, as more people converted to Islam, Arabic became the region's main language. Other major languages include Hebrew in Israel, Berber in southern Morocco and Algeria, Turkish in Turkey and Cyprus, Greek in Cyprus, Pushtu in Afghanistan, and Farsi in Iran.

REGION

The Arts

T he arts of North Africa and Southwest Asia are based on the achievements of early civilizations. Later, Judaism, Christianity, and Islam provided inspiration for architects, writers, and artists. Today, the arts reflect the influence of East and West as well as the old and the new.

Architecture and Art

The region's early civilizations produced fine metal craftswork and stone sculptures. These civilizations, however, were best known for their architecture. In Mesopotamia large temples—**ziggurats**—made of mud brick rose in step-like fashion above the flat landscape. In Egypt large blocks of stone were painstakingly fitted to form the towering pyramids. The Persians later built great palaces of stone decorated with beautifully patterned woven textiles.

The best-known forms of Islamic architecture are its mosques and palaces. Because Islam did not encourage the images of living figures in religious art, artists have used geometric patterns and floral designs to decorate buildings. Beautiful writing is also often used for decoration. Many mosques are decorated with passages from the Quran.

Literature

The region's strong oral tradition has made epics and poetry the dominant literature among the Arabs and other Muslim peoples. The epic *Shahnameh (King of Kings)* describes heroic events in early Persian history. A well-known example of another kind of literature is the *Arabian Nights*—a collection of Arab, Indian, and Persian stories. These stories often reflect life in the early period of the Muslim empires.

Today poets and writers in many parts of the region deal with the problems of change in traditional society. Much of the modern literature also has nationalistic themes. Many new rhythms and rhyme patterns in recent poetry reflect the increased influence of the West.

REGION

Varying Ways of Life

During the 1900s the way of life of the people of North Africa and Southwest Asia has changed dramatically. Since 1900 the population of the region has grown rapidly. This growth has led to many lifestyle changes as more people have moved from rural to urban areas. Current estimates are that less than 50 percent of the region's people cultivate the land and that only a very small percent are **bedouins**, or desert nomads.

Standards of Living

Countries in the region with economies based on manufacturing and trade or oil, such as Israel and Qatar, enjoy a relatively high standard of living. Many countries, however, have poverty-stricken populations. Population growth in such countries as Afghanistan and Egypt has surpassed economic growth. As a result, economic systems often cannot provide people with basic necessities.

Most hospitals in the region are government-owned. In addition, medical care in many of the wealthy oil-producing countries is free. Medical treatment, however, is available mainly in the region's towns and cities. There also is a shortage of doctors in many countries. These factors contribute to low life expectancies in much of the region.

Geographic Themes

Place: Southwest Asian Markets
In many cities of the region, the traditional *sūq* provides a marked contrast to modern department stores. *What are the staple foods of North Africa and Southwest Asia?*

Meeting Human Needs

Methods of meeting the needs of the people vary throughout the region. Housing, for example, differs from country to country. In many areas the people live without running water and electric lights. As a result, people must carry water from pumps and use lanterns or candles for light.

In some cities, such as Jerusalem, many of the buildings are made of stone and are hundreds of years old. Farmers and rural workers in North Africa and Southwest Asia usually live in tin or stone structures, or shelters made from wood and iron. A writer describes a typical Egyptian rural home:

Houses, mostly flat roofed, are generally built around a courtyard and face south to absorb the winter sun. Within the compact enclosure live dozens of people of all ages with their water buffalo, cattle, an ox or camel, an ass, and a few scrawny chickens. Furniture, if it exists at all, is sparse, and the average hut is furnished only with a crude grass mat or carpet to cover the earthen floor. Bread is the staff of peasant life, supplemented by some vegetables. Occasionally, on festive days such as the Prophet's [Muhammad's] birthday, there are eggs, meat, and fruit.

The staple foods of the region consist of wheat, barley, and rice, sometimes supplemented by meat, dairy products, fruits, and vegetables. People often buy food at a *sūq,* or an enclosed marketplace.

Many of the people of the region wear traditional long, loose cotton clothing. They also wear a head covering to reflect the hot sunlight. In many cities, however, people wear clothing like that found in North America and Europe.

Education

Primary education is free, and enrollment is increasing in the region. Many students complete both primary and secondary school, and a small percentage enroll in universities. Well-known institutions of higher learning in the region include Cairo's University of Al-Azhar, which was founded in A.D. 970. It is one of the oldest universities in the world.

Leisure Time

Family ties are important to the people of the region. Family hospitality is taken very seriously, and leisure time is often spent visiting and entertaining family members.

Popular sports include soccer, hunting, and fishing. Board games such as backgammon are popular in some countries. The people also enjoy going to movies and watching television.

Religious holidays are important throughout the region. *Īd al Adha,* or the Feast of Sacrifice, is a very important Muslim celebration during which many Muslims go on pilgrimage to Makkah. Such Jewish holidays as Passover, Yom Kippur, and Hanukkah and such Christian holidays as Christmas and Easter are observed in some countries in the region.

SECTION 3 REVIEW

Checking for Understanding
1. **Define** ziggurat, bedouin, *sūq.*
2. **Locating Places** What ancient civilization built pyramids?
3. **Region** Why does the art of the region use geometric patterns, floral designs, and beautiful writing?
4. **Human/Environment Interaction** What economic factors have enabled some countries in the region to enjoy a high standard of living?

Critical Thinking
5. **Making Generalizations** Why did the cultures in the region often borrow from each other and from cultures outside the region?

MAP AND GRAPH SKILLS

Interpreting a Special-Purpose Map

Maps fall into two basic categories: general-purpose maps and special-purpose maps. General-purpose maps contain the most basic physical and/or political information about a region, such as international boundaries, major cities, rivers, large bodies of water, and key physical features. Maps that illustrate information on specialized subjects, or themes, are called special-purpose maps, or thematic maps.

REVIEWING THE SKILL

A special-purpose map can illustrate almost any kind of information. It can contain physical, political, economic, climatic, historic, or cultural information—almost anything that can be expressed geographically.

To interpret a special-purpose map, apply the following steps:

- Read the map title to determine the subject and purpose of the map.
- Read all the labels to identify the geographic region and other information listed on the map.
- Identify each symbol and color shown in the map key.
- Locate each symbol and color on the map.
- Form hypotheses and generalizations based on the map information.

PRACTICING THE SKILL

Use the map below to answer the following questions:

1. What is the subject of the map?
2. What geographic region is shown on the map?
3. What do the colors represent?
4. What percentage of the population of Iran can read and write?
5. In which country is the literacy rate 40–50 percent?
6. Which countries have the highest literacy rate?

For additional practice in this skill, see Practicing Skills on page 388 of the Chapter 18 Review.

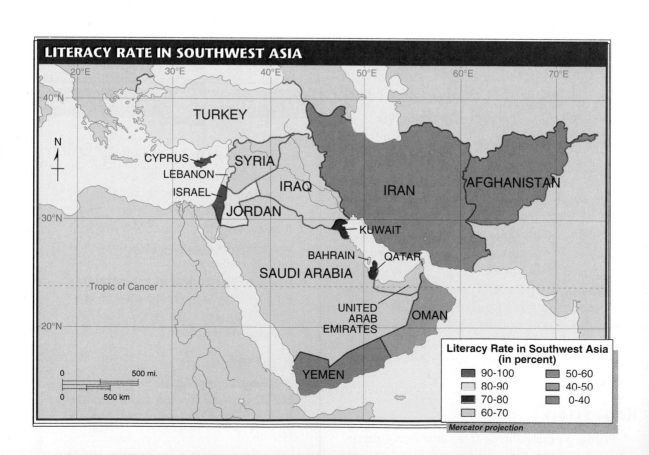

LITERACY RATE IN SOUTHWEST ASIA

Literacy Rate in Southwest Asia (in percent)
- 90-100
- 80-90
- 70-80
- 60-70
- 50-60
- 40-50
- 0-40

Mercator projection

SECTION	KEY TERMS	SUMMARY
1 Population Patterns Istanbul's mosques and palaces along the Golden Horn harbor	ethnic diversity (p. 371)	• The culture region of North Africa and Southwest Asia has been a crossroads for the peoples and cultures of Asia, Africa, and Europe. • The heaviest concentrations of population in North Africa and Southwest Asia are in coastal and river valley areas where water is available. • Rapid population growth and rising urbanization have characterized the region since World War II.
2 History and Government Israelis celebrate their Independence Day	domesticate (p. 376) cuneiform (p. 377) hieroglyphics (p. 377) qanat (p. 377) monotheism (p. 377) prophet (p. 378) mosque (p. 378) nationalism (p. 379) nationalize (p. 379)	• North Africa and Southwest Asia was the birthplace of two of the world's earliest civilizations—Mesopotamia and Egypt—and three of the world's major religions—Judaism, Christianity, and Islam. • After centuries of European influence, independent states arose in North Africa and Southwest Asia during the 1900s.
3 Cultures and Lifestyles Makkah's Grand Mosque, Islam's holiest shrine	ziggurat (p. 383) bedouin (p. 384) *sūq* (p. 385)	• Islam and the Arabic language have been the primary unifying forces in North Africa and Southwest Asia. • The people living in countries based on manufacturing and trade generally enjoy a high standard of living. The people living in countries where the economies are based on agriculture, however, have a lower standard of living. • Family relationships are important to people in the region. Popular leisure activities include soccer, hunting, and fishing.

Reviewing Key Terms

Choose the vocabulary term that best completes each of the sentences below. Write your answers on a separate sheet of paper.

ethnic diversity (p. 371)
cuneiform (p. 377)
qanats (p. 377)
prophet (p. 378)
mosque (p. 378)
ziggurats (p. 383)
bedouin (p. 384)

SECTION 1

1. Differences in groups of people based on their national origins, languages, customs, beliefs, and/or religions is known as _____ .

SECTION 2

2. The Sumerian writing system was called _____ .

3. Muslims regard Muhammad as a _____, or messenger, of God.

4. A Muslim house of worship is known as a _____ .

5. The Persians constructed a system of _____, or underground canals, to carry water from the mountains across the deserts.

SECTION 3

6. The Sumerians built step-like pyramids called _____ .

7. A desert nomad is often called a _____ .

Reviewing Facts

SECTION 1

8. How are population patterns in North Africa and Southwest Asia affected by the environment?

9. What large cities in the region are located near or on bodies of water?

SECTION 2

10. Why did two early civilizations originate in North Africa and Southwest Asia?

11. What are the three major religions that originated in the region?

SECTION 3

12. What was the outstanding architectural achievement of Islamic civilization?

13. How do the people of North Africa and Southwest Asia spend their leisure time?

Critical Thinking

14. **Drawing Conclusions**   Why do most of the people in North Africa and Southwest Asia live in areas near water?

15. **Predicting Consequences**   What might have been the future of the nations in North Africa and Southwest Asia if there had not been the discovery of oil?

16. **Analyzing Information**   What factors account for varying standards of living in North Africa and Southwest Asia?

Geographic Themes

17. **Movement**   How has the movement of peoples into North Africa and Southwest Asia affected its cultures?

18. **Location**   Why did early civilizations develop in the Tigris-Euphrates and Nile river valleys?

19. **Region**   How is the Islamic influence reflected in the languages of the region?

Practicing Skills

Interpreting a Special-Purpose Map

Refer to the special-purpose map on page 386.

20. Which countries have literacy rates of 40 percent or below?

21. Why do you think North Africa and Southwest Asia have such wide differences in literacy rates?

Using the Unit Atlas

Refer to the cultural geography section of the Unit Atlas on pages 350–351.

22. Where do most people in Algeria live?
23. What city is a major religious center for Jews, Christians, and Muslims?

Projects

Individual Activity

Select one North African country for study. Research that nation's population growth, and write a brief report about how that growth is affecting the way people live.

Cooperative Learning Activity

Working together in a small group, put together a meeting of representatives from each of four or five oil-producing nations. Each group member will research and report to the rest of the group on his or her nation's oil production and revenues and how the revenue should be spent. Upon completion, the report can be compiled and an overall summary can be presented to the entire class.

Writing About Geography

Description

Imagine you are traveling for your hometown newspaper in Saudi Arabia to write about the way of life and the type of housing of the people in one of the major cities Your description should include the effects of the climate on the way people live.

Locating Places

THE POLITICAL GEOGRAPHY OF NORTH AFRICA AND SOUTHWEST ASIA

Match the letters on the map with the places in North Africa and Southwest Asia. Write your answers on a separate sheet of paper.

1. Suez Canal
2. Riyadh
3. Istanbul
4. Iran
5. Tehran
6. Israel
7. Cairo
8. Cyprus
9. Tripoli
10. Casablanca

North Africa and Southwest Asia Today

CHAPTER FOCUS

Geographic Setting

Because of the unequal distribution of fertile lands, rainfall, and natural resources, wealth and standards of living vary from one nation to another in North Africa and Southwest Asia.

Geographic Themes

Section 1 Living in North Africa and Southwest Asia
REGION The culture region of North Africa and Southwest Asia includes some of the world's wealthiest and poorest nations.

▲ Photograph: *Harbor of Haifa, Israel*

Section 2 People and Their Environment
HUMAN/ENVIRONMENT INTERACTION Arid conditions in the region have led to technological and scientific efforts to improve the supply of water for drinking and for irrigation.

Living in North Africa and Southwest Asia

Saudi Arabia

Salam (peace),
Although a large part of my country is desert, by using efficient irrigation systems we produce and export agricultural products such as wheat and dates. Oil is our main resource and our major income. While oil is our main energy source, we also use solar energy.

Abdullah Alhamdan

The economies of the nations within the culture region of North Africa and Southwest Asia vary greatly. Abdullah Alhamdan comes from Saudi Arabia, one of the wealthiest nations. Some of the nations, however, are poor. The reasons for these differences are related to geography or history.

PLACE

Meeting Food Needs

Producing food for the rapidly growing population of North Africa and Southwest Asia is a major concern.

Agriculture

Only a small portion of the region is suitable for crops or grazing, although a large percentage of the people in poorer nations work in agriculture. Only 15 percent of Afghanistan's land is arable, yet about 75 percent of its workers are farmers. In wealthier nations, such as Kuwait, only about 5 percent of the workforce raises crops or livestock. Farmers and herders in the region often live and work separately.

In areas having a Mediterranean climate, cereal crops, citrus fruits, grapes, and dates are important products. Egypt, Saudi Arabia, Iraq, Iran, and Algeria are the largest producers of dates. Egypt exports cotton to countries in Asia, Europe, and North America.

Livestock

Another source of food for the people of the region is an estimated 330 million livestock, mostly cattle and sheep.

The effect of climate on livestock is seen by comparing two countries: Turkey and Saudi Arabia. Turkey is one of the region's leading producers of livestock, largely because it has adequate rainfall and its land is suitable for grazing. Saudi Arabia, in contrast, has almost 3 times as much land but most of it is desert. As a result, it produces only about 10 percent as much livestock as Turkey.

Fishing

The fishing industry, which provides only about 2 percent of the world's fish, is another source of food. Tuna, sardines, and sturgeon are caught in the Mediterranean Sea, Black Sea, Caspian Sea, and the Persian Gulf. The region's two largest producers of fish are Turkey and Morocco.

Industrial Growth

The most important natural resource in North Africa and Southwest Asia is petroleum, with the region producing about 25 percent of the world's supply.

Oil, Natural Gas, and Mining

The wealth from oil has brought industrial growth throughout the region. Iran and Saudi Arabia have large oil-refining and oil-shipping facilities. Some countries have developed industries that use **petrochemicals**—products derived from petroleum or natural gas—to make fertilizers, medicines, plastics, and paints. Less than 5 percent of the oil produced is refined in the region. Most is exported in crude form to industrialized countries.

Natural gas has also advanced the region's industrial growth by powering steel-making, textile, and diamond-cutting industries. This economic growth has provided thousands of jobs and helped improve the standard of living for many people in the region.

LAND USE IN SELECTED COUNTRIES OF NORTH AFRICA AND SOUTHWEST ASIA

Country	Total Land Area sq. mi.	(sq. km)	Arable Land	Forests and Woodlands	Herding
			(as a percentage of the total land area of each country)*		
Afghanistan	251,770	(652,084)	20	5	75
Algeria	919,590	(2,381,738)	3	2	15
Egypt	384,340	(995,441)	3	*	*
Iran	631,660	(1,635,999)	9	11	27
Israel	7,850	(20,332)	21	6	40
Jordan	34,340	(88,941)	4	1	1
Lebanon	3,950	(10,231)	29	7	1
Morocco	172,320	(446,309)	19	12	28
Saudi Arabia	830,000	(2,149,700)	1	1	40
Tunisia	59,980	(155,348)	32	4	20
Turkey	297,150	(769,619)	35	26	12

Columns will not total 100 percent as some land uses are omitted
*Less than 1 percent
Sources: *World Population Data Sheet of the Population Reference Bureau, Inc., 1994; The Cambridge Atlas of the Middle East; Britannica Year Book, 1993*

CHART STUDY

The climate of North Africa and Southwest Asia directly affects land use in the region. The amount of arable land and the land that can support forest and woodlands is usually relatively small. *What percentage of Turkey's land is forested? What percentage of Egypt's land is suitable for farming?*

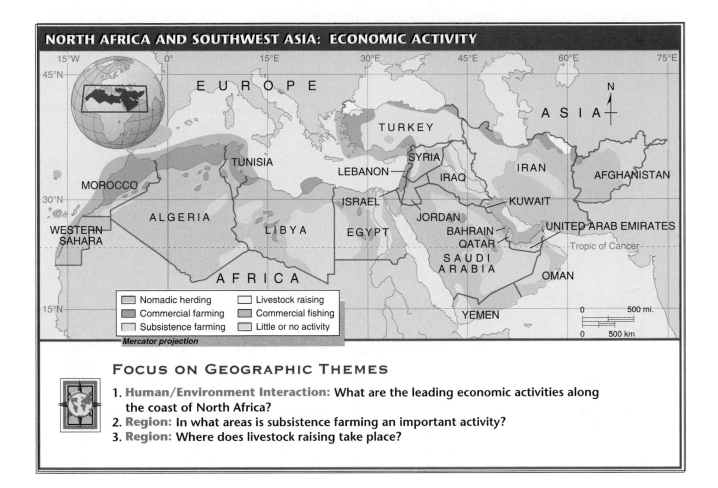

NORTH AFRICA AND SOUTHWEST ASIA: ECONOMIC ACTIVITY

Nomadic herding
Commercial farming
Subsistence farming
Livestock raising
Commercial fishing
Little or no activity

Mercator projection

FOCUS ON GEOGRAPHIC THEMES

1. **Human/Environment Interaction:** What are the leading economic activities along the coast of North Africa?
2. **Region:** In what areas is subsistence farming an important activity?
3. **Region:** Where does livestock raising take place?

Service Industries

The businesses that provide services—banking, insurance, financial services, or tourism—are known as **service industries.** These industries also play an important role in the economies of this region. In Bahrain the banking, real estate, and insurance industries provide more than 60 percent of that nation's **gross domestic product (GDP)**—the value of the goods and services created in a country in a year.

One important service industry—because of the region's historical importance and closeness to Europe—is tourism. Over the years the region's ancient monuments and religious sites have drawn millions of visitors.

Tourism, however, has not grown rapidly in all nations. Some governments discourage outside influences. Regional conflicts, political upheavals, and violence in parts of the region have also affected tourism.

Geographic Themes

Movement: Jidda Airport, Saudi Arabia
Oil revenue has enabled Saudi Arabia to build modern transportation facilities, such as this airport in the city of Jidda. *What service industries have developed in the region?*

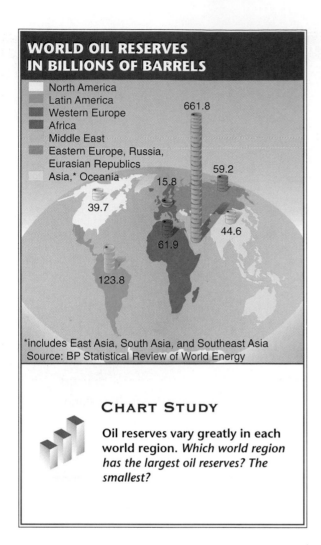

WORLD OIL RESERVES IN BILLINGS OF BARRELS

- North America
- Latin America
- Western Europe
- Africa
- Middle East
- Eastern Europe, Russia, Eurasian Republics
- Asia,* Oceania

661.8

59.2

15.8

39.7

44.6

61.9

123.8

*includes East Asia, South Asia, and Southeast Asia
Source: BP Statistical Review of World Energy

CHART STUDY

Oil reserves vary greatly in each world region. *Which world region has the largest oil reserves? The smallest?*

MOVEMENT

Transportation and Communication

North Africa and Southwest Asia's systems of transportation and communication are growing rapidly. Most development is concentrated in the eastern Mediterranean area.

Roads and Highways

The most extensive road systems are found in Iran, Turkey, and Egypt where roads connect the major cities with oil fields and seaports. Iran, with 94,072 miles of roads (151,485 km), is the leader. Mountainous and desert land have made it costly to build roads in some areas. The increased number of vehicles and the need to link cities, however, has continued to increase highway development.

Railroads and Airlines

In parts of the region new railroad construction has boomed. Some rapid transit systems were built in crowded urban areas. In addition, national rail lines have been constructed to connect urban areas, industrial areas, and seaports.

After World War II, North Africa and Southwest Asia benefited from the development of airports and airlines. One reason for this was their location at the crossroads between the East and the West. A second reason for the growth of air traffic has been the trade of the region's oil-rich nations with countries in Europe, Asia, and North America. The total area of the region is a third reason for the development of airlines. Relatively long distances separate one nation or urban center from another.

Waterways and Pipelines

Inland waterways, with the exception of the Nile River and the Suez Canal, play a far lesser role in the movement of goods and people in this region. The Tigris and the Euphrates rivers are too shallow for large boats. Although the Shatt al Arab, formed where the two rivers meet, is deeper, its control has been a matter of dispute between Iraq and Iran for years.

An elaborate system of pipelines is the major means of transporting oil. Pipelines transport oil to seaports on the Mediterranean Sea, where the huge oil tankers that are too large to pass through the Suez Canal dock.

Communication Systems

Television and radio communication systems are developing rapidly in some areas of North Africa and Southwest Asia. Newspapers are also a major means of communication although the number varies widely from country to country.

Telephone communication is difficult in some areas, because of vast stretches of desert. New technology, especially that of solar-powered radiophones, is opening telephone service to more people.

CRUDE OIL PRODUCTION IN SELECTED COUNTRIES OF NORTH AFRICA AND SOUTHWEST ASIA

Country	1991 Crude Oil Reserves (in barrels)	1990 Crude Oil Production (in metric tons)	1991 Crude Oil Production (in metric tons)
Algeria	9,200,000,000	56,673,000	58,454,000
Egypt	4,500,000,000	43,805,000	45,264,000
Iran	92,800,000,000	157,084,000	166,024,000
Iraq	100,000,000,000	100,681,000	14,876,000
Kuwait	97,000,000,000	58,729,000	9,567,000
Libya	22,800,000,000	65,990,000	73,567,567
Saudi Arabia	260,000,000,000	321,928,000	409,839,000
United Arab Emirates	98,100,000,000	102,004,000	117,940,000

Sources: Energy Information/U.S. Dept. of Energy; *Statesman's Year Book* 1992-1993

CHART STUDY

The nations of North Africa and Southwest Asia have the largest known oil reserves of any world region. *Which nation has the largest known reserves? Which nation had the smallest crude oil production in 1990? In 1991?*

Interdependence

The wealthier countries have helped their poor neighbors by providing foreign aid, trade concessions, and development loans. This aid has built hospitals, schools, and roads.

In 1960, five oil-producing countries—Iran, Iraq, Kuwait, Saudi Arabia, and Venezuela—formed the Organization of Petroleum Exporting Countries (OPEC). This organization was formed to give these oil-producing nations greater control over the production and price of oil. In the 1970s OPEC placed and later cancelled an embargo on the shipment of oil to the United States and other industrial countries, to raise the price of oil. More recently, the large supply of oil and a worldwide recession has forced the price of oil to fall.

SECTION 1 REVIEW

Checking for Understanding

1. **Define** petrochemical, service industry, gross domestic product (GDP).
2. **Locating Places** From what bodies of water do most countries of this region obtain fish?
3. **Place** Why is Turkey the leading producer of livestock?
4. **Movement** What are the three reasons for the growth of airlines in the region?

Critical Thinking

5. **Drawing Conclusions** Why do you think only 5 percent of the oil produced in this region is refined there?

THE WAR FOR WATER

*I*n the year 2000, water will be more expensive than oil."

Joyce Starr, founder of the Global Water Summit Initiative, a private study group

In 1974, the flow of the Euphrates River into Iraq slowed from a roaring 1,185 cubic yards (907 cu. m) a second to a trickle of just 75 cubic yards (57 cu. m) a second. President Saddam Hussein prepared to invade Syria, convinced that Syrians were pirating an unfair share of the region's scanty water resources. Only last-minute peacemaking efforts by a third party, Saudi Arabia, stopped hostilities from breaking out.

In actuality, Iraq's dwindling water supply was caused by a combination of natural events, none of them intentionally war-like.

The year was one of the driest on record, and both Turkey and Syria were filling their reservoirs from the river as protection against potential water shortages.

THE ISSUE

Iraq's dwindling water supply, however, was an early sign of the crisis now facing the three countries: insufficient water for their populations.

To ensure its water supply, Turkey is building a series of huge dams on the Euphrates. These dams will slow the water flow into Syria.

Syria also is building dams on the Euphrates. The dams will further reduce the water that Iraq receives.

THE BACKGROUND

Of the three countries, only Turkey receives frequent and consistent rainfall, and that rainfall occurs only in its northern mountains. The well-watered mountains, in turn, give rise to the Tigris and Euphrates rivers.

Originating in Turkey, the Euphrates River provides irrigation water for the Anatolian highlands, where most of Turkey's farms are located. The reservoirs from the dams also provide electricity for Turkey's expanding industries and cities.

Most of Syria's rural people are farmers who raise a variety of crops for a living. Syria's rainfall, however, is too light and inconsistent to provide the needed amount for the country's extensive farmlands. So Syria, too, uses the Euphrates to provide irrigation water. In addition, the dams will provide electricity for the country.

A hydroelectric dam on Syria's portion of the Euphrates River

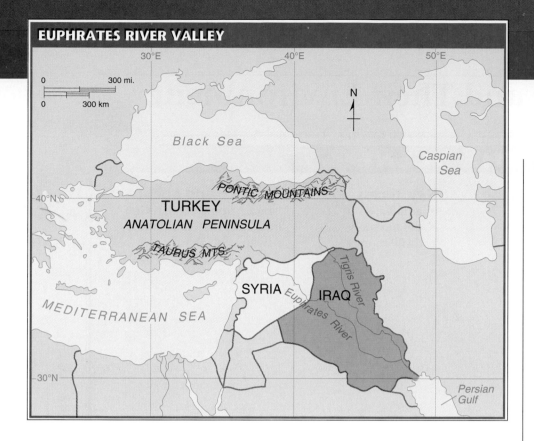

EUPHRATES RIVER VALLEY

Iraq receives little rain. Its sole sources of water are the Tigris and Euphrates rivers, both of which flow through the country and join to empty into the Persian Gulf. Turkish and Syrian dams will reduce the amount of water flowing to Iraq by 50 to 80 percent.

THE POINTS OF VIEW

The Turks defend their right to use the rivers that rise within their borders to improve economic and social conditions. They hope to turn most of the Anatolian Peninsula into farmland. Crops grown there must feed Turkey's growing population, they say.

Syria retorts that Turkey does not own the entire Euphrates River. Syrian officials point out that not only will they lose water from the re-

duced flow, but that more will be lost through evaporation from the Turkish reservoirs.

Like Syria, Iraq accuses Turkey of using water to control the politics and economics of the surrounding countries. Isolated from its neighbors by its leaders, the country seems ready to take a militant stand if its water supply is drastically reduced.

THE ISSUE TODAY

Water management experts and negotiators for the three countries feel that a number of practices could ease the crisis.

Iraq uses desalinated, or salt-free, water for domestic purposes. Current desalination techniques, however, are expensive, so the country, along with allies, is working to develop extremely low-cost salt re-

moval technology. All three countries need to repair existing equipment, improve their irrigation and water conservation techniques, and expand their water recycling. The countries also need to grow some crops that do not require so much water.

These are only short-term solutions, water management experts say. Recent expansion of populations, along with the demand for a higher standard of living, strain a water supply that cannot be increased and whose cycle cannot be changed.

Southwest Asia's water crisis cannot be separated from the population crisis. So far, though, most political and religious leaders have failed to address this issue. Until the overpopulation problem is solved, experts maintain, no long-term solution to the water shortage is possible.

Reviewing the Case

1. **What nations are concerned about the water supply from the Tigris and Euphrates rivers?**

2. **Human/Environment Interaction** What concerns do the Syrians and Iraqis have about Turkey?

2 People and Their Environment

SETTING THE SCENE

Read to Discover . . .
- the challenges facing the culture region of North Africa and Southwest Asia because of the scarcity of water.
- the steps being taken to utilize groundwater and sea water in the region.
- the environmental effects of the Persian Gulf War.
- how efforts to control the flow of river water can affect the environment.

Key Terms
- aquifer
- desalination
- distillation

Identify and Locate
Libya, Tripoli, Persian Gulf, Iraq, Kuwait, Saudi Arabia, Aswan High Dam

Because almost 70 percent of the earth is covered by water, we often think that water is an abundant natural resource. About 97 percent of the world's water, however, is salty and not usable in many instances. In certain regions of the world, the issue of freshwater for people is a serious problem.

REGION

Need for Water

Some experts predict that by the year 2050 about 10 billion people will be living on the earth. By that time, without some human action, an increased population will be forced to share approximately the same amount of water as is now available.

Water Resources

According to the United Nations, about 1.2 billion people worldwide cannot obtain clean water to drink. It also is estimated that about two-thirds of the world's households must find water outside of their homes. Meanwhile, in the United States, people use approximately 300 billion gallons of water each day.

In most parts of North Africa and Southwest Asia, providing freshwater for drinking and for irrigation is often difficult. The need for water has been fulfilled by rivers and oases and wells that draw water from **aquifers**—underground layers of porous rock, gravel, or sand that contain water. These aquifers have been used as sources of water for thousands of years. The increase in the use of this groundwater, however, has increased with the region's growing population.

The only major freshwater rivers in North Africa and Southwest Asia are the Nile, Tigris, and Euphrates rivers. Thus, only the nations of Turkey, Egypt, Iraq, and Syria have abundant fresh river water to meet their irrigation needs. Israel gets much of its irrigation water from the Jordan River through an elaborate complex of human-made canals that take freshwater from north to south. The remaining nations in the region have to turn to a few smaller rivers and to other sources of water.

The "Great Human-Made River"

The most ambitious effort to find water in recent years is Libya's "great human-made river." This project, a multibillion-dollar-pipeline, will carry water from two large aquifers beneath the Sahara to farm areas near the Mediterranean coast. Recently, a 13-foot (4-m) diameter pipeline was completed and now carries freshwater across eastern Libya to the growing coastal population. The second phase of the project will lengthen this pipeline. Another pipeline in western Libya will carry water from the desert aquifer to areas near Tripoli, the nation's capital.

A number of scientists question the long-term value of this human-made river. They believe that the aquifers in Libya and neighboring countries are in danger of being drained. They also claim that pumping aquifers near the Mediterranean coast could draw in salt water from the sea or salt from the surrounding land.

Desalination

There has been an increased search for other water sources in the region. The most widely used method is **desalination**—the removal of salt from seawater.

Desalination was used to provide fresh drinking water during World War II. United States naval ships had simple desalination units that boiled salt out of seawater.

Today it is estimated that the world's desalination plants can produce about 3.4 billion gallons (12.8 billion l) of freshwater a day. In North Africa and Southwest Asia desalination was first tried in Israel and then in other countries. About 60 percent of the world's water-producing capacity—the production of more than 2 billion gallons (7.6 billion l) a day—takes place in this region.

Recent improvements in desalination have moved beyond the simple **distillation**—the boiling and condensing of water—and producing freshwater has decreased in price. Nevertheless the cost can still be too great for

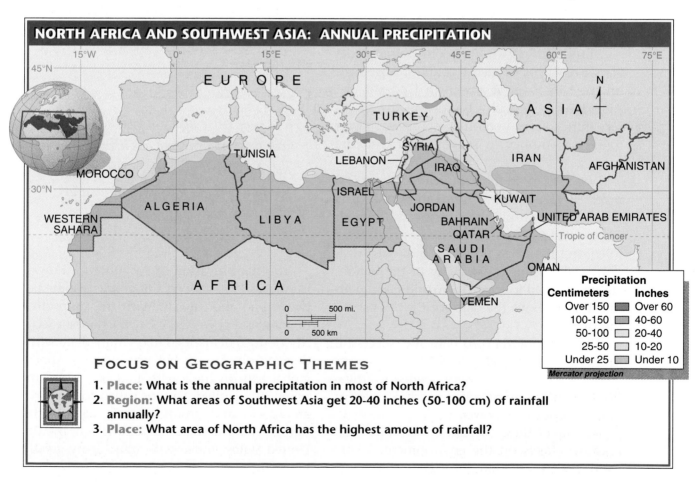

NORTH AFRICA AND SOUTHWEST ASIA: ANNUAL PRECIPITATION

Precipitation	
Centimeters	Inches
Over 150	Over 60
100-150	40-60
50-100	20-40
25-50	10-20
Under 25	Under 10

Mercator projection

FOCUS ON GEOGRAPHIC THEMES

1. **Place:** What is the annual precipitation in most of North Africa?
2. **Region:** What areas of Southwest Asia get 20-40 inches (50-100 cm) of rainfall annually?
3. **Place:** What area of North Africa has the highest amount of rainfall?

some nations. The oil-rich nations along the Persian Gulf have been among the few countries able to afford desalination.

About 3,500 desalination plants operate in some 105 world countries. Many nations around the Persian Gulf are dependent upon their desalination plants for water.

Environmental Concerns

In recent decades, the introduction of new technology and the destructive effects of war have heightened environmental concerns in the region. In some instances a nation's action to harness nature, such as the building of dams for hydroelectricity, has caused problems for the environment. This was true in Egypt with the construction of the Aswan High Dam.

The Aswan High Dam

In the early 1950s, President Gamal Abdel Nasser of Egypt wanted to build a huge dam on the Nile River at Aswan in Upper Egypt. After having difficulty borrowing the necessary funds from wealthier countries, Egypt found the money to move ahead with the project.

Work began on the dam in 1958 about 600 miles (955 km) south of Cairo and 4 miles (6.5 km) south of an old dam at Aswan. In building the Aswan High Dam, Nasser's goals were to control the Nile's floods, to improve irrigation, and to supply electricity to the nation. He also wanted to create the world's largest artificial lake above the dam for Egypt's fishing industry.

The 364-foot (111-m) dam was successful in meeting these goals. Nearly 3 million acres (about 1.2 million ha) were opened to irrigation. The dam also provided nearly 50 percent of Egypt's electrical power.

In spite of these successes, the project had negative effects on the environment. Before the dam's construction, the annual Nile floods had deposited fertile alluvial soil along the river banks. Now, the soil was trapped above the dam. Egyptian farmers soon faced the problem of using expensive fertilizers to maintain the land's fertility. The dam also prevented the annual floods from washing away salt from the soil.

The dam also affected humans and their livestock. Following its completion, there was an increase in diseases and death caused by parasites. These parasites lived in the Nile waters and formerly were washed toward the sea.

Although the Aswan Dam has had some negative effects upon the environment, geographers point out that these must be weighed against the gains. With aid from other nations and international organizations, Egypt is overcoming many of the difficulties created by the dam.

The Persian Gulf War

Another area of the region that has faced environmental challenges is the Persian Gulf. A reporter who flew into the Persian Gulf area immediately after the Persian Gulf War ended wrote about the war's effect on the environment:

---◆---

The Gulf War's legacy of pollution has been felt the world over and has left millions in the Middle East wondering whether their air is fit to breathe, their water fit to drink, their food fit to eat.

---◆---

The Iraqi invasion of neighboring Kuwait in August 1990 capped a lingering dispute between Iraq and Kuwait. With the support of major world powers, the United Nations Security Council demanded Iraq's immediate withdrawal from Kuwait but was ignored. After a global ban on trade with Iraq had been imposed, the United Nations called for massive air attacks and ground attacks against the Iraqis. The international effort, led by the United States, ended with Iraq's army greatly reduced.

Geographic Themes

Human/Environment Interaction: Persian Gulf
During the Persian Gulf War, Iraqi oil spills brought danger to the wildlife and vegetation of the region. *What other effect did the conflict have on the environment?*

Unfortunately for the region, the Iraqi forces set fire to a large number of Kuwait's oil wells before being driven out of that country. Huge black clouds of smoke polluted the area. Iraqi troops also dumped an estimated 250 million gallons (950 million l) of Kuwait's oil into the Persian Gulf.

The total effect of the Persian Gulf War on the environment is still being studied by scientists and environmentalists. Thousands of fish and other forms of marine life died when the oil spill spread for 350 miles (563 km) along the Gulf coastline. Most environmentalists believe that the shallowness of the Persian Gulf—the average depth is about 110 feet (about 30.5 m) deep—will delay the recovery of much of the area's marine life. The pools of oil left in Kuwait after the oil-well fires were put out have also threatened millions of birds.

SECTION 2 REVIEW

Checking for Understanding

1. **Define** aquifer, desalination, distillation.
2. **Locating Places** What area in Libya receives water from the "human-made river"?
3. **Human/Environment Interaction** Why are so many desalination plants found in the Persian Gulf?
4. **Human/Environment Interaction** What were the environmental effects of the Aswan High Dam and the Persian Gulf War?

Critical Thinking

5. **Identifying Central Issues** How is the relationship between population and the supply of freshwater a problem in North Africa and Southwest Asia?

CRITICAL THINKING SKILLS

Making Comparisons

Suppose you want to buy a portable compact disc (CD) player, and you must choose among three models. To make this decision, you would probably compare the three models according to various qualities or characteristics such as features, price, sound quality, weight, and so on. By making comparisons, you will figure out which model is best for you.

REVIEWING THE SKILL

Making comparisons involves identifying similarities and differences between two or more things. As long as two things share one common quality, they can be compared. In the example above, all the objects were CD players, so they shared many common qualities. However, you could compare a CD player with an audiocassette player. Even though they are different kinds of machines, both are kinds of audio equipment. When making comparisons, apply the following steps:

- Decide what items will be compared.
- Determine which characteristics you will use to compare them.
- Identify similarities and differences in these characteristics.
- If possible, look for causes that explain the similarities and differences.

PRACTICING THE SKILL

Study the chart below. Then answer the following questions.

1. Which countries are compared in the chart?
2. What characteristics are used to compare these countries?
3. What are the two smallest countries in population size? Which country is growing the fastest in population?
4. Which countries have about the same literacy rate?
5. How are Egypt, Kuwait, and Saudi Arabia all similar in their exports?

For additional practice in this skill, see Practicing Skills on page 404 of the Chapter 19 Review.

COMPARING SELECTED COUNTRIES OF NORTH AFRICA AND SOUTHWEST ASIA

	1994 Population (millions)	Annual % Population Growth Rate	Literacy Rate	Annual Oil Production (metric tons)	Major Imports	Major Exports
Egypt	58.9	2.3	48%	45.264m	Foodstuffs Machinery	Petroleum products Cotton products
Iraq	19.9	3.7	60%	14.876m	Machinery Vehicles	Fuels Energy
Israel	5.4	1.5	92%	250m in reserves (oil bearing shale)	Consumer goods Fuels	Machinery Chemicals
Kuwait	1.3	3.3	74%	9.567m	Machinery Manufactured goods	Petroleum products Machinery
Saudi Arabia	18.0	3.2	62%	409.839m	Machinery Foodstuffs	Petroleum products

Sources: *The Statesman's Year Book*, 1992-1993; The Population Reference Bureau, Inc., 1994

SECTION	KEY TERMS	SUMMARY
1 **Living in North Africa and Southwest Asia**	petrochemical (p. 392) service industry (p. 393) gross domestic product (GDP) (p. 393)	• Although the region has limited arable land, a relatively large percentage of the people are engaged in some type of agriculture. • The raising of livestock and fishing are two other sources of needed food in the region. • The level of industrialization is uneven among the nations of the region with a higher level usually found in many of the oil-producing nations. • The need to connect urban and economic centers with each other has led to a recent growth in transportation and communication systems. • Although there has been an increase in the interdependence among the nations of the region, disputes and warfare have disrupted some of the region's economies.

Airport in Jidda, Saudi Arabia

SECTION	KEY TERMS	SUMMARY
2 **People and Their Environment**	aquifer (p. 398) desalination (p. 399) distillation (p. 399)	• Nations in North Africa and Southwest Asia have taken steps to modify their environment to meet their peoples' needs for water for drinking and irrigation. • River water needed for extensive irrigation is scarce in most of the nations in the region. • Desalination is widely used to provide water, particularly in the Arabian Peninsula. • The Aswan High Dam has brought benefits to Egypt, but it has also had negative effects upon the environment. • The Persian Gulf War severely damaged the natural environment in the Persian Gulf area.

Burning oil spills in the Persian Gulf

Reviewing Key Terms

Choose the vocabulary term that best completes each of the sentences below. Write your answers on a separate sheet of paper.

petrochemicals (p. 392)
service industries (p. 393)
gross domestic product (GDP) (p. 393)
aquifers (p. 398)
desalination (p. 399)
distillation (p. 399)

SECTION 1

1. Banking and insurance are two types of _____.

2. A nation's _____ is an indication of that nation's goods and services created in a year.

3. _____ are products produced from petroleum.

SECTION 2

4. _____ was an early method used to create salt-free water.
5. Oases and wells draw water from _____.
6. Freshwater is produced by _____, which removes salt.

Reviewing Facts

SECTION 1

7. What are the major export crops of Iraq and Egypt?
8. Why does Saudi Arabia produce so little livestock?
9. Why is tourism discouraged by some countries in the region?

SECTION 2

10. What percentage of the world's water is salty?
11. What, and where, is the "great human-made river" project?
12. Why is the desalination process not used to provide water for irrigation in poorer nations?

Critical Thinking

13. **Expressing Problems Clearly** Explain why the need for industrialization is so important in some nations in North Africa and Southwest Asia.
14. **Determining Cause and Effect** How has the production of oil caused changes in the natural environment in parts of the region?

Geographic Themes

15. **Location** How has the region's location affected transportation?
16. **Region** What is a desperately needed but scarce natural resource in North Africa and Southwest Asia?

Practicing Skills

Making Comparisons

Refer to the chart on page 402.

17. Which characteristic shows the widest differences among these countries—oil production or population?
18. How would you explain these differences?
19. Compare literacy rates among the countries. What relationship do you find between these characteristics?

Using the Unit Atlas

Refer to the physical geography section of the Unit Atlas on pages 352–353.

20. What is the most important resource of the countries in the Arabian Peninsula?
21. What large body of water is the saltiest body of water on the earth?
22. What is the highest point in the region?

Projects

Individual Activity

You have learned about the importance of the process of desalination in providing freshwater for North Africa and Southwest Asia. Research current developments in the process. Write a brief report describing some of the new and more efficient methods of desalination that are being used or developed today.

Cooperative Learning Activity

Working in a group of four, have a meeting of representatives of nations that are members of OPEC. Each student will represent a different member nation. Each representative should prepare a written statement of his or her nation's position on the amount and the price of oil to be produced next year. Once each representative has prepared a written statement of his or her country's position, the group should try to reach a decision on pricing policy that should be presented to the class as a whole.

Writing About Geography

Cause and Effect

Imagine that you are a farmer in Egypt. Write a letter to a close friend in another country explaining how the construction of the Aswan High Dam has affected you and others living in your area. Use your journal, text, encyclopedias, travel books, and other reference books to help you in your research.

Locating Places

THE PHYSICAL/POLITICAL GEOGRAPHY OF NORTH AFRICA AND SOUTHWEST ASIA

Match the letters on the map with the places and physical features of North Africa and Southwest Asia. Write your answers on a separate sheet of paper.

1. Nile River
2. Suez Canal
3. Libya
4. Arabian Peninsula
5. Turkey
6. Kuwait
7. Shatt al Arab
8. Jordan
9. Morocco
10. Persian Gulf

GEOGRAPHY CONNECTION

North Africa and Southwest Asia and the United States

NORTH AFRICAN AND SOUTHWEST ASIAN CUISINE

Southwest Asian and North African cuisine has contributed several favorites to the American menu. The distinct flavor and taste most often comes from spices that are not often found in American foods: ginger, marjoram, and curry.

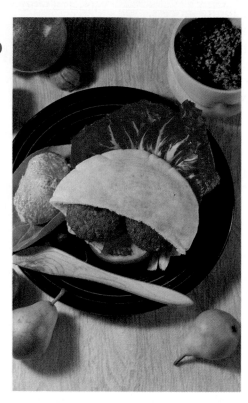

◀ **PITA BREAD,** or pita pockets, as many Americans call them, has become a great favorite with sandwich-loving Americans. A wheat bread baked in thin flat cakes, pita cakes puff out in the middle to form a pocket. The hungry diner can stuff any assortment of ingredients into the bread to make a handy, hearty meal. Pita bread is often accompanied by *tabbouleh* and *hummus.*

TABBOULEH ▶ is a salad of chopped tomatoes, green and white onions, radishes, parsley, and mint dressed up with *burghul,* a final ingredient that adds a nut-like flavor and a chewy texture.

◀ **BAKLAVA** is a favorite of Americans with a sweet tooth. Baklava is a rich pastry made of finely chopped nuts—pistachio or walnuts— baked between thin layers of dough. The pastry is drenched with honey or syrup flavored with cinnamon and lemon juice.

▲ **COUSCOUS** is a North African dish of finely ground wheat meal combined with salted water to make a kind of pasta. Americans and North Africans alike top a bowl of couscous with powdered sugar and nuts to make a sumptuous dessert.

◀ **YOGURT** is another Southwest Asian staple that Americans enjoy. Yogurt, a tart source of nutrients with few calories, is the preferred form of milk in Southwest Asia. Americans use yogurt as a basis for salad dressings and dips, mix it with fruit for a light dessert, and eat it right out of the carton. Many Americans also enjoy frozen yogurt as a treat.

▲ **SHISH KABOB** is one of the best known "American" foods from Southwest Asia and North Africa. It consists of skewered cubes of succulent spiced meat alternating with chunks of vegetables or fruit. The name comes from the Turkish words *sis* meaning "sword" or "skewer," and *kebab*, meaning "lamb" or "mutton." Americans generally substitute beef, their favorite meat, for lamb.

Checking for Understanding

1. What ingredients make North African and Southwest Asian cooking unique?
2. Place Which of the foods shown are offered by restaurants in your area?

Africa South of the Sahara

GeoJournal Activity

On a piece of poster-board, make a calendar for the month you will be studying this region. Make the boxes large enough for notes. Each day, record something that you learned about Africa south of the Sahara. After each entry, list the source of information, such as text, TV and radio reports, magazines, and newspaper articles.

Frans Lanting

NATIONAL GEOGRAPHIC SOCIETY

Picturing the World

A sheet of water a few feet deep spreads over the sands of the Kalahari. Farther north at the edge of the Kalahari, the Okavango Delta—the world's largest inland delta—fans out across northern Botswana. This unique freshwater system grows during the October–to–May wet season, allowing many animals to expand their range into the Kalahari. The rivers and wetlands shrink during the dry season, drawing thirsty animals back to the delta. Look at the map on page 425.

1. What climates are found in Botswana?
2. How do these climates differ from the climates of Gabon and other countries of central Africa?
3. How do you think wildlife survive in the harsh climate of Botswana?

Picture Atlas CD-ROM Enrichment Corner

Create a photo album of animal life of Africa south of the Sahara. Include the following photographs: bullfrog and lionesses in Botswana; rhinos in Kenya; elephants in Namibia; buffalo in South Africa; savanna in Tanzania. Read the captions and identify the following:

1. A famous animal reserve in South Africa
2. An animal that estivates
3. A national park in Tanzania larger than the state of Connecticut

Then divide into groups to search for more wildlife facts on the CD-ROM and create a Jeopardy game to test other groups' knowledge of African wildlife.

AFRICA
Cultural Geography

EXPLORING CULTURAL DIVERSITY

1. **What areas of Africa south of the Sahara are most heavily populated? Most sparsely populated?**

2. **What nations make up Africa south of the Sahara?**

Ethiopian tradition says that **Ethiopia's** first emperor, Menelik I, was the son of the Biblical Queen of Sheba and Israel's King Solomon.

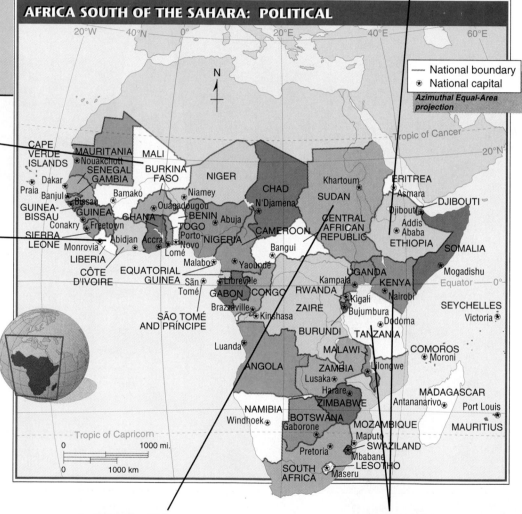

AFRICA SOUTH OF THE SAHARA: POLITICAL

— National boundary
⊛ National capital

Azimuthal Equal-Area projection

Mali was home to three great trading empires: **Ghana**, **Mali**, and **Songhai**.

Liberia is Africa's oldest republic. It was settled by African Americans freed from slavery.

The oldest bones and fossils ever discovered have been found in eastern and southern sites in **Africa**. These findings give Africa the title "birthplace of the human race."

In **Sudan**, African blacks are a majority and live in the south; Arab Muslims live in the north and central regions.

Arab and European minorities live along the coasts of **Kenya** and **Tanzania**.

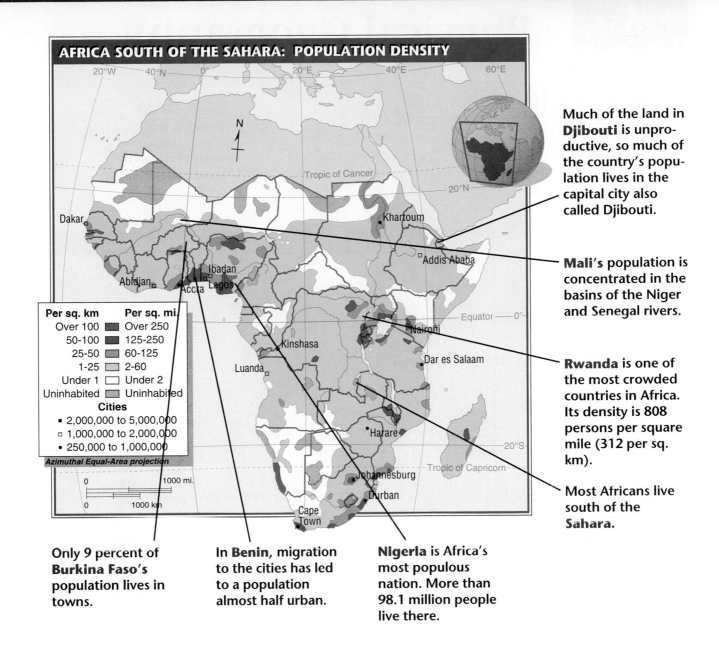

AFRICA SOUTH OF THE SAHARA: POPULATION DENSITY

Per sq. km	Per sq. mi.
Over 100	Over 250
50-100	125-250
25-50	60-125
1-25	2-60
Under 1	Under 2
Uninhabited	Uninhabited

Cities
- 2,000,000 to 5,000,000
- 1,000,000 to 2,000,000
- 250,000 to 1,000,000

Azimuthal Equal-Area projection

0 — 1000 mi.
0 — 1000 km

Much of the land in **Djibouti** is unproductive, so much of the country's population lives in the capital city also called Djibouti.

Mali's population is concentrated in the basins of the Niger and Senegal rivers.

Rwanda is one of the most crowded countries in Africa. Its density is 808 persons per square mile (312 per sq. km).

Most Africans live south of the **Sahara.**

Only 9 percent of **Burkina Faso's** population lives in towns.

In **Benin**, migration to the cities has led to a population almost half urban.

Nigeria is Africa's most populous nation. More than 98.1 million people live there.

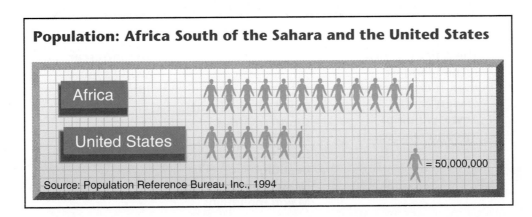

Population: Africa South of the Sahara and the United States

Africa

United States

= 50,000,000

Source: Population Reference Bureau, Inc., 1994

Africa south of the Sahara has more than twice as many people as the United States.

AFRICA
Physical Geography

CHARTING YOUR COURSE

1. *What two desert areas are located in southern Africa?*
2. *What two mountains are located in eastern Africa?*
3. *What are three natural resources found in Africa south of the Sahara?*

The **Great Rift Valley** is a series of deep, steep-sided valleys formed by parallel cracks in the earth.

The eastern and southern areas of Africa are called **High Africa.** Most of the area is more than 3,000 feet (910 m) above sea level.

The **Equator** runs through the middle of Africa. About 90 percent of the continent lies within the tropics, giving Africa the largest tropical area of any other continent.

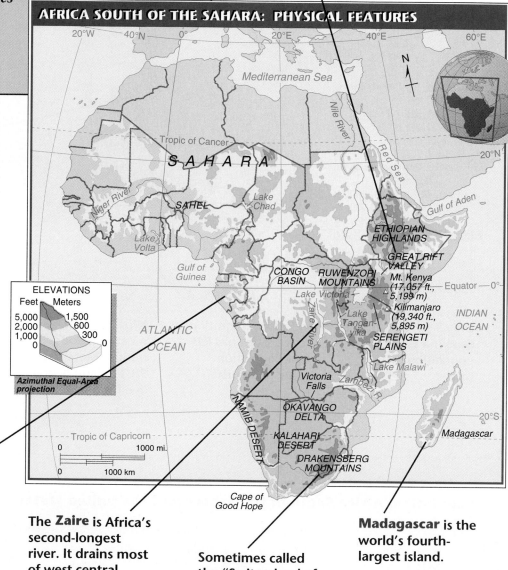

AFRICA SOUTH OF THE SAHARA: PHYSICAL FEATURES

20°W 40°N 0° 20°E 40°E 60°E

Mediterranean Sea

Nile River

Tropic of Cancer

S A H A R A

20°N

Niger River

SAHEL

Lake Chad

Red Sea

Gulf of Aden

Lake Volta

Gulf of Guinea

ETHIOPIAN HIGHLANDS

GREAT RIFT VALLEY

CONGO BASIN

RUWENZORI MOUNTAINS

Mt. Kenya (17,057 ft., 5,199 m)

Equator — 0°

Lake Victoria

Kilimanjaro (19,340 ft., 5,895 m)

INDIAN OCEAN

ELEVATIONS
Feet   Meters
5,000   1,500
2,000   600
1,000   300
0   0

ATLANTIC OCEAN

Lake Tanganyika

SERENGETI PLAINS

Lake Malawi

Azimuthal Equal-Area projection

Victoria Falls

Zambezi R.

NAMIB DESERT

OKAVANGO DELTA

20°S

Madagascar

Tropic of Capricorn

0   1000 mi.

0   1000 km

KALAHARI DESERT

DRAKENSBERG MOUNTAINS

Cape of Good Hope

The **Zaire** is Africa's second-longest river. It drains most of west central Africa, winding through rain forests.

Sometimes called the "Switzerland of southern Africa," **Lesotho** is famous for the scenery in its beautiful Drakensberg and Maloti mountains.

Madagascar is the world's fourth-largest island.

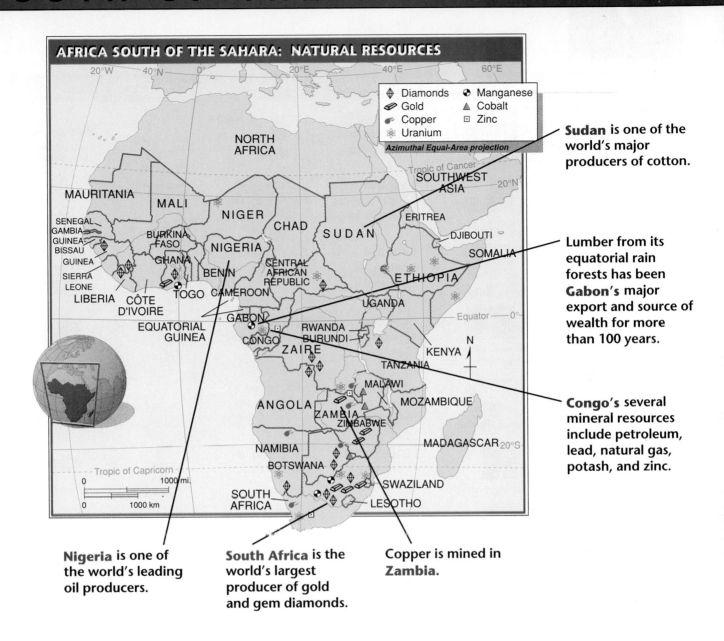

AFRICA SOUTH OF THE SAHARA: NATURAL RESOURCES

Legend:
- ◈ Diamonds
- ⬭ Gold
- ⬮ Copper
- ✳ Uranium
- ◉ Manganese
- ▲ Cobalt
- ⊡ Zinc

Azimuthal Equal-Area projection

Sudan is one of the world's major producers of cotton.

Lumber from its equatorial rain forests has been **Gabon's** major export and source of wealth for more than 100 years.

Congo's several mineral resources include petroleum, lead, natural gas, potash, and zinc.

Nigeria is one of the world's leading oil producers.

South Africa is the world's largest producer of gold and gem diamonds.

Copper is mined in **Zambia.**

Africa South of the Sahara: Physical Profile

18000 ft. — 12000 ft. — 6000 ft. — 2400 ft. — Sea level

Atlantic Ocean — COASTAL PLAIN — CRYSTAL MOUNTAINS — ZAIRE RIVER — ZAIRE RIVER — CONGO BASIN — RUWENZORI MOUNTAINS — LAKE VICTORIA — GREAT RIFT VALLEY — MT. KENYA — NGANGERABELI PLAIN — Indian Ocean

West to East at approximately 0° latitude

COUNTRY* AND CAPITAL	FLAG AND LANGUAGES	POPULATION	LANDMASS	PRINCIPAL EXPORT	PRODUCTS IMPORT
Angola Luanda	Portuguese, Bantu	11,200,000 23 per sq. mi. 9 per sq. km	481,350 sq. mi. 1,246,697 sq. km	Fuels	Transport Equipment
Benin Porto-Novo	French, Fon	5,300,000 124 per sq. mi. 48 per sq. km	42,710 sq. mi. 110,619 sq. km	Cotton	Textiles
Botswana Gaborone	English, Setswana	1,400,000 6 per sq. mi. 2 per sq. km	218,810 sq. mi. 566,718 sq. km	Diamonds	Transport Equipment
Burkina Faso Ouagadougou	French, Sudanic languages	10,100,000 95 per sq. mi. 37 per sq. km	105,710 sq. mi. 273,789 sq. km	Cotton	Machinery
Burundi Bujumbura	Rundi, French	6,000,000 606 per sq. mi. 234 per sq. km	9,900 sq. mi. 25,641 sq. km	Coffee	Machinery
Cameroon Yaoundé	French, English	13,100,000 73 per sq. mi. 28 per sq. km	179,690 sq. mi. 465,397 sq. km	Petroleum	Machinery
Cape Verde Islands Praia	Portuguese	400,000 256 per sq. mi. 99 per sq. km	1,560 sq. mi. 4,040 sq. km	Bananas	Food
Central African Republic Bangui	French, local dialects	3,100,000 13 per sq. mi. 5 per sq. km	240,530 sq. mi. 622,973 sq. km	Diamonds	Food
Chad N'Djamena	French, Arabic	6,500,000 13 per sq. mi. 5 per sq. km	486,180 sq. mi. 1,259,206 sq. km	Cotton	Petroleum
Comoros Moroni	Arabic, French	500,000 581 per sq. mi. 224 per sq. km	860 sq. mi. 2,227 sq. km	Vanilla	Rice
Congo Brazzaville	French, Kongo, Teke	2,400,000 18 per sq. mi. 7 per sq. km	131,850 sq. mi. 341,492 sq. km	Petroleum	Machinery
Côte d'Ivoire Yamoussoukro Abidjan	French, Akan	13,900,000 109 per sq. mi. 42 per sq. km	122,780 sq. mi. 318,000 sq. km	Food	Petroleum

*Country maps not drawn to scale.

COUNTRY* AND CAPITAL	FLAG AND LANGUAGES	POPULATION	LANDMASS	PRINCIPAL PRODUCTS EXPORT	IMPORT
Djibouti — Djibouti	French, Arabic	600,000 67 per sq. mi. 26 per sq. km	8,950 sq. mi. 23,200 sq. km	Livestock	Food
Equatorial Guinea — Malabo	Spanish, Fang, Bubi	400,000 37 per sq. mi. 14 per sq. km	10,830 sq. mi. 28,050 sq. km	Food & Livestock	Food and Beverages
Eritrea — Asmara	Native languages	3,500,000 73 per sq. mi. 28 per sq. km	48,260 sq. mi. 124,993 sq. km	Coffee	Food
Ethiopia — Addis Ababa	Amharic, Tigre, Oromo	55,200,000 146 per sq. mi. 57 per sq. km	376,830 sq. mi. 975,990 sq. km	Coffee	Machinery
Gabon — Libreville	French, Bantu	1,100,000 11 per sq. mi. 4 per sq. km	99,490 sq. mi. 257,679 sq. km	Petroleum	Machinery
Gambia — Banjul	English, Mandinka, Wolof	1,100,000 285 per sq. mi. 110 per sq. km	3,860 sq. mi. 9,997 sq. km	Peanuts	Food
Ghana — Accra	English, Ewe, Akan, Mossi	16,900,000 190 per sq. mi. 73 per sq. km	88,810 sq. mi. 230,018 sq. km	Cocoa Products	Machinery
Guinea — Conakry	French, Peul, Mande	6,400,000 67 per sq. mi. 26 per sq. km	94,930 sq. mi. 245,869 sq. km	Bauxite	Petroleum
Guinea-Bissau — Bissau	Portuguese, Crioulo	1,100,000 101 per sq. mi. 39 per sq. km	10,860 sq. mi. 28,127 sq. km	Cashews	Transport Equipment
Kenya — Nairobi	Swahili, English, Kikuyu	27,000,000 122 per sq. mi. 47 per sq. km	219,960 sq. mi. 569,696 sq. km	Tea	Machinery
Lesotho — Maseru	English, Sotho	1,900,000 162 per sq. mi. 63 per sq. km	11,720 sq. mi. 30,355 sq. km	Machinery	Clothing
Liberia — Monrovia	English, native dialects	2,900,000 78 per sq. mi. 30 per sq. km	37,190 sq. mi. 96,322 sq. km	Iron Ore	Machinery

*Country maps not drawn to scale.

COUNTRY PROFILE

COUNTRY* AND CAPITAL	FLAG AND LANGUAGES	POPULATION	LANDMASS	PRINCIPAL EXPORT	PRODUCTS IMPORT
Madagascar Antananarivo	Malagasy, French	13,700,000 61 per sq. mi. 24 per sq. km	224,530 sq. mi. 581,533 sq. km	Coffee	Machinery
Malawi Lilongwe	Chewa, English, Lomwe, Yao	9,500,000 262 per sq. mi. 101 per sq. km	36,320 sq. mi. 94,069 sq. km	Tobacco	Machinery
Mali Bamako	French, Bambara, Senufo	9,100,000 19 per sq. mi. 7 per sq. km	471,120 sq. mi. 1,220,201 sq. km	Cotton	Machinery
Mauritania Nouakchott	French, Arabic, Hassanya Arabic	2,300,000 6 per sq. mi. 2 per sq. km	395,840 sq. mi. 1,025,226 sq. km	Fish	Machinery
Mauritius Port Louis	English, French Créole, Bhojpuri	1,100,000 1,549 per sq. mi. 598 per sq. km	710 sq. mi. 1,839 sq. km	Clothing	Machinery
Mozambique Maputo	Portuguese, Makua, Malawl	15,800,000 52 per sq. mi. 20 per sq. km	302,740 sq. mi. 784,097 sq. km	Shrimp	Food
Namibia Windhoek	Afrikaans, English	1,600,000 5 per sq. mi. 2 per sq. km	317,870 sq. mi. 823,283 sq. km	Minerals	Petroleum
Niger Niamey	French, Fulani, Hausa	8,800,000 18 per sq. mi. 7 per sq. km	489,070 sq. mi. 1,266,691 sq. km	Uranium	Machinery
Nigeria Abuja	English, Hausa, Yoruba, Ibo	98,100,000 279 per sq. mi. 108 per sq. km	351,650 sq. mi. 910,774 sq. km	Petroleum	Machinery
Rwanda Kigali	French, Rwanda	7,700,000 808 per sq. mi. 312 per sq. km	9,530 sq. mi. 24,683 sq. km	Coffee and Tea	Machinery
São Tomé & Príncipe São Tomé	Portuguese	100,000 270 per sq. mi. 104 per sq. km	370 sq. mi. 958 sq. km	Cocoa	Food
Senegal Dakar	French, Wolof, Serer, Peul	8,200,000 110 per sq. mi. 43 per sq. km	74,340 sq. mi. 192,541 sq. km	Peanut Oil	Machinery

*Country maps not drawn to scale.

COUNTRY* AND CAPITAL	FLAG AND LANGUAGES	POPULATION	LANDMASS	PRINCIPAL PRODUCTS EXPORT	IMPORT
Seychelles Victoria	Portuguese	400,000 256 per sq. mi. 99 per sq. km	1,560 sq. mi. 4,040 sq. km	Bananas	Food
Sierra Leone Freetown	English Native Languages	4,600,000 166 per sq. mi. 64 per sq. km	27,650 sq. mi. 71,614 sq. km	Rutile	Food & Livestock
Somalia Mogadishu	Somali, Arabic	9,800,000 40 per sq. mi. 15 per sq. km	242,220 sq. mi. 627,350 sq. km	Livestock	Petroleum
South Africa Pretoria	Afrikaans, English, Nguni	41,200,000 87 per sq. mi. 34 per sq. km	471,440 sq. mi. 1,221,030 sq. km	Gold	Machinery
Sudan Khartoum	Arabic, Dinka, Nubian, Nuer	28,200,000 31 per sq. mi. 12 per sq. km	917,370 sq. mi. 2,375,988 sq. km	Cotton	Machinery
Swaziland Mbabane	Swazi, English	800,000 120 per sq. mi. 47 per sq. km	6,640 sq. mi. 17,198 sq. km	Sugar	Machinery
Tanzania Dodoma	Swahili, English	29,800,000 87 per sq. mi. 34 per sq. km	342,100 sq. mi. 886,039 sq. km	Coffee	Machinery
Togo Lomé	French, Gur and Kwa languages	4,300,000 205 per sq. mi. 79 per sq. km	21,000 sq. mi. 54,390 sq. km	Phosphates	Machinery
Uganda Kampala	English, Swahili, Luganda	19,800,000 257 per sq. mi. 99 per sq. km	77,050 sq. mi. 199,560 sq. km	Coffee	Sugar
Zaire Kinshasa	French, Kongo, Luba, Mongo	42,500,000 49 per sq. mi. 19 per sq. km	875,520 sq. mi. 2,267,597 sq. km	Copper	Machinery
Zambia Lusaka	English, Bantu	9,100,000 32 per sq. mi. 12 per sq. km	287,020 sq. mi. 743,382 sq. km	Copper	Machinery
Zimbabwe Harare	English, Shona, Sinde bele	11,200,000 75 per sq. mi. 29 per sq. km	149,290 sq. mi. 386,661 sq. km	Tobacco	Machinery

*Country maps not drawn to scale.

The Physical Geography of Africa South of the Sahara

CHAPTER FOCUS

Geographic Setting

Africa south of the Sahara comprises an area more than twice the size of the continental United States. It includes diverse landforms and climates.

Geographic Themes

Section 1 The Land
PLACE Africa south of the Sahara rises from west to east in a series of plateaus, the dominant landform on the continent.

Section 2 The Climate and Vegetation
REGION Climate regions in Africa south of the Sahara range from steamy rain forests to tropical grasslands to arid deserts.

▲ Photograph: *Cape Town, South Africa*

1 The Land

Read to Discover . . .
- the major landforms in Africa south of the Sahara.
- the physical barriers to inland travel in Africa south of the Sahara.
- how topography affects the water systems of Africa south of the Sahara.

Key Terms
- escarpment
- cataract
- fault

Identify and Locate
Eastern Highlands, Drakensberg Mountains, Ruwenzori Mountains, Kilimanjaro, Great Rift Valley, Lake Victoria, Lake Tanganyika, Lake Malawi, Lake Volta, Lake Chad, Nile River, Zaire River, Niger River, Zambezi River, Victoria Falls

> Nairobi, Kenya
>
> Jambo! Yesterday we left Nairobi and drove to the Great Rift Valley. On the way, we viewed the beautiful, snow-capped Mt. Kilimanjaro. From the top of the Mt. Kenya and valley, I could see dense forests. Thorny trees and shrubs lined the way as we descended to the bottom of the valley. What a magnificent scene!
>
> Umbisa Gusa

Africa south of the Sahara includes almost 50 countries, or about one-third of all countries on the earth. In his postcard, Umbisa Gusa describes the varied landscape of Kenya, a country in East Africa. Kenya, however, represents only a small portion of the huge African landmass that occupies almost one-fifth of the earth's total land area.

Landforms

As the world's second-largest continent, Africa is a land of immense diversity. The desert expanse of the Sahara, the largest desert in the world, blankets much of the northern third of the continent. Sub-Saharan Africa also includes about 9 million square miles (23 million sq. km) of huge plateaus, mountains, and valleys.

Continent of Plateaus

Many geographers describe Africa as a gigantic plateau. Narrow coastal plains that extend inland less than 20 miles (32 km) edge most of the continent. Until recent times, this sudden rise in land prevented easy access to the interior of Africa. One plateau follows the other as the land rises from west to east in a series of steps. Separating the plateaus are steep cliffs or slopes known as **escarpments.**

The highest and broadest plateaus and steepest escarpments lie in the south and east. Here rivers spill over escarpments in thunder-

Comparing Lands

The **continental USA** is about three times smaller than Africa south of the Sahara.

ing waterfalls, or **cataracts**, as they plunge toward the Atlantic or Indian oceans.

Because of its plateaus, Africa boasts the highest overall elevation of any other continent. In Europe, only about half the land lies at more than 500 feet (152 m) above sea level. In the region south of the Sahara, the average elevation is more than 2,000 feet (610 m) above sea level.

Mountains and Highlands

Despite its high elevations, Africa possesses surprisingly few mountains. With the exception of the Atlas Mountains in northwestern Africa, it has only scattered peaks. South of the Sahara, most mountains are found in the eastern highlands that reach from Ethiopia almost to the Cape of Good Hope.

The Drakensberg Mountains rim the edge of the southeastern plateau, while the Ruwenzori Mountains border Uganda and Zaire. The snow-clad peaks of the Ruwenzori seem to float in the sky, causing Africans to call them Mountains of the Moon.

The cone-shaped volcanic peaks of Kenya and Tanzania include Mount Kenya and Kilimanjaro, Africa's highest mountain. Each year, thousands of climbers try to reach its summit 19,340 feet (5,895 m) above the east African plateau.

The Great Rift Valley

Kilimanjaro perches on the edge of the Great Rift Valley, one of the world's natural wonders. This valley stretches from the Jordan River in Southwest Asia to the Zambezi River in Mozambique. In East Africa, it slashes a Y-shaped trench more than 3,500 miles (5,631 km) long and creates bold escarpments more than a mile high.

Scientists believe the Great Rift Valley emerged when Africa was part of a huge supercontinent they call Pangaea. Violent movements below the earth's crust began to rip Pangaea apart about 180 million years ago. Huge chunks of land drifted away from one another, creating the present-day continents.

The tremendous pressure on land surfaces caused cracks, or **faults**, and pushed up mountains. For 20 to 35 million years, East Africa seethed with volcanic activity. Another gigantic volcano to the west of Kilimanjaro blew its top and collapsed in on itself, creating the immense Ngorongoro Crater.

PLACE

Water Systems

Landforms shaped millions of years ago have influenced the water systems of Africa. Cuts in the Great Rift Valley form the continent's largest lakes, while the longest rivers all rise in the steplike plateaus. Because of high escarpments, rapids and waterfalls at the edge of the continent block easy inland travel by river.

A Chain of Lakes

A double chain of lakes lies in the Great Rift Valley. Lake Victoria—surrounded by Kenya, Tanzania, and Uganda—is the second-largest freshwater lake in the world and the source of the White Nile. To the southwest, Tanganyika reaches 420 miles (676 km) in length, making it the world's longest freshwater lake.

Surrounded by Tanzania, Mozambique, and Malawi is Lake Malawi, the third-greatest lake in Africa. Many types of fish, some that exist in no other place, live in Lake Malawi.

Few other lakes exist outside the Great Rift Valley. In West Africa, the people of Ghana built a dam across the Volta River to form Lake Volta. To the northeast lies Lake Chad. With no natural outlet to the sea, Lake Chad loses its water to evaporation and seepage.

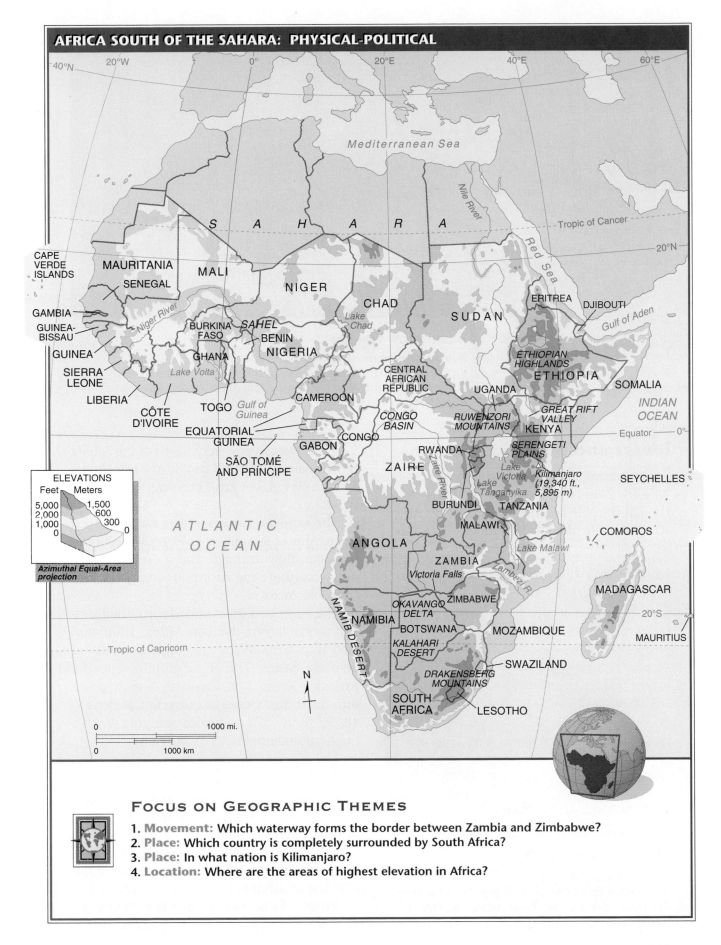

AFRICA SOUTH OF THE SAHARA: PHYSICAL-POLITICAL

Mediterranean Sea

Tropic of Cancer

20°N

S A H A R A

Nile River

Red Sea

Gulf of Aden

CAPE VERDE ISLANDS

MAURITANIA

MALI

NIGER

CHAD

SUDAN

ERITREA

DJIBOUTI

SENEGAL

Niger River

Lake Chad

GAMBIA

GUINEA-BISSAU

GUINEA

SIERRA LEONE

LIBERIA

CÔTE D'IVOIRE

BURKINA FASO

SAHEL

BENIN

GHANA

NIGERIA

Lake Volta

TOGO

Gulf of Guinea

CAMEROON

EQUATORIAL GUINEA

GABON

CONGO

SÃO TOMÉ AND PRÍNCIPE

CENTRAL AFRICAN REPUBLIC

CONGO BASIN

ZAIRE

Zaire River

UGANDA

ETHIOPIAN HIGHLANDS

ETHIOPIA

SOMALIA

RUWENZORI MOUNTAINS

GREAT RIFT VALLEY

KENYA

Equator

0°

INDIAN OCEAN

RWANDA

SERENGETI PLAINS

Lake Victoria

Kilimanjaro (19,340 ft., 5,895 m)

SEYCHELLES

BURUNDI

Lake Tanganyika

TANZANIA

MALAWI

Lake Malawi

COMOROS

ELEVATIONS

Feet	Meters
5,000	1,500
2,000	600
1,000	300
0	0

Azimuthal Equal-Area projection

ATLANTIC OCEAN

ANGOLA

ZAMBIA

Victoria Falls

Zambezi R.

ZIMBABWE

MADAGASCAR

20°S

NAMIB DESERT

NAMIBIA

OKAVANGO DELTA

BOTSWANA

MOZAMBIQUE

MAURITIUS

KALAHARI DESERT

SWAZILAND

Tropic of Capricorn

N

DRAKENSBERG MOUNTAINS

SOUTH AFRICA

LESOTHO

0		1000 mi.
0		1000 km

FOCUS ON GEOGRAPHIC THEMES

1. **Movement:** Which waterway forms the border between Zambia and Zimbabwe?
2. **Place:** Which country is completely surrounded by South Africa?
3. **Place:** In what nation is Kilimanjaro?
4. **Location:** Where are the areas of highest elevation in Africa?

Geographic Themes

Human/Environment Interaction: Victoria Falls
Victoria Falls, located on the Zambezi River, measure 350 feet (107 m) in height. *How might waterfalls affect Africa's future economic development?*

Rivers and Basins

Four great rivers slice through Africa—the Nile, the Zaire, the Niger, and the Zambezi. Although the Nile lies mostly in northern Africa, its White Nile branch starts in Lake Victoria.

Geographic Themes

Region: Zaire River, Central Africa
Many villages and markets thrive along the banks of central Africa's Zaire River. *What three other major rivers are located in Africa?*

The largest river system south of the Sahara is the Zaire. It twists and turns for almost 2,700 miles (4,344 km), crossing the Equator twice.

The Zaire has created a huge saucer-shaped basin. Almost 10 million gallons (38 million l) of water flow through the Zaire each second, creating an enormous potential for hydroelectricity.

The Niger and the Zambezi form the third- and fourth-largest rivers in Africa. Tributaries feed into both rivers, creating hollowed-out drainage basins. The Niger empties into the Atlantic Ocean. The Zambezi, which pours into the Indian Ocean at one point, widens to 18,297 feet (5,577 m) before plunging down a huge chasm known as Victoria Falls.

Waterfalls

During the rainy season, millions of gallons of water crash over Victoria Falls. Clouds of spray splash more than 1,640 feet (500 m) into the air. David Livingstone, the first European explorer to see the falls, named them after the British queen.

Victoria Falls, more than twice the height of Niagara Falls, joins dozens of smaller water-

Geographic Themes

Place: The Great Rift Valley, East Africa
The Great Rift Valley cuts a deep gash through the landscape of East Africa. *How was the Great Rift Valley formed?*

falls in offering tremendous potential for the development of hydroelectricity.

droelectric power and solar energy hold the keys to the continent's future development.

HUMAN/ENVIRONMENT INTERACTION

Natural Resources

Africa south of the Sahara is rich in resources. In South Africa and Zaire, miners extract diamonds from some of the biggest deposits on the earth. Some geologists believe that more than half the world's gold comes from South Africa and the Great Rift Valley. Central Africa, especially Zambia and Zaire, yields reserves of copper. Nigeria controls 3 percent of the world's known oil reserves. Other parts of the continent hold pockets of industrial minerals, such as uranium, manganese, cobalt, and zinc.

Africans have begun to tap two other sources of energy—waterfalls and the sun. Hy-

SECTION 1 REVIEW

Checking for Understanding
1. **Define** escarpment, cataract, fault.
2. **Locating Places** What major landform dominates Africa south of the Sahara?
3. **Location** Where is the Great Rift Valley?
4. **Region** What major lakes and rivers lie south of the Sahara?

Critical Thinking
5. **Expressing Problems Clearly** Explain what resources in Africa hold the answer to how to meet the continent's future energy needs.

SECTION 2

The Climate and Vegetation

P ainting a picture of the African landscape is much like weaving a piece of *kenta* cloth. This highly prized cloth of western Africa is made of long strips of fabric woven together in vivid patterns. Each strip is distinctly different. Yet it forms part of a pattern instantly recognized by most Africans. Like kenta cloth, the landscape of Africa is made up of distinct climate regions with their own characteristic forms of vegetation. These regions are woven together into a pattern shaped by Africa's location in the tropics.

Such climatic variations are partially explained by elevation. The combination of high plateaus, lowland coastal areas, and large interior basins strongly influence climate patterns. Higher elevations generally mean cooler climates. Wetter climates are found along escarpments that force rain-heavy clouds to drop their moisture. Such is the case with Zaire. Moisture-carrying clouds sweep inland until they run into the escarpment at the edge of the towering eastern plateau. As a result, rain falls more heavily in Zaire than in neighboring Tanzania.

LOCATION

A Diverse Continent

T hree tropical latitudes define the location of Africa south of the Sahara—the Tropic of Cancer, the Tropic of Capricorn, and the Equator. The Tropic of Cancer crosses the countries that line the southern edge of the desert. The Tropic of Capricorn extends through the southern tip of the continent. In between these two latitudes runs the Equator. No other continent on the earth straddles all three tropical latitudes.

Although all of Africa lies within 35 degrees of the Equator, the continent has great variations in climate and vegetation. Areas of steamy rain forests, desert and steppe areas, and milder climates are all found in Africa.

REGION

Climate Regions

C limate regions with distinct vegetation patterns lie both north and south of the Equator. A trip toward the Equator from either the Tropic of Cancer or the Tropic of Capricorn goes through four main climate regions: desert, steppe, tropical savanna, and tropical rain forest.

Deserts

Deserts cover a larger percentage of Africa than any other continent—about two-fifths of its land area. The Sahara sprawls across northern Africa from the Atlantic Ocean to the Red Sea. In southern Africa, the Namib Desert blankets the coast of Namibia. On the southern plateau to the west stretches the Kalahari Desert. About the size of Italy, the Kalahari covers most of Botswana.

Little rain ever falls on the deserts of Africa. The complex system of escarpments and plateaus keeps rain-laden clouds from reaching interior areas. Except for scattered cactuses and thorny shrubs, the deserts, where temperatures soar to 120°F (48.9°C), are barren. At night, heat escapes until temperatures cool to 50°F (10°C) or lower.

Desert Oases

Most oases are created by groundwater close to the surface. On the northern edge of the Kalahari Desert, however, the world's largest inland delta blooms. The delta is formed by the Okavango River. Spilling out of the highlands of distant Angola, the Okavango River spreads a sheet of water over the Kalahari sands until it disappears into the desert. The vegetation in the delta supports a variety of wildlife. "The delta," commented one scientist, "returns the pulse of life to the 'great thirstland' of the Kalahari."

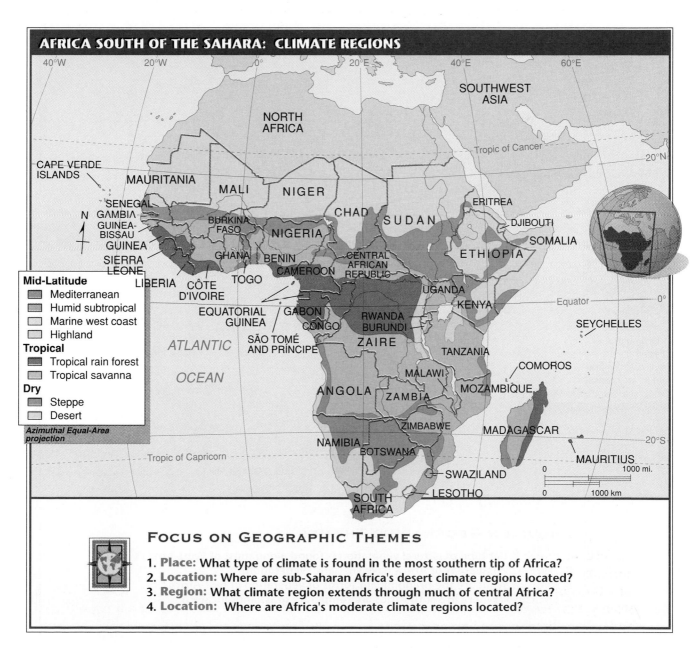

AFRICA SOUTH OF THE SAHARA: CLIMATE REGIONS

Mid-Latitude
- Mediterranean
- Humid subtropical
- Marine west coast
- Highland

Tropical
- Tropical rain forest
- Tropical savanna

Dry
- Steppe
- Desert

Azimuthal Equal-Area projection

FOCUS ON GEOGRAPHIC THEMES

1. **Place:** What type of climate is found in the most southern tip of Africa?
2. **Location:** Where are sub-Saharan Africa's desert climate regions located?
3. **Region:** What climate region extends through much of central Africa?
4. **Location:** Where are Africa's moderate climate regions located?

The Sahel

Beyond the parched deserts stretch the steppe grasslands. The western part of this area is often referred to as the Sahel, from an Arabic word that means "coast." The Sahel lies between the desert and the more fertile grasslands to the south. Its climate alternates between a long, dry season and a short, wet season. Unfortunately, in recent years the rainy seasons have almost disappeared from the Sahel. A persistent drought has brought misery, famine, and hardship to much of the region.

Tropical Savanna

Beyond the drought-ridden steppes stretch the **savannas**, or tropical grasslands containing scattered trees. The savannas also alternate between wet and dry seasons. They, however, receive considerably more rain than the Sahel. In the wetter savannas of the southern plateaus, between 30 and 60 inches (76 and 152 cm) of rain falls annually.

In some parts of the savannas, which provide grazing for livestock and wild game, elephant grass grows to more than 15 feet (4.5 m) tall. To protect wildlife, governments have cre-

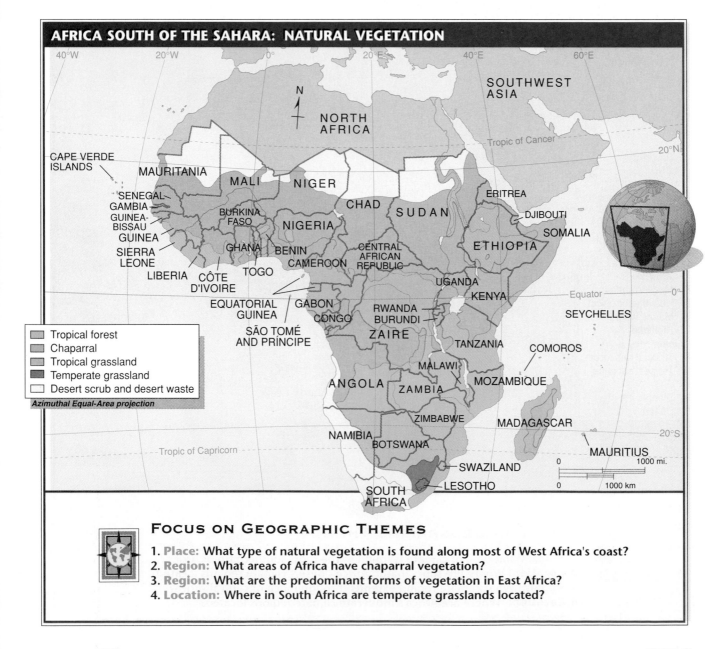

AFRICA SOUTH OF THE SAHARA: NATURAL VEGETATION

Legend:
- Tropical forest
- Chaparral
- Tropical grassland
- Temperate grassland
- Desert scrub and desert waste

Azimuthal Equal-Area projection

FOCUS ON GEOGRAPHIC THEMES

1. **Place:** What type of natural vegetation is found along most of West Africa's coast?
2. **Region:** What areas of Africa have chaparral vegetation?
3. **Region:** What are the predominant forms of vegetation in East Africa?
4. **Location:** Where in South Africa are temperate grasslands located?

Geographic Themes

Human/Environment Interaction: The Sahel
Grazing and farming lands in the Sahel have been gradually swallowed up by the advancing Sahara. *How have changes in climate affected the people of the Sahel?*

ated huge game preserves such as Tanzania's Serengeti Plains and Kenya's Nairobi National Park.

Tropical Rain Forests

Many non-Africans imagine Africa as a land of vast tropical rain forests. The steamy tropical rain forest climate region, however, covers only about 8 percent of Africa and is centered mostly on the Equator. Here temperatures hover around 80°F (27°C), and rain falls daily.

The heavy rains **leach**, or wash away, many nutrients from the soil. The rain forests provide poor farmland but are rich in other vegetation. Yet the rain forests face destruction. Cocoa, rubber, and palm-oil plantations take more and more land. Logging companies that seek valuable hardwood trees have increased their harvesting. As is the case with rain forests elsewhere in the world, this climate region may someday disappear.

Moderate Climates

The map on page 425 shows pockets of moderate climates in the highlands of Kenya

and the southern tip of Africa. These heavily populated areas have fertile soil, adequate rain, and a favorable climate—all good conditions for farming.

SECTION 2 REVIEW

Checking for Understanding
1. **Define** savanna, leach.
2. **Locating Places** What are the main climate regions that run north and south from the Equator?
3. **Place** How do elevation and rainfall affect climate in sub-Saharan Africa?
4. **Human/Environment Interaction** Why might the rain forests of Africa face possible destruction?

Critical Thinking
5. **Determining Cause and Effect** Explain the causes of the climate problem in the Sahel and its effect on human and animal life.

Evaluating Information

Remember the old expression: "Don't believe everything you read"? It's always important to question and evaluate the accuracy and reliability of information.

REVIEWING THE SKILL

There are two main purposes for evaluating information—to determine its relevance and its reliability. First, analyze the purpose and nature of the information. Decide whether it is a primary or secondary source. Both kinds of sources can provide valid information, but each has limitations. For example, primary sources (those written by eyewitnesses to events) may seem more accurate than secondary sources. However, because the author of a primary source was directly involved in the events, he or she may be less objective and more biased than a secondary source.

Second, for any kind of source, you must evaluate its *reliability.* In determining reliability, consider these factors: 1) Is this source an expert on the topic? A meteorologist may be a reliable source of information on weather, but not on sports. 2) What is the purpose of the information? A source that wants to persuade you to buy something or do something is less reliable than a source that just provides information. 3) Is the source biased, or influenced by strong beliefs and opinions? For example, two people with different political views may watch the same speech on television, but their political biases may produce very different accounts of the speech. To evaluate sources, apply the following steps:

- Determine whether it is a primary or secondary source.

- Evaluate reliability by asking these questions: Does the source know this topic well? What is the purpose? What are the biases?
- Compare the information with other sources to see if they support or contradict each other.

PRACTICING THE SKILL

Africa has extensive river systems that have played an important role in the continent's history and development. The Zaire River is Africa's second-longest river. Below, a writer discusses the river, and a part of the land through which it winds. Read the excerpt, and answer the following questions:

1. Is this a primary or secondary source? Why?
2. Is the writer an expert on the topic discussed? Why or why not?
3. Do you think the information about the river and its environment is reliable? Why or why not?

At Kisangani the river, now called Zaire, begins its long easy curl through the central forest. As it bends around toward the southwest, the river widens to 9 miles [14.5 km], its glassy waters dotted with myriad islands. Kinshasa lies at the head of Livingstone Falls, actually 220 miles [354 km] of cataracts and rapids where the river crashes through the Crystal Mountains, the western rim of the Congo Basin. The ocean port, Matadi, lies at the foot of the falls.

Now called the bas fleuve (lower river), it once again spreads out, wide and deep enough for oceangoing ships to sail down the final hundred miles to the Atlantic. But the river doesn't stop there. The current is so strong that its brown waters are hurled nearly a hundred miles into the sea and have gouged a 4,000-foot [1,200-m] canyon in the ocean floor.[1]

For additional practice in this skill, see Practicing Skills on page 430 of the Chapter 20 Review.

[1] Source: Robert Caputo. "Lifeline for a Nation–Zaire River" in NATIONAL GEOGRAPHIC, November, 1991, p. 29.

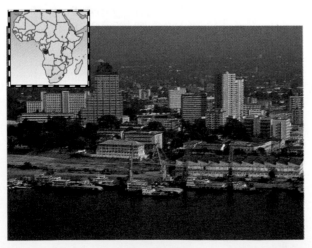

Kinshasa, Zaire

1	SECTION	KEY TERMS	SUMMARY

1 The Land

escarpment (p. 419)
cataract (p. 420)
fault (p. 420)

- A series of steplike plateaus dominates lands south of the Sahara.
- High elevations and a narrow coastal plain have historically hindered travel to the interior of Africa.
- The Great Rift Valley slices through East Africa and affects the landforms of nations from Ethiopia to Mozambique.
- Most of Africa's large freshwater lakes nestle in cuts in the Great Rift Valley.
- Four major river systems tumble over escarpments in dramatic rapids and falls as they spill off the continent.

Village and market along the Zaire River in central Africa

2	SECTION	KEY TERMS	SUMMARY

2 The Climate and Vegetation

savanna (p. 426)
leach (p. 427)

- Although most of Africa lies in the tropics, it still exhibits diverse climates and vegetation.
- Elevation and rainfall are the main factors influencing climate variations in sub-Saharan Africa.
- The main climate regions in Africa south of the Sahara include: desert, steppe, tropical savanna, and tropical rain forest.
- Africa has an abundance of mineral wealth, but it lacks the fuels to develop it.
- Deserts and steppes cover more than two-thirds of the land surface in Africa.

Desertification in western Africa

Reviewing Key Terms

Choose the vocabulary term that best completes each of the sentences below. Write your answers on a separate sheet of paper.

escarpment (p. 419)
cataract (p. 420)
fault (p. 420)
savanna (p. 426)
leach (p. 427)

SECTION 1

1. Steep cliffs or slopes that separate plateaus in Africa are called _____ .
2. The Great Rift Valley developed when volcanic activity created _____ in the earth's crust.
3. Because of Africa's plateaus, most rivers tumble off waterfalls or _____ .

SECTION 2

4. _____ relates to the rain forests of Africa.
5. An area of grasslands with scattered trees is called a _____ .

Reviewing the Facts

SECTION 1

6. Why do some geographers refer to Africa as a "continent of plateaus"?
7. What forces helped create the Great Rift Valley?
8. Why has it been historically difficult to travel into the interior of Africa by river?

SECTION 2

9. Why is Africa south of the Sahara said to be the most tropical region on the earth?
10. Why do the Kenya highlands have a milder climate than northern Zaire?
11. What vegetation exists in the tropical savannas?
12. How was a delta able to form on the sands of the Kalahari Desert?
13. What forces threaten the rain forests of Africa?

Critical Thinking

14. **Analyzing Information**   Many myths surround African mountains. What geographic data help explain the awe in which many mountains are held?
15. **Making Comparisons**   Choose two climate regions in Africa south of the Sahara. How are they different? How are they alike?

 ## Geographic Themes

16. **Movement**   What geographic factors discouraged the exchange of ideas between Europe and sub-Saharan Africa until recent times?
17. **Location**   How does location set Africa apart as a continent?

Practicing Skills

Evaluating Information

Refer to the Evaluating Information skill on page 428.

18. What biases might this source have about Africa?
19. How is the account of the Zaire River supported by the text of Chapter 20?

Using the Unit Atlas

Refer to the physical geography section of the Unit Atlas on pages 412–413.

20. What river drains most of west central Africa?
21. About what percentage of Africa has a tropical climate?

Projects

Individual Activity

Because of its great elevation, Kilimanjaro includes many climates. Research Kilimanjaro and write a short description of what climbers might see on their way to the summit.

Cooperative Learning Activity

Each summer, trucks carry European students across the continent of Africa. With a group of three or four classmates, design a three-month tour that takes students from Khartoum, Sudan, to Cape Town, South Africa that focuses on the vegetation areas of Africa. Prepare an information packet on each area crossed. The packets should include travel tips and, if possible, maps.

Writing About Geography

Cause and Effect

Imagine you are a geographer from Kenya invited to write and deliver a paper on the Great Rift Valley to the National Council of Geographic Education. Using your journal, text, and other references, write a descriptive paper about the valley's major characteristics. Be sure your paper explains the links between present-day physical features and ancient volcanic activity.

Locating Places

AFRICA SOUTH OF THE SAHARA: PHYSICAL GEOGRAPHY

Match the letters on the map with the physical features of Africa south of the Sahara. Write your answers on a separate sheet of paper.

1. Lake Chad
2. Okavango Delta
3. Zaire River
4. Great Rift Valley
5. Lake Tanganyika
6. Zambezi River
7. Kilimanjaro
8. Lake Victoria
9. Kalahari Desert
10. Lake Malawi

The Cultural Geography of Africa South of the Sahara

CHAPTER FOCUS

Geographic Setting

Africa south of the Sahara constitutes the third most populous—and fastest-growing—region in the world. More than 550 million people from some 2,000 distinct groups populate the land.

Geographic Themes

Section 1 Population Patterns

PLACE Overpopulation in sub-Saharan Africa has resulted, in part, from an uneven distribution of people and natural resources.

Section 2 History and Government

MOVEMENT The region's history

has been characterized by movements of people.

Section 3 Cultures and Lifestyles

REGION History and beliefs help bind together sub-Saharan Africa.

▲ Photograph: *Village market in Zaire*

Population Patterns

Read to Discover . . .
- the major population trends in sub-Saharan Africa.
- how economic growth rates affect Africa's population development.
- the diverse peoples who populate sub-Saharan Africa.

Key Terms
- gross domestic product (GDP)
- per capita income
- urbanization
- ethnic group

Identify and Locate
Rwanda, Chad, Gabon, Lagos, Johannesburg, Cape Town

Gonder, Ethiopia

My family and I celebrate Christmas Day by going to church. The men wear white pants, a long white shirt and a white scarf. Women wear long white dresses decorated with fringe or embroidery. We give presents to our friends and family. I like to give people fresh flowers.

Alemu Getachew

A frica south of the Sahara boasts one of the world's youngest populations. About half the region's people are no more than 15 years old. One of Africa's many teenagers wrote the postcard on this page. Alemu Getachew describes the people of Ethiopia—only a small part of the 570 million people who live in sub-Saharan Africa, the third-most populous region in the world.

A Region of Variety

S ub-Saharan Africa claims the world's highest birthrate and the world's shortest life expectancy. The region has the world's highest population growth rate and the world's lowest

economic growth rate. It possesses some of the world's most densely populated areas and some of the world's least densely populated areas. These are but a few of the characteristics of the population in sub-Saharan Africa today.

A Booming Population

With a high infant mortality and a short life expectancy, Zaire's population grows at 3.3 percent a year. In 1994 its population stood at more than 42.5 million. The example of Zaire is repeated throughout the region. As the decade of the 1990s began, the annual growth rate for Africa south of the Sahara stood at about 3 percent. If sub-Saharan Africa keeps growing at its present rate, experts predict that the region's population will double in less than 20 years.

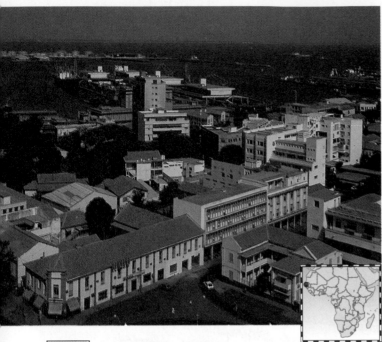

Uneven Population Density

If Africa's population were spread out evenly across the continent, there would be about 30 people per square mile. This compares favorably to the 170 per square mile (66 per sq. km) packed into western Europe. Africa's population, however, is not evenly distributed. An estimated 808 people per square mile (312 per sq. km) squeeze into Rwanda, while only 6 people per square mile (2 per sq. km) fill Namibia and Botswana.

Such uneven population distribution is closely linked to the region's physical geography. Desert and arid steppes cover nearly two-thirds of Africa. As a result, most sub-Saharan Africans crowd along the coast of western Africa, around the lakes of eastern Africa, and along the coast of southeastern Africa. They are lured to these areas by easy access to water, fertile soil, and mild climates good for farming. In describing Rwanda, the world's eleventh most densely populated nation, an expert on Africa writes:

The rugged, spectacularly beautiful hills and mountains of Rwanda are tiered like giant staircases. On each level . . . a family clan lives and farms. The dirt roads that wind through the valleys and across the hills are as busy as the sidewalks of New York's Fifth Avenue during lunch hour, a shoulder-to-shoulder procession of pedestrians. . . .

HUMAN/ENVIRONMENT INTERACTION

Population and Economics

Africa's limited farmland has strained the ability of governments to feed their people. In recent years, huge expanses of land have been exhausted through intensive cultivation, loss of soil fertility, and crippling droughts. United Nations officials estimate that food production in sub-Saharan Africa has dropped 20 percent since 1970. Yet the region's population has nearly doubled. Although some 70 percent of sub-Saharan Africans work as farmers, they are producing less and eating less.

Famine and poor nutrition claim many lives, especially infants and young children. Impure water is another cause of death. Only about 37 percent of sub-Saharan Africans have clean water to drink. Diseases are widespread. Insects such as the tsetse fly carry viruses that kill cattle, horses, and people. Acquired Immunodeficiency Syndrome (AIDS), a worldwide disease, has reached epidemic proportions in sub-Saharan Africa. The situation is worsened by a lack of both doctors to treat disease and up-to-date equipment to test and screen blood.

Sub-Saharan Africa suffers the lowest standards of living in the world. While the region's population grows at 3 percent, its economy limps ahead at about 1.5 percent. The 550 million people of sub-Saharan Africa generate a combined **gross domestic product (GDP)**, or total output of goods and services within a country or region, of about $150 billion. This is roughly the same GDP as Belgium, a nation of about 10 million people.

Standards of living vary widely in the region. In Chad, the **per capita income**, or average per person income, hovers around $220. Gabon, on the other hand, enjoys a per capita income of $4,450, which is based upon oil and mining. Yet even Gabon lags far behind the $20,880 per capita income of Belgium. The low per capita incomes of sub-Saharan Africa translate into too little capital to develop the health care, food production, and industry necessary to improve the overall standard of living.

Rapid Urbanization

A lthough Africa is the least urbanized of any continent, it is urbanizing at the world's fastest rate. In 1950, only about 35 million Africans lived in cities. By the year 2000, population experts predict that 350 million will live in cities. In less than 50 years, the number of urban Africans will have increased 10 times!

Most of the cities in sub-Saharan Africa lie on the coast, along major rivers, or near sources of valuable resources. They grew up largely as trading centers. Lagos, Nigeria, start-

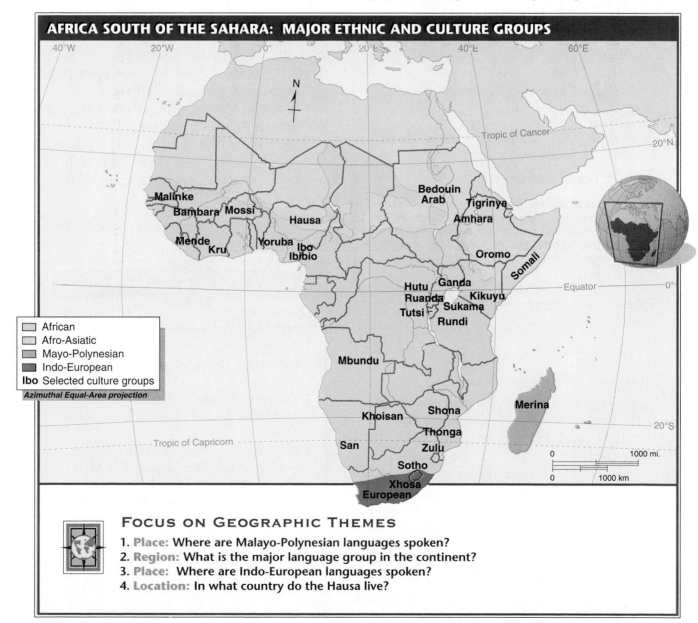

AFRICA SOUTH OF THE SAHARA: MAJOR ETHNIC AND CULTURE GROUPS

Legend:
- African
- Afro-Asiatic
- Mayo-Polynesian
- Indo-European
- **Ibo** Selected culture groups

Azimuthal Equal-Area projection

FOCUS ON GEOGRAPHIC THEMES

1. **Place:** Where are Malayo-Polynesian languages spoken?
2. **Region:** What is the major language group in the continent?
3. **Place:** Where are Indo-European languages spoken?
4. **Location:** In what country do the Hausa live?

AFRICA SOUTH OF THE SAHARA: METROPOLITAN AREAS

City and Country	Population*
Lagos, Nigeria	7,998,000
Kinshasa, Zaire	3,747,000
Abidjan, Côte d'Ivoire	2,700,000
Cape Town, South Africa	1,900,000
Johannesburg, South Africa	1,900,000
Dakar, Senegal	1,700,000
Addis Ababa, Ethiopia	1,600,000
Dar es Salaam, Tanzania	1,400,000
Ibadan, Nigeria	1,300,000
Luanda, Angola	1,100,000
Durban, South Africa	1,100,000
Lusaka, Zambia	982,000
Nairobi, Kenya	959,000
Accra, Ghana	949,000
Maputo, Mozambique	931,000

*Cities with population of 900,000 or more, based on available estimates
Source: *The World Almanac*, 1995

CHART STUDY

Africa south of the Sahara includes many rapidly growing metropolitan areas. *Which metropolitan area in sub-Saharan Africa has the most people? What large cities are located in South Africa?*

Population Diversity

Wide differences between rural and urban Africans have increased the diversity of an already incredible mix of people. Anyone who thinks of Africans as a homogeneous, or similar, mass of people is mistaken. East Africa, for example, provides home to many Asians and a variety of *mzungu,* or whites, from more than a dozen nations, including the United States. It is also home to hundreds of African **ethnic groups,** or people with similar histories and cultures.

The Maasai, for example, form one of the 70 ethnic groups that make up Kenya and the more than 100 ethnic groups that make up Tanzania. Together Africans speak more than 800 languages and numerous dialects.

Unlike the Maasai, most ethnic groups in sub-Saharan Africa do not control their own territory. Instead, they are brought together or divided by political boundaries. The Malinke people, for example, constitute part of three countries, instead of one.

ed as a slave-trading post. Johannesburg, South Africa, owes its origins to gold strikes in the area. Cape Town, South Africa, began as a port of call for Dutch ships sailing from Europe to India.

Today trade continues to play an important role in the growth of the region's cities. But so does **urbanization,** or the movement of people from rural areas into cities. Economic hardships have driven millions of people to seek new opportunities in cities such as Lagos, Nairobi, Accra, Kinshasa, and Dar es Salaam. Urban areas now comprise the most densely populated parts of sub-Saharan Africa.

SECTION 1 REVIEW

Checking for Understanding
1. **Define** gross domestic product (GDP), per capita income, urbanization, ethnic group.
2. **Locating Places** What factors determine population densities in Africa south of the Sahara?
3. **Region** What overall trend characterizes population growth in sub-Saharan Africa?
4. **Human/Environment Interaction** How is the economic growth rate linked to the standard of living in Africa?

Critical Thinking
5. **Forming Generalizations** What valid generalization can you form about the mix of people in sub-Saharan Africa?

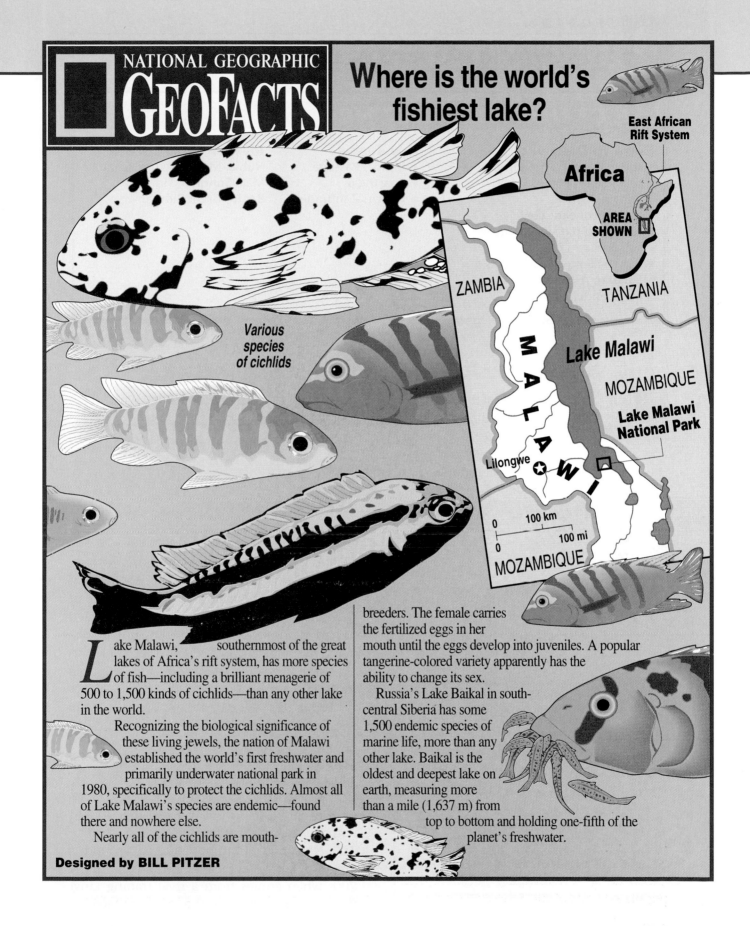

NATIONAL GEOGRAPHIC GeoFacts

Where is the world's fishiest lake?

East African Rift System

Africa

AREA SHOWN

ZAMBIA

TANZANIA

MALAWI

Lake Malawi

MOZAMBIQUE

Lake Malawi National Park

Lilongwe

0   100 km
0   100 mi

MOZAMBIQUE

Various species of cichlids

Lake Malawi, southernmost of the great lakes of Africa's rift system, has more species of fish—including a brilliant menagerie of 500 to 1,500 kinds of cichlids—than any other lake in the world.

Recognizing the biological significance of these living jewels, the nation of Malawi established the world's first freshwater and primarily underwater national park in 1980, specifically to protect the cichlids. Almost all of Lake Malawi's species are endemic—found there and nowhere else.

Nearly all of the cichlids are mouth-breeders. The female carries the fertilized eggs in her mouth until the eggs develop into juveniles. A popular tangerine-colored variety apparently has the ability to change its sex.

Russia's Lake Baikal in south-central Siberia has some 1,500 endemic species of marine life, more than any other lake. Baikal is the oldest and deepest lake on earth, measuring more than a mile (1,637 m) from top to bottom and holding one-fifth of the planet's freshwater.

Designed by BILL PITZER

SETTING THE SCENE

Read to Discover . . .
- the major accomplishments of ancient peoples in sub-Saharan Africa.
- how European rule disrupted patterns of life in sub-Saharan Africa.
- the challenges facing sub-Saharan Africa since independence.

Key Terms
- Middle Passage
- apartheid
- universal suffrage

Identify and Locate
Nubia, Meroë, Axum, Ghana, Mali, Songhai, Timbuktu, Bantu, Great Zimbabwe

E ach year, a handful of travelers heads northeast out of Agadiz, Niger. Their journey takes them past the Air Mountains and across the blazing Tenere Desert. Beyond the desert lie the Djabo Mountains. Here a guide leads travelers to caves filled with paintings created some 6,000 years ago.

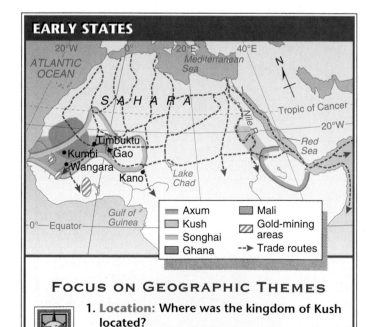

EARLY STATES

Legend:
- Axum
- Kush
- Songhai
- Ghana
- Mali
- Gold-mining areas
- --→ Trade routes

FOCUS ON GEOGRAPHIC THEMES

1. **Location:** Where was the kingdom of Kush located?
2. **Region:** What three kingdoms ruled in West Africa at different periods?
3. **Human/Environment Interaction:** What natural resource was mined in West Africa?

PLACE

African Civilizations

T he Djabo cave painters lived at a remarkable time in African history. About 5500 B.C., the fish-filled rivers and plentiful game of the Sahara lured settlers. Early peoples learned to harvest the seeds of wild grasses and domesticate, or tame, animals. Such practices led to agriculture—the cornerstone for building more complex societies.

About 2000 B.C., the Sahara began to grow warmer and drier. People slowly migrated in search of more favorable lands. These migrants helped diffuse, or spread, knowledge of agriculture throughout Africa.

The Egyptians founded the first great civilization of North Africa. In time, they fought with another civilization to the south—Nubia. The Nubian civilization centered around a kingdom known as Kush and thrived until the 700s when armies from a rival trading kingdom—Axum—captured the capital of Meroë.

At the same time, a series of trading kingdoms—Ghana, Mali, and Songhai—emerged one after the other in West Africa. The power and wealth of these kingdoms rested on control of the trans-Saharan trade, and they thrived until the late 1500s when Moroccans overpowered the Songhai.

Meanwhile, several states developed in eastern and southern Africa. These states traced their origins to a group of people called the Bantu who over the centuries fanned out over much of Africa in one of the largest migrations in history. The Bantus built several great central African states, including the kingdoms of Kongo, Luba, and Lunda. In southeastern Africa, a Bantu people called the Shona built the trading empire of Monomotapa.

MOVEMENT

European Colonization

In the 1600s and 1700s, Europeans eagerly traded with African societies. Finally, in the 1800s, Europeans seized almost the entire continent.

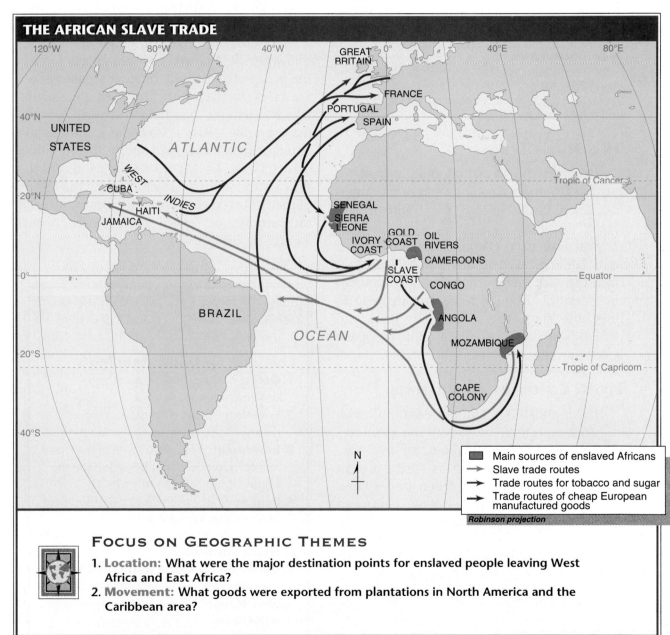

THE AFRICAN SLAVE TRADE

Legend:
- Main sources of enslaved Africans
- Slave trade routes
- Trade routes for tobacco and sugar
- Trade routes of cheap European manufactured goods

Robinson projection

FOCUS ON GEOGRAPHIC THEMES

1. **Location:** What were the major destination points for enslaved people leaving West Africa and East Africa?
2. **Movement:** What goods were exported from plantations in North America and the Caribbean area?

Geographic Themes

Region: South Africa
Nelson Mandela *(right)* won the 1993 Nobel Peace Prize for promoting peaceful change in South Africa. *What policy ended as a result of his and others' actions?*

The Slave Trade

Although the slave trade had existed for centuries, European colonization of the Americas dramatically swelled the traffic in enslaved Africans.

The slave trade claimed countless African lives. Millions died during the **Middle Passage**, the name given to the terrible trip across the Atlantic. Although some Africans tried to resist the slave trade, European guns and growing African dependence upon European goods prevailed.

From Colonies to Nations

In the mid-1800s, European nations divided Africa among themselves to use as sources of raw materials and markets for manufactured goods. By 1914, all of Africa, except Liberia and Ethiopia, had fallen under European control. Africans endured European domination until they won their independence in the mid- to late 1900s. For example, Ghana became independent in 1957, Nigeria in 1960, Kenya in 1963, Zimbabwe in 1980, and Namibia in 1990.

PLACE

Challenges for the Future

The colonial legacy has created many serious problems for sub-Saharan Africans. The political boundaries the Europeans established cut across ethnic lines, grouping diverse peoples under the same government. These groupings often led to civil wars. The colonial system caused most of the region to be underdeveloped. Few European nations prepared their colonies for independence. As a result, lack of political experience contributed to the rise of one-party states backed by the military.

In South Africa, tension remained high as the white-dominated government enforced the policy of **apartheid**, or strict separation of the races. In the 1990s, however, steps were taken to remove apartheid and work toward majority rule. Nelson Mandela, a prominent anti-apartheid leader, and South African President F. W. de Klerk held talks to turn South Africa into a nonracial democracy. One result of their efforts was the pledge to grant **universal suffrage**, or equal voting rights, to all South Africans by 1994.

SECTION 2 REVIEW

Checking for Understanding

1. **Define** Middle Passage, apartheid, universal suffrage.
2. **Locating Places** How did location affect the rise of ancient west African kingdoms?
3. **Movement** What were some of the major human migrations that helped shape the history of sub-Saharan Africa?
4. **Region** What was the major development in Africa after World War II?

Critical Thinking

5. **Determining Cause and Effect** What is the connection between colonial rule and some of the problems facing sub-Saharan Africa today?

Geography and History

AFRICA: EUROPEAN COLONIES

As you read, examine how European colonial rule affected Africa.

During the 1800s, the Industrial Revolution swept through western Europe, fueling a policy of colonial expansion. Newly industrialized countries needed raw materials for their factories and markets for their manufactured goods. By colonizing, they could acquire both while also increasing their share of global power. Africa was one of the areas targeted for expansion.

Europeans in Africa

During the late 1800s, Portugal, Spain, Italy, France, the Netherlands, and Great Britain began strengthening their hold on Africa. For the next 40 years, European governments engaged in efforts to control the most profitable sections of the region. During the mid-1920s, most of Africa was still under European control.

Effects of Colonial Rule

European governments created colonial units arbitrarily, with no regard for the ethnic homelands of the people in the regions. Colonial boundaries often cut across ethnic homelands. European administrators gave little thought to preparing Africans for future independence. Economic systems tied to production for world markets replaced the African system of production only for family or local community needs. Christian missionaries challenged beliefs and practices long a part of African life.

Colonial rule also offered expanded educational opportunities to Africans. As some Africans became politically aware, they led the demand for a share in governing. Finally, in the 1950s and 1960s, educated Africans also led independence movements that ended European rule.

AFRICA: COLONIAL RULE, 1914

Independent
Belgian
British
French
German
Italian
Portuguese
Spanish

Azimuthal Equal-Area projection

0   1000 mi.

0   1000 km

Beginning around 1870, the major European powers began a mad scramble to divide Africa, establish colonies, and exploit the wealth of natural resources found there. By 1914 only two African countries— Liberia and Ethiopia—had managed to escape European control.

Checking for Understanding

1. Why did European nations colonize Africa?

2. **Regions** Study the map. What problem can be foreseen from the colonial divisions?

SETTING THE SCENE

Read to Discover . . .
- the cultural factors that help define sub-Saharan Africa as a region.
- how language and religion have contributed to diversity in sub-Saharan Africa.
- the ways in which sub-Saharan art forms have touched upon the world.
- the obstacles to universal education in sub-Saharan Africa.

Key Terms
- mass culture
- *lingua franca*
- oral history
- extended family
- clan
- literacy rate

Identify and Locate
Sierra Leone

In recent years, certain factors have contributed to greater unity within sub-Saharan Africa. For example, colonial rule and the push for independence now form a part of the histories of most sub-Saharan nations. Also, the wider availability of television and radio has helped create a **mass culture**, or popular culture promoted by the media. In addition, sub-Saharan Africans share some common beliefs, such as the importance of family ties.

Yet despite such similarities, great diversity still exists throughout the region. In many ways, the African people are as diverse as the African landscape itself. Sometimes, they are even more diverse! Consider the city of Freetown, Sierra Leone. Its population of 469,000 includes Lebanese, Indians, Europeans, the descendants of enslaved Africans, and members of 18 ethnic groups. All these various people—their cultures and their lifestyles—help shape the human geography of sub-Saharan Africa.

REGION

Languages

Today Africans speak more than 800 languages and numerous dialects. Some of these languages originated in Africa. Others were brought to Africa by Arabs, Europeans, and other foreigners. Some African languages consist of a mixture of African and foreign words. Swahili, for example, is a major African language that is a mix of languages. Its main root is Bantu, but over the centuries, Arabic and Portuguese words have been added. Today Swahili serves as a **lingua franca,** or universal language, spoken throughout much of East Africa. It allows the people of Uganda, Rwanda, Kenya, Tanzania, and the Congo to understand each other. Such widespread use of Swahili helps define East Africa as a region.

The colonial powers imported new languages that helped Africans speak to the outside world and with one another. English is an example. Although many of these languages serve as the official languages of nations, a wide variety of ethnic languages remain in use. Language experts classify the region's many languages into three families—African, Afro-Asiatic, and Malayo-Polynesian. African languages are the most widely spoken. These include some 300 Bantu languages used in central, eastern, and southern Africa. The main Afro-Asiatic languages are the Arabic and Berber spoken in the region's northwest corner. Indo-European languages are those imported by colonial powers. In South Africa, people speak English and Afrikaans, the language of early Dutch settlers.

Religions

In describing the religion of Nigeria's Igbo, an enslaved African named Olaudah Equiano wrote:

---◆---

As to religion, [we] . . . believe that there is one Creator of all things, and that he lives in the sun, . . . and governs all events, especially our deaths.

---◆---

The religious beliefs described by Equiano form part of some of Africa's many traditional religions. Although each ethnic group might have its own religion, these tend to have some beliefs in common. Like the Igbo, most traditional religions believe in a supreme Creator and several lesser gods.

Islam and Christianity constitute the other two major religions in sub-Saharan Africa. The largest number of Muslims, or followers of Islam, can be found along the Swahili coast and in areas once held by the kingdoms of Mali and Songhai. Ethiopia embraces both Islam and Christianity. Christianity arrived in Ethiopia with missionaries and traders in the A.D. 300s. Christianity came to other nations with the European colonial powers. After independence, some Africans formed new churches that blended Christianity and traditional African religions.

The Arts

During the course of their history, sub-Saharan Africans have developed an incredible variety of art forms—from the Djabo cave paintings to the Kente cloth of West Africa to the multi-rhythmic music of traditional dances. African artists have worked in many mediums and in many styles. Because of the forced migration of enslaved Africans to other parts of the world, these styles have been widely diffused throughout the Americas, the Caribbean, and parts of Europe and Asia.

Africa South of the Sahara: Religions

Christian	201,500,000
Muslim	177,000,000
Traditional Religions	171,900,000

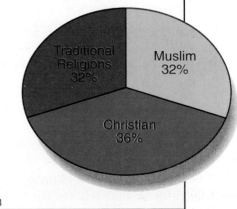

Source: Population Reference Bureau, Inc., 1993; *World Almanac*, 1993

Today the musical rhythms and instruments of Africa can be heard in popular music throughout the United States. Both the blues and jazz owe their origins to styles carried to the Americas by enslaved Africans. Even contemporary rock 'n' roll stars freely borrow from Africa. Sting, Paul Simon, and David Byrne are but a few of the artists who have looked to Africa for inspiration.

Literature

Much of the history and many of the stories of sub-Saharan Africa have been preserved in **oral history**, or the legends passed down orally from generation to generation. In more recent times, the region has produced prize-winning poets, novelists, and playwrights. In recent years, two Africans have claimed the Nobel Prize in Literature—Wole Soyinka of Nigeria (1986) and Nadine Gordimer of South Africa (1991).

Geographic Themes

Region: West Africa
Traditional dances and music in West Africa often are featured at annual festivals to honor ancestors. *What American forms of music have been inspired by African music?*

Painting, Sculpture, Weaving

African masks, sculptures, and weavings can be seen in museums and in everyday life. Modern European artists such as Pablo Picasso drew inspiration from the abstract masks of the Yoruba of Nigeria. The bronze castings of the Benin are known around the world. So are the many types of textiles designed by Africans. Prized by Africans and non-Africans alike are Ghana's Kente cloth, Nigeria's *adire* cloth, and East Africa's Konga cloth—complete with a Swahili proverb on each piece.

Music

Music forms a part of everyday life for Africans. Africans traditionally use music to bring order to life and to express themselves spiritually. Music also relieves the toil of work such as planting, hoeing, or harvesting.

PLACE

Varied Lifestyles

A journey through an African nation such as Kenya reveals the variety of lifestyles within the region. Kenya's dozens of ethnic groups all have their own customs. Wide differences also exist between rural and urban dwellers. In Nairobi, people usually wear clothes similar to those in the United States. In Maasailand, on the other hand, people wear loose-fitting clothes and brilliant jewelry.

Africans tend to share one important way of life in common. Most place great emphasis on family ties. Africans still strongly value **extended families**, or households made up of several generations. Although urbanization has made it more difficult to preserve the extended family, it is still not uncommon to find family compounds filled with relatives from grandparents to grandchildren to even great-grandchildren.

In some places, families are organized into **clans**, or large groups of people related to each other. Clan members help safeguard an ethnic

Geographic Themes

Place: Ndebele Village, South Africa
Many Africans, even those living in urban areas, maintain close connections with their families and ancestral villages. *What kind of family ties do many Africans value?*

group's traditions by passing them from one generation to the next. As in other parts of the developing world, many people also believe large families help relieve economic hardship by providing more workers. Such beliefs have made it difficult for governments to curb Africa's booming population.

REGION

Looking Ahead

The young people growing up in Africa south of the Sahara today face many challenges. Since independence, more children are attending public school. **Literacy rates**, or the ability to read and write, have risen. Still, the ideal of even an elementary education remains beyond the reach of many people.

A number of obstacles have undermined popular education. The most serious is the low standard of living. Many people simply cannot afford to send children to school. Also, some parents believe their children will profit more from survival skills, such as hunting or farming. As a result, literacy rates in sub-Saharan Africa remain the lowest in the world.

To give the region's children a more hopeful future, governments are using innovative methods to chip away at monumental problems. Television, for example, has become one of the region's most effective teaching tools.

SECTION 3 REVIEW

Checking for Understanding
1. **Define** mass culture, *lingua franca,* oral history, extended family, clan, literacy rate.
2. **Locating Places** What are some of the factors that have helped unify sub-Saharan Africa as a region in recent years?
3. **Region** How do language and religion increase diversity within sub-Saharan Africa?
4. **Movement** How have sub-Saharan Africans influenced global culture?

Critical Thinking
5. **Determining Cause and Effect** What is the connection between low standards of living and low literacy rates in sub-Saharan Africa?

Reading a Circle Graph

Suppose you must give a report that analyzes student participation in various extracurricular activities. First, you conduct a survey to find out how many students participate in sports, clubs, arts groups, and so on. After compiling this data, you must find a good way to present the information quickly, clearly, and concisely. One excellent format would be a **circle graph**.

REVIEWING THE SKILL

Circle graphs illustrate numerical information and the relationship of parts to a whole. Because it looks like a pie cut into slices, a circle graph is also called a pie graph. The complete circle represents the whole group, while each slice, or wedge, represents a fraction of the whole expressed in percentages.

When reading a circle graph, apply the following steps:

- Read the graph title to determine the subject.
- Study the labels and key to understand what each part of the graph represents.
- Compare the sizes of the parts to draw conclusions about the subject.

PRACTICING THE SKILL

Study the circle graphs below and then answer the following questions:

1. What are the subjects of the circle graphs?
2. What color represents the Luo people and their language?
3. What percentage of Kenyans are speakers of Luhya?
4. What percentage of Kenyans belong to ethnic groups other than those listed specifically on the graph?
5. What is the most striking similarity between the percentages shown on the two graphs?

For additional practice in this skill, see Practicing Skills on page 448 of the Chapter 21 Review.

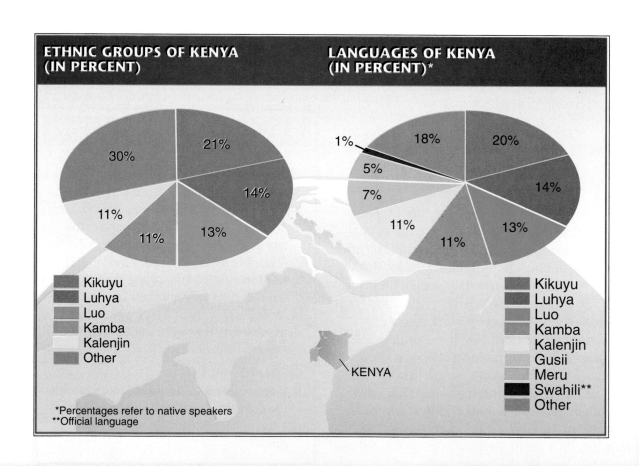

ETHNIC GROUPS OF KENYA (IN PERCENT)

30% 21% 14% 13% 11% 11%

Kikuyu
Luhya
Luo
Kamba
Kalenjin
Other

LANGUAGES OF KENYA (IN PERCENT)*

1% 18% 20% 5% 7% 14% 11% 11% 13%

Kikuyu
Luhya
Luo
Kamba
Kalenjin
Gusii
Meru
Swahili**
Other

KENYA

*Percentages refer to native speakers
**Official language

SECTION	KEY TERMS	SUMMARY
1 Population Patterns	gross domestic product (GDP) (p. 434) per capita income (p. 435) urbanization (p. 436) ethnic group (p. 436)	• With more than 570 million people, sub-Saharan Africa is the third most populous region in the world. • The uneven distribution of people in sub-Saharan Africa is linked to the region's physical geography. • Inadequate food, water, and health care contribute to short life expectancies in sub-Saharan Africa. • Sub-Saharan Africa is urbanizing faster than any other region in the world. • More than 2,000 ethnic groups, speaking some 800 languages, make up the population of Africa south of the Sahara.

West African urban scene

SECTION	KEY TERMS	SUMMARY
2 History and Government	Middle Passage (p. 440) apartheid (p. 440) universal suffrage (p. 440)	• The movement of the Bantu south from Niger formed one of the largest human migrations in history. • European colonization remapped traditional ethnic territories. • Most of Africa's nations have won independence since the 1960s. • In the 1990s, South Africans began to dismantle apartheid.

South African leader Nelson Mandela

SECTION	KEY TERMS	SUMMARY
3 Cultures and Lifestyles	mass culture (p. 442) *lingua franca* (p. 442) oral history (p. 444) extended family (p. 444) clan (p. 444) literacy rate (p. 445)	• Sub-Saharan Africa's many languages and variety of religions contribute to the region's diversity. • Sub-Saharan Africans have influenced the artistic cultures of the world. • One of the biggest challenges facing sub-Saharan African governments is how to raise literacy rates.

Nigerians celebrating annual festival

Reviewing Key Terms

Choose the vocabulary term that best completes each of the sentences below. Write your answers on a separate sheet of paper.

per capita income (p. 435)
urbanization (p. 436)
ethnic group (p. 436)
Middle Passage (p. 440)
apartheid (p. 440)
lingua franca (p. 442)
literacy rate (p. 445)

SECTION 1

1. The average annual earnings per person of a nation's population is called the _____ .
2. The movement of people from rural areas into cities is known as _____ .
3. People with similar histories and cultures are known as an _____ .

SECTION 2

4. Millions of Africans died during the _____ , the name given to the terrible trip across the Atlantic.
5. The forced separation of races in South Africa was called _____ .

SECTION 3

6. Swahili is an example of a _____ , or universal language, spoken in East Africa.
7. When a large number of people can read and write, a nation is said to have a high _____ .

Reviewing Facts

SECTION 1

8. What trend most accurately characterizes population growth in sub-Saharan Africa?
9. What factor(s) account for the diverse population patterns in sub-Saharan Africa?

SECTION 2

10. What ancient kingdoms and empires grew up in East and West Africa?

11. How will the end of apartheid affect government in South Africa?

SECTION 3

12. What are the three major language groups in sub-Saharan Africa?
13. What religions are practiced in Africa today?

Critical Thinking

14. **Predicting Consequences**   What effect do you think migration from rural areas to cities has had on traditional ways of life?
15. **Analyzing Information**   What role do you think trade played in early African societies?
16. **Making Comparisons**   Music has given the people of sub-Saharan Africa a sense of identity. Do you think this is unique to Africa? Why or why not?

Geographic Themes

17. **Place**   How has physical geography affected population densities in sub-Saharan Africa?
18. **Movement**   How did climate changes in the Sahara affect population patterns in the region?
19. **Region**   How has language helped define East Africa as a region?

Practicing Skills

Reading a Circle Graph

Refer to the circle graphs on page 446.

20. What percentage of Kenyans are speakers of Swahili?
21. What is the largest single ethnic group in Kenya?
22. What percentage of Kenyans are speakers of Gusii?

23. Which 2 ethnic groups each make up about 11 percent of Kenya's population?

Using the Unit Atlas

Refer to the cultural geography section of the Unit Atlas on pages 410–411.

24. What is the most populous nation in Africa?
25. What nation is Africa's oldest republic?
26. What is the approximate population of Africa south of the Sahara?

Projects

Individual Activity

You learned about the incredible variety of art forms in sub-Saharan Africa. Pick one of the art forms mentioned in the chapter—painting, sculpture, masks, weaving, music, poetry, or literature. Then, using an encyclo-pedia or a book on Africa, look up this art form. Pick one example of this art form and prepare an audio/visual report.

Cooperative Learning Activity

In small groups, pick two nations in sub-Saharan Africa. Using an almanac, prepare population graphics of the nations chosen. When all the student teams are done, form a committee to bind the information together alphabetically.

Writing About Geography

Description

Write a vivid description of Africa south of the Sahara based on the information recorded in your journal activity calendar. Illustrate your description with sketches based on pictures found in the text and other sources.

Locating Places

AFRICA SOUTH OF THE SAHARA: POLITICAL GEOGRAPHY

Match the letters on the map with the places in Africa south of the Sahara. Write your answers on a separate sheet of paper.

1. Angola
2. Johannesburg
3. Mali
4. Liberia
5. Namibia
6. Botswana
7. Lagos
8. Rwanda
9. Chad
10. Cameroon

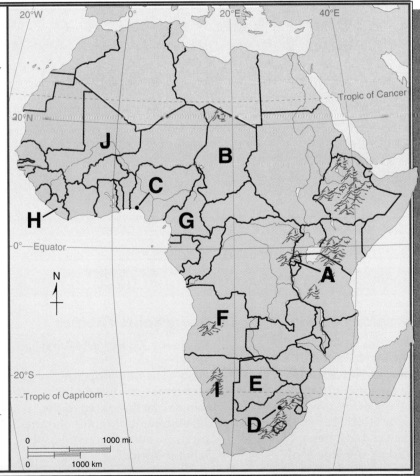

Africa South of the Sahara Today

CHAPTER FOCUS

Geographic Setting

The economy of Africa south of the Sahara, or sub-Saharan Africa, rests heavily on agriculture and the export of raw materials. Efforts to industrialize have been hindered by the legacy of colonialism, a lack of capital, and pressing environmental concerns.

Geographic Themes

Section 1 Living in Africa South of the Sahara
REGION The one-crop economies created under colonialism discouraged the development of regional trade and transportation within sub-Saharan Africa.

▲ Photograph: *Downtown Harare, Zimbabwe*

Section 2 People and Their Environment
HUMAN/ENVIRONMENT INTERACTION Over the past century, human interaction with the environment has contributed to the problem of hunger in Africa south of the Sahara.

Living in Africa South of the Sahara

SETTING THE SCENE

Read to Discover . . .

- the major types of economic activities in sub-Saharan Africa.
- the obstacles that face industrial development of Africa south of the Sahara.
- how colonialism hindered the growth of transportation and trade in sub-Saharan Africa.
- the most common form of mass communication in Africa south of the Sahara.

Key Terms

- cash crop
- commercial farming
- subsistence farming
- shifting farming
- sedentary farming

Identify and Locate

Transvaal, Dar es Salaam, Great Uhuru Railroad, Shaba Province

Johannesburg, South Africa

Although my family has an automobile, most South Africans use public transport. Because of the unnatural policies of apartheid, vast portions of the population have been forced to live far from their places of work. Over the years, the train and bus services have not been able to keep up with the demand. Mini-bus taxis have become a major form of transport.

Maurice R. DeVries

Maurice DeVries describes recent advances in transportation in South Africa. He notes it is one area of life in sub-Saharan Africa that has undergone change in recent years. Likewise, Lydiah Macharia and her family in Kenya are coping with new situations. In Kikuyu tradition, Lydiah Macharia's father will leave his tea plantation to his sons. He broke with tradition, however, when he encouraged his daughters to follow careers. Two of Lydiah's sisters became doctors. Lydiah works as a labor manager for a railroad and has used her earnings to buy land in the Great Rift Valley.

HUMAN/ENVIRONMENT INTERACTION

Agriculture

Lydiah Macharia hired several workers to till her land. She grows tea—one of Kenya's leading exports. Although Kenya is more industrialized than most nations in Africa south of the Sahara, its economy still relies on agriculture from which most Kenyans earn their living.

Colonial Legacy

Most African nations still suffer from the economies created by colonial rule, which

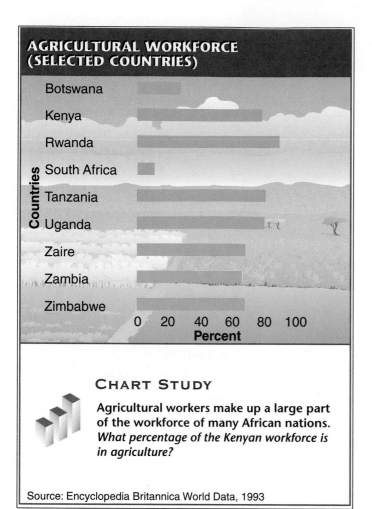

AGRICULTURAL WORKFORCE (SELECTED COUNTRIES)

Botswana
Kenya
Rwanda
South Africa
Tanzania
Uganda
Zaire
Zambia
Zimbabwe

0 20 40 60 80 100
Percent

Countries

CHART STUDY

Agricultural workers make up a large part of the workforce of many African nations. *What percentage of the Kenyan workforce is in agriculture?*

Source: Encyclopedia Britannica World Data, 1993

Despite their small number, commercial farms provide the bulk of cash crops in sub-Saharan Africa. The plantations that dot the region produce almost 75 percent of the world's palm oil, 80 percent of the peanuts, 75 percent of the cacao, and 66 percent of the world's sisal—a vegetable fiber used for making rope.

Most sub-Saharan Africans work at **subsistence farming**, or agriculture that provides just for the needs of a family or village. Some peoples, such as the Maasai, practice nomadic herding. Others support themselves by **shifting farming**, a method in which farmers move every one to three years to find better soil. Yet other farmers depend on **sedentary farming**, or farming conducted at permanent settlements. All farmers face problems caused by overgrazing, exhausted soil, and a lack of technology.

The region's population is booming, and the majority of people lack the technology to increase food production. Chemical fertilizers and farm machinery would help boost crop yields, yet few nations can afford these aids to cultivation. Hunger has become a fact of life for countless subsistence farmers.

they have tried to balance since gaining independence. Europeans used sub-Saharan Africa as a resource base. As a result, sub-Saharan Africans produced only one or two **cash crops**, or crops grown for a profit.

Ghana still depends heavily on the sale of cacao. Burundi depends on coffee. Such reliance on one product is filled with risks. An unfavorable growing season or a drop in prices on the world market can adversely affect a nation's entire economy.

Farming Methods

Only a few people work at **commercial farming**, or farming organized as a business. Most plantations that produce crops for export are owned, at least in part, by companies outside the region.

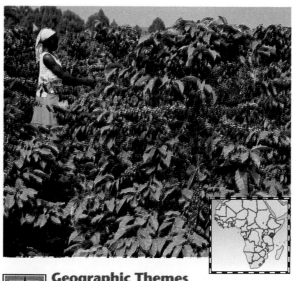

Geographic Themes

Human/Environment Interaction: East Africa

Coffee, grown on plantations, is one of the most important agricultural products of East Africa. *Why is coffee considered a cash crop?*

Forests and Seas

Forests cover almost 25 percent of Africa. These forests yield many valuable hardwood trees—Rhodesian teak, ebony, African walnut, and rosewood. Transportation systems and capital, however, are needed to develop a lumber industry. Currently, only coastal nations with rain forests export much lumber, accounting for less than 10 percent of the world's supply. The rain forests are also being cleared for farmland and fuel at an alarming rate. Their destruction has created a major environmental problem for the region and the world.

Commercial fishing has also developed slowly in sub-Saharan Africa. Few nations can afford to build fleets of ocean trawlers. The most profitable commercial fishing exists along the southwestern coast. Fish canned and exported from there include tuna, sardines, anchovies, and mackerel.

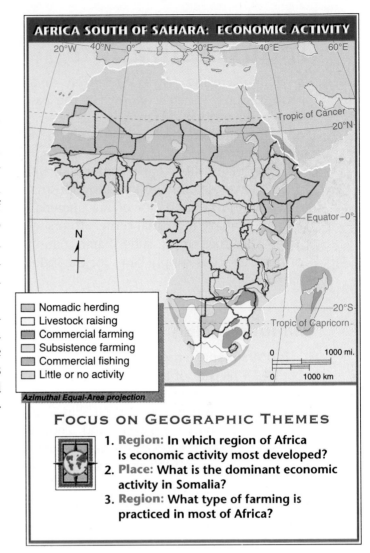

AFRICA SOUTH OF SAHARA: ECONOMIC ACTIVITY

Nomadic herding
Livestock raising
Commercial farming
Subsistence farming
Commercial fishing
Little or no activity

Azimuthal Equal-Area projection

FOCUS ON GEOGRAPHIC THEMES

1. **Region:** In which region of Africa is economic activity most developed?
2. **Place:** What is the dominant economic activity in Somalia?
3. **Region:** What type of farming is practiced in most of Africa?

Mining

Mining is an important—and difficult—economic activity in the region. Miners cope with hazardous conditions, long hours, and time away from their families.

Despite the risks thousands of black South Africans work in the mines. Their wages help support families in impoverished rural areas.

South Africa boasts a fortune of mineral wealth. A gold deposit more than 300 miles (483 km) long arcs across the Transvaal, a grassy plateau. It accounts for almost half of the world's known reserves of gold. South Africa is also a world leader in the production of gem diamonds, platinum, and minerals such as chromium, vanadium, and manganese.

South Africa's mineral wealth has made it one of the richest nations in the region, with a 1992 gross domestic product (GDP) of almost $115 billion. Most profits, however, have gone to foreign investors or companies owned by white South Africans. Little money has trickled down to black South Africans. This has caused wide gaps in the standard of living. In the late 1980s, for example, black South Africans earned a yearly per capita income of $1,467 compared to $7,276 enjoyed by white South Africans.

Resources are not spread evenly over the region, causing economic imbalances and overdependence on a single resource. Most deposits lie along the Atlantic coast and south of the Equator. Guinea has one of the world's largest deposits of bauxite, Zaire has large quantities of diamonds and important copper, and Nigeria has huge reserves of oil. Nigeria is the only sub-Saharan member of the Organization of Petroleum Exporting Countries (OPEC).

Industrialization

Manufacturing plays a relatively small role in Africa's economy. In the past, colonial rulers obtained raw materials in Africa for their home industries and left Africa industrially undeveloped.

Today many sub-Saharan nations, such as Nigeria, have used foreign loans to industrialize. Despite an abundance of raw materials, few nations have industrial centers to process them. Therefore, most sub-Saharan nations continue to act as supply bases for the industrial world.

Manufacturing

In 1993 manufacturing accounted for only about 14.4 percent of the region's entire GDP. Manufacturing, however, contributed between 38 and 44 percent of the GDP in South Africa, Swaziland, Zimbabwe, and Zambia. This was offset by the low industrial outputs of Uganda (7.4 percent), Niger (7 percent), and Guinea (less than 1 percent).

Geographic Themes

Movement: Southern Africa
Since independence, African countries have worked to improve means of transportation. *Why have landlocked countries sought to build railroads and pipelines?*

Obstacles

Obstacles to industrialization include a lack of capital, political turmoil between or within nations, and not enough skilled workers or transportation systems. The region's great hydroelectric potential also remains largely untapped.

Such conditions have forced much of Africa south of the Sahara into a cycle of poverty. Nations spend scarce revenues on feeding an ever-growing population and rely heavily on trade with industrial nations, such as the United States, Japan, and the colonial powers of Europe.

To break this dependency, some nations have attempted to form regional trading associations such as the Economic Community of West African States (ECOWAS). Others have acted on their own. For example, Nigeria has tried to further its economic growth by lifting taxes on goods shipped by landlocked nations to its ports.

Transportation and Communication

Efforts by sub-Saharan Africa to develop good transportation or communication systems have not been highly successful. Outside of cities, few paved roads exist. In rural areas travelers have to search for telephones and often must use long-wave radio transmitters. Railway and airplane travel are the most successful means of spanning the region.

Railroad Travel

Each day trains traveling the Kenya National Railroad leave Nairobi for coastal cities such as Mombasa. The 12-hour journey is considered one of the world's great train rides.

This world-famous railroad was built by the British before Kenyan independence. It spans the rugged terrain that separates the highlands from the coast to allow hauling of raw materials to port. Other colonial powers built railroads for the same purpose.

Improving Transportation

Since independence, many obstacles have hindered efforts to improve transportation. Wars and lack of funds have caused a decline of existing highways and railroads. The region's size and unfavorable terrain have made it difficult to build new routes. The region also has few harbors and navigable rivers.

For most nations air travel has overcome geographic barriers. Government-owned airlines have set up international and domestic service. International airports are found in Addis Ababa, Ethiopia; Nairobi, Kenya; Johannesburg, South Africa; and Dakar, Senegal.

Landlocked nations have also sought ground routes to coastal ports. Oil is transported through pipelines across Tanzania, Zambia, Sudan, South Africa, and Nigeria.

To transport freight, several nations have built railroads. The most successful is the Great Uhuru (Tanzam) Railroad. It connects the mineral-rich Shaba Province in southeastern Zaire to Dar es Salaam, Tanzania, a distance of about 1,153 miles (1,855 km). Many other overland routes, however, have been stopped or closed by warfare or a lack of funds.

Mass Communications

The scarcity of newsprint and the low literacy rates have limited the number of newspapers and magazines printed in the region south of the Sahara. Telephone service also is limited with the most extensive systems found in urban areas. In Chad only 1 out of every 1,114 people has access to a telephone. Even in Kenya, telephones average only about 1 per every 96 people.

The most effective means of communication in sub-Saharan Africa is radio. In Kenya, 1 out of 6 people owns a radio. In Chad, 1 out of 4.3 people owns one. Most important news is broadcast over the radio.

Television broadcasting, however, has grown slowly. Television stations offer a variety of programs, including popular reruns from the United States. Although televisions remain confined largely to urban areas, some governments are experimenting with television as an educational tool.

Geographic Themes

Region: Nigeria
Factories in Nigeria produce a wide variety of goods. Manufacturing, however, employs only a small number of Nigerians. *What percent of Africa's GDP comes from manufacturing?*

SECTION 1 REVIEW

Checking for Understanding
1. **Define** cash crop, commercial farming, subsistence farming, shifting farming, sedentary farming.
2. **Locating Places** Why do few transportation networks link sub-Saharan Africa as a region?
3. **Human/Environment Interaction** What are the most common forms of agricultural production in Africa south of the Sahara?
4. **Region** Why do sub-Saharan Africans share unequally in the region's mineral wealth?

Critical Thinking
5. **Expressing Problems Clearly** What are the most critical obstacles facing economic development in Africa south of the Sahara?

CASE STUDY

MOVING TO LAGOS

Hundreds of millions of Africans are lurching between an unworkable Western present and a collapsing African past . . . they [must] sort out new connections with their families, their tribes, and their countries.

Blain Harden, "Nigeria: Africa's Great Black Hope," *World Monitor,* August 1990

Lagos, Nigeria's capital, is the country's financial hub and headquarters of western European businesses in the country.

Factories in Lagos turn out a wide variety of items including foodstuffs, beverages, paint, soaps, textiles, and parts for auto assembly. Much of the wealth that comes from the country's petroleum, tin, coal, and iron resources is concentrated in Lagos.

THE ISSUE

Every year Lagos attracts thousands of people, mostly rural farmers, from the Nigerian countryside. To them, the city promises employment and a better way of life.

Since the 1960s, the population of Lagos has almost tripled—from a little less than 500,000 to about 8 million in the early 1990s.

This overwhelming population growth presents grim challenges for Lagos, as well as for thousands of displaced rural Africans.

THE BACKGROUND

In the mid-1960s, petroleum reserves were discovered along Nigeria's coast. During the next decade, oil exports brought a period of rapid economic growth to the country. Lagos took on the atmosphere of a boomtown.

As Lagos boomed, however, agriculture declined. Severe droughts in the early 1970s reduced crop production drastically. Many migrants from rural areas flocked to the city, hoping to improve their standard of living. At the time Lagos's businesses required more workers, both skilled and unskilled. Hundreds of thousands profited from the petroleum earnings.

Then, in the early 1980s, the oil bubble burst. World demand for petroleum dropped sharply as consumers in Western nations reacted to foreign oil prices by introducing energy conservation programs. Nigeria's foreign earnings from oil dropped also. The country's foreign debt increased; Lagos's factories slowed production or

stopped altogether for lack of imported raw materials.

Thousands of workers lost their jobs and could not find others. Agriculture was depressed even further. During the mid- and late-1980s, more and more farmers found they could not support themselves, and joined the thousands seeking work in Lagos.

This overwhelming population growth presents grim challenges for Lagos, as well as for thousands of displaced rural Africans.

Slum dwellings sprang up along the outskirts of Lagos. Unemployment was high, and the crime rate increased. In addition, agricultural production further decreased as farmers left their lands to find work in the city. By the early 1990s, Lagos was overwhelmed by an economy gone sour and a population that had tripled.

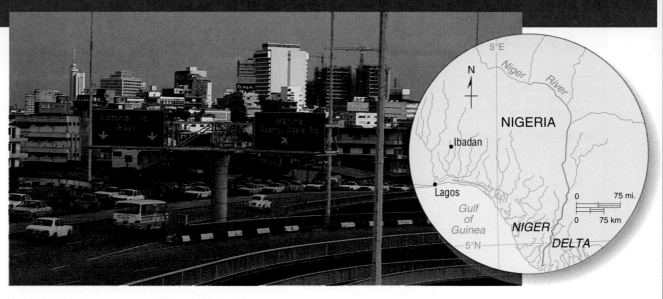

Lagos is Nigeria's chief port. High-rise buildings and overcrowded residential areas dominate the city's landscape.

THE POINTS OF VIEW

Many African leaders say that Lagos's overpopulation is part of a larger problem, that of the loss of Nigeria's traditional society. Nigeria's economic success has weakened the traditional agricultural society. Books and newspapers promoting opportunities in the cities are readily available. Even those who do not migrate to the city are becoming antagonistic to old values.

Others point out that Nigeria's population is increasing so rapidly that none of the economic gains since the 1960s could possibly keep pace. They add that a belief in a large family is one that is held in common by many of Nigeria's ethnic groups. Large families are no longer economically necessary, say these experts, yet the government has done little to develop family planning.

THE ISSUE TODAY

Overpopulation in Lagos remains a serious problem. Overcrowding has led to poor housing, a lack of good water and sanitation, and shortages of electricity and other public services. Such conditions also increase already poor health problems due to mosquitos, which breed in the city's many ponds and swampy areas. In addition, the ponds have long been used as garbage dumps, and both the land and water have become polluted.

The national government has begun water reclamation projects, and educational facilities are expanding. The government has also developed agricultural cooperatives and better markets for local surpluses. More money has been made available for investment in agriculture.

Nigerian leaders agree, however, that the runaway growth of Lagos and the country's other cities is linked directly to a loss of village life. They believe many Nigerians are torn between the old way of life and the hurried and often unrewarding pursuit of Western goals. Nigerian statesman Olusagan Obasanjo voices the hope of many Africans: "I believe that for us in Africa, our salvation lies in our own hands and nowhere else. Only we can be the architects of our future; as we have been the architects of our misfortune by and large for the past quarter of a century."

Reviewing the Case

1. What events contributed to the overpopulation in Lagos?
2. **Human/Environment**

   Interaction What are some problems Lagos faces because of overpopulation?

2 People and Their Environment

SETTING THE SCENE

Read to Discover . . .
- how hunger in Africa south of the Sahara is related to human interaction with the environment.
- the reasons many plants and animals in the region face destruction.
- the efforts sub-Saharan Africans have taken to offset decades of famine and war.

Key Terms
- desertification
- deforestation
- extinction
- habitat
- poaching
- ecotourism

Identify and Locate
Somalia, Horn of Africa, Madagascar, Serengeti Plain, Sahel

In late 1992 a Somalian woman named Muslima Aden Abdulrahman watched her mother and daughter die. A few days later, her 7-year-old son died. Muslima told a reporter:

———— ✦ ————

I have buried all my family. Almost everyone from my village is dead. I have no more tears left.

———— ✦ ————

Within weeks Muslima also died. Like her mother and children, she starved to death. Between 1991 and 1993, more than 350,000 Somalians suffered the same fate. In recent times similar stories have come out of other nations south of the Sahara. Since the 1970s, starvation and poverty have become all too familiar experiences for millions of nomadic herders and subsistence farmers of the region.

PLACE

The Shadow of Famine

The causes of famine in sub-Saharan Africa are complex and varied. As you have read, a booming population, a lack of capital, and overdependence on cash crops all contribute to food shortages. Two other factors also rob millions of sub-Saharan Africans of food—expansion of the desert and civil war.

Desertification

In the past 100 years, a band of desert more than 93 miles (150 km) wide has crept into the countries of Mauritania, Mali, Niger, Chad, and Sudan. Humans have been largely responsible for the **desertification**, or the transformation of arable land into desert, in the Sahel. Overgrazing, overplanting, and destruction of trees have left the land dangerously exposed to erosion.

A series of recent droughts have added to the misery. Two droughts in the Sahel—one from 1968 to the early 1970s and one in the early 1980s—turned farmland into wasteland. They wiped out nearly half the area's cattle. As the 1990s began, the United Nations Food and Agriculture Organization (FAO) reported 20 million people were on the brink of starvation.

Civil War

From the 1970s into the 1990s, civil war has been among the biggest human causes of famine on the Horn of Africa, the eastern bulge of land that juts into the Indian Ocean. Here political upheavals combined with droughts to create widespread suffering. Food became a weapon as rival factions battled each other in Sudan, Eritrea, Ethiopia, and Somalia. Armies burned the fields of suspected enemies. Relief agencies such as the Red Cross sent in food, only to see up to half of it stolen by rebels or corrupt warlords.

Starvation and bloodshed created millions of refugees. Famine and disease swept through many refugee camps. The situation became so critical in Somalia that the United Nations intervened in 1992. Led by 25,000 troops from the United States, the United Nations sent in a peacekeeping force made up of units from 22 nations. Armed with guns and food, the soldiers tried to stop rival warlords from interrupting food shipments to a starving nation.

PLACE

Battling Hunger

To combat hunger sub-Saharan Africans have focused on 2 tasks—restoring their battered environment and keeping the peace. The examples of Ethiopia and Eritrea show how these efforts have borne fruit. For almost 30 years, rebellion tore Ethiopia apart. For equally as long, Eritrea fought to break free of Ethiopia. At the beginning of the 1990s, the guns quieted in both nations as Eritrea finally gained its independence. As farmers went

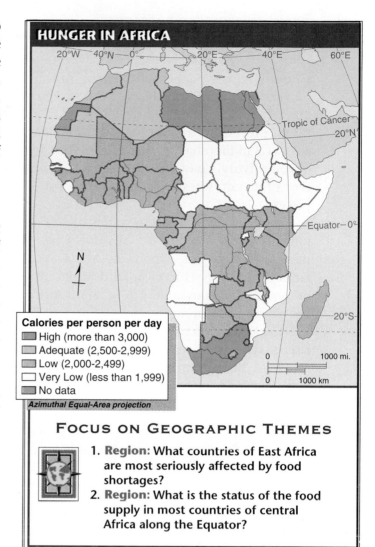

HUNGER IN AFRICA

Calories per person per day
- High (more than 3,000)
- Adequate (2,500-2,999)
- Low (2,000-2,499)
- Very Low (less than 1,999)
- No data

Azimuthal Equal-Area projection

FOCUS ON GEOGRAPHIC THEMES

1. **Region:** What countries of East Africa are most seriously affected by food shortages?
2. **Region:** What is the status of the food supply in most countries of central Africa along the Equator?

back to their land, they sought to undo the damage of drought and war.

To stop erosion, farmers in the northern Ethiopian province of Tigray terraced more than 250,000 acres (about 101,250 ha) of land. They also planted 42 million seedlings, or young trees, to hold soil in place. Using hand tools, they built earthen dams to store precious rain water. In 1992 fields in Tigray bloomed with crops such as barley, wheat, and a local grain called teff. In neighboring Eritrea farmers produced such abundant crops that the government reduced its requests for relief in 1993 by 50 percent.

The success of Ethiopia and Eritrea have held out hope for other nations. A sense of self-respect has returned. "We can make a good life," explained one Eritrean farmer with quiet pride. "All we need is rain and peace."

Saving the Forests

South of the Sahel, sub-Saharan Africans face another struggle. As this century draws to a close, the region is losing its tropical rain forests at a rate of about 3.2 million acres (1.3 million ha) per year. Since 1900 Côte d'Ivoire (Ivory Coast) has lost almost 70 percent of its rain forest. Madagascar has lost 75 percent.

Causes of **deforestation**, or destruction of forests, vary. Côte d'Ivoire cuts down many hardwood trees for export. In Madagascar, farmers burn forests to clear land for farming or grazing. Throughout sub-Saharan Africa, people cut trees for fuel.

The destruction of rain forests in Africa and elsewhere in the world has created a global problem. Plants turn carbon dioxide (CO_2) into oxygen. As the rain forests are destroyed, the amount of CO_2 rises. This gas allows the sun's rays to reach the earth. Carbon dioxide also holds in much more heat than oxygen. As a result, deforestation has very likely made the planet hotter, affecting growing seasons, rainfall patterns, and sea levels.

Destruction of the rain forests has also placed many plant and animal species at risk. Of the 200,000 plant and animal species on Madagascar, almost three-fourths exist nowhere else in the world. Deforestation is also the reason more than 20 animal species on Madagascar face **extinction**, or disappearance, from the earth.

Conflicts Over Land Use

Protection of rain forests and endangered wildlife have raised difficult questions about land use. As the population of Africa south of the Sahara grows, nomadic herders and farmers have increasingly cut into forests. They have also pushed onto savanna grasslands that provide homes to Africa's huge herds of game. The lands on which these herds thrive are the same lands needed to feed and house Africa's people.

At the beginning of the 1970s, almost 70,000 black rhinos roamed across sub-Saharan Africa. By the early 1990s, only about 3,000 could be found. Other endangered animals included the African elephant, Cape Mountain zebra, and mountain gorilla.

Such animals are endangered for a number of reasons. First, humans have pushed into the animals' natural **habitats,** or living areas. Second, in recent decades hunters in greater numbers have tracked down game for sport and profit. The rhino and elephant have suffered heavily from **poaching,** or illegal hunting. Rhino horns and ivory from elephant tusks bring high prices on the world market.

To save endangered species, some nations have created huge game preserves, such as Tanzania's Serengeti National Park, Kenya's Masai Mara, or Rwanda's Parcs des Volcans.

WILDLIFE RESERVES (SELECTED COUNTRIES)

Countries (top to bottom): Botswana, Kenya, Rwanda, South Africa, Tanzania, Uganda, Zaire, Zambia, Zimbabwe

Percent axis: 0 2 4 6 8 10 12 14 16

CHART STUDY

African nations are increasingly setting aside land as wildlife reserves, thus maintaining part of their heritage. *Which nations have preserved 10 percent or more of their land as reserves?*

![compass icon] **Geographic Themes**

Human/Environment Interaction: Madagascar Rain Forest
Many rare plant and animal species thrive in the rain forests of Madagascar, an island off the coast of southeast Africa. *What development poses a threat to their existence?*

These preserves lure millions of tourists into East Africa every year. **Ecotourism**, or tourism based on the environment, brought more than $420 million into Kenya in 1989 alone.

Despite the profits earned from such preserves, many sub-Saharan Africans object to them. "People are too desperate," explained one park official. "They need food in their stomach." To win support for conservation, governments have tried to give rural peoples an economic stake in the preserves. Zimbabwe and Zambia, for example, use money from ecotourism to build local clinics and schools.

We have to go back to the year 1500 [prior to colonialism], where we left off building an African economy, able to produce its own food, its own tools, its own weapons. . . . In short, we have to rely on ourselves.

REGION

Toward the Future

In the 1950s and 1960s, sub-Saharan Africans won political independence. In the 2000s, their foremost task will be to win economic independence.

As sub-Saharan Africans look ahead to the next century, they are searching for ways to take charge of the region. Most agree that the time has come to shake off foreign dependency. In late 1992 Ugandan President Yoweri Museveni issued a challenge to the region:

SECTION 2 REVIEW

Checking for Understanding
1. **Define** desertification, deforestation, extinction, habitat, poaching, ecotourism.
2. **Locating Places** How has growth of the desert affected life in the Sahel?
3. **Region** What was the connection between civil war and the famines of the 1980s?
4. **Human/Environment Interaction** What steps have sub-Saharan Africans taken to preserve the environment?

Critical Thinking
5. **Identifying Central Issues** What is the central issue involved in the debate over the creation of game preserves?

MAP & GRAPH SKILLS

Reading a Land-Use Map

In an earlier chapter, you learned that vegetation maps describe the natural plant life in different environments. Few places on the earth, however, are still untouched by the economic activities of humans. A **land-use map** illustrates how humans use land and other natural resources to make a living.

REVIEWING THE SKILL

Like other maps, land-use maps employ colors and symbols to represent various human uses of the land. The map key describes the meaning of each color and symbol on the map. Usually, colors show general activities such as crop farming, herding, ranching, and forestry. Symbols or labels often identify more particular kinds of information. For example, a color may show farming activities over a broad region, while a label or symbol may name the most important crop in that region.

To interpret a land-use map, first read the title and the key to identify the region and activities illustrated in the map. Then find examples of each color and symbol on the map. By comparing a land-use map with a climate or vegetation map, you can see how humans have used the natural environment and how the environment has influenced the economic development of the region.

To read a land-use map, apply the following steps:

- Read the map title to identify the region shown on the map.
- Using the map key, identify the various land uses shown on the map.
- Determine which economic activities take place in each area of the region. Look for areas where similar activities occur.
- Compare a land-use map with a climate or vegetation map to draw conclusions about how natural conditions have affected human activities.

PRACTICING THE SKILL

Use the land-use map of Africa to answer the following questions:

1. What color represents commercial farming?

2. What do the following symbols represent?

3. Which part of Africa includes ranches? What animals are raised on these ranches?

4. What minerals are found in southern Africa?

5. Which part of sub-Saharan Africa has petroleum reserves?

For additional practice in this skill, see Practicing Skills on page 464 of the Chapter 22 Review.

AFRICA SOUTH OF SAHARA: LAND USE

Minerals
- ♨ Coal
- ⚒ Petroleum
- I Iron ore
- ☯ Manganese
- ✎ Copper
- ▼ Tin
- ❇ Uranium
- ▲ Cobalt
- ◈ Diamonds
- ◿ Gold

Economic
- ░ Nomadic herding
- ☐ Livestock raising
- ▓ Commercial farming
- ☐ Subsistence farming
- ▒ Commercial fishing
- ░ Little or no activity

SECTION	KEY TERMS	SUMMARY
1 **Living in Africa South of the Sahara**	cash crop (p. 452) commercial farming (p. 452) subsistence farming (p. 452) shifting farming (p. 452) sedentary farming (p. 452)	• Most sub-Saharan nations depend on the export of one or two cash crops. • The majority of sub-Saharan Africans work as subsistence farmers. • Mineral deposits, as well as the profits from their export, are spread unevenly throughout Africa south of the Sahara. • Industrialization is hindered by a lack of capital and a shortage of skilled workers. • To reduce foreign dependence some nations are developing regional trade and transportation systems.

Coffee plantation in Kenya

SECTION	KEY TERMS	SUMMARY
2 **People and Their Environment** A lemur in the Madagascar rain forest	desertification (p. 458) deforestation (p. 460) extinction (p. 460) habitat (p. 460) poaching (p. 460) ecotourism (p. 461)	• Desertification, drought, and war have contributed to hunger in sub-Saharan Africa. • In the 1990s Ethiopia and Eritrea took steps to restore their battered environment. • Destruction of the rain forests is a global problem. • Increasing human population and hunting has placed some African wildlife at risk of extinction. • To win rural support of game preserves, some nations have shared the profits of ecotourism. • As sub-Saharan Africans head into the next century, they hope to win economic independence.

Reviewing Key Terms

Choose the vocabulary term that best completes each of the sentences below. Write your answers on a separate sheet of paper.

cash crops (p. 452)
commercial farming (p. 452)
subsistence farming (p. 452)
shifting farming (p. 452)
desertification (p. 458)
deforestation (p. 460)
extinction (p. 460)
habitat (p. 460)
poaching (p. 460)
ecotourism (p. 461)

SECTION 1

1. Crops raised and sold for a profit are known as _____ .
2. _____ supports the needs of an individual family or village.
3. Farmers who practice _____ move often to more fertile soil.
4. Farming established as an organized business is _____ .

SECTION 2

5. _____ threatens to destroy the rain forests.
6. The illegal hunting of endangered animals is known as _____ .
7. Tourism based on the environment is known as _____ .
8. An animal's living area is its _____ .
9. The disappearance of a plant or animal from the earth is _____ .
10. Transforming arable land into desert is _____ .

Reviewing Facts

SECTION 1

11. What are the key cash crops exported from this region?
12. What factors have discouraged a lumber industry in Africa?

13. What economic imbalances affect mining in sub-Saharan Africa?
14. Why has this region been slow to industrialize?
15. How did colonialism affect transportation in Africa?
16. Why is radio the most effective form of mass communication?

SECTION 2

17. Why did the United Nations intervene in Somalia in 1992?
18. What are some of the causes of deforestation in the region?
19. How have some rural farmers conserved the region's wildlife?

Critical Thinking

20. **Making Generalizations**   How has political instability in Africa south of the Sahara contributed to its lack of capital?
21. **Analyzing Information**   Based on the quote by Yoweri Museveni on page 461, what is one leading cause of current economic problems?

Geographic Themes

22. **Region**   What economic traits do many nations of sub-Saharan Africa share?
23. **Human/Environment Interaction** How has the human population boom affected the region's wildlife?

Practicing Skills

Reading a Land-Use Map
   Refer to the land-use map on page 462.
24. Compare the land-use map with the climate map on page 425. Do herding and livestock ranching take place in drier or wetter regions? Explain why.
25. Where in Africa does Mediterranean agriculture take place? Explain why.

Using the Unit Atlas

Refer to the physical geography section of the Unit Atlas on pages 412–413.

26. What natural resources are mined in Zambia?
27. What country is the world's largest producer of gold and gem diamonds?

Projects

Individual Activity

You learned about the effects of drought and civil war on Somalia. Using the *Readers' Guide to Periodical Literature,* research Somalia after the 1992 arrival of UN troops. Write a news story about your findings and post it.

Cooperative Learning Activity

Working in groups, research endangered animals in Africa south of the Sahara. Consult a variety of resources and present your findings on an outline map.

Writing About Geography

Argumentation

Review text material and your journal notes about the debate over creation of African game preserves. Put yourself in the place of a government official of Kenya, Tanzania, or Rwanda. Decide whether more or less land should be set aside for big game. Present your arguments as you would to a group of subsistence farmers.

Locating Places

AFRICA SOUTH OF THE SAHARA: PHYSICAL/POLITICAL GEOGRAPHY

Match the letters on the map with the places and physical features of Africa south of the Sahara. Write your answers on a separate sheet of paper.

1. Mauritania
2. Nigeria
3. Madagascar
4. Eritrea
5. Côte d'Ivoire
6. Sudan
7. Zambia
8. Nairobi
9. Dar es Salaam
10. Somalia

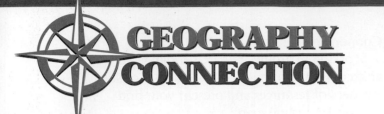
Africa South of the Sahara and the United States

THE BEAT GOES ON

Strong *rhythms form the core of African music—the music of the peoples who live south of the Sahara. Strong African rhythms beat through many kinds of American music, enriching our musical heritage.*

◀ **SPIRITUALS** were the earliest American music with an African rhythm. Deeply emotional religious songs, spirituals developed in the southern United States among enslaved Africans who added the rhythms of their lost homeland to southern biblical preaching. Spirituals became famous worldwide after the 1870s, when Nashville's Fisk University Jubilee Singers toured the United States and Europe. Today spirituals, such as "Swing Low, Sweet Chariot," "Go Down, Moses," and "Deep River," are standards of American music.

CALYPSO AND REGGAE ▶
were two forms of African-based music that entered the United States by way of the Caribbean. During the 1950s calypso, with its lively African rhythm, lilting melody, and island dialects, became popular. Reggae, which developed in the 1960s in Jamaica, combines the African beat with Jamaican folk music and American blues and soul. The Jamaican performer Bob Marley made reggae a hit in the United States during the 1970s.

◀ **RAGTIME AND DIXIELAND** arose out of blues and jazz in the early 1900s. Jazz quartets led to big band jazz in the 1920s. In 1932, bandleader Duke Ellington introduced "swing," jazz with an easy-going, relaxed rhythm. The "boogie woogie" beat also appeared in the 1930s.

ROCK 'N' ROLL ▶

made its entry in the mid-1950s when blues composer and singer Chuck Berry heightened the beat and turned out a new sound. Rock and roll led on through soul of the late 1960s and heavy metal of the 1970s. From the 1970s and into the 1990s, the African beat exploded into the insistent recurring rhythmic pattern of rap.

▼ **BLUES AND JAZZ** became popular after 1900. Blues is a highly creative personal statement, a musical response to an experience or circumstances of life. Like blues, jazz is also a highly creative musical form, because it allows the performer complete freedom to invent and vary a piece of music as it is played.

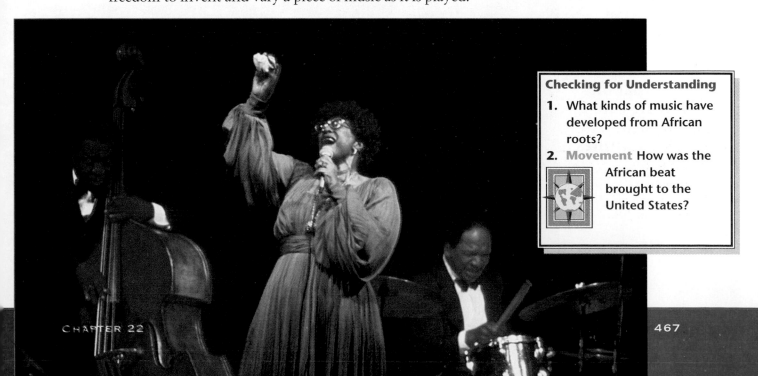

Checking for Understanding

1. What kinds of music have developed from African roots?
2. **Movement** How was the African beat brought to the United States?

South Asia

GeoJournal Activity

While you are studying about South Asia, keep a journal of recent developments in the region. Organize the material in your journal into the following categories: Physical Geography, Cultures and Lifestyles, Economy and Environment.

Picturing the World

Sherpa porters and their yaks help launch another expedition in the lofty peaks of the Himalaya range in Nepal. The world's highest mountain range, the Himalaya extend for some 1,500 miles (2,410 km) to form the northern boundary of South Asia. Look at the map on page 472.

1. What is the name and elevation of the highest peak in the Himalaya?
2. What is the highest peak in the world?
3. Now read about the people of Nepal on page 492. Where did the ancestors of the Sherpa and other Nepalese originally come from?
4. What event made the Sherpa famous worldwide?

Picture Atlas CD-ROM Enrichment Corner

South Asia has one of the highest concentrations of people and one of the most diverse populations in the world. Create a file on the religions and languages of the six countries in South Asia. (See the *Picture Atlas of the World* User's Guide on how to use the Collector button.) Read the essays, research the vital statistics, and listen to the spoken languages. Gather items from many parts of the CD-ROM and create an electronic report to explain the complex ethnic patterns of South Asia.

SOUTH ASIA
Cultural Geography

EXPLORING CULTURAL DIVERSITY

1. *What areas of South Asia are most heavily populated? Most sparsely populated?*
2. *What nations make up South Asia?*

A well-known myth of the **Himalayas** tells of the Abominable Snowman, a beast with a large apelike body and a human face.

SOUTH ASIA: POLITICAL

The state of **Kashmir** has been the scene of a Muslim-Hindu struggle since 1947.

India's people speak 14 major languages and hundreds of regional dialects.

— National boundary
⊛ National capital
Lambert Conic projection

Sri Lanka, which means "resplendent land," is home to Buddhist Sinhalese and Hindu Tamils. Continuing bitter relations between the two groups have caused much turmoil on the beautiful island.

Until 1971 **Bangladesh** was the eastern part of Pakistan. Following a short civil war, the nation declared its independence and changed its name.

SOUTH ASIA: POPULATION DENSITY

Per sq. km — **Per sq. mi.**
Over 100 — Over 250
50-100 — 125-250
25-50 — 60-125
1-25 — 2-60
Under 1 — Under 2
Uninhabited — Uninhabited

Cities
- 5,000,000 to 10,000,000
- 2,000,000 to 5,000,000
- 1,000,000 to 2,000,000
- Under 1,000,000

Lambert Conic projection

During the 1970s and 1980s, **India's** population increased by about 14 million every year. Overpopulation has caused serious overcrowding.

About three-fourths of all **Sri Lankans** live in rural agricultural villages.

Most of **Bhutan's** population live in the fertile valleys that run north and south among the country's mountain ranges.

Bangladesh has a high birthrate and a relatively small area, resulting in a population density of about 2,320 per square mile (895/sq. km). More than 85 percent of the people are rural farmers.

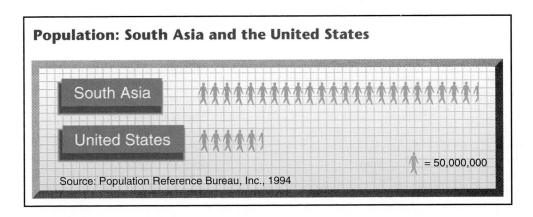

Population: South Asia and the United States

South Asia

United States

= 50,000,000

Source: Population Reference Bureau, Inc., 1994

South Asia has more than four times as many people as the United States.

Physical Geography

The Himalayas are a system of parallel mountain ranges extending in a 1,500-mile (2,410-km) curve across southern Asia.

India is a huge peninsula separated from the Asian mainland by the Himalayas.

The continental USA is about one and a half times larger than **South Asia**.

SOUTH ASIA: PHYSICAL FEATURES

60°E
70°E
80°E
90°E

HINDU KUSH

GODWIN AUSTEN PEAK (K-2) 28,251 ft. (8,611 m)

N

Indus River

30°N

HIMALAYAS

MOUNT EVEREST 29,028 ft. (8,848 m)

THAR DESERT

Ganges

River

Brahmaputra River

GANGES PLAIN

Tropic of Cancer

Narmada River

Arabian Sea

20°N

Delta of the Ganges

DECCAN PLATEAU

Bay of Bengal

ELEVATIONS
Feet   Meters
5,000   1,500
2,000   600
1,000   300
0   0

— National boundary
△ Mountain peak

Lambert Conic projection

WESTERN GHATS

EASTERN GHATS

Laccadive Islands

Andaman Islands

INDIAN OCEAN

10°N

Cape Comorin

Sri Lanka

Nicobar Islands

INDIAN OCEAN

Maldives

300 mi.

0   300 km

The country of the **Maldives** consists of about 1,200 coral islands, none of which cover more than 5 square miles (3 sq. km).

Bangladesh has the largest river delta in the world, where the Ganges and Brahmaputra rivers empty into the Indian Ocean.

SOUTH ASIA: NATURAL RESOURCES

ASIA

Nepal and **Bhutan** are both heavily forested. Nepal exports small amounts of timber from pine, oak, walnut, and poplar trees. Poplars also grow in Bhutan's forests, as do ash, oak, and willow.

PAKISTAN

NEPAL

BHUTAN

INDIA

Tropic of Cancer

BANGLADESH

Legend:
- ⚒ Petroleum
- 🝆 Natural Gas
- Coal
- ❋ Uranium
- I Iron ore
- ▲ Chromite

Lambert Conic projection

LACCADIVE ISLANDS (INDIA)

ANDAMAN ISLANDS (INDIA)

MALDIVES

SRI LANKA

NICOBAR ISLANDS (INDIA)

0   300 mi.
0   300 km

The dazzling array of tropical fish and coral formations in the clear, deep blue lagoons of the **Maldives** draw tourists from all over the world.

The Indus and its four tributaries are Pakistan's greatest natural resource, depositing fertile soil on the Punjab and Sind plains.

Sri Lanka is a leading rubber producer.

India's mica mines produce much of the world's supply.

South Asia: Physical Profile

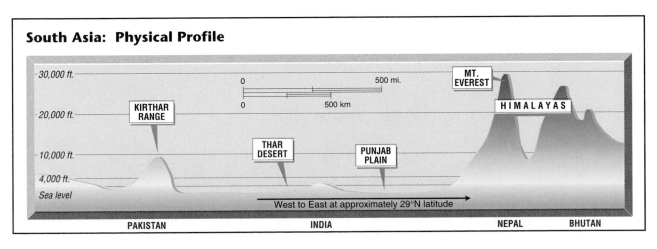

30,000 ft.

MT. EVEREST

0   500 mi.
0   500 km

KIRTHAR RANGE

20,000 ft.

HIMALAYAS

THAR DESERT

PUNJAB PLAIN

10,000 ft.

4,000 ft.

Sea level

West to East at approximately 29°N latitude

PAKISTAN   INDIA   NEPAL   BHUTAN

COUNTRY* AND CAPITAL	FLAG AND LANGUAGES	POPULATION	LANDMASS	PRINCIPAL PRODUCTS EXPORT	IMPORT
Bangladesh Dhaka	Bengali, Chakma	116,600,000 2,320 per sq. mi. 895 per sq. km	50,260 sq. mi. 130,173 sq. km	Garments	Yarns & Fabrics
Bhutan Thimphu	Dzongkha, Nepali and Tibetan dialects	800,000 44 per sq. mi. 17 per sq. km	18,150 sq. mi. 47,009 sq. km	Electricity	Petroleum
India New Delhi	Hindi, English,	919,900,000 801 per sq. mi. 309 per sq. km	1,147,950 sq. mi. 2,973,191 sq. km	Diamonds	Fuels
Maldives Male	Divehi	252,000 2,100 per sq. mi. 811 per sq. km	120 sq. mi. 311 sq. km	Clothing	Food
Nepal Kathmandu	Nepali	22,100,000 418 per sq. mi. 162 per sq. km	52,820 sq. mi. 136,804 sq. km	Food & Animals	Machinery
Pakistan Islamabad	Urdu, Punjabi, Sindhi, Pushtu	126,400,000 425 per sq. mi. 164 per sq. km	297,640 sq. mi. 770,888 sq. km	Textiles	Petroleum
Sri Lanka Colombo	Sinhalese, Tamil	17,900,000 717 per sq. mi. 277 per sq. km	24,950 sq. mi. 64,621 sq. km	Food & Animals	Machinery

*Country maps not drawn to scale.

◀ Beautiful frescoes line the walls of a Buddhist temple in Sri Lanka.

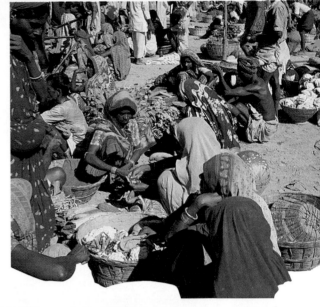

▲ Nepal's capital of Kathmandu has many outdoor markets in its traditional neighborhoods.

▼ The coasts of southern India and Sri Lanka are lined with beautiful beaches and tropical vegetation.

▲ Calcutta, India, is one of the busiest and most important port cities in Asia.

▼ India's Thar Desert receives about 10 inches (25 cm) of rain each year.

▼ This old luxury hotel reflects the architecture of the Raj, the era of British rule in India.

The Physical Geography of South Asia

CHAPTER FOCUS

Geographic Setting

South Asia includes the large, diamond-shaped peninsula that forms the southern part of the Asian continent. This peninsula is separated from the main part of Asia by the towering, snow-capped Himalayas, Karakorams, and the Hindu Kush.

Geographic Themes

Section 1 The Land

PLACE The river systems of South Asia form the world's largest continuous floodplain. These fertile valleys were home to one of the world's earliest civilizations and are still an area of great agricultural abundance.

▲ Photograph: *Mountain village in the Himalayas, Nepal*

Section 2 The Climate and Vegetation

LOCATION South Asia's climate and vegetation are strongly affected by seasonal winds. These winds bring the rains on which the region's farmers depend. Landforms, such as mountains and hills, have a powerful effect on where and how heavily the rains fall.

The Land

Laxmi chamari, Bangladesh

Assalamu - alaikum.
I am spending my vacation in the tiny village of Laxmi chamari. Now it is rainy season and the many rivers and marshy areas are filled to the brim. Every day I go out in a boat to enjoy the vast green paddy fields. The plants waver gracefully when the wind blows over them.
Md. Afsar Ali

A fsar Ali writes from Bangladesh, one of the seven countries that make up the culture region of South Asia. Separated by mountains from the rest of Asia, South Asia is often called a **subcontinent**, a landmass like a continent, only smaller. It is rimmed by three large bodies of water—the Arabian Sea to the west, the Indian Ocean to the south, and the Bay of Bengal to the east. The peninsula is about 1.7 million square miles (4.4 million sq. km), and almost 75 percent of this land belongs to India. The other nations of South Asia include Pakistan, which is located along the northwest edge of the peninsula, and the small kingdoms of Nepal and Bhutan, which are in the mountains of the northeast. Bangladesh lies at the head of the Bay of Bengal, and Sri Lanka and the Maldives are island nations south of the Indian subcontinent.

PLACE

Mountains and Plateaus

M ountains and plateaus dominate the far northern landscape of South Asia. They include some of the highest mountain ranges in the world.

The Himalayas

About 60 million years ago, when the earth's continents were still forming, a part of east Africa broke loose and began to drift slowly northward. When it rammed into Asia, the force of the collision caused the land to crumple up into a vast mountain range—the Himalayas. More than 1,000 miles (1,609 km) long and hundreds of miles wide, this range contains some of the highest mountains in the world, including jagged peaks on which the snow never melts. The most famous of these is Mount Everest, the world's highest peak, which rises to 29,028 feet (8,848 m) above sea level. A writer describes the awesome sight of the Himalayas in the following way:

To the north a deep tumult of swirling gray was all that could be seen of the Himalaya. At dusk, white egrets [birds] flapped across the sunken clouds, now black with rain; on earth, the dark had come. Then, 4 miles above these mud streets of the lowlands, at a point so high as to seem overhead, a luminous whiteness shown—the light of snows. Glaciers loomed. . . .

Other Northern Ranges

The Himalayas meet the Karakoram Mountains in the northernmost part of South Asia. Farther west, the mountains of the Hindu Kush complete the chain. Together, these northern ranges create a formidable barrier between the Indian subcontinent and the rest of Asia. In the past, invaders from the north could only enter the region through a few narrow passes. The mountain kingdoms of Bhutan and Nepal managed to remain isolated from the outside world until well into this century.

Vindhya Mountains

The Vindhya Mountains lie across the center of the Indian subcontinent. These mountains were also created by the shock of the collision between South Asia and the rest of the Asian continent. Although the Vindhya are not as lofty as the Himalayas, they separated the people of northern and southern India and contributed to the development of two very different cultures.

The Ghats and the Deccan Plateau

Forming a triangle at the base of the Indian peninsula are two chains of rugged hills and eroded mountains called the Eastern Ghats and the Western Ghats. Sandwiched between the Eastern and Western Ghats is the main tableland of South Asia—the Deccan Plateau. Here the hills are flat-topped and steep-sided. In the past, lava flowed over the plateau, creating rich, black soil. Because the coastal ranges keep the moisture-laden seasonal winds from reaching the interior, the Deccan Plateau is relatively arid.

Other Plateaus

In the northeastern part of the peninsula lies the Chota Nagpur Plateau, where the rounded hills are covered with forests of bamboo and teak. The other plateaus of South Asia include the stony tablelands that border the northwestern deserts and the humid Karnataka Plateau in the southwest, where herds of wild elephants range through dense rain forests.

Plains

Spreading between the Himalayas and the Deccan Plateau are South Asia's northern plains. Much of this vast lowland area is fertile farmland, watered by the region's three great river systems. As a result, most of South Asia's population lives on these plains.

PLACE

Major River Systems

High in the Himalayas are the sources of South Asia's three great river systems: the Indus, the Brahmaputra, and the Ganges. The

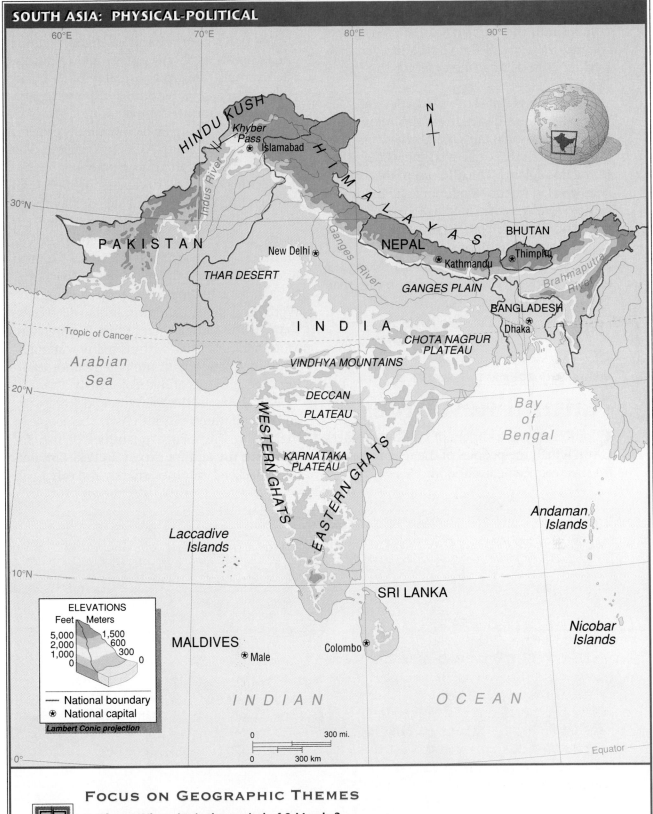

HINDU KUSH

Khyber
Pass

⊛ Islamabad

HIMALAYAS

Indus River

PAKISTAN

BHUTAN

NEPAL
⊛ Kathmandu
⊛ Thimphu

New Delhi ⊛

Ganges River

THAR DESERT

GANGES PLAIN

Brahmaputra River

BANGLADESH
Dhaka ⊛

Tropic of Cancer

I N D I A

CHOTA NAGPUR
PLATEAU

Arabian
Sea

VINDHYA MOUNTAINS

DECCAN
PLATEAU

Bay
of
Bengal

WESTERN GHATS

KARNATAKA
PLATEAU

EASTERN GHATS

Andaman
Islands

Laccadive
Islands

SRI LANKA

Nicobar
Islands

ELEVATIONS
Feet   Meters

5,000   1,500
2,000   600
1,000   300
   0   0

— National boundary
⊛ National capital

Lambert Conic projection

MALDIVES
⊛ Male

Colombo ⊛

I N D I A N   O C E A N

Equator

0   300 mi.

0   300 km

FOCUS ON GEOGRAPHIC THEMES

1. **Place:** What city is the capital of Sri Lanka?
2. **Movement:** Into what sea does the Indus River empty?
3. **Location:** Where is the highest elevation in South Asia?
4. **Region:** What ranges extend along the coasts of southern India?

Indus flows mostly through Pakistan and empties into the Arabian Sea. The Brahmaputra and the Ganges flow east and eventually join to form a broad delta along the Bay of Bengal.

As the rivers roll southward, they carry fertile soil washed down from the mountains. When the seasonal rains strike, the rivers overflow, and rich silt, or alluvial soil, is deposited in the floodplains. The **alluvial plain** that has been created by the flooding of the Indus and Ganges rivers is often referred to as the Indo-Gangetic (IN•duh•gan•JET•ik) Plain. It is the largest continuous alluvial plain in the world, and it supports a huge population. Along the eastern Ganges, densities reach more than 1,000 people per square mile.

HUMAN/ENVIRONMENT INTERACTION

Natural Resources

South Asia has a variety of natural resources on which the peoples of the region depend for their economic livelihood.

Soil and Water

The rich soil of the Indo-Gangetic Plain is one of South Asia's greatest natural resources. The rivers also are great natural resources, providing drinking water and transportation for the region's enormous population.

Today a number of dam-building projects are underway in South Asia's river valleys. The goal is to harness the rivers' potential for hydroelectric power and to create more farmland through irrigation. Pakistan already has one of the world's largest hydroelectric plants. Recently another such project was completed in Bhutan. The government of India supplied Bhutan with the money needed to construct the Chukha hydroelectric project along the Wong Chu River. In return, India will receive some of the surplus energy that is generated. Mountainous Nepal, with its many waterfalls, is another nation with the potential for creating large amounts of hydroelectricity.

Fish thrive in the many inland waterways and coastal waters of South Asia. The people of the region catch large quantities of fish for their own use and for export. In Pakistan, herring, mackerel, sardines, sharks, and other fish

Geographic Themes

Movement: Bangladesh

Many rivers and streams flow through Bangladesh and serve as the country's chief transportation routes. *What two rivers form a broad delta along the Bay of Bengal?*

are caught in the Arabian Sea. India is also a major fishing nation. A variety of fish—mackerel, sardines, shrimp, and shark—are caught in the surrounding seas. Indians catch *Bombay duck*, a small fish that is dried and used as a relish. The rivers of India yield carp and catfish.

Energy Resources

South Asia has few significant oil reserves. Some known reserves are located along India's northwestern coast and near the Ganges Delta. There are also petroleum reserves in northern Pakistan, and offshore exploration is taking place in the Arabian Sea.

Natural gas fields are found in southern Pakistan and in the Ganges Delta area of India. Central and eastern India and southern Pakistan have some coal deposits. A major uranium deposit is located in India, north of the Eastern Ghats. Bangladesh has few energy resources other than several small deposits of natural gas and some low-grade coal.

Minerals

Minerals are scattered throughout the region. Large iron-ore deposits are found in the eastern part of the Deccan Plateau. India is one of the world's leading iron-ore exporters. South Asia also has deposits of manganese, chromite, coal, iron ore, and gypsum. Many of these resources still await development. India provides nine-tenths of the world's supply of **mica**, which is needed to manufacture electrical equipment. Nepal is another producer of mica. Small amounts of copper and gold are found in the Himalayas.

Sri Lanka is one of the world's largest producers of graphite. It is also famous for its beautiful gemstones. More than 40 different varieties of precious and semiprecious stones are mined on the island. The most valuable of these are sapphires and rubies. Sri Lanka has no known deposits of coal, oil, copper, or other resources that can be used for fuel or in industry.

Timber

Another important resource of South Asia is timber. India's rain forests produce woods

Geographic Themes

Human/Environment Interaction: Sri Lanka
Sapphires and rubies come from the same mineral—corundum. Corundum with chromium oxide produces rubies. A trace of iron and titanium results in blue sapphires. *What other mineral does Sri Lanka produce?*

such as sal and teak. India also produces a prized, sweet-smelling timber called sandalwood. Forests cover much of Bhutan, and the government of Bhutan is doing its best to protect this precious natural resource. Nepal's forests, also an important resource, have been severely reduced by overcutting. To protect Sri Lanka's forests, the export of timber from that country has been banned since 1977.

SECTION 1 REVIEW

Checking for Understanding
1. **Define** subcontinent, alluvial plain, mica.
2. **Locating Places** What three bodies of water surround South Asia?
3. **Place** What is the major mountain range along South Asia's northern border?
4. **Human/Environment Interaction** What are three mineral resources of South Asia?

Critical Thinking
5. **Understanding Cause and Effect** Why are population densities so high in the Indo-Gangetic Plain?

2 The Climate and Vegetation

South Asia lies at about the same distance from the Equator as the Sahara and the other great deserts of the world. South Asia has a hot climate and a number of deserts, yet it also contains rain forests full of exotic orchids, fields of golden sunflowers, and mountainsides covered with birch trees and flowering shrubs.

REGION

South Asia's Climate Regions

South Asia is divided into five major climate regions: highland, desert, steppe, tropical rain forest, and tropical savanna.

Highland Climate

The coldest climates of South Asia are found at the northern edge of the subcontinent, in the snowy Himalayan peaks along the border of Tibet. At lower elevations of the Himalayas, the climate is mild, or temperate. In the Himalayan foothills, temperatures are actually quite warm.

Desert and Steppe Climates

A desert climate region is found along the Indus River. The land to the east of the Indus River is called the Thar Desert, or the Great Indian Desert.

A steppe climate region, made up of semi-arid grasslands, surrounds the desert climate region, except along the coast. There is also a narrow strip of steppe that runs north and south through the center of the peninsula, between the Western Ghats and Eastern Ghats.

Tropical Climates

Tropical rain forest climate regions, with a variety of trees, are found along the western coast of the Indian subcontinent, near the Ganges Delta, and in the southwestern part of Sri Lanka. Tropical savanna regions, grasslands with both wet and dry seasons, surround the steppe climate area between the Ghats and are found in the remainder of Sri Lanka.

Monsoons

The climate of South Asia is greatly affected by **monsoons**, or seasonal winds. Between October and May, the winter winds blow from the north and northeast and are dry. As summer nears, temperatures gradually rise. The heated air also rises. As the air rises, a change in the wind direction is triggered. Moist air from the ocean replaces the rising air over the land. Winds blow from the Indian Ocean in the south and southwest between June and September, carrying warm, moist air. During this time, heavy rains provide the region with the largest portion of its yearly precipitation. The map on page 520 shows the difference between the winter and summer monsoons.

The rainfall is heaviest in the eastern part of South Asia as the winds sweep up the eastern side of the peninsula. One spot in the northeast of India near Shillong receives an average of 450 inches (1,140 cm) of rain each year. Once the wind reaches the Himalayas, it is forced west across the region. Most of the precipitation falls near the mountains. The rain decreases as the winds cross the region to the west.

With a large number of South Asia's population dependent on the land, rainfall crucially affects lives. Each year millions anxiously wait and watch for the monsoon crossing the subcontinent. Most parts of South Asia receive only one spell of rain yearly, and the early part of the year is dry in most places. January is the coldest month, with temperatures below 60°F (15.6°C) in northern India. The temperature, however, rises sharply in the early spring, and by May, it often exceeds 100°F (37.8°C) in the Indo-Gangetic Plain. Thus, the people yearn for the rains.

SOUTH ASIA: CLIMATE REGIONS

Tropical
- Tropical rain forest
- Tropical savanna

Dry
- Steppe
- Desert

Mid-Latitude
- Humid subtropical
- Highland

Lambert Conical projection

FOCUS ON GEOGRAPHIC THEMES

1. **Place:** Which three climate regions dominate southern South Asia?
2. **Location:** Where are tropical rain forest climate regions located?
3. **Region:** What climate dominates the northernmost part of the region?

Geographic Themes

Region: India
Farms cover more than half of India. Rice is the major crop, making India the world's second-largest rice producer after China. *How do monsoons affect the growing of rice?*

When the monsoon arrives, it is greeted with joyous song and dance. In southwestern India, forests of teak and bamboo turn green again. In Bangladesh, farmers plant their rice. The monsoon, unfortunately, does not benefit all South Asians equally. The dry Deccan Plateau receives little rain, even in monsoon season. Parts of western Pakistan may receive no rain at all for several years in a row. In low-lying Bangladesh, the monsoon rains frequently cause disastrous floods that ruin crops and kill livestock and people. Yet without the monsoons, farming in South Asia would suffer greatly.

SOUTH ASIA: NATURAL VEGETATION

ASIA

PAKISTAN
NEPAL
BHUTAN
Tropic of Cancer
I N D I A
BANGLADESH

LACCADIVE
ISLANDS
(INDIA)

ANDAMAN
ISLANDS
(INDIA)

SRI
LANKA

NICOBAR
ISLANDS
(INDIA)

MALDIVES

0   300 mi.

0   300 km

Equator

☐ Tropical forest
▨ Temperate grassland
☐ Desert scrub and desert waste
▨ Highland (vegetation varies with elevation)

Lambert Conic projection

FOCUS ON GEOGRAPHIC THEMES

1. **Place:** What is the major type of vegetation in western South Asia?
2. **Place:** What part of the region has temperate grasslands?
3. **Region:** What type of vegetation is found in the northern part of the region?

Cyclones

Bangladesh is also dramatically affected by cyclones. A **cyclone** is a storm marked by high winds and heavy rains. Because Bangladesh is a low-lying coastal region, the violent surges of seawater typical of cyclones often cause major disasters by submerging productive farmland and causing rivers to overflow into villages and fields. In 1991, a cyclone roaring in from the Bay of Bengal pounded the country's southern coast, killing at least 131,000 people and causing losses amounting to $1.7 billion.

Vegetation

The natural vegetation of South Asia varies from one climate region to another, depending on rainfall and temperature. Long ago most of the region was probably covered with forests. Over the centuries, however, trees have been cut down for firewood and shelter and to create cropland and fields for grazing. Today only about one-sixth of the subcontinent is forested. Of this land much is covered with low, thorny scrub rather than tall trees.

Forests

When the southwestern monsoons sweep along India's west coast, they encounter the Western Ghats and drop much of their moisture. This plentiful rainfall produces a band of rain forest, dense with coconut palms and teak. Rain forests full of towering ebony trees and magnificent orchids cover much of Sri Lanka, and similar forests grow on a small section of India's southeastern coast and along the Bay of Bengal. All of these rain forests lie in the path of the monsoon.

Surrounding India's west coast rain forests are woodlands that contain a mixture of deciduous and coniferous trees. A band of temperate mixed forest extends along the northern border of the peninsula. Mixed tropical forests thrive in the damp, hot climate of Bangladesh. Bamboo and trees, such as mango and palm, grow throughout most of Bangladesh. Valuable teak forests are located in the Chittagong Hills in the southeast, while mangrove trees and other tropical plants thrive in the Sundarbans, a swampy region in the southwest.

Because the Western and Eastern Ghats prevent much rain from reaching the center of India, the climate of the Deccan Plateau and the northern plains is drier than that of the coastal regions. As a result, the natural vegetation of India's interior is tropical dry deciduous forest, rather than a type of woodland that requires more rainfall.

India and the United States

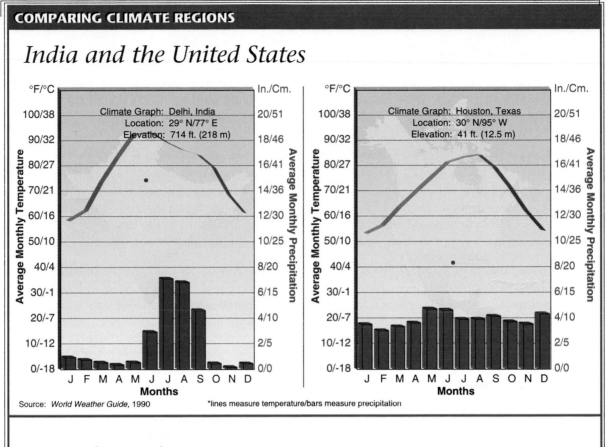

Climate Graph: Delhi, India
Location: 29° N/77° E
Elevation: 714 ft. (218 m)

Climate Graph: Houston, Texas
Location: 30° N/95° W
Elevation: 41 ft. (12.5 m)

Source: *World Weather Guide*, 1990   *lines measure temperature/bars measure precipitation*

GRAPH STUDY

The climate graphs show the average monthly temperature and the average monthly precipitation In Delhi, India, and Houston, Texas. *What is the average December temperature and precipitation in each city?*

Scrub and Grassland

The northwestern part of the Indian peninsula is extremely arid. Annual rainfall is less than 20 inches (51 cm) a year. The natural vegetation of this region is desert scrub—a mix of low trees and grasses. Some parts of this region can be used for grazing livestock, while other areas are wasteland. Irrigation projects, however, have made some parts of this desert area near the Indus River suitable for growing grains.

Grasslands and thick stands of bamboo are found in the foothills of the Himalayas. At higher elevations there are lovely alpine meadows, blooming with pink and blue flowers in spring. At the highest elevations of the mountains, however, there is little or no vegetation.

SECTION 2 REVIEW

Checking for Understanding

1. **Define** monsoon, cyclone.
2. **Locating Places** In which climate region is Sri Lanka located?
3. **Place** Why does the Deccan Plateau receive little of the monsoon rains?
4. **Place** Why does the monsoon often cause flooding in Bangladesh?

Critical Thinking

5. **Making Comparisons** How does the vegetation of northwestern India and western Pakistan compare with that of Bangladesh?

CRITICAL THINKING SKILLS

Drawing Conclusions

Suppose you come home from school and decide to put on your favorite jeans. But your jeans, which lie near an open window, are damp. The windowsill is wet, too. Putting these facts together, you conclude that it must have rained, and the jeans got wet because they were near the open window.

REVIEWING THE SKILL

In this example, you were **drawing conclusions.** You used facts, experience, and insight to form judgments about events. Drawing conclusions allows you to understand indirectly stated ideas and events, so you can apply your knowledge to a wider range of situations.

Often, however, people draw incorrect conclusions. In the example above, perhaps your brother or sister spilled water on your jeans. Maybe the jeans were washed, but not completely dried. To determine the accuracy of your conclusion, gather information that will prove or disprove it. In this case, you could find out if it had rained that day, or whether the jeans had been washed, or if anyone had spilled something on them.

When drawing conclusions, apply the following steps:

- Review the facts that are stated directly.
- Use your own knowledge, experience, and insight to form conclusions about them.
- Find information that proves or disproves your conclusions.

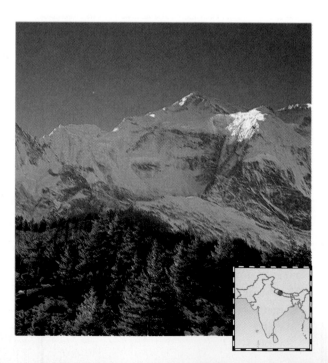

PRACTICING THE SKILL

Read the following excerpt from the diary of a mountain climber. A member of an all-woman expedition, she describes her ascent to the summit of Annapurna in the Himalayas of Nepal. Then answer the questions below.

Vera Komarkova and I and the Sherpas Mingma Tsering and Chewang Rinjing, rope together and start off shortly before 7:00 A.M. . . . I am breathing six times for each step. . . . Our oxygen tanks are only good for six hours; we must get as high as possible before starting to use them.

After climbing steadily for two and a half hours, we slow to a crawl. Time for oxygen . . . We don't talk as we climb higher. All our energy and concentration go into the steady, monotonous plod that is taking us toward our goal. There is still no wind, but we can see plumes of snow blowing off the summit in the winter gale. . . . Just below the summit pyramid the snow is again very deep, and our pace drags. But soon there is less snow, and the walking gets easier. . . . We traverse three or four bumps, and finally there we are. . . . The summit of Annapurna I at last! At 3:30 P.M. on October 15, 1978, we are at 26,504 feet on top of the world's tenth highest mountain — on top of the world.[1]

1. What conclusion can you draw about the weather conditions on this day?
2. What evidence do you have to support this conclusion?
3. Why did the climbers walk so slowly?
4. What evidence do you have to support this conclusion?

For additional practice in this skill, see Practicing Skills on page 488 of the Chapter 23 Review.

[1] Source: *Annapurna, A Woman's Place,* Arlene Blum. Sierra Club Books, San Francisco, 1980, pp. 213–214.

SECTION	KEY TERMS	SUMMARY

1 The Land

subcontinent (p. 477)
alluvial plain (p. 480)
mica (p. 481)

Brahmaputra River Delta in Bangladesh

- South Asia consists of a large peninsula with an island near its southern tip. The peninsula is also known as a subcontinent, a large landmass smaller than a continent.
- South Asia is bordered by the Himalayas in the north, the Arabian Sea on the west, the Indian Ocean on the south, and the Bay of Bengal on the east.
- Most of the region's people live on the northern plains, an agriculturally rich area.
- South Asia has three great river systems and the world's largest alluvial plain.
- South Asia has few significant oil reserves, but some natural gas, coal, and uranium. The region also has a number of substantial mineral deposits, including iron ore and mica.

SECTION	KEY TERMS	SUMMARY

2 The Climate and Vegetation

monsoon (p. 482)
cyclone (p. 484)

Indian farmer planting rice

- South Asia has highland, desert, steppe, and tropical climates.
- The monsoon is a seasonal change in wind direction that brings heavy rains to much of South Asia between June and September.
- South Asia's vegetation is affected by altitude, rainfall, and human activity.
- South Asia was once largely covered by forests. Today only a small portion of the land is forested.

Reviewing Key Terms

Choose the vocabulary term that best completes each of the sentences below. Write your answers on a separate sheet of paper.

    subcontinent (p. 477)
    alluvial plain (p. 480)
    mica (p. 481)
    monsoon (p. 482)
    cyclone (p. 484)

SECTION 1

1. Silt from a flooding river is deposited in the ＿＿＿.
2. ＿＿＿ is a mineral used in the manufacture of electrical equipment.
3. The Indian peninsula is often called a ＿＿＿.

SECTION 2

4. A severe storm marked by heavy rains and strong winds is a ＿＿＿.
5. ＿＿＿ refers to seasonal reversals in wind direction.

Reviewing Facts

SECTION 1

6. In what mountain range is Mount Everest located?
7. What are the names of the two mountain ranges that form a triangle at the base of the Indian peninsula?
8. Where are the sources of the Indus, the Ganges, and the Brahmaputra rivers?
9. What are the two goals of the dam-building projects in South Asia?
10. Which country in South Asia is known for its gemstones?

SECTION 2

11. Where are the coldest climates of South Asia found?
12. Name two locations in South Asia where tropical rain forests exist.

13. From which direction do winds blow during the June-to-September monsoon season?
14. Why have many of South Asia's forests disappeared?
15. In what part of Nepal are grains cultivated?

Critical Thinking

16. **Understanding Cause and Effect** In what way are the Himalayas responsible for the richness of the agricultural soil in the Indian subcontinent's northern plains?
17. **Making Comparisons** State the advantages and disadvantages the monsoon brings to the people of South Asia.

 ## Geographic Themes

18. **Human/Environment Interaction** How have the inhabitants of the arid regions of western Pakistan adapted their lifestyle in response to the climate and vegetation?
19. **Location** Where do the monsoon rains strike hardest?

Practicing Skills

Drawing Conclusions

Refer to the skills feature on page 486.
20. What equipment did Vera bring on her mountain climb?
21. What conclusion can you draw about her physical reaction to the climb?
22. What evidence do you have to support this conclusion?

Using the Unit Atlas

Refer to the physical geography section of the Unit Atlas on pages 472–473.

23. Where is the world's largest river delta? What two rivers form this delta?

24. What is a major natural resource of Sri Lanka?

Projects

Individual Activity

You have learned about the diversity of the physical features of South Asia. Choose one of the seven nations of the region and research the interrelationships among its physical features, climate, and vegetation.

Cooperative Learning Activity

Working in a small group, trace the path of a typical monsoon across South Asia. Research when and where the monsoon rains fall, and how they affect the different regions along their path. Present your findings to the rest of the class using maps and other visual aids (such as charts showing rainfall and/or calendars) as well as written descriptions.

Writing About Geography

Description

Imagine that you are a tourist visiting the plains of northern India for the first time. It is May, and the land is hot and dry. Describe the dust, the heat, and the vegetation. Then describe the coming of the monsoon rains and their effect on the rivers, vegetation, and people of the area. Use your journal record and other references in writing your description.

Locating Places

SOUTH ASIA:
PHYSICAL GEOGRAPHY

Match the letters on the map with the places and physical features of South Asia. Write your answers on a separate sheet of paper.

1. Deccan Plateau
2. Himalayas
3. Arabian Sea
4. Nepal
5. Indus River
6. Pakistan
7. Thar Desert
8. Ganges River
9. Bay of Bengal
10. Brahmaputra River

chapter 24

The Cultural Geography of South Asia

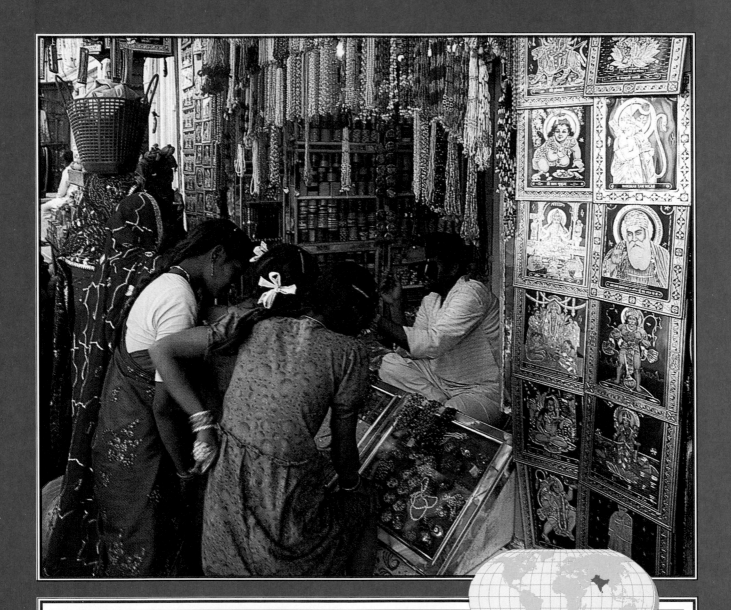

CHAPTER FOCUS

Geographic Setting

Throughout history many peoples have entered South Asia through the mountain ranges of the north and then dispersed throughout the Indian subcontinent. The result is a rich diversity of peoples, languages, and traditions.

Geographic Themes

Section 1 Population Patterns

REGION Throughout South Asia people tend to cluster in the fertile plains and lowlands.

Section 2 History and Government

MOVEMENT Two great religions, Hinduism and Buddhism, began in South Asia.

Section 3 Cultures and Lifestyles

HUMAN/ENVIRONMENT INTERACTION Lifestyles, education, and health care all vary in South Asia depending on whether people live in urban or rural environments.

▲ Photograph: *Jewelry vender in Rajasthan, India*

SETTING THE SCENE

SETTING THE SCENE

Read to Discover . . .
- the ethnic groups of South Asia.
- the density and distribution of population in South Asia.
- differences between rural and urban life in the region.

Key Term
- jati

Identify and Locate
Indo-Gangetic Plain, Thar Desert, Calcutta, Bombay, Delhi, Dhaka, Islamabad

Bangalore, India

Bangalore is a very busy, cosmopolitan city. People from all over the globe have settled here permanently. You can see children playing cricket, soccer, and field hockey wherever there is empty space. Movies are the major source of recreation, but sometimes it is impossible to get a ticket unless bought in advance. Flower shows and gardens are very popular and numerous in Bangalore.

Your friend,
Azeez Haque

Azeez Haque's description of the hectic pace of life in Bangalore, India, is typical of urban areas in the culture region of South Asia. More than 1,204 million people—about 22 percent of the world's population—live in South Asia. India's population of about 920 million people ranks second in the world and constitutes more than 76 percent of the region's total population. Bangladesh and Pakistan are home to most of the region's remaining population.

PLACE

Human Characteristics

South Asia has one of the richest and most complex mixes of people in the world. The peoples of the region are divided by six major religions, hundreds of languages, and numerous social groupings.

India

In India a person's religion may be Hindu, Muslim, Buddhist, Sikh, Jain, or Christian. The person's ancestors may have entered India from Europe or Central Asia thousands of years ago, or the individual may be part of a group whose roots go back more than 8,000 years. If the individual is a Hindu, he or she will belong to one of hundreds of **jati**—social groups that define one's occupation and social standing.

Pakistan and Bangladesh

In Pakistan and Bangladesh, more than 9 out of 10 people are Muslims. In Pakistan there are at least 5 main ethnic groups, while in Bangladesh, virtually all of the people are Bengali.

Sri Lanka

Conflict divides Sri Lanka's two main ethnic groups—the Sinhalese and the Tamils. These two groups inhabit different parts of the island, speak different languages, and practice different religions. The Sinhalese are Buddhist and the Tamils are Hindu. The Sinhalese are the majority, and they dominate the government of Sri Lanka. Many Tamils have pressured the government to create an independent Tamil state, and some have joined terrorist groups such as the Tamil Tigers.

Bhutan and Nepal

Most inhabitants of Bhutan and Nepal came originally from Mongolia and are quite different in appearance from the inhabitants of India. Tiny Nepal has one of the most complex ethnic patterns in the world. Probably the best-known Nepalese are the Sherpas, famous worldwide since their mountaineering skills helped in the first conquest of Mount Everest, the world's highest peak, located in the Himalayas.

PLACE

Population Density and Distribution

South Asia's overall population density is high—756 people per square mile (292 people per sq. km). This is about 7 times the world average. The rate of population growth in South Asia also is high. If growth continues at its present rate, the population of South Asia will double in less than 40 years.

Regional Variation

Although population densities are generally high in South Asia, they vary from one region to another. Factors such as climate, vegetation, and terrain have an impact on the number of people the land can support. Some of the most fertile farmland in South Asia is home to many thousands of people per square mile, while other areas, such as the glacier-

Geographic Themes

Place: Kathmandu, Nepal
Kathmandu, Nepal's capital and largest city, lies at the foot of the Himalayas. *What Nepalese are famous for their mountain-climbing skills?*

UNIT 8

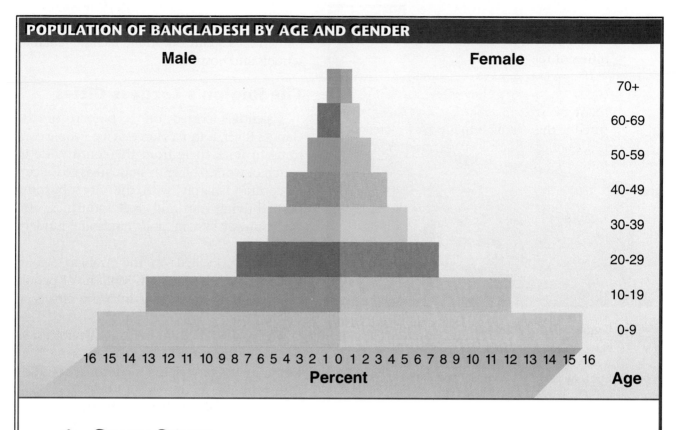

POPULATION OF BANGLADESH BY AGE AND GENDER

Male / Female

	Age
	70+
	60-69
	50-59
	40-49
	30-39
	20-29
	10-19
	0-9

16 15 14 13 12 11 10 9 8 7 6 5 4 3 2 1 0 1 2 3 4 5 6 7 8 9 10 11 12 13 14 15 16

Percent

CHART STUDY

Bangladesh has one of the most rapidly growing populations in the world. *What percentage of the male population is nine years of age or younger? What percentage of the total population is nine years of age or younger?*

dotted mountains of Nepal and Bhutan, can support only a few individuals per square mile.

Densely Populated Areas

The greatest concentration of people in South Asia is found on the fertile Indo-Gangetic Plain and along the monsoon-watered coasts of the peninsula. Because rice is an abundant and important food source, it is only natural that most South Asians live where rice is grown.

On Sri Lanka, tea and rubber are grown on large plantations. Because large plantations require large workforces, most of Sri Lanka's population live in rural villages.

The most densely populated country in the region is Bangladesh, with 2,320 people per square mile (895 people per sq. km). This is one of the highest population densities in the world. Having so many people packed into this tiny country creates serious problems. Despite rich alluvial soil and improved farming techniques, there is not enough food for all the people of Bangladesh. The situation is likely to be even more severe in the future. If the population continues to grow at its current rate, the population of Bangladesh will double in about 29 years.

Less Densely Populated Regions

India's Deccan Plateau is not as populous as the Indo-Gangetic Plain, but it is still home to an average of 125 to 250 people per square mile (48 to 97 people per sq. km).

The population of the Thar Desert is very sparse, and few people inhabit the mountainous western part of Pakistan.

Geographic Themes

Place: Bombay, India
A bustling metropolis of 12 million people, Bombay is India's financial and film-making capital. *What is India's capital?*

The southernmost parts of Bhutan and Nepal have populations of about 25 to 60 people per square mile (10 to 23 people per sq. km), but in the northern areas of both countries—where elevations are higher—the density drops to fewer than 25 people per square mile (10 people per sq. km).

PLACE

Urbanization

The percentage of South Asians living in urban areas is generally low. The urban portion of the population ranges from as low as 5 percent in Bhutan to 28 percent in Pakistan. Urbanization, however, is an important aspect of life in the region. Currently almost 300 million people in South Asia live in cities.

Rapid Urban Growth

Many South Asians are migrating to urban areas in search of better jobs and higher wages. The rapid growth of cities presents an important challenge for the governments of the region. The cities are becoming overcrowded,

and the increased population is putting a tremendous strain on public facilities such as schools and hospitals.

The Region's Largest Cities

Calcutta, located on a branch of the Ganges River, is India's largest city. People continue to flock there from the countryside in search of work. The grim slum areas of Calcutta contrast sharply with the city's bustling port, thriving iron and steel industries, efficient subway system, and handsome modern buildings.

Bombay, located on the Arabian Sea, is India's main western port. Millions of people from outlying areas pour into the city each day to work.

Delhi, India's third-largest city, traces its origins to the mid-1600s. Neighboring New Delhi, India's capital, is a modern city built by the British during the early 1900s.

The cities of Bangladesh are as crowded as the rest of that country. The capital, Dhaka, has more inhabitants per square mile than any city in the world except Lagos, Nigeria. In Islamabad, the capital of Pakistan, new housing developments are being built to accommodate the growing middle class.

SECTION 1 REVIEW

Checking for Understanding
1. **Define** jati.
2. **Locating Places** On what body of water is Bombay located?
3. **Place** Which is the most densely populated country of South Asia?
4. **Movement** What challenge have South Asia's cities faced in recent decades?

Critical Thinking
5. **Drawing Conclusions** Why are the Indo-Gangetic Plain and coastal areas the most densely populated parts of South Asia?

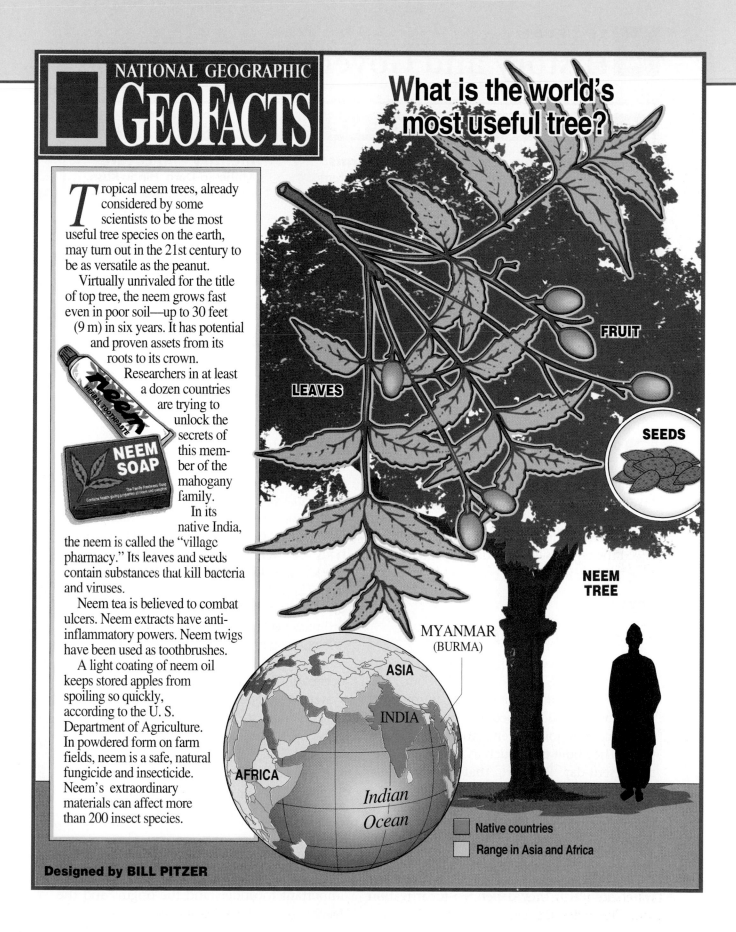

NATIONAL GEOGRAPHIC
GEOFACTS

What is the world's most useful tree?

Tropical neem trees, already considered by some scientists to be the most useful tree species on the earth, may turn out in the 21st century to be as versatile as the peanut.

Virtually unrivaled for the title of top tree, the neem grows fast even in poor soil—up to 30 feet (9 m) in six years. It has potential and proven assets from its roots to its crown.

Researchers in at least a dozen countries are trying to unlock the secrets of this member of the mahogany family.

In its native India, the neem is called the "village pharmacy." Its leaves and seeds contain substances that kill bacteria and viruses.

Neem tea is believed to combat ulcers. Neem extracts have anti-inflammatory powers. Neem twigs have been used as toothbrushes.

A light coating of neem oil keeps stored apples from spoiling so quickly, according to the U. S. Department of Agriculture. In powdered form on farm fields, neem is a safe, natural fungicide and insecticide. Neem's extraordinary materials can affect more than 200 insect species.

neem HERBAL TOOTHPASTE

NEEM SOAP The Family Freshness Soap. Contains health-giving properties of neem and camphor.

FRUIT

LEAVES

SEEDS

NEEM TREE

MYANMAR (BURMA)

ASIA

INDIA

AFRICA

Indian Ocean

Native countries
Range in Asia and Africa

Designed by BILL PITZER

2 History and Government

Over the centuries the fertile Indo-Gangetic Plain of South Asia has attracted many groups of people. The first people to invade, the Aryans, had a lasting influence on all the others. Later invaders, including Muslims and Europeans, also significantly influenced the region's cultural development.

<u>MOVEMENT</u>

Early History

One of the world's first great civilizations arose in the Indus Valley by about 2500 B.C. It was most likely founded by immigrants from Iran, who developed a writing system, a strong central government, and rich overseas trade. They built cities such as Mohenjo-Daro, in present-day Pakistan, that boasted great wealth and sophisticated technology.

Environmental changes may have led to the decline of this great civilization between 1700 B.C. and 1500 B.C. Over time, the Indus River changed its course, flooding some cities. Other cities became stranded, far from the water on which they depended for irrigation and trade networks.

About the time the Indus Valley civilization was collapsing, a new group of people known as the Aryans entered the region from the northwest. Unlike the people who built Mohenjo-Daro, the Aryans left behind few artifacts. They did, however, hand down a great body of sacred literature called the Vedas. These four books tell about Aryan religious beliefs. They also explain how Aryan society was divided into three classes: nobles, priests, and ordinary people. At first these classes were fairly flexible; people of different groups could intermarry and individuals could change their occupations. Eventually, however, a rigid **caste system** developed in which people could not change their social status. The caste system prevailed in India for centuries.

<u>PLACE</u>

Religions

Two of the world's great religions—Hinduism and Buddhism—began in India. To understand Indian history and culture, it is important to understand the origins and the teachings of these religions.

Geographic Themes

Human/Environment Interaction: Indus River valley
The Indus River valley civilization centered around planned cities:
Mohenjo-Daro (shown above) and Harappa. *What environmental changes led to the decline of the cities?*

Hinduism

Hinduism grew out of Aryan culture and incorporated the caste system first laid out in the Vedas. Hinduism is both a way of life and a set of beliefs.

Hindus believe that every individual must live according to her or his own **dharma** (DUHR•muh), or moral duty. All good actions are rewarded and bad deeds punished according to the law of **karma**. People are **reincarnated**, or reborn, repeatedly until they have overcome all their weaknesses and earthly desires. At that point, they are released from the cycle of rebirth.

Hinduism recognizes many gods and goddesses. Many Hindus see them as different forms of one being. Similarly, Hinduism sees all of the world's religions as different paths toward the same goal.

Buddhism

In approximately 563 B.C., in present-day Nepal, a prince was born—Siddhartha Gauta-

ma (sih•DAHR•tuh GAUT•uh•muh). As a man, he had everything he could want. Siddhartha's awareness of human suffering, however, made him unable to enjoy life, so he went on a pilgrimage. After years of spiritual searching and intense meditation, he perceived the true nature of human existence for the first time. In so doing, he became known as the Buddha, or the Awakened One.

Buddha spent the rest of his life trying to teach people that they suffer because they are overly attached to material things, and that to escape the chain of desire and suffering which leads to endless rebirth, one must live by certain rules. These rules include thinking clearly, acting wisely, and behaving kindly toward others.

Unlike Hinduism, Buddhism as preached by Buddha had no religious rituals. Buddha wanted to offer human beings a practical way out of their unhappiness. By following his guidelines, people could enter a state of great insight, calm, and happiness, which is called **nirvana** (nir•VAHN•uh).

Invasions and Empires

After the Aryans, many other groups of invaders entered South Asia through the Hindu Kush Mountain range in the northwest. The first invaders, the Maurya (MAU•ree•uh), established an empire that lasted from about 320 B.C. to 180 B.C. The last and greatest Mauryan emperor was named Asoka. Although officially a Hindu, he was impressed by Buddha's teachings and helped spread Buddhism.

Geographic Themes

Region: South Asia

Even though there are Hindu priests and temples, Hindu worship and meditation are mostly centered in the home. *How does Hinduism regard other religions?*

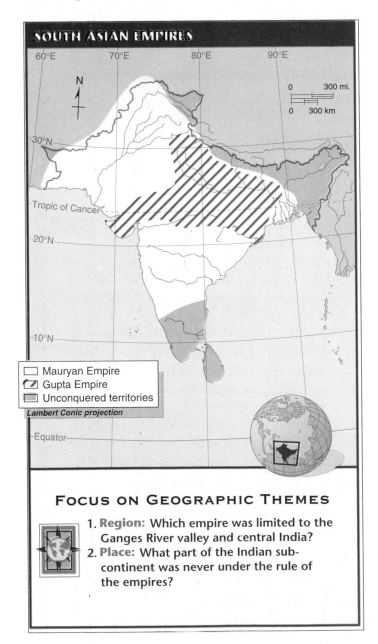

SOUTH ASIAN EMPIRES

0 300 mi.
0 300 km

Mauryan Empire
Gupta Empire
Unconquered territories

Lambert Conic projection

FOCUS ON GEOGRAPHIC THEMES

1. **Region:** Which empire was limited to the Ganges River valley and central India?
2. **Place:** What part of the Indian subcontinent was never under the rule of the empires?

About 500 years after the Mauryan Empire, the Gupta dynasty created a new empire in northern India. During the Gupta Empire, which lasted from about A.D. 320 to 550, India was one of the most advanced cultures in the world, excelling in the arts, science, and technology. The numerals we use today were most likely developed in India before being introduced to Europe by Arab traders.

Muslim merchants, adventurers, and missionaries first entered India in the 700s. By the 1100s, Muslim armies had conquered northern India. A succession of Muslim conquerors ruled the subcontinent for the next several centuries.

The final invaders were the Europeans who arrived about 1500. The Portuguese arrived first, and they came mainly to trade.

By the early 1600s, England had become the leading European power in South Asia, largely because of the success of its royal trading company, the East India Company. The company was so successful that by the mid-1700s it had occupied almost the entire region. Under the company's rule, changes were introduced, such as the reorganization of education, the introduction of the English language, and the development of a civil service.

Modern South Asia

Today the countries of South Asia are independent of European control. Independence did not come easily, however.

Independence

Many people of South Asia wanted freedom from the United Kindgom. One leader of this group was a British-trained lawyer named Mohandas K. Gandhi. Gandhi believed that Indians should rely on nonviolent methods to persuade the British to leave India. Under his guidance, many Indians refused to buy British-made goods. Known as *Mahatma,* or "Great Soul," Gandhi was often imprisoned and went on a hunger strike.

By the end of World War II, the British were tired of fighting faraway conflicts and agreed to grant independence. In 1947 British India was divided into 2 independent states. Areas with a Muslim majority became part of the Muslim nation of Pakistan, while areas with a majority of Hindus became part of the nation of India. Under this plan, Pakistan consisted of 2 sections—East Pakistan and West Pakistan—separated by about 1,000 miles (1,609 km) of Indian territory.

The departure of the British brought other changes. One year after the division of British India, British-ruled Ceylon was granted independence. In 1972 the nation changed its name to Sri Lanka. In the northern part of the subcontinent, Bhutan and Nepal had always remained independent of the British.

Today's Governments

After independence, tensions arose between Muslims and Hindus. Muslims living in mostly Hindu India fled to Pakistan, while many Hindus in Pakistan migrated to India. Rioting broke out, and tens of thousands were killed. Problems also developed between the people of East and West Pakistan. In 1971, East Pakistan revolted and declared itself the independent nation of Bangladesh.

The current governments of South Asia include democracies and monarchies. India is a federal parliamentary republic. Sri Lanka and Bangladesh also have parliamentary systems. Pakistan today has a president who is elected indirectly by members of the legislature. Bhutan and Nepal are monarchies.

Geographic Themes

Region: India
Mohandas K. Gandhi led India toward independence from British rule. *What was Gandhi's background?*

SECTION 2 REVIEW

Checking for Understanding
1. **Define** caste system, dharma, karma, reincarnated, nirvana.
2. **Locating Places** In what part of South Asia were the first great cities built?
3. **Place** What was a major feature of each empire established in South Asia?
4. **Movement** What action did Mohandas K. Gandhi recommend in the struggle for independence?

Critical Thinking
5. **Making Comparisons** Compare and contrast Buddhism and Hinduism.

Geography and History

NEPAL AND BHUTAN: ISOLATED BY GEOGRAPHY

As you read, examine how Nepal and Bhutan were affected by their geography.

Location

Cradled between the huge countries of India and China, and hidden among the imposing crags of the Himalayas, Nepal and Bhutan remained mysteries to much of the world for many centuries. Indeed, chroniclers in China refer to Bhutan as the "hidden holy land." Its present-day name came from British explorers who arrived in the mid-1770s.

Mountain Lands

Of the two countries, Bhutan is the more geographically isolated. Eight successive ranges of the Himalayas cut north to south across the tiny country, slicing it into a series of parallel valleys. The river systems that irrigate and drain the valleys provide additional obstacles that explorers or would-be invaders had to overcome.

Not until the early 1960s were roads completed across the country as well as farther south into India. Before that time, the few people who visited the country had the choice of the two methods of travel the Bhutanese themselves used: foot or horse. Most Bhutanese still travel by those two methods, while

The Himalayas cover much of Nepal and Bhutan. The mountains have long, harsh winters and short, cool summers. Steep river valleys cut through the icy glaciers and snow. Buddhist monasteries and Hindu temples often are perched on hillsides overlooking the valleys.

Bhutanese officials now use helicopters extensively.

Himalayan ranges cover the northern two-thirds of Nepal, forming the largest of the country's three parallel regions that run east and west. The remaining southern third of Nepal is divided into a strip of hills and river basins and a section that is part of India's Gangetic Plain. Steamy, tangled rain forest met intruders from the south; the freezing, hostile Himalayas met any challenge coming from the north.

Widening Contacts

During the late 1700s and early 1800s, the British increased their influence in both countries while strengthening their hold on India. Although the United Kingdom assumed control of the countries' foreign affairs and defense, it did not interfere with either nation's internal politics. Until the late 1950s, Bhutan and Nepal continued their isolation from world affairs. Since then, both nations have lessened their ties to the United Kingdom and have moved toward greater modernization.

Checking for Understanding

1. What geographical factors isolated Bhutan and Nepal?
2. **Movement** What changes have come to Nepal and Bhutan during this century?

SETTING THE SCENE

Read to Discover . . .
- the languages and religions of South Asia.
- the contrasts between rural and urban lifestyles in South Asia.
- the arts and celebrations of South Asia.

Key Terms
- mantra
- sadhu
- raga
- tala

Identify and Locate
Taj Mahal, Golden Temple

South Asia's ethnic diversity and its long and complicated history have produced a rich culture. Although the region's standard of living tends to be low when measured in terms of material wealth or life expectancy, South Asians are surrounded by beautiful art and architecture, have access to a lively film industry, and celebrate hundreds of festivals each year.

PLACE

Languages

South Asia has a diversity of languages. India alone has 14 major languages and hundreds of regional dialects. Although English is commonly spoken in government and business, Hindi is the official language of India.

Indo-Aryan Languages

Most of the languages spoken in Pakistan, Bangladesh, and northern India fall into the Indo-Aryan family of languages. These include Hindi, Urdu, and Bengali. About half of the Indian people, especially in the north and central areas, speak Hindi as a first or second language. Urdu is the official language of Pakistan, and Bengali is the official language of Bangladesh. Hindustani, a language spoken in northern India, is a mixture of Hindi and Urdu. Nepali and Sinhalese, the official languages of Nepal and Sri Lanka, are Indo-Aryan languages as well.

Other Languages

About one-fifth of the people in southern India and Sri Lanka speak languages of the Dravidian family. The Dravidian languages include Tamil, Telegu, Kannada, and Malayalam. In northern South Asia, the languages spoken in Bhutan and Nepal reflect these countries' close ethnic and historic ties with central Asia.

PLACE

Religions

The major religions of South Asia are Hinduism, Islam, and Buddhism. Most of the people in India and Nepal practice Hinduism. There are also Hindus in Bhutan, Sri Lanka, Pakistan, and Bangladesh.

The majority of people in Pakistan and Bangladesh are Muslim. In India, Muslims are the largest single minority, exceeding 100 million.

Although Buddhism had its beginnings in South Asia, its overall influence has declined in the region. This has been primarily because of the flexibility of Hinduism, which has absorbed many of the teachings of Buddhism.

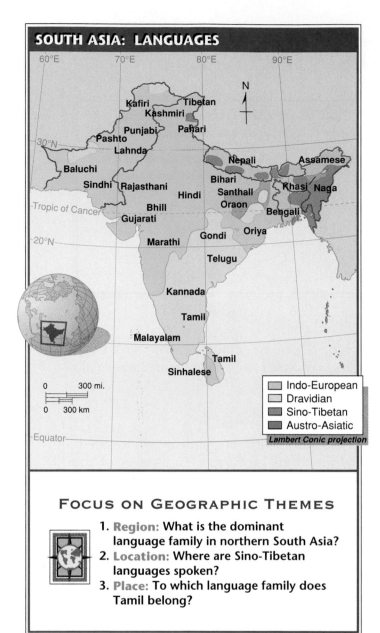

SOUTH ASIA: LANGUAGES

Kafiri
Tibetan
Kashmiri
Punjabi
Pahari
Pashto
Lahnda
Baluchi
Nepali
Assamese
Sindhi
Rajasthani
Bihari
Hindi
Santhall
Khasi Naga
Bhill
Oraon
Gujarati
Bengali
Marathi
Gondi
Oriya
Telugu
Kannada
Tamil
Malayalam
Tamil
Sinhalese

0   300 mi.

0   300 km

Equator

Indo-European
Dravidian
Sino-Tibetan
Austro-Asiatic

Lambert Conic projection

FOCUS ON GEOGRAPHIC THEMES

1. **Region:** What is the dominant language family in northern South Asia?
2. **Location:** Where are Sino-Tibetan languages spoken?
3. **Place:** To which language family does Tamil belong?

Buddhism, however, remains quite strong in Sri Lanka, Bhutan, and Nepal.

Two other religions of South Asia are Sikhism and Jainism. Jainism was founded in the 500s B.C. by a young Hindu teacher named Mahavira. Its chief characteristic is a belief in extreme nonviolence. Jains believe that every living thing has a soul, and that to kill even an insect is evil. Today, Jainism has over 3 million followers in India.

Sikhism was founded in the early 1500s by a teacher named Nanak. Nanak was interested in combining Hinduism and Islam into one united creed. Sikhs are monotheistic, like Muslims, and accept Hindu ideas on karma and reincarnation. Most of the 18 million Sikhs live in the northwestern part of India.

Another religion in South Asia is Christianity with about 28 million followers. Most Christians live in the south of India.

Influence of Religion

Religion has a powerful influence on daily life in South Asia. In Bhutan, prayer flags flap in the wind, sending out sacred messages called **mantras**. In India, Hindu teachers known as **sadhus** can be seen everywhere. Usually dressed in yellow robes, they carry just a bowl and a blanket and live on gifts from those who want to improve their karma. In India, where Hindus consider cattle sacred, thousands of cows roam the streets. In Pakistan women dress modestly as Islamic law requires.

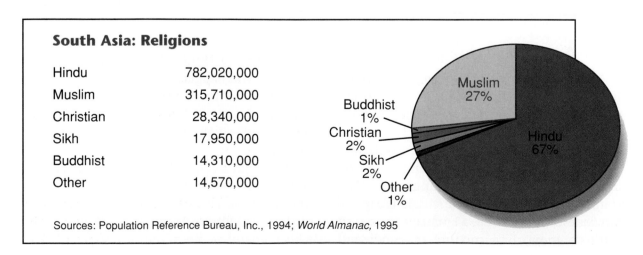

South Asia: Religions

Hindu	782,020,000
Muslim	315,710,000
Christian	28,340,000
Sikh	17,950,000
Buddhist	14,310,000
Other	14,570,000

Muslim 27%
Buddhist 1%
Christian 2%
Sikh 2%
Other 1%
Hindu 67%

Sources: Population Reference Bureau, Inc., 1994; *World Almanac*, 1995

The Arts

Like religion, the arts are an important aspect of life in South Asia. Even the humblest workers perform their tasks in an artistic way. For example, a spice or cosmetic stall in any Indian bazaar is a palette of dazzling colors piled in perfect pyramids by merchant vendors.

Architecture

One of the world's most famous buildings, the Taj Mahal, is in India. A Muslim emperor built it in the 1600s as a tomb for his beloved wife. The structure is made of white marble and has towers and domes in the Islamic style. Delicate screens, which allow air to circulate, are carved in the Hindu style.

Other outstanding architectural works include mosques in Pakistan and Bangladesh and the Golden Temple of the Sikhs in Amritsar (UHM•RIT•suhr), India. In Bhutan there are old fortified monasteries called dzong (dzawng) that developed as centers for Buddhist learning and art.

Music and Dance

Classical Indian dances are based on themes from Hindu mythology. There are numerous dance styles, each from a different region.

The style known as Bharata Natyam (bah•RAH•tah naht•yahm) is mainly danced in the south. The dancers are usually women, gorgeously dressed in bright silk saris and gold bracelets. The dances are long and elaborate, with complex hand gestures, rapid whirling, and stamping feet.

In the Kathakali (kah•thah•KAHL•lee) dances from India's west coast, the dancers wear huge, colorful masks and move violently. Very different is Manipuri, a gentle, swaying dance style from northeastern India.

Indian classical music is divided into two basic types: Hindustani—practiced in the North—and Karnatak—practiced in the South. The melody is called the **raga**, and the rhythm is called the **tala.** There is no harmony in Indi-

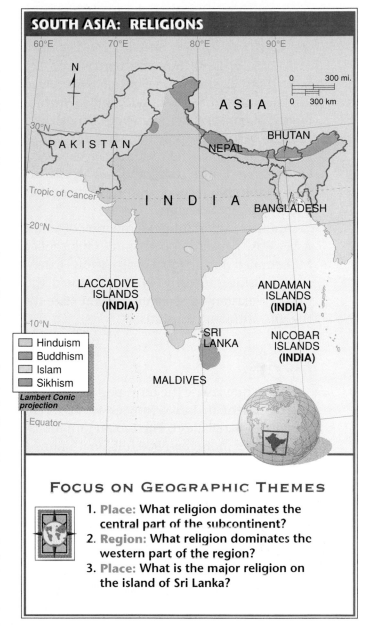

SOUTH ASIA: RELIGIONS

Hinduism
Buddhism
Islam
Sikhism

Lambert Conic projection

FOCUS ON GEOGRAPHIC THEMES

1. **Place:** What religion dominates the central part of the subcontinent?
2. **Region:** What religion dominates the western part of the region?
3. **Place:** What is the major religion on the island of Sri Lanka?

an music, and improvisation plays an important role.

Literature

Two of India's most famous works of literature are the *Mahabharata* (muh•HAH•BHA•ruh•tuh) and the *Ramayana* (rah•MAH•yah•nuh). These two great epic poems were composed between about 1500 B.C. and 500 B.C. and are still frequently read aloud or used as the basis of dramas today.

The Mahabharata includes a shorter work known as the *Bhagavad Gita* (BAH•guh•vahd GEE•tuh), meaning "the lord's song." This story takes place before a great battle and teaches people to fulfill their duties and not to fear death.

India's greatest modern writer was Rabindranath Tagore, winner of the Nobel Prize for Literature in 1913. In addition to writing poetry, fiction, and drama in both Bengali and English, Tagore composed music and painted. He lived at a time when South Asia was awakening from British rule, and his works expressed the cultural and patriotic ferment that was sweeping the region.

Another important modern writer of South Asia was Muslim poet and philosopher Muhammad Iqbal. Iqbal, who wrote extensively during the early 1900s, proposed the idea of Pakistan—a separate Muslim state for the subcontinent's Muslims.

Movies

Today movies are the most popular form of entertainment in India. Movies are also very popular in Bangladesh. The Indian film industry produces more than 800 full-length films a year—more than any other country.

Geographic Themes

Place: Taj Mahal

The white marbled Taj Mahal is considered one of the most beautiful buildings in the world. *Why was the Taj Mahal built?*

Lifestyles

Lifestyles in South Asia, like those in many developing nations, are a complicated mixture of the traditional and the modern.

Urban and Rural Contrasts

The standard of living in the rural areas of South Asia is often low. The majority of the people are peasant farmers who must struggle to raise enough food to feed their families. Large extended families live in small villages and work on small farms nearby.

Prosperous people in the cities live very different lives. These people include business leaders, industrialists, political leaders, and large landowners. They live in high-rise apartments or small houses, drive cars, and enjoy the many cultural offerings.

Many of the cities' residents, however, have little chance to appreciate these luxuries. Millions live in the streets, spreading out their beds on the sidewalks each night. Others build flimsy shelters of bamboo.

Health

Because much of South Asia has a semitropical or tropical climate, such diseases as malaria and smallpox are widespread. Governments have made some progress against these diseases. Sri Lanka was one of the first developing nations to eliminate malaria, a disease spread by mosquitoes. Nepal has also eradicated the disease through insect spraying programs.

In Bhutan, life expectancy is the shortest in the region—only 46 years. Only Sri Lanka with its life expectancy of 70 years approaches the rates of developed countries such as Japan or the United States, where life expectancy exceeds 75 years.

The availability of clean water is a problem in much of South Asia. Therefore, water-borne diseases such as cholera and dysentery are still common. In Nepal, almost one-third of the babies die from dysentery before they reach their first birthday. Infant mortality is also very high in Bangladesh.

Food Needs

Another reason for the health problems that face South Asia is poor nutrition. It has been estimated that almost one-third of the people of this region do not get enough protein to eat. The reason is simple: they are too poor to afford a variety of foods.

Governments are doing what they can to improve food production and people's diets. In Nepal, government-sponsored reforms have taken farmland away from large landowners and put it in the hands of those who actually work it. The result has been increased production. Beginning in the 1960s, the Indian government began a many-sided campaign to increase the country's food supply. So far the campaign has been very successful.

Education

Improving education is essential to improving South Asia's standard of living. In most areas of South Asia, about one-third of the people over the age of 15 can read and write. In Sri Lanka, the literacy rate is very high—more than 86 percent. The government of India is committed to expanding educational opportunities. Today's literacy rate is twice what it was when the country first became an independent nation. Advances in education are also weakening the caste system, especially in the cities. Laws have also been passed giving the lowest social class—the untouchables—the same rights as other people.

Celebrations

An example of South Asia's rich and varied cultures are the region's many celebrations. Hindu festivals, such as Diwali, the festival of lights, are joyous, colorful occasions marked by ancient symbols and community togetherness. Muslims celebrate a great day of festivity at the end of Ramadan, the month during which they abstain from food and drink from dawn to dusk. The day is marked by visiting and feasting with friends, relatives, and neighbors. Buddhists widely celebrate the birth of Buddha, and Christians celebrate the traditional holidays of the Christian calendar.

Geographic Themes

Region: South Asia
The countries of South Asia are committed to improving education and raising their standards of living. *About how many people in South Asia over the age of 15 can read and write?*

SECTION 3 REVIEW

Checking for Understanding
1. **Define** mantra, sadhu, raga, tala.
2. **Locating Places** In what part of India are the Dravidian languages spoken?
3. **Place** What has been the greatest improvement in medical care in South Asia?
4. **Region** How does religion affect lifestyles in South Asia?

Critical Thinking
5. **Expressing Problems Clearly** How does unclean water affect the health of South Asians?

MAP & GRAPH SKILLS

Reading a Line Graph

A line graph is an excellent tool for recording changes in data over time. On a line graph, time intervals (hours, weeks, years, etc.) are recorded on the horizontal axis, or **x-axis.** The vertical axis, or **y-axis,** shows numbers or units of measurement. These two axes form a grid.

REVIEWING THE SKILL

In plotting a line graph, for each time interval you must place a dot along the vertical axis showing what quantity occurred at that time. Then draw a line connecting the dots to show whether the numbers go up or down.

To read a line graph, apply the following steps:
- Read the graph title to determine its subject.
- Study the information on the x- and y-axes to identify the units of measurement and the time period.
- Look at the placement of dots on the grid.
- Study the movement of the line(s) on the graph to draw conclusions about trends over time.

PRACTICING THE SKILL

Use the graphs below to answer the following questions:
1. What is the topic of the graphs?
2. What time period is measured on these graphs?
3. What do the numbers on the y-axis represent?
4. What was the approximate population of each country in 1992?
5. Are the figures shown for the year 2000 actual or estimated? Explain your answer.

For additional practice in this skill, see Practicing Skills on page 508 of the Chapter 24 Review.

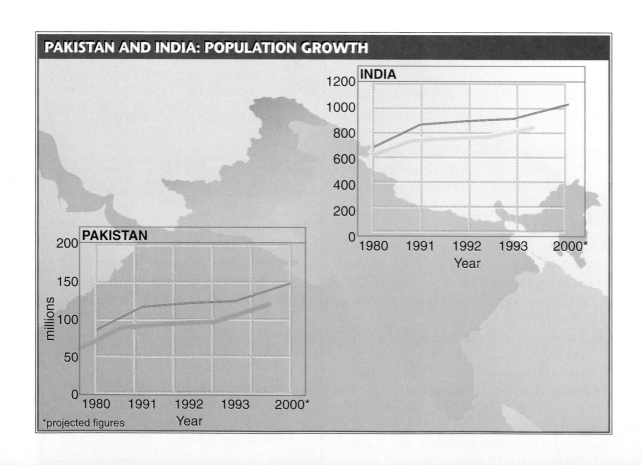

PAKISTAN AND INDIA: POPULATION GROWTH

SECTION	KEY TERMS	SUMMARY
1 **Population Patterns**	jati (p. 491)	• South Asia is an ethnically diverse area. • Population density is greatest on the Indo-Gangetic Plain. • Although most South Asians live in rural areas, an increasing number are migrating to the cities in search of work.

Victoria Railway Station, Bombay, India

SECTION	KEY TERMS	SUMMARY
2 **History and Government**	**caste system** (p. 496) **dharma** (p. 497) **karma** (p. 497) **reincarnated** (p. 497) **nirvana** (p. 497)	• The Indus Valley was home to one of the world's first great civilizations. • Many peoples have conquered South Asia, from the Aryans to the British. • Two of the world's great religions—Hinduism and Buddhism—originated in South Asia. • After World War II, the region achieved independence from the British Empire. • Today most of the people of South Asia elect their leaders.

Hindu temple and priest

SECTION	KEY TERMS	SUMMARY
3 **Cultures and Lifestyles**	**mantra** (p. 502) **sadhu** (p. 502) **raga** (p. 503) **tala** (p. 503)	• South Asians speak many different languages. India alone has 14 major languages and hundreds of dialects. • The main religions of South Asia are Hinduism, Islam, and Buddhism. People also practice Christianity, Jainism, and Sikhism. • In most of South Asia the standard of living is low and life expectancy is short. There have been improvements, however, in health care and education in recent years.

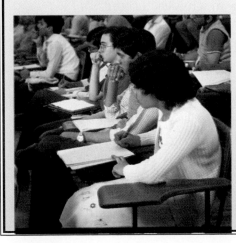

Modern university class in India

Reviewing Key Terms

Choose the vocabulary term that best completes each of the sentences below. Write your answers on a separate sheet of paper.

jati (p. 491)
caste system (p. 496)
dharma (p. 497)
sadhu (p. 502)
raga (p. 503)

SECTION 1

1. The term for a Hindu social division is ____.

SECTION 2

2. Hindus believe that each person must follow his or her moral duty, or ____.
3. India's ancient ____ consisted of four major groups.

SECTION 3

4. ____ is the melody of Indian classical music.
5. ____ are Hindu teachers.

Reviewing Facts

SECTION 1

6. South Asia is home to what percentage of the world's population?
7. Which capital is the second most densely populated city in the world?

SECTION 2

8. Which people passed on the body of literature known as the Vedas?
9. According to Buddha, what is the result of desiring things?

SECTION 3

10. What religion is followed by most of the people of Pakistan and Bangladesh?
11. Why do so many South Asians fail to eat enough protein?

Critical Thinking

12. **Cause and Effect** Why do few people live at high elevations in Nepal and Bhutan?
13. **Drawing Conclusions** What do the objects discovered at Mohenjo-Daro suggest about the people who created them?
14. **Expressing Problems Clearly** Why have the governments of South Asia been unable to improve urban living conditions?

 ## Geographic Themes

15. **Region** How does the region's overall population density compare with the world average?
16. **Movement** From what direction did most invaders enter South Asia?
17. **Place** What is the *Baghavad Gita's* theme?

 ## Practicing Skills

Reading a Line Graph

Refer to the line graph on page 506.

18. By how much did Pakistan's population grow from 1980 to 1991?
19. By how much is each country's population expected to increase in the 20-year period shown in the graphs?

Using the Unit Atlas

Refer to the cultural geography section of the Unit Atlas on pages 470–471.

20. From what country did Bangladesh win its independence? When?
21. What major social problem is India facing?

Projects

Individual Activity

You have learned about Hinduism, Buddhism, and Islam. Choose one of the religions and research one aspect of it in depth. You might examine its teachings on the deity, its rules for daily life, or its views on what happens after death. Write a report on what you learn.

Cooperative Learning Activity

Working in a small group, go to the library or media center. Have each person in the group research one topic related to South Asia, such as festivals, health, education, or ethnic diversity. Use the *Readers' Guide to Periodical Literature* to locate recent magazine articles on these subjects. Report on your findings to the rest of the class.

Writing About Geography

Description

Locate a book, magazine article, or encyclopedia entry about Mohenjo-Daro. Read the descriptions and study the pictures. Then describe Mohenjo-Daro as it would have looked to someone living there thousands of years ago. Using your journal record, compare the products of modern South Asia with those produced in the region's earliest civilization. What geographic factors account for any similarities or differences?

Locating Places

SOUTH ASIA: PHYSICAL GEOGRAPHY

Match the letters on the map with the places of South Asia. Write your answers on a separate sheet of paper.

1. Thar Desert
2. Sri Lanka
3. New Delhi
4. Calcutta
5. Nepal
6. Indus River
7. Hindu Kush
8. Bombay
9. Dhaka
10. Bhutan

chapter 25

South Asia Today

CHAPTER FOCUS

Geographic Setting

The people who live in South Asia have adapted to a rich and varied geographic setting, which includes everything from isolated mountain valleys to a long coastline that is a crossroads for international trade.

Geographic Themes

Section 1 Living in South Asia

REGION In most nations of South Asia, a large majority of the people still make their living in agriculture.

▲ Photograph: *Indian girl celebrating the Festival of Lights*

Section 2 People and Their Environment

HUMAN/ENVIRONMENT INTERACTION The rapidly expanding population of South Asia is placing an ever-increasing burden on the environment.

1 Living in South Asia

Read to Discover . . .
- the major crops of South Asia.
- the industries that are developing in South Asia.
- mining and fishing resources of South Asia.

Key Terms
- subsistence farming
- jute
- cash crop
- green revolution

Identify and Locate
Malabar Coast, Kathmandu Valley, Chittagong

Rawalpindi, Pakistan

My family lives in Rawalpindi, a city in northern Pakistan. About 65 percent of Pakistanis live on farms, but the country is rapidly setting up new industries. Communication by means of mail, telephone, and fax are reliable, and even the remotest areas are getting equipped with telephones and post offices.

Zia Raja

Z ia Raja describes the growth of industry in his homeland of Pakistan. In recent years the governments of India, Bangladesh, and the other nations in South Asia have also made tremendous progress toward modernizing their economies. India especially has increased agricultural output, slowed population growth, and established a broad and impressive industrial base. As a result, India ranks among the world's top 12 producers of goods and services. Yet India continues to have one of the world's lowest per capita incomes—about $310 a year. Furthermore, its output per person is quite low. In India—as throughout the region—traditional, labor-intensive methods are used in most occupations. As a result, the average individual produces and earns little.

HUMAN/ENVIRONMENT INTERACTION

Agriculture

M ost people in South Asia make their living by farming. In India 70 percent of the population is engaged in farming; in Bangladesh the figure jumps to 80 percent. Most people practice **subsistence farming**— managing to produce just what they need to survive. These subsistence farmers use simple tools; a peasant plowing with a wooden harrow pulled by an ox is still a common sight throughout much of the region. Gradually, however, agriculture is changing as modern methods are introduced in the hopes of producing larger harvests. Some farmers now use tractors and irrigate their fields with water pumped from electric-powered wells.

Agricultural Conditions

South Asian farms vary in size from large plantations in Sri Lanka to small plots of land in India.

The Sri Lankan plantations were originally established by the British and the Dutch. Today on these plantations, skilled workers use advanced technology to produce tea, rubber, coconut, and other products for export.

Contrasting with the vast tea and rubber plantations are the region's small farms. In India more than one-third of the farms are less than one acre in area. Their small size is a result of traditional inheritance practices. It is the custom to divide a family's land equally among all the family's sons. As generations pass and the plots are divided and then further subdivided, plots grow smaller. A family may own several such plots, scattered around the village where the family lives. This makes farming difficult. In an attempt to solve this problem, some states in India have passed laws establishing a minimum size for farms.

A Variety of Crops

The major food crop grown in South Asia is rice. Rice is grown chiefly in the tropical rain forest climate of the Ganges Delta and along the Malabar Coast—the western coast of the peninsula. India is the world's second-largest producer of rice. Tiny Bangladesh (about the size of Iowa) ranks fourth.

Wheat is a major crop of the Indo-Gangetic Plain. It is also the chief crop of the Indus Valley of Pakistan. Peanuts grown along the western coast of the peninsula are another important crop of the region.

Although rice is the major food crop of Bangladesh, **jute**—a fiber used to make string and cloth—is the country's major cash crop. When harvested, the slender stalks shine a dull gold color. Jute is called the "golden crop" for another reason: sales of this product account for 75 percent of all the money Bangladesh earns from exports.

Cotton is another important fiber crop grown in South Asia; India and Pakistan are world leaders in its production. India is also one of the world's largest producers of bananas, while citrus fruits are grown in the steppe areas of India, Pakistan, and Bangladesh.

India and Sri Lanka are two of the world's largest producers of tea. Originally grown in China, tea was introduced to India by British planters who brought plants and seeds from China. When workers on the Indian tea plantations began demanding better working conditions, the British set up new plantations in Ceylon (now Sri Lanka). When Sri Lanka gained its independence in 1948, the British planters moved on once again, but the plantations remain. The sale of tea abroad brings much-needed cash into Sri Lanka. So does the sale of rubber, the nation's second-largest plantation crop. The island's dependence on **cash crops**, however, forces it to import great quantities of rice to meet its people's food needs. This conflict—between growing the food crops a nation's people need to survive

Geographic Themes

Place: Sri Lanka
About three-fourths of all Sri Lankans live in villages and work on farms or plantations. *What agricultural products are exported from Sri Lanka?*

physically and growing the cash crops the country needs in order to survive in the global economy—exists throughout South Asia, as in many developing regions.

Improved Agricultural Practices

At the present growth rate, the population of South Asia will double in less than 40 years. Although government leaders—especially in India—have made efforts to slow the rate of population growth, they realize that agricultural production must rise dramatically if the region's people are to be adequately fed.

Government programs throughout South Asia are training farmers to use modern technology. These programs focus on how irrigation, insect control, and fertilization can raise productivity.

In some areas farmers are taught to plant two or more crops on the same piece of land in a single year. In Bangladesh, for example, farmers can harvest three crops of rice in most years. In the Kathmandu Valley of Nepal, farmers used to let their land lie fallow after harvesting their rice crops; now they plant a second crop of winter wheat. This method cannot work everywhere, however. In places where agriculture is dependent on the monsoon rains, growing more than one crop in a year is difficult. Also, farmers who have used traditional methods for centuries may be reluctant to experiment with new techniques; subsistence farmers have little room for error in their lives.

Education and government leadership are crucial—both to change attitudes and to teach specific new techniques. Agricultural research stations in Bhutan have led to the establishment of very successful fruit orchards. The government of Sri Lanka has encouraged rice production by paying high prices for rice and establishing new irrigation programs.

One of the most impressive achievements of recent years has been the **green revolution.** Worried by the rising threat of world hunger, plant breeders began in the 1960s to develop new and more productive varieties of rice, wheat, and maize. Asian rice growers planted

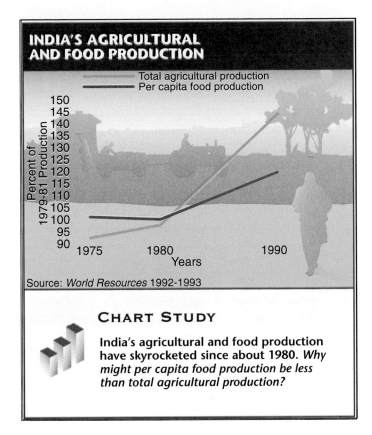

INDIA'S AGRICULTURAL AND FOOD PRODUCTION

Source: *World Resources* 1992-1993

CHART STUDY

India's agricultural and food production have skyrocketed since about 1980. *Why might per capita food production be less than total agricultural production?*

the new varieties, and rice production increased by more than 60 percent between 1965 and 1985. Wheat yields in India increased by 50 percent. These new varieties, however, are more susceptible to disease than the old strains were. They also require expensive fertilizers and much irrigation. Despite these problems, the green revolution has allowed countries such as India to store grain surpluses and even export grain. Researchers are currently working to develop strains that can better resist diseases and drought.

HUMAN/ENVIRONMENT INTERACTION

Mining and Fishing

South Asia consists of a peninsula and islands; naturally, fish are an important resource. Mining is also an important source of income.

Mining

Most of the mining in the region takes place on the Indo-Gangetic Plain and in eastern India. India produces large amounts of mica, coal, and iron ore and also has significant deposits of bauxite, silver, and copper. Pakistan has some natural-gas deposits, and precious stones such as sapphires and rubies are mined in Sri Lanka. Bhutan possesses significant mineral resources, including coal, lead, marble, zinc, and copper. Unfortunately, problems in extracting and processing these minerals have so far prevented them from being mined in large quantities.

Fishing

Fishing is an important industry in Sri Lanka and Pakistan. Fresh and dried fish, as well as lobsters and shrimp, are important exports of Pakistan. In Bangladesh, fish are a primary food source for many people. The majority of farmers in rural Bangladesh fish during the flood season, and the nation's commercial fisheries industry, though new, is very successful. Japan is a major purchaser of shrimp and frogs' legs from Bangladesh.

MOVEMENT

Industrial Growth

The pace of industrialization varies in South Asia. In India the process of industrialization was begun by the British. The nation's industries have traditionally been heavily regulated by the government. An easing of government regulations in the 1980s, however, led to a surge in development. At the other end of the spectrum is tiny Bhutan, which has remained isolated and undeveloped until recently. Government policy currently is to encourage development but to proceed very slowly, so that the nation's cultural heritage and natural resources are carefully preserved.

Light Industry

Light industry involves the production of consumer goods, such as bicycles, televisions, and textiles. Textile manufacturing is India's most important industry, and has been for hundreds of years. Roughly 24 million people are employed in India's textile industry, producing cotton, wool, and silk in an astonishing variety of colors and styles—embroidered, woven, painted, and tie-dyed. The garment industry is also thriving in Bangladesh. In 1979, the year Bangladesh first exported finished garments, the clothing industry earned $9 million in profits. Within just 10 years, profits had soared to $450 million.

Throughout South Asia many goods are manufactured by workers laboring in their own homes. Millions of these laborers weave

SOUTH ASIA: ECONOMIC ACTIVITY

Legend:
- Nomadic herding
- Commercial farming
- Subsistence farming
- ■ Manufacturing and trade
- Commercial fishing
- Little or no activity

Lambert Conic projection

FOCUS ON GEOGRAPHIC THEMES

1. **Location:** Where does manufacturing and trade take place?
2. **Human/Environment Interaction:** What is the major economic activity in most of the region?
3. **Location:** Where does most commercial farming take place?

fabrics of cotton, rayon, and silk by hand. They also make shoes, jewelry, brassware, woodcarvings, furniture, bowls, and other goods. Because these home industries provide jobs for villagers, the government has always encouraged them. Today, many of the products made in these industries are sold in different parts of the world.

South Asia also has a number of privately owned small industries. These industries generally are plants that employ fewer than 100 workers and use simple machinery. They make such goods as bicycle parts, shoes, and carpets.

Heavy Industry

South Asia also has large-scale industries that specialize in heavy industrial production. These include or are related to mining, electric power, and iron and steel manufacturing. India manufactures steel, cement, and heavy machinery. Bangladesh produces cement, iron, and steel. Bangladesh also melts down and reuses steel from one of its most unusual industries—shipbreaking. Shipowners from all over the world send their old or crippled ships to the port of Chittagong, where workers scramble over the ships with sledgehammers and torches, ripping the structure apart. Manufacturing is not an important part of the economy of Sri Lanka, and in Bhutan there are only a few large industrial employers.

Until the early 1990s, when India moved to a free market economy, more than 200 of its large-scale industries were owned solely by the government. The rest were owned jointly by the government and private investors or were still in private hands.

Under the old economy, India did not welcome foreign investments. All foreign-brand products sold in India had to have Indianized names. Since 1992, however, foreign investment has been encouraged, and products may be sold under their own brand names.

Tourism

Tourism is important to the economies of several South Asian nations. Tourists are attracted to Nepal by the opportunities to hunt, photograph wildlife, and climb or trek in the

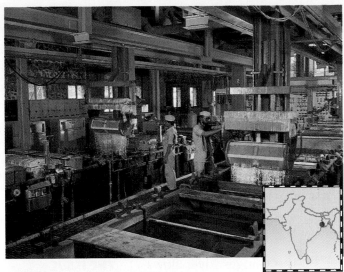

Geographic Themes

Place: India
India produces a variety of manufactured goods, including machines, tractors, cars, ships, and airplanes. *How many people are employed in India's textile industry?*

Himalayas. Tourists are also drawn to exotic Bhutan, but their activities are carefully controlled by the government. Sri Lanka has many beautiful beaches and lovely hotels to attract tourists. Unfortunately, continuing violence between the Sinhalese and the Tamils has drastically reduced tourism on the island.

SECTION 1 REVIEW

Checking for Understanding

1. **Define** subsistence farming, jute, cash crop, green revolution.
2. **Locating Places** What areas in India and Pakistan are known for growing wheat?
3. **Human/Environment Interaction** What are two problems with the new strains of wheat and rice being planted in South Asia?
4. **Place** Why is there little mining in Bhutan?

Critical Thinking

5. **Making Comparisons** Compare and contrast industrial development in India and Bhutan.

CASE STUDY

THE GANGES:
PLAGUED BY POLLUTION

The Ganges is more than a river. It is a phenomenal force that holds 5,000 years of history, culture, and tradition.

The Ganges River flows across the northern corner of India, beginning as a pair of headstreams in the Himalayas. The streams flow south-southeast, joining at Kanpur, then continue across India and Bangladesh to empty into the Bay of Bengal. The Ganges River flows a total length of 1,557 miles (2,507 km), providing water to southern Tibet, northern India, and the entire countries of Nepal and Bangladesh.

THE ISSUE

The Ganges is the most sacred river of the Hindus, India's major religious group. Every year, millions of pilgrims journey to bathe in its waters. Those waters, however, are heavily polluted, carrying industrial and human waste, as well as agricultural runoff.

THE BACKGROUND

According to the Hindu religion, the Ganges is the Hindu goddess Ganga, come to earth in the form of a river to redeem the souls of worthy men and women. To bathe in the waters of "Mother Ganges" is to be cleansed of all sins.

For years waste materials from distilleries, chemical manufacturers, fertilizer complexes, and the sewage from a steadily growing population have poured into the Ganges.

Millions of Hindus trek across India every year to bathe in the Ganges. Various points along the river provide flights of stairs, called *ghats,* down which pilgrims travel to reach the river. Many believers come, or are brought, especially to die in the Ganges. A believer so fortunate as to die while immersed in its waters is assured of a place in paradise.

"Mother Ganges" provides physical support as well as spiritual. The river and its tributaries drain a region of almost 400,000 square miles (1,040,000 sq. km). These lands have been fertilized continu-

Dams on South Asia's great river systems, especially the Ganges, supply electricity to the region's villages and factories.

ously for centuries by nutrients from the river.

The Ganges and its tributaries support roughly 300 million people, more than the entire population of the United States. Most are rural farmers, living in villages of about 1,000 or fewer people that dot the fertile plain. Drinking water for the villages is provided by a few wells dug deeply enough to tap into groundwater. Washing and bathing are usually done in the river.

Although the Ganges runs through a primarily agricultural area, several major cities are located along its banks: the commercial center Allahabad, heavily industrialized Kanpur, and Patna, a rice-producing center. Delhi, one of the world's fastest-growing cities, spreads along a northwestern tributary. Most of these cities have 1 million or more inhabitants. Kanpur has more than 2 million people; Delhi has 8.7 million residents.

In the last 40 years, factories and chemical plants have developed in these cities, as well as along the river's banks. During the 1980s alone, more than 230 million gallons (872 million L) of untreated sewage were also emptied into the river every day.

THE POINTS OF VIEW

Observers point out that it is virtually impossible for many Hindus to comprehend pollu-tion in the river's sacred waters. "A Hindu pilgrim has no knowledge of the fact that an average drop of water contains traces of cyanide, arsenic, lead, zinc, chromium, selenium and mercury," maintains photojournalist Raghubir Singh. Experts point out the continuing—and steadily increasing—pollution problems posed by India's expanding population and the advance of modern industrialization. The rapid population increase results from better preventive medical care and intensive public health measures. These, in turn, have produced a significant drop in infant deaths.

THE ISSUE TODAY

The Indian government has instituted ongoing efforts to reverse pollution in the Ganges. In 1986 a $250 million clean-up project was begun.

In addition, the government started an ambitious program of population control. Many claim it is the most ambitious in history. Radio and TV ads promote family planning programs. The government also makes generous payments to families who agree to have no more than 2 children.

Although population growth has decreased, the average couple still has 3 to 4 children. About 65,000 babies are born every day. The continued population growth, coupled with the extent of the pollution

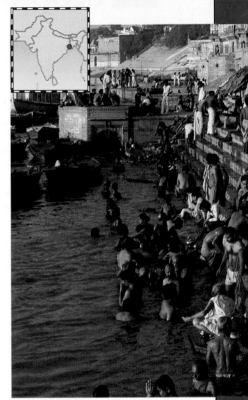

Some of India's largest cities, such as Calcutta and Varanasi, stand on the banks of the Ganges River. Pilgrims gather along the Ganges to perform ritual bathings.

from which the Ganges is already suffering, cause many to think that the river is long past the point of ecological recovery.

Reviewing the Case

1. What place does the Ganges River hold in the Hindu religion?

2. **Human/Environment** **Interaction** What factors contributed to the pollution of the Ganges?

People and Their Environment

SETTING THE SCENE

Read to Discover . . .
- how people have affected South Asia's wildlife.
- how both deforestation and reforestation are occurring.
- how water use is changing.
- how activities such as tourism affect the environment.

Key Terms
- deforestation
- trekker
- mangrove tree
- Chipko

Identify and Locate
Sundarbans, Uttar Pradesh, Narmada River basin

A s in all parts of the world, the environment of South Asia is affected in many ways by the human beings who inhabit the region. Because much of South Asia is so densely populated, the interaction between humans and the environment is especially intense.

HUMAN/ENVIRONMENT INTERACTION

Forests of South Asia

C enturies ago much of South Asia was covered with forests. Over time, much forestland has been converted into farmland or pastureland. Trees have been cut for firewood and shelter. Still, many forests survive—from the rain forests of Sri Lanka and the west coast of India to the deciduous forests of drier and cooler areas. Many experts doubt that these forests can be preserved if South Asia's population continues to expand at its present rate. They point out the severe effects of **deforestation**, or the loss of forests, and urge governments and individuals to conserve woodlands.

Deforestation

One expert estimates that half of the trees of northern India have been cut down in the past 30 years. Many trees have been cut by commercial timbering enterprises or to make way for other businesses, such as quarrying. Others have been slowly killed by impoverished villagers who use the leaves as fodder for their animals.

During the same period, almost one-third of Nepal's forests have been cut down. Nepalese farmers, pushed out of traditional farmlands because of the rising population, have been forced higher into the mountains. There they have cleared trees for farmland and grazing.

Tourists vastly increase the demand on firewood in Nepal and Bhutan. A single **trekker**, or mountain hiker, may use as much firewood as 10 Sherpas. Trekkers also leave litter and garbage behind on the once-pristine slopes of the Himalayas. To avoid these problems, the government of Bhutan closely supervises the tourists who enter the country.

Little of Sri Lanka's original vegetation remains untouched. Slash-and-burn methods of agriculture and illegal logging have caused rapid deforestation. In Bangladesh, using firewood as the main fuel has caused a severe loss of woodlands. The only forests left are in the Chittagong Hills—home to a small number of tribal people—and the Sundarbans, swampland full of **mangrove trees** along the Bay of Bengal.

Effects

The effects of deforestation can be devastating. Traditionally, dense mangroves in the Sundarbans have provided protection from cyclones and tidal waves that affect the coast of Bangladesh. As the mangroves are cut down, this defense is weakened. The forests in the Himalayas have acted like sponges—absorbing the heavy rains in the monsoon season and gradually releasing the moisture throughout the year. When these forests are cleared, heavy rains pour down the bare mountainsides. The water run-off causes serious monsoon flooding as far away as Bangladesh. Downpours wash topsoil off the mountains, sometimes causing dangerous landslides. Soil, carried along by streams and rivers, clogs dams with silt and alters the paths of the rivers.

Deforestation affects wildlife as well. As forests are cut down, animals such as tigers and elephants are slowly forced into smaller habitats. In the foothills of the Himalayas, a traditional honey hunter reports, "My grandfather took 600 nests a year. Last year we took 80." This is an example of the nature of human-environment relations. Human activity reduces the number of bee colonies, and then the people who depend on honey to make a living also suffer.

Deforestation of tropical rain forests is dangerous. These forests usually grow in poor soils. The trees' elaborate root systems efficiently absorb available nutrients and also hold the topsoil in place. The trees absorb and gradually release rainfall, and help keep the climate cooler than it would otherwise be. If the rain forests disappear, soil erodes, and climate changes occur.

Conservation

The people of Bhutan have taken steps to protect the nation's trees. The government supervises control of the forests, limiting commercial timbering and training citizens in forestry. Despite a high demand for Bhutan's wood products, roughly 70 percent of the landscape is still wooded. Pine trees have been planted on Nepalese hillsides to stop erosion. In Sri Lanka a reforestation program began in 1970, and the export of timber has been banned since 1977.

Geographic Themes

Human/Environment Interaction: Nepal
A Sherpa carries people and goods across the foothills of the Himalayas. *How have Nepalese farmers affected the environment of the foothills area?*

In India the **Chipko**—or tree-hugger—movement was started by environmental activist Sunderlal Bahaguna, a former follower of Gandhi. The tree-hugger movement is devoted to saving the remaining forests of northern India. Bahaguna tells villagers about the importance of trees and teaches them land management and reforestation techniques. In some villages Chipko has opened nurseries and provided seedlings. Bahaguna has had success in showing impoverished villagers that trees must be preserved if erosion and drought are to be avoided. He also convinced then Prime Minister Indira Gandhi to halt commercial timbering in the Himalayan forests of Uttar Pradesh.

Wildlife

South Asia is home to spectacular wildlife. For example, elephants, water buffalo, and monkeys are found in Sri Lanka. Crocodiles and the magnificent Bengal tiger roam Bangladesh. Unfortunately, many of these animals are endangered in a rapidly changing environment, especially in forested areas.

Some animals of the region have become rare through overhunting. Others have been endangered as a result of the loss of habitat.

SOUTH ASIAN MONSOONS

Winter winds
Summer winds

Lambert Conic projection

FOCUS ON GEOGRAPHIC THEMES

1. **Movement:** From what direction do the January monsoon winds come? What kind of weather do they bring?
2. **Human/Environment Interaction:** What impact do the July monsoon winds have on South Asia?

Deforestation and development projects, such as the construction of dams, have taken a severe toll on animal species.

In recent decades, the countries of South Asia have taken steps to protect animals. Governments have created wildlife reserves with help from international organizations. They also have passed laws to control hunting and development.

Water

In South Asia, humans and the environment affect each other in relation to water. The people build dams, they irrigate, they pollute, and they change the courses of rivers and the effects of the monsoons.

Dams

Dams play a crucial role in irrigating dry areas and regulating the flow of water. The Tarbela Dam of Pakistan is the world's largest earthen dam. Built in the 1970s, this dam controls floods and holds water in reserve for irrigating Pakistan's crops during the driest months. Dams also produce hydroelectric power. To build a dam, however, land must be flooded. Wildlife is displaced and plant life destroyed.

Dams trap silt that otherwise would flow downstream, and dam reservoirs can be a source of waterborne disease. In a country such as India, where many people consider the rivers holy, dams are seen as interfering with the spiritual force of the water.

Narmada River Project

Plans to build a huge dam in India's Narmada River basin have met with both intense excitement and violent disapproval. Supporting the project are those who point out that the dam will generate large amounts of electricity and irrigate millions of acres of cropland. It will also control flooding during the monsoon months.

Opposing the dam are the thousands of tribal people who will be forced out of their

Geographic Themes

Human/Environment Interaction: Endangered Species
South Asian animals, such as this tiger, are facing extinction as humans have cleared forested areas for development. *What steps are being taken to protect South Asia's wildlife?*

villages when flooding begins, and environmental activists who point out that dams ruin soils and create health problems. This controversy is an example of the complex interdependence between the human residents of South Asia and their environment.

SECTION 2 REVIEW

Checking for Understanding
1. **Define** deforestation, trekker, mangrove tree, Chipko.
2. **Locating Places** Where can the Bengal tiger still be found?
3. **Human/Environment Interaction** How do tourists affect the Himalayas?
4. **Region** How do forests prevent loss of topsoil?

Critical Thinking
5. **Drawing Conclusions** Why is it important for South Asians to preserve their forests?

Making Generalizations

Suppose you ask a friend to go roller blading. Your friend says, "I don't know. Luiz just twisted his knee on roller blades. Janet scraped up her arms and legs in a roller-blading accident. Roller blading is too dangerous." Whether you like it or not, your friend used these facts to form a **generalization**, or general statement, about roller blading. The generalization may be true or false. That depends largely on the accuracy of the supporting details.

REVIEWING THE SKILL

Using knowledge and experiences, people form generalizations to explain and understand the world. Generalizations play a key part in many fields of study. By observing animals in their natural surroundings, biologists form generalizations, or hypotheses, about such things as how animals find food, rear their young, and defend against enemies. Forming generalizations based on observation, and then testing these theories against more evidence, is a cornerstone of the scientific method.

Although generalizations help us understand the world, they also can be misleading. For example, the generalization about roller blading was based on two incidents. But what really caused these roller-blading accidents? Were Luiz and Janet using proper equipment? Were they roller blading on busy streets? Were they wearing pads and helmets? To say that roller blading is always dangerous may be an **over generalization**, or a statement that is too broad. Perhaps proper equipment and precautions make it a far less dangerous sport. Whenever making generalizations, be sure that they are based on accurate supporting details. Use the following steps in making generalizations:

- Gather facts, examples, or statements related to the topic.
- Identify similarities or patterns among these facts.
- Use these similarities or patterns to form generalizations about the topic.
- Test your generalizations against other facts and examples.

PRACTICING THE SKILL

Write a generalization based on each group of statements that follow.

1. • Using simple hand tools and oxen-drawn plows, most South Asian subsistence farmers produce just enough food to feed their families.
   • Because many people in India believe that land must be divided equally among sons, farms are becoming smaller and less efficient.
   • Many South Asian farmers are reluctant to abandon traditional practices such as leaving the land fallow after harvest.
2. • Agricultural production in South Asia must rise to meet the nutritional demands of a rapidly growing population.
   • Increasing population severely limits the abilities of South Asian governments to provide services for their people.
   • To acquire more land, people in South Asia clear forests for planting and grazing, thus causing environmental problems such as soil erosion, habitat destruction, and climate change.

For additional practice in this skill, see Practicing Skills on page 524 of the Chapter 25 Review.

1 SECTION	KEY TERMS	SUMMARY
Living in South Asia	**subsistence farming** (p. 511) **jute** (p. 512) **cash crop** (p. 512) **green revolution** (p. 513)	• Agricultural advances are helping South Asia produce enough food for its expanding population. • Main food crops include rice and wheat; main cash crops include jute and tea. • Mining, fishing, and tourism are significant sources of income in the region. • Industry—both light and heavy—is expanding in the region.

Tea plantation in Sri Lanka

2 SECTION	KEY TERMS	SUMMARY
People and Their Environment	**deforestation** (p. 518) **trekker** (p. 518) **mangrove tree** (p. 518) **Chipko** (p. 520)	• Much of South Asia has been deforested by human beings seeking wood for fuel and shelter, and land for farming and grazing. • Deforestation can lead to flooding, landslides, loss of valuable topsoil, loss of habitat for animals, and climate changes. • Governments and individuals throughout South Asia are attempting to conserve and replant forests. • Despite the loss of many animals due to overhunting and habitat loss, South Asians are working to maintain existing species in wildlife preserves and elsewhere. • Water usage is controversial in South Asia for many reasons; dams are needed to control flooding and provide water for irrigation, but they also cause environmental problems.

Tiger reserve in India

Reviewing Key Terms

Choose the vocabulary term that best completes each of the sentences below. Write your answers on a separate sheet of paper.

jute (p. 512)
cash crop (p. 512)
green revolution (p. 513)
deforestation (p. 518)
trekker (p. 518)
mangrove trees (p. 518)
Chipko (p. 520)

SECTION 1

1. A fiber used to make rope and cloth is _____ .

2. Something grown to make money rather than to use for one's own survival is known as a _____ .

3. The development and use of new, high-yield grains is called the _____ .

SECTION 2

4. A mountain hiker is known as a _____ .

5. _____ grow in the swamplands of Bangladesh.

6. A movement to save the forests of northern India is called _____ .

7. The loss of all the trees in an area is called _____ .

Reviewing Facts

SECTION 1

8. How do the majority of people in South Asia make their living?

9. What is the major food crop of South Asia?

10. What is India's most important industry?

SECTION 2

11. Which South Asian country still has forests covering 70 percent of the land?

12. Why is the Bengal tiger endangered?

13. What religious reason do people in India have for opposing dam construction?

Critical Thinking

14. **Making Generalizations**   What effect is modern technology having on the economy of South Asia?

15. **Expressing Problems**   What are several ways in which expanding human populations are having negative effects on the environment of South Asia?

 ## Geographic Themes

16. **Place**   Where does most mining take place in India? What are the key minerals?

17. **Movement**   How has Bhutan's isolation helped to preserve its environment?

Practicing Skills

Making Generalizations

18. Write a generalization based on the group of statements below.
    A. The government of Bhutan strictly controls commercial use of its forests.
    B. Nepal, Sri Lanka, and India employ reforestation projects to replace forests.
    C. South Asian governments have restricted hunting of endangered species, used experimental methods for removing large animals from populated areas, and established wildlife reserves.

Using the Unit Atlas

Refer to the physical geography section of the Unit Atlas on page 472–473.

19. What mineral is mined in India?

20. What is Pakistan's greatest natural resource?

21. What is South Asia's highest point?

Projects

Individual Activity

You have learned a little about the economic activities in the various nations of South Asia. Choose the nation that interests you most and research one form of economic activity. You might research the garment industry of India, the tourist business in Nepal, or shipbreaking in Bangladesh. Write a brief report on the subject.

Cooperative Learning Activity

Working in a small group, organize a debate on one of the aspects of the environmental issues in South Asia. For example, half of the group might assemble arguments and data to support the building of dams in the region, while the other half might compile arguments against dam-building. Each group should hold its debate in front of the rest of the class. Afterward, the class as a whole should evaluate the issue and try to form judgments.

Writing About Geography

Cause and Effect

Choose one aspect of human-environment interaction in South Asia and write an essay that shows how humans both cause changes in the environment and then are affected in turn by those changes. You may use your journal, text, encyclopedias, guide books, or magazine articles to help you write your essay.

Locating Places

SOUTH ASIA: PHYSICAL GEOGRAPHY

Match the letters on the map with the places and physical features of South Asia. Write your answers on a separate sheet of paper.

1. Calcutta
2. Arabian Sea
3. Kathmandu Valley
4. Narmada River
5. Indus Valley
6. Ganges River
7. Indo-Gangetic Plain
8. Malabar Coast
9. Bay of Bengal
10. Himalayas

GEOGRAPHY CONNECTION

South Asia and the United States

COTTONS, CASHMERE, AND TIE-DYE

South Asia's textile industry has an ancient past. Experts have dated some printed cottons of the region to 3000 B.C. The materials calico and chintz have been part of our heritage since colonial times. Cashmere, madras, and tie-dye appeared later in our fashion history, but have become popular and enduring favorites as well.

▲ **CHINTZ** is a cotton export from South Asia that quickly became an American favorite. A medium-weight cotton fabric with a soft, lustrous glaze, chintz has been used in home decorating since the 1700s. Its wide variety of colors and patterns, as well as its durability and easy care, keep it in demand.

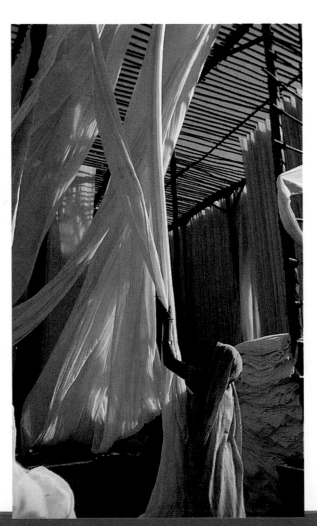

◀ **MADRAS** is a cotton fabric from South Asia that has found a place in American wardrobes. First produced in the Indian city of Madras, the fabric's strong bright designs are colored with vegetable dyes. The colors "bleed," or run, when washed, resulting in the soft, subtle coloring that is the fabric's trademark. Madras fabric reached the height of its popularity in the United States during the late 1950s and early 1960s.

▼ **CALICO,** a lightweight cotton fabric, originated in and was named for the Indian city of Calcutta. It quickly became one of the most popular products imported to the United Kingdom by the British-owned East India Company. Hundreds of designs and colors were eventually available in Europe and North America as a result of the Industrial Revolution. Fragments of cotton calicos became the basic ingredient of an American art form developed by pioneer women—the patchwork quilt. Colorful calicos remain a contemporary textile for shirts, blouses, and casual summer clothing.

▲ **CASHMERE,** a lightweight luxury fabric, is made from the fine, soft hair fibers that grow as the undercoat on goats in the Vale of Kashmir in northern South Asia. An especially supple and elegant textile, cashmere tops the list of the best dressed for coats and sweaters.

TIE-DYE ▶
refers to a special technique developed in central India to decorate fabrics. A length of fabric, usually cotton or silk, is twisted, and sections are tied with thread or rope before dying. Tie-dying most often produces spectacular circular or zigzag designs of brilliant hue. Fashion seekers prize tie-dye for its unique one-of-a-kind look.

Checking for Understanding

1. What South Asian textiles are part of American fashion?
2. **Movement** How did calico and chintz first get to the United States?

East Asia

GeoJournal Activity

While studying East Asia, follow news reports about the region either on television or in newspapers and magazines. Keep a record of the developments under the following categories: Environment, Culture and Daily Life, History and Government.

National Geographic photographer Jodi Cobb

NATIONAL GEOGRAPHIC SOCIETY

Picturing the World

These Buddhist temple pagodas in southern China date from the Tang Dynasty, which ruled China from A.D. 618-907. China was governed by emperors of different dynasties for some 3,600 years. Today, China is ruled by a Communist government. Buddhism spread from India, where it originated, to China about 2,000 years ago. Look at the circle graph on page 562.

1. What percentage of East Asians practice Buddhism?
2. Read to learn about the religions of East Asia. Why are so many East Asians considered as nonreligious in the chart?

Picture Atlas CD-ROM Enrichment Corner

Create a file of East Asia information. (See the *Picture Atlas of the World* User's Guide on how to use the Collector button.) Read the essays and vital statistics, look at the photos, map, and videos, and listen to the musical selections for each country. Make sure your file includes the following information:

1. Most heavily and sparsely populated nations
2. Where the majority of the people of East Asia live
3. Examples of cultural phenomena that date back more than a thousand years
4. National dishes or pastimes
5. Major physical features of the region
6. Major tourist sites of the region
7. Major problems in the region

EAST ASIA

Cultural Geography

EXPLORING CULTURAL DIVERSITY

1. *What nations make up East Asia?*
2. *What areas of China are most heavily populated? Most sparsely populated?*
3. *What is the approximate population of East Asia?*
4. *What are the national capitals for the six nations of East Asia?*

During the 1200s, the **Mongols** built the largest empire in history, conquering the area from eastern Asia to eastern Europe.

The **Japanese** enjoy a mixture of Eastern and Western cultures. Their favorite spectator sports, for example, are baseball and sumo wrestling.

EAST ASIA: POLITICAL

70°E 90°E 110°E 130°E
50°N

Ulan Bator
MONGOLIA

NORTH KOREA
Beijing Pyongyang
JAPAN
Seoul
SOUTH KOREA
Tokyo

CHINA

30°N

N

Tropic of Cancer

Taipei

Macao (Port.)
TAIWAN

0   500 mi.
0   500 km

Hong Kong (U.K.)

—— National boundary
⊛ National capital
Conic projection

China's largest ethnic group is the Han nationality, which includes 94 percent of the population. The remaining 6 percent is divided among 50 ethnic groups.

The Chinese leased **Hong Kong** to the British for 99 years in 1898. Hong Kong will revert to Chinese rule in 1997.

North and South Korea are divided by a heavily policed 2.5 mile- (4.0 km-) wide demilitarized zone. The zone was established in 1953, after the Korean War.

The Chinese Nationalist government rules **Taiwan.**

Although almost 75 percent of all Chinese live in rural villages, **China** has at least 31 major cities with populations of 1 million or more. More than 90 percent of China's 1.2 billion people live crowded into one-sixth of the country's land.

About half of all people of **Mongolia** live and work on livestock farms.

About 70 percent of all Koreans live in cities. **South Korea**, however, has almost three times the number of large cities as **North Korea.**

EAST ASIA: POPULATION DENSITY

Per sq. km	Per sq. mi.	Cities
Over 100	Over 250	■ Over 5,000,000
50-100	125-250	□ 2,000,000 to 5,000,000
25-50	60-125	• 1,000,000 to 2,000,000
1-25	2-60	○ Under 1,000,000
Under 1	Under 2	
Uninhabited	Uninhabited	

Conic projection

The majority of **Hong Kong's** people live in the capital, Victoria, and Kowloon. The cities are Hong Kong's major centers of economic activity.

Almost all of **Taiwan's** people live on the western third of the island, which is a coastal plain.

So much of **Japan's** land is covered with mountains and hills that its population of 125 million lives densely packed along the islands' coasts.

The population of East Asia is more than 5½ times that of the United States.

Population: East Asia and the United States

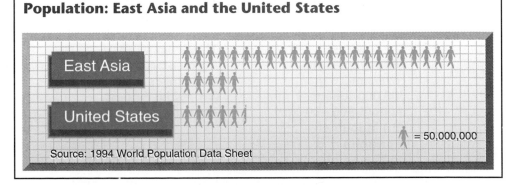

East Asia

United States

Source: 1994 World Population Data Sheet

👤 = 50,000,000

EAST ASIA
Physical Geography

CHARTING YOUR COURSE

1. **What four large islands make up Japan?**
2. **What desert area is found in Mongolia and northern China?**
3. **What are three natural resources found in East Asia?**
4. **What is the highest point in East Asia?**

Mongolia is a land of high plateaus and towering mountains. No part of Mongolia is less than 1,700 feet (518 m) above sea level.

Japan consists of four large islands and thousands of smaller ones.

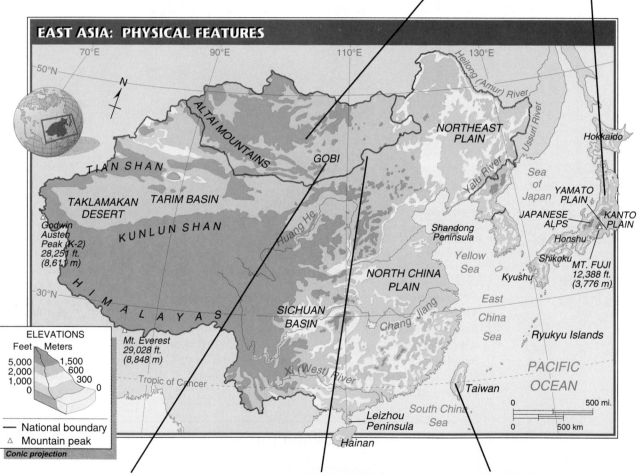

EAST ASIA: PHYSICAL FEATURES

ALTAI MOUNTAINS

TIAN SHAN

GOBI

NORTHEAST PLAIN

Heilong (Amur) River

Ussuri River

Hokkaido

TAKLAMAKAN DESERT

TARIM BASIN

Yalu River

Sea of Japan

YAMATO PLAIN

Godwin Austen Peak (K-2) 28,251 ft. (8,611 m)

KUNLUN SHAN

Huang He

Shandong Peninsula

JAPANESE ALPS

KANTO PLAIN

Honshu

HIMALAYAS

Yellow Sea

NORTH CHINA PLAIN

Shikoku

MT. FUJI 12,388 ft. (3,776 m)

Kyushu

East China Sea

Ryukyu Islands

SICHUAN BASIN

Chang Jiang

Mt. Everest 29,028 ft. (8,848 m)

Xi (West) River

PACIFIC OCEAN

Tropic of Cancer

Taiwan

Leizhou Peninsula

South China Sea

Hainan

ELEVATIONS

Feet	Meters
5,000	1,500
2,000	600
1,000	300
0	0

— National boundary
△ Mountain peak

Conic projection

0   500 mi.

0   500 km

The treeless, windswept Gobi covers more than 500,000 square miles (1,300,000 sq. km) in southern **Mongolia** and northern **China**.

The **Great Wall of China**, stretching 4,000 miles (6,437 km), is the longest structure ever built.

Taiwan's thickly forested mountains blanket about half of the island. Many plunge sharply to the sea along the eastern coast.

Mongolia has rich deposits of coal, copper, gold, iron, and petroleum.

Anthracite (hard coal) and tungsten are **South Korea's** chief mining products.

Although **Japan** has few natural resources, it is a world industrial superpower. It imports most of its raw materials.

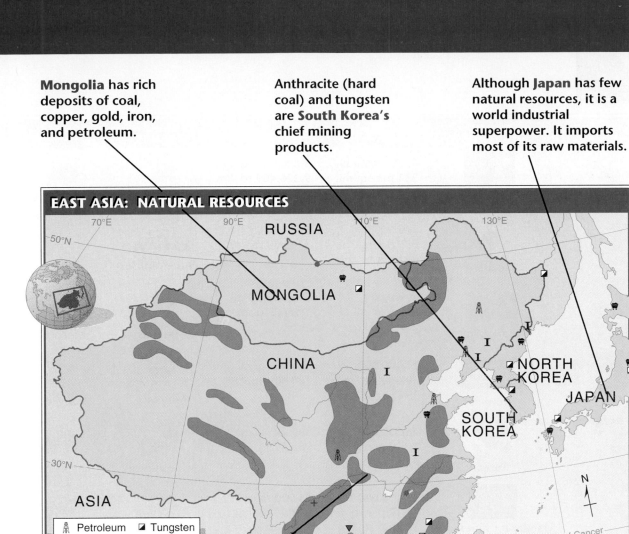

EAST ASIA: NATURAL RESOURCES

70°E 90°E 110°E 130°E
50°N
RUSSIA
MONGOLIA
CHINA
NORTH KOREA
SOUTH KOREA
JAPAN
ASIA
30°N
TAIWAN
Tropic of Cancer
MACAO
HONG KONG

Petroleum
Coal
Iron ore
Tin
Tungsten
Bauxite
Copper

Conic projection

0   500 mi.
0   500 km

N

The **Sichuan Basin's** mild climate and long growing season make it one of **China's** main agricultural regions.

An accessible location and excellent natural harbor have helped make **Hong Kong** a world center of trade, finance, manufacturing, and transportation.

Cedar, hemlock, and oak trees grow in **Taiwan's** forests, its most important natural resource.

China and the Korean Peninsula: Physical Profile

15000 ft. — TIAN SHAN
10000 ft.
5000 ft.
2000 ft.
Sea level

TARIM BASIN
GOBI
KOREAN PENINSULA
East China Sea
Sea of Japan
Beijing

0   500 mi.
0   500 km

West to East at approximately 40°N latitude

COUNTRY* AND CAPITAL	FLAG AND LANGUAGES	POPULATION	LANDMASS	PRINCIPAL EXPORT	PRODUCTS IMPORT
China Beijing	Mandarin, Yue Wu Hakka, Xiang	1,192,000,000 331 per sq. mi. 128 per sq. km	3,600,930 sq. mi. 9,326,409 sq. km	Textiles	Machinery
Japan Tokyo	Japanese	125,000,000 859 per sq. mi. 331 per sq. km	145,370 sq. mi. 376,508 sq. km	Motor Vehicles	Fuels
Mongolia Ulan Bator	Mongolian	2,400,000 4 per sq. mi. 2 per sq. km	604,830 sq. mi. 1,566,510 sq. km	Minerals	Machinery
North Korea Pyongyang	Korean	23,100,000 497 per sq. mi. 192 per sq. km	46,490 sq. mi. 120,409 sq. km	Minerals	Petroleum
South Korea Seoul	Korean	44,500,000 1,170 per sq. mi. 452 per sq. km	38,120 sq. mi. 98,731 sq. km	Machinery	Machinery
Taiwan Taipei	Mandarin Chinese, Taiwanese, Hakka dialects	21,100,000 1,517 per sq. mi. 586 per sq. km	13,900 sq. mi. 36,001 sq. km	Machinery	Machinery

*Country maps not drawn to scale.

The Potala Palace in Lhasa, Tibet, was once home of the Dalai Lama, Tibet's exiled Buddhist leader.

Japan's ancient Shinto religion is still practiced at shrines throughout the country.

Taiwan has a booming industrial economy that exports products to other parts of the world.

Yurts, or tentlike structures, are common living quarters in the far western part of China.

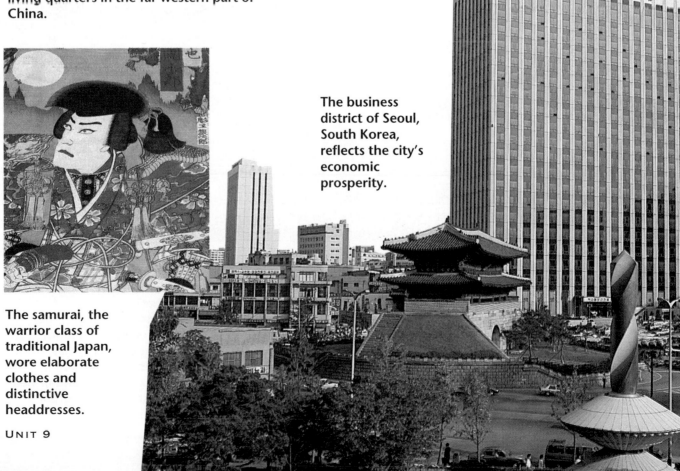

The business district of Seoul, South Korea, reflects the city's economic prosperity.

The samurai, the warrior class of traditional Japan, wore elaborate clothes and distinctive headdresses.

The Physical Geography of East Asia

CHAPTER FOCUS

Geographic Setting

The culture region of East Asia includes much of the Asian mainland south of Russia, along with nearby islands. High inland mountains and plateaus separate mainland East Asia from the rest of the continent.

Geographic Themes

Section 1 The Land
PLACE East Asia has a varied landscape. Landforms range from towering mountains to barren deserts to rich river valleys.

▲ Photograph: *Mount Fuji, Japan*

Section 2 The Climate and Vegetation
LOCATION East Asia's large landmass puts it in many different climate zones, from subarctic to tropical rain forest. Location inland or near the coast also has a great effect on climates.

SETTING THE SCENE

Read to Discover . . .
- the variety of landscapes in East Asia.
- the importance of East Asian rivers.
- the natural resources of East Asia.

Key Terms
- archipelago
- tsunami
- loess

Identify and Locate
Mongolia, Korean Peninsula, Japan, Taiwan, Huang He, Chang Jiang, Xi River, Plateau of Xizang, the Himalayas, Gobi, Tarim Basin, North China Plain, Hong Kong

Tokyo, Japan

Konnichiwa. My hometown, Tokyo, is very crowded. I live close to the Metropolitan Office, which is the most crowded place in Japan. There are a lot of advertising signs with bright blinking lights, so we hardly see the stars. But when it's a beautiful sunny day, I can see Mt. Fuji in the distance. Some people always speak ill of a big city but I like my city. Hope you'll come and visit me.

Ema Ito

his postcard from Japan mentions Mount Fuji, one of many amazing sights in the lands that make up East Asia. A few hundred miles away, Ema Ito would have seen a very different landscape. East Asia is a place of immense contrast—towering, snow-covered mountains in the west, barren deserts in the north, lush green fields in the southeast, and hundreds of islands.

PLACE

Land and Sea

The huge People's Republic of China dominates the geography of East Asia, occupying almost 3,600,000 square miles (9,326,000 sq. km)—about 81 percent of the land area. With about 1.2 billion people, China has the largest population of any nation.

Mongolia, north of China, covers more than 604,000 square miles (1,567,000 sq. km)—an area larger than Texas, New Mexico, Arizona, and Colorado combined. Its population, however, is only about 2,400,000.

The other countries in East Asia are Japan, North Korea, South Korea, and Taiwan. The region also includes the colonies of Hong Kong and Macao.

Peninsulas, Islands, and Seas

The smaller nations of East Asia are located on peninsulas and islands. These landforms divide this part of the Pacific Ocean into small seas.

The Korean Peninsula juts out from northern China, between the Sea of Japan and the Yellow Sea. To the southwest, between Japan and the mainland, is the East China Sea. Still farther south, beyond the island of Taiwan, the South China Sea lies between the Philippines and the peninsula of Southeast Asia.

The Japanese Islands

Japan is an **archipelago**, a group of islands made up of four large, mountainous islands and thousands of smaller ones. Most of Japan's major cities are on the large island of Honshu. The other islands, from north to south, are Hokkaido (hah•KY•doh), Shikoku (shi•KOH•KOO), and Kyushu (kee•OO•shoo).

Other Islands

South from Japan, a curving arc of small islands sweeps toward the mainland of Asia. The Ryukyu (ree•YOO•KYOO) Islands end near Taiwan (ty•WAHN), a mountainous island about 100 miles (about 161 km) from the coast of mainland China. This island is the home of the Republic of China. This small country also includes 2 other offshore islands, Quemoy and Matsu, and an island chain called the Pescadores.

The island arc that includes Japan, the Ryukyus, Taiwan, and the Philippines is at a boundary where tectonic plates meet. The islands are part of the Pacific Rim's Ring of Fire, where violent earthquakes and volcanoes are frequent.

Volcanoes originally formed most of these islands. Japan still has about 50 active volcanoes, and more than 1,000 small earthquakes shake the country every year. Violent quakes occur less often but bring disaster to people and buildings. An undersea earthquake can send a huge **tsunami** (tsu•NAH•mee), or sea wave, crashing against the islands.

Macao and Hong Kong

Farther south, on the China coast, are two small European colonies on offshore islands and peninsulas. British Hong Kong and Portuguese Macao are both bustling commercial shipping ports.

REGION

Mountains and Lowlands

Mountain ranges and rugged highlands cover much of East Asia. The only large lowland areas are on the mainland, in eastern China.

The world's highest mountains mark the western edge of East Asia where many peaks soar more than 25,000 feet (7,620 m) high. This area is known as "the roof of the world." Mount Everest, the highest mountain in the world, is found here.

The region has several other mountain ranges. They fan out in different directions from this center. They include the Himalayas, the Karakoram Range, the Kunlun Shan, the Tian Shan, and the Altai Mountains.

The mountain ranges of Manchuria extend southward through the center of Korea. Coastal plains edge both sides of the peninsula. Japan is even more mountainous than Korea and also has coastal plains.

The highest plateau region in East Asia is the Plateau of Xizang, at elevations ranging from 13,000 to 15,000 feet (3,962 to 4,572 m)—higher than many mountain peaks in other places. North and east of the plateau are other rugged highlands, at elevations ranging from 3,300 to 6,500 feet (1,006 to 1,981 m). The huge Mongolian Plateau extends over much of Mongolia and parts of northern China.

Between the highlands are broad, flat basins. For example, the huge Tarim Basin lies between the Kunlun Shan and Tian Shan. It is part desert and part salt marshes. By contrast, much of Sichuan (SSU•CHWAN) province in southwestern China lies in a great fertile basin that is heavily cultivated.

Large parts of northwestern China and Mongolia are dry, windswept desert waste-

EAST ASIA: PHYSICAL-POLITICAL

FOCUS ON GEOGRAPHIC THEMES

1. **Location:** What East Asian country lies north of the Gobi?
2. **Place:** Which areas of East Asia are under European rule?
3. **Movement:** What river has its outlet near the port city of Shanghai?
4. **Location:** Where are lowland areas located in East Asia?

---

lands. The sandy Taklamakan Desert and the treeless Gobi are among these deserts. The Gobi stretches across southern Mongolia and parts of China.

PLACE

River Systems

Extensive river systems have always been important on the mainland of East Asia. Chinese civilization began in these river valleys, and they are still crucial to China's economic well-being.

China's Rivers

China's major rivers begin in the highlands of the Plateau of Xizang and flow eastward to the sea. The northernmost is the Huang He (HWAHNG•HUH), which flows across the North China Plain and empties into the Yellow Sea. This river is known as the Yellow River because it carries tons of fine, yellowish-brown topsoil called **loess** (LES), which is blown from the western deserts into the air and water by winds. This rich soil, along with water from the river, makes the North China Plain a rich wheat-farming area.

The Huang He is also known as "China's sorrow." For thousands of years, the river's frequent and terrible floods have destroyed villages and towns, killing hundreds of thousands of people.

The Chang Jiang, Asia's longest river, flows 3,964 miles (6,378 km) through mountains and across fertile plains. It empties into the East China Sea.

The basin the Chang Jiang and its tributaries form is China's "rice bowl." More than half of China's crops grow here, especially rice and other grains.

A third major river, the Xi (SHEE), or West, crosses southeastern China and flows into the South China Sea near Guangzhou (GWANG•JOH). There it has built up a delta of fertile soil. Farmers in this warm region grow rice and other food crops, often growing two crops on the same piece of land, one after the other.

China also has the world's longest artificial waterway. The Grand Canal runs from Beijing (BAY•JING), the capital, to Hangzhou, a distance of 1,114 miles (1,792 km).

Japan and Korea

In contrast to the long rivers of China, Japan and Korea have many short, swift-flowing rivers that run from the mountains to the sea. They flow through deep valleys with

Geographic Themes

Place: Huang He Valley
The Huang He flows through one of China's important agricultural and industrial areas. *Why is the Huang He River also known as the Yellow River?*

forested hillsides, often forming spectacular waterfalls.

HUMAN/ENVIRONMENT INTERACTION

Natural Resources

East Asia is rich in minerals, forests, and other resources, but they are distributed unevenly among the countries. Because of its great land area, China has the most abundant supplies of natural resources.

Mineral Resources

The continent of Asia, as a whole, has the largest reserves of coal in the world. Although more than half the world's coal is in Russia, China is the third-largest coal producer in the world. Nearly all parts of China have coal deposits, but the richest are in the north, especially Manchuria. China also has petroleum reserves as well as tin, tungsten, and bauxite deposits.

Like the neighboring region of Manchuria, the Korean Peninsula has good mineral resources. They include iron ore, coal, gold, and copper.

Japan is East Asia's leading industrial country, but mineral resources are scarce in its islands. It does have coal, copper, some iron ore, and a few other minerals. Still, Japan must import a variety of minerals.

Land and Forest Resources

Asia's many mountains provide little available land that is flat enough or rich enough for farming and growing food. In China, only about 11 percent of the land—most of it in the north—can be used for growing crops. Larger areas in western China and Mongolia are grasslands where animals can graze. The soil in much of north China's farmland is made up of thick deposits of loess blown from the Gobi. Loess can also pile up and form thick, rounded cliffs. Since ancient times, people in areas of northern China have dug cave homes in such loess cliffs.

Forests once covered huge areas of China, but over many centuries, the Chinese people have cut down trees for heating, building, and

Geographic Themes

Place: Inland Sea, Japan
Hundreds of hilly, wooded islands dot Japan's beautiful Inland Sea, which separates Honshu from Shikoku. *Why are the people of East Asia so dependent on the sea?*

other uses. Today, about 12 percent of the country is forested.

In Japan farmland is very scarce. Japanese farmers try to make good use of every inch of land, and they have the most efficient agriculture in Asia. While urban areas are crowded and farmland is scarce, most of the steep hillsides of Japan are still covered with thick forests. Some trees supply lumber for building.

Korea's best farmland is on the coastal plain in the south. Many trees have been cleared for farmland, but forests still grow in the mountains.

Farmers use about one-third of the land on the island of Taiwan, growing rice and tropical fruits like bananas and pineapples. About half of the island is thickly forested mountains.

Water and Ocean Resources

For thousands of years, farmers in East Asia have depended on water from the rivers for irrigating their fields. Where the weather is warm enough, irrigation lets farmers grow two or three crops a year. The rivers also carry fertile soil and deposit it on the flood plains and in deltas.

Because farmland is scarce throughout East Asia, island nations and coastal areas depend on the oceans as an important food source. Their fishing fleets bring back food both for people at home and for export. Japan is one of the world's two main fish producers, while China ranks third.

2 The Climate and Vegetation

SETTING THE SCENE

Read to Discover . . .
- the different climate regions in East Asia.
- how seasonal winds affect climates in East Asia.
- the kinds of plants and trees that grow in different parts of East Asia.

Key Terms
- monsoon
- typhoon

Identify and Locate
Japan Current, Climate regions: humid continental, humid subtropical, steppe, desert, highland, tropical rain forest

E ast Asia has a large landmass. In latitude, it spans a greater range than the contiguous United States. Heilongjiang (HAY•LUNG•jee•AHNG) Province in northern Manchuria is about as far north as Hudson Bay in Canada, while the Chinese island of Hainan is at about the same latitude as Mexico City. As the *People's Republic of China Yearbook* says:

When Heilongjiang Province in the north is snow-bound in winter, it is stifling hot on the islands in the South China Sea. And when the sun rises over the Wusuli River in the east, it is still night on the Pamir Plateau in the west.

East Asia's location as well as factors such as ocean winds, storms, and mountains, give the region a great variety of climates and vegetation.

REGION

East Asia's Climate Regions

M uch of East Asia is in one of the mid-latitude climate zones, while the rest is generally divided among highland, desert, and steppe climates. Small parts of northern Mongolia are subarctic. Small areas in southern China are tropical rain forest.

Monsoons

As in South Asia, the seasonal winds called **monsoons** have a great effect on East Asia's climate. In the summer, warm monsoon winds blow from the Pacific. They bring hot, humid weather and soaking downpours of rain, especially near the coast. Most rain falls between April and October.

In the fall and winter, the winds switch direction. Icy winds blow from Siberia and Mongolia. Because of these winds, winters in monsoon areas of China are colder and drier than in other countries at the same latitudes. When these cold winds blow across the Sea of Japan, however, they pick up moisture and bring heavy snow to northern Japan.

The monsoons are necessary to life in Asia, especially for farmers to grow crops. If the summer monsoons are late or do not bring enough rain, even the coastal plains in northern China may have droughts.

Violent hurricanes called **typhoons** also blow across coastal East Asia from the Pacific Ocean. Most occur between late August and October. High winds and heavy rains can do great damage, but typhoons also may bring welcome rain in the dry season.

Ocean Currents

Ocean currents also influence the climate of island countries in East Asia. The warm-water Japan Current flows along the southern and southeastern coasts of the Japanese islands, making winters milder there.

Along the coasts of Hokkaido, the northernmost island of Japan, the cold Okhotsk Current flows from the Arctic. It brings harsh, cold winters to Hokkaido.

Mid-latitude Climates

Southeastern China, southern Korea, Taiwan, and the southern islands of Japan have a humid subtropical climate. Summers here are

Geographic Themes

Place: Hokkaido, Japan

Winters are cold and snowy in the northern part of the Japanese archipelago. *What type of climate is found in southern Japan?*

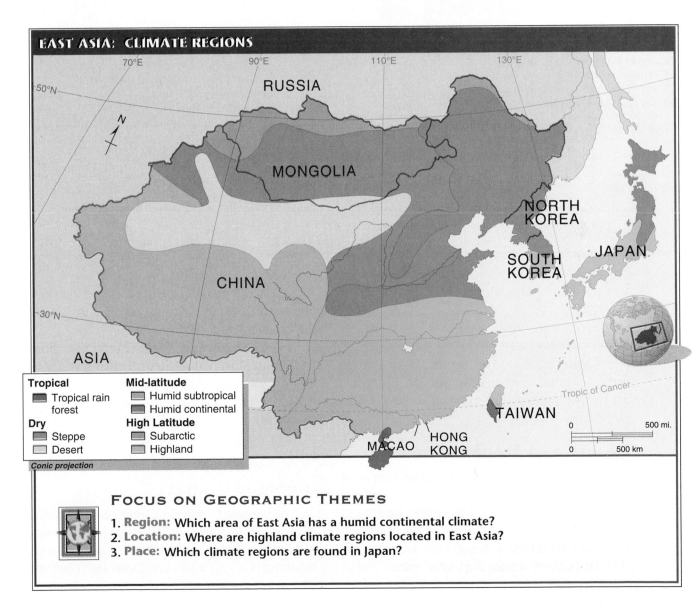

EAST ASIA: CLIMATE REGIONS

RUSSIA

MONGOLIA

NORTH KOREA

JAPAN

SOUTH KOREA

CHINA

ASIA

TAIWAN

Tropic of Cancer

MACAO   HONG KONG

Tropical
- Tropical rain forest

Dry
- Steppe
- Desert

Mid-latitude
- Humid subtropical
- Humid continental

High Latitude
- Subarctic
- Highland

Conic projection

0   500 mi.

0   500 km

FOCUS ON GEOGRAPHIC THEMES

1. **Region:** Which area of East Asia has a humid continental climate?
2. **Location:** Where are highland climate regions located in East Asia?
3. **Place:** Which climate regions are found in Japan?

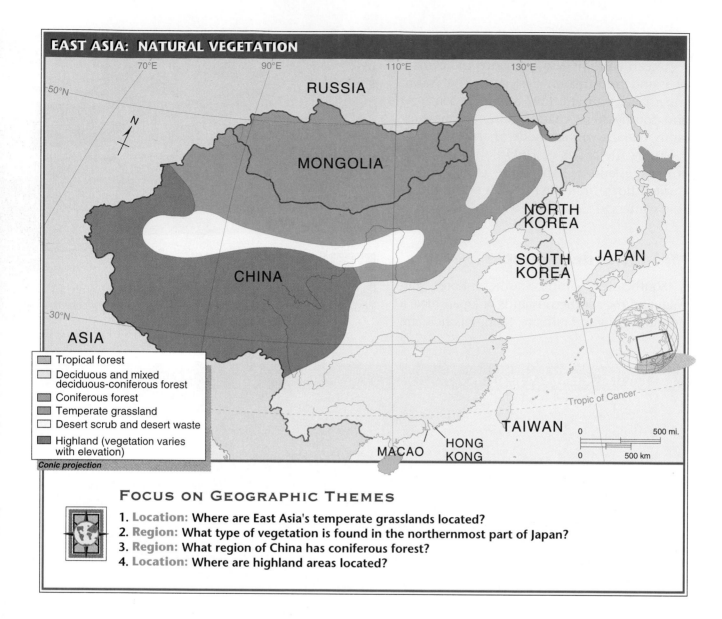

EAST ASIA: NATURAL VEGETATION

Legend:
- Tropical forest
- Deciduous and mixed deciduous-coniferous forest
- Coniferous forest
- Temperate grassland
- Desert scrub and desert waste
- Highland (vegetation varies with elevation)

Conic projection

FOCUS ON GEOGRAPHIC THEMES

1. **Location:** Where are East Asia's temperate grasslands located?
2. **Region:** What type of vegetation is found in the northernmost part of Japan?
3. **Region:** What region of China has coniferous forest?
4. **Location:** Where are highland areas located?

warm or hot. The summer monsoons bring heavy rains.

Climates in northeastern China, northern Korea, and northern Japan are still temperate, but cooler than in the south. These places have a humid continental climate. Summers are warm or hot, but winters are cold and sometimes very snowy.

Desert and Steppe Climates

Much of Mongolia and the inland areas of northern China have dry climates—desert and steppe. These great arid areas lie so far inland that moist winds from the ocean do not reach them. In addition, the high mountains that surround these areas trap any rainfall that might reach them.

In both steppe and desert climates, temperatures are extreme. It often is very hot in the daytime and very cold at night.

Because many deserts in the world are close to the Equator, people tend to think of them as hot and dry. The Gobi and Taklamakan, however, are often cold and windy. While the Gobi may have summer heat waves, average winter temperatures there are only 10°F (−12°C).

Highland Climates

The climate in mountainous areas depends mainly on elevation. It is usually cool or cold. As you climb higher, the air temperature drops by about 3.5°F (2°C) every 1,000 feet (305 m) of elevation. For example, the Plateau of

Xizang averages more than 13,000 to 15,000 feet (3,962 to 4,572 m) in elevation. Even in summer, average temperatures there are only about 58°F (14°C).

Tropical Climates

A small strip of land along China's southern coast, part of Taiwan, and the island of Hainan have a tropical rain forest climate. Here it is hot year-round, with a rainy season brought by the summer monsoons.

REGION

East Asia's Vegetation

Forests once covered more of East Asia than they do today. Over thousands of years, however, forests have been cut for timber and cleared for farms. In many places, this has led to serious erosion problems on hillsides and along river valleys.

Vegetation in the Middle Latitudes

In the mid-latitude climate of most of East Asia, forests are a mix of needleleaf evergreen trees, or conifers; broad-leaved deciduous trees; and broad-leaved evergreens.

Both deciduous trees and broad-leaved evergreens grow in humid subtropical climates. Bamboos, which are not trees but tree-like grasses, grow in many warm areas of East Asia. Other valuable plants are the tea bush and the mulberry tree, whose leaves provide food for silkworms.

Tropical Vegetation

Where the climate is tropical, palms and tropical hardwoods grow along with broad-leaved evergreens and tropical fruits such as bananas. A lush rain forest covers much of the tropical island of Hainan.

Steppe and Highland Vegetation

Natural vegetation on the steppe is mainly grasses and a few trees. Many of the original

Geographic Themes

Place: Southern China
A small part of southern China has a tropical climate with warm temperatures and plenty of rain. *How does the climate of northern China compare with that in southern China?*

forests have been cut, leaving grasses and shrubs that can grow in the dry climate.

The lower slopes of mountains may have small alpine meadows with grass, flowers, and trees. Above a certain elevation—the treeline—trees cannot grow. Vegetation is similar to that found on the tundra. Mosses and colorful lichens grow on the rocky slopes.

SECTION 2 REVIEW

Checking for Understanding
1. **Define** monsoon, typhoon.
2. **Locating Places** In what two climate zones is Japan located?
3. **Region** How do the monsoons affect climate in much of East Asia?
4. **Place** What are the summers like in southern Korea and southeastern China?

Critical Thinking
5. **Determining Cause and Effect** Why do northern China and Mongolia have a steppe climate and vegetation?

CHAPTER 26

545

MAP & GRAPH SKILLS

Interpreting a Contour Map

If you went hiking in the mountains, what kind of map would help you find your way? A trail map would show the paths you could follow. But how would you know if the trail follows a gentle easy route, or cuts straight up the side of a mountain? To get this kind of information, you need a **contour map.**

REVIEWING THE SKILL

Contour maps use lines, called **isolines**, to describe the shape, or contour, of the landscape. Isolines connect all the points that are at the same elevation. The number on each isoline indicates its elevation. If you walked along one isoline, you would always be at the same height above sea level.

The relationship of the isolines to one another indicates the slope of the terrain. Where the lines are far apart, the land rises gradually. Where the lines are close together, the land rises steeply. Rivers often flow through valleys between mountains and hills. Because they outline the topography of an area, contour maps are also called **topographic maps.**

When interpreting a contour map, apply the following steps:

- Identify the area shown in the map.
- Read the labels on the isolines to determine how much the elevation increases with each line.
- Locate the highest and lowest points on the map.
- Figure out which areas have the most gradual and steepest grades.

PRACTICING THE SKILL

Study the contour map below and then answer the following questions:

1. What area is shown on the map?
2. What is the interval, or difference, between each isoline?
3. What is the highest point on Taiwan?
4. Which side of Taiwan has the steepest topography?
5. Which cities are located more than 1,000 feet (305 meters) above sea level?
6. If you were to hike to the top of Hsinkao Shan, what would be the most gradual route?
7. If you hiked straight up Hsinkao Shan from the city of Taitung, how many miles would you walk? On this route, how much elevation would you gain for every mile you walk?

For additional practice in this skill, see Practicing Skills on page 548 of the Chapter 26 Review.

	SECTION	KEY TERMS	SUMMARY
1	**The Land**	**archipelago** (p. 538) **tsunami** (p. 538) **loess** (p. 539)	• The region of East Asia is made up of China, Mongolia, and North and South Korea on the continent of Asia, and two island nations, Japan and Taiwan. • China occupies 90 percent of the land area in East Asia. Other nations occupy peninsulas and islands. • Mainland East Asia has mountains and highlands in the west, plateaus and basins in the central and northern regions, and coastal plains in the east. • Because so much of East Asia is mountainous, population and cities are densely crowded on the coastal plains. • East Asia is rich in minerals, but they are unevenly distributed and sometimes poorly located. • Because population pressure is high and farmland is limited, the ocean is an important food source for East Asia.

Japan's Inland Sea

	SECTION	KEY TERMS	SUMMARY
2	**The Climate and Vegetation**	**monsoon** (p. 542) **typhoon** (p. 542)	• East Asia has a wide variety of climates because of its great land area. • Seasonal monsoon winds have a major influence on climates in East Asia. • Much of East Asia is in the middle latitudes with humid continental or humid subtropical climates. • Inland steppe and desert areas have dry climates with extremes of hot and cold temperatures. • Many parts of East Asia, especially Japan, North and South Korea, and Taiwan, are thickly forested.

Tropical vegetation and village in southern China

Reviewing Key Terms

Choose the vocabulary term that best completes each of the sentences below. Write your answers on a separate sheet of paper.

archipelago (p. 538)
tsunami (p. 538)
loess (p. 539)
monsoon (p. 542)
typhoon (p. 542)

SECTION 1

1. Farmlands in eastern China are richer because of thick deposits of ____ carried by wind and water.
2. A ____ caused by an earthquake can do great damage to coastal areas.
3. Like Japan, the Ryukyu Islands are an ____ .

SECTION 2

4. In Asia, a violent tropical hurricane is known as a ____ .
5. China is cold and dry in the winter because of ____ winds from Siberia.

Reviewing Facts

SECTION 1

6. What highland area covers much of western China?
7. What are China's three great rivers?
8. Which is the largest and most densely populated of the Japanese islands?
9. What is China's richest energy resource?
10. Why are the oceans a valuable resource for East Asian countries?

SECTION 2

11. What is the pattern of monsoon winds in East Asia?
12. How does the Japan Current influence climate in Japan?
13. What are the characteristics of a humid subtropical climate? What parts of East Asia have this climate?

14. What are the climate and vegetation like on the steppes of East Asia?

Critical Thinking

15. **Predicting Consequences**   China and East Asia are separated from the rest of Asia by steep mountains and highlands. How might this have affected the ways in which East Asian cultures developed?
16. **Making Comparisons**   How do climate and vegetation differ between northern and southern China? Why?

 ## Geographic Themes

17. **Interaction**   How have the Huang He and Chang Jiang been important to the people of China?
18. **Location**   What is the most important factor in the climate of a mountain region?

Practicing Skills

Interpreting a Contour Map
Refer to the contour map on page 546.

19. If you were to hike to the top of Hsinkao Shan, what would be the steepest route that you would take on your trip?
20. Look at the locations of the cities shown on the contour map. In what general areas are they located? Why are no major cities located on the central portion of the map?

Using the Unit Atlas

Refer to the cultural geography section of the Unit Atlas on pages 530–531.

21. Where do about 75 percent of most Chinese people live?
22. How vast was the Mongol Empire?
23. What kind of culture is dominant in Japan today?

Projects

Individual Activity

You have read about the three great rivers that have been important in China. Choose one of those rivers—Huang He, Chang Jiang, or Xi—and research its individual profile: Where does it begin and end? Through what kind of terrain does it flow? How does the river influence the people who live near it? Has the river changed over time? How? Prepare a short oral or written report telling what you have discovered about the river.

Cooperative Learning Activity

Work with two or three classmates to prepare questions for a game of Geography Jeopardy that the whole class can play. As in the television quiz show, players are given the answer and must supply the question. Organize your "answers" into at least five different categories, such as "Rivers," "Begins with *T*," or "Climate Regions." For example, in the category "Begins with *T*," players might be given this answer: This island nation is located in the East China Sea. (The appropriate response is "What is Taiwan?")

Writing About Geography

Description

The environment of East Asia helped the peoples of the region to develop unique civilizations. Consult your journal, text, and reference sources to find out how landforms and bodies of water have shaped the countries of the region. Select one country and describe how its physical features might affect the lifestyles of its people.

Locating Places

EAST ASIA: PHYSICAL GEOGRAPHY

Match the letters on the map with the places and physical features of East Asia. Write your answers on a separate sheet of paper.

1. Tibetan Plateau
2. Mongolia
3. Korean Peninsula
4. Honshu
5. Yellow Sea
6. Huang He
7. Yangzi River
8. Taiwan
9. North China Plain
10. Himalayas

The Cultural Geography of East Asia

CHAPTER FOCUS

Geographic Setting

The geography of East Asia has greatly influenced how and where people live. The rugged mountains and plateaus are thinly populated, while the coastal plains are some of the most crowded places on the earth.

Geographic Themes

Section 1 Population Patterns

MOVEMENT East Asian cultures began in river valleys.

Section 2 History and Government

MOVEMENT Throughout much of history, Chinese influences spread throughout the region.

Section 3 Cultures and Lifestyles

REGION Although Chinese influence has been strong, each country in East Asia has a unique culture.

▲ Photograph: *Bustling Taipei, Taiwan*

Population Patterns

Chuncheon, South Korea

Ahnnoung haseyo!
I live in Chuncheon, South Korea. In my spare time I enjoy hobbies such as swimming, playing the piano, singing, being with friends, reading, and taking long walks in the park. I like a variety of foods, such as Italian, Mexican, and American, but my favorite is Korean.

Sonmin Kim

Sonmin Kim describes the typical lifestyle of a teenager in South Korea, one of the countries in East Asia. East Asia is a region made up of many different religions, languages, and lifestyles. The majority of people in East Asia live in China, the world's most populous country.

PLACE

Human Characteristics

The East Asia culture region contains more than 1.5 billion people—a little more than 25 percent of the world's population. East Asians are members of many different **ethnic groups**—groups that share a common language, religion, ancestry, or a combination of such characteristics.

China

About 94 percent of the people of China belong to the group, or nationality, called the Han. They live mainly in eastern and southern China. The rest of China's 1.2 billion people belong to about 50 different ethnic groups. The non-Chinese peoples live mainly in the far north and west. Although they live in China, non-Chinese peoples such as the Tibetans have long cultural histories and traditions of their own.

Most of the people of Taiwan are Chinese, some of whom are descendants of Nationalist Chinese who fled the mainland after the defeat of the Nationalists by the Communists in a civil war that ended in 1949. A small minority are the original inhabitants of the island, who are related to the peoples of Indonesia.

Japan

Japan is ethnically **homogeneous**—of the same kind. That is, most Japanese belong to the same ethnic group. They share language, customs, and ancestry. Koreans are the largest minority group in Japan.

One minority ethnic group in Japan is the Ainu. They were probably the earliest inhabitants of the islands. When the present-day Japanese migrated from Asia, several thousand years ago, the Ainu gradually moved north. Today they live mostly on the island of Hokkaido.

Korea

Although Korea is now divided politically into North and South Korea, it had a long history as a unified nation until after World War II. The people of Korea are also a distinct ethnic group. People throughout the peninsula share a common ancestry, language, and ap-

pearance. Only about 35,000 people of foreign descent live in Korea. People of Chinese descent make up the largest non-Korean group.

Mongolia

The people of Mongolia are also homogeneous, with about 90 percent being Mongols. Mongols are divided into several tribes but share a common language and ancestry. About three-fourths belong to one tribe, the Khalkhas. A number of Mongol groups live across the border in northern China. Others live in Russia.

Population Distribution

Population is distributed very unevenly throughout East Asia, because much of the area is barren and mountainous. The dry, cold deserts and remote mountains are empty and almost uninhabited. The fertile river valleys and coastal plains, however, are some of the most crowded places on the earth.

China

China has almost 1.2 billion people, and more than 90 percent of them are crowded onto only one-sixth of the land. Most live in the fertile valleys and plains of China's three great rivers: the Huang He, Chang Jiang, and Xi. In this thickly settled part of China, average population density is more than 518 people per square mile (200 per sq. km).

Population is scarcest in the rugged western provinces of Xinjiang (SHIN•jee•AHNG) and Xizang. A few farmers and herders live on scattered oases.

Chinese government officials worry that the country's huge population may grow faster than the food supply. In the past, China often had serious famines in which thousands died of hunger. Today the government encourages smaller families. People with only one child are rewarded—perhaps with better income through reduced taxation or the chance to go to a good school.

Geographic Themes

Place: Tokyo, Japan
Japanese shoppers stroll on the Ginza, Tokyo's most famous street, which is known for its modern buildings and neon signs. *How are the Japanese described ethnically?*

Japan

Japan, with a much smaller land area, is even more crowded than China. Forested mountains cover the center of the Japanese islands. Most of its 125 million people, therefore, live in the valleys and on coastal plains at the base of the mountains. As in most other industrial nations, population growth is slow.

The average population density in Japan is about 850 people per square mile (328 per sq. km). Around large cities, however, population density is much greater.

Japan has few uninhabited areas like those in China. The northern island of Hokkaido, which is rural and mountainous, still has a population density of about 250 people per square mile (96 per sq. km).

Korea

In both North and South Korea, most people live on the coastal plains. The two nations are quite different, however.

Only about 34 percent of Koreans live in the north. Even though its population is growing rapidly, North Korea is short of workers. More than 3 million people have migrated to South Korea since the Korean War in the early 1950s.

The rest of the people of the divided peninsula live in South Korea, making it another crowded country. Average population density is about 1,170 people per square mile (452 per sq. km).

Mongolia

With much of its land covered by deserts and mountains, Mongolia's small population of 2.4 million is spread thinly over the broad steppes. Population density for the country as a whole is only about 4 people per square mile (2 per sq. km). About one-fourth of Mongolia's people live in the capital, Ulan Bator, which is located in a river basin.

Taiwan and Hong Kong

By contrast the island nation of Taiwan has a population density of about 1,517 people per square mile (586 per sq. km). As in Japan,

Geographic Themes

Place: Seoul, South Korea
Since the mid-1950s, South Korea's capital of Seoul has grown into a busy, modern city. *How does Seoul rank among the world's cities in terms of population and living conditions?*

most people live in cities on the coastal plain rather than in the wooded mountains in the center of the island.

The prosperous United Kingdom colony of Hong Kong includes two islands and mainland territory, a total of less than 400 square miles (1,036 sq. km). Almost 6 million people are squeezed into this small area—a density of about 14,000 people per square mile (5,405 per sq. km).

HUMAN/ENVIRONMENT INTERACTION

Urbanization

The mountainous or dry nature of the land in East Asia and the attraction of cities have caused millions of people to crowd into large, urban industrial areas. Small farming villages, however, are still an important part of life in East Asia.

China

Only about one-fourth of China's people live in cities. The rest live and work on farms. However, since the country has more than 1 billion people, there are more than 35 major cities with populations well over 1 million. The largest cities are the seaport of Shanghai, with about 7 million, and Beijing, the capital, with about 6 million.

Like other cities in Asia, China's cities are very crowded. Population density in Shanghai, for example, is more than 87,000 people per square mile (33,590 per sq. km). At rush hour, thousands of bicycles fill the streets. People in cities live in crowded apartments, often behind a store or shop. Sometimes many families share what was once the private home and courtyard of a wealthy family.

Japan

Unlike China, Japan is very urbanized. This is not a new development. Even in the 1700s, city life flourished in Japan. In 1721 Edo, present-day Tokyo, had about 1 million people. Today more than three-fourths of the people in Japan live in cities.

About half of all Japan's people live in the crowded coastal corridor about 320 miles (515 km) long on the island of Honshu. This is the Tokaido **megalopolis**—a super-city that includes several large cities and the smaller cities near them.

The largest urban center in the corridor is the area around Tokyo-Yokohama, with a population of about 27 million in 1990. The other centers are Nagoya and the industrial areas of Osaka, Kobe, and Kyoto.

Japan's busy modern cities have glass and concrete skyscrapers and huge neon signs advertising cars, cameras, and watches. Private homes are small and crowded closely together. A suburban family of four typically lives in a three-room wooden house—with a tiny garden if they are lucky. An average city couple probably has a small, two-room apartment.

Korea

About two-thirds of the people in both North and South Korea live in cities. Seoul (SOHL), the capital of South Korea, had more than 16 million people in 1990, making it one of the world's largest—and most crowded—cities. Korean urban life first expanded after Japan seized control of the country in 1910. The Japanese brought industry to Korean cities and took much farmland away from farmers. As a result, many Koreans moved to the cities to find work. After World War II, the division of Korea into two countries, the Korean conflict, and the continued growth of industry furthered urbanization.

Today, population density in Seoul is about 46,000 per square mile (17,760 per sq. km)—4 times that of New York City. South Korea's cities are growing as many people move there in search of jobs.

Taiwan

On the island of Taiwan, too, about three-fourths of the people live in cities. The largest city is Taipei with a population of about 7 million. Taipei is the capital of Taiwan and a growing manufacturing center. The Chinese Nationalist government moved to Taipei in 1949 after the Chinese Communists conquered mainland China. Since then, the city and its suburbs have grown rapidly both in area and population.

SECTION 1 REVIEW

Checking for Understanding
1. **Define** ethnic group, homogeneous, megalopolis.
2. **Locating Places** Where is the Tokaido megalopolis located?
3. **Place** In what part of China does most of the population live?
4. **Place** Which has the greater population density—North or South Korea?

Critical Thinking
5. **Determining Cause and Effect** Why are some parts of East Asia overcrowded while others are almost uninhabited?

NATIONAL GEOGRAPHIC
GEOFACTS

Where is the world's longest escalator?

Among the longest single escalators are two at Metro subway stations, one in downtown Moscow, the other in suburban Washington, D. C. The 115-foot (35-m) Wheaton, Maryland, escalator is the longest in the Western Hemisphere.

0 10 km
0 10 mi

CHINA

Shenzhen

HONG KONG
(U.K.)

South China Sea

Hong Kong Island

Europe Asia China Pacific Ocean Africa Indian Ocean

Victoria Harbor

Connaught Rd.

ESCALATOR SYSTEM

MID-LEVELS

CENTRAL

Queens Rd.

Des Voeux Rd.

Caine Rd.

Conduit Rd.

ESCALATOR

MOVING SIDEWALK

The world's longest escalator system is a half-mile-long (800-m) covered outdoor network that snakes through the crowded streets of Hong Kong.

It opened in October 1993 to ease rush-hour traffic congestion on densely populated Hong Kong Island. The series of moving sidewalks and escalators, with 23 exits and entrances, links the central business district with residences about midway up Victoria Peak.

The 28-million-dollar escalator network runs downward for the morning commute, and then reverses direction at 10 a.m. and runs uphill until its 10 p.m. closing. The entire ride, which is free, takes about 20 minutes. At least 27,000 people are expected to use the system every day.

Designed by BILL PITZER

SETTING THE SCENE

Read to Discover . . .
- where civilization began in East Asia.
- how ideas spread from the Chinese Empire throughout East Asia.
- how East Asia has changed in the 20th century.

Key Terms
- culture hearth
- dynasty
- clan
- shogun
- samurai

Identify and Locate
Huang He, North China Plain, Kyoto

S ome of the world's longest continuous civilizations can be found in East Asia. Their history is filled with the rise and fall of powerful ruling families.

LOCATION

River Valley Civilization

T he culture of East Asia began in China about 2000 B.C., in the valley of the Wei River, a major tributary of the Huang He. China is considered East Asia's **culture hearth**, the center from which ideas and traditions spread.

Dynasties

Recorded Chinese history begins about 1700 B.C. with the Shang (SHAHNG) **dynasty**, or ruling house. The Shang and all succeeding dynasties faced similar problems—rebellions by local lords, attacks by central Asian nomads, and natural disasters, such as floods or famine. When the government was stable, it could defend its people against these problems. Sooner or later, however, the dynasty would weaken and fall. People explained this event by saying that its rulers had lost "the mandate of heaven," the approval of the deities.

Imperial China

Shang rulers set up a city-state in the North China Plain. Evidence shows that the Shang were skillful metalworkers and had a writing system.

The Zhou (JAU) dynasty conquered the Shang in about 1100 B.C. and ruled for 900 years. During that time Chinese culture spread, trade increased, and China entered the Iron Age. China's best-known philosopher and teacher Kung Fu-tzu, known as Confucius (Konfuzi), lived during this time. Another philosophy, Daoism (DOW•ism) also appeared. The Zhou were followed by a series of powerful dynasties that expanded Chinese territory.

By 221 B.C. the Qin (CHIN) dynasty had established the Chinese Empire. It would continue to influence East Asia for centuries. The Great Wall, stretching about 4,000 miles (6,437 km) along China's northern border, was built in the Qin dynasty. Rulers of a later dynasty—the Tang—continued to make the empire larger. By 620 A.D. merchants, travelers, missionaries, and silk traders were taking Chinese culture to all of East Asia.

CHINESE EMPIRES

Qin Empire
Han Empire
Tang Empire
Great Wall (Qin and Han times)
Great Wall (Tang times)
Grand Canal (Tang times)

GOBI

Beijing

Xi'an
(Chang'an)

Huang He

YELLOW
SEA

PLATEAU
OF XIZANG

30°N

Chang Jiang

EAST
CHINA
SEA

Tropic of Cancer

Xi (West) River

Guangzhou

SOUTH CHINA SEA

FOCUS ON GEOGRAPHIC THEMES

1. **Movement:** What barrier did the Chinese build to keep out nomadic invaders?
2. **Place:** Which rivers are linked by the Grand Canal?
3. **Place:** What city developed in central China under the empires?

PLACE

Japan and Korea

Many people borrowed Chinese ideas but shaped them to fit their own cultures.

Ancient Japan

The people of early Japan lived in **clans**, small tribal communities. From China and Korea, they learned metalworking and ways of growing rice in irrigated fields.

The Yamato people, whose main clan became the imperial family, ruled Japan by the A.D. 400s.

During the 500s and 600s, Japanese leaders sent students to China to learn technology, government, and the arts.

Feudal Japan

By the 1100s, local nobles and their armies were fighting to control Japan. The country's first military ruler, or **shogun**, took power in 1192. He was supported by professional soldiers, or **samurai**, who lived by a strict code of loyalty. Military dictators would rule Japan until the late 1800s.

Korea

The Korean Peninsula was for centuries a cultural bridge between Japan and the mainland of Asia.

The kingdom of Silla ruled Korea as a unified state until 936 when it was overthrown by the Koryo Dynasty. Military rulers took power in the late 1100s but were conquered by the Mongols.

MOVEMENT

The Mongols

In the 1200s the fierce Mongols swept out of the steppes of central Asia, into China. Mongols established the first non-Chinese dynasty there in 1260, and the two cultures existed side by side.

Japanese samurai fought off two huge Mongol invasions in 1274 and 1281.

MOVEMENT

Contacts with the West

By the 1600s leaders in China, Japan, and Korea wanted to remain isolated from Western nations. They discouraged trade with Europe whose countries wanted a share of the rich trade in tea and silk.

China

The Chinese Empire limited trade with all foreigners to the port city of Guangzhou.

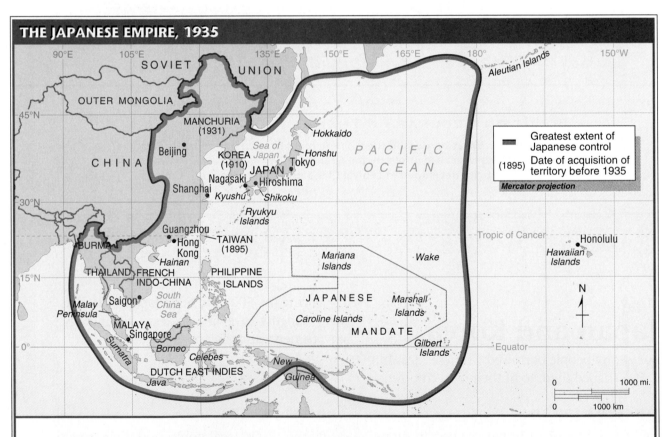

THE JAPANESE EMPIRE, 1935

Legend:
— Greatest extent of Japanese control
(1895) Date of acquisition of territory before 1935
Mercator projection

FOCUS ON GEOGRAPHIC THEMES

1. **Region:** What areas of mainland East Asia were ruled by Japan during World War II?
2. **Place:** What major islands form the Japanese archipelago?
3. **Place:** In what year did Taiwan come under Japanese rule?
4. **Location:** What Chinese-owned island lies southwest of Hong Kong?

Eventually the United Kingdom, Germany, Russia, and France all forced trade treaties on China. They also made China give them "spheres of influence" in various parts of the country.

Japan

In 1853 United States steamships sailed into Tokyo Bay. Rather than fight, Japanese officials signed trade treaties with the United States and European nations.

Foreign influence gave the Japanese a chance to introduce changes. Japan quickly built factories and railroads and modernized its government, military forces, and economy. It also began to build an empire in Asia, taking over Korea and parts of Manchuria.

 Geographic Themes

Region: China
In 1989, Chinese students unsuccessfully tried to limit the power of China's Communist government. *Who was the first Communist leader of China?*

MOVEMENT

War and Revolution

The 20th century involved East Asia in two world wars, brought two revolutions to China, and divided the Korean Peninsula.

Wars and Recovery

Japan aided the Allies in World War I, gaining Germany's former possessions in China and the Pacific. During World War II, Japan took over parts of China and Southeast Asia. After that war ended in its defeat, Japan lost its empire. In 1948, Korea, once its colony, was divided into pro-American South Korea and Communist-ruled North Korea.

Postwar Japan transformed itself into a democracy. Within a few decades, an economic boom made the country one of the richest in the world.

Revolutions in China

The Chinese Empire came to an end in 1911 when a Nationalist revolution led by Dr. Sun Yat-sen (SUN YAHT•SEN) overthrew the Manchu dynasty. In 1927 Chiang Kai-shek set up a Nationalist government, but his rival Communist Mao Zedong (MAU ZUH•DUNG), gained huge support from peasants.

During World War II, Nationalists and Communists together resisted Japan. At the end of the war, the two groups fought each other again. By 1949 the Communists set up the People's Republic of China on the mainland. The Nationalists fled to the island of Taiwan and set up the Republic of China.

In 1924 Mongolia set up a Communist government. After the fall of the Soviet Union, the Mongolians in the 1990s began to move toward democracy and free enterprise.

SECTION 2 REVIEW

Checking for Understanding
1. **Define** culture hearth, dynasty, clan, shogun, samurai.
2. **Locating Places** Where did East Asian civilization begin?
3. **Movement** What elements of Chinese culture did the Japanese borrow and adapt?
4. **Place** How did China's government change during the 20th century?

Critical Thinking
5. **Drawing Conclusions** Why would the East Asian nations want to be isolated from Western countries in the 1800s?

Geography and History

HONG KONG: HARBOR OF FREE ENTERPRISE

As you read, examine the change facing Hong Kong.

Leading Asian Port

Hong Kong, on the southeast coast of China, has been a dependency of the United Kingdom since the 1840s. British officials approved and appointed by Britain's monarch control the government.

As a British dependency, Hong Kong has grown and prospered. An excellent natural harbor has made the territory a major Asian port. Hong Kong's low taxes and free port status—no duties are collected on imported goods—have made it a center of trade. More than 100 banks and 4 stock exchanges make Hong Kong Asia's second-largest international financial center.

Hong Kong has also become an industrial center, making use of a large and cheap labor force. More than 2 million tourists visit Hong Kong yearly, spending money that stimulates the economy.

A Change of Hands

Although Hong Kong has been governed by the United Kingdom, it is powerfully influenced by the neighboring Republic of China. Chinese citizens hold many of the government's lower offices, and 98 percent of Hong Kong's population is Chinese.

Hong Kong is one of East Asia's busiest ports. Most of Hong Kong's people are Chinese, but the territory has been under British rule since the 1800s. In 1997, the United Kingdom will finally return Hong Kong to China.

CHINA
Guangdong Province
114°E
22°30'N
N
Shenzhen
Hong Kong (U.K.)
Hong Kong
0   10 mi.
0   10 km
South China Sea

Through wars and treaties, Great Britain gained control of Hong Kong Island in 1842, then Kowloon peninsula in 1860. In 1898, China leased the New Territories to the United Kingdom for 99 years.

The Chinese Communists have governed China since 1949, but have never officially recognized the United Kingdom's control of Hong Kong. Neither have they opposed British rule.

Changing Hands Again

On July 1, 1997, the United Kingdom's 99-year lease of the New Territories expires, and all of Hong Kong will return to Chinese rule. In 1984 the two nations signed a joint declaration that pledged Hong Kong's return to China in 1997, but with a high degree of independence from the Chinese Communist regime.

Checking for Understanding

1. **Place** Study the map on this page. How does Hong Kong's coastline contribute to its success as a trading center?
2. How did the United Kingdom acquire control of Hong Kong?

SETTING THE SCENE

Read to Discover . . .
- the languages and religions of the peoples of East Asia.
- how standards of living differ among countries in East Asia.
- the importance of arts and leisure activities in the countries of East Asia.

Key Terms
- ideogram
- shamanism
- calligraphy
- haiku

Identify and Locate
Xizang (Tibet), Mongolia, Korea, Mount Fuji, Kyoto

T he people of East Asia have a long and rich cultural tradition. The ideas of Confucianism, Daoism, Buddhism, and Shinto have been major influences. Communism has also had a major impact on the cultures of China, North Korea, and Mongolia.

REGION

Languages

P eople in East Asia speak languages from several different language families. The largest, Sino-Tibetan, which includes Chinese and Tibetan, is spoken by more than 1.1 billion people.

Chinese Languages

Chinese has many dialects, pronounced very differently from one another. Mandarin, the northern dialect, is the most widely spoken and is taught in schools.

The Chinese written language is based on **ideograms**, or pictorial characters, that each carry one meaning. When each character becomes a spoken syllable, however, it takes on a different meaning—these pronunciations form a dialect. Chinese languages are also tonal. The same syllable has different meanings depending upon tone and pitch. Other languages spoken in China include Mongolian, Manchu, and Uygur.

Japanese and Korean

Japanese and Korean languages are related. Learning to read and write Japanese is challenging because three different writing systems are used. The Japanese borrowed many ideograms from Chinese. Then, in the ninth century, two phonetic alphabets were invented to represent the actual sounds of Japanese.

Koreans have their own writing system developed by a 15th-century ruler.

PLACE

Religion

P eople in East Asia may follow more than one religion. Many Japanese, for example, practice both Buddhism and the traditional Japanese religion of Shinto. Confucian ideas have also influenced the entire region.

Communist governments in China and North Korea have discouraged religious practices, but many people have held to their beliefs. In China these beliefs can mean a blend of Buddhism or Christianity with Confucian and Daoist ideas. In the far western province of Xinjiang, the Uygurs are Muslims.

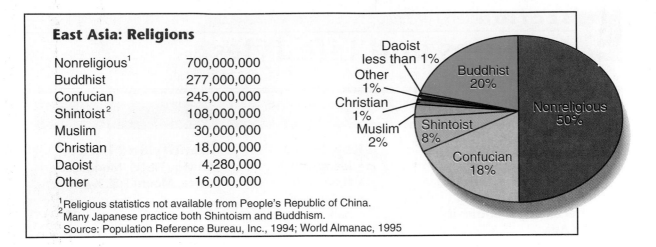

East Asia: Religions

Nonreligious[1]	700,000,000
Buddhist	277,000,000
Confucian	245,000,000
Shintoist[2]	108,000,000
Muslim	30,000,000
Christian	18,000,000
Daoist	4,280,000
Other	16,000,000

[1]Religious statistics not available from People's Republic of China.
[2]Many Japanese practice both Shintoism and Buddhism.
Source: Population Reference Bureau, Inc., 1994; World Almanac, 1995

Many Koreans are Buddhists, with some ideas taken from Confucianism. Others follow **shamanism,** a belief in a leader who can communicate with spirits, or belong to the nationalistic sect called Chundo Kyo. About 20 percent of South Koreans are Christians.

Before Communist governments took power, Xizang (Tibet) and Mongolia were religious states led by Buddhist monks.

<u>PLACE</u>

Standards of Living

Standards of living in East Asia have steadily improved as these nations' economies have developed. Contrasts are still great, however—from glittering skyscrapers to mud houses in rural parts of the region.

Japan

Japan is the most modern and industrialized country in East Asia. In 1992 its average annual household income was $48,900, one of the highest in the world. Most Japanese live in cities where housing shortages are a continuing problem.

Consumer costs in Japan are high by American standards, but income is distributed more evenly. Japanese businesses emphasize teamwork and cooperation. A *sarariman*, the Japanese term for a white-collar worker, can usually enjoy the security of a lifetime job and good benefits. Breaking with tradition, many Japanese women now have professional careers.

Korea and Taiwan

Both South Korea and Taiwan have developed quickly into modern industrial nations, with rising standards of living.

Prosperity in Taiwan has improved living standards for both farmers and city dwellers.

China

Communist leaders in China have tried new approaches to running the economy, reforming land ownership, and increasing food production.

After the death of Mao Zedong, new leaders began to allow people to improve their own standard of living through opening businesses and working private farm plots.

<u>PLACE</u>

Education and Health

East Asians respect learning. Today elementary education is free and compulsory throughout the region. Opportunities for higher education have increased greatly since the 1950s.

Literacy

Japan has a long tradition of literacy. Today almost all Japanese adults can read and write. North and South Korea, and Taiwan also have literacy rates of more than 90 percent. In

Mongolia, 89 percent of the people can read and write.

Historically, only the wealthiest people in China were literate. Since the 1940s the Communist government has built more elementary schools and has started adult education. Today the literacy rate in China is about 76 percent.

Schools

Japan's demanding school system teaches students to work together and value cooperation. Students must finish ninth grade, attending school almost year-round. More than 90 percent of all students also finish high school, but a difficult entrance exam is required for most colleges or technical schools.

Advanced education has been one of the reasons for the economic development in much of East Asia.

Health Care

Better health care has caused life expectancies to rise and infant deaths to decline in East Asia. In general, the life expectancy for women is more than 70 years, and for men—

65 years. Japan, with the most up-to-date medical facilities, has the longest life expectancies—82 years for women, and 76 years for men.

In the Communist countries, medical treatment is free. In Korea, Taiwan, and China both Western medical techniques and traditional herbal medicine and acupuncture are used.

Leisure Time

People in East Asia participate in a variety of free-time enjoyments from music to sports. Family life is at the center of many activities.

Food

East Asia has many national and regional styles of cooking with some staple foods in common. Grains such as rice, wheat, and millet are basic foods, often made into noodles or dumplings. Asians eat less red meat than North Americans or Europeans, getting more

Geographic Themes

Region: Japan

Japanese workers at a Tokyo plant perform exercises before beginning a busy day. The Japanese workforce is one of the most highly skilled in the world. *What values does it stress?*

protein from soybeans and fish. Many strict Buddhists are vegetarians.

Sports

East Asians enjoy many sports such as baseball, soccer, and volleyball. Olympic champions in skiing, swimming, gymnastics, table tennis, and other sports have come from this region. Many people, old and young, also practice traditional exercises and martial arts.

Ceremonies and Holidays

Several Asian philosophies and religions, such as Shinto and Zen Buddhism, require followers to celebrate rituals. Each Asian country also celebrates traditional ethnic and national holidays. Many celebrate the New Year according to the lunar calendar, in late January or early February.

Arts and Architecture

Chinese styles in art and architecture have influenced all of East Asia. Religion has also inspired much great art.

In 1966, communism changed the standards for Chinese arts with Mao Zedong's Cultural Revolution. It tried to wipe out the memory of centuries of art. After Mao died, however, many Chinese artists returned to traditional forms.

Painting, Sculpture, and Pottery

Daoism's emphasis on quiet contemplation of nature has influenced both Chinese

Geographic Themes

Place: Seoul, Korea
This Buddhist temple in Korea reflects the historical influence of Buddhism on the arts of East Asia. *In what arts do East Asians excel?*

and Japanese painting. Many paintings include a verse or inscription done in **calligraphy,** the art of beautiful writing.

Japanese artists of the 1700s and early 1800s also developed a style of wood-block printing with vivid colors. Famous print artists, such as Hiroshige and Hokusai, influenced Western artists.

Asian sculptors have often portrayed the Buddha or traditional deities. Buddhist temples in Korea, China, and Japan contain many statues and images of stone, bronze, or jade.

Pottery makers worked in Japan as long ago as 10,000 B.C. During the Tang dynasty, Chinese potters learned how to make fine, thin porcelain called china. Korean potters in the Koryo dynasty were famous for their pale green celadon vases.

Music and Theater

East Asian music is based on a five-tone, or pentatonic, scale that has a melody line but no harmony. Music originally was used in temple rituals and to accompany dancers with flutes, drums, and gongs. Stringed instruments included the lute, guitar, and *koto,* a zither.

Traditional musical dramas, combining music and story, are popular. The Chinese perform opera, and the Japanese enjoy serious *Noh* plays, and the livelier Kabuki theater. Several countries have motion picture industries.

Literature

In about 1010, what is thought to be the world's first novel, *The Tale of Genji,* was written in Japan. The author was a noblewoman at the Heian court, Lady Murasaki Shikibu.

Poetry has long been important in East Asian culture, from the Chinese Confucian writing to the 17-syllable form of Japanese poetry, the **haiku.**

Architecture

Except for modern city skyscrapers, most East Asian architecture is based on simple wood construction, often with gracefully curved tile roofs. People also build with brick or stone if it is locally available. One common style is the pagoda, derived from Buddhist

Geographic Themes

Place: Tokyo, Japan
Lavish costumes and colorful stage sets characterize Kabuki theater, which has been popular in Japan for centuries. *What other type of play developed in traditional Japan?*

temples in India. It is a multistory building, with each story smaller than the one below.

SECTION 3 REVIEW

Checking for Understanding
1. **Define** ideogram, shamanism, calligraphy, haiku.
2. **Locating Places** Where do people speak languages from the Sino-Tibetan family?
3. **Place** What religions are practiced by people in different parts of China?
4. **Place** When and where was the first real novel written? By whom?

Critical Thinking
5. **Making Generalizations** How have rising standards of living changed the lives of people in East Asia?

MAP & GRAPH SKILLS

Reading a Population Density Map

In most countries, population is concentrated in particular areas—in cities, along coastlines, in moderate climates, near rivers, and so on. Because of uneven distribution, population density varies within each country.

REVIEWING THE SKILL

Population density is the number of people living in a square mile or square kilometer. A **population density map** illustrates the distribution of population in a given region. Mapmakers can show population density in two ways. On some maps, different colors represent various population densities. On other maps, a dot represents a particular number of people, such as 1,000 or 100,000. The number of dots clustered in an area indicates the population density.

When reading a population density map, apply the following steps:

• Study the map key to determine what the colors and symbols represent.

• Find the areas that have the greatest and least population density.

• Compare the map with other information about the region to draw conclusions about the causes and effects of the population density patterns in this area.

PRACTICING THE SKILL

Study the population density map below and then answer the following questions:

1. What does the color yellow represent?
2. What symbols stand for cities of more than 2,000,000 people?
3. Which areas of China are least densely populated?
4. What physical features affect population distribution in China?

For additional practice in this skill, see Practicing Skills on page 568 of the Chapter 27 Review.

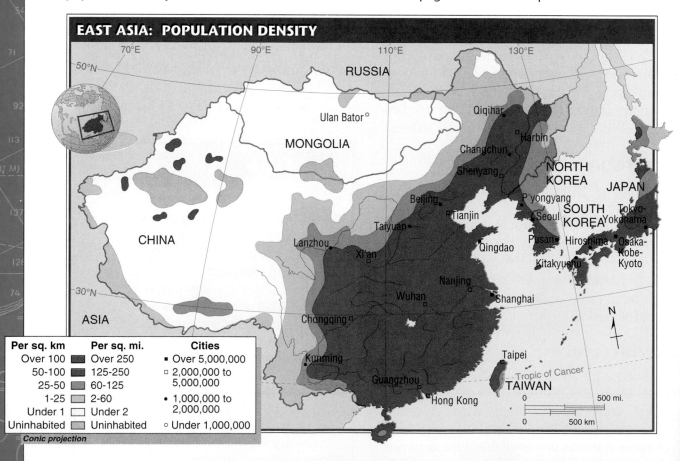

EAST ASIA: POPULATION DENSITY

Per sq. km	Per sq. mi.	Cities
Over 100	Over 250	▪ Over 5,000,000
50-100	125-250	▫ 2,000,000 to 5,000,000
25-50	60-125	
1-25	2-60	• 1,000,000 to 2,000,000
Under 1	Under 2	
Uninhabited	Uninhabited	○ Under 1,000,000

Conic projection

SECTION	**KEY TERMS**	**SUMMARY**
1 **Population Patterns** The Ginza, the main shopping street of Tokyo, Japan	**ethnic group** (p. 551) **homogeneous** (p. 552) **megalopolis** (p. 554)	• The people of East Asia belong to many different ethnic groups, the largest of which is the Han of China. • Population in East Asia is unevenly distributed. It is concentrated in river valleys and on coastal plains. • Japan is the most urbanized nation in East Asia; China remains predominantly rural with hundreds of millions of its citizens living in a nonurban setting.
2 **History and Government** Student protests in China, 1989	**culture hearth** (p. 556) **dynasty** (p. 556) **clan** (p. 557) **shogun** (p. 557) **samurai** (p. 557)	• East Asian culture began in the Huang He valley of China and spread to other countries in the region. • Confucianism and Daoism, two influential schools of thought, developed in China about 500 B.C.; Buddhism was brought from India. • The Chinese Empire dominated East Asia for several centuries. • Contact with the West weakened China but led Japan to modernize.
3 **Cultures and Lifestyles** A Buddhist temple in Korea	**ideogram** (p. 561) **shamanism** (p. 562) **calligraphy** (p. 565) **haiku** (p. 565)	• Sino-Tibetan languages are the most widely spoken in Asia, while Korean and Japanese are spoken in their native countries. • Rising standards of living have brought improvements in education and health care. • People in East Asia practice traditional arts and leisure activities but also enjoy modern recreations.

Reviewing Key Terms

Choose the vocabulary term that best completes each of the sentences below. Write your answers on a separate sheet of paper.

    ethnic group (p. 551)
    homogeneous (p. 552)
    dynasty (p. 556)
    shogun (p. 557)
    calligraphy (p. 565)
    haiku (p. 565)

SECTION 1

1. The population of Mongolia is quite _____ .

2. The largest _____ in China is the Han.

SECTION 2

3. Japan's feudal military leaders were called the _____ .

4. The Great Wall of China was built during the Qin _____ .

SECTION 3

5. _____ is an artful form of handwriting.

6. One Japanese verse form is the _____ .

Reviewing Facts

SECTION 1

7. Which countries in East Asia are the most homogeneous in ethnic groups?

8. Which country in East Asia has the largest percentage of rural people?

SECTION 2

9. How did Japan respond to contact with the West in the 1800s?

10. How did China's government change after World War II?

SECTION 3

11. What are the major religions in East Asia?

12. Which Asian nation has the highest standard of living?

Critical Thinking

13. **Drawing Conclusions** How has geography influenced population density and distribution in East Asia?

14. **Identifying Central Issues** How did Confucianism influence government and society in China?

15. **Making Generalizations** Why do you think Japanese schools emphasize cooperation and teamwork? How has this philosophy helped Japan's economic growth?

Geographic Themes

16. **Human/Environment Interaction** Why are the valleys and coastal plains of China and Japan such crowded areas?

17. **Location** Where was the original center of East Asian culture?

18. **Movement** What religious ideas traveled from China to Korea and Japan?

Practicing Skills

Reading a Population Density Map

Refer to the population density map on page 566.

19. Which of the following cities have fewer than 2 million people—Beijing, Nanjing, Xi'an, Guangzhou, Hong Kong, Kunming?

20. Along which major rivers lie the most densely populated areas of China?

21. What is the largest city in Taiwan?

Using the Unit Atlas

Refer to the physical geography section of the Unit Atlas on pages 532–533.

22. What geographic factors have made Hong Kong a world center of trade, manufacturing, and transportation?

23. What is the Great Wall and why is it extraordinary?

Projects

Individual Activity

From your textbook or other sources about East Asian art and architecture, choose one object or building from China, Japan, or Korea. Then write several paragraphs about the object, explaining the creator's skill, the material used, and how it represents the creator's culture.

Cooperative Learning Activity

Flags often include important symbols. Divide the class into six groups to each research the flag of one nation: China, Japan, Taiwan, North Korea, South Korea, Mongolia. Each group should draw a picture of the flag, and research its symbols and what changes it may have gone through, to report to the class.

Writing About Geography

Argumentation

Imagine that you are a Japanese official in 1851 as an American fleet arrives in Tokyo Bay. How do you think the Japanese should respond to this development? Using your journal and other source materials, write a short essay in which you argue either *for* adapting Western technology and ideas or *against* accepting anything that comes from these intrusive foreigners. Highlight issues such as available resources, population pressure, international trade, and international relations.

Locating Places

EAST ASIA:
PHYSICAL GEOGRAPHY

Match the letters on the map with the places in East Asia. Write your answers on a separate sheet of paper.

1. Taiwan	6. Taipei
2. Mongolia	7. Guangzhou
3. Tokyo	8. Ulan Bator
4. Chiang Jiang	9. Shanghai
5. Seoul	10. Beijing

chapter 28
East Asia Today

CHAPTER FOCUS

Geographic Setting

Like population, most agriculture and industry are concentrated in the river valleys and coastal plains of East Asia. The climate and terrain in much of the region make huge areas unsuitable for human habitation.

Geographic Themes

Section 1 Living in East Asia

MOVEMENT Most of the countries of East Asia depend heavily on both regional and international trade for their growth and prosperity.

▲ Photograph: *Farm market in Beijing, China*

Section 2 People and Their Environment

HUMAN/ENVIRONMENT INTERACTION The intense concentration of people and industries in a fairly small part of the region has had a severe impact on the natural environment.

Living in East Asia

SETTING THE SCENE

Read to Discover . . .

- the importance of agriculture and fishing in East Asian economies.
- how smaller nations are challenging Japan's economic dominance in Asia.
- what the economic future holds for East Asia.

Key Terms

- commune
- cooperative
- trading partner
- merchant marine

Identify and Locate

Xinjiang, Tian Shan, Shanghai, Hong Kong, Fujian (province), Wuhan, Guangzhou

Wuhan, China

Ni Hao! Early morning grocery shopping at farm markets is a Chinese ritual. Items such as meat, fish, fruit, eggs and vegetables are bought fresh every day. Besides shopping, people in China come to the market to walk, meet friends, eat breakfast, or just watch the shoppers and farmers bargain for produce. *Bing Liu*

Bing Liu, who lives in central China, describes the importance of agriculture in Chinese daily life. Until recently most people in East Asia depended on agriculture for a living. Today industry and trade have become very important. Japan remains the leading industrial nation, but the Four Tigers—South Korea, Taiwan, Hong Kong, and Singapore (in Southeast Asia)—are becoming stronger economically.

HUMAN/ENVIRONMENT INTERACTION

Agriculture

Politics and economic development have changed farming styles in East Asia since the 1950s. Supplying enough food, however, remains crucially important.

China

China is the most agricultural of the nations of East Asia, with a huge land area and a growing population. More than 60 percent of the people in China work in agriculture. It is one of the world's leading producers of rice, wheat, and tea. Chinese farmers also produce large quantities of soybeans, cotton, jute, and silk. Livestock is an important product in the rugged western province of Xinjiang.

Since 1949, China's Communist government has made many changes in the country's agriculture. In the Great Leap Forward in 1958, farmers were organized into huge **communes**, collective farming communities whose members share work and products equally. An average commune had 5,000 households, divided into units called production brigades.

Most peasants disliked the communes, and crop production fell, bringing famine. Since then, smaller farms and smaller groups of workers have been allowed. Many farmers also have private garden plots and sell extra crops or animals.

Japan

Because farmland is scarce in the Japanese islands, farmers use every inch of it carefully. In the warmer southern islands, they may plant and harvest three crops a year. Farmers terrace their fields and use machinery, fertilizers, and irrigation.

Most farms—usually about three acres—are family businesses. In some families, women and grandparents run the farm while men commute to city jobs.

Even with limited land, Japan grows all the rice, and many of the vegetables, that it needs. In higher areas, tea and mulberry bushes—to feed silkworms—are grown.

Korea

Much of the land in the Korean Peninsula is too rugged for farming. As industries and cities grow, fewer Koreans work in agriculture, causing farmers to depend on machines.

Rice is the main crop in both North and South Korea. South Korean farmers plant two crops of rice a year using special seeds and farming methods to produce high yields. They grow other grains and potatoes and raise farm animals such as chickens, cattle, and pigs.

Taiwan

Taiwanese farmers also terrace their fields to grow rice. Most farms there are only two or three acres. The warm climate lets farmers plant pineapples, bananas, tea, peanuts, and vegetables.

Mongolia

Most of the land in Mongolia, in north-central East Asia, is used for grazing herds of sheep, goats, camels, and cattle.

Until the early 1990s, Mongolia followed the Soviet Union as its economic model. Herders were organized into collectives with quotas for producing milk and wool. State farms also grew food for people and fodder for animals. Today Mongolian farmers are slowly moving toward free enterprise.

Geographic Themes

Region: Eastern China

China's farmers rely on human and animal labor as well as machinery. *What percent of China's people work in agriculture?*

HUMAN/ENVIRONMENT INTERACTION

Fishing

Three of the world's leading fishing nations are in East Asia—Japan, China, and South Korea.

Fishing is an important food source and export of the region. In China, people depend on freshwater fish while the Japanese catch and eat more seafood than any other people.

Commercial fishing is especially important for peninsular and island nations. Fleets of trawlers catch tons of snapper, tuna, squid, shrimp, and other seafood. Factory ships often travel along to clean and freeze the fish soon after it is caught.

Most Japanese fishing communities have organized **cooperatives**, or co-ops. Co-op members work together to buy boats, sell the catch, and provide housing and benefits for their members.

POPULATION OF JAPAN BY AGE AND SEX

Male | Female

POPULATION OF CHINA BY AGE AND SEX

Male | Female

Age
70+
60-69
50-59
40-49
30-39
20-29
10-19
0-9

14 13 12 11 10 9 8 7 6 5 4 3 2 1 0 1 2 3 4 5 6 7 8 9 10 11 12 13 14
Percentage

14 13 12 11 10 9 8 7 6 5 4 3 2 1 0 1 2 3 4 5 6 7 8 9 10 11 12 13 14
Percentage

CHART STUDY

Japan's population is stable, but China's population had been growing rapidly. In recent years, however, the Chinese government has attempted to reduce population growth. *Using the population pyramid, determine whether the Chinese government has been successful at slowing population growth.*

MOVEMENT

Industry and Trade

Since the 1950s most nations of East Asia have become prosperous trading and industrial nations. Many have invited foreign investors.

Despite political differences regional nations are economically interdependent. Japan, Taiwan, and Hong Kong have all made investments in China, and state-owned Chinese companies have invested in Hong Kong.

Japan

Japan has long had flourishing industries, trade, and finance. As Japan became an imperial and military power in the 1890s, it developed heavy industries such as shipbuilding and steelmaking.

Recovering from World War II, Japan became Asia's economic miracle. Japanese

Geographic Themes

Region: South Korea
South Korea has one of the world's fastest-growing economies. A major industry is shipbuilding. *What is a major source of South Korea's prosperity?*

industries such as Honda, Sony, and Toyota prospered. Japanese-made cars, VCRs, stereos, cameras, and other electronic equipment have a world market.

One reason for Japan's success is that its workers turn out more goods per hour than workers in Europe or the United States. Japanese-style management encourages workers to feel part of a team. Also, factories continually modernize their equipment.

Because Japan has few industrial raw materials, it depends on trade. Although the country is a major steelmaker, for example, it imports iron ore. It also imports some food and most energy fuels—coal, oil, and natural gas, for example.

Japan's export trade, on the other hand, is extremely successful with its **trading partners**—countries that buy from or sell to the Japanese. The United States is Japan's largest partner, with Europe and other East Asian countries also its customers.

Taiwan

The island of Taiwan—the Republic of China—depends on thousands of smaller businesses, which make textiles, appliances, and other goods. Many Taiwanese operate factories in China's Fujian province and in other countries where land is available, the workforce is large, and labor is cheap.

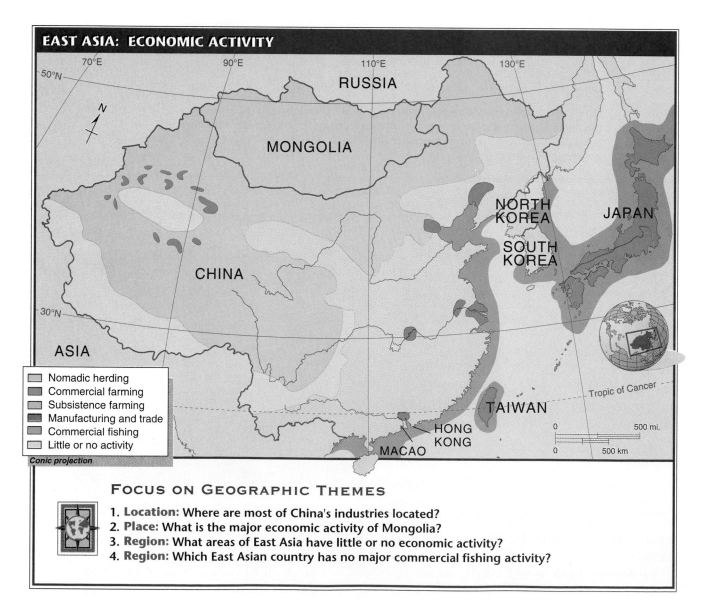

EAST ASIA: ECONOMIC ACTIVITY

Nomadic herding
Commercial farming
Subsistence farming
Manufacturing and trade
Commercial fishing
Little or no activity

Conic projection

FOCUS ON GEOGRAPHIC THEMES

1. **Location:** Where are most of China's industries located?
2. **Place:** What is the major economic activity of Mongolia?
3. **Region:** What areas of East Asia have little or no economic activity?
4. **Region:** Which East Asian country has no major commercial fishing activity?

China and Hong Kong

Outdated technology, poor government planning, and a lack of skilled workers have all slowed industrial growth in the People's Republic of China. The government owns and runs most major industries. China's natural resources, however, make it a leading producer of coal, steel, and cement. In the 1990s, Chinese leaders proposed many changes in the economy, encouraging foreign investments.

Entrepreneurs from Hong Kong and Taiwan have invested billions of dollars in plants in the nearby mainland provinces of Fujian and Guangdong. Beijing and cities in Manchuria in northern China are centers for iron and steel, petrochemicals, and cars. Shanghai produces textiles, steel, and ships.

Many economists believe that "greater China"—the People's Republic, Taiwan, and Hong Kong—will become an economic giant with the return of Hong Kong to China in 1997.

Korea

"Greater Korea" is also expected to become an economic center. It would include North and South Korea as well as northern China and far eastern Russia.

South Korea is one of Asia's new economic powers. Its prosperity since the Korean War has come mainly from trade with the United States and Japan. South Korea exports electronic equipment, textiles, ships, steel, and cars and trucks.

The Communist government of North Korea, which has large mineral reserves, emphasizes heavy industry such as machinery, chemicals, and iron and steel.

Mongolia

Most industries in Mongolia are based on its livestock, farms, and forests. Factories make textiles from wool and leather shoes and coats from hides. They also process meat and milk products and make furniture, paper, and other wood products.

Before the fall of communism in Russia, Mongolia traded mainly with China and Soviet bloc countries. In the 1990s Mongolia began to move gradually toward capitalism.

JAPAN'S BALANCE OF TRADE

Year	Value of Imports (in billions of dollars)	Value of Exports (in billions of dollars)	Balance of Trade (in billions of dollars)
1978	79.3	97.5	+18.2
1979	110.7	103.0	-7.7
1980	140.5	129.9	-10.6
1981	152.0	143.3	-8.7
1982	139.0	132.0	-7.0
1983	126.0	146.0	+20.0
1984	136.5	170.1	+33.6
1985	130.0	177.0	+47.0
1986	126.4	209.2	+82.8
1987	149.5	229.2	+79.7
1988	187.4	264.9	+77.5
1989	210.8	275.2	+64.40
1990	234.8	286.9	+52.10
1991	236.7	314.5	+77.80

Source: *The Statesman's Yearbook*, 1992-1993
Encyclopedia Britannica Yearbook, 1993

CHART STUDY

Japan has maintained a positive balance of trade since 1983. *In what year did the value of Japan's exports start to exceed $200 billion?*

MOVEMENT

Transportation and Communication

Before air travel was common, rugged mountains isolated East Asia. Today every country in the region has at least one scheduled air service. Overland travel in mainland Asia, however, involves long journeys by railroad or road. Transportation and communication networks are concentrated in the heavily populated areas.

Water

Rivers in China are important routes from inland industrial cities to seaports. The Chiang

Geographic Themes

Region: Honshu, Japan
Japan's bullet-shaped, high-speed electric trains run the length of the main island of Honshu. *How fast can the bullet trains travel?*

Jiang is the longest navigable river and the major port of Shanghai lies at its mouth. Large oceangoing ships can travel upriver 680 miles (1,090 km) to the transportation center of Wuhan in central China.

Other major ports are also at the mouths of rivers: Tianjin (TYEN•JIN) on the Huang He, and Guangzhou, on the Xi River. The world's oldest and longest artificial waterway, the Grand Canal, connects the Chiang Jiang and the Huang He.

Much of the trade of East Asian nations depends on their **merchant marine**, ships that engage in commerce. The leading nation is Japan, with a merchant fleet of nearly 10,000 ships, the second largest in the world. Japan's coast, especially the Inland Sea, has many fine harbors. Major ports are Yokohama, Kobe (KOH•bee), and Nagoya.

Land Travel

Japan has had busy highways since the 1600s. Railroads were an important part of Japan's drive toward modernization in the late 1800s. Today Japanese railway systems include high-speed trains, known as bullet trains, that can travel at 145 miles per hour (240 kmph).

Outside Japan few East Asians own cars. Railroads are important for long-distance travel, especially for the great distances within China. In the northwest a major railway line links Beijing with the Trans-Siberian Railway in Russia. Locally, buses connect towns. In rural areas people still travel by animal-drawn carts. Bicycles are popular everywhere.

North Korean railroads link that country with China. Railroads connect major South Korean cities. South Korea also built new highways for the 1988 Olympic Games held in Seoul.

Communications

In the Communist nations of East Asia, governments keep tight control of communications media. China's largest newspaper is the *People's Daily*, the official paper of the Communist Party.

Access to mass communications varies with a country's standard of living. Most people in Japan and Taiwan own television sets; a typical Chinese working family, on the other hand, is lucky to have a radio.

The Japanese have more than 125 daily newspapers, 2,000 magazines, and a large book publishing industry. A Tokyo paper, *Asahi Shimbun*, has a circulation of 11 million copies a day, the largest in the world.

SECTION 1 REVIEW

Checking for Understanding
1. **Define** commune, cooperative, trading partner, merchant marine.
2. **Locating Places** What Chinese port city is located on the Chiang Jiang?
3. **Place** What are China's major food crops?
4. **Movement** Why is trade important to Japan's prosperity?

Critical Thinking
5. **Analyzing Information** Why are the nations of East Asia interdependent in spite of their political differences?

People and Their Environment

SETTING THE SCENE

Read to Discover . . .
- how industrialization has harmed the environment in East Asia.
- what actions East Asians are taking to fight pollution and other environmental problems.
- how natural forces affect East Asia.

Key Terms
- acid rain
- chlorofluorocarbon

Identify and Locate
Beijing, Guangzhou, Guangdong

In terms of the environment, the people of East Asia have paid a high price for economic growth and prosperity. Industry and development have caused serious pollution problems. The region is also subject to natural disasters such as floods and earthquakes.

HUMAN/ENVIRONMENT INTERACTION

Environmental Concerns

In many parts of East Asia, industrial growth has seemed so important that its effects on the environment have been largely ignored. This has created serious environmental problems that affect not only this region but the entire world.

China

Coal is an inexpensive fuel—and China has huge reserves of it. As China works to industrialize, coal provides about 70 percent of its energy, running factories and heating homes. Burning coal, however, causes serious air pollution, especially in industrial cities. In Beijing where the air is already polluted by wind-blown dust, coal adds soot and poisonous fumes. In regions of China devoted to heavy industry, large numbers of people suffer from lung disease.

Burning coal gives off sulfur dioxide, a major ingredient of **acid rain**. When sulfur dioxide and other acids mix with water in the air, the rain that falls can be more acid than vinegar. It damages trees and can kill wildlife in lakes and rivers. Acid rain is a serious problem in the industrial region of southeast China, especially Guangdong, Guangxi, and Guizhou provinces. Winds spread acid rain across the sea to Japan's forests.

As China industrializes, problems with polluted water and toxic wastes increase. Thousands of acres of forests are cleared every year, adding to desert land and making floods worse. Government policies such as the Great Leap Forward caused damage to the environment by neglect. Although China has laws regulating pollution, they often are not enforced.

As a nation industrializes, its people tend to use more goods, consume more energy, and create more waste. Because China has more than 1 billion people, its continuing economic growth will have a great impact on the world's environment.

Japan

Japan is highly industrialized and very crowded. Waste products from factories, plus the trash of a rich "throwaway society," have polluted the air and water.

For many years the Japanese were criticized for ignoring the environmental problems their technologies were creating. In the 1970s, however, the Japanese government began to encourage industries to prevent pollution. Today its pollution-control laws are among the world's strictest.

Japanese industries sought new technologies to clean up or prevent air and water pollution. Japan soon became efficient in using energy. Of all the industrialized nations, it produces the least carbon dioxide, which contributes to the greenhouse effect. The United States, on the other hand, produces the most carbon dioxide, about 24 percent of the world total.

In the 1990s Japan became a world leader in environmental issues. It urged other nations to reduce their emissions of carbon dioxide and **chlorofluorocarbons**, or CFCs. These

substances, found in liquid coolants, destroy parts of the earth's protective ozone layer. Japan also offered "clean" technology and financial help for environmental projects to neighboring East Asian countries and other developing nations.

Other Countries

Rapid economic growth also brought environmental problems in Korea and Taiwan. In Taiwan, for example, computer factories were producing toxic waste, and petrochemical plants polluted river water. Both countries took steps to regulate industries.

Conservation

Other threats to the environment in East Asia are caused by growing populations, overfishing, and trade in rare animal products. Carved elephant ivory is valued in Asian art, and rhinoceros horn is used in traditional medicine. Yet both animals are endangered.

Japan has been criticized worldwide for some of its fishing methods. It is one of the few countries in the world that still hunts whales. In 1991 Japan agreed to stop fishing with drift nets, huge deep-sea nets that drastically lowered fish populations and killed anything caught in them, including dolphins and birds.

REGION

Natural Disasters

Because of its geography, East Asia constantly faces catastrophic natural disasters. Throughout its history, China has had to deal with disastrous floods on the Huang He and the Chiang Jiang. A young Chinese worker in 1969 described how the government and commune members worked to control floods:

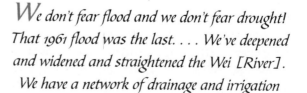

We don't fear flood and we don't fear drought! That 1961 flood was the last. . . . We've deepened and widened and straightened the Wei [River]. We have a network of drainage and irrigation

Geographic Themes

Place: Tokyo, Japan
Some Japanese often wear masks on days when pollution is severe. *How has Japan sought to improve the environment of East Asia?*

Geographic Themes

Place: Huang He valley, China
Because the Huang He often floods over a large area and causes great destruction, it has been called "China's sorrow." *How have the Chinese sought to control floods?*

canals and channels that can carry off or bring in water quickly. From source to mouth the work of harnessing the Yellow River [Huang He] is going ahead. That settles the danger of flood.

Several parts of China also suffer from frequent, damaging earthquakes. Typhoons often devastate coastal areas.

The island nations of East Asia are part of the Pacific Ocean's Ring of Fire. Located at plate boundaries where the earth's crust sometimes shifts, this region has frequent earthquakes and volcanic activity. Japan has about 50 active volcanoes and many hot springs from underground sources.

Every year Japan has about 1,500 small earthquakes. The most devastating, in 1923, destroyed large parts of Tokyo and Yokohama and killed about 130,000 people. Earthquakes on the sea floor can be equally serious for coastal areas. In 1993 an earthquake sent huge tsunami crashing onto the shores of Hokkaido and nearby small islands.

SECTION 2 REVIEW

Checking for Understanding
1. **Define** acid rain, chlorofluorocarbon.
2. **Locating Places** In what part of China is the problem of acid rain most serious?
3. **Place** What is the Ring of Fire?
4. **Human/Environment Interaction** What kinds of natural disasters are a threat to East Asia?

Critical Thinking
5. **Predicting Consequences** Why will China's continued economic growth have an effect on the world environment?

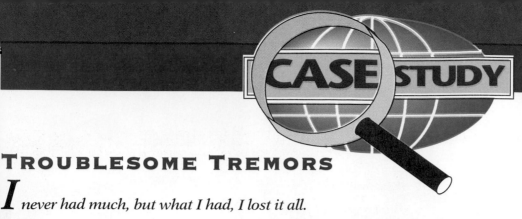

TROUBLESOME TREMORS

I never had much, but what I had, I lost it all.

Fujiharu Hatsuzuka, 63-year-old fisher who
survived a 1993 earthquake in northern Japan.

O n January 17, 1995, a 7.5-magnitude earthquake struck central Japan, demolishing the city of Kobe, the country's second-largest port. Within minutes the quake triggered landslides and raging firestorms. More than 6,000 people were killed, another 250,000 were made homeless, and the city experienced nearly $120 billion in damage. The quake was the worst to hit Japan in seven decades.

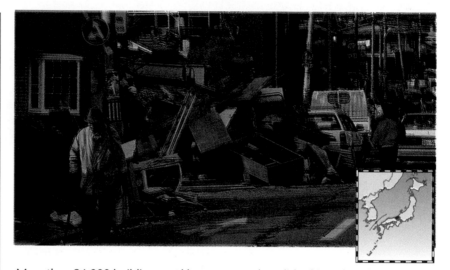

More than 94,000 buildings and houses were demolished in Kobe when a devastating earthquake struck the city in early 1995.

THE ISSUE

The 1995 quake was one of about 1,500 that shake Japan every year. Building construction and city planning are areas of intense interest as the Japanese study ways to minimize the devastating effects of major earthquakes.

THE BACKGROUND

Japan lies in a region where three huge plates of the earth's surface crunch against one another. The collisions are continuous, accounting for the thousands of earthquakes that are part of Japan's geological make-up.

Most quakes are short tremors. Every few years, however, a serious quake occurs. Major crunches usually cause several other natural catastrophes, such as landslides and tsunami.

Through the centuries the Japanese have developed housing that is remarkably resilient to quakes. Most famous is the traditional Japanese house— one story, of wood, constructed on a sturdy skeletal frame. The frames are able to sustain the repeated shocks of frequent earthquakes. Luckily, Japan has tremendous timber resources, so wooden houses can be quickly and easily rebuilt.

Although wooden houses can withstand a quake's jolts, they are vulnerable to the firestorms that often occur in conjunction with quakes.

Traditional Japanese cooking is done over an open charcoal fire: the earth's shaking upsets the stoves, spilling smoldering charcoal on the floor, which catches fire. Tokyo's 1923 quake—the century's worst—began during lunch hour. Overturned cookstoves fired the rubble, producing two great walls of fire that pushed fleeing crowds into the Sumida River.

To reduce the chance of fire, brick construction was introduced in the early 1890s. By the turn of the century, Japanese architects had learned how to strengthen brick walls with steel frame construction, build with composite brick-and-steel frame structures, and use reinforced concrete.

Through the centuries the Japanese have developed housing that is remarkably resilient to quakes.

THE POINTS OF VIEW

Although several construction techniques now exist for quake-proofing buildings, some Japanese architects say that such construction is not used as widely as it could be. In addition, say these architects, no time is ever given to examine ways in which destruction from a quake could be lessened through better city planning. Says a leading architect, "Our authorities only recognize the need for reconstruction and clearance after a catastrophe.

TECTONIC PLATES NEAR JAPAN

- Eurasian Plate
- Philippine Plate
- Pacific Plate

RUSSIA
CHINA
N. KOREA
S. KOREA
Sea of Japan
JAPAN
PACIFIC OCEAN
East China Sea

◄ Plate boundary
◄ Direction of plate movements

They see no necessity to prevent the recurrence of catastrophes by a new program of building."

Experts also point out that Japan's urban population is rapidly increasing. More people crowding in the cities means potentially more victims during a quake.

THE ISSUE TODAY

Japan continues to build. While more concrete buildings are going up, they do not necessarily replace wooden houses. Most are built in addition to wooden housing.

Charcoal stoves have been replaced by kerosene for heating and bottled gas for cooking. Unfortunately, both are much more highly flammable than charcoal.

Engineers and earthquake scientists are working together to design buildings that will not collapse during a quake. Cities have passed strict zoning laws requiring tall buildings to conform to certain rigorous standards. Japanese citizens participate in frequent earthquake drills. Many families keep survival kits ready. Fire extinguishers are handy everywhere, even in buses and taxicabs.

Experts admit, however, that a large quake could demolish buildings—wooden or cement—by the thousands. As many as one-half million people could die.

Reviewing the Case

1. Why does Japan have many earthquakes?
2. What steps have the Japanese taken to minimize earthquake damage?
3. **Human/Environment** **Interaction** What nongeographical problem contributes to earthquake damage in Japan?

MAP & GRAPH SKILLS

Reading an Economic Activity Map

Most people in any region practice one or two basic types of economic activity—the dominant economic activities of that region. These can be illustrated in an **economic activity map**.

REVIEWING THE SKILL

The economic activity maps in this textbook use colors to represent dominant economic activities. Other sources may use patterns or symbols to represent economic activities. In all maps, however, the key or legend defines the colors and symbols.

To read an economic activity map, apply the following steps:

- Read the map title to identify the geographic region shown by the map.
- Study the map key to understand all colors, symbols, and patterns used on the map.
- Study the map to determine what activities dominate the economy of each area.
- Compare the map with maps showing landforms, climate, and resources of the region to draw conclusions about the interaction of humans and the environment.

PRACTICING THE SKILL

Use the map below to answer the following questions:

1. What color represents subsistence agriculture? Manufacturing and trade?
2. What economic activity dominates eastern China?
3. How do landforms and climate determine the economic activity in eastern China?
4. In what areas do most people practice nomadic herding? Why is there little agriculture in these regions?
5. What activities dominate Japan's economy?
6. How has Japan's physical geography influenced its economy?

For additional practice in this skill, see Practicing Skills on page 584 of the Chapter 28 Review.

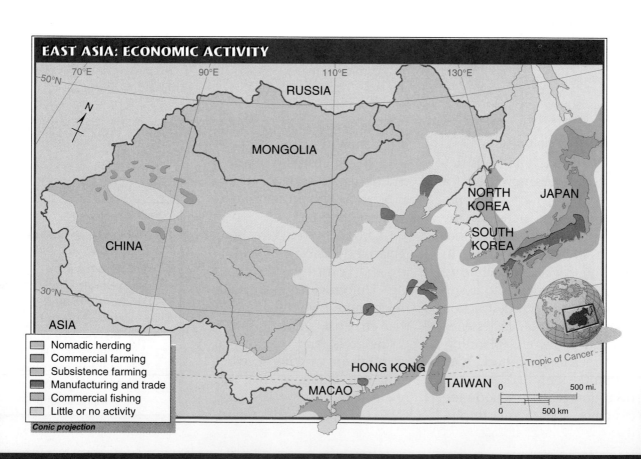

EAST ASIA: ECONOMIC ACTIVITY

RUSSIA
MONGOLIA
NORTH KOREA
JAPAN
SOUTH KOREA
CHINA
ASIA

HONG KONG
MACAO
TAIWAN
Tropic of Cancer

- Nomadic herding
- Commercial farming
- Subsistence farming
- Manufacturing and trade
- Commercial fishing
- Little or no activity

0   500 mi.
0   500 km

Conic projection

SECTION	KEY TERMS	SUMMARY
1 **Living in East Asia**	**commune** (p. 571) **cooperative** (p. 572) **trading partner** (p. 574) **merchant marine** (p. 576)	• East Asia was once mainly agricultural, but trade and industry have brought prosperity and economic growth to most of its nations. • A majority of Chinese people still work in agriculture, following policies set by the Communist government. • Fishing is important both for food and for export. • Japan is East Asia's leading industrial nation but is being challenged by Taiwan and South Korea. • Trade and business investment bring together capitalist and Communist countries in East Asia. • Ships and railroads are important links within East Asia; transportation is most developed in the eastern part of the region.

Japanese bullet train

SECTION	KEY TERMS	SUMMARY
2 **People and Their Environment**	**acid rain** (p. 577) **chlorofluorocarbon** (p. 578)	• Rapid industrial growth in East Asia has caused air and water pollution and toxic wastes; such environmental problems were ignored for several decades. • Japan has become a leader in protecting and cleaning up the environment, with strict anti-pollution laws. • China's huge population increases the impact of its economic development on the environment. • East Asia is subject to natural disasters such as flooding, earthquakes, tsunami, and typhoons.

Chinese town on the banks of the Huang He

Reviewing Key Terms

Choose the vocabulary term that best completes each of the sentences below. Write your answers on a separate sheet of paper.

   commune (p. 571)
   cooperative (p. 572)
   trading partner (p. 574)
   merchant marine (p. 576)
   acid rain (p. 577)
   chlorofluorocarbons (p. 578)

SECTION 1

1. South Korea is a major _____ of Japan's.
2. Members of a farming or fishing _____ voluntarily work together to share the work and the profits.
3. Japan's _____ carries its exports to other countries.
4. During the Great Leap Forward, several thousand farm households were organized into a single _____ .

SECTION 2

5. The greatest danger to the earth's ozone layer comes from _____ .
6. _____ endangers forests in China and neighboring countries.

Reviewing Facts

SECTION 1

7. What is the most important food crop in North and South Korea?
8. What kinds of things must Japan import? Why?
9. How do industries in Taiwan differ from those in Japan and Korea?
10. Why do businesses in Taiwan and Hong Kong invest in factories in mainland China?

SECTION 2

11. What is the most important energy source in China? How does this affect the environment?

12. What steps has Japan taken to solve environmental problems?
13. Why are earthquakes and volcanoes common in the islands of East Asia?

Critical Thinking

14. **Making Predictions** How might "greater China"—China, Taiwan, and Hong Kong—challenge Japan's economic power?
15. **Identifying Central Issues** Why did pollution problems develop in industrialized East Asia?

Geographic Themes

16. **Location** Why is fishing important and necessary for the people of East Asia?
17. **Human/Environment Interaction** How does acid rain in China affect pollution in Japan?

Practicing Skills

Reading An Economic Activity Map
   Refer to the map on page 582.
18. How has physical geography affected the location of manufacturing and trade centers in China?
19. In which parts of East Asia is fishing an important economic activity?
20. Compare the map on page 582 with the climate map of East Asia on page 543. How would you explain areas of little or no economic activity?

Using the Unit Atlas

Refer to the physical geography section of the Unit Atlas on pages 532–533.
21. Describe the physical makeup of Japan.

22. What are the major natural resources of Mongolia?

23. What is China's main agricultural area? What makes it good for growing crops?

Projects

Individual Activity

You have learned how important trade is to the nations of East Asia. Research and write a brief report about the imports and exports of one country or territory. Try to answer these questions: Does the country import/export mostly food and agricultural products or industrial goods? What does this show about the country and its people?

Cooperative Learning Activity

The United States is an important trading partner for East Asia. Work with four or five classmates to find out what products from East Asia you use every day. Check all parts of your homes and schools for products. Make a group list of what you find to share with the class.

Writing About Geography

Comparison

Imagine that you are a reporter making a tour of farming communities in two or more places in East Asia—for example, Taiwan and China, or two distinct regions of China. Write a short news article comparing and contrasting the farms and farm families. You may want to compare the size of farms, farming methods, crops grown, or other factors. Use your journal record to help you write your article.

Locating Places

EAST ASIA: PHYSICAL GEOGRAPHY

Match the letters on the map with the places and physical features of East Asia. Write your answers on a separate sheet of paper.

1. Shanghai
2. Tian Shan
3. Hong Kong
4. Guangzhou
5. Yokohama
6. Mongolia
7. Taiwan
8. Grand Canal
9. North Korea
10. Nagasaki

GEOGRAPHY CONNECTION

East Asia and the United States

THE MARTIAL ARTS

Martial arts is a catch-all phrase identifying various fighting methods developed from ancient Asian combat skills. Experts believe that the martial arts began as forms of exercise and self-defense practiced by Buddhist monks in India and Tibet. The monks then introduced the skills in China; from there, they spread to Korea and Japan. Today, hundreds of martial arts systems and styles exist.

The most popular martial arts in the United States are tae kwan do, karate, kung fu, and judo. Millions of Americans participate for recreation, physical fitness, or competition.

JUDO ▶
gets its name from the Japanese words *ju* (gentle) and *do* (way). Judo uses no hand or foot blows; rather, its purpose is to neutralize an opponent with various throws and locks. The "gentle way" refers to the participant's use of pretended weakness to take an opponent off balance.

▲ THE AMERICAN MARTIAL ARTS system advocates that practitioners pick and choose from all available techniques to find the most practical and realistic for personal use. Since the introduction of judo, Americans have embraced hundreds of styles and substyles of East Asian martial arts.

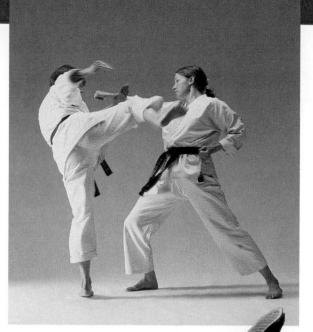

KARATE is a Japanese term: *kara* is most often translated "empty"; *te* means "hand." The name refers to the sport's beginning: Originally, karate skills were hand-and-foot blows learned by soldiers as defense if they became weaponless ("empty-handed") during battle. Today, the term includes any martial art using hand-and-foot blows as basic techniques. Japanese karate employs hard, quick, powerful blows. Introduced in the United States in the 1940s, karate has more American participants than anywhere else in the world.

▼TAE KWAN DO,
or Korean karate, is by far the favorite of all the martial arts. Known as the art of kicking and punching, this sport combines the abrupt movements of Japanese karate with the circular movement patterns of kung fu. The Koreans added their own touches—spectacular jumping and spinning kicks—which punctuate tae kwan do performances.

▲
KUNG FU—Chinese karate—is the best known of the Chinese martial arts. Kung fu practitioners incorporate their blows and kicks into a flowing, circular motion.

Checking for Understanding

1. What martial arts are popular in the United States?
2. **Movement** How did martial arts spread from India and Tibet to China?

587

Southeast Asia

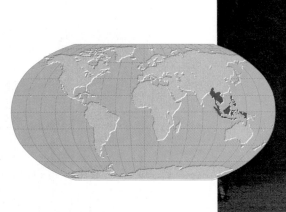

GeoJournal Activity

While studying Southeast Asia, keep track of photo images and descriptions about the region published in newspapers and magazines. Record your thoughts about each photo and description in your journal.

Picturing the World

Boats mob a canal of the Mekong River Delta in southern Vietnam. The Mekong River begins in China and flows 2,600 miles (4,183 km) through Myanmar, Laos, Thailand, Cambodia, and Vietnam. The river has few bridges, no industrial centers, and is the least developed of Asia's great rivers. Look at the map on page 591.

1. Where do most Laotians live, and what crop do they grow?
2. Now look at the map on page 592. What are other major rivers in Southeast Asia?

Picture Atlas CD-ROM Enrichment Corner

Rivers are very important for communication and transportation on the mainland of Southeast Asia. Create a file of photographs showing life along these rivers. (See the *Picture Atlas of the World* User's Guide on how to use the Collector button.) Include the following photographs: the Irrawaddy River in Myanmar; the houses on a canal in Bangkok and the barges on the Chao Phraya River in Thailand; gold panning in Laos; the Mekong Delta in Vietnam; and the Mekong River in Cambodia. Get together in groups. Use the information in the photo captions in your file and any other sources you can find to write questions about the rivers of Southeast Asia that will challenge your classmates in other groups.

SOUTHEAST ASIA
Cultural Geography

1. *What areas of Southeast Asia are the most heavily populated? Most sparsely populated?*
2. *What nations make up Southeast Asia?*
3. *What cities in Southeast Asia have more than 2 million people?*
4. *What countries of Southeast Asia are made up of islands?*

After nearly 400 years of Spanish colonial rule, **the Philippines** was governed by the United States from 1898 to 1946.

Houses in **Myanmar** (Burma) are built on poles above the ground to protect the inhabitants against floods and wild animals.

Bangkok, Thailand's capital, has more than 300 Buddhist temples.

Cambodia has faced almost constant warfare since the 1960s.

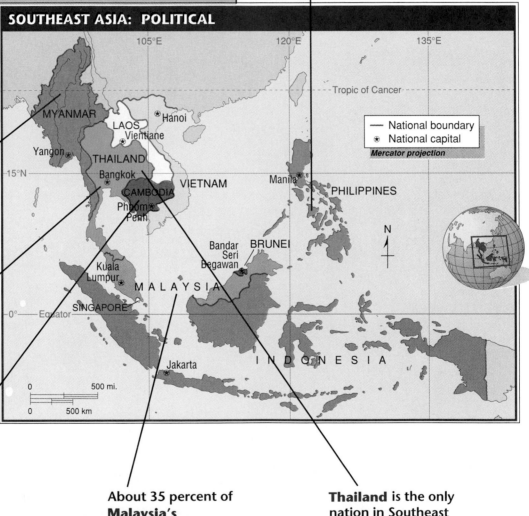

SOUTHEAST ASIA: POLITICAL

— National boundary
⊛ National capital
Mercator projection

About 35 percent of **Malaysia**'s population is Chinese, most of whom live in cities.

Thailand is the only nation in Southeast Asia that has never been ruled by a Western power.

About four-fifths of Thailand's population lives in rural areas.

Most Laotians live along the Mekong River and its tributaries and grow rice.

Fertile plains created by the Mekong River's floodwaters are home to most Cambodians.

About 65 percent of Brunei's people live in urban areas.

SOUTHEAST ASIA: POPULATION DENSITY

N

105°E   120°E   135°E

Tropic of Cancer

Hanoi

Yangon

15°N

Bangkok

Manila

Phnom Penh
Ho Chi Minh City

Kuala Lumpur

Medan

Singapore

0° — Equator

Jakarta

Bandung   Surabaya

Per sq. km	Per sq. mi.
Over 100	Over 250
50-100	125-250
25-50	60-125
1-25	2-60
Under 1	Under 2
Uninhabited	Uninhabited

Cities
- ■ Over 10,000,000
- □ 2,000,000 to 10,000,000
- • 1,000,000 to 2,000,000
- ○ Under 1,000,000

Mercator projection

0   500 mi.

0   500 km

With a population of almost 200 million, Indonesia is the fourth most populous country in the world, after China, India, and the United States.

Only about 900 of the Philippines's 7,000 islands are inhabited.

About half of the Philippines's population of 69 million live on the island of Luzon.

Population: Southeast Asia and the United States

Southeast Asia

United States

= 50,000,000

Source: 1994 World Population Data Sheet

Southeast Asia has one and a half times as many people as the United States.

SOUTHEAST ASIA
Physical Geography

CHARTING YOUR COURSE

1. *What body of water separates the Malay Peninsula and the island of Sumatra?*
2. *What Southeast Asian country is landlocked?*
3. *What are three natural resources found in Southeast Asia?*
4. *What major rivers are located in Southeast Asia?*

Laos is the only landlocked country in Southeast Asia. The Mekong River, however, flows through the country, providing Laotians with their chief means of transportation.

Of the more than 7,000 islands in the **Philippines**, the 11 largest make up 95 percent of the country.

Vietnam is composed of two river deltas. The Mekong River delta is at the southern end of the country, while the Hong (Red) River delta is at the northern end.

Most of **Brunei** is flat and forest-covered.

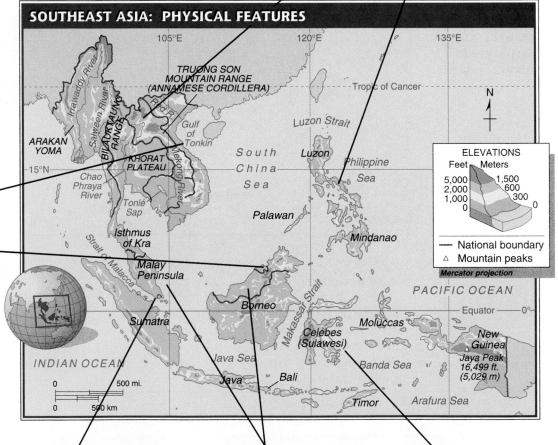

SOUTHEAST ASIA: PHYSICAL FEATURES

105°E — 120°E — 135°E

TRUONG SON
MOUNTAIN RANGE
(ANNAMESE CORDILLERA)

Tropic of Cancer

Irrawaddy River
Salween River
BILAUKTAUNG RANGE

ARAKAN YOMA

Gulf of Tonkin

KHORAT PLATEAU

15°N

Chao Phraya River

Mekong River

Tonlé Sap

Luzon Strait

South China Sea

Luzon

Philippine Sea

Palawan

Mindanao

N

ELEVATIONS

Feet	Meters
5,000	1,500
2,000	600
1,000	300
0	0

—— National boundary
△ Mountain peaks

Mercator projection

Isthmus of Kra

Malay Peninsula

Strait of Malacca

Sumatra

Borneo

Makassar Strait

PACIFIC OCEAN

Equator — 0°

Moluccas

Celebes (Sulawesi)

New Guinea

Jaya Peak
16,499 ft.
(5,029 m)

INDIAN OCEAN

Java Sea

Banda Sea

Java

Bali

Timor

Arafura Sea

0   500 mi.
0   500 km

Singapore consists of one main island and more than 50 offshore islets. Most of Singapore lies near sea level.

The country of **Malaysia** lies partly on the Malay Peninsula and partly on the island of Borneo.

Indonesia consists of more than 13,600 islands. They lie along the Equator and stretch more than 3,000 miles (4,827 km).

Myanmar's forests contain about 80 percent of the world's teakwood.

Rubber trees thrive in **Thailand's** southern region. The area also has large tin deposits.

Cambodia's flat land, plentiful water, and tropical climate are ideal for growing rice, the country's chief crop.

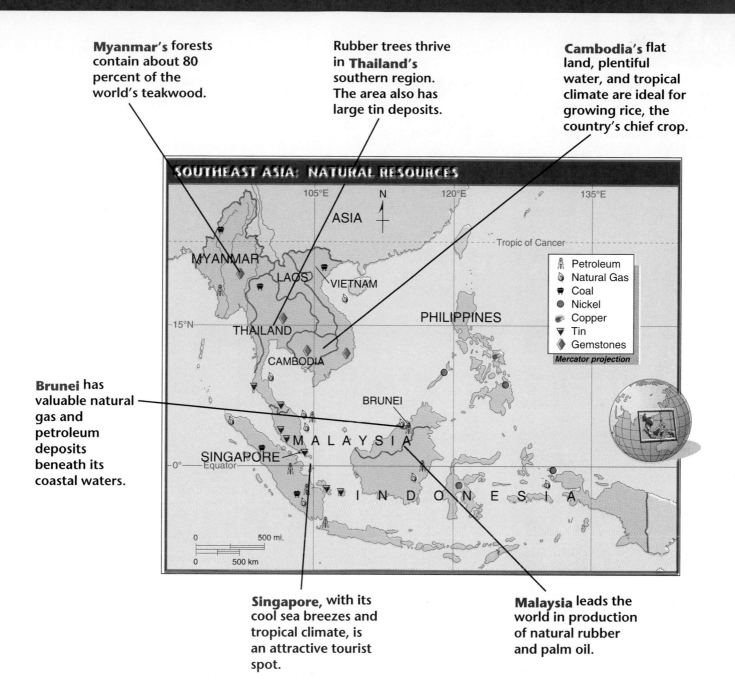

SOUTHEAST ASIA: NATURAL RESOURCES

105°E   N   120°E   135°E

ASIA

- - - Tropic of Cancer - - -

MYANMAR

LAOS

VIETNAM

15°N

THAILAND

PHILIPPINES

CAMBODIA

	Petroleum
	Natural Gas
	Coal
	Nickel
	Copper
	Tin
	Gemstones

Mercator projection

BRUNEI

Brunei has valuable natural gas and petroleum deposits beneath its coastal waters.

M A L A Y S I A

SINGAPORE

0°
Equator

I N D O N E S I A

0   500 mi.

0   500 km

Singapore, with its cool sea breezes and tropical climate, is an attractive tourist spot.

Malaysia leads the world in production of natural rubber and palm oil.

Mainland Southeast Asia: Physical Profile

9000 ft.

ANNAMESE CORDILLERA   Phu Bia (9,252 ft.)   0   150 mi.

BILAUKTAUNG RANGE   0   150 km

6000 ft.

SALWEEN RIVER

MEKONG RIVER

MOUTHS OF THE IRRAWADDY RIVER   PING RIVER   RED RIVER

3000 ft.

1200 ft.   *Bay of Bengal*   *Gulf of Martaban*   *Gulf of Tonkin*

Sea level

Yangon   SW to NE from approx. 17°N to 22°N latitude   Hai-phong

COUNTRY* AND CAPITAL	FLAG AND LANGUAGES	POPULATION	LANDMASS	PRINCIPAL PRODUCTS EXPORT	IMPORT
Brunei Bandar Seri Begawan	Malay, English, Chinese	300,000 148 per sq. mi. 57 per sq. km	2,030 sq. mi. 5,258 sq. km	Petroleum	Machinery
Cambodia Phnom Penh	Khmer, French	10,300,000 151 per sq. mi. 58 per sq. km	68,150 sq. mi. 176,509 sq. km	Rubber	Machinery
Indonesia Jakarta	Bahasa Indonesia (Malay), Javanese	199,700,000 283 per sq. mi. 109 per sq. km	705,190 sq. mi. 1,826,442 sq. km	Petroleum	Machinery
Laos Vientiane	Lao	4,700,000 52 per sq. mi. 20 per sq. km	89,110 sq. mi. 230,795 sq. km	Wood	Food
Malaysia Kuala Lumpur	Malay, English, Chinese, Indian languages	19,500,000 154 per sq. mi. 59 per sq. km	126,850 sq. mi. 328,542 sq. km	Machinery	Machinery
Myanmar Yangon	Burmese, Karen, Shan	45,400,000 179 per sq. mi. 69 per sq. km	253,880 sq. mi. 657,549 sq. km	Agricultural Products	Machinery
Philippines Manila	Pilipino, English, Cebuano, Bicol	68,700,000 597 per sq. mi. 230 per sq. km	115,120 sq. mi. 298,161 sq. km	Food & Animals	Machinery
Singapore Singapore City	Chinese, English, Malay, Tamil	2,900,000 12,083 per sq. mi. 4,664 per sq. km	240 sq. mi. 622 sq. km	Office Machines	Petroleum
Thailand Bangkok	Thai, Chinese, Malay, regional dialects	59,400,000 301 per sq. mi. 116 per sq. km	197,250 sq. mi. 510,878 sq. km	Machinery	Machinery
Vietnam Hanoi	Vietnamese, Chinese	73,100,000 582 per sq. mi. 225 per sq. km	125,670 sq. mi. 325,485 sq. km	Fuels	Machinery

*Country maps not drawn to scale.

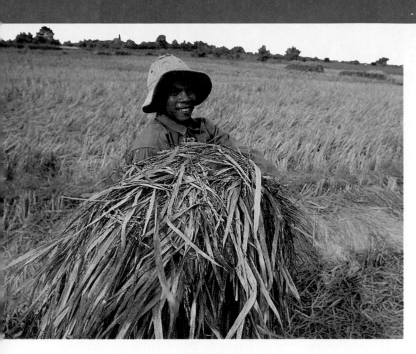

Rice is an important crop grown on the Philippine island of Luzon.

The Akha people are one of many different ethnic groups living in the mountains of northern Thailand and Myanmar (Burma).

This European-style church reflects the influence of Spain and the Roman Catholic Church on the Philippines.

Yangon, the capital of Myanmar, is known for its elaborate Buddhist temples.

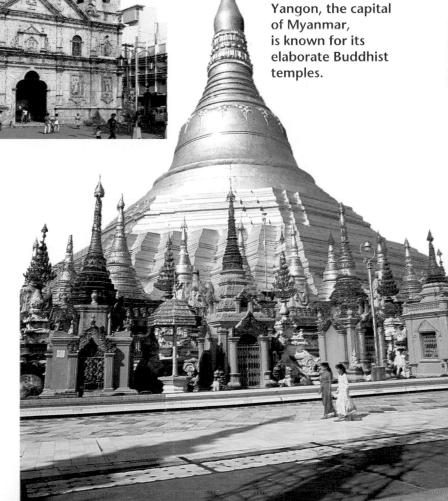

Villages and farms line the banks of the Mekong River in Vietnam.

The Physical Geography of Southeast Asia

CHAPTER FOCUS

Geographic Setting

About half of the nations of Southeast Asia lie on the Indochina and Malay peninsulas, while the others are in the Malay Archipelago. Because Southeast Asia is located astride the Equator, the region's climate is largely tropical.

Geographic Themes

Section 1 The Land
PLACE The mainland and the islands differ geographically in important ways.

▲ Photograph: *Mountains on the island of Sumatra, Malaysia*

Section 2 The Climate and Vegetation
LOCATION The climate and vegetation of Southeast Asia are consistent with their tropical location—the hot, humid, rainy climate gives rise to rain forest vegetation throughout much of the region.

1 The Land

SETTING THE SCENE

Read to Discover . . .
- the natural forces that shaped Southeast Asia.
- how mainland and island Southeast Asia are alike and how they are different.
- the kinds of natural resources found in Southeast Asia.

Key Terms
- cordillera
- archipelago
- flora
- fauna

Identify and Locate
Indochina Peninsula, Malay Peninsula, Ring of Fire, Annamese Cordillera, Makassar Strait, Irrawaddy River, Chao Praya River, Mekong River

Bangkok, Thailand
Swatdee! Right now I'm on vacation on a small island south of Thailand. The island is called Pooket Island, and it has beautiful beaches. Tourists come here to relax and have fun. Wish you were here.
Noy Khunviset

Phuket Island—Noy Khunviset's vacation spot—is one of many scenic coastal areas in the culture region of Southeast Asia. Having mostly a tropical climate, Southeast Asia is mountainous, with fertile river valleys. The region is made up of 10 countries: Thailand, Vietnam, Laos, Cambodia, Myanmar (formerly called Burma), Malaysia, Singapore, the Philippines, Indonesia, and Brunei. The similarities and differences among the cultures of these countries often reflect the influence of other Asian countries and European colonial rule.

Since World War II, the countries of Southeast Asia have seen continual political upheaval and warfare. At the same time, the region has made great advances economically.

Southeast Asian countries are also taking steps to cooperate in solving regional problems.

PLACE

Peninsulas and Islands

Southeast Asia was formed by the collision of the Eurasian, Philippine, and Indo-Australian tectonic plates millions of years ago. The clashing of the plates where India joined Asia forced up the mighty Himalayas and created **cordilleras**, or parallel mountain ranges, and river valleys in the Indochina Peninsula. To the east, volcanic and earthquake activity gave rise to a number of **archipelagoes**, or island groups.

Until 15,000 years ago, when sea levels were lower, there was a continent that connected what are now the islands of Sumatra, Java, Bali, Borneo, and Palawan (one of the western islands of the Philippines) with the mainland. With the rise in water levels caused by the melting at the end of the last Ice Age, much of the exposed land mass was covered, leaving a series of islands. This development had several important effects. It isolated the **flora**, the plants, and **fauna**, the animals, of the islands. It created a region with a longer coastline than any other comparable area in the world. In addition, it made the region's trade and communication dependent on water routes.

Mainland Southeast Asia

With only one exception, Southeast Asia can be divided into mainland and island countries. Five countries of Southeast Asia lie entirely on the mainland. Vietnam, Laos, Cambodia, and Myanmar lie entirely on the Indochina Peninsula. Thailand lies mainly on the Indochina Peninsula, but also trails southward to the Malay Peninsula.

Malaysia includes the southern end of the Malay Peninsula, as well as the northern part of the island of Borneo.

Island Southeast Asia

Singapore, sometimes referred to as a city-state, lies on an island at the southern tip of the Malay Peninsula. Another island country, Indonesia, is made up of 13,677 islands from the Indian Ocean to Papua New Guinea.

Brunei, a small country on the north edge of the island of Borneo, and the Philippines, an archipelago made up of 7,107 islands, are the remaining island countries.

HUMAN/ENVIRONMENT INTERACTION

Mountains

The mountains of mainland Southeast Asia run mainly in north-south ridges. Three of these ridges are the Arakan Range in western Myanmar; the Bilauktaung (bi•LOWK•towng) Range, which runs along the border of Myanmar and Thailand; and the Annamese Cordillera, which separates Vietnam from Laos and Cambodia.

Although few peaks rise above 10,000 feet (about 3,000 m), these ranges are dominant landforms. The highlands in the west and north meet to form a natural barrier between India and China. The ridges also form barriers between and within the Southeast Asian countries.

Mountains on the islands of Southeast Asia are part of the spectacular Pacific Ring of Fire. These volcanoes—many still active—have formed craters on the islands of Indonesia and the Philippines.

Indonesia alone has 327 volcanoes, 200 of which were once active, and 127 that are active today. One of the most famous, Krakatoa, was located in the strait between the islands of Java and Sumatra. In 1883, Krakatoa erupted violently, causing many deaths and great destruction.

Today a staff of volcano watchers in Java regularly checks active sites, prepared to alert the population when there is danger of an eruption.

The 1991 eruption of Mt. Pinatubo some 55 miles (about 90 km) north of Manila, the Philippine capital, was one of the most recent examples of volcanic action in the Ring of Fire. It is said to have been the most powerful volcanic eruption in the 20th century. The lava severely damaged the town of Angeles and destroyed the American-controlled Clark Air Base, covering it with nearly a foot of ash.

SOUTHEAST ASIA: PHYSICAL-POLITICAL

ELEVATIONS
Feet | Meters
5,000 | 1,500
2,000 | 600
1,000 | 300
0 | 0

— National boundary
⊛ National capital

Mercator projection

FOCUS ON GEOGRAPHIC THEMES

1. **Place:** What neck of land connects the Malay Peninsula to the rest of the mainland?
2. **Region:** What region includes Vietnam, Laos, and Cambodia?
3. **Place:** What city is the capital of Myanmar?
4. **Location:** What seas lie to the east and west of the Philippines?

The volcanoes of the region, however, do not only bring destruction. They are also the source of the fertile soil regions in the islands, which are some of the most productive agricultural areas in the world. Volcanic ash, full of rich nutrients, enriches the soil so much that even wooden fence posts sometimes sprout and grow into dense thickets within a few years.

Rivers

The rivers of mainland Southeast Asia flow in the north-south valleys between mountain ranges. The food supply, communication, and transportation throughout the region depend heavily on these waterways. The major rivers include the Irrawaddy in Myanmar; the Chao Phraya (chau PRY•uh) in Thailand; the Mekong, which runs along the Thailand/Laos border through Cambodia and southern Vietnam; and the Hong (Red) River in northern Vietnam.

Mainland rivers have their origins in the northern highlands. Some of them—like the Mekong which flows for 2,600 miles (about 4,180 km)—begin as far north as China. Silt and sediment deposits left by mainland rivers create fertile agricultural regions. The sediment deposits left by the Mekong are increasing shorelines as much as 50 feet (15 m) per year.

Rivers on Southeast Asian islands are generally shorter than the mainland rivers and flow in all directions. In Indonesia most rivers run in a northerly direction, cutting horizontally across the narrow islands. On the island of Borneo, the rivers tend to start near the center and run out toward the edges like spokes on a wheel.

Natural Resources

The Sultan of Brunei, one of the richest people in the world, made his fortune from oil and natural gas discovered on the northern coast of the island of Borneo. Fossil fuels are also found in Malaysia, Indonesia, Myanmar, and Vietnam. Coal is found in Vietnam and the Philippines.

Minerals

Minerals and gems are another important resource and product of regional trade. Deposits of nickel and iron in Indonesia, copper-concentrates in the Philippines, and tin in Thailand, Myanmar, Laos, and Malaysia—which has the world's largest tin deposits—are mined.

Myanmar, Thailand, Cambodia, and Vietnam produce breathtaking sapphires and ru-

Geographic Themes

Place: Luzon, The Philippines
Volcanic mountains rise on most of the islands of the Philippines. *What recent Philippine volcanic eruption is said to have been the most powerful in this century?*

bies. Burma rubies, as they are called, are especially prized by gem dealers.

Pearls are found near Sulu and Palawan in the Philippines. In 1934, the largest natural pearl ever found, weighing about 14 pounds (6.4 kg), was discovered in Palawan.

Another product from the earth, natural steam, is also a valuable resource. Trapped in volcanoes the steam has been tapped through wells. It is a source of geothermal energy used to generate electricity.

Flora and Fauna

Mahogany from the Philippines, teak from Myanmar, and rubber from Malaysia are among the trees that are an important resource in Southeast Asia. Because of heavy and unregulated deforestation, several Southeast Asian nations have restricted logging.

The forests also provide important pharmaceuticals. More than 10 percent of prescription drugs are made from products of tropical forests. Thailand has also developed the 1,000-plus species of orchids found there into a valuable trade resource.

The wildlife of Southeast Asia, such as elephants, tigers, several species of rhinoceros, and orangutans, is also considered a resource. Hundreds of animals in the region are found nowhere else in the world. Some of these include the bearded pig of Borneo, the Malayan lacewing butterfly, and Indonesia's Komodo dragon, the largest lizard in the world.

The people of Southeast Asia have an invaluable resource in the 2,500 fish species that thrive in the surrounding tropical waters. Fish are especially found in large quantities in the rivers of mainland Southeast Asia and in the seas near the Philippines, Indonesia, and Myanmar. Seafood, a major source of protein, is eaten in Southeast Asia at almost twice the world average.

Traditionally, local fishers in the region have gone out in sailing boats or canoes to make their catches with lines or traps. In recent decades, the region's small fishers have had to compete with a rapidly growing fleet of trawlers. The result has been an increased

Geographic Themes

Place: Malaysia
Malaysia's economy depends heavily on the use of natural resources. Malaysia is the world's leading producer of natural rubber. *What mineral resource is mined in Malaysia?*

yield everywhere in the region. Fish farming is now a major supplement to the economies of Southeast Asian countries. Concerns about the dangers of overfishing, however, have been raised; and the production of seafood for export has started to level off.

SECTION 1 REVIEW

Checking for Understanding
1. **Define** cordillera, archipelago, flora, fauna.
2. **Locating Places** Through which countries does the Mekong River flow?
3. **Region** What are two ways in which the mainland and the islands of Southeast Asia differ? In what two ways are they similar?
4. **Region** What are some of the natural resources found in Southeast Asia?

Critical Thinking
5. **Analyzing Information** Where on the mainland would you expect to find the most densely populated areas?

2 The Climate and Vegetation

SETTING THE SCENE

Read to Discover . . .
- the climate regions of Southeast Asia.
- the different kinds of vegetation in Southeast Asia.

Key Terms
- monsoon
- endemic
- deforestation

Identify and Locate
Climate regions: tropical rain forest, tropical savanna

Most of Southeast Asia lies within the tropics and has a tropical climate controlled by the **monsoons**, or seasonal winds. In summer, the moisture-laden monsoons blow from the cooler seas toward the warmer land. In the winter, the dry monsoons blow from the cooling land out to sea.

REGION

Southeast Asia's Climate Regions

Although Southeast Asia largely has a tropical climate, there are exceptions in the region's climate patterns due mainly to latitude, elevation, and local wind patterns. For example, the northernmost parts of Laos and Vietnam are humid subtropical and from November to April are cool and dry with temperatures averaging around 61°F (16°C). The Shan Plateau in Myanmar, called by one traveller a "tropical Scotland," is elevated and cooler than the rest of the country.

Tropical Rain Forest

A tropical rain forest climate—uniformly hot, humid, and rainy throughout the year—is found throughout the islands of Southeast Asia, as well as on the eastern and western coasts of the Indochina Peninsula. The average daily temperature in much of this area hovers around 79°F (26°C). Regional rainfall averages 79 to 188 inches (201 to 478 cm) per year, and the humidity reaches between 80 and 90 percent.

Even within this climate region there is some variation. For example, the farther away an area is from the Equator, the more concentrated the wet season becomes and the more pronounced the dry season becomes. The farther inland, the more rainfall there is likely to be. Other examples of local peculiarity are found in peninsular Malaysia, where most of the rain falls during thunderstorms, and in Singapore, where there are about 180 days with lightning each year.

Tropical Savanna Climate

A tropical savanna climate region extends southeastward across the Indochina Peninsula to the Philippines. It is characterized by alternate wet and dry seasons. In this climate region, monsoon winds bring rain from May or June through October. October to April is the dry season, with the first few months being cooler and the last few being hot. In most of the region monsoon winds blow during the dry months.

An exception is in eastern Indonesia. There, the rainy seasons are reversed, with the South Pacific trade winds bringing the hot, dry season from May to September, and the monsoons bringing the wet season from December to March.

Local peculiarities on the mainland include Sittwe (Akyab) in Myanmar, which gets an average of 204 inches (5,182 mm) of rain each year. Temperatures can drop to freezing in December and January in the Kieng Khoung province of Laos.

Importance of Rains

The heavy rains in Southeast Asia are important in several ways. They cause the flooding of the rivers, which is essential to wet rice cultivation—a crucial element in the agricultural life of the region. The rains also nourish the tropical rain forests that cover most of the area.

Vegetation

The vegetation of Southeast Asia is varied and abundant, characteristic of tropical rain forest and savanna climate regions. Southeast Asia contains 13 different types of tropical rain

SOUTHEAST ASIA: CLIMATE REGIONS

Tropical
- Tropical rain forest
- Tropical savanna

Mid-Latitude
- Humid subtropical
- Highland

Mercator projection

0   500 mi.
0   500 km

FOCUS ON GEOGRAPHIC THEMES

1. **Region:** How does the climate of the mainland countries differ from the climate of the island countries?
2. **Location:** Where are highland climates located in Southeast Asia?
3. **Location:** What part of Southeast Asia has a humid subtropical climate?

forest, and Malaysia alone has more than 145,000 species of flowering plants. The flora of Southeast Asia consists mainly of tropical and subtropical species, but also includes such rarities as cacti in central Myanmar. Tropical-savanna grasslands extend southeastward across the Indochina Peninsula and are also found in some of the easternmost islands, the areas in the region farther from the Equator.

Forests

The forests of Southeast Asia are very old. The Malaysian rain forest is believed to be the oldest in the region, dating back 130 million years. The makeup of Malaysia's forests is an example of the mix of different types of tropical rain forest. Below 2,000 feet (610 m) are the lowland rain forests. Above 2,000 feet (610

SOUTHEAST ASIA: NATURAL VEGETATION

- Tropical forest
- Deciduous and mixed deciduous-coniferous forest
- Temperate grassland

Mercator projection

FOCUS ON GEOGRAPHIC THEMES

1. **Region:** What is the dominant natural vegetation of Southeast Asia?
2. **Place:** What part of Southeast Asia has grasslands?

m), highland forest areas are found, while above 4,000 feet (1,220 m) there are mossy forests. In the river valleys, peat swamp forests thrive, while sandy coastal soil supports various shrubs, and the tidal mud flats are covered with mangrove swamp forests.

An Unusual Case

Singapore's vegetation makes it an exception in the region. Although Singapore is a highly developed urban area with one of the highest population densities in the world, it is one of the only two cities in the world to have areas of tropical rain forest within its boundaries (the other is Rio de Janeiro, Brazil). It may be hard to believe that where towering apartment blocks now house 2.7 million people, dense rain forest surrounded by mangroves once covered the island.

Singapore's vegetation is also unusual in that many of the **endemic** species—those native to a particular area—are now gone. Almost 80 percent of the trees and shrubs now growing in Singapore were imported, some from as far away as Central and South America. Along with the loss of its natural habitat, Singapore has lost many of its larger mammals and its variety of exotic animals.

Deforestation

During the 1970s and 1980s, the demand for natural resources, the creation of jobs, and the need for more open land led Southeast Asian nations to introduce deforestation programs. **Deforestation** refers to the removal of large areas of forest by loggers and farmers. Although a useful short-term solution to economic problems, deforestation has had disastrous consequences in the region, often reducing rich forest areas to wastelands. Thailand, for example, has lost half of its forests as a result of logging. Throughout the region, the loss of rain forest has decreased soil quality, created erosion problems, and caused water contamination. Logging has also encroached on lands belonging to local groups, affecting their traditional livelihoods and causing political dissent.

Geographic Themes

Human/Environment Interaction: Northern Thailand
Southeast Asia's forests and plains produce an abundance of flowers that are used for decoration and for festivals. *What human activity poses a threat to Southeast Asia's forests?*

Since the late 1980s, the governments of a number of Southeast Asian countries have tried to reduce logging and the export of timber, but without complete success. Brunei, for example, forbade lumber exports starting in 1989, and Thailand did the same.

SECTION 2 REVIEW

Checking for Understanding
1. **Define** monsoon, endemic, deforestation.
2. **Locating Places** In which climate region is Southeast Asia mainly located?
3. **Region** What are the variations found in the climates of Southeast Asian countries?
4. **Region** How does the tropical climate affect vegetation in Southeast Asia?

Critical Thinking
5. **Determining Cause and Effect** How does deforestation affect the livelihood of Southeast Asia's people?

CRITICAL THINKING SKILLS

Determining Cause and Effect

Suppose you leave for school one morning and forget to put a carton of milk back into the refrigerator. When you return in the afternoon, the milk has spoiled. What is the connection between these two events?

REVIEWING THE SKILL

Events occur because other events make them happen. An event or person that makes something happen is called a **cause**. In the example above, forgetting to refrigerate the milk caused it to spoil. The **effect**, or result, was the spoilage. The relationship between these two events is called a cause-and-effect relationship. Cause-and-effect relationships explain why things happen and how actions produce other actions.

Cause-and-effect relationships can be simple or complex. Sometimes several different causes produce a single effect. For example, a car accident may have several causes—poor road conditions, a tired or ill driver, bad weather, faulty equipment. On the other hand, one cause can produce several effects. Burning fossil fuels, such as gasoline and coal, may improve productivity and standard of living but also increases air pollution and global warming.

In addition an effect often becomes the cause of yet another event. For example, burning fossil fuels causes more greenhouse gases in the atmosphere; the greenhouse gases increase the global temperature. Global warming may cause ice caps to melt, which would increase the amount of water in the sea, which in turn may cause floods in coastal areas. Strings of causal relationships are called **cause-effect chains.**

When determining cause and effect, apply the following steps:
- Ask questions about why events occur.
- Identify the outcomes of events.
- Look for cause-and-effect relationships among events. Sometimes clue words or phrases, such as *caused, led to, brought about, produced, because, as a result of, so that, thus, as a consequence,* and *therefore,* indicate these relationships.

PRACTICING THE SKILL

A. Identify causes and effects in the following statements. Remember that there may be more than one cause or effect in each statement.

1. The mountain ridges, river valleys, and volcanic islands of Southeast Asia were formed by the collision of the Eurasian and Indo-Australian tectonic plates millions of years ago.
2. The mountain ridges of Southeast Asia produce natural barriers with India and China and also between peoples living within the region.
3. Erupting volcanoes bring destruction but also produce fertile soil and a source of geothermal energy.
4. Water has been the primary method of transportation and trade in Southeast Asia because of its enormous coastline and long rivers.
5. As distance from the Equator increases, wet and dry seasons become more concentrated and defined.
6. Heavy rainfall brings about river flooding, which is essential to rice cultivation.

B. Use the material in Chapter 29 to identify these cause-and-effect relationships.
1. Name three effects produced by the rising water levels after the last Ice Age.
2. Identify two causes and three effects of deforestation in Southeast Asia.

For additional practice in this skill, see Practicing Skills on page 608 of the Chapter 29 Review.

SECTION	KEY TERMS	SUMMARY
1 **The Land** Rubber plantation in Malaysia	**cordillera** (p. 597) **archipelago** (p. 598) **flora** (p. 598) **fauna** (p. 598)	• The region of Southeast Asia includes the 2 peninsulas east of India and south of China and the 20,000 islands of the Malay Archipelago. • Southeast Asia's mountains were formed by the collision of the Indo-Australian plate and the Philippine plate with the Eurasian plate. • The rivers on the mainland of Southeast Asia are important for agriculture, communication, and transportation. • Southeast Asia has major reserves of fossil fuels, tropical hardwoods, tin, and gems.

SECTION	KEY TERMS	SUMMARY
2 **The Climate and Vegetation** Floral festival in Thailand	**monsoon** (p. 602) **endemic** (p. 605) **deforestation** (p. 605)	• Most parts of Southeast Asia have a hot and humid climate affected by monsoons. • A tropical rain forest climate region is found throughout the islands of Southeast Asia, as well as on the eastern and western coasts of the Indochina Peninsula. • A tropical savanna climate region extends southeastward across the Indochina Peninsula. Some of the southernmost islands in the region also share this climate. • The vegetation of Southeast Asia consists largely of varieties of tropical rain forest. • Deforestation in Southeast Asia has affected the ecology, the economy, and the culture of some of the peoples.

Reviewing Key Terms

Choose the vocabulary term that best completes each of the sentences below. Write your answers on a separate sheet of paper.

cordilleras (p. 597)
archipelago (p. 598)
flora (p. 598)
fauna (p. 598)
monsoons (p. 602)
endemic (p. 605)
deforestation (p. 605)

SECTION 1

1. A(n) _____ is a group of islands.
2. _____ refers to the vegetation of a region.
3. Parallel mountain ranges, such as those found on the Indochina Peninsula, are known as _____ .
4. _____ refers to the animals of a region.

SECTION 2

5. _____ means native to one particular area.
6. _____ occurs when many trees are logged without regard for the environment.
7. _____ are winds that shift with the seasons.

Reviewing Facts

SECTION 1

8. What are three important landform types in Southeast Asia?
9. What geographic factor is responsible for the most fertile soils on mainland Southeast Asia? On the islands?
10. Name a Southeast Asian resource found underground, underwater, and in a tropical rain forest.

SECTION 2

11. Describe the two dominant climate regions found in Southeast Asia.
12. Why is deforestation a problem for Southeast Asia?

Critical Thinking

13. **Predicting Consequences** What kinds of transportation difficulties might Southeast Asians face on the mainland?
14. **Drawing Conclusions** Southeast Asia has a diversity of peoples and cultures. How might physical geography have shaped this diversity on the mainland? On the islands?

Geographic Themes

15. **Place** Why are the many volcanoes of the Ring of Fire useful as well as dangerous?
16. **Region** What vegetation is found in Southeast Asia's tropical rain forest climate region?

Practicing Skills

Determining Cause and Effect

Refer to the Determining Cause and Effect skill feature on page 606.

Find three cause-and-effect relationships in Chapter 29. For each one, identify the causes and effects.

Using the Unit Atlas

Refer to the physical geography section of the Unit Atlas on pages 592–593.

17. What body of water separates the two major land areas of Malaysia?
18. What landforms make up the nation of Indonesia?

Projects

Individual Activity

You have learned about some of the resources of Southeast Asia, such as gems, orchids, timber, and minerals. Imagine that you work in an exporting business in a Southeast Asian country. What are some of the problems you might encounter as you try to prepare a particular resource for export? Use your journal record, the text, encyclopedias, and other resources to prepare a brief report about your resource.

Cooperative Learning Activity

Working in a group of four, plan a trip through Southeast Asia. Decide what areas to visit, noting the kinds of landforms to be seen in each place. Determine how to get from one place to another, and work together on a map that shows the route. Finally, prepare a written itinerary and present the travel plans to the class.

Writing About Geography

Description

Use your journal, a film, a book, or a magazine with photographs to investigate a variety of physical features in Southeast Asia. Then write a newspaper story about a volcanic area in the Philippines, a rain forest in Malaysia, or the Mekong Delta in Vietnam.

Locating Places

SOUTHEAST ASIA: PHYSICAL GEOGRAPHY

Match the letters on the map with the places and physical features of Southeast Asia. Write your answers on a separate sheet of paper.

1. Singapore
2. Irrawaddy River
3. Thailand
4. Malay Peninsula
5. Mekong River
6. Vietnam
7. Philippines
8. Java
9. Sumatra
10. Borneo

chapter 30

The Cultural Geography of Southeast Asia

CHAPTER FOCUS

Geographic Setting

The culture region of Southeast Asia lies on the trade route from the Western nations to China and the East. As a result, the region has attracted traders and colonizers throughout history.

Geographic Themes

Section 1 Population Patterns
PLACE Most of Southeast Asia's peoples live in rural areas.

Section 2 History and Government
MOVEMENT The region's resources have long attracted foreigners.

Section 3 Cultures and Lifestyles
REGION The cultures of Southeast Asia reflect great ethnic diversity.

▲ Photograph: *Kuala Lumpur, the capital of Malaysia*

Population Patterns

LUANG PRABANG, LAOS

SAYBAYDEE! FROM MY HOME I CAN SEE THE BEAUTIFUL OLD TEMPLE ON TOP OF PHOU SI MOUNTAIN. BELOW THE MOUNTAIN IS THE OLD ROYAL PALACE THAT IS NOW THE NATIONAL MUSEUM. MANY PEOPLE COME TO LOOK AT THE BEAUTIFUL THINGS ON DISPLAY THERE.

BOUN SINGRATH SOMBOUN

Boun Singrathsomboun describes the rich cultural heritage of Laos, a landlocked country in mainland Southeast Asia. About 484 million people, about 9 percent of the world's population, live in the Southeast Asia culture region. The population of the region is growing rapidly and will likely double in about 37 years. This growth will present special challenges for the countries of the region.

PLACE

Population Growth

Southeast Asia's population is divided among 10 countries. Brunei, the country with the smallest population in the region, has about 300,000 people. By contrast more than 199 million people live in Indonesia, one of the most populous countries in the world. Vietnam, the Philippines, Thailand, and Myanmar all have between 45 million and 73 million people. Malaysia has about 20 million people, and the other nations—Cambodia, Laos, and Singapore—have fewer than 10 million.

Population Density

The majority of people in Southeast Asia live either in the river valley lowlands or on the coastal plains. A ready supply of water, fertile land, adequate transportation, and job availability are factors that have contributed to this concentration of people. In general the highlands and mountains have fewer people than the lowlands, and rural areas have fewer people than the cities.

The population density of the region varies widely. The overall density in Indonesia is 283 people per square mile (109 people per sq. km), and the island of Java is one of the most densely populated islands in the world. Singapore, the country with the least area, also has the greatest population density—more than 12,000 people per square mile (4,660 people per sq. km).

SOUTHEAST ASIA: URBAN AND RURAL POPULATION (SELECTED COUNTRIES)

Country	Percent Urban	Percent Rural	Annual Urban Growth %	Annual Rural Growth %
Indonesia	31	69	4.18	0.67
Malaysia	51	49	4.34	0.94
Thailand	19	81	4.70	0.80
Vietnam	20	80	3.75	1.83
Philippines	43	57	3.81	1.56
Myanmar	24	76	2.65	1.91
Cambodia	13	87	3.96	2.29
Laos	19	81	6.10	1.82

Sources: Population Reference Bureau, Inc., 1993; *Encyclopedia of the Third World,* Facts on File

CHART STUDY

Most nations of Southeast Asia are predominantly rural, but are rapidly becoming urban nations as more people move to the region's cities. *Which nation has the highest annual urban growth rate? Which nation has the highest percentage of urban population?*

Population Growth Rate

For a long time, the population growth rate was lower in Cambodia than in any other nation in the region. Between 1975 and 1979, Cambodia lost 38 percent of its population as a result of starvation, torture, and executions by the Communist Khmer Rouge government that was ruling the country. It has only recently approached its population figure of 10 million. Malaysia, on the other hand, has one of the highest growth rates in the region—2.3 percent, due in part to efforts of the government to increase the population from the current figure of 20 million to 70 million by 2095. The other countries in the region have a growth rate between 1.2 percent and 2.9 percent.

The Indonesian government in recent years has tried to encourage Indonesians in heavily populated areas to limit the size of their families. This effort has met with some success, but Indonesia's population continues to increase by almost 1.5 million people a year. The Singapore government has also carried out a campaign to slow population growth. One measure was to cut government child-care payments to parents having three or more children. By the early 1990s, these efforts had steadily reduced the birthrate.

PLACE

Rural and Urban Populations

The mainland countries of Southeast Asia have a higher percentage of **arable land,** land suitable for growing crops, than the island countries. Therefore, in mainland Southeast Asia, about 75 percent of the population

Geographic Themes

Region: Sumatra, Indonesia
The great majority of Indonesians are farmers who live in small towns or rural villages.
How does Indonesia's population compare with that of other island Southeast Asian countries?

is rural and works in agriculture. On Southeast Asian islands, the rural population ranges from 0 percent in urbanized Singapore to 87 percent in Cambodia.

The populations of several Southeast Asian countries are undergoing a shift from rural to urban areas. This shift has largely been the result of political conflicts and governmental policies, but economic and educational opportunities available in cities have also been factors.

The cities, however, have suffered from this rapid growth. Bangkok, Thailand, for example, had a population of about 1 million people in 1950. By 1992 the city had an estimated population of 10 million. The area of the city has expanded to accommodate the increased population, growing from about 37 square miles (96 sq. km) in 1958 to about 618 square miles (1,601 sq. km) today. Nevertheless it is estimated that more than 1 million residents of Bangkok live in densely populated areas characterized by poverty and poor housing.

In Southeast Asia, there are at least 12 cities with populations of more than 1 million people. The largest cities in the region—except

Bangkok, Thailand, and Hanoi, Vietnam—were first developed as colonial ports by European powers. In nearly every country in the region, the largest city is now a **primate city**—a city that serves as the capital of the country as well as the major port and industrial center.

SECTION 1 REVIEW

Checking for Understanding
1. **Define** arable land, primate city.
2. **Locating Places** Where do most people in Southeast Asia live?
3. **Movement** What geographic characteristic led to the development of most of Southeast Asia's cities?
4. **Movement** What are two ways in which the population of Southeast Asia is changing?

Critical Thinking
5. **Analyzing Information** How have government policies in Southeast Asia affected population characteristics?

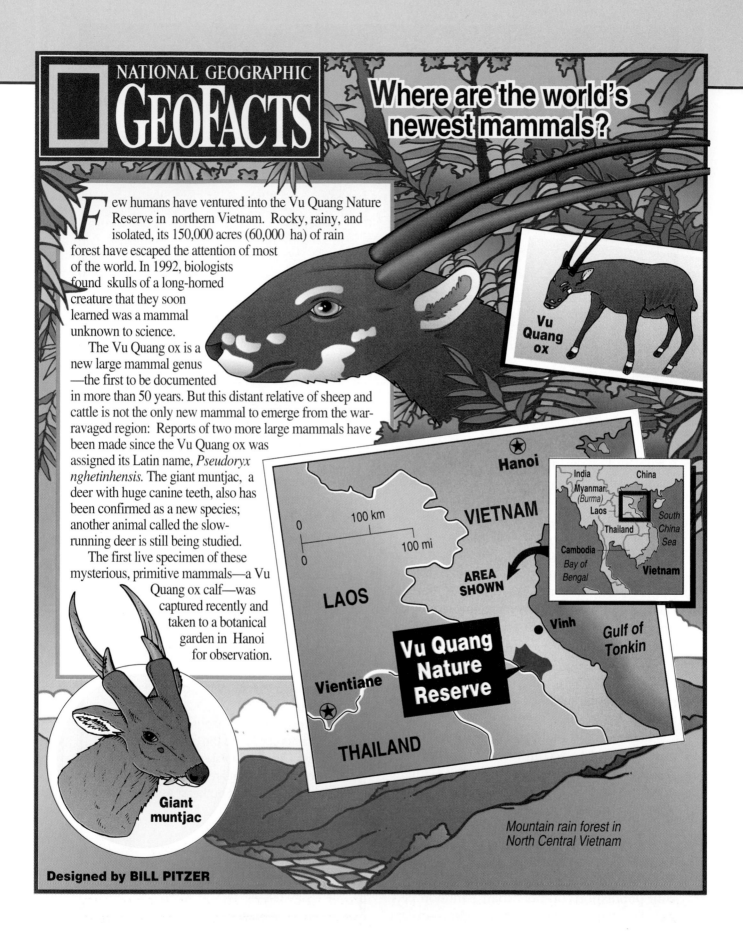

NATIONAL GEOGRAPHIC
GEOFACTS

Where are the world's newest mammals?

Few humans have ventured into the Vu Quang Nature Reserve in northern Vietnam. Rocky, rainy, and isolated, its 150,000 acres (60,000 ha) of rain forest have escaped the attention of most of the world. In 1992, biologists found skulls of a long-horned creature that they soon learned was a mammal unknown to science.

The Vu Quang ox is a new large mammal genus —the first to be documented in more than 50 years. But this distant relative of sheep and cattle is not the only new mammal to emerge from the war-ravaged region: Reports of two more large mammals have been made since the Vu Quang ox was assigned its Latin name, *Pseudoryx nghetinhensis*. The giant muntjac, a deer with huge canine teeth, also has been confirmed as a new species; another animal called the slow-running deer is still being studied.

The first live specimen of these mysterious, primitive mammals—a Vu Quang ox calf—was captured recently and taken to a botanical garden in Hanoi for observation.

Vu Quang ox

Giant muntjac

Hanoi

VIETNAM

0   100 km

0   100 mi

LAOS

AREA SHOWN

Vinh

Vu Quang Nature Reserve

Gulf of Tonkin

Vientiane

THAILAND

India   China
Myanmar (Burma)
Laos   South China Sea
Thailand
Cambodia
Bay of Bengal   Vietnam

Mountain rain forest in North Central Vietnam

Designed by BILL PITZER

History and Government

SETTING THE SCENE

Read to Discover . . .
- how location influenced the development of empires in Southeast Asia.
- the cultural influences that have affected the people of Southeast Asia.
- the changes that resulted from European and American colonization of Southeast Asia.

Key Terms
- maritime
- indigenous
- sphere of influence

Identify and Locate
Strait of Malacca, Sunda Strait, Gulf of Thailand, Indian Ocean, South China Sea, Mekong Delta

Many empires in early Southeast Asia developed around strategic ports. About 2,000 years ago, ports along the Gulf of Thailand were most important.

Sumatra's Srivijaya Empire (A.D. 600 to A.D. 1400) was one of the region's most powerful **maritime**, or seafaring, powers. It controlled shipping along the Strait of Malacca and through the Sunda Strait. Today Singapore, located on the shortest sea route between the Indian Ocean and the South China Sea, is one of the world's most prosperous seaports.

Some Southeast Asian empires were land-based and gained their wealth from the fertile soil. The Khmer Empire of Angkor in present-day Cambodia and the Kingdom of Srivijaya in Java grew three to four crops of rice along with other crops each year.

MOVEMENT

Outside Influences

Countries outside the region wanted involvement in sea routes between China and the West and in the region's resources of rice, forest products, tin, pearls, gold, and spices.

South Asia

In the A.D. 100s Indian traders introduced Hinduism and later Buddhism to the **indigenous**, or local, peoples. By the A.D. 1400s, Buddhism was the primary religion in Myanmar, Thailand, Laos, and Cambodia.

China

The Chinese began maritime trading routes through Southeast Asia early. The Hong (Red) River valley was dominated by the Chinese from the A.D. 100s to the A.D. 900s.

Islam

Islam was brought by Arab and Indian traders in the A.D. 1300s. Melaka (Malacca) on the Malay Peninsula grew into a Muslim center and important seaport by the early 1500s.

The West

Western influence in Southeast Asia lasted until the 1900s. Portugal, Spain, the Netherlands, Great Britain, and France came to trade, spread Christianity, and claim territory. They spread their **spheres of influence**—agreed-upon areas of control—over all of Southeast Asia except Thailand.

By the mid-1900s the United Kingdom had claimed what is now Brunei, Myanmar, Malaysia, and Singapore. France ruled present-day Cambodia, Vietnam, and Laos. The Netherlands colonized the islands of Indonesia, and Spain ruled the Philippine Islands, which were later acquired by the United States.

Change and Modernization

Westerners expanded tin mining and oil drilling. They also displaced small farms with large rice, rubber, and coffee plantations. They managed these estates using immigrant labor from India and China and imported machinery. Many of the foreign laborers stayed in the region.

The Westerners boosted economic production in the region for their own benefit, not

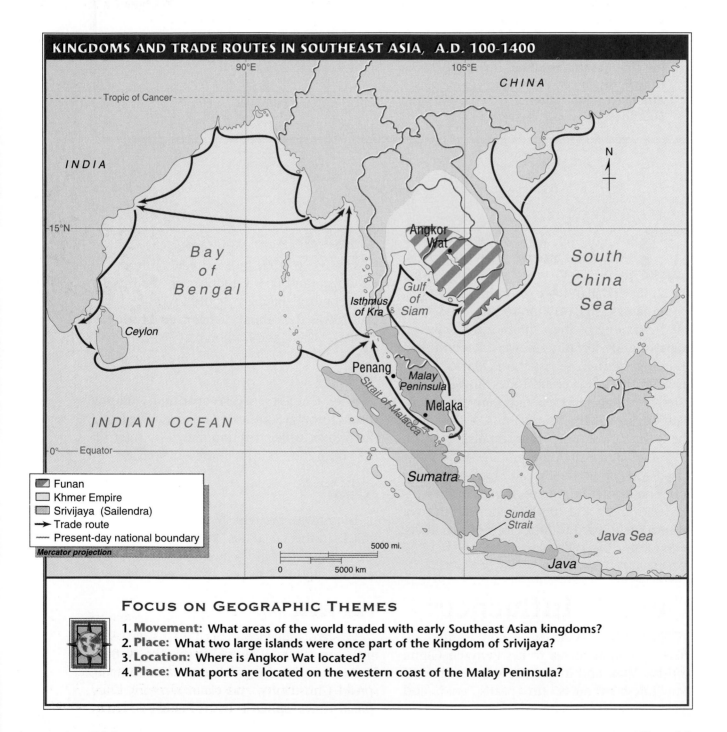

KINGDOMS AND TRADE ROUTES IN SOUTHEAST ASIA, A.D. 100-1400

Legend:
- Funan
- Khmer Empire
- Srivijaya (Sailendra)
- → Trade route
- -- Present-day national boundary

Mercator projection

0 — 5000 mi.
0 — 5000 km

FOCUS ON GEOGRAPHIC THEMES

1. **Movement:** What areas of the world traded with early Southeast Asian kingdoms?
2. **Place:** What two large islands were once part of the Kingdom of Srivijaya?
3. **Location:** Where is Angkor Wat located?
4. **Place:** What ports are located on the western coast of the Malay Peninsula?

FOREIGN COLONIES IN SOUTHEAST ASIA, 1914

Legend:
- Independent
- British
- French
- Dutch
- United States

Mercator projection

BURMA

SIAM

FRENCH INDOCHINA

MALAY STATES

SARAWAK

BRUNEI

BRITISH NORTH BORNEO

PHILIPPINE ISLANDS

DUTCH EAST INDIES

Tropic of Cancer

15°N

Equator

0 500 mi.

0 500 km

FOCUS ON GEOGRAPHIC THEMES

1. **Region:** What European powers established colonies in Southeast Asia?
2. **Place:** Which area of Southeast Asia was under American rule?
3. **Place:** What was the traditional name of present-day Thailand?
4. **Place:** What present-day countries were parts of French Indochina?

for that of Southeast Asians. In Myanmar's Irrawaddy River valley, about 988,400 acres (400,302 ha) of land were cultivated for rice in 1855. By 1930 there were 9,844,000 acres (4 million ha) of rice under cultivation. In Malaysia, rubber trees were introduced by the British in the early 1800s. By 1939 there were about 3.4 million acres (1.4 million ha) of rubber plantations. The Europeans also built networks of roads and railways to link inland production to overseas trade.

REGION

Independence and Conflicts

During World War II, Japan forced Western nations out of Southeast Asia. After Japan's defeat in 1945, the Western powers tried to regain control. They, however, faced growing Southeast Asian demands for freedom. By 1965, all of the region's peoples had won independence.

Geographic Themes

Place: Angkor Wat

The temple of Angkor Wat, built in the 1100s, is considered one of the finest architectural monuments in Southeast Asia. *In what modern nation is Angkor Wat located?*

New Nations

After World War II, European powers tried to regain control in Southeast Asia; they too had to face the growing strength of Southeast Asian moves toward independence. All the countries of Southeast Asia are now independent.

Independence, however, did not come without problems. Many countries have suffered ethnic wars, conflicts between Communist and non-Communist groups, and border disputes.

Governments Today

Three types of government are represented in Southeast Asia today. Indonesia, the Philippines, and Singapore are republics. Brunei, Malaysia, and Thailand are constitutional monarchies. Vietnam, Laos, and Myanmar are socialist republics. In May 1993, Cambodia held the first free election in its history. By the end of the year, it had become a constitutional monarchy under King Norodom Sihanouk.

SECTION 2 REVIEW

Checking for Understanding

1. **Define** maritime, indigenous, sphere of influence.

2. **Locating Places** Which parts of Southeast Asia border on the Sunda Strait? The Strait of Malacca?

3. **Movement** What outside influences shaped the historical development of Southeast Asia?

4. **Movement** What major religions were brought to Southeast Asia before World War II?

Critical Thinking

5. **Analyzing Information** Why were European nations interested in colonizing Southeast Asia?

SINGAPORE: MODEL OF PROSPERITY

As you read, examine how Singapore became an economic leader.

Trading Center

The city of Singapore surrounds an excellent natural harbor on the southern edge of Singapore Island. Singapore is Southeast Asia's busiest port; in terms of annual tonnage handled, it is also one of the world's largest.

Crowding around the harbor are deep-water facilities for immense oil tankers and cargo ships as well as wharves and docks for local trade. Warehouses stand filled with—or waiting for—thousands of tons of exports and imports. Singapore is a free port: goods can be unloaded, stored, and shipped again without payment of import duties.

Adjoining the docks and port area is the city's commercial and business section. In the towering glass-and-steel skyscrapers are department stores, banks, insurance companies, financial firms— national and international— and Singapore's stock exchange.

To the west of the city, beyond the older shopping and residential areas, is the Jurong industrial park region. Here, more than 800 manufacturing plants produce clothing, textiles, machinery, metals, and electronic, scientific, and transportation equipment.

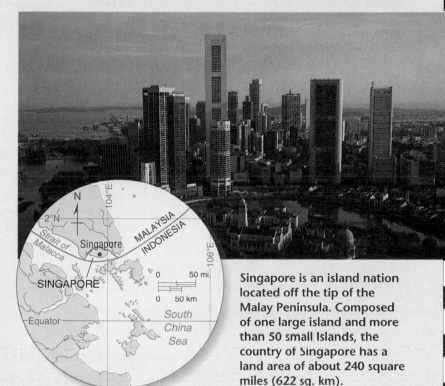

Singapore is an island nation located off the tip of the Malay Peninsula. Composed of one large island and more than 50 small Islands, the country of Singapore has a land area of about 240 square miles (622 sq. km).

Strict Government

Singapore's government plays a major role in the economy. Although the economy is based on free enterprise, the government exercises strict control over economic and social affairs. The government determines what benefits, such as sick leave and vacation time, employers shall provide for their workers.

In 1965, when Singapore became independent, the government embarked on a crash course of industrialization. The People's Action Party, the ruling political party, drove significant opposing parties underground. A government licensing system was established for national newspapers and magazines, and laws were established to keep labor unions politically powerless.

Checking for Understanding

1. What natural feature helped Singapore become an economic center in Southeast Asia?

2. **Place** What is unusual about the relationship between Singapore's economy and its government?

Cultures and Lifestyles

SETTING THE SCENE

Read to Discover . . .
- how ethnic diversity in Southeast Asia has led to a rich and varied culture.
- the effects of religious beliefs on culture in Southeast Asia.

Key Terms
- wat
- batik
- longhouse

Identify and Locate
Indochina Peninsula, Bangkok, Angkor Wat

The cultures of Southeast Asia reflect migrations by people from other regions. Several major world religions have had a great impact on the region.

The region's artistic development was greatly influenced by the early Indian civilization. Local artists, however, soon adapted the Indian culture to their own needs. Later, Southeast Asian art continued to be influenced by foreign styles but kept its distinctive quality.

SOUTHEAST ASIA: RELIGIONS

105°E   120°E   135°E
Tropic of Cancer
N
15°N

Chinese religions
Hinduism
Buddhism
Islam
Catholicism
Traditional religions
Mercator projection

0   300 mi.
0   300 km

Equator

FOCUS ON GEOGRAPHIC THEMES

1. **Place:** What four major religions are found in Southeast Asia?
2. **Place:** Where is Catholicism the major religion?

REGION

Languages and Religions

Hundreds of languages and dialects are spoken in Southeast Asia. These languages stem from three major language families: Malayo-Polynesian, Sino-Tibetan, and Mon-Khmer.

Many of the languages that are spoken in the region are the result of migration and colonization. For example, in the Philippines, Tagalog and English are the official languages. Spanish is also spoken in the Philippines. Chinese, Malay, Tamil, and English are the official languages of Singapore, which reflect the importance of commerce in this tiny island nation. In Malaysia, English is often used in business and daily life. The Malaysian government, however, has taken steps to make Malay the official language, especially in schools and universities. In Vietnamese cities, most people can speak English, French, Chinese, or Russian as well as Vietnamese.

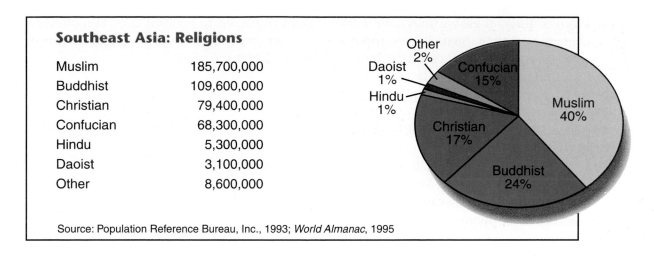

Southeast Asia: Religions

Muslim	185,700,000
Buddhist	109,600,000
Christian	79,400,000
Confucian	68,300,000
Hindu	5,300,000
Daoist	3,100,000
Other	8,600,000

Source: Population Reference Bureau, Inc., 1993; *World Almanac*, 1995

The people of Southeast Asia practice many different religions. This is the result of the cultural influences of the many peoples who migrated to the region. Buddhism is the major religion of the Indochina Peninsula. Many people who live on the Malay Peninsula and in parts of Indonesia are followers of Islam. Most people who live in the Philippines are Roman Catholics. This religious tradition began when the Philippines came under the control of Spain in the 1500s. A great number of the region's people—mainly those of Chinese ancestry—follow Confucianism or Daoism.

REGION

The Arts

Buddhism and Hinduism have inspired Southeast Asia's art and architecture. Beautiful Indian-style **wats**, or temples, and Chinese-style pagodas are found throughout the region. Some of the greatest ancient structures were built of stone, which was scarce. The temples were often partly coated with a thin, gleaming layer of gold. One of the most famous Hindu temples is Angkor Wat in Cambodia, built by a Khmer king more than 800 years ago. The numerous stone buildings of the temple housed priests as well as libraries. The walls are covered with carvings that described Hindu epics and legends.

Around A.D. 800, a well-known Buddhist shrine called Borobudur was built on the Indonesian island of Java. To build the shrine, 2 million cubic feet (56,000 cu. m) of stone were taken from a riverbed. The stones were carved and decorated with scenes depicting Buddhist beliefs. In the shrine are about 500 smaller shrines, each with a seated Buddha. The hand gestures of each Buddha vary to show different moods. In the city of Pagan, Myanmar, more than 3,000 Buddhist monasteries were built.

Crafts

The rich cultures of Southeast Asia have produced many fine crafts. The people of Myanmar and Vietnam produce fine lacquerware. Boxes, trays, dishes, and furniture are covered with many layers of resin from Asian sumac trees. Colored powders are used to paint the lacquerware.

The Indonesians and Malaysians make beautiful patterns on cloth by a method known as **batik.** Wax or rice paste is placed on cloth to resist dyes. The cloth is then dyed, and a pattern is formed by the dye's reaching only the uncovered parts of the cloth. Finally, the cloth is boiled to remove the wax.

In the Philippines a delicate cloth is made from pineapple fibers. Throughout Southeast Asia the weaving of palm leaves, bamboo, and other plants produce many goods—such as baskets, mats, and hats—for everyday use.

Literature

Early literature in Southeast Asia consisted of oral folktales and legends. Indian literature had a great influence on the development of local writings. Today these writings have a distinct character of their own. For example a well-known story from Java, called "Arjunavivaha," tells about the life of a Javanese king. This story comes from a similar tale about an Indian thinker.

In recent times writers of Southeast Asia have been heavily influenced by non-Asian writing. Some writers, however, have worked to translate classic Southeast Asian literature into modern language that can be read and understood by more people.

Music, Dance, and Drama

Traditional folk, religious, and court music remain strong throughout Southeast Asia. Music, dance, and drama are combined to describe legends or historical events. Dancers perform formal traditional dances that often have religious themes. Mostly percussion instruments, such as gongs, drums, and instruments similar to the xylophone are used.

Puppet plays are popular in many parts of Southeast Asia. These plays use local and religious characters to perform tales. Sometimes a human dancer who imitates a puppet's movements performs the play.

Lifestyles

Despite the recent growth of large urban centers, most Southeast Asians are farmers who live in small villages. A typical village has about 25 or 30 houses made of bamboo or wood. These houses have tiled, corrugated iron, or tin roofs to keep out the heavy rains that are typical of Southeast Asia. In coastal lowlands the houses are often built on raised platforms supported by wooden poles for protection from insects, animals, and flooding. In some rural areas of Indonesia and Malaysia, the people live in **longhouses**—buildings that house up to 100 people who are usually from several related, or extended, families. In general rural homes lack running water, electricity, and other services found in cities.

Most people in the cities live in traditional houses built of brick or wood. Many people still live in poor conditions, but governments are building housing projects to improve this situation. Some people in the cities live in new high-rise apartments or in single-family houses.

Varieties of Food and Clothing

Most people in Southeast Asia live on the food they raise themselves. Rice is the staple, usually served with fish, chicken, or vegetables. Various countries have their own specialties. Some use curry and other spices; some cook in coconut milk and oil. Tea, coffee, and coconut-milk drinks are the region's most popular beverages. Religion also plays an important role in the diet of many Southeast Asians. Buddhists, Muslims, and Hindus must obey the different dietary laws of their religions prescribing specific meat they can eat and periods of fasting.

Rural dwellers wear traditional clothing, which often includes loose-fitting shirts and

Geographic Themes

Place: Bangkok, Thailand
Thai classical dancers wear elaborate costumes as they act out traditional stories and religious themes. *What kinds of musical instruments are played in Southeast Asia?*

skirts or pants necessary because of the hot climate. In many of the cities people prefer to dress in Western styles.

Health and Education

Since achieving their independence, many Southeast Asian countries have enjoyed an improved quality of life. Independence has brought industrialization. Per capita incomes in many areas have risen. Life expectancy and infant survival rates have also increased. The general levels of health in Southeast Asia still vary widely, with Singapore having the best overall health conditions. In Laos and Cambodia, life expectancy is only 50 years as compared to 74 years in Singapore.

Since 1945 literacy has increased dramatically in the region although education is still limited. Governments continue efforts to make education available to everyone. The average number of years of schooling range from 2 in Cambodia to 8 in Brunei. Thailand has the highest literacy rate in the region (89 percent), while Cambodia has the lowest (50 percent).

Recreation and Celebration

Southeast Asians enjoy a variety of activities in their leisure time. They sometimes mix their social pleasures with daily chores. In large cities, such as Bangkok, Kuala Lumpur, Jakarta, and Singapore, people visit libraries, museums, theaters, parks, restaurants, and nightclubs. In rural areas, visiting neighbors is enjoyed.

People throughout Southeast Asia enjoy sports, such as soccer, basketball, and badminton. Indonesia has produced some world-class badminton players. Traditional sports and pastimes are also popular. The Indonesians practice a combination of dancing and self-defense known as *silat*. The Thai enjoy a form of boxing in which boxers use both feet and hands.

Many public holidays are celebrated and include Buddhist, Muslim, and Christian religious holidays. New Year's Day is also an important holiday throughout Southeast Asia.

 Geographic Themes

Place: Thailand
Rural and urban Southeast Asians alike celebrate festivals that include parades and processions. *What religions influence celebrations and holidays in Southeast Asia?*

SECTION 3 REVIEW

Checking for Understanding
1. **Define** wat, batik, longhouse.
2. **Locating Places** Where is the temple of Borobudur located?
3. **Movement** What country outside Southeast Asia had the most influence on the architecture, literature, dance, and drama in the region?
4. **Region** What are three recreational activities enjoyed by Southeast Asians?

Critical Thinking
5. **Making Comparisons** How does housing and clothing in rural areas of Southeast Asia compare with housing and clothing in urban areas?

STUDY AND WRITING SKILLS

Interpreting Primary Sources

If you witness a fire in your neighborhood and write a letter describing this event, you are a **primary source.**

REVIEWING THE SKILL

Primary sources are firsthand or eyewitness accounts of events. These include letters, journals, oral histories, interviews, autobiographies, and photographs. As primary sources, people recount events in their own words, describing details and personal reactions. By making events seem real, primary sources enable us to feel the impact of events on individuals.

When interpreting primary sources, first identify the speaker and the events being described. Determine when and where these events took place and when the account was actually written. If the account was written years later, the speaker may have forgotten some details. Finally, identify the speaker's emotions, opinions, and biases to determine how they have influenced the account. In interpreting primary sources, use the following steps:

- Identify the speaker and the speaker's relation to the events described.
- Identify when and where the events took place and when the account was written.
- Separate facts from the speaker's emotions, opinions, and biases.
- Determine what kind of information the document provides and what questions are left unanswered.

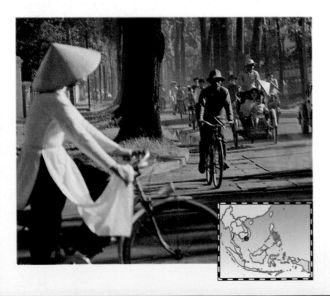

PRACTICING THE SKILL

In the following interview, a Vietnamese student explains why and how he became involved in the resistance movement. After reading the account, answer the questions that follow.

In September 1961 I enrolled in the school of science at Saigon University. . . . I started my studies in Saigon with the same enthusiasm I had before. . . . But even though I was so involved in my studies, I was also learning other things in Saigon. I started to come alive politically. I started with a critical view of Ngo Dinh Diem's government because of the arrests and religious favoritism that I knew about in my home province. Now I saw that Saigon had two faces. In one way it was exactly the rich fairyland I had dreamed about, a city of magnificent buildings, luxurious cars, and wealth. But it was also a place where people lived in the most miserable shanties, or just out on the street. Beggars were all over the place. . . .

The summer of 1963 was when the conflict between Catholics and Buddhists was most intense. . . . One day . . . I went down to Hai Duc [a Buddhist temple] with a friend of mine. . . . I thought maybe there would be some demonstrations or speeches. . . . But when we got there, nothing was going on. . . . We turned around to leave. Just as we did, three men grabbed us and threw us into a car. . . . It took only a couple of minutes to get to the police station. They searched me and took my wallet and ID. Then they shoved me into a cell by myself.[1]

1. When and where did these events take place?
2. How did the speaker's observations of Saigon affect his political views?
3. From this account, what conclusions can you draw about the political system in Vietnam in the early 1960s?

For additional practice in this skill, see Practicing Skills on page 626 of the Chapter 30 Review.

[1] Source: Interview with Nguyen Cong Hoan, *Portrait of the Enemy,* David Chanoff and Doan Van Toai. Random House, New York, 1986, pp. 17–18.

SECTION	KEY TERMS	SUMMARY
1 Population Patterns Town on the island of Sumatra, Indonesia	arable land (p. 612) primate city (p. 613)	• The population of Southeast Asia is growing rapidly. • Although most of Southeast Asia is rural, the number of large, densely populated cities in the region is growing.

SECTION	KEY TERMS	SUMMARY
2 History and Government Ruins of Angkor Wat, Cambodia	maritime (p. 615) indigenous (p. 615) sphere of influence (p. 615)	• Early in its history, Southeast Asia became a zone of contact between East Asia and South Asia. • All Southeast Asian countries except Thailand were colonized by foreign powers and are now independent. • The forms of government in Southeast Asia today include constitutional monarchies, republics, and socialist republics.

SECTION	KEY TERMS	SUMMARY
3 Cultures and Lifestyles Festival procession, Thailand	wat (p. 621) batik (p. 621) longhouse (p. 622)	• Culture in Southeast Asia reflects earlier migrations by people from other regions as well as regional folk traditions. • Among the major religions, Buddhism and Hinduism have greatly influenced Southeast Asian art, architecture, drama, and celebrations. • In spite of rapid population growth, economic development has led to many improvements and brought many challenges.

Reviewing Key Terms

Choose the vocabulary term that best completes each of the sentences below. Write your answers on a separate sheet of paper.

arable land (p. 612)
primate city (p. 613)
maritime (p. 615)
indigenous (p. 615)
spheres of influence (p. 615)
wats (p. 621)
batik (p. 621)
longhouses (p. 622)

SECTION 1

1. A _____ is a country's capital as well as its largest city, chief port, and industrial center.
2. An area suitable for the growing of crops is called _____ .

SECTION 2

3. Colonial powers in Southeast Asia established _____ to decide who had power in a certain area.
4. _____ people are native to the place in which they live.
5. When the Chinese lost their land route to trade with the West, they used a _____ route instead.

SECTION 3

6. _____ are religious temples.
7. In some rural areas of Indonesia and Malaysia, people from several related families often live in _____ .
8. Some Southeast Asians make patterns on cloth using a method known as _____ .

Reviewing Facts

SECTION 1

9. What geographic areas in Southeast Asia are the most populous?
10. Which country in Southeast Asia has the largest population? The smallest?

SECTION 2

11. What was the first foreign influence to reach Southeast Asia?
12. Which Southeast Asian country avoided becoming a colony?

SECTION 3

13. What is the predominant religion in the Indochina Peninsula?
14. What are some of the distinctive crafts created by the region's peoples?

Critical Thinking

15. **Drawing Conclusions**   Why do you think the island of Java has a high population density?
16. **Analyzing Information**   Why would huge plantations make it hard for small farms to compete?

Geographic Themes

17. **Movement**   What factors have influenced many people in Southeast Asia to move from rural to urban areas?
18. **Movement**   How did the early empires of Southeast Asia profit from trade?
19. **Place**   In what ways do Southeast Asians have a better quality of life?

Practicing Skills

Interpreting Primary Sources

Refer to the Interpreting Primary Sources skills feature on page 624.
20. How long after these events was this account written?
21. How do you think the speaker's opinions have affected his account of these events?
22. What kind of information is provided in this account? What other information gives you a fuller understanding of the political situation in Vietnam at this time?

Using the Unit Atlas

Refer to the cultural geography section of the Unit Atlas on pages 590–591.

23. In what geographic areas of Vietnam do most people live?
24. What Southeast Asian nation was once under American rule?
25. What ethnic group controls most of Malaysia's businesses?

Projects

Individual Activity

You have learned about elements of the culture of Southeast Asia. Find an example of Southeast Asian culture, such as a painting or a piece of literature from the region, or record someone from Southeast Asia speaking his or her native language. Introduce your find to the rest of your class.

Cooperative Learning Activity

Working in a group of four, think about ways in which other cultures have influenced the cultures of Southeast Asia. Then reread the section in the text as well as other reference books and make a list of the evidence. After completing the list, share your response with other groups and have them share their findings.

Writing About Geography

Narration

Find a book on Borobudur or Angkor Wat. Pretend that you are the first person to "find" one of these "lost" wonders of the world. Write an entry in your journal sharing your first impressions. Your writing should vividly describe the temple you have chosen.

Locating Places

SOUTHEAST ASIA: PHYSICAL GEOGRAPHY

Match the letters on the map with the places and physical features of Southeast Asia. Write your answers on a separate sheet of paper.

1. Cambodia
2. Bangkok
3. Hanoi
4. Strait of Malacca
5. Gulf of Thailand
6. Manila
7. Sumatra
8. Java
9. Indian Ocean
10. South China Sea

chapter 31
Southeast Asia Today

▲ Photograph: *Floating market in Bangkok, Thailand*

CHAPTER FOCUS

Geographic Setting

Southeast Asia contains a rich variety of natural resources. The people of the region, however, face many environmental challenges as they develop industrialized economies.

Geographic Themes

Section 1 Living in Southeast Asia

HUMAN/ENVIRONMENT INTERACTION Agriculture is an important part of the economies of Southeast Asia. In addition, about half of the countries depend on expanding industry for economic growth.

Section 2 People and Their Environment

REGION Environmental hazards such as typhoons, volcanoes, earthquakes, and floods often disrupt daily life and economic productivity in Southeast Asia. Air and water pollution are also affecting the quality of urban life in the region.

SETTING THE SCENE

Read to Discover . . .
- the importance of rice cultivation in Southeast Asia.
- how Southeast Asian countries are industrializing their economies.
- the ways in which the countries of Southeast Asia are interdependent.

Key Terms
- sickle
- cash crop
- interdependent
- Association of Southeast Asian Nations (ASEAN)
- free port

Identify and Locate
Strait of Malacca, Manila, Chao Phraya River, Bangkok, Mekong River, Jakarta

> Kuala Lumpur, Malaysia
>
> I am helping my father in his business. Due to heavy foreign investment by Americans, Europeans and Japanese, Malaysia has enjoyed an economic boom in the last five years. This surge in the economy has helped my father to be successful in his trading business.
>
> Chee Ng

MALAYSIA

15¢ LAPANGAN TERBANG ANTARABANGSA KUALA LUMPUR INTERNATIONAL AIRPORT

Chee Ng lives in Malaysia, one of the most economically successful countries in Southeast Asia today. The economies of the other Southeast Asian countries are developing at varying rates. Almost 65 percent of Southeast Asia's labor force is engaged in agriculture. Manufacturing and commerce, however, are an important factor in the economics of about half of the region's countries.

HUMAN/ENVIRONMENT INTERACTION

Agriculture

Rice farming is the most important agricultural activity in the region. More than 50 percent of the farmland in Southeast Asia is used for growing rice.

Rice Cultivation

Rice grows well in Southeast Asia because most of the region has fertile soil, an abundant water supply, and a warm, wet climate. In addition to providing a major source of food, rice has long been an important export of Myanmar, Cambodia, Thailand, and Vietnam. Rice is also a major crop in Indonesia. For the most part, farmers in Southeast Asia do not use modern machinery. They plant and harvest their crops by hand or with simple hand tools, such as **sickles**—sharp, curved knives. Water buffalo or oxen are used to plow the fields.

Rice needs an abundance of water to grow. Rains provide sufficient water for growing rice in parts of the Philippines and in the Irrawaddy River delta in Myanmar. Seasonal flooding

Geographic Themes

Place: Bali, Indonesia
The island of Bali is known for its beautiful scenery, elaborate temples, and fertile soil. *What major crop is grown in Indonesia and other countries of Southeast Asia?*

of the Chao Phraya and Mekong rivers irrigates rice fields in parts of Thailand, Cambodia, and Vietnam. Rice is planted at the beginning of the rainy season in May and is ready for harvest in October. During the dry season, a second rice crop can be grown by irrigating rice fields with water stored from the rains and the flooding river.

Other Crops

Southeast Asian nations also grow edible roots, such as cassavas and yams, and bananas. Many people in Southeast Asia have small garden plots that produce a variety of fruits and vegetables, and they also raise pigs and poultry for food.

Plantations in the coastal lowlands provide many of the region's **cash crops**—crops raised to be sold. Sugar cane is grown on Java and in the Philippines. Rubber, brought to the region from South America less than 100 years ago, is an important cash crop. Malaysia is the world's leading natural-rubber producer. Other regional cash crops are coconuts, coffee, palm oil, and spices.

HUMAN/ENVIRONMENT INTERACTION

Forestry and Mining

Forestry is an important industry in Southeast Asian countries. Myanmar leads the world in teakwood exports. Lumber and products made from teak, ebony, mahogany, and bamboo are important to the economies of Malaysia, the Philippines, Indonesia, and Thailand.

Environmental Protection

Logging, however, has often led to serious deforestation and environmental damage. In recent years, some countries have taken steps to limit the exploitation of the forests. The governments of Thailand, Indonesia, the Philippines, and Malaysia have passed laws to limit certain timber exports, but these restrictions are often not adequately enforced.

Oil and Mining

Oil extraction and mining are important to Southeast Asia's economic growth. Brunei has become rich from its oil industry. Crude oil, natural gas, and petroleum products account for 95 percent of Brunei's export income. One of the world's largest natural gas plants is found in Brunei.

Indonesia is the largest producer of petroleum in the region and is one of the top 10 producers in the Organization of Petroleum Exporting Countries (OPEC). Economic development has been spurred by the building of pipelines to carry oil from drilling sites to the coasts for shipment. Pipelines have been built on the islands of Sumatra, Java, Borneo, and New Guinea.

Tin mining is a major industry in Southeast Asia. Malaysia, Thailand, and Indonesia are three of the world's leading tin producers. Iron ore is also important in Malaysia and in the Philippines. Manganese, an important mineral for strengthening steel, is found in the Philippines and in Indonesia. Tungsten,

SOUTHEAST ASIA: ECONOMIC ACTIVITY

Legend:
- Commercial farming
- Subsistence farming
- Manufacturing and trade
- Commercial fishing

Mercator projection

FOCUS ON GEOGRAPHIC THEMES

1. **Region:** What is the dominant economic activity in Southeast Asia?
2. **Place:** Where is manufacturing and trade an important economic activity? Why?

which is used for electrical purposes and for steel alloys, greatly adds to the economic growth of Myanmar and Thailand.

PLACE

Commercial and Industrial Growth

Newly industrializing countries in Southeast Asia are Malaysia, the Philippines, Singapore, and Thailand. Foreign companies have moved manufacturing and assembly plants to Southeast Asia because of the large supply of inexpensive labor in the region. Foreign investments have stimulated the economies of Southeast Asian nations.

Singapore

Singapore's location and good harbors have led to its development as an important port and manufacturing center. Major indus-

tries in Singapore produce chemicals, electronic equipment, transportation equipment, machinery, metals, paper, rubber, textiles, and processed foods. Oil refining and shipbuilding are also important industries in Singapore.

Other Industrialized Countries

Malaysia has used the capital from its mineral and rubber exports to develop many industries. Major manufactured products include cement, chemicals, rubber goods, textiles, and processed foods. Malaysia and the Philippines are developing profitable automobile assembly industries. Textile and clothing industries are important in Thailand and the Philippines. In increasing their exports, Thailand and the Philippines have tried to balance industrial growth with more traditional ventures in agricultural production and fish farming.

Less Industrialized Countries

Other countries of the region, such as Laos, Cambodia, and Vietnam, are developing their industries at a slower rate. Only a small percentage of the people in these countries work in industry. Manufacturing has yet to be developed on a scale larger than small craft industries for a number of reasons.

Wars and political changes in Laos, Cambodia, and Vietnam have affected economic development for many years. A policy of isolationism in Myanmar has long slowed the country's economic growth. Indonesia's economic development is offset somewhat by its rapidly growing population. This means that Indonesia must import many kinds of manufactured goods. Indonesian leaders, however, hope to finance future industrial development and expansion with income from Indonesia's oil exports.

MOVEMENT

Interdependence

Some countries in Southeast Asia have become more **interdependent**, or reliant on each other, as a result of the formation of two organizations designed to increase regional development and trade. In 1967 Indonesia, Malaysia, the Philippines, Singapore, and Thailand formed the **Association of Southeast Asian Nations (ASEAN)**. Brunei joined ASEAN in 1984. One goal of ASEAN is to promote tourism in member countries. ASEAN also works to lower trade barriers in the region. In addition, members of ASEAN share products during shortages.

Although ASEAN is a political and economic alliance, it does not have full political or economic unity as one of its major goals. This is primarily because of Southeast Asia's great diversity. Yet, the association has allowed its members to understand one another through regular meetings of leaders and cultural exchanges of citizens. ASEAN also has provided a sense of security in a region that has long known political instability and conflict.

Another development group is the Asian Development Bank (ADB), based in Manila, the capital of the Philippines. This organization helps the economic development of member countries by lending them money. The ADB helps to finance agricultural, transportation, and industrial-development projects throughout Southeast Asia.

MOVEMENT

Transportation

Water transportation is the most common way to move people and goods in Southeast Asia. In recent years overland transport networks have been developed in many urban areas. Modern and efficient transportation, however, has yet to reach most parts of rural Southeast Asia.

Water Transportation

Because of the long coastlines and many rivers, water transportation is very important in Southeast Asia. Throughout the region's history, boats have carried people and goods to the islands and along rivers and seacoasts. All but one of the countries of the region have at least one harbor for oceangoing vessels. Laos, the only exception, is landlocked.

For centuries Southeast Asia has been the crossroads of major ocean trade routes. Even today most shipping traffic between Europe and East Asia passes through the Strait of Malacca. All the largest cities of Southeast Asia are located near waterways, making these cities trade centers.

The **free port** of Singapore, which lies near the southeastern end of the Strait of Malacca, is one of the world's busiest ports. A free port is a place where goods can be unloaded, stored, and reshipped without the payment of import duties. Thus, Singapore is an important port for Southeast Asia. Other major ports include the Indonesian cities of Palembang, on Sumatra, and Jakarta, on Java. Jakarta is the center for most of Indonesia's trade and is also a leading cultural and manufacturing center.

Manila, in the Philippines, has one of the best natural harbors in the world. Its location makes Manila one of the most important centers for oceangoing trade in Asia. Bangkok, near the mouth of the Chao Phraya, is a port for both Thailand and landlocked Laos.

Overland Transportation

Throughout the region, the quality of transportation varies dramatically. Highways and railroads have been developed on the peninsulas and on some of the larger islands in the region. In general, however, these systems connect only the major cities. Travel outside urban areas is mainly on unpaved roads.

In most countries of the region, bicycles, motor scooters, and oxcarts are common means of transportation. The Philippines, Singapore, and Thailand have better overland transportation systems than the other countries of the region. This has largely been the result of the process of economic development in these countries and their ties with other industrialized countries of the world. The island of Singapore is connected to the Malay Peninsula by a 16-mile (25.6 km) railway. In Jakarta,

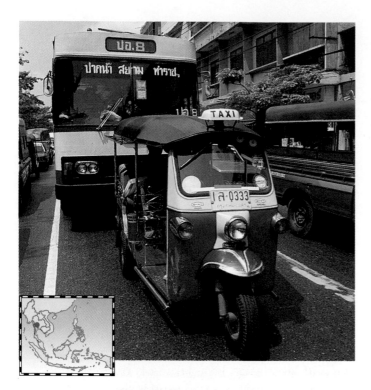

Communications

Communications services are readily available in the cities of Southeast Asia. These services help to develop the economies of the region by providing rapid communication between businesses. Because of the rugged terrain of Southeast Asia, satellite communication is used to help countries provide telephone service to rural areas. Post offices are found mostly in major urban centers.

Southeast Asia has many daily newspapers and magazine and book publishers. Most publishers are located in cities, such as Bangkok, Jakarta, Yangon, and Singapore. Television networks and radio stations are typically government-owned and controlled. Most people either own or have access to a radio, while television sets are less common. Singapore, Brunei, and the Philippines have the greatest number of television sets per person. Most of the countries of Southeast Asia are making great strides toward the development of modern communication systems. It will take more time, however, for these systems to reach every part of the region.

Geographic Themes

Place: Bangkok, Thailand
Small jeep-like vehicles carry people through the busy streets of many Southeast Asian cities. *What are other types of overland transportation in Southeast Asia?*

Indonesia, paved roads are choked with trucks, automobiles, buses, bicycles, and motorcycles. This problem is often made more difficult by peddlers who set up their stalls along major streets.

In rural areas of Southeast Asia, travel is difficult. Heavy rains often wash out unpaved roads. Dense forests, rugged terrain, and the seas that separate the islands of the region also interfere with road and railway development.

In many Southeast Asian countries, governments are working to improve transportation. For example, bridges are being built between the main islands of the Philippines to link major highways. In Vietnam and Cambodia, roads and railroads damaged from recent wars have been repaired.

Air travel links the major cities of the region with the rest of the world. All of Southeast Asia's countries have at least one major airport. In some remote areas, supplies are moved only by air.

SECTION 1 REVIEW

Checking for Understanding
1. **Define** sickle, cash crop, interdependent, Association of Southeast Asian Nations (ASEAN), free port.
2. **Locating Places** In what type of areas are many of Southeast Asia's cash crops grown?
3. **Region** Why is rice an important agricultural product in Southeast Asia?
4. **Movement** How have certain industries in the region managed to prosper?

Critical Thinking
5. **Synthesizing Information** In what ways have many Southeast Asian countries become more interdependent?

SETTING THE SCENE

Read to Discover . . .
- the causes of air and water pollution in Southeast Asia.
- the dangers posed by typhoons, volcanic activity, and earthquakes in Southeast Asia.

Key Terms
- cyclone
- typhoon

Identify and Locate
Ring of Fire, Philippines, Bali, Bangkok

Southeast Asians face a variety of environmental challenges. Some of these problems stem from human activities. Others are caused by nature, and some by a combination of human and natural factors.

HUMAN/ENVIRONMENT INTERACTION

Environmental Pollution

As Southeast Asian countries become more urbanized and industrialized, air, water, and noise pollution pose increasing dangers to the region's environment. More people living close together means more concerns about housing, water supply, sanitation, and traffic. Increased manufacturing creates industrial waste matter. As societies become wealthier and people purchase more automobiles, toxic emissions are added to the air.

Rapid economic development in Thailand, for example, has brought prosperity to many Thais, but it has also negatively affected their quality of life. Bangkok, Thailand's capital, has become a commercial and industrial center for Southeast Asia. It is a busy city of skyscrapers, factories, noisy expressways, and traffic jams. A rapid increase in population has also brought overcrowding in the city's residential areas. As a result of these changes, the people of Bangkok must deal with air, water, and noise pollution.

Pollution in Southeast Asia even extends beyond the major cities. In the Tai Phi National Park of Thailand, for example, 80 percent of the freshwater wells are contaminated as a result of increased human usage. Other causes of air pollution in rural areas are volcanic eruptions and forest fires. Forest fires in the Indonesian part of Borneo in 1991 created medical problems for people as far away as mainland Malaysia, and disrupted both air traffic and shipping.

HUMAN/ENVIRONMENT INTERACTION

Volcanoes

Because much of Southeast Asia is located on the Ring of Fire, many people in the region have to cope with the threat of volcanic activity. In the Philippines, volcanic mountains rise in most of the country's larger islands, and many of the volcanoes are active. Indonesia also has many volcanoes that have been active in historic times. The Indonesian island of Bali is noted for its 10,308-foot-high (3,142-m) volcano, Gunung Agung. The Balinese people regard the volcano as a sacred centerpiece of their Hindu faith. They continue to live near Gunung Agung, despite a 1963 eruption that took the lives of more than 1,500 people.

In June 1991, after a 600-year period of dormancy, 5,770-foot-high (1,759-m) Mount Pinatubo erupted. Philippine scientists were able to predict the eruption, and government authorities ordered the evacuation of nearby towns. Still, more than 900 people died and about 100,000 homes were destroyed. Pinatubo began erupting again in July 1992. During the next three months, 40,000 more people became homeless. As a result of the eruptions, a cloud of ash and dust spewed into the atmosphere and affected climate and weather thousands of miles away.

PLACE

Floods and Typhoons

Flood conditions are a natural problem in Southeast Asia. The major rivers on the Indochina Peninsula, for example, undergo seasonal flooding every year. Flash floods in Southeast Asia yearly kill hundreds of people and ruin about 10 million acres (about 4 million ha) of crops. The dangers and damage caused by flooding in Southeast Asia, however, have been increased by human activity. In November 1991, for example, a major storm struck the central Philippine islands. Because the land had been cleared of forest, the storm caused extensive damage from runoff and mudslides that would not have occurred otherwise.

Flooding is also a serious problem in Bangkok, which is built on unstable land. Some sections of the city sink as much as 25 inches (about 64 cm) each year. The city's most recent serious flooding occurred in 1983 when one-fourth of its area was submerged.

A **cyclone**—the name means "coil"—is an area of low atmospheric pressure surrounded by circulating winds. Tropical cyclones are among the deadliest storms on the earth. A **typhoon** is a tropical cyclone located in the Pacific area. Typhoons form north of the Equator, usually between July and October, and their winds circulate in a counterclockwise direction.

Geographic Themes

Human/Environment Interaction: Bangkok, Thailand
Bangkok's rapid industrial development has significantly increased air pollution over the city. *What other change has seriously affected Bangkok's quality of life?*

Geographic Themes

Human/Environment Interaction: Indonesia
Indonesia has a number of active volcanoes. Some of these volcanoes have erupted, killing people and destroying property. *What other natural disasters occur in Southeast Asia?*

The typhoons that affect Southeast Asia form in the North Pacific Ocean, north of the island of New Guinea. Some travel north to Japan, others go through the northern Philippines and on to the Chinese mainland. Still others pass through the Philippines and across the Indochina Peninsula. Typhoons may have winds from 150 to 180 mph (241 to 290 kmph), and may be accompanied by rain, thunder, and lightning. Typhoons disrupt shipping, and high ocean waves that sometimes accompany typhoons can be devastating.

Asian meteorologists do not participate in the naming system used in the United States to identify tropical storms. Instead, they number storms using the last two digits of the year and a number to designate which storm of the year is being watched—for example, 1:97 would be the first typhoon in 1997.

SECTION 2 REVIEW

Checking for Understanding

1. **Define** cyclone, typhoon.
2. **Locating Places** Name two Southeast Asian countries that are part of the Ring of Fire.
3. **Human/Environment Interaction** What factors account for environmental pollution in Southeast Asia?
4. **Region** How much crop damage does flooding cause in Southeast Asia each year?

Critical Thinking

5. **Predicting Consequences** What effect do you think uncontrolled economic development will have on Bangkok's future?

CASE STUDY

LOGGING IN THAILAND

Some day, I'd like to take my children out to where we were today. . . . I'd like to show them a new forest. . . . I'd like to . . . be able to say, 'Your father helped to make this.'

Nai Mong, Thai forestry official

Thailand's teak forests are one of its most valuable natural resources. Teak, a strong, durable wood, is in great demand for making fine furniture. Its rich red color and beautiful grain patterns add to its high value.

In 1961 Thailand introduced a national plan to develop industry. Under the plan, teak exports became a leading source of income for the country.

THE ISSUE

Before Thailand's economic program, forests covered 60 percent of the country's land. During the 1960s and 1970s, Thailand's economy prospered: Each year its GDP increased. By the mid-1970s, however, it became obvious that Thailand's forests were diminishing as the forestry sector of the country's economy prospered.

THE BACKGROUND

Like most of the other Southeast Asian countries, Thailand is a newly industrialized nation. To stimulate its economy and provide a better standard of living for its peo-

A truck carries logs of teakwood from a northern Thai forest.

ple, Thailand opened its forests to foreign logging companies. The companies established modern logging processes, and provided training, equipment, and jobs for many Thais. The Thai economy benefited from payments by the companies, as well as the additional spending power of the Thai workers.

The companies, however, made little effort to replant as they harvested. Teak trees take about 70 years to produce a full-grown harvestable tree. Logged areas were leveled, then abandoned.

Without the trees' root systems, surface soil was no longer held in place. Topsoil was easily eroded by heavy tropical rains. The soil washed into the streams that crisscross Thailand, clogging them and reducing the amount of water available for irrigation.

THE POINTS OF VIEW

Scientists pointed out that Thailand's forests were a renewable source. With proper management, forests could continue to be a stable part of Thailand's economy.

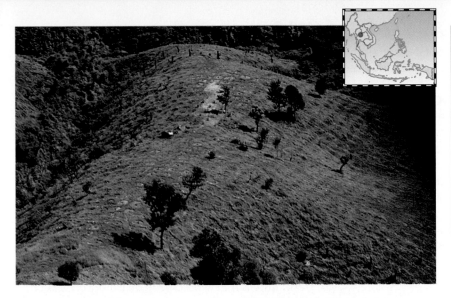

The overcutting of forests has exposed bare hillsides to the effects of violent rainstorms.

> By the mid-1970s, however, it became obvious that Thailand's forests were diminishing as the forestry sector of the country's economy prospered.

As it was, not only were the forests being devastated, but other ecological areas—Thailand's rivers and topsoil—were suffering as well.

The Thai government defended its decision to allow the logging companies into Thailand, saying that they provided jobs and income for Thailand.

The logging companies protested that a replanting program would force them to raise their prices and decrease wages to keep returns profitable for their investors.

THE ISSUE TODAY

The Thai government banned the export of teak in 1978, and announced a reforestation program. Illegal logging, however, continued. By the early 1990s, only 20 percent of Thailand's forests remained.

Excessive logging is believed responsible for a major disaster that occurred in Thailand during the late 1980s. A violent thunderstorm that hit one of the deforested regions in November 1988 created flash floods on the bare, muddy hillsides. These floods killed 400 people and left thousands more injured and homeless.

Environmentalists stated that, if the forests had re-mained to absorb the downpour, floods would not have threatened the valley's residents. They charged, that, by ignoring the consequences of their actions, Thai officials and loggers not only destroyed a vital resource but also created a disaster. Economic experts believed that the destructive floods had set the region's economy back 20 years.

Thailand's reforestation program is moving slowly, under the leadership of the Thai Royal Forestry Department. Although the government is financially prosperous by Southeast Asian standards, it cannot afford a large conservation corps.

Those Thais who work for the corps have begun the tough work of clearing logged land of debris and dead tree stumps. Their work is made doubly hard—as well as dangerous—by illegal loggers who continue to defy the government's ban, and who will kill forestry personnel coming too close to their operations.

Reviewing the Case

1. Why did Thailand invite foreign logging companies into its teak forests?

2. **Human/Environment**
 Interaction How did overlogging harm the forests?

Understanding Time Zones

The earth revolves 360° in 24 hours; therefore, when it is day on one side, it is night on the other. To clarify time relationships, the earth's surface has been divided into 24 **international time zones**.

REVIEWING THE SKILL

Each zone represents 15° longitude, or the distance the earth rotates in 1 hour. The base time zone, called Greenwich Mean Time (GMT), is set at the Prime Meridian (0°). Traveling west from Greenwich, it becomes 1 hour earlier; traveling east, it becomes 1 hour later. The international date line is set at the 180° meridian. Traveling west across this imaginary line, you add a day; traveling east, you subtract a day. Use the following steps to determine time zones:

- Choose a place for which you already know the time and locate it on the map.
- Locate the place for which you wish to know the time, and determine if it is east or west of the first place.
- Count the time zones between the two places.
- Calculate the time by either adding or subtracting an hour for each time zone.
- Determine whether you have crossed the date line, and identify the day of the week.

PRACTICING THE SKILL

Use the map to answer the following questions.

1. If it is 4 P.M. in Honolulu, what time is it in Rio de Janeiro?
2. If it is 10:00 A.M. in Tokyo on Tuesday, what day and time is it in Moscow? In Washington, D.C.?
3. How many time zones does Southeast Asia have?

For additional practice in this skill, see Practicing Skills on page 642 of the Chapter 31 Review.

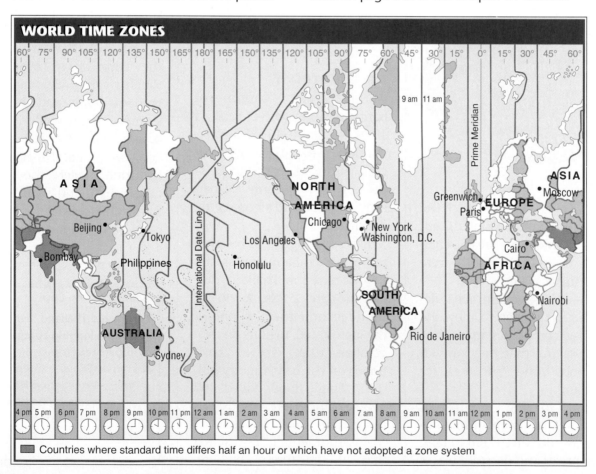

WORLD TIME ZONES

Countries where standard time differs half an hour or which have not adopted a zone system

SECTION	KEY TERMS	SUMMARY
1 Living in Southeast Asia	sickle (p. 629) cash crop (p. 630) interdependent (p. 632) Association of Southeast Asian Nations (ASEAN) (p. 633) free port (p. 633)	• Agriculture is the basis for most of the economies of Southeast Asia. The major crops are rice, sugar cane, rubber, coffee, and coconuts. • The lush forests of Southeast Asia yield many wood products; mining has also been important to the economies of the region. • In recent years manufacturing has become increasingly important, and many new industries have developed in Southeast Asia. • The main form of transportation in Southeast Asia is by water. Land transportation is less developed.

Indonesian farmer with water buffalo

SECTION	KEY TERMS	SUMMARY
2 People and Their Environment	cyclone (p. 636) typhoon (p. 636)	• Industrialization, urbanization, and rapid population increases have brought environmental pollution to many urban and rural areas in Southeast Asia. • Because they live within the Ring of Fire, large numbers of Southeast Asians are surrounded by volcanoes, many of them active. • Each year, flash floods destroy lives and crops in Southeast Asia. • Typhoons are dangerous storms that occur in Southeast Asia between July and October.

Busy expressway in Bangkok, Thailand

Reviewing Key Terms

Choose the vocabulary term that best completes each of the sentences below. Write your answers on a separate sheet of paper.

>sickles (p. 629)
>cash crops (p. 630)
>interdependent (p. 632)
>free port (p. 633)
>cyclone (p. 636)
>typhoon (p. 636)

SECTION 1

1. Some Southeast Asian countries have become more _____ as a result of regional development and trade organizations.
2. Southeast Asian farmers harvest their crops with simple hand tools, such as _____ .
3. The _____ of Singapore is a leading center of trade in Southeast Asia.
4. Rubber, coconuts, palm oil, and spices are _____ exported from Southeast Asia.

SECTION 2

5. The term _____ means "coil."
6. A _____ is a tropical storm located in the Pacific area.

Reviewing Facts

SECTION 1

7. What is the most important agricultural product in Southeast Asia?
8. What factors have led to Singapore's development as an important port and manufacturing center?
9. What is a major goal of the Association of Southeast Asian Nations (ASEAN)?

SECTION 2

10. What impact did the eruption of Mount Pinatubo have on the Philippines?
11. Why is Bangkok's flooding problem getting worse?

12. How do Asian meteorologists designate different typhoons?

Critical Thinking

13. **Predicting Consequences** Brunei reportedly has enough oil reserves to last until 2018. What might happen to other economies in the region if Brunei's oil runs out?
14. **Analyzing Information** How does living within the Ring of Fire affect daily life for many Southeast Asians?

 ## Geographic Themes

15. **Movement** Why have many foreign countries moved their manufacturing and assembly plants to Southeast Asia?
16. **Human/Environment Interaction** What have humans done in Southeast Asia that increases the danger and damages from flooding?

 ## Practicing Skills

Understanding Time Zones

Refer to the Understanding Time Zones skills feature on page 640.

If you take a noon flight from New York to Paris, what time will it be in Paris when you land six hours later?

Using the Unit Atlas

Refer to the physical geography section of the Unit Atlas on pages 592–593.

17. What natural resources have brought wealth to Brunei?
18. What environmental factor accounts for the fertile soil in Indonesia?

Projects

Individual Activity

You have learned about some environmental hazards in Southeast Asia. Research one type of hazard (such as volcanoes or typhoons) and write a brief report telling what the dangers are and what is being done to safeguard people and property.

Cooperative Learning Activity

Work in groups of four with each student representing one of the following countries: Thailand, Cambodia, Vietnam, and Singapore. Organize a presentation for the United Nations on whether or not Cambodia, Laos, and Vietnam should be allowed to join ASEAN. Think about why it would be advantageous or a problem for your country. Your stand on the issue should be presented to the other group members. In conclusion, each group may present its recommendation to the class as a whole.

Writing About Geography

Classification

Southeast Asians face a number of environmental problems that could be grouped in a variety of ways. Using your journal record as a reference, think about several ways to divide the environmental problems into groups or categories. Then write a short essay explaining and defending your classification system. Tell why the way you have grouped the environmental problems is useful or instructive.

Locating Places

SOUTHEAST ASIA: PHYSICAL GEOGRAPHY

Match the letters on the map with the places and physical features of Southeast Asia. Write your answers on a separate sheet of paper.

1. Bangkok
2. Philippines
3. Singapore
4. Bali
5. Jakarta
6. Strait of Malacca
7. Mekong River
8. Gulf of Thailand
9. Indian Ocean
10. Chao Phraya River

GEOGRAPHY CONNECTION

Southeast Asia and the United States

SOUTHEAST ASIAN DINING

In the 1840s many Chinese people emigrated to Southeast Asian countries, where Chinese influence was already strong. Other Chinese emigrants went to the United States, taking their unique foods and cooking methods. These have become as popular as New England Yankee pot roast and apple pie.

Since the 1960s immigrants and refugees from Thailand and Vietnam have made the United States their home. They, too, have brought their cuisines, which also reflect the influence of the Chinese.

▲ **RICE OR NOODLES** is the most basic ingredient in Chinese, Thai, and Vietnamese cooking. Rice has been a staple food in Southeast Asia and China for thousands of years. Rice and noodles were excellent ways of providing food inexpensively.

◄ **THAI COOKING** has been strongly influenced by Chinese cuisine. It combines flavors in daring, tantalizing ways—sweet and sour, salty and sweet—sometimes all of these in a single dish. Many Thai dishes have an unusual, sharp taste. The sharpness results from the Thai fondness for lemon grass and chilis. Another seasoning found in Thai cooking is coconut milk, which laces foods with a delicate sweetness during steaming.

◀ **THE CANTONESE STYLE** of Chinese food is familiar to most Americans, because most of the Chinese who emigrated to the United States came from the southern Chinese city of Canton, now known as Guangzhou. Chinese cooking is also popular in urban centers of Southeast Asia that have large Chinese communities.

VIETNAMESE FOOD ▶
reflects a number of influences, the strongest of which is Chinese. Vietnamese dishes can be spicy, although not so hot as Thai. Also, many dishes often seem like salads to Americans because they are served with large platters of lettuces, fresh herbs, and raw vegetables, such as beans, sprouts, carrots, and cucumbers.

▼ **FISH** is a favorite item on Vietnamese and Thai menus. A standard Vietnamese dish is *nuoc mam,* a clear, salty golden sauce made from fish or shrimp. Thai and Vietnamese dinners may also include other fish dishes, such as eel soup, seafood pancakes, and grilled shrimp balls.

Checking for Understanding

1. Why are Chinese, Thai, and Vietnamese cuisines similar?

2. **Movement** Which Southeast Asian cuisine would best fit into your daily diet? Why?

Australia, Oceania, and Antarctica

GeoJournal Activity

While studying Australia, Oceania, and Antarctica, check for travel or other kinds of advertisements either on television or in newspapers and magazines. List any that mention the places, people, cultures, and economies of the region. Write your impressions on each advertisement: How does it present the region? Do you agree or disagree with its viewpoints?

646

NATIONAL GEOGRAPHIC SOCIETY

Picturing the World

Symbol of the outback and sacred to Aborigines, Uluru, or Ayers Rock, bulges above the plains of Australia's vast Northern Territory. Uluru, the world's largest sandstone monolith, stands 1,142 feet (348 m) high in the middle of two million square miles of flat outback desert. Australia has a wide range of vegetation, from tropical rain forests to desert scrub. Look at the map on page 662.

1. What is the dominant vegetation of Australia?

2. Read to learn about the climate and vegetation of Australia. What geographic factor contributes to this vegetation?

Picture Atlas CD-ROM Enrichment Corner

Many indigenous peoples still live in Oceania. Create a file on these indigenous peoples. (See the *Picture Atlas of the World* User's Guide on how to use the Collector button.) Include the video for Australia and the following photographs: Aboriginal father and daughter in Australia; Huli wigmen and pig hunters in Papua New Guinea; Maori boy in New Zealand getting his face painted; fishers and mother in feathers in Vanuatu; dancers and shoppers in Micronesia; stone dancers and ceremonial drinkers in Fiji. Using these various indigenous groups as topics, create electronic reports and present your reports to the class.

EXPLORING CULTURAL DIVERSITY

1. *What areas of Australia, Oceania, and Antarctica are most heavily populated? Most sparsely populated?*
2. *What countries make up Australia, Oceania, and Antarctica?*

Hundreds of languages are spoken on the Pacific Islands; **Papua New Guinea** alone has more than 700.

AUSTRALIA AND OCEANIA: POLITICAL

Oceania's population is made up of three main ethnic groups: Melanesian, Micronesian, and Polynesian.

A little more than 90 percent of all New Zealanders are descended from European settlers. The rest are Maori, descendants of **New Zealand's** first settlers.

Forty-five percent of **Fiji's** population is of Melanesian descent; 55 percent are descendants of laborers imported from India.

Australia has about 18 million people. If Australians were evenly spread out across the continent, there would be only 6 persons to every square mile (2 per sq. km). Indeed most of Australia's people crowd into the southeastern corner of the continent.

About three-fourths of all New Zealanders live on North Island. About 80 percent of New Zealand's population are city dwellers.

Nauru, Tuvalu, and the Marshall Islands are the most densely populated island areas of Oceania.

AUSTRALIA AND OCEANIA: POPULATION DENSITY

Per sq. km	Per sq. mi.
Over 100	Over 250
50-100	125-250
25-50	60-125
1-25	2-60
Under 1	Under 2
Uninhabited	Uninhabited

Cities
□ 2,000,000 to 5,000,000
• 1,000,000 to 2,000,000
○ Under 1,000,000

Mercator projection

The United States has more than 11 times as many people as Australia, Oceania, and Antarctica.

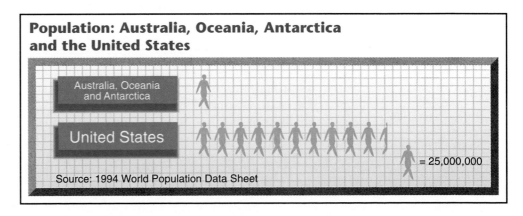

Population: Australia, Oceania, Antarctica and the United States

Australia, Oceania and Antarctica

United States

= 25,000,000

Source: 1994 World Population Data Sheet

CHARTING YOUR COURSE

1. *What body of water separates Australia and New Zealand?*
2. *What large island lies north of Australia's Cape York Peninsula?*
3. *What are three natural resources found in Australia, Oceania, and New Zealand?*

All the islands of **Oceania**—some 20,000 to 30,000 of them—do not cover as much land as the state of Alaska. The islands of **New Zealand** and **New Guinea** make up 80 percent of Oceania's total land area.

AUSTRALIA, OCEANIA, AND ANTARCTICA: PHYSICAL

120°E 135°E 150°E 165°E 180° 165°W 150°W 135°W

Tropic of Cancer

MICRONESIA

PACIFIC

15°N

MELANESIA

OCEAN

POLYNESIA

0°

Equator

New Guinea

Arafura Sea

New Britain

Solomon Islands

Timor Sea

CAPE YORK PENINSULA

ARNHEM LAND

Coral

Fiji

15°S

GREAT SANDY DESERT

MACDONNELL RANGES

GREAT ARTESIAN BASIN

Great Barrier Reef

New Caledonia

Tropic of Capricorn

GIBSON DESERT

Eyre Lake

Darling R.

Sea

30°S

GREAT VICTORIA DESERT

NULLARBOR PLAIN

GREAT DIVIDING RANGE

Tasman

Murray River

Sea

North Island

Great Australian Bight

45°S

Tasmania

South Island

SOUTHERN ALPS

International Date Line

ELEVATIONS

Feet	Meters
5,000	1,500
2,000	600
1,000	300
0	0

— National boundary
— Regional boundary

Mercator projection

N

0 500 mi.
0 500 km

South Pole

20°W 0° 20°E
40°W 40°E
60°W 60°E
80°W 80°E
100°W 100°E
120°W 120°E
140°E
160°W 180° 160°E

Antarctic Circle

☐ Ice Cap
▨ Ice Shelf

0 500 mi.
0 500 km

Although it is surrounded by water, geographers classify **Australia** as a continent rather than an island because of its great size.

The island of **Tasmania** is the smallest of Australia's seven states.

No matter where a person is in **New Zealand**, the sea is never more than 80 miles (129 km) away.

Antarctica, the world's coldest and iciest region, has mountains, valleys, and lowlands under its ice cap.

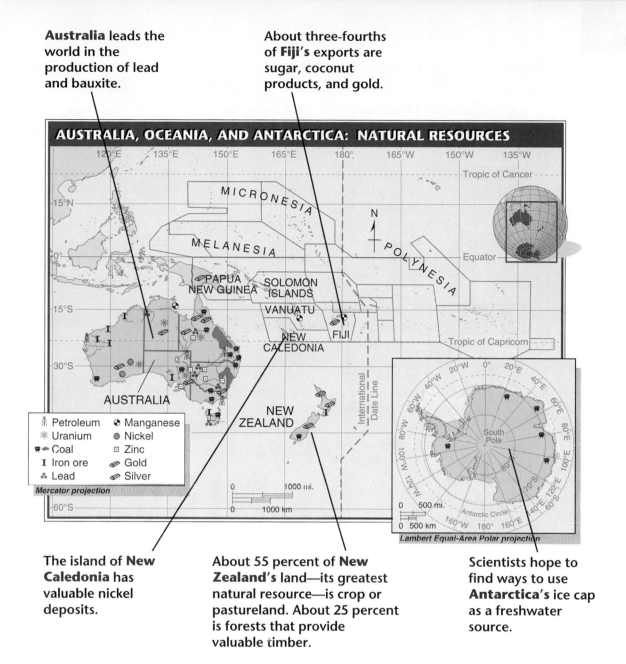

Australia leads the world in the production of lead and bauxite.

About three-fourths of **Fiji's** exports are sugar, coconut products, and gold.

AUSTRALIA, OCEANIA, AND ANTARCTICA: NATURAL RESOURCES

Petroleum
Uranium
Coal
Iron ore
Lead
Manganese
Nickel
Zinc
Gold
Silver

Mercator projection

Lambert Equal-Area Polar projection

The island of **New Caledonia** has valuable nickel deposits.

About 55 percent of **New Zealand's** land—its greatest natural resource—is crop or pastureland. About 25 percent is forests that provide valuable timber.

Scientists hope to find ways to use **Antarctica's** ice cap as a freshwater source.

Australia: Physical Profile

6000 ft.
HAMMERSLEY RANGE
MACDONNELL RANGES
4000 ft.
Mt. Bruce (4,024 ft.)
GREAT SANDY DESERT
Mt. Ziel (4,955 ft.)
GREAT DIVIDING RANGE
COASTAL PLAINS
SIMPSON CENTRAL LOWLANDS
GREAT ARTESIAN BASIN
COASTAL PLAINS
2000 ft.
800 ft.
Indian Ocean
Pacific Ocean
Sea level
West to East at the Tropic of Capricorn, 23.5°S

COUNTRY* AND CAPITAL	FLAG AND LANGUAGES	POPULATION	LANDMASS	PRINCIPAL EXPORT	PRODUCTS IMPORT
Australia Canberra	English, Aboriginal languages	17,800,000 6 per sq. mi. 2 per sq. km	2,941,290 sq. mi. 7,617,941 sq. km	Crude Oil	Machinery
FEDERATED STATES OF Micronesia Kolonia	English	100,000 370 per sq. mi. 143 per sq. km	270 sq. mi. 699 sq. km	Copra	Food
Fiji Suva	English, Fijian, Hindi	800,000 113 per sq. mi. 44 per sq. km	7,050 sq. mi. 18,260 sq. km	Sugar	Machinery
Kiribati Bairiki	English, Gilbertese	76,900 246 per sq. mi. 95 per sq. km	313 sq. mi. 811 sq. km	Copra	Machinery
Marshall Islands Majuro	English, Marshallese, Japanese	100,000 1,429 per sq. mi. 552 per sq. km	70 sq. mi. 181 sq. km	Coconut Oil	Food
Nauru Yaren	Nauruan, English	9,460 1,183 per sq. mi. 450 per sq. km	8 sq. mi. 21 sq. km	Phosphates	Food
New Zealand Wellington	English, Maori	3,500,000 33 per sq. mi. 13 per sq. km	103,470 sq. mi. 267,987 sq. km	Food	Petroleum
Papua New Guinea Port Moresby	English, Melanesian, Papuan languages	4,000,000 22 per sq. mi. 8 per sq. km	174,850 sq. mi. 452,862 sq. km	Gold	Machinery
Solomon Islands Honiara	Melanesian, English, Papuan, Polynesian languages	400,000 37 per sq. mi. 14 per sq. km	10,810 sq. mi. 27,998 sq. km	Fish	Machinery
Tonga Nuku'alofa	Tongan, English	99,100 329 per sq. mi. 127 per sq. km	301 sq. mi. 780 sq. km	Squash	Food
Tuvalu Funafuti	Tuvaluan, English	9,500 1,056 per sq. mi. 396 per sq. km	9 sq. mi. 24 sq. km	Copra	Food
Vanuatu Port Vila	English, French, Bislama	200,000 42 per sq. mi. 16 per sq. km	4,710 sq. mi. 12,199 sq. km	Copra	Machinery

*Country maps not drawn to scale.

COUNTRY* AND CAPITAL	FLAG AND LANGUAGES	POPULATION	LANDMASS	PRINCIPAL PRODUCTS EXPORT	IMPORT
Western Samoa Apia	Samoan, English	200,000 183 per sq. mi. 71 per sq. km	1,090 sq. mi. 2,823 sq. km	Coconut Oil	Food

*Country maps not drawn to scale.

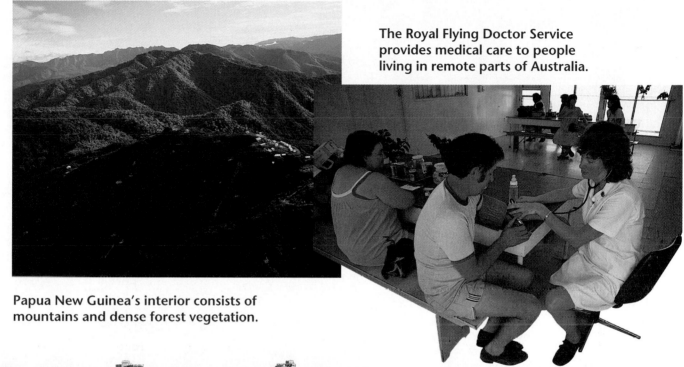

The Royal Flying Doctor Service provides medical care to people living in remote parts of Australia.

Papua New Guinea's interior consists of mountains and dense forest vegetation.

Modern hotels and beaches line the coast of northeast Australia.

The Physical Geography of Australia, Oceania, and Antarctica

CHAPTER FOCUS

Geographic Setting

The culture region of Australia, Oceania, and Antarctica contains the two continents of Antarctica and Australia as well as thousands of islands of varying size in the Pacific Ocean.

Geographic Themes

Section 1 The Land
PLACE Australia and Antarctica are mostly flat plateaus at both high and low elevations.

▲ Photograph: *Harbor in French Polynesia*

Section 2 The Climate and Vegetation
LOCATION Winds from the Pacific Ocean bring the island country of New Zealand moist warm air in the winter and cool breezes in the summer.

SETTING THE SCENE

Read to Discover . . .
- the mammoth rocks and endless deserts of Australia's interior.
- the volcanic mountains and coral reefs of the Pacific Islands.
- the icy landscape and ice cap climate of Antarctica.

Key Terms
- artesian water
- coral
- atoll
- lagoon
- continental island
- krill

Identify and Locate
Australia, Oceania, New Zealand, Antarctica, Melanesia, Micronesia, Polynesia, Great Dividing Range, Great Barrier Reef, Western Plateau, Murray River, North Island, South Island, Transantarctic Mountains

ANTARCTICA

GREETINGS FROM ANTARCTICA! WE ARE TRAVELING ON SLEDS AND SNOWMOBILES ON THE POLAR PLATEAU, WHERE THE ICE IS IN PLACES OVER 10,000 FEET THICK! WE ARE ON A SCIENTIFIC EXPEDITION DRILLING ICE CORES FOR INFORMATION ABOUT OUR CHANGING WORLD CLIMATE. SO LONG!   DAVID REED

AUSTRALIAN ANTARCTIC TERRITORY

ADELIE PENGUIN   7c

David Reed carries out scientific work in Antarctica, one of the coldest areas on the earth. Antarctica, along with Australia and the islands of Oceania, is part of the diverse South Pacific culture region. Covering a huge portion of the world, the South Pacific region contains both polar and tropical landscapes.

REGION

Australia: A Continent and a Country

Australia is unique. It is the only place on the earth that is both a country and a continent.

Great Dividing Range

The major area of hills and mountains in Australia is the Great Dividing Range. The range stretches from the northernmost Cape York Peninsula southward along Australia's eastern coast to the island of Tasmania. Most of Australia's freshwater begins in the Great Dividing Range.

Central Lowlands

West of the Great Dividing Range the land takes on a very different appearance. A thick ribbon of pastureland known as the Central Lowlands runs through the middle of Australia. Underneath the lowlands lies a vast pool of underground water known as the Artesian Basin. **Artesian waters** are pressurized and rise to the surface into ranchers' wells without any pumping.

Western Plateau

A low expanse of flat land called the Western Plateau covers nearly two-thirds of Australia. Australians call this area where few people care to live the outback. Three deserts—the Great Sandy, the Great Victoria, and the Gibson—cover much of the outback. In these deserts are mammoth rock formations—some as much as 6 billion years old. South of the Great Victoria Desert is the Nullarbor Plain. Although the plain borders the Great Australian Bight—a huge arm of the Indian Ocean—the plain receives little rainfall.

Great Barrier Reef

The Great Barrier Reef, one of the world's most famous natural wonders, lies a short distance off Australia's northeastern coast. Made of **coral** formed by the limestone skeletons of tiny sea animals, the reef is a long strip of coral-covered land that is home to a spectacular array of brilliantly colored tropical fish and underwater creatures. A writer described the Great Barrier Reef as follows:

...A place of beauty, a kaleidoscope of colour and a refuge for a host of strange but interesting animals and plants ... a major challenge to scientists wishing to unlock the storehouse of new knowledge it contains.

Natural Resources

Only about 10 percent of Australia's land is arable. Because Australia's farmers use their land and water resources effectively, however, it is one of the world's leading producers of wheat, cattle, and sheep. Australia is one of the world's leading exporters of beef, mutton and lamb, and wool.

Australians are also tapping their country's great wealth of mineral resources. These resources include uranium, bauxite, iron ore, copper, lead, manganese, nickel, zinc, gold, silver, diamonds, and opals.

REGION

Oceania: Island Lands

To understand the very large region of Oceania more easily, geographers identify three major island groups based on location, how the islands were formed, and the culture of the inhabitants. These island groups are Melanesia, Micronesia, and Polynesia. Melanesia lies north and east of Australia, and Micronesia is located north of Melanesia and south of the Japanese islands. Polynesia includes the area from Midway Island on the north to New Zealand on the south.

High Islands

Many of the islands of Oceania were formed millions of years ago as a result of colliding tectonic plates. They are part of the Ring of Fire that is known for its earthquake and volcanic activity. These volcanic islands are the high islands of Oceania. The earth beneath them is still not quiet, and gas can sometimes be seen belching into the sky from volcanic mountains that rise high above sea level.

Low Islands

The low islands of Oceania also began with volcanoes. On these islands, coral has grown along the rim of an underwater volcano, creating a ring-shaped island called an

AUSTRALIA AND OCEANIA: PHYSICAL-POLITICAL

ELEVATIONS

Feet	Meters
5,000	1,500
2,000	600
1,000	300
0	0

— National boundary
— State boundary
⊛ National capital

Mercator projection

0   500 mi.

0   500 km

FOCUS ON GEOGRAPHIC THEMES

1. **Place:** What city is the capital of Fiji?
2. **Location:** Which nation occupies part of a large island north of Australia?
3. **Region:** What are the three major island regions of the South Pacific?

atoll. At the center of the atoll is shallow, often transparent water called a **lagoon.** Atolls are often so low-lying that waves wash them in and out of view. They have little soil and few natural resources.

Continental Islands

The remaining islands of Oceania, and most of its largest islands, are **continental is-** **lands.** They are made of rock that has risen from continental shelves on the ocean floor. Papua New Guinea, New Caledonia, the Bismarck Archipelago, and the Solomon Islands are all continental islands. Although they were not formed by volcanoes, many do have active volcanoes. The continental islands possess the most significant mineral resources in Oceania. These minerals include oil, gold, nickel, and copper.

land and South Island—form most of the country's landmass.

North Island has at its center a plateau of volcanic stone crossed by a chain of volcanic peaks, many of which are active. Sparkling freshwater lakes, including Lake Taupo, New Zealand's largest lake, are common in this part of the island as well. To the east of the plateau, running north and south along the island, is a band of hills, their slopes dotted with sheep and dairy cattle.

Longer than North Island, South Island is dominated by the towering Southern Alps. Beyond, along the South Island's jagged western coastline, are numerous finger-like inlets formed centuries ago by glaciers.

Natural Resources

Fast-flowing rivers on both North and South Island provide the people of New Zealand with an abundant supply of hydroelectric power. Another energy source is steam from volcanic hot water, which is used to generate geothermal power. New Zealand also has coal and natural gas.

Like Australia, New Zealand is a global supplier of sheep and wool products. Pine forests and Pacific Ocean fish are other important resources.

PLACE

New Zealand: A Rugged Landscape

Located 1,200 miles (1,931 km) southeast of Australia, New Zealand is a group of mountainous islands. Two islands—North Is-

Geographic Themes

Human/Environment Interaction: North Island, New Zealand
The central plateau of New Zealand's North Island contains volcanoes, hot springs, and geysers. *How have the hot springs benefited New Zealanders?*

Geographic Themes

Region: Antarctica

Animals, such as penguins, seals, and whales, thrive in Antarctica's coastal waters. *What Antarctic shellfish may one day help feed the world's hungry?*

PLACE

Antarctica: A White Plateau

Nearly twice the size of Australia, Antarctica sits astride the southern end of the globe under an enormous white shield. The ice, which is as much as 2 miles (3.2 km) thick in some places, covers about 95 percent of the continent's landmass.

Landforms

The Transantarctic Mountains cross the continent and extend northward on the Antarctic Peninsula to within 600 miles (965 km) of South America's Cape Horn. The mountains and the peninsula divide the continent into two regions. To the east is a high, flat plateau. To the west of the mountains, the landmass is largely below sea level.

Although significant mineral resources are present in Antarctica, its greatest resources are the scientists who conduct research there. They research weather patterns and observe the sun and stars without obstruction. They also have observed—more clearly in Antarctica than in other parts of the world—the effect of human industrialization on the earth's ozone layer. The waters around Antarctica also contain a wealth of sea resources, such as **krill**, a shrimplike animal that may one day help feed the world's hungry.

SETTING THE SCENE

Read to Discover . . .
- the climate regions of Australia, Oceania, and Antarctica.
- the vegetation patterns of Australia, Oceania, and Antarctica.

Key Terms
- wattle
- doldrums
- typhoon
- manuka
- crevass
- lichens

Identify and Locate
Climate regions: desert, steppe, tropical rain forest, marine west coast, ice cap, tundra

In the South Pacific, water is crucial in creating great contrasts in climate and vegetation. Pacific Ocean currents bring moisture to many islands in Oceania, where lush landscapes prevail. In arid areas, such as Australia's Western Plateau, the land is dry and barren.

REGION

Australia's Climate and Vegetation

Australia is one of the driest continents in the world. The driest area of Australia is the Western Plateau.

Desert

Subtropical high-pressure air masses above central Australia block moisture-bearing Pacific Ocean winds from reaching the Western Plateau. This geographic factor contributes to a desert climate on large areas of the continent.

Steppe

Surrounding Australia's desert region is a ring of steppe climate. Here the landscape changes as more regular rainfall brings vegetation to life. Rains, however, fall only during the wet season. A woman who grew up in southwestern Australia describes the effects of the rains on the steppe landscape:

The transformation of the countryside was magical. As far as the eye could see wild flowers exploded into bloom. Each breeze would waft [the flowers'] pollen round the house, making it seem as though we lived in an enormous garden. . . . Trees sprung up . . . and before long a new clump of . . . saplings was well formed. On walks we would find enormous mushrooms, as large as a dinner plate, but perfectly formed . . . . Stranger still, the whole countryside was green, a color we scarcely knew.

Two native forms of vegetation—acacia and eucalyptus trees—dominate the landscape of the steppe climate region. Early settlers who wattled, or interwove, acacia saplings to create walls and roofs for their homes named the trees **wattles.**

Coasts

Australia's coastal areas have a variety of moister climates. The southern coasts have a Mediterranean climate, while a humid subtropical climate dominates the northeast coast, and a marine west coast climate prevails on the southeastern coast.

AUSTRALIA, OCEANIA, AND ANTARCTICA: CLIMATE REGIONS

Tropical
- Tropical rain forest
- Tropical savanna

Dry
- Steppe
- Desert

Mid-Latitude
- Mediterranean
- Humid subtropical
- Marine west coast

High Latitude
- Tundra
- Ice cap
- Highland

Mercator projection

Lambert Equal-Area Polar projection

FOCUS ON GEOGRAPHIC THEMES

1. **Region:** What climate region extends through most of central Australia?
2. **Location:** Where are tropical climate regions located in Australia?
3. **Place:** What is the predominant climate region of Antarctica?
4. **Place:** How might climate affect settlement patterns in Australia?

REGION

Oceania's Climate and Vegetation

Oceania lies primarily north of the Tropic of Capricorn. It generally has a tropical rain forest climate, in which warm days follow one another in an almost unbroken chain. Most of the region has distinct wet and dry seasons. During the wet season, days are con-stantly rainy and humid. In the dry season, rainfall decreases, and a brilliant blue sky and ocean blend into one at the endless horizon.

The amount of rain that falls during the wet season varies from island to island. On some of the low coral islands, very little rain falls, and there is little or no vegetation. Tropical plants such as coconut palms cover islands that receive more rain.

The mountainous high islands receive the most rainfall—as much as 150 inches (381 cm) a year in western Melanesia. On these islands, steamy rain forests cover the land.

The combination of high temperatures and strong rains have made agriculture difficult for Pacific islanders. Where the rain forest has been cleared, the soil is left exposed to the strong tropical sun and torrential rains that wash away its nutrients.

The Pacific Ocean has many competing winds and currents. In the Northern Hemisphere, the Pacific's currents flow in an enormous clockwise circle. In the Southern Hemisphere, that circle flows counterclockwise. As the two circular flows pass each other, they form an area called the **doldrums.** In the doldrums, the wind may be eerily calm. It may also be devastatingly fierce. Each year intense storms called **typhoons** bring high winds and heavy rains to the islands. These storms can cause enormous damage.

AUSTRALIA, OCEANIA, AND ANTARCTICA: NATURAL VEGETATION

Tropical rain forest
Chaparral
Deciduous and mixed deciduous-coniferous forest
Tropical grassland
Temperate grassland
Desert scrub and desert waste
Tundra
Ice cap

Mercator projection

Lambert Equal-Area Polar projection

FOCUS ON GEOGRAPHIC THEMES

1. **Region:** Which region has an ice cap?
2. **Location:** Where is chaparral located?
3. **Region:** What type of natural vegetation is suitable for raising livestock?

New Zealand's Climate and Vegetation

With the exception of its mountain areas, New Zealand has only one climate region—marine west coast. Rain falls throughout the year and temperatures are mild.

The central volcanic plateau of the North Island and the Southern Alps on the South Island strongly affect New Zealand's climate. Atop the plateau it is warm and sunny in summer. Small shrubs called **manuka** carpet the region, replacing forest that prehistoric eruptions destroyed long ago. Throughout both islands, it is wettest on the western slopes of the mountains. Here, the air coming off the Pacific Ocean drops its moisture.

REGION

Antarctica's Climate and Vegetation

Antarctica is one of the coldest places on the earth. It is also one of the highest and driest of the continents.

Antarctica's plateau, covered year-round by a vast sheet of ice, is drier than Australia's deserts. As the air rises across the plateau, moisture is lost. This dryness in turn makes the air colder. During the long winter, temperatures may fall as low as −100°F (−73°C).

Antarctica's ice is always moving, inching slowly toward the ocean. In the warmer, moister parts of the continent, it moves more quickly, often breaking into pieces. Between the pieces huge cracks called **crevasses** develop.

A small area of Antarctica lies in a tundra climate zone. In this zone, located on the Antarctic Peninsula, summer temperatures may reach almost 60°F (15.6°C). Here, a surprising array of vegetation breaks the endless white of the continent's interior. Mosses dot the rocks, algae tints the ice itself with red, green, or yellow. Sturdy plants called **lichens** flourish.

Geographic Themes

Place: Australian Outback
Part of Australia's interior consists of open countryside and has a steppe climate. *What two native forms of vegetation are found in Australia's steppe climate region?*

SECTION 2 REVIEW

Checking for Understanding
1. **Define** wattle, doldrums, typhoon, manuka, crevass, lichens.
2. **Locating Places** What areas in the South Pacific and Antarctica have the wettest climates? The driest climates?
3. **Region** In which climate region is the Antarctic Peninsula located?
4. **Movement** How do Pacific Ocean currents and winds affect the climate of Oceania?

Critical Thinking
5. **Making Comparisons** How does the general climate of New Zealand compare with that of Australia?

MAP & GRAPH SKILLS

Interpreting Routes on a Map

Throughout history, merchants have followed trade routes across land and sea. To aid navigation, traders have developed maps of these routes. Since traders usually find the shortest or easiest paths between cities, trade route maps reveal the interaction of human activity with natural landscape.

REVIEWING THE SKILL

Trade routes usually follow the least difficult path between population centers. Because of geography, though, the least difficult route may not be the shortest.

On a trade-route map, some areas have many interlacing routes. These areas generally have much population and commerce. When interpreting routes on a map, apply the following steps:

- Identify the area covered and symbols used in the map.
- Locate major population centers.
- Identify the trade routes on the map and points of connection between routes.
- Use the map to draw conclusions about how the physical geography affects transportation and trade in the region.

PRACTICING THE SKILL

Study the map below and then answer the following questions.

1. What modes of transportation does Australia have?
2. What color represents inland waterways on the map?
3. Where are major airports located?
4. How many railroads connect western and eastern Australia?
5. Why do you think there are so many routes in eastern Australia?
6. What are the major seaports of Australia?

For additional practice in this skill, see Practicing Skills on page 666 of the Chapter 32 Review.

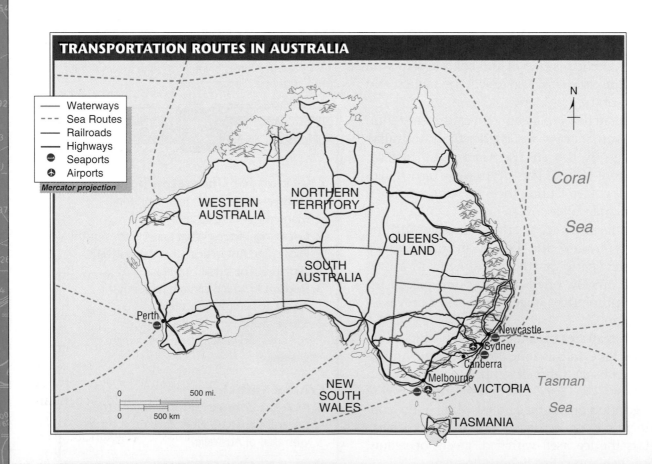

TRANSPORTATION ROUTES IN AUSTRALIA

SECTION	KEY TERMS	SUMMARY
1 **The Land** Penguins along the Antarctic coast	artesian water (p. 656) coral (p. 656) atoll (p. 657) lagoon (p. 657) continental island (p. 657) krill (p. 659)	• The South Pacific region includes the large continents of Antarctica and Australia, and thousands of islands of varying size that comprise Oceania. • The islands of Oceania were created either directly or indirectly by volcanic activity. • New Zealand has a rugged geography with very jagged coastlines, tall mountains, and rapidly flowing rivers. • While Antarctica may have important mineral resources, its key resource is the information it offers to scientists.

SECTION	KEY TERMS	SUMMARY
2 **The Climate and Vegetation** The Australian outback, an area of vast expanses	wattle (p. 660) doldrums (p. 662) typhoon (p. 662) manuka (p. 663) crevass (p. 663) lichens (p. 663)	• Australia generally has a hot, dry climate. Its interior is a vast desert bordered by a wide steppe. Mountains separate the moister coastal areas from the drier interior. • A tropical rain forest climate is found throughout much of Oceania. • Because of Pacific Ocean currents and winds that collide with one another, Oceania experiences violent typhoons at certain times of the year. • New Zealand has a mild, moist marine climate with a moderate range of temperatures throughout the year, especially on North Island. • An ice cap climate covers nearly all of Antarctica. Except for lichens and mosses in the tundra areas, Antarctica has no vegetation.

Reviewing Key Terms

Choose the vocabulary term that best completes each of the sentences below. Write your answers on a separate sheet of paper.

artesian water (p. 656)
atoll (p. 657)
lagoon (p. 657)
continental islands (p. 657)
doldrums (p. 662)
typhoons (p. 662)
manuka (p. 663)
crevasses (p. 663)
lichens (p. 663)

SECTION 1

1. In Australia's Central Lowlands, _____ rises to the ground's surface without pumping.
2. The ring of land that forms around a sunken volcano is called an _____. A _____ of warm water is created inside the ring.
3. _____ form when portions of an ocean shelf are pushed upward.

SECTION 2

4. Unstable winds in the _____ of the Pacific Ocean cause violent storms called _____.
5. Explorers in Antarctica must be careful to avoid _____.
6. Where volcanic activity has destroyed New Zealand's trees, _____ shrubs flourish.
7. Hardy plants called _____ grow inside the rocks of Antarctica's coast.

Reviewing Facts

SECTION 1

8. Why are Australia's highlands called the Great Dividing Range?
9. How were the low islands of Oceania formed?
10. Which mountains cross the continent of Antarctica?

SECTION 2

11. What kind of climate is found on New Zealand's North Island?

12. What is Antarctica's greatest resource?
13. Where in Oceania can you find volcanoes?

Critical Thinking

14. **Drawing Conclusions**   Most Australians live along the continent's coast. How might physical geography have determined this pattern of settlement?
15. **Making Generalizations**   What geographic factors are responsible for Antarctica's cold, dry climate?

 ## Geographic Themes

16. **Region**   What landforms dominate the South Pacific region?
17. **Human/Environment Interaction** How has clearing the rain forests affected agriculture in the Pacific islands?

 ## Practicing Skills

Interpreting Routes on a Map

Refer to the Interpreting Routes on a Map skills feature on page 664.

18. Why do you think there is so little transportation in west central Australia?
19. What kinds of transportation are found in the area around Perth?
20. Which seaport appears to have the most traffic? Why?

Using the Unit Atlas

Refer to the physical geography section of the Unit Atlas on pages 650–651.

21. Why is Australia classified as a continent?
22. What is the world's coldest and iciest region?

Projects

Individual Activity

As discussed in the chapter, volcanic activity played a role in the formation of many islands of Oceania. Choose one island from each of the three types of islands—high, low, and continental. Research the geographic and natural history of each kind of island and summarize your findings in a brief oral report.

Cooperative Learning Activity

Working in pairs, create a visual presentation capturing the climate and vegetation of either Australia, New Zealand, Antarctica, or Oceania. Select visual images—photographs, maps, drawings, paintings. Then exchange the images and write captions to accompany the images you have received. Finally, work together to organize your material in either booklet or bulletin board format for presentation to the class.

Writing About Geography

Proposal

Imagine you live somewhere in Australia, Oceania, or Antarctica. Write a proposal explaining why your area should be used to relieve world overpopulation. Describe the land and climate of your area, and discuss the conditions new residents would find. Use your journal record and text as well as encyclopedias and other reference books.

Locating Places

PHYSICAL GEOGRAPHY: AUSTRALIA AND NEW ZEALAND

Match the letters on the map with the places and physical features of Australia and New Zealand. Write your answers on a separate sheet of paper.

1. Great Barrier Reef
2. Great Victoria Desert
3. Great Dividing Range
4. Tasmania
5. Cape York Peninsula
6. Great Australian Bight
7. Lake Eyre
8. North Island
9. South Island

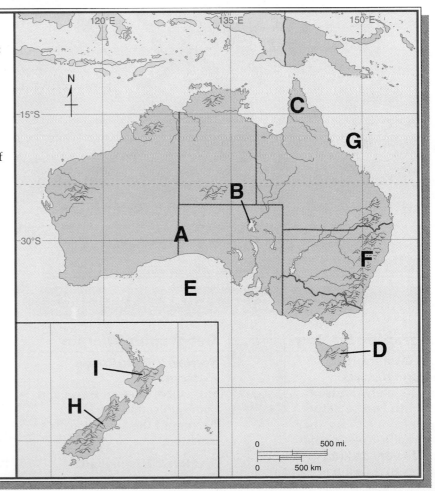

The Cultural Geography of Australia, Oceania, and Antarctica

CHAPTER FOCUS

Geographic Setting

Great distances and landform barriers separate many parts of the South Pacific culture region from one another. Geographic isolation has allowed very distinct cultures to develop.

▲ Photograph: *Sydney Opera House, Sydney, Australia*

Geographic Themes

Section 1 Population Patterns

MOVEMENT Modern travel and communication have decreased the South Pacific's isolation.

Section 2 History and Government

HUMAN/ENVIRONMENT INTERACTION The development of the South Pacific was guided by foreign powers struggling for control.

Section 3 Cultures and Lifestyles

PLACE Ways of life in the South Pacific reflect a vibrant blend of Western and traditional influences.

SETTING THE SCENE

Read to Discover . . .
- the blend of peoples living in the South Pacific region.
- how sparsely and unevenly the population is distributed.

Key Term
- primate city

Identify and Locate
Sydney, Melbourne, Auckland, Wellington

Albury, Australia
G'Day! I live in Albury, which is about a three-hour drive from Melbourne. I work after school at a store called "Big W" where I price the stock. I play the electric guitar and hope to be in a heavy metal band one day. I also write poetry and songs. Your friend,
Bernadine Cook

AUSTRALIA 50¢

Bernadine Cook lives in southeastern Australia, one of the most densely populated areas in an otherwise sparsely settled country. Australia, Oceania, and Antarctica together make up the world's most sparsely populated culture region. Its 28 million inhabitants are unevenly distributed across the area.

REGION

Human Characteristics

Most Australians and New Zealanders trace their roots to Great Britain and its settlement of both countries in the late 1700s. In recent years government-sponsored immigration policies, especially in Australia, have encouraged immigration from other parts of the world. Many new Australians have roots in southern and eastern Europe. Others have come from China, Southeast Asia, and various areas of the Pacific.

There are, however, peoples living in the South Pacific that settled in the region long before the arrival of European settlers. In Australia, these native people are called Aborigines from the Latin phrase *ab origine*, which means "from the beginning." During the early period of European settlement, the number of Aborigines declined sharply. Today their population is once again growing.

New Zealand's earliest inhabitants were the Maori (MOWR•ee). Like Australia's Aborigines, the Maori are now a minority in the lands they once dominated.

Over the centuries, as settlers and immigrants have arrived in the South Pacific from different parts of the world, they have added their unique social patterns, languages, and physical characteristics to those already in place. Now the region reflects a wide human diversity. In Papua New Guinea, for example, more than 700 different languages and dialects are spoken. Throughout the other islands, there are people with Polynesian, Asian, Indonesian, European, and mixed heritages.

Population Distribution

The South Pacific's most heavily populated areas are found in the mild climate regions. The region's most sparsely populated places are its deserts and its polar climate regions. In some parts of the South Pacific, such as Australia's deserts and Antarctica, there is little or no permanent settlement.

Australia is the South Pacific's most heavily populated country, with about 18 million people. Almost all the country's major cities are found in coastal areas. Australian cities of more than 1 million people are all found along the country's coasts, in its mild climate zones. These cities include Sydney and Brisbane on the eastern coast and Melbourne and Adelaide on the southern coast. Perth is the major city along Australia's southwestern coast.

The largest cities in Oceania are the New Zealand ports of Auckland, Wellington, and Christchurch. Most countries in Oceania have a single major city called a **primate city**. These cities generally serve as their countries' capitals and their largest ports.

PLACE

Population Density and Urbanization

Population density in the South Pacific varies greatly throughout the region. The Micronesian island of Nauru, for example, has a population density of more than 1,183 people per square mile (450 per sq. km). Antarctica, on the other hand, does not have a permanently settled population.

Geographic Themes

Region: New Zealand
The Maori were the first people to live in New Zealand. They came from Polynesian islands northeast of New Zealand. *Which group of people settled Australia before the arrival of Europeans?*

Geographic Themes

Place: Auckland, New Zealand
Auckland is New Zealand's largest city. Many of its residential areas consist of single-family houses. *What percent of New Zealanders live in urban areas?*

Population density figures for the South Pacific are often misleading because unfavorable climates, terrains, or soil conditions make large parts of the region uninhabitable. The South Pacific's density figures would be much higher if they were based on the amount of living land area only.

Australia and New Zealand are urbanized countries. About 85 percent of Australia's people live in cities or towns. About 80 percent of New Zealand's population is urban. Other South Pacific countries are somewhat less urbanized.

Several factors account for the extensive urbanization in Australia, New Zealand, and other areas of the South Pacific. One factor is that much of the productive land supports grazing but not farming. Sheep need a great deal of land and leave little room for people. Today, as ranchers and farmers replace workers with machines, even fewer people are needed in the rural areas.

Another factor is that Pacific islanders, especially the young, are leaving their homes, where jobs and industry are scarce, and heading to the region's major cities in search of opportunity.

An additional factor is that communication and technology have made the South Pacific area accessible from anywhere in the world. Businesses from around the world have been established in the region's cities—many of which are ports—to tap into its many resources. As the cities of the region have reacted to these different factors, they have blossomed into modern, multicultural urban centers.

SECTION 1 REVIEW

Checking for Understanding
1. **Define** primate city.
2. **Locating Places** Where are the most sparsely populated parts of the South Pacific culture region?
3. **Place** Why is the South Pacific unevenly populated?
4. **Region** What are two reasons New Zealand and Australia have become highly urbanized?

Critical Thinking
5. **Drawing Conclusions** Improved technology has greatly changed the relative location of Australia and New Zealand, bringing them closer to the world. How do you think this increased interaction might have affected the human diversity of the region?

NATIONAL GEOGRAPHIC
GEOFACTS

What is the most poisonous animal?

Scourge of the coastal waters of Australia, the infamous box jellyfish is the earth's most venomous animal. A single box jelly, also known as a marine stinger or sea wasp, carries enough venom to kill 60 people. Its victims can die in four minutes or less.

Over the past century, these ghostly assassins have killed at least 65 people. The pain of their sting is instantaneous and unbearable. Avoiding these creatures is difficult. Their bodies can be as big as basketballs, but are 95 percent water. Their deadly 15-foot (4.6-m) tails of nearly 60 thin tentacles are almost invisible.

Box jellyfish do not attack their prey. They react when something blunders into them. Not all contacts are fatal. It takes at least 10 feet (3 m) of tentacle to kill a human. Quick treatment with antivenom can save lives. Australian surfers wear "stinger suits" —often made of pantyhose—to protect their skin from lethal punctures.

EQUATOR

INDONESIA

Indian Ocean

Darwin•

Coral Sea

Cairns•

Tropic of Capricorn

A U S T R A L I A

0   500 km
0   500 mi

Sydney•

Canberra ⊛

Australian range of box jellyfish

TASMANIA

Stings

TOXIC DART GUN

Tiny stinging capsules called nematocysts (A) are cocked (B) and fired upon contact with a victim, releasing two types of toxin (C) as the capsules puncture the skin.

HUMAN SKIN TISSUE

Capillary

A

B

C

Gonads

Mouth

Eye

Tentacles

ADULT BOX JELLYFISH

Designed by BILL PITZER

History and Government

SETTING THE SCENE

Read to Discover . . .
- the earliest settlers in the South Pacific.
- the impact of European settlement in the region.
- how the governments in the region have changed over time.

Key Terms
- nomadic
- boomerang
- trust territory

Identify and Locate
Southeast Asia, Papua New Guinea, Marquesas Islands, Guam, Iwo Jima, Guadalcanal, Kiribati, Sydney Harbor, Nauru, Vanuatu, Tonga, Western Samoa, Society Islands

Throughout its history, the South Pacific culture region has been greatly affected by its location, its resources, and its climates. The native cultures that developed in the region were influenced very little by outsiders.

MOVEMENT

Early Peoples

Historians today are still uncertain about many aspects of the South Pacific region's earliest history. It is known that people were living in Australia and in parts of Melanesia more than 40,000 years ago.

Migrations

The ancestors of these early people probably reached the South Pacific from East Asia or from Southeast Asia. Some may have migrated over land bridges during the Ice Age, when ocean levels were far lower than they are today. Others probably used canoes and rafts to reach the South Pacific.

Not until about A.D. 300 did advances in shipbuilding and navigation enable people to reach and to settle the far islands of Melanesia and Micronesia. By about A.D. 1000, these excellent seafarers had also discovered and set-tled almost all of Polynesia. Remote location and harsh climate prevented the discovery of Antarctica until about 1820.

Early Lifestyles

The early peoples who settled the coastal areas of the South Pacific region made their livings mainly by fishing. A fishing lifestyle, however, was not possible in the hot, dry Australian interior. Thus, the Aborigines followed a **nomadic** way of life, traveling from place to place, never establishing permanent settlements. For food, they hunted animals using a slightly curved stick called a **boomerang**, and gathered fruits or seeds. When these foods became scarce, they moved on to a new home.

Unlike the Australian Aborigines, the people who settled the inland parts of Papua New Guinea found much fertile land. These people were able to farm and raise livestock.

The earliest Micronesians developed trade with the distant islands of Melanesia and parts of Asia. The peoples who settled the islands of Polynesia also engaged in overseas trade as well as farming and fishing. The large Polynesian islands of New Zealand were first settled by the Polynesian Maori. They probably arrived as early as A.D. 750 from the Marquesas (mahr•KAY•zuhz) Islands, which lie northeast of New Zealand.

Europeans in the South Pacific

During the early 1500s, Spanish and Portuguese explorers became the first Europeans to reach the South Pacific. Within 250 years, Europeans had reached virtually all of the lands in the region.

Early Explorers

During the early and mid-1600s, Dutch navigators discovered Australia and New Zealand. The British sailor Captain James Cook explored and charted many of the more remote stretches of the South Pacific. Between 1768 and 1779, Cook explored the islands of Hawaii, claimed the east coast of Australia for Great Britain, and sailed completely around Antarctica.

AUSTRALIA AND OCEANIA: COLONIES, 1900

British
French
United States
German

Mercator projection

0   500 mi.
0   500 km

FOCUS ON GEOGRAPHIC THEMES

1. **Location:** Which European nation ruled Tahiti?
2. **Place:** How did the status of Papua differ from that of most other islands?
3. **Location:** What island chain is northwest of the Hawaiian Islands?
4. **Place:** What non-European nation acquired possessions in the Pacific area?

Continuing European Interest

During the 1800s the British settled and colonized Australia and New Zealand. Initially the British used Australia as a safe and distant place to set up a colony for convicts. British colonists were attracted to New Zealand's rich soil and fine fishing. The British introduced sheep, cattle, and horses to the region, and raising livestock soon became a profitable business for many British colonists. The discovery of gold in Australia in the 1800s brought thousands of immigrants from the United Kingdom and aided the settlement of the continent.

Antarctica remained largely unexplored during these years. Serious exploration of the continent was not undertaken until the late 1800s. The South Pole was reached first, in 1911, by the Norwegian explorer Roald Amundsen. Large areas of Antarctica's interior remain unexplored today.

Much of Oceania was opened to European settlement by Christian missionaries. Western religious leaders worked to spread their beliefs throughout Oceania during the 1800s. By the end of the century, Christianity had become widespread among the native peoples of Oceania.

REGION

Struggle for Imperial Power

By the early 1900s, Australia and New Zealand had gained independence from the United Kingdom. Even though both nations had won the right to govern themselves, they maintained close ties with the United Kingdom and accepted the British king or queen as their chief of state. This was not the case, however, with many of the island peoples of Oceania.

Throughout the late 1800s and early 1900s, Oceania was the scene of a struggle for imperial control. Many Western countries, including the United Kingdom, France, Germany, and the United States, sought to establish naval bases in the South Pacific. In addition, these countries hoped to extend their overseas trading interests and to find new sources of raw materials to be used in manufacturing.

In 1898, as a result of the American victory in the Spanish-American War, the United States gained control of many of Spain's island possessions in Micronesia. During this same period, Germany, France, and the United Kingdom expanded their holdings in the South Pacific.

The defeat of Germany in World War I led to a new balance of power in the South Pacific. Japan—an increasingly influential Asian and world leader—took over some of Germany's possessions in the region. The struggle for control began anew as the Japanese spread their power throughout the South Pacific. In December 1941, as World War II raged in Europe, the Japanese bombed the United States military bases at Pearl Harbor in Hawaii. Japanese soldiers also captured American, British, and French holdings in the South Pacific.

The region became the scene of some of the bloodiest fighting in World War II as the Allies moved from island to island in an effort to get within striking distance of Japan. Hundreds of thousands of Japanese and Allied soldiers fought savage battles in places such as Iwo Jima and Guadalcanal. By the end of the war in 1945, the Japanese had been driven out of the islands by the United States and its allies.

After World War II, the United Nations placed some parts of Oceania under temporary Western control. Areas of the islands of Micronesia, for example, became a **trust territory** under the United States. While some islands are now self-governing, the United States still helps manage the affairs of some island nations. Many developed nations compete for trade in the Pacific region and try to exert political and economic influence there.

REGION

Governments Today

The European powers that first colonized the South Pacific brought their forms of government to the lands. Some of the countries of the South Pacific region, such as Aus-

Geographic Themes

Place: Canberra, Australia
Australia's federal parliament building is located in Canberra, a modern capital that serves as an example of successful urban planning. *What type of government does Australia have?*

tralia and New Zealand, adopted these forms of government when they became independent. Thus, Australia and New Zealand, former British colonies, have parliamentary democracies based on the British form of government.

Some of the recently independent countries of the South Pacific region have developed democratic forms of government. Among these are Kiribati, Nauru, and Vanuatu. A few South Pacific nations, such as Tonga and Western Samoa, are monarchies.

Several South Pacific island groups, including American Samoa and the Northern Marianas, are governed by the United States. Other islands are territories of European nations. French claims in Polynesia, for example, include the Society Islands and the Marquesas Islands. Although various countries claim parts of Antarctica, the continent has no official government, because it has no permanent settlement.

SECTION 2 REVIEW

Checking for Understanding

1. **Define** nomadic, boomerang, trust territory.
2. **Locating Places** Where did the ancestors of the earliest Australians and Melanesians originally live?
3. **Movement** How did Christianity reach the South Pacific culture region?
4. **Movement** What event greatly aided the settlement of the Australian continent?

Critical Thinking

5. **Determining Cause and Effect** Why are the governments of Australia and New Zealand parliamentary democracies?

Geography *and* History

LIVING IN ANTARCTICA

As you read, examine how people are learning to live in Antarctica's hostile environment.

Location

Antarctica lies at the "bottom of the world," isolated by stormy seas. It is the highest, coldest, and driest of the continents. Temperatures rarely rise above freezing, and winds sweeping the land often reach hurricane strength.

Because it is so forbidding, Antarctica has had little human settlement. Its harsh environment, however, is also the earth's most unspoiled. This rigorous environment is proving an excellent site for scientific research.

Threatened Environment

Many environmentalists worry that the increasing number of people on the continent will damage the land's ecological systems and pollute its unspoiled environment.

Environmentalists charge scientists living there with dumping untreated sewage into the ocean. Garbage dumps have appeared near some research stations. Fishing fleets from Russia, Poland, Japan, and South Korea seek krill and other fish off the northern Antarctic shores during the continent's short summer. Tourists, mountaineers, boaters, and vacationers in increas-

A thick ice cap makes Antarctica the highest continent in terms of average elevation. Towering mountain peaks and glacier-filled valleys are prominent features of the Antarctic coastline. Glaciers and ice sheets often extend out over the ocean to form gigantic ice shelves. Large chunks of ice break off the shelves to form icebergs. Antarctica produces about five thousand large icebergs each year.

ing numbers also find Antarctica fascinating.

Many countries also want to open Antarctica for mining. Studies indicate that valuable deposits of oil, gold, and copper could exist in quantities large enough to make the expense of operations worthwhile.

Treaty Signed

In 1991, 26 countries signed the Madrid Protocol Treaty. It included a 50-year ban on mining and oil exploration. Mindful, too, of the habitat erosion already taking place on the fragile continent, the nations set Antarctica aside as a natural reserve dedicated to peace and science.

Environmentalists and scientists alike hope that the

treaty will help reverse any adverse effects that human habitation has caused. They also hope that, in 50 years, the world's nations will be sufficiently aware of ecological disaster and that the treaty will be extended, not repealed.

Checking for Understanding

1. Study the photo on this page. What elements contribute to Antarctica's harsh environment?
2. **Human/Environment Interaction** What are the concerns of ecologists regarding Antarctica?

SETTING THE SCENE

Read to Discover . . .
- the factors that have influenced culture in the South Pacific.
- the traditional and Western artforms of the region.
- the varied South Pacific lifestyles and standards of living.

Key Terms
- strine
- pidgin English
- subsistence farming
- fale

Identify and Locate
Easter Island, French Polynesia

The cultural traditions of the native peoples of the South Pacific have contributed much to the region's present-day lifestyles. Later immigrants have also had an impact on the region's lifestyles.

A Blend of Cultures

The cultural patterns found in the South Pacific today are a result of many different forces. Climate, natural resources, and landforms have strongly influenced life and culture in the region.

Culture and Environment

The movement of different peoples into the South Pacific region has contributed to shaping cultural patterns there. The earliest peoples of the region developed very distinct cultural traditions. In large part, these patterns grew out of lifestyles that were in harmony with the natural environment. Instead of working to change their environment, Aboriginal hunter-gatherers adapted to its demands. For Australia's Aborigines, this meant a lifestyle that worked with, rather than against, the harsh outback. It meant the development of an idea about their relationship to nature

that dominates their way of life. This idea, called Dreamtime, is explained by Aboriginal leader Silas Roberts:

---❖---

Aboriginals have a special connection with everything that is natural. . . . We see all things natural as part of us. All the things on earth we see as part human.

---❖---

The early fishing peoples of Melanesia also developed cultures and lifestyles that were closely bound to nature. The sea provided for many of their basic needs. Thus, they lived in small villages at the water's edge. The forms of social organization these people followed were generally based on a fishing way of life, and much of their folklore revolved around the sea.

The European Influence

As Europeans began to move into the South Pacific, the region's cultural patterns began to change. By the early 1900s, many parts of the South Pacific, such as Australia and New Zealand, had cultural patterns and lifestyles that were a mixture of traditional and European customs and beliefs.

Today many of the countries in the South Pacific are strongly Western in their lifestyles and forms of cultural expression. For example, a street scene in downtown Sydney, Australia's largest city, easily could be mistaken for a scene in a British city. Nevertheless, large parts of the South Pacific have maintained much of their traditional culture.

Religious Beliefs

The native peoples of the South Pacific followed many different religious beliefs before the Europeans arrived. When Western missionaries and settlers began moving into the region, however, they brought the ideas and values of Christianity. Although traditional religious beliefs continue to be followed in many parts of the area, Christianity is the most widely held religion in the region today.

 Geographic Themes

Region: Australia
Rugby, imported from the United Kingdom, is a popular sport in Australia. *How have European influences affected the South Pacific area?*

PLACE

Languages

As the cultures of the South Pacific blended, their peoples faced the challenge of communicating with one another. Mountains, interior deserts, and isolated islands separated one group of people from another. As a result, people speak many different languages.

The most widely spoken languages in the region today are of the Indo-European language family. English is spoken throughout Australia and New Zealand. The English spoken in Australia, known as **strine**, reflects the easygoing Australian culture.

In Oceania, English is also common in areas that the United States and the United Kingdom have influenced. French is widespread in French Polynesia and in other areas of Oceania that remain under French control.

Most of the languages native to Oceania belong to the Malayo-Polynesian language family. The native language of the Australian

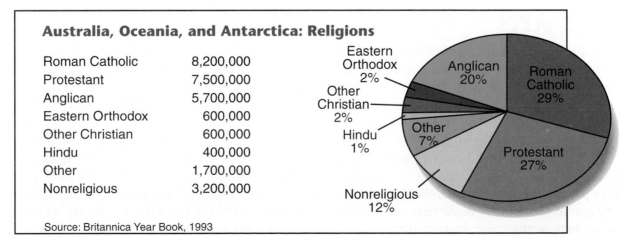

Australia, Oceania, and Antarctica: Religions

Religion	Population
Roman Catholic	8,200,000
Protestant	7,500,000
Anglican	5,700,000
Eastern Orthodox	600,000
Other Christian	600,000
Hindu	400,000
Other	1,700,000
Nonreligious	3,200,000

Source: Britannica Year Book, 1993

Pie chart:
Roman Catholic 29%
Protestant 27%
Anglican 20%
Nonreligious 12%
Other 7%
Eastern Orthodox 2%
Other Christian 2%
Hindu 1%

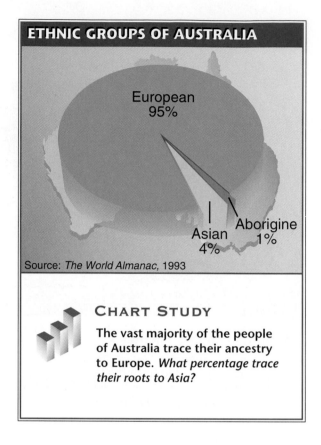

ETHNIC GROUPS OF AUSTRALIA

European
95%

Asian
4%

Aborigine
1%

Source: *The World Almanac*, 1993

CHART STUDY

The vast majority of the people of Australia trace their ancestry to Europe. *What percentage trace their roots to Asia?*

Aborigines, however, belongs to its own separate family.

As trade and contact throughout the South Pacific have increased during recent times, the need for a commonly understood language has become greater. Thus, language forms based upon mixtures of native and European languages have gradually developed. One of these languages is **pidgin English,** a blend of English and native speech.

The Arts

Most of the native peoples in the region did not have a written language. History, customs, and beliefs were passed down from generation to generation through music, dance, and storytelling.

Today some of the stories of these cultures can be observed through the art each has passed on to later generations. For example, the people of Easter Island in Polynesia carved huge and mysterious stone figures. While experts believe they may have had religious sig-

nificance, the stone carvings reflect the artistry of their creators.

In many South Pacific cultures, the arts still derive inspiration from these earlier times. A few Aborigines still paint on the bark of the stringybark tree. Other native artists, in New Zealand for example, are outstanding wood-carvers and woodworkers, creating beautifully carved masks and figurines. By continuing these traditional arts, the region's artists have maintained their heritage of powerful and lively art.

Western forms of art also thrive. In this region described as "a land for the soul to expand into," artists have focused on their individual experiences. Painters such as Arthur Streeton, Charles Conder, and Fred Williams captured their view of the stark Australian outback. In New Zealand, teacher Sylvia Ashton-Warner wrote of her experiences among the Maori people. Australian writer Patrick White received the 1973 Nobel prize in literature for his moving portrayal of life in Australia. The values of native cultures are revealed in the works of Aboriginal poet Kath Walker or Maori novelists such as Patricia Grace.

Lifestyles

Two general lifestyle patterns are found in the region. One pattern is largely traditional. The other reflects a European background.

Traditional Lifestyles

For many Pacific islanders, daily life is a struggle. Sometimes the soil is too poor to support much agriculture. On these islands, such as Vanuatu or Tonga, native people work at **subsistence farming,** growing only enough food for their own needs. These foods might be bananas, coconuts, or sweet potatoes. Where possible islanders raise chickens and pigs, and fish in the oceans around them. Others work in relatively low-paying jobs for either local or federal governments.

A typical traditional South Pacific home is very simple in design. In Western Samoa for example, the traditional type of home is called a **fale.** Its open sides allow cooling ocean breezes to circulate, and the thatched roof shields dwellers from the hot tropical sun. For privacy, blinds of coconut palm leaves can be lowered.

European Lifestyles

People in Australia and New Zealand, where the strongest European influences exist, live a very different life. Even those living in the Australian outback or working in isolated mining towns enjoy modern conveniences. Some may even commute thousands of miles to and from nearby cities, leading a dual existence that brings current trends and ideas into remote areas.

In the cities, life is typically modern with elegant shopping malls, large sports stadiums, and towering skyscrapers. Ethnic neighborhoods such as the Cabramatta district of Sydney lend an international flavor.

Both in cities and rural areas, Australians and New Zealanders dress in Western styles. Shorts and other casual clothes are popular because of the mild climate.

Health and Education

Many Pacific islanders are in poor health because of the difficulties of life and the remoteness of many islands. Fresh foods and meats are often scarce, and water and electricity are often unavailable. As a result, many of the people have chronic illnesses.

Lack of education may make it difficult for Pacific islanders to improve their lives. In many nations, despite help from wealthier Western countries, most people cannot read or write. Some nations have made great progress. On these islands, children regularly attend government or missionary schools, and literacy rates are much higher.

Geography also poses a challenge to health care and education in Australia. Modern technology, however, allows doctors to consult with patients through the use of 2-way radios or the Royal Flying Doctor Service.

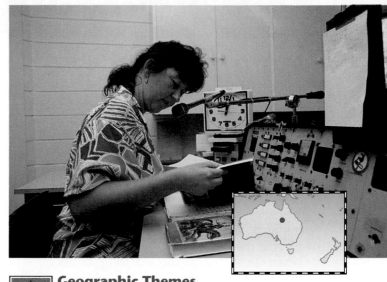

Geographic Themes

Region: Australia
Children in remote areas of Australia receive daily school lessons over "schools of the air." *How does modern technology aid health care in Australia?*

Modern technologies also help Australia's young people in the outback to receive an education. If an area does not have the 8 or 9 children necessary to start a school, students take classes by 2-way radio or through the mail with correspondence courses.

SECTION 3 REVIEW

Checking for Understanding
1. **Define** strine, pidgin English, subsistence farming, fale.
2. **Locating Places** What is Australia's largest city?
3. **Movement** What communications problems has geography created for the peoples of Australia, New Zealand, and Oceania?
4. **Region** Why is the health of many Pacific Islanders poor?

Critical Thinking
5. **Making Generalizations** In what ways have geographic factors worked to shape cultural development in the South Pacific region?

Reading Tables and Analyzing Statistics

Reading lists of facts and figures can be confusing. Therefore, statistics are often organized into **tables**, which condense numerical information into a compact format.

REVIEWING THE SKILL

In a table, similar kinds of information are organized into columns and rows. Labels across the top and left-hand sides explain what the numbers in the table represent. Identifying patterns and relationships among the figures can reveal a great deal about the topic.

When reading tables and analyzing statistics, apply the following steps:

- Read headings and labels to determine the kinds of information included in the table.
- Look up unfamiliar terms.
- Identify similarities, differences, and other relationships among the data.
- Use the data to draw conclusions.

PRACTICING THE SKILL

▼ Study the table below and answer the following questions.

1. Which countries are compared in the table?
2. How do the countries rank according to total population? Population density?
3. Which country has the highest GDP per capita? The lowest GDP per capita?
4. What is the relationship between infant mortality and life expectancy? Between infant mortality and per capita GDP?
5. What is the relationship between urbanization and electricity consumption?

For additional practice in this skill, see Practicing Skills on page 684 of the Chapter 33 Review.

COMPARATIVE DATA (SELECTED NATIONS)

	Australia	Fiji	New Zealand	Papua New Guinea
Population	17,800,000	800,000	3,500,000	4,000,000
Population density (per square mile)	6/sq. mi.	113/sq. mi.	33/sq. mi.	22/sq. mi.
Annual population growth	0.8%	2.0%	0.9%	2.3%
Urbanization	85%	39%	85%	13%
GDP - US dollars GDP per capita	$311,000,000,000 $18,054	$1,300,000,000 $1,840	$40,000,000,000 $12,200	$2,700,000,000 $725
Life Expectancy	77 years	64.5 years	75.5 years	55.5 years
Infant Mortality Rate (per 1000 births)	7/1000	15/1000	7/1000	72/1000
Population per physician	472	2,745	518	13,827
Literacy Rate	100%	86%	99%	52%
Electricity Consumption per capita (kw hours)	8,258	590	8,235	435

Sources: *The World Almanac*, 1995; The Population Reference Bureau, 1994

SECTION	KEY TERMS	SUMMARY
1 **Population Patterns** Auckland, New Zealand	primate city (p. 670)	• Many different groups of people have settled in the South Pacific, creating a blend of peoples, cultures, and lifestyles. • The population of the South Pacific is unevenly distributed because many areas cannot support life.
2 **History and Government** Parliament buildings in Canberra, Australia	nomadic (p. 673) boomerang (p. 673) trust territory (p. 675)	• The first humans to settle the South Pacific probably came from Southeast Asia. Settlement then spread eastward. • In the late 1700s, the British began settling Australia and then New Zealand. • European nations and Japan struggled throughout the late 1800s and early 1900s for control of the Pacific islands.
3 **Cultures and Lifestyles** Australian rugby match	strine (p. 679) pidgin English (p. 680) subsistence farming (p. 680) fale (p. 681)	• European culture has become dominant in the South Pacific. Traditional cultural elements, however, continue to shape lifestyles in the region today. • Settlement patterns in the South Pacific have been largely determined by climates and landforms. Cultural and economic backgrounds have also affected lifestyles and standards of health and education in the South Pacific.

Reviewing Key Terms

Choose the vocabulary term that best completes each of the sentences below. Write your answers on a separate sheet of paper.

primate city (p. 670)
nomadic (p. 673)
boomerang (p. 673)
strine (p. 679)
pidgin English (p. 680)
subsistence farming (p. 680)
fales (p. 681)

SECTION 1

1. A _____ serves as its country's capital, port, and single major urban area.

SECTION 2

2. _____ people do not establish permanent settlements.
3. A _____ is used for hunting.

SECTION 3

4. _____ involves growing only enough food for one's own needs.
5. Australians speak _____ .
6. _____ has made it easier for Pacific islanders to understand each other.
7. Many Pacific islanders live in homes called _____ .

Reviewing Facts

SECTION 1

8. Who were the first settlers in Australia and New Zealand?
9. From what country can most Australians and New Zealanders trace their roots?

SECTION 2

10. How did the earliest settlers reach Australia?
11. Why were the first British people sent to settle Australia?

SECTION 3

12. What is the dominant religion in the South Pacific region?
13. In the past how did traditional South Pacific peoples pass their history to the next generation?

Critical Thinking

14. **Analyzing Information** Why are Australia and New Zealand largely urbanized?
15. **Identifying Central Issues** Why did European nations and Japan struggle to control Oceania in the 1800s and 1900s?
16. **Expressing Problems Clearly** How has geography affected health and education in Oceania?

Geographic Themes

17. **Place** Why do most people in Australia live in coastal cities?
18. **Movement** How did the discovery of gold affect the settlement of Australia?
19. **Human/Environment Interaction** How do Australia's Aborigines view their relationship to nature?

Practicing Skills

Reading Tables and Analyzing Statistics
Refer to the statistical table on page 682. Which country has the lowest standard of living? On what figures do you base this conclusion?

Using the Unit Atlas

Refer to the cultural geography section of the Unit Atlas on pages 648–649.
20. Where do most of Australia's people live?
21. What major ethnic groups make up Oceania's population?

Projects

Individual Activity

The work of many writers and artists of the South Pacific culture region reflects their personal view of the region. Study the work of a writer or artist from the region (such as Kath Walker or Sydney Nolan) and explain in a brief oral report how the work captures the spirit of the South Pacific.

Cooperative Learning Activity

Working with a partner, create pairs of sister city locations from throughout the region. One student should choose locations for each pair that are heavily populated while the other student chooses locations with sparse population. List two advantages and disadvantages to human settlement in your areas. Then work together to pair locations with compatible features. If you wish, present the pairs to the rest of the class and invite their input.

Writing About Geography

Cause and Effect

Imagine you are a time traveler who has traveled to the South Pacific islands before European settlement. Write a description of how European settlement has affected your island and its people. Be sure to identify the causes for any changes you discuss. Use your journal, text, and other reference sources to help you gather the necessary information.

Locating Places

PHYSICAL GEOGRAPHY: AUSTRALIA AND WESTERN OCEANIA

Match the letters on the map with the places and physical features of Australia and western Oceania. Write your answers on a separate sheet of paper.

1. Papua New Guinea
2. Sydney
3. Auckland
4. Melbourne
5. Canberra
6. Perth
7. Brisbane
8. Adelaide
9. Wellington

chapter 34

Australia, Oceania, and Antarctica Today

CHAPTER FOCUS

Geographic Setting

Long distances and harsh climates have often posed economic and environmental challenges that Australia, Oceania, and Antarctica have met with varying success.

▲ **Photograph:** *Sheep farm in New Zealand*

Geographic Themes

Section 1 Living in Australia, Oceania, and Antarctica
MOVEMENT Modern transportation and communication has brought the Australia, Oceania, and Antarctica culture region closer to the rest of the world.

Section 2 People and Their Environment
LOCATION The unique environment of the South Pacific, no longer protected by distance and isolation, has been damaged by human settlement.

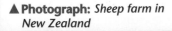

Living in Australia, Oceania, and Antarctica

SETTING THE SCENE

Read to Discover . . .
- the kinds of agriculture practiced in the South Pacific region.
- the reasons for economic interdependence in Australia and Oceania.
- the transportation and communication challenges facing the Australia, Oceania, and Antarctica culture regions.
- the industries that thrive in Australia, Oceania, and Antarctica.

Key Terms
- grazier
- station
- copra
- subsistence farming
- rail gauge

Identify and Locate
St. George Island, Bougainville, Western Australia, Pilbara, Kimberley, Tuvalu, New South Wales, Federated States of Micronesia, the South Island

Wellington, New Zealand

I live in Wellington, which is a hilly city and the capital of New Zealand. We use trains and buses for transportation, and there is even a cable car. I earn money delivering newspapers, which I do on foot because of the steep hills. My country relies on meat and farm produce for income, so there is always a lot of fresh fruit in the stores, and sheep on the hillsides. Dave Ferguson

kahu-huruhuru / Maori feather cloak (detail)

50c NEW ZEALAND

As Dave Ferguson's postcard reveals, people who live in the Australia, Oceania, and Antarctica culture region produce a variety of food products. Agriculture is by far the region's most important economic activity.

Food Production

Farmers in the culture region vary their agriculture according to geographic conditions. Australian farmers, using scientific methods and machinery, adapt their farming methods to the generally dry climate. New Zealand and Australia export large quantities of farm products—especially meat, wool, dairy products, and wheat.

Ranching

Sheep and cattle graze over much of the land in Australia and New Zealand. In Australia livestock, tended by cowhands and sheep **graziers**, or herders, must search a large area to find enough vegetation. As a result some Australian **stations**, or ranches, are

Geographic Themes

Human/Environment Interaction: Fiji
Unlike many other Pacific island countries, Fiji has much commercial farming. Sugar cane is one of Fiji's major agricultural exports. *What agricultural items are raised elsewhere in the Pacific area?*

mammoth—as large as 6,000 square miles (15,540 sq. km). The largest stations are almost self-sufficient economic units, complete with stores and post offices.

Australia and New Zealand have used scientific research and advertising to establish new markets for farm products. Improved machinery and fertilizers and innovative packaging have expanded sales to western Europe and Japan.

Subsistence Farming

In much of Oceania, climate and soil conditions do not support widespread commercial farming. On the low Micronesian islands, **copra**, the dried meat from the coconut palms, is often the only farm product exported. Island farmers generally practice **subsistence farming**, growing only enough food to feed themselves.

Farming is more widespread on the high islands of Oceania, where rich volcanic soil and ample rainfall support a variety of crops. Some people produce cash crops including tropical fruits, sugar, coffee, and copra and other coconut products.

Fishing is also an important source of food, especially on the low islands, and some fish are exported as well.

Because of its harsh climate, Antarctica produces no farm crops. Its icy coastal waters are a rich source of seafood.

HUMAN/ENVIRONMENT INTERACTION

Mining and Manufacturing

Scattered unevenly throughout the region are mineral deposits of copper, iron ore, lead, and coal. Australia has many mines and is a leading exporter of diamonds, gold, bauxite, and iron ore.

Most of the region's ore is exported to Japan to be made into cars and appliances. Australia has a growing economic interdependence with nearby Asia.

The other areas of Oceania have only scattered mining industries. Melanesians, for example, mine copper and in Micronesia, phosphate mining has become important. The possibility of one day reaching the large deposits of valuable minerals believed to lie under the Antarctic ice cap also exists.

Domestic Manufacturing

Geography has limited manufacturing in the South Pacific. Importing equipment and raw materials is too difficult and too expensive. In Oceania a lack of skilled workers, modern transportation, and communications systems are also factors. Almost all manufacturing is done in Australia, near Sydney and Melbourne, and in New Zealand, near Auckland.

Challenges to Growth

Many of Oceania's islands are too small to produce large amounts of goods and are located too far from trading markets.

Modern air travel has increased island tourism. Visitors enjoy the region's scenery and beaches, while boosting island economies. Aid from Western nations also helps many Pacific island countries.

AUSTRALIA AND OCEANIA: ECONOMIC ACTIVITY

Legend:
- Hunting and gathering
- Forestry
- Livestock raising
- Commercial farming
- Subsistence farming
- Manufacturing and trade
- Commercial fishing
- Little or no activity

Mercator projection

FOCUS ON GEOGRAPHIC THEMES

1. **Location:** Where are manufacturing centers concentrated?
2. **Region:** Which area of Australia has little or no economic activity?
3. **Place:** In what area of New Zealand is forestry a major economic activity?

Transportation and Communication

Australia, Oceania, and Antarctica are partially inaccessible. The region contains thousands of miles of solid ice, endless desert, and vast oceans.

Ground Travel

Australia and New Zealand have the most well-developed road and rail systems in the region. Still, large parts of the Australian outback are without any roads.

Travelers on Australia's rail system are sometimes frustrated. Not all of the country's railroads are built to the same standards. The **rail gauge**—or distance between the rails—from state to state does not match. This results in the use of different rail cars, so traveling across the country means changing trains.

New Zealand's rail and road system is quite good. Even though the terrain is often mountainous, most of New Zealand can be reached.

In Oceania, entire countries do not have well-developed road or rail systems. Countries are working hard to improve the roads and bridges necessary for industrial growth.

Antarctica poses special problems. Lacking permanent settlements, the icy continent has

Geographic Themes

Region: Australian Outback
A four-wheel-drive vehicle is ideally suited to Australia's rugged outback. Only about 36 percent of Australia's roads are paved, and few roads exist in the outback region. *What is rail travel like in Australia?*

Geographic Themes

Human/Environment Interaction: Antarctica
Air travel is available to Antarctica during the long winter months when ice blocks all forms of water transportation. *Why is air travel an important method of transportation in the Pacific area?*

no need for road or rail systems, and specially designed vehicles are required.

Air and Water Travel

Air and water travel are the most essential to the region. Pacific islanders started traveling by outrigger canoe thousands of years ago. Small wind- or motor-powered boats are still used. New Zealanders ride ferries from the North Island to the South Island.

Scientists in Antarctica's coastal stations depend on cargo ships and airplanes to deliver needed goods. On Australia's large stations, cattle owners use helicopters to reach their cattle. Small airplanes are needed to travel between the islands of Oceania.

The development of modern communication, such as telephones and radios, has had a major effect upon life in Australia, Oceania, and Antarctica. Two-way radios offer people emergency help, education, and social communication.

SECTION 1 REVIEW

Checking for Understanding
1. **Define** grazier, station, copra, subsistence farming, rail gauge.
2. **Locating Places** Where in New Zealand does most manufacturing take place?
3. **Movement** What country is an important trading partner for Australia's mining industry?
4. **Human/Environment Interaction** Why do many Pacific island countries lack manufacturing centers?

Critical Thinking
5. **Making Comparisons** How is farming in Oceania different from the agriculture practiced in both Australia and New Zealand?

PRESERVING THE GREAT BARRIER REEF

The next ten years will determine whether there is sufficient commitment in the minds and hearts of Australians to ensure that the reef is protected from insidious degradation.

Graeme Kelleher, chairman of the Great Barrier Marine Park Authority, 1992, *Sea Frontiers*

Running along the northeast coast of Australia, the Great Barrier Reef is the largest structure on the earth made by living organisms. Between 500,000 and 1 million years old, the reef is made up of about 2,500 separate coral reefs whose combined length stretches 1,250 miles (about 2,012 km). Most of the reef lies between 10 and 150 miles (16 and 241 km) from the shore of the Australian state of Queensland.

A rich variety of plant life grows in this beautiful underwater garden. The great formation is also home to about 400 species of coral and 1,500 kinds of fish.

THE ISSUE

Because of the richness of its marine environment, the Great Barrier Reef is important to biologists and marine scientists. Its beauty and diverse marine life also attract thousands of tourists and marine enthusiasts each year.

Many kinds of human activities, however, are weakening the Great Barrier Reef. Wide areas appear to be dead. Scientists fear that if overuse continues, the entire reef may break up.

THE BACKGROUND

The surface of the Great Barrier Reef is living, made up of tiny animals called coral polyps. Coral polyps are the reef's builders as well as its foundation. They, however, are only one part in the Great Barrier Reef's delicately balanced environment of plant and animal life. One change, such as a shift in temperature or a change in the amount of sunlight or salt in the water, can damage one part of the reef or interfere with one of the species living on or around the reef.

In recent years the Great Barrier Reef has grown in popularity with tourists. Shell hunting, snorkeling, and spearfishing are among the favorite activities of tourists. Unfortunately, such activities harm the reef.

Shell hunters contribute to the destruction of the reef's coral polyps. Snorkelers bump against or hit the reef with their fins, breaking off pieces or damaging underwater plants. Spearfishers overhunt various species of the reef's fish. Water content is also changing through human activity. Sewage from the resort areas and gasoline from motor boats are polluting the sea. Farmers along the coast use fertilizers that drain into streams and rivers that empty into the Great Barrier Reef's waters. Cities along the coast dump wastes directly into the ocean. Some reefs have been covered with silt and debris from such pollution.

Many kinds of human activities, however, are weakening the Great Barrier Reef. Wide areas appear to be dead.

In the late 1960s, mining companies tried to strip-mine the reef for its limestone content. Oil companies prepared to drill for petroleum they

The Great Barrier Reef lies on the shallow shelf that fringes Australia.

claimed was under the Great Barrier Reef.

THE POINTS OF VIEW

Farmers, city and state governments, and mining and oil companies said that the Australian government should not pass any new laws that would restrict development and growth. Resort owners, shop owners, or other types of tourist-related businesses did not want the Australian government to limit use of the reef. Restrictions, they stated, would decrease the number of people coming to the reef. If the number of tourists dropped off, the area would lose money and jobs.

Environmentalists pointed out that the coral reef could be destroyed easily by tourists. They also warned that sewage and chemicals from farm fields would change the balance of the coastal waters in which the coral reef grows. With human activity and pollution, the Great Barrier Reef could disappear.

THE ISSUE TODAY

In 1981 the Australian government dedicated the Great Barrier Reef as a World Heritage Site. Most of the reef is still open for general use, but the park management is working on a plan to carefully control use of the reef. About 10 percent of the park is open on a "look-but-don't-touch" basis.

Some development is permitted. It is contained, however, in areas traditionally used for that purpose. Oil exploration, mining, and spearfishing are banned. Oil shipping is permitted, though the tankers must be guided by trained reef pilots.

Park rangers have increased efforts to improve their relationships with farm and business owners. Some businesses have hired teams of scientists who monitor changes on the reef, as well as giving tours and talks about the reef. Although the Great Barrier Reef is not entirely safe from business concerns, many more businesses are agreeing that they have as much at stake in the reef's continued existence as scientists and tourists.

Reviewing the Case

1. What changes in the ecosystem can damage the coral reef?

2. **Human/Environment** **Interaction** What steps have been taken to protect the Great Barrier Reef?

People and Their Environment

THE ENVIRONMENT

SETTING THE SCENE

Read to Discover . . .
- the impact on the environment of new animal species introduced to Australia and Oceania.
- how industrial development has affected the land and climate of South Pacific countries.
- the impact of human exploration on the environment of Antarctica.

Key Terms
- marsupial
- global warming
- ecosystem

Identify and Locate
Bikini Atoll, Queensland, Banaba, Northern Territory

Distance and isolation make the Australia, Oceania, and Antarctica culture region home to a unique and fragile environment. Separated from the rest of the world by the vast Pacific Ocean, the region abounds with plants and animals not found anywhere else in the world. In many cases the absence of large mammals as predators also helped this special natural world to develop. Now, as modern travel allows humans to visit and settle almost every corner of the region, they have left their footprints on this delicate balance with sometimes devastating effects.

HUMAN/ENVIRONMENT INTERACTION

Animal Life

The Europeans introduced a variety of animals and plants—camels, rabbits, sheep, and sugarcane—to Australia. Some were brought and raised for profit, such as sheep. Others, such as camels, were used as beasts of burden.

The plants and animals already in Australia had never been exposed to these new species. While a few flourished, most suffered. Australia's most well-known native animals include kangaroos, koalas, wallabies, and other **marsupials**, mammals that give birth to offspring that mature in their mothers' pouches. Only a few of these and other native species have been able to survive newly added predators, such as European foxes and rats. Native grasses were also destroyed by the millions of rabbits brought for use in hunting.

Cane Toad

In the 1930s sugarcane farmers in the Australian state of Queensland tried to solve a crop problem by using the system of predator and prey. They introduced a small number of toads into the sugarcane fields to eat the grubs that were destroying their crops. The toads did eat grubs, but they then moved out of the fields, eating native plants, other insects, garbage, and even pet food. Because they were highly poisonous when eaten, the toads had few predators.

In the 1990s the cane toad moved out of Queensland into neighboring New South Wales and the Northern Territory. In the moist, tropical Northern Territory, the toads are upsetting nature's balance by killing lizards, snakes, birds, and other animals. So far scientists have been unable to solve this problem.

Animal Overpopulation

In 1837 merchants and shippers hoping to start a fur industry brought the brushtail possum to New Zealand. Without natural predators, it quickly spread throughout the country. Until the 1980s some balance was achieved by trapping thousands of possums each year. Then as possums and other animals came under special protection, the world fur market all but disappeared. Now the possums are everywhere. They eat some of New Zealand's most unique and fragile trees. They also carry a highly contagious disease that is deadly to New Zealand's cattle industry.

HUMAN/ENVIRONMENT INTERACTION

Industry and Science

The growth of industry has brought great advantages to Australia, Oceania, and Antarctica. It has brought costs as well. Throughout the region, human efforts to improve conditions, boost economic activity, or carry military experiments also have caused problems that must now be solved.

Phosphate Mining

The people of Nauru have lived a comfortable life financed by enormous phosphate deposits, mined and sold for fertilizer. Now the phosphate is running out and the topsoil has long been destroyed. The Naurans must find a way to reclaim this barren land or their economy will fall apart.

Logging

In other parts of Oceania intense logging has caused problems. The land, once thick with rain forest, now lies exposed to the tor-

Geographic Themes

Region: Australia
The koala bear is one of about 150 marsupials that live in every part of Australia. *What impact has human settlement had on Australia's animal life?*

rential rains and the baking sun. In mountainous Papua New Guinea, landslides have washed away the earth. On other islands the soil has been so stripped of nutrients that crops cannot grow.

Nuclear Testing

In the late 1940s and 1950s, the United States and other nations did not recognize the long-term danger from nuclear testing in the South Pacific. The United States government promised the people of Bikini Atoll, in the Marshall Islands, that they would only be leaving their home for a short time while atomic tests were being conducted.

Almost 50 years later Bikini Atoll is still unsafe for human occupation. Although the land may be recovered one day, its people, relocated and supported by the United States government, have lost their livelihood and the traditional structure of their society.

Geographic Themes

Place: Uranium Mine, South Australia
Australia has the world's largest undeveloped deposits of uranium, an important element in creating nuclear weapons. *How has the testing of nuclear weapons affected the Pacific area?*

HUMAN/ENVIRONMENT INTERACTION

The Antarctic Wilderness

The British explorer James Cook never reached continental Antarctica in the 1770s; he was defeated by the thick ice. The harsh climate has protected Antarctica. The continent's scientific and economic potential, however, have inspired people to overcome the challenge of reaching it.

What will it mean for Antarctica's environment if people can fly there in a few hours? How will the Antarctic wilderness be protected? These are urgent questions for the nations of the world.

The Scientific Impact

The key to Antarctica's scientific value has always been its isolation. The air and seas are almost untouched by humans, the ice and land almost unchanged for millions of years. This means that experiments about weather patterns, the ozone layer, ancient glaciers, and the living community that are conducted there are not distorted by humans and the environmental changes they make.

Surprisingly the scientists who cherish Antarctica's relatively untouched environment are now causing some of the problems the continent faces. Along with several thousand tourists who visit the continent each summer, an equal number of scientists are leaving garbage and graffiti behind, and disturbing wildlife nesting sites.

Ozone Hole

Perhaps the greatest danger to Antarctica is the change occurring in the ozone layer. Some scientists believe that pollution has made a hole in this protective covering, allowing more of the sun's radiation to reach the earth's surface.

Kiribati and other low atoll islands face the danger of **global warming**, or greenhouse effect, according to some scientists. Experts claim that global warming, created in part by human pollution, will eventually cause the polar regions to melt, raising sea levels more than 8 inches (about 20 cm) thus submerging many Pacific islands.

Scientists also worry that this added radiation will seriously harm the fragile Antarctic **ecosystem**, its community of living things that depend on each other for survival.

Concern is mostly focused on possible damage to the microscopic plants that feed krill, or tiny crustaceans. Like a falling domino, a reduced krill population will, in turn, cause other changes. Without the krill for food, the number of fish will shrink, leaving less food for the penguins and affecting marine life throughout the Antarctic area.

Solving the Problems

Because no one nation controls Antarctica, protecting its environment is an especially difficult challenge. So far, the nations of the world have mostly worked together to gradu-

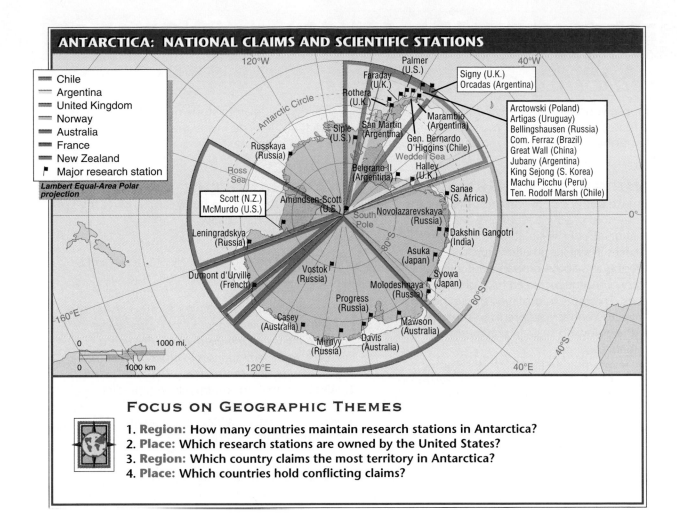

ANTARCTICA: NATIONAL CLAIMS AND SCIENTIFIC STATIONS

Chile
Argentina
United Kingdom
Norway
Australia
France
New Zealand
Major research station

Lambert Equal-Area Polar projection

120°W

Palmer (U.S.)

Faraday (U.K.)

Signy (U.K.)
Orcadas (Argentina)

40°W

Rothera (U.K.)

Arctowski (Poland)
Artigas (Uruguay)
Bellingshausen (Russia)
Com. Ferraz (Brazil)
Great Wall (China)
Jubany (Argentina)
King Sejong (S. Korea)
Machu Picchu (Peru)
Ten. Rodolf Marsh (Chile)

Antarctic Circle

Siple (U.S.)

San Martin (Argentina)

Marambio (Argentina)

Russkaya (Russia)

Gen. Bernardo O'Higgins (Chile)

Ross Sea

Belgrano II (Argentina)

Weddell Sea

Halley (U.K.)

Scott (N.Z.)
McMurdo (U.S.)

Amundsen-Scott (U.S.)

Sanae (S. Africa)

South Pole

Novolazarevskaya (Russia)

0°

Leningradskaya (Russia)

Dakshin Gangotri (India)

Asuka (Japan)

Dumont d'Urville (French)

Vostok (Russia)

Syowa (Japan)

Molodeshnaya (Russia)

Progress (Russia)

160°E

0   1000 mi.

0   1000 km

Casey (Australia)

Mawson (Australia)

120°E

Mirnyy (Russia)

Davis (Australia)

40°E

FOCUS ON GEOGRAPHIC THEMES

1. **Region:** How many countries maintain research stations in Antarctica?
2. **Place:** Which research stations are owned by the United States?
3. **Region:** Which country claims the most territory in Antarctica?
4. **Place:** Which countries hold conflicting claims?

ally explore Antarctica. The Antarctic Treaty, signed in 1959, defined Antarctica as a "continent for science and peace." There would be no political borders, no military activity, no nuclear waste or explosions and, most importantly, no national claims to ownership.

Without national claims, however, who owns the resources of the continent and will guide its future? In 1989 France and Australia, and Greenpeace and other environmental groups proposed that the continent become a wilderness reserve, owned and protected by all. While the World Park concept remains challenged, 31 nations did agree in the 1991 Madrid Protocol to ban oil and gas exploration in Antarctica for 50 years. As Antarctica moves toward the 21st century, it will test the world's willingness to preserve the earth's last wilderness.

SECTION 2 REVIEW

Checking for Understanding

1. **Define** marsupial, global warming, ecosystem.
2. **Locating Places** What country claims the Amundsen-Scott research station at the South Pole?
3. **Human/Environment Interaction** What problems has the cane toad caused in Australia?
4. **Region** Why are the plants and animals of the South Pacific region unique?

Critical Thinking

5. **Determining Cause and Effect** How might the hole in the ozone layer threaten Kiribati and Antarctica's marine life?

CRITICAL THINKING SKILLS

Predicting Consequences

Suppose your teacher has scheduled a test for Monday morning. You plan to study on Sunday evening so the material will be fresh in your mind the next day. Unexpectedly, a friend invites you to go to a movie Sunday night. If you go to the movie, will you perform well on the test the next day?

REVIEWING THE SKILL

To make this decision, you must **predict the consequences** of your actions. We can use information about the situation and our experiences in similar situations to make an intelligent guess about probable outcomes. Predicting consequences can help produce better decisions. The more information and experience you have, the better your predictions will be.

Use the following steps in predicting consequences:

- Gather information about the decision or action.
- Use your knowledge and past experiences to formulate possible consequences of the decision or action.
- Analyze each possible consequence by asking, "How likely is it that this will occur?"
- When considering actions that affect many individuals or groups, predict consequences for the various groups involved.

PRACTICING THE SKILL

Read the passage below and answer the questions that follow.

In 1959, 12 nations signed the Antarctic Treaty to preserve the continent for scientific study; to prohibit military activities, nuclear testing, and waste dumping; and to prevent mining for 50 years. As the end of the treaty period approaches, disagreement among nations about mineral use in Antarctica increases. As mineral supplies in other parts of the world decrease, this controversy will grow.

1. What information would help you predict consequences of mining in Antarctica?
2. What are three possible consequences of allowing mining in Antarctica?

For additional practice in this skill, see Practicing Skills on page 700 of the Chapter 34 Review.

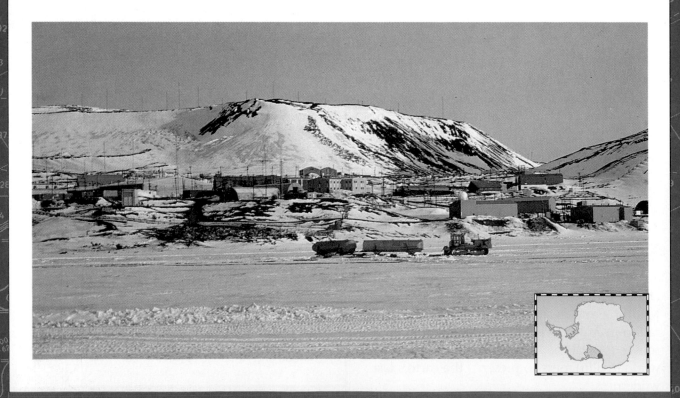

SECTION	KEY TERMS	SUMMARY
1 **Living in Australia, Oceania, and Antarctica**	grazier (p. 687) station (p. 687) copra (p. 688) subsistence farming (p. 688) rail gauge (p. 690)	• Agriculture is the most important economic activity in the South Pacific. • Farmers in Oceania farm mostly for their own use while those in Australia and New Zealand produce large farm exports, especially livestock and dairy products. • Antarctica produces no farm crops and has no mining or manufacturing industries. Its waters are a source of seafood. • Almost all the South Pacific's major manufacturing centers are in Australia and New Zealand. • Air and water travel has helped to bridge the distances to bring goods and services to remote parts of the South Pacific.

Airplane flying over Antarctica

SECTION	KEY TERMS	SUMMARY
2 **People and Their Environment**	marsupial (p. 694) global warming (p. 696) ecosystem (p. 696)	• Many of the plants and animals in the South Pacific, previously isolated, have suffered from human introduction of new species into the region. • The efforts of industry and government to pursue political and economic goals in Oceania have caused environmental problems that remain unsolved. • Antarctica's fragile environment is no longer protected by isolation. Scientists, industry, and tourists alike may be damaging its delicately balanced natural world.

Uranium mine in Australia

Reviewing Key Terms

Choose the vocabulary term that best completes each of the sentences below. Write your answers on a separate sheet of paper.

graziers (p. 687)
stations (p. 687)
copra (p. 688)
rail gauges (p. 690)
marsupials (p. 694)
global warming (p. 696)
ecosystem (p. 696)

SECTION 1

1. Train travel in Australia can be difficult because the _____ do not match throughout the system.
2. _____ raise sheep in Australia and New Zealand.
3. Livestock ranches in Australia are called _____ .
4. _____ can be found on most Pacific islands.

SECTION 2

5. Many native Australian mammals, called _____, were killed by foxes.
6. Scientists worry that _____ will seriously damage the marine life in Antarctica.
7. Antarctica's fragile _____ may suffer from increased tourism.

Reviewing Facts

SECTION 1

8. What are the main farm products exported from Oceania?
9. Where are most of Australia's manufactured products used?
10. How is air travel used in the South Pacific region?

SECTION 2

11. Until recently, what human activity helped to control New Zealand's possum population?
12. Why is Bikini Atoll now uninhabited?

13. What does the Madrid Protocol do?

Critical Thinking

14. **Determining Cause and Effect** How has the development of modern communication systems affected life in the South Pacific today?
15. **Expressing Problems Clearly** How has industrial activity in Oceania affected the region's environment?

 Geographic Themes

16. **Location** Where are the South Pacific's major manufacturing centers?
17. **Human/Environment Interaction** How have tourists and scientists contributed to the problems facing Antarctica's environment?

 Practicing Skills

Predicting Consequences
Refer to the skill on page 698.
18. What are two possible consequences of a permanent ban on mining in Antarctica?
19. What are three possible consequences of allowing livestock production in Australia and New Zealand to continue unchecked?

Using the Unit Atlas

Refer to the physical geography section of the Unit Atlas on pages 650–651.
20. What are Fiji's major exports?
21. How do scientists hope to use the Antarctic ice cap?

Projects

Individual Activity

Find out more about the economies of two South Pacific countries. In a short written report, compare the countries' economies and the factors that have contributed to the development of each.

Cooperative Learning Activity

In small groups, role-play a meeting of the Antarctic Treaty countries. Each student will focus on a different issue affecting Antarctica. When the group meets, individual members should present their findings, arguing for or against the World Park concept from the viewpoint of their specific issue. If students wish, they may draft a class letter that includes all the arguments.

Writing About Geography

Narration

Imagine you are developing a newspaper or radio station to link remote parts of the South Pacific with one another. Write an article describing the impact that improved communication would have on your community. Use your journal record, text, magazine articles, encyclopedias, and other books. Be sure to consider both positive and negative results of greater interaction between parts of the region—for example, changes to traditional cultures as well as improved economies.

Locating Places

ANTARCTICA: PHYSICAL GEOGRAPHY

Match the letters on the map with the places and physical features of Antarctica. Write your answers on a separate sheet of paper.

1. Weddell Sea
2. Antarctic Circle
3. South Pole
4. Ross Sea
5. Antarctic Peninsula

GEOGRAPHY CONNECTION

Connections to the United States

AUSTRALIA AND THE UNITED STATES

*T*he American fascination with Australia and its people may stem from the undeniably intriguing animal and plant life, the striking similarity in national character and lifestyle, or the shared parentage with the United Kingdom. Whatever its cause, the fascination is real and has influenced American popular culture in several ways.

PAUL HOGAN ▶ was one of Australia's "favorite sons" in the United States during the 1980s. Americans first met him on television in early 1984, when he appeared in commercials for the Australian Tourist Commission. His relaxed friendliness, from his opening "G'day" to his closing "Slip another shrimp on the barbie" (barbeque), seemed to embody the breezy Australian manner. In the late 1980s, he wrote and starred in several movies about Australian outback hero Crocodile Dundee.

▲ **AUSTRALIAN CLOTHING** has been popular among Americans interested in hiking and other outdoor activities. Outback shorts or pants have pockets aplenty; some have pockets on pockets, some on the sides of the legs. Like the pockets of a kangaroo or a koala, the pants pockets have a hidden fold, so the pockets can expand to hold objects picked up on a trek.

◀ **AUSTRALIAN CINEMA** has thousands of American fans. Whether meeting a feisty heroine such as Muriel in "Muriel's Wedding" or laid-back crocodile hunter Crocodile Dundee, Americans have come to appreciate Australian films.

AUSTRALIAN MUSICIANS ▶
have been great favorites, too, particularly since the mid-1970s and 1980s. During those years, Olivia Newton John and the BeeGees topped American pop charts continuously. In the 1990s, the group Midnight Oil used their musical talents to warn listeners of the consequences of destroying the earth's environment.

▼ **THE AUSTRALIAN ARMY "DIGGER" HAT**
is also a popular item. The brim can be worn down all the way around to shed rain, or flipped up on one side, in the more traditional Australian style.

Checking for Understanding

1. In what areas of American culture has Australian influence made a mark?
2. Movement What signs of Australian influence can you find in your community? Why?

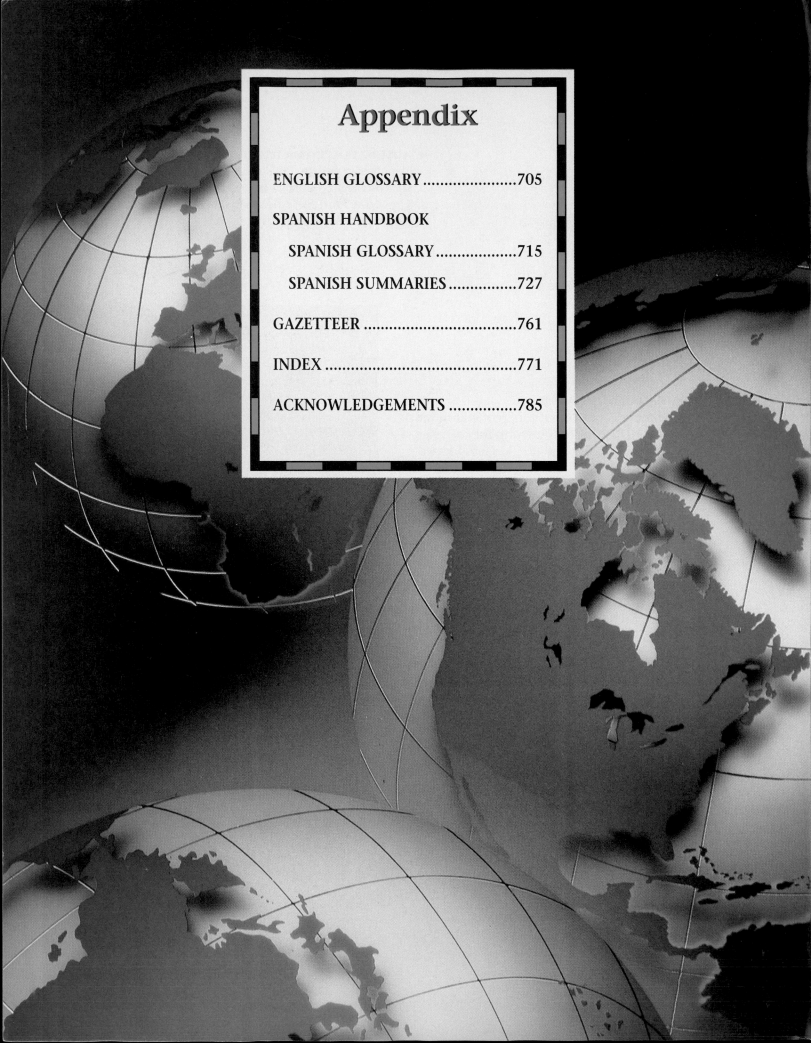

Appendix

ENGLISH GLOSSARY 705

SPANISH HANDBOOK

    SPANISH GLOSSARY 715

    SPANISH SUMMARIES 727

GAZETTEER 761

INDEX 771

ACKNOWLEDGEMENTS 785

Glossary

A

absolute location the position of a place on the earth's surface (p. 5)

abstract art form that expresses the artist's attitudes and emotions (p. 121)

acid deposition wet or dry airborne acids that fall to the earth (p. 271)

acid rain precipitation carrying large amounts of dissolved acids, especially sulfuric acid and nitric acid, which damages buildings, forests, and crops and kills wildlife (pp. 137, 270, 577)

alluvial plain floodplain on which flooding rivers have deposited rich soil, such as the Indo-Gangetic Plain in South Asia (p. 480)

alluvial-soil deposits rich soil made up of sand and mud deposited by running water (p. 359)

amendment in U.S. history, official changes made to the Constitution (p. 117)

apartheid policy of strict separation of the races adopted in South Africa in the 1940s (p. 440)

aquifer underground water-bearing layers of porous rock, sand, or gravel (p. 398)

arable land land suitable for growing crops (p. 612)

archipelago a group or chain of islands (pp. 34, 538, 598)

artesian water underground water supply that is under enough pressure to rise into wells without being pumped (p. 656)

Association of Southeast Asian Nations (ASEAN) organization formed in 1967 to promote regional development and trade in Southeast Asia (p. 633)

atheist person who does not believe in God (p. 317)

atmosphere the air that surrounds the earth (p. 27)

atoll ring-shaped island formed by coral building up along the rim of an underwater volcano (p. 657)

avalanche mass of ice, snow, or rock that slides down a mountainside (p. 232)

axis referring to the earth, an imaginary line that runs through its center between the North Pole and the South Pole (p. 45)

B

batik method of dyeing cloth to produce beautiful patterns, developed in Indonesia and Malaysia (p. 621)

bedouin member of the nomadic desert peoples of North Africa and Southwest Asia (p. 384)

bilingual speaking or using two languages (p. 121)

biologist scientist who studies plant and animal life (p. 274)

biosphere the part of the earth where life—people, plants, and animals—exists (p. 28)

black market any illegal market where scarce or illegal goods are sold, usually at high prices (p. 328)

blizzard a heavy snowstorm with winds of more than 35 miles per hour (p. 100)

boomerang curved throwing stick used for hunting by Aborigines in Australia (p. 673)

bycatch unwanted fish, marine mammals, and birds caught by fishing trawlers and thrown away (p. 141)

C

cabinet heads of departments in the executive branch of the U.S. government who advise the President (p. 118)

calligraphy the art of beautiful and decorative handwriting (p. 565)

campesinos farm workers; generally, people who live and work in rural areas (p. 196)

canopy top layer of a rain forest, where the tops of tall trees come together (p. 167)

capitalism economic system based on free enterprise, in which individuals own and use capital (p. 76)

cash crop farm crop grown to be sold or traded rather than used by the farm family (pp. 113, 195, 452, 512, 630)

caste system in traditional South Asian society, the division of society into rigid groups, based mainly on occupation, that determined social standing, marriage choice, and other actions (p. 496)

cataract a large waterfall (p. 420)

caudillo term for a Latin American political leader from the late 1800s on, often a military dictator (literally, "strong man") (p. 184)

cereal any grain, such as barley, oats, or wheat, grown for food (p. 364)

chaparral type of vegetation made up of dense forests of shrubs and short trees, common in Mediterranean climates (pp. 54, 232)

chart visual presentation of data in rows and columns (p. 22)

chernozem (cher•nuh•ZYAWM) rich black topsoil found in the North European Plain, especially in Russia and Ukraine (p. 291)

chinampas floating artificial farming islands made by the Aztec (p. 181)

chinook seasonal warm wind that blows down the Rocky Mountains in late winter and early spring (p. 100)

Chipko in India, an environmental movement known by the term for "tree-hugger," aimed at saving forests (p. 520)

chlorofluorocarbon chemical substance, found mainly in liquid coolants, that damages the earth's protective ozone layer (p. 578)

city-state in ancient Greece, independent community consisting of a city and the surrounding lands, where democracy first developed (p. 245)

civilization a culture that has organized a social, economic, and political system, built cities, and achieved a certain level of development in the arts and sciences (p. 69)

clan tribal community or large group of people related to one another (pp. 444, 557)

climate weather patterns typical for an area over a long period of time (p. 45)

cold war refers to the power struggle between the Soviet Union and the United States (p. 248)

collective farm under communism, a large, state-owned farm on which farmers received wages plus a share of products and profits; also called a *kholkoz* (p. 264)

command economy economic system in which economic decisions about production and distribution are made by some central authority (p. 328)

commercial farming farming organized as a business (p. 452)

commune in China, a collective farming community whose members were supposed to share work and products (p. 571)

communism social and political movement developed by Marx and Lenin that favored revolution to establish a classless society in which workers would control industrial production (pp. 247, 313)

compass rose directional marker on a map (p. 12)

conquistador Spanish term for "conqueror," referring to soldiers who conquered Native Americans in Latin America (p. 182)

Constitution plan of government made for the new United States in 1787 (p. 117)

consumer goods household goods, shoes, and clothing that individuals buy (pp. 264, 328)

continental divide a line or ridge that separates rivers flowing toward opposite sides of a continent (p. 94)

continental island island formed of rock that has risen from the continental shelf, such as Papua New Guinea (p. 657)

continental shelf shallow ocean area near the coast of a continent (p. 34)

contour lines on a map, lines that connect points of land at the same elevation (p. 14)

contour plowing farming method in which plowed furrows follow the natural curve of the land, lessening erosion (p. 131)

cooperative a voluntary organization whose members work together and share the expenses and profits from their enterprise; also called "co-op" (p. 572)

copra dried meat of a coconut (p. 688)

coral tiny marine animals and the rock-like structures (islands, reefs) formed by the skeletons of coral colonies (p. 656)

cordillera chain or range of mountains (p. 597)

crevass huge, deep crack that forms in thick ice or snow (p. 663)

crop rotation farming method in which different crops are alternated in the same field, preserving soil nutrients (p. 131)

Crusades series of religious wars (c. 1100-1300) in which European Christians tried to retake Palestine from Muslim rule (p. 246)

cultural diffusion the spread of ideas, customs, goods, and people from one culture to another (p. 70)

culture way of life of a group of people who share traditions, interests, beliefs, and ways of making a living (pp. 10, 63)

culture hearth a center where cultures developed and from which ideas and traditions spread outward (pp. 69, 556)

culture region division of the earth based on a variety of factors, including government, social groups, economic systems, language, or religion (p. 74)

cuneiform sumerian writing system using wedge-shaped symbols pressed into clay tablets (p. 377)

current cold or warm "river" of seawater that flows in the oceans, generally in a circular pattern (p. 50)

cyclone storm with heavy rains and high winds that blow in a circular pattern around an area of low atmospheric pressure (pp. 484, 636)

czar in Russian history, the emperor or supreme ruler (p. 312)

D

deciduous describing trees, usually broad-leaved such as oak and maple, that lose their leaves in autumn (p. 54)

deforestation the loss or destruction of forests, due mainly to trees being cleared for logging or farming (pp. 202, 460, 518, 605)

delta triangular section of land built up at a river's mouth that looks like the Greek letter *delta* (Δ) (p. 359)

desalination the removal of salt from sea water to make it usable for drinking and farming (p. 399)

desertification process in which arable land is turned into desert, usually due to destruction of vegetation (p. 458)

developing country country in the process of becoming industrialized (p. 195)

dharma in Hinduism, a person's moral duty, based on class distinctions, which guides his or her life (p. 497)

diagram drawing that shows what something is or how something is done, such as the steps of a process or cycle (p. 22)

dialect local form of a language used in a particular place or by a certain group (pp. 177, 251)

distillation method of desalination in which water is boiled and condensed (p. 399)

doldrums a frequently windless area near the Equator (pp. 50, 662)

domesticate to take plants and animals from the wild and tame them or otherwise make them useful to people (p. 376)

dry farming farming method used in dry regions in which land is plowed and planted deeply to hold water in the soil (p. 116)

dynasty a ruling house or continuing family of rulers, especially in China (p. 556)

E

economic system the way in which the people of a country produce and distribute goods and services (p. 75)

ecosystem the complex community of interdependent living things in a given environment (pp. 202, 696)

ecotourism tourism based on concern for the environment (p. 461)

endemic describing plant or animal species native to a particular area (p. 605)

environmentalist person actively concerned with the quality and protection of the environment (p. 271)

equinox one of two days (about March 21 and September 23) on which the sun is directly above the equator, making day and night equal in length (p. 46)

erosion wearing away of the earth's surface, by wind, flowing water, or glaciers (p. 31)

escarpment steep cliff or slope between a higher and lower land surface (pp. 162, 419)

ethnic diversity differences among groups of people based on their origins, languages, customs, or beliefs (p. 371)

ethnic group group of people who share a common ancestry, language, customs, religion, or combination of such characteristics (pp. 305, 436, 551)

eutrophication process by which the water of a lake or stream becomes too rich in dissolved nutrients, leading to plant growth that depletes oxygen (p. 139)

evaporation the changing of liquid water into water vapor, a gas (p. 36)

exports resources or goods sent from one country to another (pp. 39, 195)

extended family household made up of several generations; for instance, aunts, uncles, and grandparents as well as parents and children (pp. 189, 444)

extinction the disappearance or end of a species of animal or plant (p. 460)

F

fale traditional type of home in Western Samoa, with open sides and thatched roof (p. 681)

farm cooperative organization in which farmers share in growing and selling farm products (p. 264)

fault a crack or break in the earth's crust, usually caused by intense folding (pp. 29, 420)

fauna the animal life of a region (p. 598)

fazenda Portuguese term for huge sugar plantations in Brazil (p. 182)

feudalism in medieval Europe and Japan, system of government in which powerful lords gave land to nobles in return for pledges of loyalty (p. 245)

fishery areas (freshwater or saltwater) where fish or other sea animals are caught (p. 97)

fjord (fee•YORD) long, steep-sided glacial valley now filled by seawater (p. 223)

flora the plant life of a region (p. 598)

foehn (FUHN) warm dry wind that blows from the leeward side of mountains, sometimes melting snow and causing an avalanche; used mainly in Europe (p. 232)

fold a bend in layers of rock, sometimes caused by plate movement (p. 29)

free enterprise an economic system in which private businesses operate with little interference from government (pp. 76, 129)

free port port city, such as Singapore, where goods can be unloaded, stored, and reshipped without the payment of import duties (p. 633)

fútbol Latin American name for soccer (p. 189)

G

general purpose map map showing a wide range of general physical and/or political information about an area (p. 14)

geography the study of the earth and the ways people live and work on it (p. 5)

glacier large bodies of ice that move across the surface of the earth (p. 31)

glasnost Russian term for a new "openness," part of Gorbachev's reform plans (p. 314)

global warming gradual warming of the earth and its atmosphere that may be caused in part by pollution and an increase in the greenhouse effect (p. 696)

government a group or nation's political system (p. 74)

graph way of presenting and comparing information visually, as in a line graph, bar graph, or circle graph (p. 20)

grazier person who raises and herds sheep or cattle (p. 687)

great circle shortest distance between any two places on the earth's surface (p. 16)

green revolution program, begun in the 1960s, to produce higher-yielding, more productive strains of wheat, rice, and other food crops (p. 513)

grid system pattern formed as the lines of latitude and longitude cross one another (p. 6)

gross domestic product (GDP) the value of goods and services created within a country in a year (pp. 393, 434)

groundwater water that lies beneath the surface of the earth, supplied mainly by rain filtering through the soil (p. 35)

H

habitat area with conditions suitable for certain plants or animals to live (p. 460)

haiku form of Japanese poetry consisting of 17 syllables, often about nature (p. 565)

headwaters the sources of river waters (p. 96)

heavy industry the manufacture of machinery and equipment needed for factories and mines (p. 263)

hemisphere half of a sphere or globe, as in the earth's Northern and Southern Hemispheres (p. 5)

hieroglyphics Egyptian writing system using pictures and symbols to represent words or sounds (p. 377)

history the study of written information about events and people in the past (p. 69)

Holocaust term given to the mass killings of 6 million European Jews by Germany's Nazi leaders during World War II (p. 248)

homogeneous describing a group of people or things that are very like one another (p. 552)

hurricane a large, powerful windstorm that forms over warm ocean waters (pp. 66, 100)

hydroelectric power electrical energy generated by falling water (p. 165)

hydrosphere the watery areas of the earth, including oceans, lakes, rivers, and other bodies of water (p. 28)

hypothesis one step in the scientific method, suggesting a scientific explanation for observed events (p. 57)

I

icon religious image, usually including a picture of Jesus, Mary, or a saint, used mainly by Orthodox Christians (p. 317)

ideogram a pictorial character or symbol that has a specific meaning or stands for a syllable (p. 561)

imports resources or goods brought into one country from another (p. 39)

immigrant person who has left his or her home country and settled permanently in another country (p. 107)

impressionism artistic style that developed in Europe in the late 1800s and tried to show the natural appearance of objects with dabs or strokes of color (p. 253)

indigenous native to a place; the original inhabitants—plant, animal, or human (p. 615)

industrialization process of turning to the use of machinery in manufacturing (p. 115)

industrialize to develop industry (p. 336)

interdependent relying on one another for goods, services, and ideas (pp. 8, 133, 632)

isthmus narrow piece of land connecting two large landmasses (p. 33)

J

jai alai (HY•LY) traditional handball-type game popular with Mexicans and Cubans (p. 189)

jazz musical form that developed in the United States in the early 1900s, blending African rhythms and European harmonies (p. 122)

jati in traditional Hindu society, a social group that defines a family's occupation and social standing (p. 491)

jute plant fiber used to make string and cloth (p. 512)

K

karma in Hindu belief, the sum of good and bad actions in one's present and past lives, leading to rewards or punishment (p. 497)

key part of a map that explains the symbols used (p. 12)

kolkhoz in the Soviet Union, a large collective farm (p. 329)

krill tiny shrimplike sea animals that live in cold Antarctic oceans (p. 659)

kums regional term for the sandy deserts in the Turan Lowland, as in Kara Kum (p. 292)

L

lagoon shallow pool of water at the center of an atoll (p. 657)

language family group of related languages that have all developed from one earlier language (pp. 76, 251)

latifundia in modern Latin America, large estates owned by families or corporations (p. 196)

latitude imaginary lines running east and west around the globe, used to measure the distance north and south of the Equator in degrees; also called parallels (p. 5)

leach to wash nutrients out of the soil (p. 427)

leeward facing away from the direction from which the wind is blowing (p. 51)

lichens sturdy small plants that grow like a crust on rocks or tree trunks (p. 663)

light industry manufacturing aimed at making consumer goods rather than heavy machinery, such as textiles or food processing (p. 263)

lingua franca a language (such as Swahili) used for communication among people with different native languages (p. 442)

literacy rate the percentage of people in a given place who can read and write (pp. 123, 445)

lithosphere surface land areas of the earth's crust (about 30 percent), including continents and ocean basins (p. 28)

llanos (YAHN•ohz) fertile plains along the Caribbean coast of South America, in Colombia and Venezuela (p. 164)

loess (LES) fine, yellowish-brown topsoil made up of particles of silt and clay, usually carried by the wind (p. 539)

longhouse in rural areas of Indonesia and Malaysia, a large building where people from several related families live (p. 622)

longitude imaginary vertical lines running from pole to pole on the globe, used to measure distance east or west of the Prime Meridian; also called meridians (p. 6)

M

malnutrition poor nutrition due to a badly balanced diet or lack of food (p. 187)

mangrove tree tropical evergreen tree or shrub that usually grows in thick groves near water (p. 518)

mantle thick middle layer of the earth's interior structure, consisting of dense, hot rock made up of silicon, oxygen, aluminum, iron, and magnesium (p. 29)

mantra in Hinduism, a sacred word or phrase repeated in prayers and chants (p. 502)

manuka small shrubs that grow in plateau regions of New Zealand (p. 663)

map projection way of drawing a map to represent the rounded earth on a flat surface (p. 17)

maquiladoras in Mexico, manufacturing plants set up by foreign firms (p. 197)

maritime concerned with travel or shipping by sea (p. 615)

market economy an economic system based on free enterprise, in which businesses are privately owned and production and prices are determined by supply and demand (p. 328)

marsupial type of mammal (such as kangaroos or koalas) that gives birth to offspring that mature in a pouch on the mother's abdomen (p. 694)

mass culture popular culture spread by media such as radio and television (p. 442)

megalopolis a "super-city" that is made up of several large cities and the smaller cities near them, such as the area between Boston and Washington, D.C., or around Tokyo-Yokohama, Japan (pp. 109, 554)

meltwater water formed by melting snow and ice (p. 271)

merchant marine a country's fleet of ships that engage in commerce or trade (p. 576)

mesa flat-topped, elevated landform (from the Spanish term for "table") (p. 94)

mestizo in Latin America, person of mixed Native American and European descent (p. 176)

metropolitan area region that includes a central city and its surrounding suburbs (p. 109)

mica silicate mineral that typically splits into thin, shiny sheets (p. 481)

Middle Passage name given to the route used by slave ships across the Atlantic from West Africa to the Americas (p. 440)

minifundia in Latin America, small farms that produce food chiefly for family use and the local market (p. 196)

mistral strong northerly wind from the Alps that can bring cold air to southern France (p. 231)

mixed farming raising several kinds of crops and livestock on the same farm (p. 264)

mixed forest forestland with both evergreen and deciduous trees (p. 54)

mobile describing things or people that move easily from place to place (p. 122)

modernism Latin American literary movement of the late 1800s, focusing on artistic expression and experimentation (p. 188)

monotheism belief in one God (p. 377)

monsoon in Asia, seasonal wind that brings warm moist air from the oceans in summer, cold dry air from inland in winter (pp. 482, 542, 602)

mosaic picture or design made with small pieces of colored stone, glass, or tile (p. 188)

mosque in Islam, a house of public worship (p. 378)

mulatto person of mixed African and European descent (p. 176)

multicultural having elements that come from more than one culture (pp. 120, 239)

N

nationalism belief in the right of each people to be an independent nation (p. 379)

nationalities large, distinct ethnic groups within a country, used especially in Russia and the Eurasian republics (p. 305)

nationalize to place a company or industry under government control (p. 379)

natural resource element or substance from the earth that is not made by people but can be used by them, such as minerals (p. 37)

natural vegetation plant life that grows in a certain area if people have not changed the natural environment (p. 52)

nirvana in Buddhism, ultimate state of peace and insight toward which people strive (p. 497)

nomadic describing a way of life in which a group travels from place to place rather than establishing a permanent settlement (p. 673)

nonrenewable resource resource that cannot be replaced by natural growth or human action, such as most minerals (p. 38)

North American Free Trade Agreement (NAFTA) trade agreement made in 1993 by Canada, the United States, and Mexico (p. 134)

O

oasis small area in a desert where water and vegetation are found, usually because of underground springs (pp. 53, 362)

oral history legends and stories passed on by word of mouth from generation to generation (p. 444)

organic farming the use of natural substances to enrich the soil and grow crops rather than chemical fertilizers and pesticides (p. 264)

P

Pampas grassy, treeless plains of southern South America, used for growing grain and grazing animals (p. 164)

pastoralism the raising and grazing of livestock (p. 364)

patriarch in church history, an important Christian bishop or leader; today, the head of an independent Eastern Orthodox church or of the Armenian Apostolic Church (p. 318)

peat vegetable matter, mainly mosses, usually found in swamps; sometimes cut and burned as fuel in parts of western Europe (p. 229)

per capita income the total income of a country or region divided by the number of people; income per person (pp. 76, 435)

perestroika (pehr•ehs•TROY•kah) in Russian, "restructuring"; part of Gorbachev's plan for reforming Soviet government (p. 314)

permafrost permanently frozen layer of soil beneath the surface of the ground (pp. 55, 231, 297)

pesticide chemical used to kill insects, rodents, and other pests (p. 341)

petrochemical chemical product derived from petroleum or natural gas (p. 392)

phosphate natural mineral containing chemical compounds often used in fertilizers (p. 361)

pidgin English a dialect mixing English and local languages (p. 680)

plateau flat landmass higher than the surrounding land, with at least one steep side, called a cliff (pp. 34, 94)

GLOSSARY

poaching illegal hunting of protected animals (p. 460)

pogrom in czarist Russia, an attack on Jews carried out by government troops or officials (p. 318)

polder low-lying area of the Netherlands from which seawater has been drained to create new farmland (p. 228)

polluted contaminated by harmful or impure substances (p. 338)

pollution the existence of impure, unclean, or poisonous substances in the air, water, and land environment (p. 67)

population density average number of people in a square mile or square kilometer (p. 65)

population distribution the pattern of population—where people live—in a country, a continent, or the world (p. 65)

prairie an inland grassland area (p. 54)

precipitation moisture that falls to the earth as rain, sleet, hail, or snow (p. 51)

prehistory the time in a people's past before written records were kept (p. 69)

prevailing wind wind in a region that blows in a fairly constant directional pattern, such as the trade winds that blow toward the Equator in low latitudes (p. 50)

primate city city that dominates a country's economy, culture, and government and in which population is concentrated; usually the capital (pp. 179, 613, 670)

prophet person believed to be a messenger from God (p. 378)

Q

qanat underground canals used in water systems of ancient Persians (p. 377)

quipu (KEE•poo) rope with knotted cords of various lengths and colors used by the Inca to keep records and send messages (p. 182)

R

raga in Indian classical music, a basic melody on which the player improvises or plays variations (p. 503)

rail gauge the distance between the rails on a railroad track, which determines the position of wheels on a railroad car (p. 690)

rain shadow dry area found on the leeward side of a mountain range (p. 51)

realism artistic style portraying everyday life that developed in Europe during the mid-1800s (p. 252)

reforestation replanting young trees or seeds on lands where trees have been cut or destroyed (p. 203)

Reformation religious movement that began in Germany in the 1400s, leading to the establishment of Protestant churches (p. 246)

refugee person who must leave his or her home and flee elsewhere for safety (p. 240)

reincarnated in Hindu belief, being reborn repeatedly in different forms, until one has overcome earthly desires (p. 497)

relative location where a place is located in relation to other places (p. 7)

relief differences in elevation, or height, of land and landforms (p. 14)

religion organized way of worshiping a spiritual being or thinking about life (p. 77)

Renaissance in Europe, a 300-year period of renewed interest in classical learning and the arts, beginning in the 1300s (p. 246)

renewable resource resource that can be grown by people or renewed naturally, such as trees (p. 38)

republic form of government without a monarch, in which people elect their officials, including the head of state (p. 114)

revolution in astronomy, the earth's yearly trip around the sun, taking 365 1/4 days (p. 46)

romanticism artistic style emphasizing individual emotions that developed in Europe in the late 1700s and early 1800s as a reaction to industrialization (p. 252)

russification in 19th-century Russia, a government program that required everyone in the empire to speak Russian and to become a Christian (p. 313)

S

sadhu a Hindu hermit or holy man and teacher (p. 502)

samurai in medieval Japan, a class of professional soldiers who lived by a strict code of personal honor and loyalty to a noble (p. 557)

savanna a tropical grassland containing scattered trees (p. 426)

scale on a map, the relationship of measures on the map to actual measurements in feet, miles, meters, or kilometers on the earth's surface (p. 12)

sedentary farming farming carried on at permanent settlements (p. 452)

seismic related to earthquakes (p. 358)

serf laborer owned by a noble and obliged to remain on the land where he or she worked (p. 312)

service industry business that provides a service—such as banking, insurance, or transport—instead of making goods (pp. 132, 196, 393)

shamanism belief in a leader who can communicate with spirits (p. 562)

shifting farming method in which farmers move every few years to find better soil (p. 452)

shogun in medieval Japan, a military ruler of the country (p. 557)

sickle large, curved knife with a handle, used to cut grass or tall grains (p. 629)

sirocco hot desert wind that can blow air and dust from North Africa to western Europe's Mediterranean coast (p. 231)

slash-and-burn farming traditional farming method in which all trees and plants in an area are cut and burned to add nutrients to the soil (p. 202)

smog irritating haze caused by the interaction of ultraviolet solar radiation with chemical fumes from automobile exhausts and other pollution sources (from the words *smoke* and *fog*) (pp. 57, 138)

socialism political philosophy that originally called for ownership of all land and factories by peasants and workers, now refers to government ownership of some or all means of production (pp. 76, 312)

socialist realism in the Soviet Union, realistic style of art and literature that glorified Soviet ideals and goals (p. 320)

solstice one of two days (about June 21 and December 22) on which the sun's rays strike directly at latitude 23 1/2°N (Tropic of Cancer) or 23 1/2°S (Tropic of Capricorn), marking the beginning of summer or winter (p. 47)

sovkhoz in the Soviet Union, a large farm owned and run by the state (p. 329)

special purpose map map emphasizing a special subject matter, such as resources or population (p. 15)

sphere of influence area of a country in which a foreign power has political or economic control (p. 615)

standard of living a measure of people's quality of life, based on access to material goods such as income, food, and housing (p. 75)

state farm under communism, a state-owned farm managed by government officials; also called *sovkhoz* (p. 264)

station Australian term for an outlying ranch or large farm (p. 687)

steppe wide grassy plains of Eurasia, stretching from the Black Sea to the Altai Mountains; also, similar semi-arid climate regions elsewhere (p. 298)

strait narrow waterway connecting two large bodies of water (p. 111)

strine colloquial, informal English spoken in Australia (p. 679)

subcontinent large landmass that is part of a continent but still distinct from it, such as India (p. 477)

subsistence farming traditional agriculture whose goal is to produce just enough to eat for a family or a village to survive (pp. 63, 452, 511, 680, 688)

suburbs outlying communities around a central city (p. 109)

Sunbelt southern part of the United States, so named because of its mild climate (p. 108)

sūq an enclosed marketplace in the region of North Africa and Southwest Asia (p. 385)

T

taiga Russian term for the vast subarctic forest, mainly evergreens, that begins where the tundra ends; also used for subarctic climate regions in general (pp. 55, 297)

tala in Indian classical music, a rhythm pattern, often played on a drum (p. 503)

tariff a tax on imports or exports (p. 265)

temperature a measure of how hot or cold something is, generally measured in degrees on a set scale, such as Fahrenheit

GLOSSARY

or Celsius (p. 45)

tierra caliente Spanish term for "hot country"; the lowest zone (sea level-3,000 feet elevation) of a highland climate near the Equator (p. 167)

tierra fría Spanish term for "cold country"; the highest altitude zone of highland climates in Central and South America (p. 167)

tierra templada Spanish term for "temperate country"; the middle zone (3,000-6,000 ft. elevation) of Latin American highland climates (p. 167)

timberline elevation above which it is too cold for trees to grow (pp. 56, 101)

topography physical features of the earth's surface (p. 14)

tornado a violent windstorm with rotating winds and a funnel-shaped cloud (pp. 66, 100)

trading partner a country that buys from or sells to another country (p. 574)

trekker a mountain hiker; more generally, anyone on a difficult journey (p. 518)

tributary smaller rivers and streams that feed into a larger river (p. 96)

truck farm farm, especially in the northeastern United States, that grows vegetables for markets in nearby cities (p. 131)

trust territory region, such as Micronesia, placed by United Nations under temporary political and economic control of another country after World War II (p. 675)

tsunami Japanese term used for a huge sea wave caused by an undersea earthquake (pp. 67, 538)

tundra vast treeless plains in cold northern climates, characterized by permafrost and small, low plants such as mosses and shrubs (p. 297)

typhoon a hurricane (cyclone), or violent tropical storm, that forms in the Pacific Ocean, usually in late summer (pp. 100, 542, 636, 662)

U

universal suffrage equal voting rights for all adult residents of a nation (p. 440)

urbanization the movement of people from rural areas into cities (p. 436)

V

viceroy representative of the Spanish monarch appointed to enforce laws in American colonies (p. 182)

W

wadi in the desert, a streambed that is dry except during a heavy rain (p. 360)

wat in Southeast Asia, a temple (p. 621)

water cycle regular movement of water from ocean to air to ground and back to the ocean (p. 36)

wattle name given to acacia trees by early Australian settlers who built houses of interwoven (wattled) acacia saplings (p. 660)

weather condition of the atmosphere in one place during a short period of time; for example, a "cold, windy, wet day" (p. 45)

weathering chemical or physical processes, such as freezing, that break down rocks (p. 30)

welfare state nation, such as Great Britain, Norway, or Sweden, in which the government assumes major responsibility for people's welfare in areas such as health and education (p. 253)

windward facing toward the direction from which the wind is blowing (p. 51)

Z

ziggurat large step-like temple of mud brick built in ancient Mesopotamia (p. 383)

Glossary/Glosario

A

absolute location/ubicación absoluta La posición de un lugar en la superficie de la tierra (pág. 5)

abstract/abstracto estilo de arte que expresa las emociones y la actitud del artista. (pág. 121)

acid deposition/deposición ácida Ácidos secos o húmedos que lleva el viento y que caen a la tierra (pág. 271)

acid rain/lluvia ácida Precipitación que lleva grandes cantidades de ácidos disueltos, especialmente ácido sulfúrico y ácido nítrico, los cuales dañan los edificios, los bosques y las cosechas y matan la fauna (págs. 137, 270, 577)

alluvial plain/llanura aluvial Llanura en la que los ríos inundados han depositado tierra rica, como la Llanura Indogangéctica en el Asia del Sur (pág. 480)

alluvial-soil deposits/depósitos de tierra aluvial Tierra rica compuesta de arena y lodo depositados por aguas corrientes (pág. 359)

amendment/enmienda En la historia de los Estados Unidos, cambios oficiales que se le hacen a la Constitución (pág. 118)

apartheid/segregación racial Política de estricta separación de las razas adoptada en Sudáfrica en los años 40 (pág. 440)

aquifer/acuífero/aguas freáticas Capas subterráneas de roca porosa, arena o grava que acumulan agua (pág. 398)

arable land/tierra arable Tierra idónea para cultivar cosechas (pág. 612)

archipelago/archipiélago Un grupo o cadena de islas (pgs. 34, 538, 598)

artesian water/agua artesiana Abastecimiento de agua subterránea que está bajo suficiente presión para subir a los pozos sin tener que ser bombeada (pág. 656)

Association of Southeast Asian Nations (ASEAN)/Asociación de Naciones del Asia del Sudeste (ANSEA) Organización formada en 1967 para promover el desarrollo y el comercio regional en el Asia del Sudeste (pág. 632)

atheist/ateo Persona que no cree en Dios (pág. 317)

atmosphere/atmósfera El aire que rodea la Tierra (pág. 27)

atoll/atolón Isla en forma de aro formada por coral que se acumula por todo el borde de un volcán submarino (pág. 657)

avalanche/avalancha Masa de hielo, nieve o roca que se desliza por el lado de una montaña (pág. 231)

axis/eje Referente a la Tierra, una línea imaginaria que le atraviesa por el centro entre el Polo Norte y el Polo Sur (pág. 45)

B

batik/batik Método de teñir tela para producir bellos estampados, desarrollado en Indonesia y Malasia (pág. 621)

bedouin/beduíno Miembro de los pueblos nómadas del desierto del Africa del Norte y Asia del Sudoeste (pág. 384)

bilingual/bilingüe Que habla o usa dos idiomas (pág. 121)

biologist/biólogo Científico que estudia la vida vegetal y animal (pág. 274)

biosphere/biosfera La parte de la Tierra donde la vida, la gente, las plantas y los animales—existe (pág. 28)

black market/mercado negro Cualquier mercado ilegal donde se vende productos escasos o ilegales, por lo general a precios altos (pág. 328)

blizzard/ventisca Una fuerte tormenta de nieve con vientos de más de 35 millas por hora (pág. 101)

boomerang/bumerang Palo curvo que se tira, lo usan los aborígenes de Australia para cazar (pág. 673)

bycatch/pezca residua los peces, mamiferos marinos y aves que quedan atrapados sin querer en las redes de los pescadores profesionales y luego se desechan (pág. 141)

C

cabinet/gabinete Directores de departamentos en la rama ejecutiva del gobierno de EE.UU. quienes aconsejan al Presidente (pág. 118)

calligraphy/caligrafía El arte de escribir a mano de forma decorativa y bella (pág. 565)

campesinos Trabajadores agrícolas; generalmente gente que vive y trabaja en áreas rurales (pág. 196)

canopy/follaje o copa Capa superior del bosque de lluvia, donde se juntan las puntas de los árboles altos (pág. 167)

capitalism/capitalismo Sistema económico basado en el libre comercio, en el cual los individuos son dueños del capital que usan (pág. 76)

cash crop/cosecha comercial Cosecha agrícola cultivada para venderse o trocarse en lugar de usarse para la familia del agricultor (págs. 113, 195, 452, 512, 630)

caste system/sistema de casta En la sociedad tradicional del Asia del Sur, la división de la sociedad en rígidos grupos, basada principalmente en la ocupación, que determina la posición social, la selección de conyuge y otras acciones (pág. 496)

cataract/catarata Un gran salto de agua (pág. 420)

caudillo Término para un líder político de Latinoamérica desde los últimos años de los 1800 en adelante, con frecuencia un dictador militar (pág. 184)

cereal/cereal Cualquier grano, como la cebada, la avena o el trigo, que se cultiva para alimento (pág. 364)

chaparral/chaparral Tipo de vegetación compuesta de densos bosques de matorrales y arbustos, común los en climas mediterráneos (págs. 54, 232)

chart/tabla Representación visual de datos en filas y columnas (pág. 22)

chernozem Capa vegetal de tierra negra y rica que se halla en la llanura del norte de Europa, especialmente en Rusia y Ucrania (pág. 291)

chinampas Islas flotantes de agricultura artificial hechas por los aztecas (pág. 181)

chinook/chinuco Viento cálido estacional que sopla por las Montañas Rocosas al final del invierno y al principio de la primavera (pág. 101)

Chipko/chipko En la India, un movimiento ambiental conocido por el término "abraza-árbol," con fines de salvar los bosques (pág. 520)

cholorofluorocarbons/clorofluorocarbonos También llamados CFCs; sustancias químicas que se hallan principalmente en enfriantes líquidos, dañan la capa de ozono que protege la tierra (pág. 578)

city-state/ciudad-estado En la antigua Grecia, comunidad independiente que consistía de una ciudad y las tierras circundantes, donde primero se desarrolló la democracia (pág. 245)

civilization/civilización Una cultura que ha organizado un sistema social, económico y político; que ha construido ciudades y logrado un cierto nivel de desarrollo en las artes y las ciencias (pág. 69)

clan/clan Comunidad tribal o grupo grande de gente relacionas entre sí (pgs. 444, 557)

climate/clima Patrones del tiempo típicos de un área durante un largo período de tiempo (pág. 45)

cold war/querra fría Se refiere a la lucha por el poder entre la Unión Soviética y los Estados Unidos (pág. 248)

collective farm/granja colectiva Bajo el comunismo, una granja enorme, propiedad del estado, en la cual los agricultores recibían sueldos más una parte de los productos y ganancias; también denominada *kholkoz* (pág. 264)

command economy/economía controlada Sistema económico en el que las decisiones económicas acerca de la producción y la distribución las toma alguna autoridad central (pág. 328)

commercial farming/agricultura comercial Agricultura organizada como un negocio (pág. 452)

commune/comuna En la China, una comunidad agrícola colectiva cuyos miembros estaban supuestos a compartir el trabajo y los productos (pág. 571)

communism/comunismo Movimiento sociopolítico desarrollado por Marx y Lenín que favorecía la revolución para establecer una sociedad sin clases en la que los trabajadores controlarían la producción (págs. 247, 313)

compass rose/rosa del compás Marcador direccional en un mapa (pág. 12)

conquistador Término español para referirse a los soldados que conquistaron a los indios de Latinoamérica (pág. 182)

Constitution/Constitución Plan que hizo el gobierno en 1787 para los nuevos Estados Unidos (pág. 118)

consumer goods/bienes de consumidor Enseres domésticos, zapatos y ropas que la gente compra (págs. 264, 328)

continental divide/divisoria continental
Una línea o cordillera que separa ríos que fluyen hacia distintos lados de un continente (pág. 96)

continental island/isla continental Isla formada de roca que se ha levantado de la plataforma continental, como Papua Nueva Guinea (pág. 657)

continental shelf/plataforma continental Área no profunda del océano cerca de la costa de un continente (pág. 34)

contour lines/líneas de contorno En un mapa, las líneas que conectan puntos de tierra a la misma elevación (pág. 14)

contour plowing/labranza de contorno Método de labranza en el que los surcos siguen la curva natural de la tierra para reducir la erosión (pág. 131)

cooperative/cooperativa Una organización voluntaria cuyos miembros trabajan juntos y comparten los gastos y ganancias de su empresa (pág. 572)

copra/copra La masa seca del coco (pág. 688)

coral/coral Diminutos animales marinos y estructuras como roca (islas, arecifes) formados por los esqueletos de colonias de coral (pág. 656)

cordillera/cordillera Cadena de montañas (pág. 597)

crevasse/grieta Una brecha enorme y honda que se forma en la nieve o en el hielo grueso (pág. 663)

crop rotation/rotación de cultivo Método de agricultura en el que distintos cultivos se alternan en el mismo terreno para preservar los nutrientes de la tierra (pág. 132)

Crusades/Cruzadas Serie de guerras religiosas (c. 1100-1300) en las que los cristianos europeos trataron de tomar Palestina del control musulmán (pág. 246)

cultural diffusion/difusión cultural La difusión de ideas, costumbres, bienes y personas de una cultura a otra (pág. 70)

culture/cultura Modo de vida de un grupo de gente que comparte tradiciones, intereses, creencias y modos de ganarse la vida (págs. 10, 63)

culture hearth/hogar de la cultura Un centro donde las culturas se desarrollan y desde el cual las ideas y las tradiciones se difunden (págs. 69, 556)

culture region/región cultural División de la Tierra basada en una variedad de factores que incluyen el gobierno, los grupos sociales, los sistemas económicos, el lenguaje o la religión (pág. 74)

cuneiform/cuneiforme Sistema de escritura sumeria que usa símbolos en forma de cuñas hundidas en tabletas de arcilla (pág. 377)

current/corriente "Río" de agua de mar fría o cálida que fluye hacia los océanos, por lo general de forma circular (pág. 50)

cyclone/ciclón Tormenta con lluvias fuertes y vientos altos que sopla en círculo alrededor de un área de baja presión atmosférica (págs. 484, 636)

czar/zar En la historia de Rusia, el emperador o gobernante supremo (pág. 312)

D

deciduous/deciduo Describe árboles, usualmente de hojas anchas como los robles y arces, que pierden las hojas en el otoño (pág. 54)

deforestation/desforestación La pérdida o destrucción de los bosques, debido principalmente a la tala de árboles para el madereo o la agricultura (págs. 202, 460, 518, 605)

delta Sección triangular de tierra que se forma en la boca de un río y que se parece a la letra griega *delta* (Δ) (pág. 359)

desalination/desalación La eliminación de la sal del agua de mar para que se pueda usar para beber y en la agricultura (pág. 399)

desertification/desertificación Proceso en el cual la tierra arable se vuelve desierto, usualmente debido a la destrucción de la vegetación (pág. 458)

developing country/país en vías de desarrollo País en el proceso de industrialización (pág. 195)

dharma En hinduismo, el deber moral que guía la vida de una persona, de acuerdo a las diferencias de clase (pág. 497)

diagram/diagrama Dibujo que muestra lo que algo es o cómo algo se hace, como los pasos de un proceso o ciclo (pág. 22)

dialect/dialecto Variedad local de un lenguaje usado en un lugar en particular o por cierto grupo (págs. 177, 251)

distillation/destilación Método de desalación en el cual el agua se hierve y se condensa (pág. 400)

doldrums/zona de calmas ecuatoriales Un área cerca del Ecuador frecuentemente sin viento (págs. 50, 662)

domesticate/domesticar El tomar plantas y animales silvestres y domarlos o hacerlos útiles para la gente (pág. 376)

dry farming/agricultura seca Método de agricultura que se usa en regiones secas en que la tierra se ara y se siembra bien hondo para retener el agua en la tierra (pág. 117)

dynasty/dinastía Una casa gobernante o la continuación de una familia de gobernantes, especialmente en la China (pág. 556)

E

economic system/sistema económico La forma en que la gente de un país produce y distribuye los bienes y servicios (pág. 75)

ecosystem/ecosistema La compleja comunidad de seres vivientes que, en cierto medio ambiente, dependen los unos de los otros (págs. 202, 697)

ecotourism/ecoturismo Turismo basado en preocupación por el medio ambiente (pág. 461)

endemic/endémico Que describe especies de plantas o animales nativos de un área particular (pág. 605)

environmentalist/ambientalista Persona activamente preocupada con la calidad y la protección del medio ambiente (pág. 271)

equinox/equinoxio Uno de dos días (entre el del 21 marzo y el 23 de septiembre) cuando cual el Sol está directamente encima del ecuador, haciendo que el día y la noche sean de igual duración (pág. 46)

erosion/erosión El desgaste de la superficie de la Tierra por el viento, el fluir del agua o los glaciares (pág. 31)

escarpment/escarpa Risco o escarpadura entre una superficie de tierra alta y otra más baja (págs. 162, 419)

ethnic diversity/diversidad étnica Diferencias entre grupos o gente basadas en sus orígenes, lenguajes, costumbres o creencias (pág. 371)

ethnic group/grupo étnico Grupo de personas quienes comparten los mismos antepasados, lenguaje, costumbres o una combinación de tales características (págs. 305, 436, 551)

eutrophication/eutroficación Proceso por el cual el agua de un lago o arroyo se hace demasiado rica en nutrientes disueltos, haciendo que la abundancia de plantas agote el oxígeno (pág. 139)

evaporation/evaporación El cambio de agua líquida a vapor de agua, un gas (pág. 36)

exports/exportaciones Recursos o bienes que se envían desde un país a otro (pág. 39)

extended family/parentela Una familia compuesta de varias generaciones de parientes; por ejemplo los tíos y abuelos al igual que los padres y los hijos (pág. 444)

extinction/extinción La desaparición o fin de una especie de animal o planta (pág. 460)

F

fale Tipo de casa tradicional en Samoa occidental, con los lados abiertos y el techo de paja (pág. 681)

farm cooperative/cooperativa agrícola Organización en la que los agricultores comparten en el cultivo y la venta de los productos agrícolas (pág. 264)

fault/falla Una grieta o hendidura en la corteza terrestre, usualmente causada por intensos pliegues (págs. 29, 420)

fauna/fauna La vida animal de una región (pág. 598)

fazenda Término portugués para una enorme plantación azucarera en Brasil (pág. 182)

feudalism/feudalismo Sistema de gobierno durante la época medieval en Europa y el Japón, en que poderosos señores feudales daban tierras a los nobles a cambio de su lealtad (pág. 245)

fishery/pesquería Zonas (de agua fresca o salada) donde se pescan peces u otros animales marinos (pág. 98)

fjord/fiordo Valle glacial con largos acantilados llenos de agua de mar (pág. 223)

flora/flora La vida de las plantas de una región (pág. 598)

foehn/fohn Viento seco y cálido que sopla del lado sotavento de las montañas, a veces derrite la nieve y provoca avalanchas; se usa predominantemente en Europa (pág. 231)

fold/pliegue Una dobladura en las capas de roca, a veces causada por el movimiento de las placas (pág. 29)

free enterprise/libre comercio Un sistema económico en el cual los negocios privados operan con poca interferencia del gobierno (págs. 76, 129)

free port/zona libre Ciudad portuaria, como Singapur, donde los bienes se desembarcan, se almacenan y se vuelven a embarcar sin pago de impuestos portuarios (pág. 633)

fútbol Se conoce en Norteamérica como el "soccer" (pág. 189)

G

general purpose map/mapa de propósito general Mapa que muestra un amplia variedad de información física y/o política acerca de un área (pág. 14)

geography/geografía El estudio de la Tierra y la forma en que la gente vive y trabaja (pág. 5)

glacier/glaciar Grandes cuerpos de hielo que se mueven a través de la superficie de la Tierra (pág. 31)

glasnost/glasnost Término ruso para una nueva "libertad"; parte de los planes de reforma de Gorbachev (pág. 314)

global warming/calentamiento global Calentamiento gradual de la Tierra y su atmósfera que puede ser causado en parte por la contaminación y un aumento del efecto de invernadero (pág. 697)

government/gobierno El grupo o sistema político de una nación (pág. 74)

graph/gráfica Modo de representar y comparar información visualmente, como una gráfica lineal, gráfica de barra o gráfica circular (pág. 20)

graziers/ganaderos Personas que crían y pastorean ganado ovejuno y vacuno (pág. 687)

great circle/gran círculo La distancia más corta entre dos lugares cualquiera en la superficie de la Tierra (pág. 16)

green revolution/revolución verde Programa comenzado en los años 60 para producir cepas de mayor rendimiento de trigo, arroz y otras cosechas de alimento (pág. 513)

grid system/sistema de cuadrícula Patrón formado a medida que las líneas de latitud y longitud se intersectan (pág. 6)

gross domestic product (GDP)/producto interno bruto (PIB) El valor de los bienes y los servicios creados dentro de un país en un año (págs. 393, 435)

groundwater/agua subterránea Agua que yace debajo de la superficie de la Tierra, abastecida mayormente por la filtración de la lluvia a través de la tierra (pág. 35)

H

habitat/hábitat Area con condiciones idóneas para que vivan ciertas plantas y animales (pág. 460)

haiku/haiku Forma de poesía japonesa que consiste de 17 sílabas, con frecuencia trata de la naturaleza (pág. 565)

headwaters/cabeceras Las fuentes de aguas de río (pág. 96)

heavy industry/industria pesada La manufactura de maquinaria y equipo necesario para fábricas y minas (pág. 263)

hemisphere/hemisferio Mitad de una esfera o globo, como en los Hemisferios Norte y Sur de la Tierra (p. 5)

hieroglyphics/jeroglíficos Sistema de escritura egipcia que usa dibujos y símbolos para representar palabras y sonidos (pág. 377)

history/historia El estudio de información escrita acerca de los acontecimientos y personas del pasado (pág. 69)

Holocaust/Holocausto Término designado a la muerte masiva de 6 millones de judíos europeos por los líderes Nazi de Alemania durante la Segunda Guerra Mundial (pág. 248)

homogeneous/homogéneo Describe a un grupo de gente o cosas que son muy parecidas (pág. 552)

hurricane/huracán Una gran tormenta de vientos fuertes que se forma sobre

SPANISH HANDBOOK

SPANISH HANDBOOK

las aguas cálidas del océano (págs. 66, 101)

hydroelectric power/energía hidroeléctrica Energía eléctrica generada por la caída del agua (pág. 165)

hydrosphere/hidrosfera Las zonas acuosas de la Tierra que incluyen los océanos, lagos, ríos y otros cuerpos de agua (pág. 28)

hypothesis/hipótesis Un paso en el método científico que sugiere una explicación científica para los fenómenos que se observan (pág. 57)

I

icon/icono Imagen religiosa, usualmente incluye un cuadro de Jesús, María o un santo, usado principalmente por los cristianos ortodoxos (pág. 317)

ideogram/ideograma Un caracter pictórico o un símbolo que tiene un significado específico o representa una sílaba (pág. 561)

imports/importaciones Recursos o bienes que vienen de otro país (pág. 39)

immigrant/inmigrante Persona que ha dejado su país y se ha establecido permanentemente en otro país (pág. 107)

impressionism/impresionismo Estilo artístico que se desarrolló en Europa en los últimos años de los 1800 y que trató de mostrar la apariencia natural de los objetos con toques o pinceladas de color ligeros (pág. 253)

indigenous/indígeno Nativo a un lugar; los habitantes originales, ya sean plantas, animales, o seres humanos (pág. 615)

industrialization/industrialización Proceso de usar maquinaria en la manufactura (pág. 116)

industrialize/industrializar Desarrollar industria (pág. 336)

interdependent/interdependiente Depender los unos de los otros para bienes, servicios e ideas (págs. 8, 135, 632)

isthmus/istmo Porción angosta de tierra que conecta a otras dos masas de tierra más grandes (pág. 33)

J

jai alai/jai alai Juego de mano tradicional popular en México y Cuba (pág. 189)

jazz/jazz Forma musical que se desarrolló en los Estados Unidos a principios de siglo, mezcla ritmos africanos con harmonías europeas (pág. 122)

jati/jati En la sociedad tradicional hindú, un grupo social que define la ocupación de una familia y su pocisión social (pág. 491)

jute/yute Fibra vegetal que se usa para hacer cordón y tela (pág. 512)

K

karma/karma En la creencia Hindú, la suma de las acciones buenas y malas en la vida presente y las vidas pasadas de una persona, conduce a premio o castigo (pág. 497)

key/clave Parte de un mapa que explica los símbolos que se usan (pág. 12)

kolkhoz En la Unión Soviética, una enorme granja colectiva (pág. 329)

krill Diminutos animales marinos parecidos a los camarones que viven en los frígidos océanos de la Antártica (pág. 659)

kums Término regional para los desiertos arenosos en las tierras bajas de Turán, como en Kara Kum (pág. 292)

L

lagoon/laguna Estanque de poca profundidad en el centro de un atolón (pág. 657)

language family/familia de lenguajes Grupo de lenguajes relacionados que se desarrollaron de un lenguaje anterior (págs. 76, 251)

latifundia/latifundios En la moderna Latinoamérica, grandes estancias que pertenecen a familias o corporaciones (pág. 196)

latitude/latitud Líneas imaginarias que corren de este a oeste alrededor del globo, se usan para medir la distancia al norte o sur del Ecuador en grados; también se llaman paralelos (págs. 5, 13)

leach/deslave Lavar la tierra para sacarle los nutrientes (pág. 426)

leeward/sotovento Con cara en contra de la dirección de donde sopla el viento (p. 51)

lichens/líquenes Plantas diminutas y fuertes que crecen como una corteza sobre las rocas y los troncos de los árboles (pág. 663)

light industry/industria ligera Manufactura con fines de producir bienes para el consumidor en vez de maquinaria pesada, como textiles o el procesamiento de alimentos (pág. 263)

lingua franca/lengua franca Un lenguaje, como el Swahili, usado para facilitar la comunicación entre personas que hablan diferentes idiomas nativos (pág. 442)

literacy rate/índice de alfabetización El porcentaje de personas en un lugar dado que puede leer y escribir (págs. 123, 445)

lithosphere/litosfera Áreas de superficie terrestre de la corteza de la Tierra (como el 30 por ciento), incluye los continentes y las cuencas de los océanos (pág. 28)

llanos Llanuras fértiles a lo largo de las costas del Caribe de Sudamérica, en Colombia y Venezuela (pág. 164)

loess/loes Capa superficial del suelo, fina, amarillenta y marrón compuesta de partículas de limo y arcilla, usualmente arrastrada por el viento (pág. 539)

longhouse/casa larga En zonas rurales de Indonesia y Malasia, un edificio grande donde vive la gente de varias familias que están relacionadas entre sí (pág. 622)

longitude/longitud Líneas verticales imaginarias que corren de polo a polo del globo, se usan para medir distancias de este u oeste desde el primer meridiano; también se les llama meridianos (págs. 6, 13)

M

malnutrition/malnutrición Nutrición pobre debido a una dieta mal balanceada o a la falta de comida (pág. 187)

mangrove/árbol de Ámanglar Árbol o arbusto tropical perenne que generalmente crece en densas arboledas cerca del agua (pág. 518)

mantletree/manto Gruesa capa mediana de la estructura interior de la Tierra, consiste de densa piedra caliente compuesta de silicio, oxígeno, aluminio, hierro y magnesio (pág. 29)

mantra/mantra En Hinduismo, una palabra o frase sagrada que se repite en los rezos y cantos (pág. 502)

manuka Pequeños arbustos que crecen en las mesetas de Nueva Zelandia (pág. 663)

map projection/proyección de mapa Modo de trazar un mapa para representar en una superficie plana la redondez de la Tierra (pág. 17)

maquiladoras En México, plantas manufactureras montadas por firmas extranjeras (pág. 197)

maritime/marítimo Que concierne los viajes o la transportación por mar (pág. 615)

market economy/economía de mercado Un sistema económico basado en libre comercio, en el que los negocios son de propiedad privada y la producción y los precios se determinan por la oferta y la demanda (pág. 328)

marsupial/marsupio Tipo de mamífero (como canguros o coalas) que dan a luz a crías que maduran en una bolsa en el abdomen de la madre (pág. 694)

mass culture/cultura de las masas Cultura popular extendida por los medios de comunicación como la radio y la televisión (pág. 442)

megalopolis/megalópolis Una "super-ciudad" compuesta por varias grandes ciudades y las pequeñas ciudades cerca de ellas, como el área entre Boston y Washington, D.C. o los alrededores de Tokio-Yokohama, Japón (págs. 109, 554)

meltwater/aguanieve Agua formada al derretirse la nieve y el hielo (pág. 271)

merchant marine/marina mercante La flota de barcos de un país que participa en el intercambio comercial (pág. 576)

mesa/meseta Formación terrestre elevada con la cima plana (pág. 94)

mestizo En Latinoamérica, persona de descendencia mixta de indios y europeos (pág. 176)

metropolitan area/área metropolitana Región que incluye una ciudad central y sus suburbios circundantes (pág. 109)

mica/mica Mineral silicato que típicamente se parte en delgadas láminas brillantes (pág. 481)

Middle Passage/Pasaje Medio Nombre dado a la ruta que usaron los barcos de

SPANISH HANDBOOK

esclavos para atravesar el Atlántico desde el África Occidental hasta las Américas (pág. 440)

minifundia/**minifundios** En Latinoamérica, pequeas granjas que producen alimento principalmente para el uso de la familia y el mercado local (pág. 196)

mistral/mistral Viento fuerte del norte desde los Alpes que trae aire frío al sur de Francia (pág. 231)

mixed farming/agricultura mixta Cultivo de varias clases de cosechas y ganado en la misma granja (pág. 264)

mixed forest/bosque mixto Tierras forestales con árboles perennes y deciduos (pág. 54)

mobile/móviles Describe cosas o personas que se mueven fácilmente de lugar en lugar (pág. 122)

modernism/modernismo Movimiento literario latinoamericano de fines de los años 1800, que enfocó la expresión artística y la experimentación (pág. 188)

monotheism/monoteísmo Creencia en un sólo Dios (pág. 377)

monsoon/monzón En Asia, viento veraniego que trae aires cálidos y húmedos desde los océanos, aire seco y frío desde la tierras interiores en el invierno (págs. 482, 542, 602)

mosaic/mosaico Dibujo o diseño hecho con pequeños pedazos de piedra, vidrio o azulejo de colores (pág. 188)

mosque/mezquita En Islam, una casa de oración pública (pág. 379)

mulatto/mulato Persona de descendencia mixta africana y europea (pág. 176)

multicultural/multicultural Que posee elementos que vienen de más de una cultura (págs. 120, 239)

N_____

nationalism/nacionalismo Creencia en el derecho de cada pueblo a ser una nación independiente (pág. 380)

nationalities/nacionalidades Grandes y diversos grupos étnicos distintis dentro de un país, se usaron especialmente en Rusia y las repúblicas euroasiáticas (pág. 305)

nationalize/nacionalizar Colocar una compañía o industria bajo el control del gobierno (pág. 380)

natural resource/recurso natural Elemento o sustancia de la tierra que no está hecha por la gente pero que ellos la pueden usar, como los minerales (pág. 37)

natural vegetation/vegetación natural Vida vegetal que crece en ciertas zonas si la gente no cambia el medio ambiente (pág. 52)

nirvana En Budismo, el máximo estado de paz y entendimiento que la gente trata de alcanzar (pág. 497)

nomadic/nómada Describe una forma de vida en la cual un grupo viaja de sitio en sitio en vez de establecer un poblado permanente (pág. 673)

nonrenewable resource/recurso no renovable Recurso que no se puede reponer por crecimiento natural o acción humana, como la mayoría de los minerales (pág. 38)

North American Free Trade Agreement (NAFTA)/Tratado de Libre Comercio de Norteamericano (TLCNA) Tratado comercial hecho en 1993 entre Canadá, los Estados unidos y México (pág. 135)

O_____

oasis Pequeña área en el desierto donde hay agua y vegetación, usualmente debido a manantiales subterráneos (págs. 53, 362)

oral history/historia oral Leyendas y cuentos que se pasan por tradición oral de generación en generación (pág. 444)

organic farming/agricultura orgánica El uso de sustancias naturales en lugar de fertilizantes y pesticidas para enriquecer la tierra y cultivar cosechas (pág. 264)

P_____

pampas/pampa Llanos herbosos, sin árboles en América del Sur, los cuales, se usan para cultivar cereales y para el pastoreo (pág. 164)

pastoralism/pastoreo críar y pastorear ganado (pág. 364)

patriarch/patriarca En la historia de la iglesia, obispo o líder importante; actualmente, el dirigente de una Iglesia Ortodoxa del Este o de la Iglesia Apostólica Armenia (pág. 318)

peat/turba Materia vegetal, mayormente musgos, se halla usualmente en pantanos; en algunos lugares de Europa occidental, a veces se corta y se quema como combustible (pág. 228)

per capita income/ingresos per cápita Los ingresos totales de un país o región divididos por el número de personas; ingresos por persona (págs. 76, 435)

perestroika En Rusia, "restructuración"; parte del plan de Gorbachev para reformar el gobierno soviético (pág. 314)

permafrost Capa de tierra por debajo de la superficie del suelo que está permanentemente congelada (págs. 55, 231, 297)

pesticide/pesticida Sustancia química que se usa para matar insectos, roedores y otras plagas (págs. 64, 341)

petrochemical/petroquímico Producto químico derivado del petróleo o del gas natural (pág. 392)

phosphate/fosfato Mineral natural que contiene compuestos químicos que a menudo se usan en fertilizantes (pág. 361)

pidgin English/Inglés corrompido Un dialecto que mezcla el inglés con los idiomas locales (pág. 680)

plateau/altiplano Masa de tierra plana más alta que la tierra que le rodea, con al menos un lado escarpado (págs. 34, 94)

poaching/cazar o pescar en vedado La caza o pesca prohibida de animales protegidos (pág. 460)

pogrom En la Rusia zarista, un ataque contra los judíos llevado a cabo por las tropas o los oficiales del gobierno (pág. 318)

polder/pólder Zona en Holanda, bajo el nivel del mar, de la cual se ha drenado el agua del mar para crear nuevas tierras de agricultura (pág. 228)

polluted/contaminado afectado por sustancias dañinas o impuras.

pollution/polución La existencia de sustancias sucias, impuras o venenosas en el aire, el agua y la tierra (pág. 67)

population density/densidad demográfica Número promedio de personas en una milla o kilómetro cuadrado (pág. 65)

population distribution/distribución demográfica La configuración demográfica; donde vive la gente en un país, continente o en el mundo (pág. 65)

prairie/pradera Zona herbosa tierra adentro (pág. 54)

precipitation/precipitación Humedad que cae a la tierra, como lluvia, nevisca, granizo o nieve (pág. 51)

prehistory/prehistoria La época en el pasado de un pueblo antes de que existiera un registro escrito (pág. 69)

prevailing wind/viento dominante Viento en una región que sopla en una dirección casi constantemente, como los alisios que soplan hacia el Ecuador en latitudes bajas (pág. 50)

primate city/ciudad prócer Ciudad que domina la economía, cultura y el gobierno de un país y en la que la población está concentrada; usualmente la capital (págs. 179, 613, 670)

prophet/profeta Persona de quien se cree ser un mensajero de Dios (pág. 379)

Q

qanat Canales subterráneos que se usaban en los sistemas de acueductos en la antigua Persia (pág. 378)

quipu Cuerda con cordones anudados de varios largos y colores que usaban los incas para anotar sus registros y mandar mensajes (pág. 182)

R

raga En la música clásica de la India, una melodia básica sobre la cual el músico improvisa o toca variaciones (pág. 503)

rail gauge/ancho de vía La distancia entre los rieles en las ferrovías, lo cual determina la posición de las ruedas de los vagones (pág. 691)

rain shadow/sombra de lluvia Zona seca que se halla del lado sotovento de una cordillera (pág. 51)

realism/realismo Estilo artístico que capta la vida cotidiana que se desarrolló en Europa a mediado de los años 1800 (pág. 252)

reáforestation/reforestación La siembra de árboles jóvenes o semillas en terrenos donde los árboles han sido talados o destruídos (pág. 203)

Reformation/Reforma Movimiento religioso que comenzó en Alemania en los

1400 y que condujo al establecimiento de Iglesias Protestantes (pág. 247)

refugee/refugiado Persona que tiene que dejar su hogar y huir a otro lugar para estar a salvo (pág. 240)

reincarnated/reincarnado En la creencia Hindú, el renacer repetidas veces en distintas formas, hasta que uno ha vencido todos los deseos terrenales (pág. 497)

relative location/ubicación relativa La posición de un lugar en relación a otros lugares (pág. 7)

relief/relieve Las diferencias de elevación de la tierra (pág. 14)

religion/religión Forma organizada de alabar a un ser espiritual o de pensar acerca de la vida (pág. 77)

Renaissance/Renacimiento En Europa, un período de renovado interés por las enseñazas y artes clásicas que comenzó cerca del 1300 y duró 300 años (pág. 246)

renewable resource/recurso renovable Recurso que se puede cultivar o que se renueva naturalmente, como los árboles (pág. 38)

republic/república Forma de gobierno sin monarca, en el cual la gente elige a sus oficiales, incluso al jefe de estado (pág. 114)

revolution/revolución En astronomía, el viaje de la Tierra alrededor del Sol que toma 365 1/4 días (pág. 46)

romanticism/romanticismo Estilo artístico que enfatizaba las emociones individuales que se desarrolló en Europa en los últimos años de los 1700 y principios de los 1800 como una reacción a la industrialización (pág. 252)

russification/rusificación En la Rusia del siglo XIX, programa de gobierno que requería que todo el mundo en el imperio hablara ruso y se convirtiera al Cristianismo (pág. 313)

S

sadhu Un hermitaño hindú o un hombre santo y maestro (pág. 502)

samurai/samurai En el Japón medieval, una clase de soldados profesionales quienes se regían por un código estricto de honor personal y lealtad a un noble (pág. 558)

savanna/sabana Un herbazal tropical que contiene árboles dispersos (pág. 425)

scale/escala la relación entre las medidas de un mapa y las verdaderas medidas en pies, millas, metros o kilómetros sobre la superficie de la tierra (pág. 12)

sedentary farming/agricultura sedentaria Agricultura que toma lugar en asentamientos permanentes (pág. 452)

seismic/sísmico Relacionado con los terremotos (pág. 359)

serf/siervo Obrero de la propiedad de un noble y obligado a permanecer en la tierra donde trabajaba (pág. 312)

service industry/industria de servicios Negocios que proveen servicios, como los bancos, las compañías de seguros o transportación, en vez de producir bienes (págs. 134, 196, 393)

shaminism/shamanismo Creencia en un líder que se puede comunicar con los espíritus (pág. 562)

shifting farming/cultivo migratorio Método en el cual los agricultores se mudan cada cuantos años para hallar mejor tierra (pág. 452)

shogun/shogún En el Japón medieval, un gobernante militar del país (pág. 557)

sickle/hoz Cuchillo grande y curvo con un mango, usado para cortar hierba o cereales altos (pág. 629)

sirocco/siroco Viento caliente del desierto que sopla aire y polvo desde el África del Norte hasta la costa mediterránea de Europa (pág. 231)

slash-and-burn farming/agricultura de corte y quema Método tradicional de cultivo en que todos los árboles y plantas en el área se cortan y se queman para añadirles nutrientes al suelo (pág. 202)

smog/smog Calina irritante causada por la interacción de la radiación solar ultravioleta con humos químicos del escape de los automóviles y otras fuentes de contaminación (de las palabras inglesas *smoke*=humo y *fog*=neblina) (págs. 57, 138)

socialism/socialismo Filosofía política que originalmente dictaba que los campesinos y obreros fueran los propietarios de la tierra y de las factorías; ahora se refiere a la propiedad del gobierno de algunos o todos los medios de producción (págs. 76, 312)

socialist realism/realismo socialista En la

SPANISH HANDBOOK

Unión Soviética, estilo realista de arte y literatura que glorificaba los ideales y las metas soviéticas (pág. 320)

solstice/solsticio Uno de dos días (aproximadamente entre el 21 de junio y el 22 de diciembre) en que los rayos del Sol dan directamente en la latitud 23 1/2°N (Trópico de Cancer) o 23 1/2°S (Trópico de Capricornio), para marcar el principio del verano o el invierno (pág. 47)

sovkhoz En la Unión Soviética, una enorme granja del estado y que el estado mismo opera (pág. 329)

special purpose map/mapa de propósito especial Mapa que enfatiza un tema especial, como recursos o población (pág. 15)

sphere of influence/esfera de influencia Zona del país en la que una potencia extranjera tiene control político o económico (pág. 615)

standard of living/estándar de vida Una medida de la calidad de vida, basada en el acceso a bienes materiales como ingresos, alimentos y vivienda (pág. 75)

state farm/granja estatal Bajo el comunismo, una granja de propiedad del estado dirigida por oficiales del gobierno; también denominada *sovkhoz* (pág. 264)

station/estación Término australiano para un rancho o granja grande en áreas remotas (pág. 687)

steppe/estepa Vastas llanuras herbosas de Eurasia que se extienden desde el Mar Negro hasta los Montes Altai; también, regiones en otros lugares con climas semiáridos similares (pág. 298)

strait/estrecho Vía fluvial estrecha que conecta dos grandes cuerpos de agua (pág. 111)

strine Inglés coloquial que se habla en Australia (pág. 679)

subcontinent/subcontinente Gran área de tierra que forma parte de un continente pero situada bastante lejos de él, como la India (pág. 477)

subsistence farming/agricultura de subsistencia Agricultura tradicional cuya meta es producir lo suficiente para que una familia o una aldea coma y sobreviva (págs. 63, 452, 511, 681, 688)

suburbs/suburbios Comunidades en las afueras y que circundan una ciudad cen-

tral (pág. 109)

Sunbelt/franja del Sol Parte sur de los Estados Unidos, denominada así debido a su clima suave (pág. 108)

sūq En el África del Norte y el Asia del Sudoeste, plaza de mercado encerrada (pág. 385)

T

taiga Término ruso para un vasto bosque subártico, principalmente de siempreverdes, que comienza donde termina la tundra; también se emplea para regiones climatológicas subárticas en general (págs. 55, 297)

tala En la música clásica de la India, un modelo rítmico, a menudo tocado con tambor (pág. 503)

tariff/tarifa Un impuesto sobre bienes importados o exportados (pág. 265)

temperature/temperatura Una medida de cuán caliente o cuán frío está algo, generalmente se mide en grados con una escala fija, como Fahrenheit o Celcio (pág. 45)

tierra caliente La zona más baja (nivel del mar -3,000 pies de elevación) de un clima de montaña cerca del Ecuador (pág. 167)

tierra fría La zona de altitud más alta de los climas de montaña en Centro y Sudamérica (pág. 167)

tierra templada La zona mediana (3,000-6,000 pies de elevación) de los climas de montaña de Latinoamérica (pág. 167)

timberline/límite de la vegetación selvática Elevación por encima de la cual hace demasiado frío para que crezcan los árboles (págs. 56, 101)

topography/topografía Características físicas de la superficie de la Tierra (pág. 14)

tornado Una violenta tormenta de viento con vientos giratorios y una nube en forma de embudo (págs. 66, 101)

trading partner/socios comerciales Países que comercian entre sí (pág. 574)

trekker/excursionista Alguien que escala montañas; generalmente, cualquiera que emprende un viaje difícil (pág. 518)

tributary/tributario Pequeños ríos y arroyos que alimentan los ríos más grandes (pág. 97)

truck farm/granja de hortalizas Granja,

especialmente en el noreste de los Estados Unidos, que cultiva vegetales para los mercados en las ciudades circundantes (pág. 131)

trust territory/territorio en fideicomiso Región, tal como Micronesia, que después de la Segunda Guerra Mundial fue colocada temporáneamente por las Naciones Unidas bajo el control político y económico de otra nación (pág. 676)

tsunami Término japonés para una ola de mar enorme causada por un maremoto (págs. 67, 538)

tundra Vastas llanuras sin árboles en climas fríos del norte, caracterizadas por la capa del subsuelo congelada y pequeñas plantas como musgos y arbustos (pág. 297)

typhoon/tifón Un huracán, ciclón o tormenta tropical violenta que se forma en el Océano Pacífico, usualmente al final del verano (págs. 101, 542, 636, 663)

U

universal suffrage/sufragio universal Derechos de votación iguales para todos los adultos residentes de una nación (pág. 440)

urbanization/urbanización El movimiento de personas de las áreas rurales a las ciudades (pág. 436)

V

viceroy/virrey Representante del monarca español asignado para hacer cumplir las leyes en las colonias americanas (pág. 182)

W

wadi En el desierto, cauce seco excepto durante la lluvias pesadas (pág. 359)

wat En el Asia del Sudeste, un templo (pág. 620)

water cycle/ciclo de agua Movimiento regular del agua desde el océano hasta el aire y el suelo y de vuelta al océano (pág. 36)

wattle/zarzo Árboles de acacia; los primeros colonos de Australia entretejían los zarzos jóvenes para construir sus casas

(pág. 660)

weather/tiempo Condición de la atmósfera en un lugar durante un corto período de tiempo; como la de un día frío, con viento y lluvia (pág. 45)

weathering/desgaste Procesos químicos o físicos, como congelación, que desbaratan las rocas (pág. 30)

welfare state/estado benefactor Nación, como Gran Bretaña, Noruega o Suecia, en la que el gobierno asume la responsabilidad principal por el bienestar de la gente en en cuanto a salud y educación (pág. 253)

windward/barlovento Con la cara hacia la dirección desde donde el viento está soplando (pág. 51)

Z

ziggurat/zigurat En la antigua Mesopotamia, gran templo escalonado hecho de ladrillos de arcilla (pág. 383)

Puntos de interés

SECCIÓN Temas de geografía

Los cinco temas: localidad, lugar, interacción humana con el medio ambiente, movimiento y región son importantes para el estudio de la geografía. Los geógrafos usan los temas para comprender las relaciones entre las personas y los lugares. Los geógrafos tambien usan la información de otras disciplinas para ayudarles a entender la interacción de las personas con el medio ambiente.

SECCIÓN Manual de destrezas en geografía

Los geógrafos usan mapas y gráficas para interpretar y analizar datos geográficos. El leer un mapa requiere el conocer sus elementos. Los elementos de un mapa incluyen la clave, la rosa del compás, la escala y la cuadrícula global.

Ya que los mapas son planos, es difícil que representen con precisión la superficie curva de la Tierra. Las diferentes proyecciones de los mapas planos muestran la Tierra redonda aunque con algunas distorciones.

Puntos de interés

SECCIÓN **El planeta Tierra**

La Tierra consiste de agua, tierra y aire. El agua compone la hidrosfera de la Tierra. La tierra compone parte de la litosfera de la Tierra, mientras que el aire compone la atmósfera.

Secciones de la corteza terrestre flotan y se mueven en el estrato de manto haciendo que algunos continentes se separen y otros se acerquen. También hay fuerzas externas como el agua, el viento y la gravedad que afectan la superficie de la Tierra. Éstas ayudan a configurar la superficie de la Tierra por medio de la erosión, el movimiento y las nuevas formaciones de tierra.

SECCIÓN **2** **Características de la Tierra**

Las formaciones de tierra son las características que componen la superficie de la Tierra. Los cuatro tipos principales son las montañas, las lomas, las praderas y las mesetas.

El agua es tanto una característica física como un recurso. Los océanos, los ríos, los lagos y los arroyos son características del agua. El agua es un recurso limitado que se circula y se purifica repetidamente por medio del ciclo de agua.

SECCIÓN **Recursos de la Tierra**

Los muchos recursos naturales de la Tierra no están divididos equitativamente entre los países del mundo. El uso, el abastecimiento y los cambios a través del tiempo son factores para determinar la importancia de los recursos naturales.

Los recursos renovables se reemplazan a sí mismos naturalmente o la gente puede cultivarlos para abastecerse continuamente de ellos. Los recursos no renovables, como los combustibles de fósil, jamás se pueden reponer.

Puntos de interés

SECCIÓN ## Relación de la Tierra y el Sol

La relación entre la Tierra y el Sol afecta el clima de la Tierra. El Sol provee a la Tierra con calor y luz. Las diferentes áreas del planeta, sin embargo, reciben distintas cantidades de luz solar a distintas horas.

SECCIÓN ## Factores que afectan el clima

El sol afecta el clima de la Tierra; sin embargo, el Sol no calienta ni enfría todos los lugares de la Tierra de la misma manera. Otros factores que afectan el clima de la Tierra son la latitud, la elevación, el viento, las corrientes marítimas y las formaciones de tierra.

SECCIÓN ## Modelos del clima mundial

Los geógrafos a menudo dividen la Tierra en cinco importantes regiones climatológicas, basándose por lo general en la latitud. Las regiones son la tropical, la seca, la latitud media, la latitud alta y la montañosa.

Las regiones climatológicas se vuelven a dividir en regiones más pequeñas basado en factores tales como su flora, ubicación, paisaje y temperatura. Los climas cambian con el tiempo debido a causas naturales y humanas.

Puntos de interés

  Límites y oportunidades

L as naciones se pueden clasificar como desarrolladas o en vías de desarrollo. Los países desarrollados están altamente industrializados, mientras que los países en vías de desarrollo son agrícolas.

Tanto las naciones desarrolladas como las que están en vías de desarrollo enfrentan muchos retos. La población del mundo tiene que hacer frente a las tareas de satisfacer las necesidades alimenticias y conservar los recursos. Los peligros del medio ambiente, como los fenómenos relacionados al clima y la contaminación, presentan obstáculos para lograr estas metas.

  Expresión cultural

L as culturas se expresan de distintos modos, como el lenguaje, la religión y las artes. Las primeras culturas altamente desarrolladas, o civilizaciones, se desarrollaron cerca de ríos importantes en áreas donde el clima era templado y los terrenos fértiles. Al evolucionar las culturas a través de los siglos, el comercio aumentó y se hicieron una variedad de contactos culturales.

  Regiones culturales del mundo en la actualidad

P ara ayudarles a describir pueblos y culturas, los geógrafos dividen el mundo en regiones culturales. Entre los factores que se usan para determinar las regiones culturales se hallan el medio ambiente, la historia, el lenguaje, la religión, el gobierno, la estructura social y la economía.

Puntos de interés

SECCIÓN **1** — Geografía física de los Estados Unidos y Canadá

Los Estados Unidos y Canadá forman una región que compone casi todo el continente de América del Norte. Dos cordilleras dominan las formaciones terrestres del oeste, con altiplanos y depresiones entre ellas. Las cordilleras del oeste y otra importante cordillera en el este bordean los enormes llanos del interior que marcan la porción central de la región. Varios ríos importantes ayudan a arrastrar las aguas de la tierra hacia los océanos que bordean la región. Los Estados Unidos y Canadá son ricos en muchos recursos renovables y no renovables.

SECCIÓN **2** — Clima y vegetación

Aunque Canadá y los Estados Unidos comparten algunas regiones climatológicas, otras son peculiares de cada nación. Sin embargo, la mayoría de estas regiones—desde el desierto hasta la tundra—están representadas. Los vientos del Océano Pacífico, el Océano Ártico y el Golfo de México ejercen una tremenda influencia sobre los climas de la región. La diversa vegetación natural de las regiones climatológicas ha sido profundamente afectada por la población humana.

capítulo 6

Puntos de interés

SECCIÓN 1   Configuración demográfica

La mayoría de los inmigrantes que vinieron a los Estados Unidos y Canadá eran de origen europeo. Gran Bretaña aportó el mayor número de ellos. Otros grupos étnicos incluyen franceses, afroamericanos, hispanos y los de origen asiático.

El clima limita la población en dos terceras partes del territorio norte de Canadá. La mayoría de los canadienses viven a lo largo de la frontera con los Estados Unidos. Tanto en los Estados Unidos como en Canadá, la mayoría de las personas viven en áreas urbanas.

SECCIÓN 2   Historia y gobierno

Los científicos creen que los primeros seres humanos que se establecieron en la región cruzaron un puente de tierra entre Asia y América del Norte. Otros inmigrantes siguieron con el tiempo y surgieron dos naciones. En los años 1700, los colonos americanos pelearon la Guerra de Independencia contra los ingleses para establecer los Estados Unidos de América. Casi un siglo después, el Acta Británica Norteamericana (1867) hizo a Canadá una nación autónoma con lazos con Gran Bretaña.

SECCIÓN 3   Culturas y estilos de vida

Las personas de los Estados Unidos y Canadá siempre han valorado su libertad religiosa. Los Estados Unidos tiene una población mayormente angloparlante, aunque muchos americanos hablan español y otros idiomas. Canadá reconoce tanto el inglés como el francés como sus idiomas oficiales. Los ciudadanos de ambos países disfrutan de la variedad de culturas y de un alto estándar de vida.

Puntos de interés

SECCIÓN 1 — La vida en los Estados Unidos y Canadá

Los suelos ricos, las abundantes aguas y los variados climas de las fincas en los Estados Unidos y Canadá estimulan la producción de una amplia variedad de carnes, cereales, vegetales y frutas. Los adelantos tecnológicos en la agricultura han aumentado el rendimiento de la cosecha y el tamaño de la finca, pero han disminuído el número de trabajadores agrícolas.

La región cultural de los Estados Unidos y Canadá es una de las más adelantadas mundialmente en cuanto a la manufactura de bienes y sus industrias de servicio emplean a la mayor cantidad de personas. La abundancia de productos agrícolas y manufacturados de las dos naciones ponen a la región al mando del comercio mundial. Complejas redes de transporte y de comunicación sostienen a la gente y a la economía de la región.

SECCIÓN 2 — La gente y su medio ambiente

La contaminación es un problema ambiental importante en los Estados Unidos y Canadá. Las emisiones de las fábricas y los automóviles producen contaminantes como la lluvia ácida y el smog. El abastecimiento de agua en la región está contaminado por los deshechos industriales, las sustancias químicas de la agricultura y las aguas residuales.

Otros tipos de actividad humana también han tenido un impacto en el medio ambiente de la región. La explotación forestal, especialmente en los terrenos públicos, está poniendo en peligro los bosques de antiguos árboles en el área del noroeste del Pacífico. La pesca excesiva y el desperdicio en la industria marítima han disminuído seriamente el número de peces y, como resultado, ha traído dificultades económicas a las áreas que dependen del mar.

Puntos de interés

  ## El terreno

Latinoamérica consiste de México, Centroamérica, Sudamérica y las Islas del Caribe. Enormes cordilleras, la mayor de las cuales es la de los Andes, dominan la mayor parte de América Latina y a menudo bloquean las comunicaciones. Grandes altiplanos, que se usan para el pastoreo y para la agricultura decoran el paisaje latinoamericano.

A elevaciones más bajas, las áreas llanas de Latinoamérica proveen importantes terrenos para el pastoreo, la agricultura y el terreno boscoso. La mayoría de los sistemas fluviales importantes de Latinoamérica, incluyendo el Amazonas y el Río de la Plata, se hallan en Sudamérica.

  ## Clima y vegetación

Los climas tropicales, como el bosque de lluvia tropical y la sabana tropical, son los climas más comunes en Latinoamérica. Un clima subtropical de inviernos moderados, veranos calientes y una corta temporada seca se halla en las áreas de pradera. Otras partes de la región tienen un clima desértico o un clima de estepa.

La vegetación natural de Latinoamérica varía de acuerdo al clima e incluye desde la llujuriante vegetación perenne del bosque de lluvia tropical hasta los cactus del desierto. Una de las características más significativas del clima y la vegetación de Latinoamérica es las tres zonas montañosas basadas en la elevación. Entre los recursos principales de Latinoamérica están el petróleo, el gas natural, la bauxita, el estaño, el cobre, el oro, la plata y las gemas preciosas.

Puntos de interés

SECCIÓN **Configuración demográfica**

La diversidad étnica de la población de Latinoamérica incluye a indios, europeos, africanos, asiáticos, mestizos y mulatos. La población no está parejamente distribuída por toda la región. La población urbana ha aumentado rápidamente a medida que la gente se ha mudado de las áreas rurales a las urbanas.

SECCIÓN **Historia y gobierno**

Los mayas, los aztecas y los incas desarrollaron civilizaciones altamente avanzadas mucho antes de que los europeos llegaran a las Américas. Los países europeos de España y Portugal controlaron la mayor parte de Latinoamérica por más de 300 años. Hoy, la mayoría de los líderes latinoamericanos desean gobiernos estables y una calidad de vida mejor para sus pueblos.

SECCIÓN **Culturas y estilos de vida**

Los españoles y los portugueses trajeron a Latinoamérica la cultura europea y el Catolicismo Romano, la religión principal de la región. En décadas más recientes, las artes y la literatura se han vuelto menos europeas y más peculiarmente latinoamericanas.

A pesar de las diferencias de clase social, estilos de vida y pasatiempos, los latinoamericanos comparten un fuerte sentido de la familia. Sus familias se han beneficiado de los recientes adelantos en el cuidado de la salud y en la educación.

SPANISH HANDBOOK

Puntos de interés

SECCIÓN **1** **La vida en Latinoamérica**

La economía de muchos países latinoamericanos se basa en la agricultura. Hay dos clases importantes de fincas en la región—*latifundios* y *minifundios*.

La mayoría de los países de Latinoamérica han tardado en industrializarse debido a la falta de fondos, fuerza de trabajo calificada, materias primas y fuentes de energía. El costo y las barreras físicas han retrasado el desarrollo de la transportación y las redes de comunicación en la región. A pesar de estas dificultades, el deseo de Latinoamérica de industrializarse ha hecho que aumente la interdependencia que existe entre la región y algunas naciones del exterior.

SECCIÓN **2** **La gente y su medio ambiente**

Grandes áreas de la cuenca del río Amazonas están sufriendo la deforestación. La construcción de carreteras, la agricultura a escala menor, la ganadería y la explotación comercial de los árboles ha contribuído a este problema ambiental. Se necesita mejor planificación y regulaciones gubernamentales más fuertes para desarrollar los recursos de la cuenca del río Amazonas sin hacerle daño al medio ambiente.

El rápido crecimiento de las ciudades latinoamericanas también ha causado problemas sociales y del medio ambiente. Los gobiernos de Latinoamérica están cada vez más conscientes de los problemas y están tratando de resolverlos.

Puntos de interés

SECCIÓN **1** El terreno

El continente europeo es una enorme península que se extiende hacia el oeste desde las masas terrestres de Eurasia. Europa tiene una costa larga e irregular con muchas penínsulas e islas rodeadas por distintos mares.

Europa consiste de llanos rodeados de montañas a lo largo de sus bordes sur y norte. Los ríos desempeñan un papel importante de rutas de transporte que unen el interior de Europa con los puertos costeños. Además de estas características físicas, Europa tiene grandes depósitos de carbón, hierro, petróleo y gas natural.

SECCIÓN **2** Clima y vegetación

Debido a las cálidas corrientes marítimas, gran parte de Europa tiene climas más templados que otras partes del mundo que están en las mismas latitudes. La parte noroeste de Europa tiene un clima marino occidental con temperaturas moderadas tanto en verano como en invierno. La mayor parte del sur de Europa tiene un clima mediterráneo con inviernos moderados y lluviosos y veranos secos y calurosos. El interior de Europa experimenta más extremos de temperatura durante las estaciones que las otras partes del continente. Tanto el clima como las personas afectan la vegetación natural de la región.

capítulo 12

Puntos de interés

SECCIÓN Configuración demográfica

La diversidad de la población europea refleja una historia de migraciones por todo el continente. La distribución demográfica en Europa ha sido influída por las características físicas, el clima y los recursos. Como resultado de la industrialización, casi tres cuartos de los europeos viven en áreas urbanas.

SECCIÓN Historia y gobierno

La antigua civilización greco romana ha sevido de modelo para el mundo occidental. La admiración europea de sus ideas dió origen al Renacimiento, cuyos logros científicos hizo que los europeos se interesaran y se sintieran capaces de explorar remotos lugares del mundo. La civilización europea se difundió por otros continentes por medio del comercio, la colonización y la inmigración.

Después de la sequnda Guerra Mundial, Europa se convirtió en el centro de la guerra fría, la cual dividió la Europa occidental anticomunista de la oriental, controlada por los comunistas. En años recientes, la Comunidad Europea ha promovido la unidad entre las naciones europeas.

SECCIÓN Culturas y estilos de vida

Las diferencias en los estilos de vida europeos reflejan cultura y tradición, desarrollo económico y sistemas políticos. La industrialización y la urbanización, sin embargo, han reducido muchas de estas diferencias en los últimos años. Otro factor importante de la unificación es el papel que muchos gobiernos europeos ahora desempeñan para proveer bienestar a sus ciudadanos.

Puntos de interés

SECCIÓN **1** La vida en Europa

Europa tiene diversas economías basadas en la agricultura, la manufactura y los servicios. Además, sus sistemas de comunicación y de transporte están entre los mejores del mundo. Las ferrovías son un medio importante de transportación de pasajeros y cargas por toda Europa.

En las últimas décadas, las 12 naciones de la Comunidad Europea han colaborado para lograr la unidad económica a pesar de las dificultades que traen los cambios. Mientras tanto, los países del este de Europa han luchado para ajustarse a una economía de libre comercio después de 40 años de control comunista.

SECCIÓN **2** La gente y su medio ambiente

Europa se enfrenta a un número de problemas ambientales. La lluvia ácida ha dañado bosques, fauna y edificios en muchas partes del continente. La contaminación del aire debido a las factorías pone en peligro la salud y contribuye al efecto de invernadero. La contaminación debida a los deshechos industriales, las aguas negras, la basura y el petróleo amenaza el mar Mediterráneo y la fauna que el mar sostiene.

Los europeos, no obstante, comparten una preocupación por el medio ambiente y un sentido de responsabilidad hacia las generaciones futuras. Sus gobiernos han tomado medidas para reducir la contaminación y limpiar el medio ambiente.

Puntos de interés

SECCIÓN **El terreno**

El terreno que ocupa Rusia y las Repúblicas de Eurasia cubre dos continentes—Europa y Asia. Todas las repúblicas menos Rusia, Georgia y Ucrania carecen de acceso al mar. Áreas de pastoreo cubren la mayor parte de la región. Hay también numerosas cordilleras, mesetas y cuerpos de agua en el interior. La mayoría de los ríos en la región fluyen hacia el norte y están congelados durante gran parte del año. Los minerales, los recursos de energía, los suelos fértiles, la fauna y la pesca abundan en Rusia y las repúblicas de Eurasia.

SECCIÓN **2** **Clima y vegetación**

Debido a su ubicación al norte, la lejanía de grandes cuerpos de agua y la falta de montañas cerca de las áreas de praderas, la mayoría de las partes de Rusia y de las repúblicas de Eurasia tienen un clima continental o subártico. A través de la región, los veranos son cortos y los inviernos son largos y fríos. Casi la mitad de la tierra rusa y de las repúblicas eurasianas está cubierta de nieve durante casi todo el año. El *permafrost* (subsuelo permanentemente congelado) se halla debajo del 40 porciento del área de la región. En Rusia y las repúblicas de Eurasia, la vegetación natural varía desde la tundra desprovista de árboles en el norte, hasta los densos bosques de la taiga en el centro y los desiertos yermos del sur.

Puntos de interés

SPANISH HANDBOOK

SECCIÓN **Configuración demográfica**

Tres grupos étnicos importantes—los eslavos, los turcos y los caucásicos— viven en Rusia y las repúblicas de Eurasia. Cada una de las repúblicas tiene su propio lenguaje principal.

La población no está distribuída parejamente a través de Rusia y las repúbli- cas eurasiáticas. En los últimos años, también ha habido un cambio en la relación rural/urbana. Mientras que en el pasado la mayoría de la gente de la región vivía en el campo, hoy viven en la ciudad.

SECCIÓN **Historia y gobierno**

Los eslavos y varangianos fundaron ciudad-estados a lo largo de los ríos en la parte occidental de la región. Bajo los zares, surgió en Rusia un poderoso estado que creó uno de los imperios más grandes del mundo. A principios de siglo, el imperio ruso se convirtió en una nueva nación llamada la Unión de Repúblicas Socialistas Soviéticas y por más de siete décadas estuvo bajo el poder comunista. Cuando el estado soviético se derrumbó a principios de los 90, las antiguas repúblicas soviéticas se convirtieron en naciones independientes.

SECCIÓN **Culturas y estilos de vida**

En la actualidad, las tres religones principales, el Cristianismo, el Islam y el Judaismo, al igual que un número de otras religiones, se practican abierta- mente en Rusia como en las repúblicas de Eurasia. Las personas de la región tienen fuertes tradiciones culturales y están dedicados a las artes. Tienen diver- sos estilos de vidas y gozan de una var- iedad de celebraciones.

Puntos de interés

SECCIÓN ## La vida en Rusia y las Repúblicas Eurásicas

Durante muchas décadas, Rusia y las repúblicas eurásicas tenían una sola economía controlada por el gobierno soviético. Al hacerse independiente, cada república tomó control de su propia economía y ahora está tratando de moverse hacia un sistema de libre comercio. Cada una está también tomando medidas para privatizar la agricultura y la industria. Debido al largo período de control central soviético, las repúblicas todavía están dependiendo económicamente las unas de las otras.

La independencia, sin embargo, les ha traído mayor libertad de expresión a los sistemas de comunicaciones y a la mayoría de los medios de información. Aunque las vías fluviales, las carreteras y las ferrovías continúan siendo métodos vitales para la transportación de cargas y pasajeros, las líneas aéreas y los oleoductos están creciendo en importancia.

SECCIÓN ## La gente y su medio ambiente

En su lucha por industrializarse, los soviéticos descuidaron y abusaron el medio ambiente. Comprometidos a la energía nuclear como fuente económica de energía eléctrica, construyeron numerosas estaciones nucleares en varias partes de la nación. El desastre de Chernobyl generó dudas y protestas acerca de la energía nuclear y las armas nucleares. Otros problemas ambientales que se heredan de la era soviética y que aún siguen siendo significativos son la contaminación causada por la industria pesada y el uso de los pesticidas.

Puntos de interés

capítulo **17**

SECCIÓN 1 — El terreno

La región de África del Norte y Asia del Sudoeste se extiende desde Marruecos en el oeste hasta Afganistán en el este. Cubriendo más del 10 por ciento de la superficie total de la tierra, la región de África del Norte y Asia del Suroeste tiene un número de penínsulas y varios mares.

La precipitación en el África del Norte y en el Asia del Sudoeste varía grandemente, yendo desde menos de 4 pulgadas (10cm) en algunas mesetas hasta cantidades mucho más altas en algunas de las áreas montañosas. A pesar de la escasez de lluvia en muchas áreas, el fértil valle del río Nilo y el área cerca de los ríos Tigris y Éufrates provee el terreno donde la agricultura florece. También de gran importancia son el petróleo y el gas natural, dos recursos naturales vitales que proveen ingresos sustanciosos para algunas naciones de la región.

SECCIÓN 2 — Clima y vegetación

Las cuatro regiones climatológicas del África del Norte y del Asia del Sudoeste son el desierto, la mediterránea, la estepa y la montañosa. Mucha de la agricultura del África del Norte y del Asia del Sudoeste ocurre a lo largo de zonas costeras que tienen un clima mediterráneo. La precipitación es más prevalente allí que en otras zonas de la región. En zonas donde la precipitación es menos abundante, el desmonte del terreno para la agricultura y el pastoreo excesivo en zonas de estepa han hecho estragos a la vegetación.

Puntos de interés

 SECCIÓN **1** Configuración demográfica

La región cultural del África del Norte y del Asia del Sudoeste ha sido la encrucijada donde se encuentran los pueblos y las culturas del Asia, África y Europa. Las concentraciones demográficas más grandes en el África del Norte y en el Asia del Sudoeste están en las zonas costeras y las cuencas de los ríos donde hay agua disponible. El rápido crecimiento demográfico y el aumento de urbanización ha caracterizado la región desde la Segunda Guerra Mundial.

 SECCIÓN **2** Historia y gobierno

El África del Norte y el Asia del Sudoeste fue el lugar donde se originaron dos de las civilizaciones más antiguas del mundo—Mesopotamia y Egipto. También se originaron allí tres de las religiones más importantes del mundo—el Judaismo, el Cristianismo y el Islam. Tras siglos de influencia europea, fue en este siglo que surgieron los estados independientes de esta región.

 SECCIÓN **3** Culturas y estilos de vida

La gente del África del Norte y del Asia del Sudoeste que vive en países cuyas economías están basadas en la manufactura y el comercio por lo general disfrutan de un alto estándar de vida. Sin embargo, las personas que viven en países donde las economías se basan en la agricultura, tienen un estándar de vida bajo. El Islam y la lengua árabe han sido las fuerzas unificadoras más importantes de casi todo el África del Norte y el Asia del Sudoeste. Las relaciones familiares también son muy importantes para la gente de esta región. Los pasatiempos más populares incluyen el fútbol, la caza y la pesca.

Puntos de interés

SECCIÓN **1** La vida en África del Norte y Asia del Sudoeste

Aunque la región del África del Norte y el Asia del Sudoeste tiene un terreno arable limitado, un porcentaje relativamente grande de la gente participa en algún tipo de agricultura. La cría de ganado y la pesca son dos fuentes más de alimento para la región.

El nivel de industrialización es disparejo entre las naciones del África del Norte y del Asia del Sudoeste, con más industrialización en muchas de las naciones productoras de petróleo. El gran desarrollo industrial, junto con la necesidad de conectar los centros urbanos y económicos ha producido recientemente un crecimiento en los sistemas de transportación y comunicación. Aunque la dependencia mutua ha aumentado entre las naciones de la región, varios conflictos y guerras han interrumpido la economía de algunos países.

SECCIÓN **2** La gente y su medio ambiente

La gente del África del Norte y del Asia del Sudoeste ha tomado medidas para modificar su medio ambiente y para poder tener agua para tomar y para el riego. El agua fluvial necesaria para el regadío extensivo está escasa en la mayoría de las naciones de la región. La desalación se emplea ampliamente para proveer agua, particularmente en la península arábiga.

Recientemente, las actividades humanas en la región han tenido efectos mixtos. La construcción de la Presa del Alto Aswan ha traído beneficios a Egipto, pero también ha tenido efectos negativos sobre el medio ambiente. La Guerra del Golfo Pérsico dañó severamente el medio ambiente natural de esa zona.

SPANISH HANDBOOK

Puntos de interés

SECCIÓN El terreno

El África al sur del Sahara se caracteriza grandemente por una serie de altiplanos escalonados. Altas elevaciones y estrechas praderas costeras han impedido históricamente el viajar al interior del África. Cuatro sistemas fluviales importantes saltan por escarpaduras en dramáticos rápidos y cataratas en su recorrido por el continente. El Valle de la Gran Grieta atraviesa el África oriental, desde Etiopía en el norte, hasta Mozambique en el sur. Muchos de los lagos de agua dulce de la región están situados en el valle.

SECCIÓN Clima y vegetación

Aunque la mayor parte del África yace en el trópico, exhibe diversos climas y vegetaciones. La elevación y la precipitación son los factores principales que influyen en la variedad del clima de África al sur del Sahara. Las principales regiones climatológicas son el desierto, la estepa, la sabana tropical y el bosque de lluvia tropical.

Los desiertos y las estepas cubren más de dos tercios de la superficie de la tierra en África. La región tiene una abundancia de riqueza mineral, pero carece de petróleo para desarrollarla.

Puntos de interés

SECCIÓN Configuración demográfica

Con más de 530 millones de personas, el África al sur del Sahara es la tercera región con más habitantes del mundo. Más de 2,000 grupos étnicos, que hablan unos 800 idiomas, componen la población del África al sur del Sahara. La geografía física de la región contribuye a la distribución dispareja de esta diversa población.

El África al sur del Sahara está urbanizándose más rápido que cualquier otra región del mundo. Además de este reto, la gente de la región tiene una expectativa de vida corta debido a la alimentación, el agua y el cuidado médico inadecuado.

SECCIÓN Historia y gobierno

En la antigua África, el movimiento de los Bantú de Niger hacia el sur formó una de las mayores inmigraciones humanas en la historia. En tiempos modernos, la colonización europea cambió las fronteras territoriales que han sido tradicionalmente étnicas. Desde los

años 60, la mayoría de las naciones del África ha logrado su independencia. El último baluarte europeo que queda es Sudáfrica, donde en 1990 el sistema de segregación racial fue desmantelado.

SECCIÓN Culturas y estilos de vida

La cantidad de idiomas y la variedad de religiones del África del sur del Sahara contribuyen a la diversidad de la región. Con esta diversidad, los africanos del sur del Sahara han influído

en las culturas artísticas del mundo. A pesar de los logros pasados y presentes, el África del sur del Sahara tiene que enfrentarse al reto de reducir su tasa de analfabetismo.

Puntos de interés

SECCIÓN 1 — La vida en África al sur del Sahara

La mayoría de la naciones del África del sur del Sahara depende de la exportación de uno o dos cultivos comerciales. La mayoría de las personas de la región, sin embargo, trabajan como agricultores de subsistencia.

Los depósitos de minerales, al igual que las ganancias de su exportación, no están distribuídos parejamente a través del África al sur del Sahara. El desarrollo industrial lo impide la falta de capital y la escasez de mano de obra adiestrada. Para reducir la dependencia extranjera, algunas naciones en la región están desarrollando sistemas regionales de comercio y transporte.

SECCIÓN 2 — La gente y su medio ambiente

A medida que los africanos del sur del Sahara se dirigen hacia el próximo siglo, esperan obtener la independencia económica. Esta meta está siendo retada por una serie de problemas ambientales. La desertificación, las sequías y la guerra han contribuído al hambre en esta región. En los años 90, dos de las naciones afectadas por estos problemas—Etiopía y Eritárea—han tomado medidas para reparar los daños a su medio ambiente.

La destrucción de los bosques de lluvia no es sólo un problema africano sino mundial. A través del África al sur, el aumento demográfico y la caza han puesto a algunos animales en peligro de extinción. Para ganarse el apoyo rural para preservar las reservas de caza, algunas naciones en la región han compartido las ganacias del ecoturismo.

Puntos de interés

capítulo
23

SECCIÓN **1** El terreno

Asia del Sur consiste de una enorme península con una isla cerca de la punta sur. La península se conoce como un subcontinente, una masa de tierra grande más pequeña que un continente. La región está limitada por el Himalaya en el norte, el mar Arábigo al oeste, el océano Índico en el sur y el Golfo de Bengala en el este.

La mayoría de la gente de la región vive en las llanuras del norte, una zona agrícola rica. El Asia del Sur tiene tres grandes sistemas fluviales y la llanura aluvial más grande del mundo. La región tiene pocas reservas de petróleo, pero tiene gas natural, carbón y uranio y unos importantes depósitos de hiero y mica.

SECCIÓN **2** Clima y vegetación

El Asia del Sur tiene tierras altas, desierto, estepa y climas tropicales. Un cambio de estación en la dirección del viento conocido como monzón trae lluvias fuertes a la región entre junio y septiembre. La vegetación del Asia del Sur está afectada por la altitud, la lluvia y la actividad humana. En un entonces la región estaba cubierta de bosques, pero en la actualidad tan sólo tiene una pequeña porción de tierras forestales.

SPANISH HANDBOOK

Puntos de interés

 SECCIÓN 1 Configuración demográfica

El Asia del Sur es una región étnicamente diversa. Su densidad demográfica es mayor en la llanura Indogangética. Aunque la mayoría de los asiáticos del sur viven en áreas rurales, un número creciente está migrando a las ciudades en busca de trabajo.

 SECCIÓN 2 Historia y gobierno

El Valle Indio del Asia del Sur fue la cuna de una de las primeras grandes civilizaciones del mundo. Otras civilizaciones que siguieron en la región produjeron dos de las principales religiones del mundo—el Hinduismo y el Budismo.

A través de los siglos, muchos pueblos han conquistado el Asia del Sur, desde los arianos hasta los británicos. Después de la Segunda Guerra Mundial, la región ha logrado independizarse del Imperio Británico. En la actualidad, la mayoría de la gente del Asia del Sur vive en naciones independientes y eligen a sus líderes.

 SECCIÓN 3 Culturas y estilos de vida

Los asiáticos del sur hablan muchos idiomas diferentes. La India tiene 14 idiomas principales y cientos de dialectos. Las religiones principales del Asia del Sur son el Hinduismo, el Islam y el Budismo. La gente también practica el Cristianismo, el Jainismo y el Sikhismo.

En la mayor parte del Asia del Sur el estándar de vida es bajo y la expectativa de vida es corta. En años recientes, sin embargo, se ha mejorado el cuidado de la salud y la educación.

Puntos de interés

SECCIÓN La vida en el Asia del Sur

Los adelantos agrícolas están ayudando al Asia del Sur a producir suficiente alimento para su creciente población. Las principales cosechas de alimento son el arroz y el trigo; las principales cosechas comerciales son el yute y el té.

Las minas, la pesca y el turismo son también importantes fuentes de ingresos para el Asia del Sur. La industria, tanto ligera como pesada, está creciendo en la región.

SECCIÓN La gente y su medio ambiente

La gente ha deforestado muchas partes del Asia del Sur en busca de madera para combustible, para hacer casas y para la agricultura y el pastoreo. La deforestación trae la amenaza de inundaciones, deslices de tierra, la pérdida de la valiosa capa vegetal y del hábitat de los animales además de cambios climatológicos. Los gobiernos e individuos por toda el Asia del Sur están tratando de conservar y volver a sembrar los bosques. A pesar de la pérdida de

muchos animales debido a la caza excesiva y la pérdida del hábitat, los surasiáticos están tratando de preservar las especies que todavía existen en las reservas de fauna y en otros lugares.

El uso del agua es controvertido en el Asia del Sur por muchas razones. Las presas se necesitan para controlar las inundaciones y proveer agua para el regadío, pero también causan problemas para el medio ambiente.

SPANISH HANDBOOK

Puntos de interés

 SECCIÓN **El terreno**

La región del Asia Oriental consite de la China, Mongolia y Corea en el continente de Asia y dos naciones islas, Japón y Taiwán. La China ocupa el 90 por ciento del área del Asia Oriental. Otras naciones ocupan penínsulas e islas.

El continente de Asia Oriental tiene montañas y en el oeste, mesetas y cuencas en las regiones del centro y el norte y llanos costeros en el este. Debido a que una gran parte del Asia Oriental es mon-

tañosa, las ciudades de las llanuras costeras tienen una densa población. Las presiones del exceso de población al igual que las limitadas tierras de agricultura han hecho que los asiáticos del Este consideren el océano una fuente importante de alimento. Respecto a otros recursos, el Asia del Este es rica en minerales, pero no siempre están parejamente distribuídos y a veces son difíciles de encontrar.

 SECCIÓN **Clima y vegetación**

El Asia Oriental tiene una variedad de climas debido a su gran masa de terreno. Mucha de la región está entre latitudes con clima húmedo continental o húmedo subtropical. Los vientos con lluvias de la estación de monzón afectan grandemente el clima del Asia Oriental.

Muchas partes de la región, especialmente el Japón, Corea y Taiwán, tienen espesos bosques. Las estepas del interior y las zonas de desiertos, sin embargo, tienen climas secos con temperaturas extremas y escasa vegetación.

Puntos de interés

SECCIÓN **Configuración demográfica**

La gente del Asia del Este pertenece a distintos grupos étnicos, el mayor de los cuales es el Han de la China. La población en la región no está distribuída parejamente y está concentrada en las cuencas y en las llanuras costeras. El Japón es la nación más urbanizada del Asia del Este. La China permanece predominantemente rural con cientos de millones de sus ciudadanos viviendo en las afueras de las zonas urbanas.

SECCIÓN **2** **Historia y gobierno**

La cultura del Asia del Este comenzó en el valle de Huang He en la China y se dispersó a otros lugares de la región. El Confusianismo y Daoismo, dos influyentes escuelas de pensamiento, se desarrollaron en la China cerca del año 500 A.C. El Budismo, una importante religión del Asia del Este, se originó en la India. Durante varios siglos, el Imperio Chino fue la potencia dominante en el Asia del Este. El contacto con el Occidente debilitó a la China pero condujo al Japón a modernizarse.

SECCIÓN **Culturas y estilos de vida**

El Asia del Este tiene diversos idiomas, culturas y estilos de vida. Los idiomas sinotibetanos son los más hablados de la región, mientras que el coreano y el japonés se hablan en sus respectivos países. En los últimos años, el aumento en el estándar de vida ha traído mejorías en la educación y el cuidado de la salud. La gente del Asia del Este practica las artes y los pasatiempos tradicionales pero también goza de las recreaciones modernas.

SPANISH HANDBOOK

Puntos de interés

SECCIÓN 1 — La vida en el Asia del Este

Hubo una época en que el Asia del Este era principalmente agrícola, pero el comercio y la industria han traído prosperidad y crecimiento económico a la mayoría de sus naciones. A pesar del progreso industrial de la China, la mayoría de su gente todavía trabaja en la agricultura, siguiendo las políticas establecidas por el gobierno comunista. Por todas las zonas costeras del Asia del Este, la pesca es importante tanto para la alimentación como para la exportación.

El Japón es la nación industrial principal, pero Taiwán y Corea del Sur también están compitiendo. El comercio y las inversiones comerciales unen a los países capitalistas y comunistas de la región. Las embarcaciones y las ferrovías son vínculos importantes dentro del Asia del Este. La transportación está más desarrollada en la parte oriental de la región.

SECCIÓN 2 — La gente y su medio ambiente

El rápido crecimiento industrial del Asia del Este ha causado contaminación del aire y del agua y ha producido deshechos tóxicos. Pero, durante varias décadas, estos problemas ambientales fueron ignorados. En la actualidad, el Japón se ha convertido en un líder en la protección y en la limpieza del medio ambiente, con leyes estrictas contra la contaminación.

Otros factores impactan el medio ambiente del Asia del Este. La enorme población de la China intensifica el efecto que tiene su desarrollo económico sobre el medio ambiente. El medio ambiente del Asia del Este está propenso a desastres naturales, como las inundaciones, los terremotos, los tsunamis y los tifones.

Puntos de interés

SECCIÓN **1** El terreno

La región del Asia del Sudeste incluye las 2 penínsulas al este de la India y al sur de la China y las 20,000 islas del archipiélago de Malaya. Las montañas del Asia del Sudeste se formaron cuando las placas indoaustralianas y filipinas chocaron contra la placa eurásica. Los ríos del continente del Asia del Sudeste son importantes para la agricultura, la comunicación y la transportación. Otro beneficio vital para el Asia del Sudeste son sus reservas enormes de petróleo, maderas tropicales duras, estaño y gemas.

SECCIÓN **2** Clima y vegetación

Casi todas las partes del Asia del Sureste tienen un clima caliente y húmedo afectado por los monzones. Por todas las islas del Asia del Sureste al igual que en las costas del este y oeste de la península Indochina hay un clima de bosque de lluvia tropical. Un clima de sabana tropical se extiende hacia el sureste y atraviesa la península. Algunas de las islas más al sur en el Asia del Sudeste también comparten este clima.

La vegetación del Asia del Sudeste consiste principalmente de variedades de bosques de lluvia tropical. La desforestación en la región ha afectado la ecología, la economía y la cultura de algunas de sus gentes.

Puntos de interés

SECCIÓN 1 — Configuración demográfica

La población del Asia del Sureste está aumentando rápidamente. Aunque gran parte de la región es rural, hay un número creciente de grandes ciudades que están densamente pobladas.

SECCIÓN 2 — Historia y gobierno

Temprano en su historia, el Asia del Sudeste se convirtió en una zona de contacto entre el Asia del Este y el Asia del Sur. En siglos posteriores toda la región, con la excepción de Tailanda, fue colonizada por potencias extranjeras.

Después de la Segunda Guerra Mundial, los países del Asia del Sudeste se hicieron independientes. Hoy en día, las formas de gobierno en la región son las monarquías constitucionales, las repúblicas democráticas y las repúblicas socialistas.

SECCIÓN 3 — Culturas y estilos de vida

Las culturas y los estilos de vida del Asia del Sudeste reflejan las primeras migraciones de los pueblos que vinieron desde otras regiones así como las tradiciones folclóricas regionales. Entre las principales religiones de la región el Budismo, el Hinduismo y el Islam han influído grandemente en el arte, la arquitectura, el drama y las celebraciones del Asia del Sudeste. A pesar del enorme crecimiento demográfico, el desarrollo económico ha traído muchas mejoras y ha presentado muchos retos al Asia del Sudeste.

Puntos de interés

SECCIÓN ## La vida en Asia del Sudeste

La agricultura es la base de la mayoría de las economías del Asia del Sudeste. Las cosechas principales son el arroz, la caña de azúcar, el caucho, el café y el coco. Los lujuriantes bosques de la región ofrecen muchos productos de madera.

En años recientes, la mina y la manufactura han aumentado en importancia y muchas nuevas industrias se han desarrollado en el Asia del Sudeste. El medio de transporte principal de la región es el agua; la transportación terrestre está menos desarrollada.

SECCIÓN ## La gente y su medio ambiente

La industrialización, la urbanización y el rápido aumento demográfico han traído la contaminación ambiental a muchas áreas urbanas y rurales del Asia del Sudeste. La gente y el medio ambiente del Asia del Sudeste también están afectados por acontecimientos naturales. Esto se debe a que grandes números de asiáticos del sudeste viven en el Aro de Fuego, o sea rodeados de volcanes, muchos de ellos activos. Además, cada año en la región, las inundaciones repentinas y violentas destruyen vidas y cosechas. Los tifones son tormentas peligrosas que ocurren en el Asia del Sudeste entre julio y octubre.

SPANISH HANDBOOK

Puntos de interés

SPANISH HANDBOOK

SECCIÓN 1   El terreno

La región del Pacífico del Sur incluye los grandes continentes de Antártida, Australia y las miles de islas de variados tamaños que componen Oceanía. Las islas de Oceanía fueron creadas directa o indirectamente por actividad volcánica. Nueva Zelandia, un importante grupo de islas de Oceanía, tiene una geografía accidentada con costas muy irregulares, altas montañas y ríos con fuertes corrientes. Mientras que la Antártida tiene importantes recursos minerales, su recurso principal es la información que ofrece a los científicos.

SECCIÓN 2   Clima y vegetación

La región del Pacífico del Sur tiene una diversidad de clima y vegetación. Casi toda la Antártida tiene un clima polar. A excepción de los líquenes y los musgos en las zonas de la tundra, la Antártida no tiene vegetación. Australia, sin embargo, generalmente tiene un clima caliente y seco. Su interior es un vasto desierto rodeado por una amplia estepa. Las montañas separan las zonas húmedas de las costas de las más secas del interior.

Nueva Zelandia tiene un clima marino templado y húmedo con una variedad de temperaturas moderadas durante el año, especialmente en la Isla Norte. La mayor parte de Oceanía, sin embargo, se caracteriza por un clima de bosque de lluvia tropical. Otra característica del medio ambiente de Oceanía son los violentos tifones durante ciertas épocas del año. Estas tormentas se producen por el choque de las corrientes y los vientos del Océano Pacífico.

Puntos de interés

SECCIÓN **1**   Configuración demográfica

Muchos grupos distintos de personas se han establecido en el Pacífico del Sur y han creado una mezcla de gente, culturas y estilos de vida. La población de la región no está distribuída parejamente ya que muchas zonas no pueden sostener vida.

SECCIÓN **2**   Historia y gobierno

Los primeros seres humanos que se establecieron en el Pacífico del Sur probablemente vinieron del Asia del Sudeste. Los poblados luego se esparcieron hacia el este. A fines de los 1700, Gran Bretaña comenzó a colonizar Australia y luego Nueva Zelandia. Durante el final de los 1800 y a principios de los 1900 las naciones europeas y el Japón lucharon por el control de las islas del Pacífico.

SECCIÓN **3**   Culturas y estilos de vida

La cultura europea ha vuelto a dominar en el Pacífico del Sur. Sin embargo, en la actualidad, los elementos culturales tradicionales continúan formando los estilos de vida de la región.

Los patrones de población en el Pacífico del Sur han sido grandemente determinados mayormente por el clima y la configuración de la tierra. Las condiciones geográficas como éstas, al igual que la herencia cultural y económica, han afectado los estilos de vida y los estándares de salud y educación del Pacífico del Sur.

Puntos de interés

 SECCIÓN **1** La vida en Australia, Oceanía y Antártida

La agricultura es la actividad económica más importante en el Pacífico del Sur. Los agricultores en las islas del Pacífico cultivan mayormente para su propio consumo mientras que los agricultores de Australia y Nueva Zelandia producen grandes exporta-ciones agrícolas, especialmente ganado y productos lácteos. La Antártida no tiene minas ni industrias manufactureras. En las últimas décadas, el transporte aéreo y marítimo ha ayudado a reducir las distancias y llevar bienes y servicios a las remotas partes del Pacífico del Sur.

 SECCIÓN **2** La gente y su medio ambiente

Muchas de las plantas y animales del Pacífico del Sur, que antes se encontraban aislados, han sufrido al introducirse nuevas especies. Además, los esfuerzos de la industria y el gobierno por alcanzar metas políticas y económicas han causado muchos problemas ambientales en la región.

El frágil medio ambiente de Antártica ya no está protegido por el aislamiento. Es posible que tanto los científicos, como la industria y los turistas estén dañando este mundo natural tan delicadamente equilibrado.

Gazetteer

A Gazetteer (GAZ•uh•TIR) is a geographic index or dictionary. It shows latitude and longitude for cities and certain other places. Latitude and longitude are shown in this way: 48°N 2°E, or 48 degrees north latitude and 2 degrees east longitude. This Gazetteer lists most of the world's largest independent countries, their capitals, and several important geographic features. The page numbers tell where each entry can be found on a map in this book. As an aid to pronunciation, many entries are spelled phonetically.

A

Abidjan (A•bih•JAHN) Capital and port of Côte d'Ivoire, Africa. 5°N 4°W (p. 410)

Abu Dhabi (AH•boo DAH•bee) Capital of the United Arab Emirates, on the Persian Gulf. 24°N 54°E (p. 359)

Abuja (ah•BOO•jah) Capital of Nigeria. 8°N 9°E (p. 410)

Accra (uh•KRAH) Port city and capital of Ghana. 6°N 0° longitude (p. 410)

Addis Ababa (A•duhs A•buh•buh) Capital of Ethiopia. 9°N 39°E (p. 410)

Adriatic (AY•dree•AT•ihk) **Sea** Arm of the Mediterranean Sea between the Balkan Peninsula and Italy. 44°N 14°E (p. 225)

Afghanistan (af•GA•nuh•STAN) Country in central Asia, west of Pakistan. 33°N 63°E (p. 359)

Albania (al•BAY•nee•uh) Country on the east coast of the Adriatic Sea, south of Serbia and Montenegro. 42°N 20°E (p. 225)

Algeria (al•JIHR•ee•uh) Country in North Africa. 29°N 1°E (p. 359)

Algiers (al•JIHRZ) Capital of Algeria. 37°N 3°E (p. 359)

Almaty (al•MAH•tee) Capital of Kazakhstan. 43°N 77°E (p. 293)

Alps (ALPS) Mountain system extending east to west through central Europe. 46°N 9°E (p. 225)

Amazon (A•muh•ZAHN) **River** Largest river in the world by volume and second-largest in length. 2°S 53°W (p. 163)

Amman (ah•MAHN) Capital of Jordan. 32°N 36°E (p. 359)

Amsterdam (AM•stuhr•DAM) Capital of the Netherlands. 52°N 5°E (p. 225)

Andes (AN•DEEZ) Mountain system extending north to south along the western side of South America. 13°S 75°W (p. 163)

Andorra (an•DAWR•ah) Small country in southern Europe, between France and Spain. 43°N 20°E (p. 243)

Angola (ang•GOH•luh) Country in Africa, south of Zaire. 14°S 16°E (p. 410)

Ankara (ANG•kuh•ruh) Capital of Turkey. 40°N 33°E (p. 359)

Antananarivo (AN•tuh•NA•nuh•REE•voh) Capital of Madagascar. 19°S 48°E (p. 410)

Argentina (AHR•juhn•TEE•nuh) Country in South America, east of Chile on the Atlantic Ocean. 36°S 67°W (p. 163)

Armenia (ahr•MEE•nee•uh) Southeastern European country between the Black Sea and the Caspian Sea. 40°N 45°E (p. 293)

Ashkhabad (ASH•kuh•BAD) Capital of Turkmenistan. 40°N 58°E (p. 293)

Asunción (uh•SOONT•see•OHN) Capital of Paraguay. 25°S 58°W (p. 163)

Athens (A•thuhnz) Capital and largest city in Greece. 38°N 24°E (p. 225)

Atlas (AT•luhs) **Mountains** Mountain range on the northern edge of the Sahara. 31°N 5°W (p. 359)

Australia (aw•STRAYL•yuh) Country and continent southeast of Asia. 23°S 135°E (p. 648)

Austria (AWS•tree•uh) Country in central Europe, east of Switzerland. 47°N 12°E (p. 225)

Azerbaijan (A•zuhr•BY•JAHN) European-Asian country on the Caspian Sea. 40°N 47°E (p. 293)

B

Baghdad (BAG•DAD) Capital of Iraq. 33°N 44°E (p. 359)

Bahamas (buh•HAH•muhz) Country made up of many islands, between Cuba and the United States. 26°N 76°W (p. 163)

Baku (bah•KOO) Port city and capital of Azerbaijan. 40°N 50°E (p. 293)

Balkan (BAWL•kuhn) **Peninsula** Peninsula in southeastern Europe. 42°N 20°E (p. 225)

Bamako (BAH•muh•KOH) Capital of Mali. 13°N 8°W (p. 410)

G
A
Z
E
T
T
E
E
R

Bangkok (BANG•KAHK) Capital of Thailand. 14°N 100°E (p. 599)

Bangladesh (BAHN•gluh•DESH) Country in South Asia, bordered by India and Myanmar. 24°N 90°E (p. 479)

Bangui (BAHN•GEE) Capital of the Central African Republic. 4°N 19°E (p. 410)

Banjul (BAHN•JOOL) Port city and capital of Gambia. 13°N 17°W (p. 410)

Barbados (bahr•BAY•DOHS) Island country between the Atlantic Ocean and the Caribbean Sea. 14°N 59°W (p. 152)

Beijing (BAY•JIHNG) Capital of China. 40°N 116°E (p. 539)

Beirut (bay•ROOT) Capital of Lebanon. 34°N 36°E (p. 359)

Belarus (BEE•luh•ROOS) Eastern European country west of Russia. 54°N 28°E (p. 293)

Belgium (BEL•juhm) Country in north-western Europe, south of the Netherlands. 51°N 3°E (p. 225)

Belgrade (BEL•GRAYD) Capital of Serbia. 45°N 21°E (p. 225)

Belize (buh•LEEZ) Country in Central America, east of Guatemala. 18°N 89°W (p. 163)

Belmopan (BEL•moh•PAN) Capital of Belize. 17°N 89°W (p. 163)

Benin (buh•NIHN) Country in western Africa. 8°N 2°E (p. 410)

Berlin (BUHR•LIHN) Capital of Germany. 53°N 13°E (p. 225)

Bermuda (BUHR•MYOO•duh) Islands in western Atlantic Ocean, self-governing British colony. 32°N 65°W (p. 199)

Bern (BUHRN) Capital of Switzerland. 47°N 7°E (p. 225)

Bhutan (boo•TAHN) Country in the eastern Himalayas, northeast of India. 27°N 91°E (p. 479)

Bishkek (bihsh•KEK) Largest city and capital of Kyrgyzstan. 43°N 75°E (p. 293)

Bissau (bih•SAU) Capital of Guinea-Bissau. 12°N 16°W (p. 410)

Bogotá (BOH•guh•TAW) Capital of Colombia. 5°N 74°W (p. 163)

Bolivia (buh•LIH•vee•uh) Country in the central part of South America, north of Argentina. 17°S 64°W (p. 163)

Bosnia-Herzegovina (BAHZ•nee•uh HERT•suh•goh•VEE•nuh) Southeastern European country between Yugoslavia and Croatia. 44°N 18°E (p. 225)

Botswana (baht•SWAH•nuh) Country in Africa, north of the Republic of South Africa. 22°S 23°E (p. 410)

Brasília (bruh•ZIHL•yuh) Capital of Brazil. 16°S 48°W (p. 163)

Bratislava (BRA•tuh•SLAH•vuh) Capital and largest city of Slovakia. 48°N 17°E (p. 225)

Brazil (bruh•ZIHL) Largest county in South America. 9°S 53°W (p. 163)

Brazzaville (BRA•zuh•VIHL) Capital of the Congo Republic. 4°S 15°E (p. 410)

Brunei (bru•NY) Country on the northern coast of the island of Borneo. 5°N 114°E (p. 590)

Brussels (BRUH•suhlz) Capital of Belgium. 51°N 4°E (p. 225)

Bucharest (BOO•kuh•REST) Capital of Romania. 44°N 26°E (p. 225)

Budapest (BOO•duh•PEST) Capital of Hungary. 48°N 19°E (p. 225)

Buenos Aires (BWAY•nuhs AR•eez) Capital of Argentina. 34°S 58°W (p. 163)

Bujumbura (BOO•juhm•BUR•uh) Capital of Burundi. 3°S 29°E (p. 410)

Bulgaria (BUHL•GAR•ee•uh) Country in southeastern Europe, south of Romania. 42°N 24°E (p. 225)

Burkina Faso (bur•KEE•nuh FAH•soh) Country in western Africa, south of Mali. 4°N 2°W (p. 410)

Burundi (bu•ROON•dee) Country in central Africa at the northern end of Lake Tanganyika. 3°S 30°E (p. 410)

C

Cairo (KY•ROH) Capital of Egypt, on the Nile River. 31°N 32°E (p. 359)

Cambodia (kam•BOH•dee•uh) Country in Southeast Asia, south of Thailand. 12°N 104°E (p. 599)

Cameroon (KA•muh•ROON) Country in west Africa, on the northeast shore of the Gulf of Guinea. 6°N 11°E (p. 410)

Canada (KA•nuh•duh) Country in North America. 50°N 100°W (p. 95)

Canberra (KAN•buh•ruh) Capital of Australia. 35°S 149°E (p. 657)

Cape Town Legislative capital of the Republic of South Africa. 34°S 18°E (p. 411)

Caracas (kuh•RAH•kuhs) Capital of Venezuela. 11°N 67°W (p. 163)

GAZETTEER

Caribbean (KAR•uh•BEE•uhn) **Sea** Part of the Atlantic Ocean, bordered by the West Indies, South America, and Central America. 15°N 76°W (p. 163)

Caspian (KAS•pee•uhn) **Sea** Salt lake between Europe and Asia that is the world's largest inland body of water. 40°N 52°E (p. 293)

Central African Republic Country in central Africa, south of Chad. 8°N 21°E (p. 410)

Chad (CHAD) Country in central Africa, west of Sudan. 18°N 19°E (p. 410)

Chang (CHANG) **River** Principal river of China that rises in Tibet and flows into the East China Sea near Shanghai. 31°N 117°E (p. 539)

Chile (CHIH•lee) South American country, west of Argentina. 35°S 72°W (p. 163)

China (CHY•nuh) Country in eastern and central Asia, known officially as the People's Republic of China. 37°N 93°E (p. 539)

Chisinau (KEE•shih•NAU) Largest city and capital of Moldova. 47°N 29°E (p. 293)

Colombia (kuh•LUHM•bee•uh) Country in South America, west of Venezuela. 4°N 73°W (p. 163)

Colombo (kuh•LUHM•BOH) Capital of Sri Lanka. 7°N 80°E (p. 479)

Comoros (KAH•muh•rohs) **Islands** Small island country in Indian Ocean between the island of Madagascar and the southeast African mainland. 13°S 43°E (p. 421)

Conakry (KAH•nuh•kree) Capital of Guinea. 10°N 14°W (p. 410)

Congo Republic Country in equatorial Africa, south of the Central African Republic. 3°S 14°E (p. 410)

Copenhagen (KOH•puhn•HAY•guhn) Seaport, largest city, and capital of Denmark. 56°N 12°E (p. 225)

Costa Rica (KAHS•tuh REE•kuh) Central American country, south of Nicaragua. 11°N 85°W (p. 163)

Côte d'Ivoire (KOHT dee•VWAHR) West African country, south of Mali. 8°N 7°W (p. 410)

Croatia (kroh•AY•shuh) Southeastern European country on the Adriatic Sea. 46°N 15°E (p. 225)

Cuba (KYOO•buh) Island in the West Indies. 22°N 79°W (p. 163)

Cyprus (SY•pruhs) Island country in the eastern Mediterranean Sea, south of

Turkey. 35°N 31°E (p. 359)

Czech (CHEK) **Republic** Central European country south of Germany and Poland. 50°N 15°E (p. 225)

D

Dakar (DA•KAHR) Port city and capital of Senegal. 15°N 17°W (p. 410)

Damascus (duh•MAS•kuhs) Capital of Syria. 34°N 36°E (p. 359)

Dar es Salaam (DAHR•es suh•LAHM) Indian Ocean seaport of Tanzania. 7°S 39°E (p. 411)

Denmark (DEN•MAHRK) Country in northwestern Europe, between the Baltic and North Seas. 56°N 9°E (p. 225)

Dhaka (DA•kuh) Capital of Bangladesh. 24°N 90°E (pp. 479)

Djibouti (juh•BOO•tee) Country in east Africa, on the Gulf of Aden. 12°N 43°E (pp. 410)

Dodoma (DOH•doh•mah) Capital of Tanzania. 7°S 36°E (p. 410)

Doha (DOH•HAH) Capital of Qatar. 25°N 51°E (p. 359)

Dominican (duh•MIH•nih•kuhn) **Republic** Country in the West Indies on the eastern part of Hispaniola Island. 19°N 71°W (p. 163)

Dublin (DUH•bluhn) Port city and capital of Ireland. 53°N 6°W (p. 225)

Dushanbe (doo•SHAM•buh) Largest city and capital of Tajikistan. 39°N 69°E (p. 293)

E

Ecuador (EH•kwuh•DAWR) Country in South America, south of Colombia. 1°S 79°W (p. 163)

Egypt (EE•juhpt) Country in northern Africa on the Mediterranean Sea. 27°N 27°E (p. 359)

El Salvador (el SAL•vuh•DAWR) Country in Central America, southwest of Honduras. 14°N 89°W (p. 163)

Equatorial Guinea (EE•kwuh•TOHR•ee•uhl GIH•nee) Country in western Africa, south of Cameroon. 2°N 17°E (p. 410)

Estonia (e•STOH•nee•uh) Northern European country on the Baltic Sea. 59°N 25°E (p. 225)

GAZETTEER

Ethiopia (EE•thee•OH•pee•uh) Country in eastern Africa, north of Somalia and Kenya. 8°N 38°E (p. 410)

Euphrates (yu•FRAY•TEEZ) **River** River in southwestern Asia that flows through Syria and Iraq and joins the Tigris River. 36°N 40°E (p. 352)

F

Fiji (FEE•JEE) Country comprised of an island group in the southwest Pacific Ocean. 19°S 175°E (p. 657)

Finland (FIHN•luhnd) Country in northern Europe, east of Sweden. 63°N 26°E (p. 225)

France (FRANTS) Country in western Europe, south of the English Channel. 47°N 1°E (p. 225)

Freetown (FREE•TAUN) Port city and capital of Sierra Leone, in western Africa. 9°N 13°W (p. 410)

G

Gabon (ga•BOHN) Country in western Africa, on the Atlantic Ocean. 0° latitude 12°E (p. 410)

Gaborone (GAH•buh•ROH•NAY) Capital of Botswana, in southern Africa. 24°S 26°E (p. 410)

Gambia (GAM•bee•uh) Country in western Africa, along the Gambia River. 13°N 16°W (p. 410)

Georgetown (JAWRJ•TAUN) Capital of Guyana. 8°N 58°W (p. 163)

Georgia (JAWR•juh) Asian/European country bordering the Black Sea, south of Russia. 42°N 43°E (p. 293)

Germany (JUHR•muh•nee) Country in north central Europe, officially called the Federal Republic of Germany. 52°N 10°E (p. 225)

Ghana (GAH•nuh) Country in western Africa, on the Gulf of Guinea. 8°N 2°W (p. 410)

Greece (GREES) Country in southern Europe, on the Balkan Peninsula. 39°N 22°E (p. 225)

Greenland (GREEN•luhnd) Island in northwestern Atlantic Ocean and the largest island in the world. 74°N 40°W (p. A10)

Guatemala (GWAH•tuh•MAH•luh) Country in Central America, south of Mexico. 16°N 92°W (p. 163)

Guatemala City Capital of Guatemala and the largest city in Central America. 15°N 91°W (p. 163)

Guinea (GIH•nee) West African country, on the Atlantic coast. 11°N 12°W (p. 410)

Guinea-Bissau (GIH•nee bi•SAU) West African country on the Atlantic coast. 12°N 20°W (p. 410)

Gulf of Mexico Gulf on the southeast coast of North America. 25°N 94°W (p. 95)

Guyana (gy•A•nuh) South American country on the Atlantic coast, between Venezuela and Suriname. 8°N 59°W (p. 163)

H

Haiti (HAY•tee) Country on Hispaniola Island in the West Indies. 19°N 72°W (p. 163)

Hanoi (ha•NOY) Capital of Vietnam. 21°N 106°E (p. 599)

Harare (huh•RAH•RAY) Capital of Zimbabwe. 18°S 23°E (p. 410)

Havana (huh•VA•nuh) Seaport, capital city of Cuba, and largest city of the West Indies. 23°N 82°W (p. 163)

Helsinki (HEL•SIHNG•kee) Capital of Finland. 60°N 24°E (p. 225)

Himalayas (HIM•uh•LAY•uhz) Mountain range in South Asia, bordering the Indian subcontinent on the north. 30°N 85°E (p. 479)

Honduras (hahn•DUR•uhs) Central American country, on the Caribbean Sea. 15°N 88°W (p. 163)

Hong Kong (HAHNG KAHNG) British-owned territory and port in southern China. 22°N 115°E (p. 530)

Huang He (HWAHNG HE) **River** in north central and eastern China that is also known as the Yellow River. 35°N 114°E (p. 539)

Hungary (HUHN•guh•ree) Central European country, south of Slovakia. 47°N 18°E (p. 225)

I

Iberian (y•BIR•ee•uhn) **Peninsula** Peninsula in southwest Europe, occupied by Spain and Portugal. 41°N 1°W (p. 225)

Iceland (YS•luhnd) Island country between the North Atlantic and the Arctic oceans. 65°N 20°W (p. 225)

India (IHN•dee•uh) South Asian country, south of China and Nepal. 23°N 78°E (p. 479)

Indonesia (IHN•duh•NEE•zhuh) Group of islands that forms the Southeast Asian country known as the Republic of Indonesia. 5°S 119°E (p. 599)

Indus (IHN•duhs) **River** River in Asia that rises in Tibet and flows through Pakistan to the Arabian Sea. 27°N 68°E (p. 479)

Iran (ih•RAHN) Southwest Asian country that was formerly named Persia. 31°N 54°E (p. 359)

Iraq (ih•RAHK) Southwest Asian country, south of Turkey. 32°N 43°E (p. 359)

Ireland (YR•luhnd) Island west of England, occupied by the Republic of Ireland and by Northern Ireland. 54°N 8°W (p. 225)

Islamabad (is•LAH•muh•BAHD) Capital of Pakistan. 34°N 73°E (p. 479)

Israel (IHZ•ree•uhl) Country in southwest Asia, south of Lebanon. 33°N 34°E (p. 359)

Italy (IH•tuhl•ee) Southern European country, south of Switzerland and east of France. 44°N 11°E (p. 225)

J

Jakarta (juh•KAHR•tuh) Capital of Indonesia. 6°S 107°E (p. 599)

Jamaica (juh•MAY•kuh) Island country in the West Indies. 18°N 78°W (p. 163)

Japan (juh•PAN) Country in East Asia, consisting of the four large islands of Hokkaido, Honshu, Shikoku, and Kyushu, plus thousands of small islands. 37°N 134°E (p. 539)

Jerusalem (juh•ROO•suh•luhm) Capital of Israel and a holy city for Christians, Jews, and Muslims. 32°N 35°E (p. 359)

Jordan (JAWR•duhn) Country in southwest Asia, south of Syria. 30°N 38°E (p. 359)

K

Kabul (kah•BUHL) Capital of Afghanistan. 35°N 69°E (p. 359)

Kampala (kahm•PAH•luh) Capital of Uganda. 0° latitude 32°E (p. 410)

Kathmandu (KAT•MAN•DOO) Capital of Nepal. 28°N 85°E (p. 479)

Kazakhstan (KA•ZAK•STAN) Large Asian country south of Russia, bordering the Caspian Sea. 48°N 65°E (p. 293)

Kenya (KEH•nyuh) Country in eastern Africa, south of Ethiopia. 1°N 37°E (p. 410)

Khartoum (kahr•TOOM) Capital of Sudan. 16°N 33°E (p. 410)

Kiev (KEE•EF) Capital of Ukraine. 50°N 31°E (p. 293)

Kigali (kih•GAH•lee) Capital of Rwanda, in central Africa. 2°S 30°E (p. 410)

Kingston (KIHNG•stuhn) Capital of Jamaica. 18°N 77°W (p. 163)

Kinshasa (kihn•SHAH•suh) Capital of Zaire. 4°S 15°E (p. 410)

Kuala Lumpur (KWAH•luh LUM•PUR) Capital of Malaysia. 3°N 102°E (p. 599)

Kuwait (ku•WAYT) Country between Saudi Arabia and Iraq, on the Persian Gulf. 29°N 48°E (p. 359)

Kyrgyzstan (KIR•giz•STAN) Small central Asian country on China's western border. 41°N 75°E (p. 293)

L

Lagos (LAY•GAHS) Port city of Nigeria. 6°N 3°E (p. 411)

Laos (LOWS) Southeast Asian country, south of China and west of Vietnam. 20°N 102°E (p. 599)

La Paz (luh PAHZ) The administrative capital of Bolivia, and the highest capital in the world. 17°S 68°W (p. 163)

Latvia (LAT•vee•uh) Northeastern European country on the Baltic Sea, west of Russia. 57°N 25°E (p. 225)

Lebanon (LE•buh•nuhn) Country on the Mediterranean Sea, south of Syria. 34°N 34°E (p. 359)

Lesotho (luh•SOH•TOH) Country in south Africa, within the borders of the Republic of South Africa. 30°S 28°E (p. 410)

Liberia (ly•BIR•ee•uh) West African country, south of Guinea. 7°N 10°W (p. 410)

Libreville (LEE•bruh•VIHL) Port city and capital of Gabon. 1°N 9°E (p. 410)

Libya (LIH•bee•uh) North African country on the Mediterranean Sea, west of Egypt. 28°N 15°E (p. 359)

Liechtenstein (LIHK•tuhn•SHTYN) Small country in central Europe, between Switzerland and Austria. 47°N 10°E (p. 243)

Lilongwe (lih•LAWNG•way) Capital of Malawi, in southeastern Africa. 14°S 34°E (p. 410)

Lima (LEE•muh) Capital of Peru. 12°S 77°W (p. 163)

Lisbon (LIHZ•buhn) Port city and capital of Portugal. 39°N 9°W (p. 225)

Lithuania (LIH•thuh•WAY•nee•uh) European country on the Baltic Sea, west of Belarus. 56°N 24°E (p. 225)

Ljubljana (lee•OO•blee•AH•nuh) Capital of Slovenia. 46°N 14°E (p. 225)

Lomé (loh•MAY) Port city and capital of Togo in Africa. 6°N 1°E (p. 410)

London (LUHN•duhn) Capital of the United Kingdom, on the Thames River. 52°N 0° longitude (p. 225)

Luanda (lu•AN•duh) Port city and capital of Angola. 9°S 13°E (p. 410)

Lusaka (loo•SAH•kuh) Capital of Zambia. 15°S 28°E (p. 410)

Luxembourg (LUHK•suhm•BUHRG) Small European country between France, Germany, and Belgium. 50°N 7°E (p. 214)

M

Macedonia (MA•suh•DOH•nee•uh) Southeastern European country north of Greece. 42°N 22°E (p. 225). Macedonia also refers to a geographic region covering northern Greece, the country Macedonia, and part of Bulgaria.

Madagascar (MA•duh•GAS•kuhr) Island in the Indian Ocean off the southeast coast of Africa. 18°S 43°E (p. 410)

Madrid (muh•DRIHD) Capital of Spain. 40°N 4°W (p. 225)

Malabo (mah•LAH•BOH) Capital of Equatorial Guinea. 4°N 9°E (p. 410)

Malawi (muh•LAH•wee) Southeastern African country, south of Tanzania and east of Zambia. 11°S 34°E (p. 410)

Malaysia (muh•LAY•zhuh) Federation of states in Southeast Asia on the Malay Peninsula and the island of Borneo. 4°N 101°E (p. 599)

Maldive (MAHL•DEEV) **Islands** Island country in the Indian Ocean near South Asia. 5°N 42°E (p. 470)

Mali (MAH•lee) Country in western Africa, south of Algeria. 16°N 0° longitude (p. 410)

Managua (muh•NAH•gwuh) Capital of Nicaragua. 12°N 86°W (p. 163)

Manila (muh•NIH•luh) Port city and capital of the Republic of the Philippines. 15°N 121°E (p. 599)

Maseru (MA•suh•ROO) Capital of Lesotho, in southern Africa. 29°S 27°E (p. 410)

Mauritania (MAWR•uh•TAY•nee•uh) Western African country, north of Senegal. 20°N 14°W (p. 410)

Mauritius (maw•RIH•shuhs) Small island country in the Indian Ocean east of Madagascar. 21°S 58°E (p. 410)

Mbabane (EM•bah•BAH•nay) Capital of Swaziland, in southeastern Africa. 26°S 31°E (p. 410)

Mexico (MEK•sih•KOH) Country in North America, south of the United States. 24°N 104°W (p. 163)

Mexico City Capital and most populous city of Mexico. 19°N 99°W (p. 163)

Minsk (MINTSK) Capital of Belarus. 54°N 28°E (p. 293)

Mogadishu (MAH•guh•DIH•SHOO) Major seaport and capital of Somalia, in eastern Africa. 2°N 45°E (p. 410)

Moldova (mahl•DOH•vuh) Small European country between Ukraine and Romania. 47°N 29°E (p. 293)

Monaco (MAH•nuh•KOH) Small country in southern Europe, on the French Mediterranean coast. 44°N 8°E (p. 243)

Mongolia (mahn•GOHL•yuh) Country in Asia between Russia and China 46°N 100°E (p. 539)

Monrovia (MUHN•ROH•vee•uh) Major seaport and capital of Liberia, in western Africa. 6°N 11°W (p. 410)

Montevideo (MAHN•tuh•vuh•DAY•OH) Capital of Uruguay. 35°S 56°W (p. 163)

Morocco (muh•RAH•KOH) Country in northwestern Africa on the Mediterranean Sea and the Atlantic Ocean. 32°N 7°W (p. 359)

GAZETTEER

Moscow (MAHS•KOH) Capital and largest city of Russia. 56°N 38°E (p. 293)

Mount Everest (EV•ruhst) Highest mountain in the world, in the Himalayas between Nepal and Tibet. 28°N 87°E (p. 472)

Mozambique (MOH•zuhm•BEEK) Country in southeastern Africa, south of Tanzania. 20°S 34°E (p. 410)

Muscat (MUHS•KAT) Seaport and capital of Oman. 23°N 59°E (p. 359)

Myanmar (MYAN•mahr) Country in Southeast Asia, south of China and India, formerly called Burma. 21°N 95°E (p. 599)

N

Nairobi (ny•ROH•bee) Capital of Kenya. 1°S 37°E (p. 410)

Namibia (nuh•MIH•bee•uh) Country in southwestern Africa, south of Angola on the Atlantic Ocean. 20°S 16°E (p. 410)

Nassau (NA•SAW) Capital of the Bahamas. 25°N 77°W (p. 163)

N'Djamena (EN•juh•MAY•nuh) Capital of Chad. 12°N 15°E (p. 410)

Nepal (nuh•PAWL) Mountain country between India and China. 29°N 83°E (p. 479)

Netherlands (NE•thuhr•lundz) Western European country on the North Sea, north of Belgium. 53°N 4°E (p. 225)

New Delhi (NOO DEH•lee) Capital of India. 29°N 77°E (p. 479)

New Zealand (NOO ZEE•luhnd) Major island country in the South Pacific, southeast of Australia. 42°S 175°E (p. 657)

Niamey (nee•AH•may) Capital and commercial center of Niger, in western Africa. 14°N 2°E (p. 410)

Nicaragua (NI•kuh•RAH•gwuh) Country in Central America, south of Honduras. 13°N 86°W (p. 163)

Nicosia (NIH•kuh•SEE•uh) Capital of Cyprus. 35°N 33°E (p. 359)

Niger (NY•juhr) Landlocked country in western Africa, north of Nigeria. 18°N 9°E (p. 410)

Nigeria (ny•JIR•ee•uh) Country in western Africa, south of Niger. 9°N 7°E (p. 410)

Nile (NYL) **River** Longest river in the world, flowing north and east through eastern Africa. 27°N 31°E (pp. 359, 410)

North Korea (kuh•REE•uh) Asian country in the northernmost part of the Korean Peninsula. 39°N 127°E (p. 539)

Norway (NAWR•WAY) Country on the Scandinavian Peninsula. 64°N 11°E (p. 225)

Nouakchott (noo•AHK•SHAHT) Capital of Mauritania. 18°N 16°W (p. 410)

O

Oman (oh•MAHN) Country on the Arabian Sea and the Gulf of Oman. 20°N 58°E (p. 359)

Oslo (AHZ•loh) Capital and largest city of Norway. 60°N 11°E (p. 225)

Ottawa (AH•tuh•wuh) Capital of Canada. 45°N 76°W (p. 95)

Ouagadougou (WAH•guh•DOO•goo) Capital of Burkina Faso, in western Africa. 12°N 2°W (p. 410)

P

Pakistan (PA•ki•STAN) South Asian country on the Arabian Sea, northwest of India. 28°N 68°E (p. 479)

Palau (pah•LOW) Island country in the Pacific Ocean. 7°N 135°E (p. 648)

Panama (PA•nuh•MAH) Country in Central America, on the Isthmus of Panama. 9°N 81°W (p. 163)

Panamá Capital of Panama. 9°N 79°W (p. 163)

Papua New Guinea (PA•pyuh•wuh NOO GIH•nee) Independent island country in the South Pacific Ocean. 7°S 142°E (p. 657)

Paraguay (PAR•uh•GWY) Country in South America, north of Argentina. 24°S 58°W (p. 163)

Paramaribo (PAIR•uh•MAIR•uh•BOH) Port city and capital of Suriname. 6°N 55°W (p. 163)

Paris (PAIR•uhs) River port and capital of France. 49°N 2°E (p. 225)

Persian (PUHR•zhuhn) **Gulf** Arm of the Arabian Sea between Iran and Saudi Arabia. 28°N 51°E (p. 359)

GAZETEER

Peru – Skopje

Peru (puh•ROO) Country in South America, south of Ecuador and Colombia. 10°S 75°W (p. 163)

Philippines (FIH•luh•PEENZ) Country in the Pacific Ocean, southeast of Asia. 14°N 125°E (p. 599)

Phnom Penh (NAWM•PEN) Capital of Cambodia. 12°N 106°E (p. 599)

Poland (POH•luhnd) Country on the Baltic Sea in eastern Europe. 52°N 18°E (p. 225)

Port-au-Prince (POHRT•oh•PRINTS) Capital of Haiti. 19°N 72°W (p. 163)

Port Moresby (MOHRZ•bee) Capital of Papua New Guinea. 10°S 147°E (p. 657)

Porto-Novo (POHR•tuh•NOH•voh) Port city and capital of Benin, in western Africa. 7°N 3°E (p. 410)

Portugal (POHR•chih•guhl) Country on the Iberian Peninsula, south and west of Spain. 38°N 8°W (p. 225)

Prague (PRAHG) Capital of the Czech Republic. 50°N 15°E (p. 225)

Pretoria (prih•TOHR•ee•uh) Capital of South Africa. 26°S 28°E (p. 410)

Puerto Rico (PWEHR•tuh•REE•koh) Island in the Caribbean Sea; U.S. commonwealth. 19°N 67°W (p. 163)

Pyongyang (pee•AWNG•YAHNG) Capital of North Korea. 39°N 126°E (p. 539)

Q

Qatar (KAH•tuhr) Country on the south-western shore of the Persian Gulf. 25°N 53°E (p. 359)

Quito (KEE•toh) Capital of Ecuador. 0° latitude 79°W (p. 163)

R

Rabat (ruh•BAHT) Capital of Morocco. 34°N 7°W (p. 359)

Reykjavík (RAY•kyuh•VIK) Capital of Iceland. 64°N 22°W (p. 225)

Riga (REE•guh) Capital and largest city of Latvia. 57°N 24°E (p. 225)

Riyadh (ree•YAHD) Capital of Saudi Arabia. 25°N 47°E (p. 359)

Romania (ruh•MAY•nee•uh) Country in eastern Europe, south of Ukraine. 46°N 23°E (p. 225)

Rome (ROHM) Capital of Italy, on the Tiber River. 42°N 13°E (p. 225)

Russia (RUH•shuh) Largest country in the world, covering parts of Europe and Asia. 60°N 90°E (p. 293)

Rwanda (roo•AHN•duh) Country in Africa, south of Uganda. 2°S 30°E (p. 410)

S

St. Thomas Island that is part of U.S. Virgin Islands, in the Caribbean Sea 18°N 65°W (p. A9)

San'a (sa•NAH) Capital of Yemen. 15°N 44°E (p. 359)

San José (SAN uh•ZAY) Capital of Costa Rica. 10°N 84°W (p. 163)

San Marino (SAN mah•REE•noh) Small European Country, located in the Italian peninsula. 44°N 13°E (p. 243)

San Salvador (san SAL•vuh•DAWR) Capital of El Salvador. 14°N 89°W (p. 163)

Santiago (SAN•tee•AH•goh) Capital of Chile. 33°S 71°W (p. 163)

Santo Domingo (SANT•uh duh•MIN•goh) Capital of the Dominican Republic. 19°N 70°W (p. 153)

São Tomé and Príncipe (SOWN•tuh•MAY PRIN•suh•pah) Small island country in Gulf of Guinea off the coast of Central Africa. 1°N 7°E (p. 410)

Sarajevo (SAR•uh•YAY•voh) Capital of Bosnia and Herzegovina. 43°N 18°E (p. 225)

Saudi Arabia (SOW•dee uh•RAY•bee•uh) Country on the Arabian Peninsula. 23°N 46°E (p. 359)

Senegal (SEH•nih•GAWL) Country on the coast of western Africa, on the Atlantic Ocean. 15°N 14°W (p. 410)

Seoul (SOHL) Capital of South Korea. 38°N 127°E (p. 539)

Serbia (SUHR•bee•uh) European country south of Hungary. 44°N 22°E (p. 225)

Seychelles (say•SHELZ) Small island country in the Indian Ocean near East Africa. 6°S 56°E (p. 410)

Sierra Leone (see•EHR•uh lee•OHN) Country in western Africa, south of Guinea. 8°N 12°W (p. 410)

Singapore (SIHNG•uh•POHR) Multi-island country in Southeast Asia near tip of Malay Peninsula. 2°N 104°E (p. 590)

Skopje (SKAW•pyah) Capital of the country of Macedonia. 42°N 21°E (p. 225)

GAZETTEER

768

Slovakia (sloh•VAH•kee•uh) Central European country south of Poland. 49°N 19°E (p. 225)

Slovenia (sloh•VEE•nee•uh) Small central European country on the Adriatic Sea, south of Austria. 46°N 15°E (p. 225)

Sofia (SOH•fee•uh) Capital of Bulgaria. 43°N 23°E (p. 225)

Somalia (soh•MAH•lee•uh) Country in Africa, on the Gulf of Aden and the Indian Ocean. 3°N 45°E (p. 410)

South Africa Country at the southern tip of Africa. 28°S 25°E (p. 410)

South Korea Country in Asia on the Korean Peninsula between the Yellow Sea and the Sea of Japan. 36°N 128°E (p. 539)

Spain Country on the Iberian Peninsula. 40°N 4°W (p. 225)

Sri Lanka (sree•LAHNG•kuh) Country in the Indian Ocean south of India, formerly called Ceylon. 9°N 83°E (p. 479)

Stockholm (STAHK•HOHLM) Capital of Sweden. 59°N 18°E (p. 225)

Sucre (SOO•kray) Constitutional capital of Bolivia. 19°S 65°W (p. 163)

Sudan (soo•DAN) Northeast African country on the Red Sea. 14°N 28°E (p. 410)

Suriname (SUR•uh•NAH•muh) South American country on the Atlantic Ocean between Guyana and French Guiana. 4°N 56°W (p. 163)

Suva (SOO•vuh) Port city and capital of Fiji. 18°S 177°E (p. 657)

Swaziland (SWAH•zee•LAND) South African country west of Mozambique, almost entirely within the Republic of South Africa. 27°S 32°E (p. 410)

Sweden (SWEE•duhn) Northern European country on the eastern side of the Scandinavian Peninsula. 60°N 14°E (p. 225)

Switzerland (SWIT•suhr•luhnd) European country in the Alps, south of Germany. 47°N 8°E (p. 225)

Syria (SIHR•ee•uh) Country in Asia on the east side of the Mediterranean Sea. 35°N 37°E (p. 359)

T

Taipei (TY•PAY) Capital of Taiwan. 25°N 122°E (p. 539)

Taiwan (TY•WAHN) Island country off the southeast coast of China, and the seat of the Chinese Nationalist government. 24°N 122°E (p. 539)

Tajikistan (tah•JIH•kih•STAN) Central Asian country north of Afghanistan. 39°N 70°E (p. 293)

Tallinn (TA•luhn) Largest city and capital of Estonia. 59°N 25°E (p. 225)

Tanzania (TAN•zuh•NEE•uh) East African country on the coast of the Indian Ocean, south of Uganda and Kenya. 7°S 34°E (p. 410)

Tashkent (tash•KENT) Capital of Uzbekistan and a major industrial center. 41°N 69°E (p. 293)

Tbilisi (tuh•BEE•luh•see) Capital of the Republic of Georgia. 42°N 45°E (p. 293)

Tegucigalpa (tuh•GOO•suh•GAL•puh) Capital of Honduras. 14°N 87°W (p. 163)

Tehran (TAY•RAN) Capital of Iran. 36°N 52°E (p. 359)

Thailand (TY•LAND) Southeast Asian country south of Myanmar. 17°N 101°E (p. 599)

Thimphu (THIHM•boo) Capital of Bhutan. 28°N 90°E (p. 479)

Tiranë (tih•RAH•nuh) Capital of Albania. 42°N 20°E (p. 225)

Togo (TOH•goh) West African country between Benin and Ghana, on the Gulf of Guinea. 8°N 1°E (p. 410)

Tokyo (TOH•kee•OH) Capital of Japan. 36°N 140°E (p. 539)

Trinidad and Tobago (TRIH•nih•DAD tuh•BAY•goh) Island country off the coast of Venezuela. 11°N 61°W (p. 152)

Tripoli (TRIH•puh•lee) Capital of Libya. 33°N 13°E (p. 359)

Tunis (TOO•nuhs) Port city and capital of Tunisia. 37°N 10°E (p. 359)

Tunisia (too•NEE•zhuh) North African country on the Mediterranean Sea between Libya and Algeria. 35°N 10°E (p. 359)

Turkey (TUHR•kee) Country in southeastern Europe and western Asia. 39°N 32°E (p. 359)

Turkmenistan (TUHRK•MEH•nuh•STAN) Central Asian country on the Caspian Sea. 40°N 60°E (p. 293)

U

Uganda (oo•GAN•duh) East African country south of Sudan. 2°N 32°E (p. 410)

Ukraine (yoo•KRAYN) Large eastern European country west of Russia, on the Black Sea. 49°N 30°E (p. 293)

Ulan Bator (OO•LAHN BAH•TAWR) Capital of Mongolia. 48°N 107°E (p. 539)

United Arab Emirates (ih•MIR•uhts) Country made up of seven states on the eastern side of the Arabian Peninsula. 24°N 54°E (p. 359)

United Kingdom Country in Western Europe made up of England, Scotland, Wales, and Northern Ireland. 57°N 2°W (p. 225)

United States of America Country in North America made up of 50 states, mostly between Canada and Mexico. 38°N 110°W (p. 95)

Uruguay (UR•uh•GWY) South American country, south of Brazil on the Atlantic Ocean. 33°S 56°W (p. 163)

Uzbekistan (OOZ•BEH•kih•STAN) Central Asian country south of Kazakhstan, on the Caspian Sea. 41°N 65°E (p. 293)

V

Vanuatu (VAHN•WAH•TOO) Country made up of islands in the Pacific Ocean, east of Australia. 17°S 170°W (p. 657)

Vatican (VA•tih•kuhn) **City** Headquarters of the Roman Catholic Church, located in the city of Rome in Italy. 42°N 13°E (p. 243)

Venezuela (VEH•nuh•ZWAY•luh) South American country on the Caribbean Sea, between Columbia and Guyana. 8°N 65°W (p. 163)

Vienna (vee•EH•nuh) Capital of Austria. 48°N 16°E (p. 225)

Vientiane (VYEHN•TYAHN) Capital of Laos. 18°N 103°E (p. 599)

Vietnam (vee•ET•NAHM) Southeast Asian country, east of Laos and Cambodia. 18°N 107°E (p. 599)

Virgin Islands Island territory of the United States, east of Puerto Rico in the Caribbean Sea. 18°N 65°W (p. 152)

W

Warsaw (WAWR•SAW) Capital of Poland. 52°N 21°E (p. 225)

Washington, D.C. Capital of the United States, in the District of Columbia. 39°N 77°W (p. 95)

Wellington Capital of New Zealand. 41°S 175°E (p. 657)

West Indies (IHN•deez) Islands in the Caribbean Sea, between North America and South America. 19°N 79°W (p. 163)

Windhoek (VIHNT•HOOK) Capital of Namibia, in southwestern Africa. 22°S 17°E (p. 410)

Y

Yamoussoukro (YAH•muh•SOO•kroh) Second capital of Côte d'Ivoire, in western Africa. 7°N 6°W (p. A19)

Yangon (YAHN•GOHN) Capital of Myanmar. 17°N 96°E (p. 599)

Yaoundé (yown•DAY) Capital of Cameroon, in western Africa. 4°N 12°E (p. 410)

Yemen (YEH•muhn) Country on the Arabian Peninsula, south of Saudi Arabia on the Gulf of Aden and the Red Sea. 15°N 46°E (p. 359)

Yerevan (YEHR•uh•VAHN) Largest city and capital of Armenia. 40°N 44°E (p. 293)

Z

Zagreb (ZAH•grehb) Largest city and capital of Croatia. 46°N 16°E (p. 225)

Zaire (zah•IHR) African country on the Equator, north of Zambia and Angola. 1°S 22°E (p. 410)

Zambia (ZAM•bee•uh) Country in south central Africa, south of Zaire and Tanzania. 14°S 24°E (p. 410)

Zimbabwe (zim•BAH•bwee) Country in south central Africa. 18°S 30°E (p. 410)

GAZETTEER

Index

c = chart	m = map
d = diagram	p = photo
g = graph	ptg = painting

A

Aborigines, 669, 673, 678; art of, 680
abstract art, 121
Abu Simbel, *p 376*
acid deposition, 271
acid rain, 137-38, *m 138, p 139,* 270-71, *p 271,* 274, 577
Acquired Immunodeficiency Syndrome (AIDS), 434
ADB. *see* Asian Development Bank
Adelaide, Australia, 670
adire cloth, 444
Aegean Islands, 244
Aegean Sea, 224
Afghanistan, 352, 358, 373, 383
Africa. *see* Africa South of the Sahara; North Africa and Southwest Asia; South Africa
Africans; in Latin America, 176, 182, 183, 188; in the United States, 113
Africa South of the Sahara, *m 410, m 421;* agriculture in, 438, 451-52, *p 452, c 452,* 456-57, 459; air travel in, 455; Arabs in, 437; arts in, 424, 443-44; atlas of, 412-17; cities in, *p 418,* 435-36, *c 436,* 442, 456-57; civil war in, 459; clans in, 444-45; communications in, 155; conflicts over land use in, 460-61; conservation in, 427, 459; crafts in, 424, 444; cultures in, 457, 466-67; deforestation in, 460; desertification in, 458-59; deserts in, 424-25; disease in, 434; early civilizations in, 438-49; economies in, 434-35, 451-52, 453, *m 453,* 454, 457; ecotourism in, 461; education in, 445, 457; energy sources in, 422, 423; environmental problems in, 427, 457; ethnic groups in, 410, *m 435,* 436, 440, 442, 443, 444-45; European colonization in, 439-40, 441, *m 441,* 451-52; extended family in, 444; famine in, 434-35, 458-59, *m 459;* fishing in, 453; food production in, 434, 452; forests in, 453, 460; game preserves in, 427, 460; history of, 438-41; industry in, 427, 454, *p 455;* lakes in, 420; landforms of, *m 412,* 419-20; languages and dialects in, 436, 442-43; lifestyles in, 444-45; literature in, 444; logging in, 427; mineral resources in, 413, 423, 453, 456; mining in, 453; mountains and highlands of, *p 408-09,* 412, 420; music in, 444, 466, 467; Muslims in, 443; natural resources in, *m 413,* 423; oil in, 423, 456; oral history in, 444; overpopulation in, 433, 434, 456-57; plateaus in, 419-20; population density in, *m 411,* 434-36, 456-57; population growth rate in, 433, 434-35, 456-57; poverty in, 457; railroads in, *p 454,* 454, 455; rain forests in, 413, 427; reli-

gions in, 443; rivers in, 412, 422; slave trade in, *m 439,* 440; standards of living in, 434-35, 445, 453; trade in, 410, *c 414-17,* 437, 439; transportation in, 454-55; urbanization in, 435-36, 444; vegetation in, *m 426,* 426-27, 453; waterfalls in, 422-23; water systems in, 420-23; wildlife in, 460-61. *See also* North Africa and Southwest Asia; South Africa
Age of Classical Greece, 71
agriculture, 63-64; cash crops, 113, 195-96, 452, 512-13, 630, 688; cattle ranching, 114, 130, 164, 195-96, 202-03, 392; collective farms, 264, 329-30; commercial farming, 64, 452; communes, 571-72; contour plowing, 131; crop rotation, 38, 131; dry farming, 116; estate farming, 196, 617; farm cooperatives, 264; green revolution, 513; irrigation, 8, 57, 112, *p 131,* 334, 339, 359, 630; mixed farming, 264; organic farming, 264; plantation, 116, 155, 169, 182, 493, 512, 630; sedentary farming, 452; shifting cultivation, 381, 452; slash-and-burn farming, 202; state farms, 264, 329-30, 572; subsistence farming, 63-64, 452, 511, 513, 680, 688; technology in, 117, 131-32, 242, 513; traditional, 63-64; truck farms, 131. *See also* names of culture regions
AIDS. *see* Acquired Immuno deficiency Syndrome
Ainu, 552
air pollution. *see* pollution
air travel, 198-99, 266, 332, *p 393,* 394, 455, 575, 634, 691, *p 691*
Akha people, 595
Alaska, 98, 108, 116, 136, 296
Alaska Range, 93
Albania, 224, 252
Alberta, 115, 123, 130
Aleppo, Syria, 350
Algeria, 351, 359, 360, 371, 374
alluvial plain, 480
alluvial-soil deposits, 359, 377
alphabet, 377
Alps, *p 56,* 216, 227, 231, 241, 292
Altai Mountains, 538
Althing, 214
altiplano, 162, 196
Altmuhl Valley, 267
Amazon River, 154, 164, 198
Amazon River basin, 52, 162, 164, 167, 198, 202-04, *p 203*
amendments, 117, 118
American Samoa, 676
Amur River, 294
Anáhuac, *p 162*
Anatolian Peninsula, 358, 397
Andes Mountains, 154, 162
Andorra, 243
Angkor Wat, Cambodia, *m 618, p 618,* 621
animal, most poisonous, 672
Annamese Cordillera, 598
Antarctica, 33, *m 651, p 659,* 676, *m 697;* air travel in, *p 691;* climate in, *m 661,* 663; environmental problems in, 696-97; explorations of,

673, 675; ice cap of, 32, 35, 663, 677, *p 677,* 688; landforms of, 650, 659, 677, *p 677;* living in, 677; natural resources of, 688; ozone above, 72, *p 73,* 659, 696; population in, *m 649,* 669, 670; protecting the wilderness of, 696-97; scientific research in, 651, 655, 659, 677, 696-97 *m 697;* sea resources of, 659, 688; vegetation in, *m 662,* 663
Antarctic Circle, 48, 49
Antarctic Treaty, 697
anthropologists, 10, 77
anthropology; and geography, 10
apartheid, 440
Apennine Peninsula, 224
Appalachian Mountains, 94
aquifers, 398
Arabian Peninsula, *p 38,* 352, 353, 358, 363, 371
Arabian Sea, 358, 477
arable land, 612
Arabs, 371, 372, *p 372,* 379
Arafat, Yasser, *p 372;* and West Bank Accord, 372
Arakan Range, 598
Aral Sea, 293, 334-35, *p 335;* pollution of, 334-35, *p 335*
Ararat, Mount, 358
archaeologists, 69
archipelago, 34, 598
Arctic Circle, 48, 49, 224, 296
Arctic Ocean, 34, 94, 111
Argentina, 152, 153, 154, 155, 164, 169, 185, 197, 198
Arizona, 86, 87, 113, 115
Armenia, 284, 286, 288, 307, 308, *p 309,* 318, 319, 332, 333, 373; earthquake in, 67
art, *p 82-83, ptg 122;* Aboriginal, 680; abstract 121, 253; abstract expressionism, 346; African, 189; assemblages, 346; Byzantine, 248, 252; of calligraphy, 565; classical, 280; cubism, 347; European influence in, 253, 281; Gothic, 248, 252; impressionism, 253; modernism, 188; mosaics, 188, 189; Native American, 121, 188; realism, 252; and religion, 252, 564, 672; of the Renaissance, 246-47, 248, 252; romanticism, 252; socialist realism, 320. *See also* names of regions
Artesian Basin, 655-56
artesian waters, 656
artifacts, 69
Aryans, 496, 497
ASEAN. *see* Association of Southeast Asian Nations
Asia, 33. *See also* East Asia; North Africa and Southwest Asia; South Asia; Southeast Asia
Asian Development Bank (ADB), 633
Asir Mountains, 358
Asoka, 498
assembly lines, *p 83,* 117
Association of Southeast Asian Nations (ASEAN), 633
asteroids, 27
Aswan High Dam, 359, 400
Atacama Desert, *p 165,* 165, 166
atheists, 317
Atlantic Coastal Plain, 94

INDEX

Atlantic Ocean, 34; islands of, 224, 226

Atlas Mountains, 358, *p 361*, 365, 420

atmosphere; earth's, 27, 49, 50; greenhouse effect and, 45, 57, 72-73, 578

atoll, *p 36*

Auckland, New Zealand, 670, *p 671*, 689

Australia, *m 648, m 651, m 657;* Aborigines in, 669, 673, 678, 680; agriculture in, 656, 687-88; air travel in, 691; animal life in, 672, 694-95, *p 695;* animal overpopulation in, 695; arts in, 680, 703; British in, 669, 675; cattle stations in, 687-88, 691; Central Lowlands of, 655-56; cities of, *p 668*, 670, 681; climate regions in, 660, *m 661;* coastal regions of, 660; communications in, 691; cultural patterns of, 678-81; deserts of, 656; economic activity in, *m 689*, 689; education in, 681; environmental problems in, 692-93; 694-97; ethnic origins of, 669, *c 680;* European influence in, 669, 678-79, 680; explorations of, 674; fishing in, 673; food production in, 687-88; government in, *p 676*, 676; Great Barrier Reef of, 656, 692-93, *m 693, p 693;* health care in, 653, 681; history of, 669, 673-75, *m 674*, 678-79; immigration in, 669, 675; independence of, 675; influence on United States culture, 702-03; language in, 679; lifestyles in, 679, 680-81; literature of, 680; manufacturing in, 689; mineral resources of, *m 651*, 656, 675, 688; mining in, 688, *p 696;* mountains and hills of, 655, 660; natural resources of, *m 649*, 656; outback in, 656, *p 663*, 680, 681, *p 690;* plains of, 656; population density in, 649, *m 649*, 669, 670; population distribution in, 669, 670; road and rail systems in, 690; sea pollution in, 692-93; size of, 241, 650; sports in, *p 679;* tourism in, 653, 692-93; urbanization in, 671; vegetation in, 660, *m 662;* western plateau of, 656. *See also* South Pacific

Austria, 214, *p 241*

authoritarian government, 74

autobahn, 266, *p 266*

automobiles, 90, 117, 134-35, 266, 274; pollution from, 138, 205

autopistas, 198

avalanche, 232

axis, of the earth, 45-46

Axum, 138

Ayers Rock, *p 658*

Azerbaijan, 285, 288, 292, 295, 298, 306, 315, 318, 319, 330-31, 333

azimuthal projection, 18

Aztec civilization, 181

B

Babylonians, 371

Bahamas, *m A2, m A5, m A10,* 161, *m 163*

Bahrain, 350, 374

Baikal, Lake, 293, *p 339*, 339-40, 437

Baku, Azerbaijan, 287, 295, 331

Balaton, Lake, 229, 272, *p 274*

Balearic Islands, 226

Bali, Indonesia, *p 630*, 635

Balkan Peninsula, 224, 229, 231, 240, 245

bamboo, 484

Bangkok, Thailand, 590, 613, *p 628*, 633, *p 634*, 635, *p 636*

Bangladesh, 471, 472, 474, 477, *p 480*, 491, 501, 515, 518; agriculture in, 512, 513; cyclones in, 484, 519; independence of, 470, 499; population density in, 471, 493, 494

Bantu, 439, 442-43

bar graph, 20, 322

bark painting, 680

batik, 621

bauxite, 165, 229

Bavaria, 267

Bay of Bengal, 35, 477, 518

bays, 34

Beatles, 281

bedouins, 350

Beethoven, Ludwig van, 280

Beijing, China, 540, *p 570*, 575, 577

Belarus, 285, 306, *p 328*, 333; forests in, 295, 299; radiation in, 330, 337; refineries in, 333

Belgium, 240, 264

Belize, 152

Benin, 411

Bering Sea, 293

Bering Strait, 111, 181

Bermuda, *m A9, m A10, p 199*

Bhutan, 471, 492, 494, 501, 502, 513, 515; forests in, 473, 481, 519; isolation of, 477, 478, 499, 500; natural resources of, 480, 481, 514; tourism in, 515, 518

Bikini Atoll, 695

Bilauktaung Range, 598

bilingual, 121

biologists, 274

biosphere, 28

birthrate, 65

Bismarck Archipelago, 657

Black Earth Belt, 287, 295

Black Forest, 230, 233, 270

black market, 328

Black Sea, 224, 293, *p 294*, 332, 340, 358

Blanc, Mount, 216, *p 227*

blizzards, 100

Bogotá, Colombia, 205

Bolivia, 153, 155, 164, 165, 178, 197, 202

Bolsheviks, 313

Bombay, India, 494, *p 494*

boomerang, 673

Borneo, 592, 598, 600, 631, 635

Borobudur, 621

Bosnia-Herzegovina, 240, *p 240*, 252

Bosphorus Sea, 224

Botswana, 425, 434

box jellyfish, 672

Brahmaputra River, 478, 480

Brasília, Brazil, 189

Brazil, 152, 153, *p 160*, 164, 165, 167, 202; agriculture in, 155; Carnival in, *p 174*, 189; industry in, 197; population density in, 178; Portuguese in, 182. *See also* Amazon River basin

Brazilian Highlands, 162, 164

British Columbia, 108, 109, 115

British Isles, 216, 226, 229

British North America Act, 118

Brunei, 593, 597, 598; natural resources in, 592, 600, 631; population density in, 591, 611

Brussels, Belgium, *p 238*, 242, *p 275*

Buddhism; in East Asia, 561, 562, *p 564;* in South Asia, 496-97, 501-02; in Southeast Asia, 621; in the United States and Canada, 120

Buenos Aires, Argentina, 153, 164, 178, 185, *p 185*, 205

buffalo, 112

Bulgaria, 224, 231, 252

Burkina Faso, 411

Burma, 597, 601

Burundi, 452

bycatch, 141

Byzantine Empire, 245

C

cabinet, 118

Cairo, Egypt, *p 370*, 374

Cajuns, 121

Calcutta, India, *p 475*

California, 86, 87, 110, 113, 131

calligraphy, 565

Cambodia, 593, 597, 598, 623; population density in, 611, 612; war and political change in, 590, 615, 618, 632

Cameroon, 414

campesinos, 196

Canaanites, 371

Canada, *m 95;* acid rain in, 138; agriculture in, 89, 97, 101, *m 101*, 129-32; arts in, 121-22; atlas of, 88-91; borders of, 86, 117; cattle in, 130; celebrations in, 123; cities of, *g 100*, 109, *p 128;* climate regions of, 98-100, *m 99, g 100*, 111, 112; communication networks in, 134, 136; cultures of, 82-83, 121-22; Dominion established in, 115; economy of, 90, 129, *m 130*, 132-34; education in, 123; energy resources in, 97, 115; environmental problems in, 137-39; ethnic groups in, 107, 111, 119; European colonization of, 111, 112-14; European influence in, 121-22; fishing in, 89, 97, 139, 141; food processing in, 132; foreign trade of, 132-33; forests in, 89, 97, 100, 140; French Canadians in, 86, 115, 119; government in, 90, 115, *d 117*, 118-19; health care in, 122-23; history of, 111, 119; housing in, 122; industrialization in, 115; industry in, 90, 115-16, 132, 135; inland waterways of, 91, *d 91*, 94-96, 108, 109, 113, 135; interdependence of, 133-34; Inuit in, 86, 111, 118; lakes in, 88, 97, 138, 139; landforms of, 88-89, *p 90*, 93-96, *m 94*, 100-01; languages in, 115, 119, 120-21; lifestyles in, 122-23; literature in, 121; logging in, 97, 140; Loyalists in, 115, 119; mineral resources of, 89, 97, 117; mountains in, 88, *p 90*, 93-94; music in, 121-22; national parks in, 90, 123; natural resources of, *m 87*, 89, 97, 111, 112, 117, 139-41; overuse of resources in, 139-41; plains in, 89, 94, 97, 101, 130; plateaus of, 94; polar regions of,

100, 108, 111; population density in, 65, *m 87*, *g 87*, 107-08; population distribution in, 107-08; provinces of, 115, 118; railroads in, *p 116, p 117*, 135; religion in, 120, *g 121*; rivers of, 94-96, 97, 113; roads in, 134-35; service industries in, 132; sports and recreation in, 123, 148-49; standard of living in, 122; territories of, 118; trade in, 132-34; transportation in, 117, 134-36; vegetation in, 100-01, *m 101*
Canadian Pacific Railway, *p 116*
Canadian Shield, 88, 89, 94, 96
canals, 267, 331, 335, 377, 394
Canberra, Australia, *p 676*
cane toad, 694-95
canopy, 167
canyons, 31, 34
Cape Horn, 659
Capetown, South Africa, *p 418,* 436
Cape York Peninsula, 655
capitalism, 76; in the United States and Canada, 129
Caracas, Venezuela, 153, *p 194*
cardinal directions, 12
Caribbean islands, 109, 176, 183; landforms of, 161, 178. *See also* Latin America
Carpathian Mountains, 227, 292
cartograms, 144, *m 144*
cartographers, 11, 40, 58
Cascade Range, 93
Case Studies, 72-73, 142-43, 200-01, 268-69, 334-35, 396-97, 456-57, 516-17, 580-81, 638-39, 692-93
cash crops, 113; in Africa South of the Sahara, 452; in Latin America, 195-96; in South Asia, 512; in Southeast Asia, 630; in the South Pacific, 688; in the United States and Canada, 113, 116
Caspian Sea, 227, 286, 293, 338-39, 358, 373
caste system, 196, 197
cataracts, 420
cattle ranching; in Australia, 687-88, 691; in Latin America, 164, 195-96, 202-03; in North Africa and Southwest Asia, 392; in the United States and Canada, 114, 116, 130
Caucasians, 305, 307
Caucasus Mountains, 292, 332
caudillos, 184
cause and effect relationships, 606
Celts, 240
Central America, 113, 161, 181; landforms of, 154. *See also* Latin America
Central Lowlands, 94, 97, 655-56
Central Plateau, 358
Central Siberian Plateau, 293, 339
Central Uplands, 226, 227
cereals, 364
Chad, 435, 455
Chad, Lake, 420
Chang Jiang River, 540
Channel Tunnel, 250
Chao Phraya River, 600, 630
chaparral, 54, 232
charts, 20-22
Chernobyl disaster, 330, 336-37, *p 337*
chernozem, 291
Chiang Kai-shek, 559
Chile, 164, 165
China; agriculture in, 533, 540,

571-72, *p 572*; arts in, 564; communism in, 559, 564, 571, 576; Cultural Revolution in, 564; culture of, 71, 246; dynasties in, 556, *m 558;* early civilization in, 556; earthquakes in, 579; economy of, 72-73, 562; ethnic groups in, 530, 551-52; European trade with, 558-59; flooding in, 577, 578-79, *p 579;* Grand Canal in, 576; Great Leap Forward, 571, 577; Great Wall of, *p 70,* 71, 532, *p 557;* industrialization in, 575, 577; landforms of, 538; Mongols in, 558; Nationalists in, 530, 551, 554, 559; natural resources of, 533, 540-41; population density in, 554; population distribution in, 552; population of, 531, 537; population policy in, 552; railroads in, 576; revolutions in, 559; rivers of, 539-40; trade in, 615; transportation centers in, 576. *See also* East Asia
Chinese; in Latin America, 176; in the United States, 117
chinook, 100
chlorofluorocarbons (CFCs), 72-73, *d 73,* 578
Chota Nagpur Plateau, 478
Christianity; in Africa South of the Sahara, 443; in East Asia, 561, *c 562;* in Europe, 245; in North Africa and Southwest Asia, 378, 382; in Russia and the Eurasian Republics, 307; in Southeast Asia, 615; in the South Pacific, 675, 679; in the United States and Canada, 114, 120
circle graph, 21, 446
CIS. *see* Commonwealth of Independent States
city-states, 245
Ciudad Juárez, Mexico, 196-97
civilization, 69; African, 438-39; Aztec, 181; in China, 556; culture hearths, 69; Egyptian, 376-77; Incan, 181-82; Indus Valley, 496; Mayan, 181; Mesopotamian, 377, *m 377*
clans, 444-45, 557-58
clearcutting, 140
climate, 45; adaptations to, 56-57, 70; changes in, 57; culture and, 78; dry, 53; elevation and, 49-50, 170, 234; factors affecting, 48-51, 170, 234; highland, 56, 98, 167, 231, 234; high latitude, 55-56; landforms and, 51; latitude and, 48-49, 234; midlatitude, 49, 54; ocean currents and, 50-51, 234; sun's effect on, 45, 46, 48-51; temperature and, 49, 234; tropical, 52, 234; wind and, 50, 51. *See also* names of climate regions
climate graph, 78, *g 78*
climate maps, 234, *m 234*
climate regions, 48, 52-56, *m 53,* 234; desert, 53, 87; humid continental, 54, 234; humid subtropical, 54, 234; ice cap, 56; marine west coast, 54, 234; Mediterranean, 54, 234; steppe, 53, 234; subarctic, 55, 234; tropical rain forest, 52; tropical savanna, 52; tundra, 55-56, 234. *See also* names of climate regions; names of culture regions

clouds, 36
coal, 97, 229, 271, 540, 577
coastal plains, 34
coffee, 169, 195-96, *p 196*
Colca Canyon, 180
cold war, 248, 314
collective farms; in Europe, 264; in Russia and the Eurasian Republics, 329-30
Colombia, 155
Colorado River, 88, 96
Columbia Icefield, 90
Columbia Plateau, 94
comets, 27
commercial farming, 64; in Africa South of the Sahara, 452
Commonwealth of Independent States (CIS), 315
communes, 571-72
communication networks, 71. *See also* names of culture regions
communications; through language, 77
communism, 247-48, 254, 313, 331; in China, 559, 564, 571; in East Asia, 576; in Europe, 247-48, 262, 265; in Russia and the Eurasian Republics, 313-14; in Southeast Asia, 612
Communism Peak, 292
Como, Lake, 229
comparisons, making, 402
compass, magnetic, 70
compass rose, 4, 12, 58
Confucianism, 561, 621
Confucius, 556
Congo, 413
conic projection, 17
coniferous forests, 232
conquistadors, 182
Constitution, United States, 117, 120
constitutional monarchy, 74
consumer goods, 264, 328
continental divide, 94
continental drift, 30
continental islands, 657
continental shelf, 34, 96
continents, 33
contour lines, 14
contour maps, 170, 546
contour plowing, 131
Cook, James, 674, 696
cooperatives, fishing, 572
copper, 37, *m 155,* 217, 413
copra, 688
coral, 473, 656, 692-93
cordilleras, 597
core, of the earth, 29
corn, 130
Corn Belt, 131
Corsica, *m 225*
Costa Rica, 164
cotton, 116, 131, 339, 353, 413, 512, 526
cotton mills, 115, 116
Council for Mutual Economic Assistance (COMECON), 265
crafts; in Africa South of the Sahara, 424, 443, 444; in Latin America, 197; Native American, 121; in Southeast Asia, 621
crevasses, 663
Crimean Peninsula, 298
Critical Thinking Skills, 276, 342, 402, 428, 486, 522, 606, 698
Croatia, 217, 252

Croats, 240
crop rotation, 38; in the United States and Canada, 131
Crusades, 246
Cuba, 183, 196, *p 205*
Cuban Americans, *p 211*
cultural barriers, 70-71
cultural contacts, 70
cultural diffusion, 70-71
cultural origins, 69
culture, 10, 63; change, 71; climate and, 78; global, 82-83, *p 82-83;* mass, 442
culture hearths, 69-70, *m 71,* 556
culture regions, 74-77, *m 75;* Africa South of the Sahara, 408-67; East Asia, 528-87; Europe, 212-81; Latin America, 150-211; North Africa and Southwest Asia, 348-407; Russia and the Eurasian Republics, 282-347; South Asia, 468-527; Southeast Asia, 588-645; South Pacific, 646-703; United States and Canada, 84-149
cuneiform, 377
currents, ocean, *see* ocean currents
Cuzco, Peru, 181
cyclones, 484, 636
Cyprus, 373, 382
czars, 312, 316
Czech Republic, 230, 231, 233, 263, 264, 265, 271

D

Dallas, Texas, *m 9, p 9*
dams, 57; in Africa South of the Sahara, 420; in Europe, 268-69; in North Africa and Southwest Asia, 359, 396, *p 396,* 400; in Russia and the Eurasian Republics, 335, 340, *p 340;* in South Asia, *p 516,* 521
Danube River, *m 225,* 228
Daoism, 556, 561, 564, 621
Dardanelles strait, 224
Dead Sea, 28, 352, 358, 375
Death Valley, *p 32,* 88, 94, 98
Deccan Plateau, 478, 483, 484, 493
deciduous trees, 54, 232, 545
deforestation; in Africa, 460; in the Amazon River basin, 202-04; consequences of, *p 201,* 203-04, 519, 638-39; in Costa Rica, 200-01, *p 204;* in South Asia, 518-20; in Southeast Asia, 601, 605, 638-39
Delhi, India, 517
delta, 359
democracy, 74; in Europe, 248; in Latin America, 184; in the South Pacific, 676; in the United States, 90
demography, 190
Denmark, 223, 263, 274
desalination, 397, 399-400
desert climate region, 8, 53, *m 53,* 234, *m 234;* in Australia, 660; in Canada, 111; in East Asia, 538-39, 544; in Latin America, 166, *m 167,* 169; in North Africa and Southwest Asia, 351, 362-63; in Russia and the Eurasian Republics, 292, *p 296,* 297; in South Asia, 482; in the United States, 98, 111
desertification, 381, 458-59
developed countries, 64; damage to

ozone layer by, 73
developing countries, 64-65, 195; Montreal Protocol and, 72-73; population growth in, 65
dharma, 497
diagrams, 22
dialects, 177, 251
dictatorships; in Europe, 248; in Latin America, 184
dikes, 268
distillation, 399
Djabo cave painters, 438
Djabo Mountains, 438
Djibouti, 411
Dnieper River, 291, 294, 311
Dniester River, 291, 294
doldrums, 50, 662
domestication, 376
Don River, 291, 294
Drakensberg Mountains, 412, 420
Dreamtime, 678
dry farming, 116
dunes, 31
Dutch, *see* Netherlands
dynasty, 556

E

earth, *p 26,* 26-43; atmosphere of 27, 45, 49, 50, 72-73; axis of, 45-46; hemispheres of, 5; landforms of, 33-34; measurements of, 27; resources of, 37-39; revolution of, *d 46,* 46-47; rotation of, 45-46, 50-51; structure of, *d 29,* 29-32; surface of, 27-28, 38; viewed from outer space, 27-28; water bodies of, 34-36
earthquakes, 29, 30, *d 31,* 286, 538, 579, 580-81
East Africa, 420, 437
East Asia; acid rain in, 577; agriculture in, 540-41, 571-72; air pollution in, 577; air travel in, 575; arts and architecture of, 564-65; atlas of, 530-35; capitalism in, 575; ceremonies and holidays in, 564; cities of, 554; climate in, 542-45, *m 543;* communications in, 576; communism in, 575, 576; conservation in, 578; countries of, 537; crafts in, 565; earthquakes in, 579, 580-81; economic activity in, 531, 533, 538, 560, *m 574;* education in, 562-63; environmental problems in, 577-78; ethnic groups in, 551; fishing in, 541, 572; floods in, 578-79; foods of, 563-64; forests of, 533; governments in, 559; health care in, 563; history of, 559; housing in, 562; industry and trade in, 573-75; land and forest resources in, 540-41; landforms of, 532, 537-38; languages in, 561; leisure time in, 563-64; literature in, 565; martial arts in, 586-87; mineral resources of, 540; monsoons in, 542; mountains of, 538-39; music and theater in, 565, *p 565;* natural disasters in, 578-79; natural resources of, *m 533,* 540-41; peninsulas, islands, and seas of, 537-38; pollution control in, 578; population in, *m 531,* 551-53, *m 573;* religions of, 561-62, *g 562, p 564,* 565; rivers in, 539-40, 575-76; sculpture and pottery in,

565; sports in, 564; standards of living in, 562; trade balance in, *c 575;* transportation in, 575-76; typhoons in, 542, 579; urbanization in, 553-54; vegetation of, *m 544,* 545; volcanic activity in, 579; war and revolution in, 559; water and ocean resources of, 541
East China Sea, 537
Easter Island, 680
Eastern Ghats, 478, 484
Eastern Hemisphere, 33
Eastern Orthodox Church, 245, 252, 317-18
East Siberian Uplands, 293
economic activity maps, 582, *m 582*
Economic Community of West African States (ECOWAS), 454
economics; and geography, 10
economic systems, 10, 75-76; capitalism, 76; communism, 314; free enterprise, 76, 129; socialism, 76, 312; tariffs, 265
economy; agricultural, 195; changing, 71, 261-62, 327-28; command, 328; exports, 195; market, 328. *See also* names of culture regions
ecosystem, 202, 696
ecotourism, 461
ECOWAS. *see* Economic Community of West African States
Ecuador, *p 48,* 50, 178
education, *see* literacy rates; names of culture regions
Egypt, 350, 359, 373, 374, 383; early civilization in, 376-77, *p 376, m 378*
Elbrus, Mount, 292
Elburz Mountains, 358
elevation, and climate, 49-50, 170
endangered species, 140, 204, 295, 460, 520, 578
endemic species, 605
energy sources; geothermal power, 658; hydroelectric power, 165; nuclear power 336-37; peat, 229; tidal power, 229. *See also* names of culture regions
English Channel, 250
environmentalists, 271
environmental problems, 66-68; deforestation, 200-01, 202-04, *p 204,* 460, 518-20; upsetting the ecosystem, 202; volcanic activity, *p 68;* waste disposal, 142-43; weather and, 66-67, 268. *See also* acid rain; pollution; names of culture regions
Equator, 5, 13, 51, 412, 424
equinox, 46
Erie, Lake, 138
Eritrea, 459
erosion, 31-32
escalator, longest, 555
escarpment, 162, 164, 419
estate farming, 196, 616
Estonia, 315
Ethiopia, 410, 443, 459
ethnic diversity, 371
ethnic groups, 305, 436, 551
Etruscans, 245
Euphrates River, 359, 360, 396-97
Eurasia, 33, 223
Europe, 33, *m 214, m 215, m 225, m 249;* acid rain in, 270-71, *p 271;* African influence in, 243; agriculture in, 233, 242, 262-64; air travel in, 266; architecture in, *p 246,* 252-

53; art in, 243, *ptg 243*, 252-53, 280-81; Asian influence in, 246; Atlantic islands of, 224, 226; atlas of, 214-21; canals in, 267; caves in, 244; celebrations in, 214, 255; Chunnel in, 250; cities in, 215, 238, 242, 244, 251, *p 260*; climate regions of, 216, 230-32, *m 231, g 233*, 241; cold war in, 248; communications in, 265-66; communism in, 214, 247-48, 255, 262, 264, 265; conflicts in, 214, 248; conservation projects in, 268-69; Crusades in, 246; culture of, 246-47, 251-53, 280-81; democracy in, 24, 264, 265; early peoples in, 239, 240, 244; eastern, 248, 262, 265, 266, 275; economy of, 261-62, 263-64, 265; education in, 253; empires in, 214; energy sources of, 229; environmental problems in, 233, 268-69, 270-75; ethnic groups in, 239-40, 245; European Union in, 249, 261, 262, *m 262*, 265, *g 265*, 275, *p 275*; explorations by, 247; family in, 240, 254; feudalism in, 245; fishing in, 217, 263; food supply in, 263; forests in, 230, 232, 233, 270; governments of, 247-49, 251, 253-54; grasslands in, 232; Greek and Roman influences in, 244-45, 252; health care in, 253; history of, 244-49; immigrants in, 239, 240; industrialization in, 242, 247, 251, 262-63; Industrial Revolution in, 242, 247, 263; industries of, 217, 233, 242, 262-65, *p 263*; iron and coal in, 229; lakes in, 229, *p 274*; landforms of, 214, 216, 223-28, 230; languages in, 214, 239, 240, 251, *m 252*; lifestyles in, 254-55; logging in, 233; manufacturing in, 264; Mediterranean islands in, 225, 244; Middle Ages in, 245; mineral resources of, 214, 229, 263; mountains in, 216, 226-27, *p 227*, 241; musical heritage from, 280-81; Muslim influence in, 245-46; natural resources of, *m 217*, 229; oil and natural gas fields in, 217, *p 228*, 229; peninsulas of, 223-24; plains in, 227-28; pollution in, 271-73, *p 272*; population density in, *m 215*; population distribution in, 241-242; post World War II, 261-267; quality of life in, 253; railroads in, 250, 266, *p 267*; Reformation in, 246-47; reform movements in, 248-49; refugees in, 240; religions of, 240, 245, 246-47, 252; Renaissance in, 246-47; revolutions in, 247-48; rivers in, 228-29, 267; roads in, 266, *p 266*; Roman Catholic Church in, 240, 245, 246; service industries in, 264-65; sports and recreation in, *p 254*, 254; telecommunications in, 265; tourism in, 265, 272; trade in, 246, 249, 264-65; transportation in, 250, 266-67; universities in, 253; urbanization in, 242, 251; vegetation in, 230, 232-33; waterways in, 267; world wars in, 248

European colonies, *see* names of culture regions

European Union (EU), 73, 249, 261, 262, *m 262, g 264*, 265, 275, *p 275*

eutrophication, 139
evaporation, 36
Everest, Mount, 28, *p 32*, 478, 492, 538
Everglades, 88
evergreen trees, 54, 55
explorations, 247, 674, 675
exports, 39, 133, 195
extended family, 189, 254, 444
extinction, 460

F

Fabergé eggs, *p 319*
fale, 681
family; in Africa South of the Sahara, 444, 457; in Europe, 240, 254; in Latin America, 189; in North Africa and Southwest Asia, 385
farm cooperatives, 264
faults, 29, 420
fauna, 598, 601
fazendas, 182
Federal Communications Commission (FCC), 136
Federal Interstate Highway System, 134-35
Federal State Highway System, 134
Fertile Crescent, 353
fertilizers, 39, 67
feudalism, 245
Fiji, 648, 651, *p 688, m 688*
Finland, 229, 230, 231, 232
fishing; bycatch and, 141; conservation measures, 141; eutrophication and, 139; over-fishing, 141; pollution and, 139, 141, 271, 334-35, 340; technology, 141. *See also* names of culture regions
fjords, 223, *p 224*
Flemings, 240
flora, 598, 601
foehns, 232
folds, 29
food chain, 67
forests; acid rain and, 270; clearcutting, 140, *p 639*; old-growth, 140; reforestation and, 203, 233, 519, 639; sustainable forestry and, 141. *See also* lumber industry; rain forests; names of culture regions
fossil fuels, 37, 38, 39; burning of, 57, 67, 271, 577
France, *m 58*, 248, 263, 265; Bastille Day in, 255; and Haiti, 183; high-speed trains in, 266; landforms in, *m 225*; and North America, 113, 116, 119; prehistoric life in, 244; and Southeast Asia, 240, 615, 616; territories in the South Pacific, 676, 679 Fraser Plateau, 94; free enterprise, 76, 129
free port, 633
Freetown, Sierra Leone, 442
French Canadians, 86, 115, 119
Fuji, Mount, *p 536*, 537
fur trade, 113
fútbol, 189

G

Gabon, 413, 435

Gall-Peters projection, 19
game preserves, 427, 460, 461
Gandhi, Mohandas K., 499, *p 499*
Ganges River, 472, 478, 480; pollution of, 516-17
Gautama, Siddhartha, 497
general-purpose maps, 14, 386
Geneva, Lake, 229
GeoFacts, 40, 110, 180, 243, 310, 375, 437, 495, 555, 614, 672
Geographic Information Systems, 9
geography, 5; and other subjects, 9; skills handbook, 11-22; themes of, 5-9
Geography and History, 119, 185, 250, 316, 381, 441, 500, 619, 677
Geography Connection, 82-83, 148-49, 210-11, 280-81, 346-47, 406-07, 466-67, 526-27, 586-87, 644-45, 702-03
Geography Skills Handbook, 11-22
Georgia, Republic of, 292, 298, 307, 318
geothermal power, 658
Germanic tribes, 245
Germany, 267; acid rain in, 270-71, 274; population in, 215, 240, 241; South Pacific interests, 675; and World War II, 248, 675
geysers, *m 658, p 658*
Ghana, 410, 420, *m 438*, 452
Giant muntjac, 614
Gibson Desert, 656
glaciers, 32, 35, 90, *p 90*, 96, 223, 224-25, 226, 229, 292
glasnost, 314, 334
global warming, 271-72, 696
globes, 16
Gobi Desert, 53, 532, 539, 544
gold, 413, 453
Goode's Interrupted Equal-Area projection, 18
Gorbachev, Mikhail, 314, 315
government, forms of, 17, *d 117*; authoritarian, 74; cabinet, 118; city-states, 245; communist, 247-48, 254, 262; constitutional, 118; constitutional monarchy, 74, 618; democratic, 74, 245; dictatorships, 248; executive branch, 118; judicial branch, 118; legislative branch, 118; monarchies, 499, 676; parliamentary, 118; representative democracy, 118; republic, 114, 245; study of, 74; welfare states, 253. *See also* names of culture regions
Gran Chaco, 164
Grand Banks, 141
Grand Canal, China, 540, 576
Grand Canyon, 31, 88, 94, 180
graphs, 20; bar, 20, 322; circle, 21, 446; climate, 78, *g 78*; line, 20, 506; pictographs, 21, 86
grasslands; in Europe, 232; in Latin America, 169
graziers, sheep, 687
Great Australian Bight, 656
Great Barrier Reef, 656, *m 693, p 693*; preserving, 692-93
Great Basin, 94, 108
Great Bear Lake, 96
Great Britain, 229, 247, 250, 253, 263; and Australia and New Zealand, 669, 672, 675; and Hong Kong, 560; and India, 498, 499, 500, 512; landforms of, 226; pollution laws in, 273; and Southeast

INDEX

Asia, 616; and the United States and Canada, 112, 114, 118, 119. *See also* United Kingdom
great circle routes, 16
Great Dividing Range, 655, 660
Greater Antilles, 161
Great Lakes, 88, 96, 108, 109, 131, 135; pollution of, 138-39
Great Plains, *p 47;* climate of, 100-01; elevation of, 94; farming on, 89, *p 98,* 101, *m 101,* 112, 130; settlement of, 116
Great Rift Valley, 412, 420, *p 423*
Great Salt Lake Desert, 98
Great Sandy Desert, 656
Great Slave Lake, 96
Great Uhuru Railroad, 455
Great Victoria Desert, 656
Great Wall of China, *m 70, p 70,* 71, 532, 557
Greece, *c 219,* 224, 230, 255, *m 262;* classical, 71, 214, 244-45, *p 255;* culture of, 245
greenhouse effect, 45, 57, 72-73, 578, 696
Greenland, 32, 56
green revolution, 513
grid system, 6, *m 6,* 102, 506
gross domestic product (GDP), 76, 393, 434
gross national product (GNP), 76
groundwater, 35, 398
Guadalajara, Mexico, *p 187*
Guatemala, *p 63*
Guiana Highlands, 162
Guinea, 453
Gulf Coastal Plain, 94
gulfs, 34
Gulf Stream, 51, 231
Gunung Agung, 635-36
Gupta Empire, 498
Guyana, 165, 176

H

habitats, 460
Haifa, Israel, 351
haiku, 565
Haiti, 183, 199
Han, 530, 551
Hawaiian Islands, *p 68,* 98, 101, 649; climate in, 100; discovery of, 674
headwaters, 96
health care. *see* names of culture regions
heavy industry, 263
Hebrews, 377
Height of Land, 94
Hejaz Mountains, 358
hemispheres, 5, *d 7,* 33
herding, 572, 687
hieroglyphics, 377
highland climate; in East Asia, 544-45; in Europe, 231; in Latin America, 167; in North Africa and Southwest Asia, 363-64; in South Asia, 482; in the United States and Canada, 98
hills, 33-34. *See also* landforms; names of culture regions
Himalayas, 162, 164, 470, 472, *p 476,* 477-78, 482, 492, 500, *p 500, m 519, p 519,* 597
Hinduism, 246; in South Asia, 497,

499, 501-02, 516-17; in Southeast Asia, 615
Hindu Kush, 352, 359, 478, 498
Hispanics, 210-11
history; of Africa South of the Sahara, 437, 438-41; of Europe, 214, 239, 240, 244-49; and geography, 9-10, 69, 71; of Latin America, 176, 181-84, 185; of North Africa and Southwest Asia, 376-79; of Russia and the Eurasian Republics, 284, 311-15, 316; of South Asia, 496-99, 500; of Southeast Asia, 615-18; of the South Pacific, 673-75; of the United States and Canada, 86, 110, 111-18, 119
Hokkaido, Japan, 538, 543, *p 543,* 552, 553, 579
Holland, 268
Holocaust, *p 248,* 248, *p 309*
homogeneous, 552
Honduras, 196
Hong Kong, 555, *m 560, p 560,* 573; British control of, 530, 537, 553, 560, 575; economic activity in, 531, 533, 538, 560
Hong River, 600, 615
houses and housing; climate and, 56; in East Asia, 562; in Europe, 254; in Latin America, 205; Native American, 111, *p 112;* in North Africa and Southwest Asia, 385; in Russia, 321; in Southeast Asia, 590, 622; in the South Pacific, 681; in urban areas, 205
Houston, Texas, 109
Huang He, 539-40, *p 540,* 556, *m 557,* 578, *p 579*
human/environment interaction, 7-8
humid continental climate region, 54, 234; in Europe, 231; in Japan, *g 78;* in Russia and the Eurasian Republics, 296; in the United States and Canada, 99
humid subtropical climate region, 54, 234; in Australia, 660; in East Asia, 543-44; in Europe, 231; in Latin America, 166, 169; in Russia and the Eurasian Republics, 298; in Southeast Asia, 602; in the United States and Canada, 99
Hungarian Basin, 228
Hungary, *p 226,* 229, 230, 231, 233, 239, 254, 272, 274
hunting, 111, 112, 244, 673
hurricanes, 66-67, 100
Hussein, Saddam, 380, 396
hydroelectric power; in Africa South of the Sahara, 422, 423; in Latin America, 165; in New Zealand, 658; in North Africa and Southwest Asia, *p 396;* in Russia and the Eurasian Republics, 295; in South Asia, 480; in the United States and Canada, 115
hydrosphere, 28
hypothesis, 57

I

Iberian Peninsula, 224, 225, 228, 241
Ice Age, 32, 57, 70, 96, 111, 223, 229, 598, 673
icebergs, 677

ice cap climate region, 56, 111, 663
ice caps, 36, 663
Iceland, 214, 224-26, 230, 231, 241
ideograms, 561
Igbo, 443
immigrants, 107; in Australia, 669, 675; in Canada, 107, 116, 119; in Europe, 239, 240; in Latin America, 176; in the United States, 107, 116, 121
imports, 39, 133
impressionism, 253
Inca civilization, 181-82
India, 477, 483, 495, 498; British in, 474, 498, 499, 500; caste system in, 496, 497; climate in, 483; culture of, 470, 501, 503, 516-17, 526; early empires in, 498; economy of, 480, 497, 511-15; environmental problems in, 516-17, 518-19, 521; landforms in, 472, 477; Narmada River Project in, 521; overpopulation in, 471, 491, 493, 517. *See also* South Asia
Indian Ocean, 34, 477
indigenous peoples, 615
Indochina Peninsula, 597, 598, 636
Indo-Gangetic Plain, 480, 483, 493, 496
Indonesia, 597, 600, 612; batik art in, 621; economy in, 631, 632; islands of, 592, 598; mountains in, *p 596,* 598; population density in, 591, 611
Indus River, 478, 480, 482, 496
Indus River Valley, 496, *m 497, p 497,* 512
industrialization, 115, 336; and social change, 184. See also names of culture regions
Industrial Revolution, 71, 117, 242, 247, 263, 441
industry, 64-65; heavy, 263, 341, 515; light, 263, 514-15; manufacturing, 132-33, 264; and pollution, 68, 138-39, 340-41; service, 132-33, 196, 263, 264, 393; state-owned, 264. *See also* names of culture regions
infant survival rate, 74
Inland Sea, Japan, *p 541,* 576
inland waterways. *see* names of culture regions
interdependence, 8, 134, 632; climate/environment/people, 56-57; human/environment, 7-8; resources and, 39. *See also* names of culture regions
interior plains, 34
Intermontane basins and plateaus, 94
international date line, 640
International Telecommunications Satellite Organization (Intelsat), 265
Interprovincial Pipeline, 135
Inuit, 86, 111, 118
Iran, 359, 373, 374, 380, 395
Iran, Plateau of, 359
Iraq, 360, 373, 374, 391-92, 395; and the Persian Gulf War, 380, 400; water supply in, 396-97
Ireland, 224-35, 230
Irish, 117
Irkutsk, Russia, 230
iron, 229
Irrawaddy River, 599-600, 629

irrigation, 8, 57; in North Africa and Southwest Asia, 359; in Russia and the Eurasian Republics, 334, 339; in Southeast Asia, 630; in the United States and Canada, 112, *p 131*
Irtysh River, 294
Islam, 120; in Africa South of the Sahara, 443; in East Asia, 561-62; in Europe, 245; in North Africa and Southwest Asia, 373, 378-79, 382; in Russia and the Eurasian Republics, 306, 318, 319; sects of, 318; in South Asia, 501; in Southeast Asia, 561, 562, 615
islands, 34; archipelagos 34, 538, 598; atolls, 656-57; continental, 657
Israel, 350; cities in, 351; climate in, *p 54;* landforms in, 357, 358; wars in, 379
Israelis, 372
Istanbul, Turkey, *p 374*
isthmus, 33
Italy, 217, 224, 229, 230, 231, 245, 248, 263

J

jai alai, 189
Jainism, 502
Jakarta, Indonesia, 633-34
Jamaica, 165
Japan; agriculture in, 572; arts in, 565; climate in, *g 78;* culture of, 530; early clans in, 557-58; earthquakes in, 579, 580, *p 580;* economy in, 133, 134, 562, 574; education in, 562-63; empires of, *m 558,* 559; ethnic homogeneity in, 552; European trade in, 558-59; feudal, 557; fishing in, 541, 572, 578; Ginza district in, *p 552;* heavy industry in, 573-74; high-speed trains in, 576, *p 576;* housing in, 554, 562, 580-81; industrialization in, 559, 574, 578; industry in, 82; islands of, 538; Kabuki theater in, 565, *p 565;* landforms of, 531, 532, 537, 538; management style in, 562, *p 563,* 574; martial arts in, 586-87; Mongols in, 558; natural resources of, 533; pollution-control laws in, 578; pollution in, 578; population density in, 553; population distribution in, 554; postwar, 559, 573-74; religion in, 535; resources of, 39; samurai in, 557; shipping in, 576; shoguns in, 557; South Pacific interests of, 675; Tang dynasty in, 565; trade in, 134, 559; urbanization in, 554; in World War II, 675. *See also* East Asia
Java, 598, 611, 621, 622, 633, 634
jazz, 122, 467
Jerusalem, Israel, 351, *m 372, p 372*
Jews, 248, 252, 318, 350, 371, 372, 378, 379, 382
Jordan, 358, *p 372*
Jordan River, 358, 398
Judaism, 120, 318, 377, 382
judo, 586
jute, 512
Jutland, 223
Jutland Peninsula, 267

K

Kalahari Desert, 425
Karachay, Lake, 310
Karakoram Mountains, 478, 538
Kara Kum, 286, *p 296,* 299
karate, 587
karma, 497
Karnataka Plateau, 478
Kashmir, 470, 526-27
Kathmandu, Nepal, 474, *p 492,* 513
Kazakhs, 284, 305, 306
Kazakhstan, 293, 306, 330, 338, 341
Kente cloth, 424, 443, 444
Kenya, 410, 419, 427, *p 450,* 451, 455, 460, 461
Kenya, Mount, 420
Khyber Pass, 352
Kiev, Ukraine, 291, *p 308,* 309, 311, 312
Kikuyu, 451
Kilimanjaro, *p 408,* 420
Kobe, Japan, 580, *p 580*
Konga cloth, 444
Korea, 541, 562; agriculture in, 572; division of, 530, 552, 554, 559; early kingdoms in, 558; economy and trade in, 534, 575; Japan's influence on, 554; landforms of, 537; Mongols in, 558; natural resources of, 533; population density in, 531, 553, 554; urbanization in, 554. *See also* East Asia
Korean Peninsula, 537, 558
Koryo dynasty, 565
Krakatoa, 598
krill, 659, 696
Kuala Lumpur, Malaysia, *p 610*
kung fu, 587
Kunlun Shan, 538
Kurds, 373
Kush, 438
Kuwait, 380, 391, 395, 400
Kyrgyz, 284

L

lagoon, 473, *p 654,* 657
Lagos, Nigeria, 435, 456-57, *m 457, p 457;* population growth in, 456-57
Lake Plateau, 229
lakes, 35; glacial 35, 96. *See also* names of culture regions
landfills, 142-43
landforms, 33-34, *d 34;* in Africa South of the Sahara, 419-20; and climate, 52; in East Asia, 532, 537-39; in Europe, 214, 216, 223-28, 230; in Latin America, 154, 161-64; in North Africa and Southwest Asia, 352, 357-58, 381; in Russia and the Eurasian Republics, 286, 287, 291-93; in South Asia, 472, 477-78; in Southeast Asia, 592, 597-99; in the South Pacific, 655-59; in the United States and Canada, 88, 90, 93-94
land-use maps, 462
language families, 76, 251, 305, 373, 443, 501, 561, 620, 679; of the world, *m 76,* 77
languages, 77; African 442-43; Balto-Slavic, 251; bilingual, 121; communications through, 77; dialects, 177, 251; European, 251, *m 252;* Germanic, 251; of Native

Americans, 177; Romance, 251. *See also* names of culture regions
Laos, 592, 597, 598, 603, 611
La Paz, Bolivia, 153
Lapps, 254
Lascaux Cave, 244
latifundia, 196
Latin America, *m 152, m 163;* Africans in, 176, 182, 183, 188; agriculture in, 155, 169, 181, 195-96, *p 196,* 202; air pollution in, 205; air travel in, 198; Amazon River Basin in, 202-05; arts and architecture in, *ptg 188,* 188-89; Asians in, 176; atlas of, 152-59; Aztecs in, 181; cattle in, 164, 196, 202-03; celebrations in, 7, *p 174,* 189, 211; cities in, 153, 178, 179, *p 179,* 185, *p 185, p 194,* 204-05, *p 205;* climate regions in, *p 164,* 166-69, *m 167, g 168,* 178, 195-96; communications in, 199; countries of, 161; cultures in, 186-89; deforestation in, 200-01, 202-04, *p 204;* deserts in, 169; dictatorships and democracies in, 183-84; early civilizations in, 181-82; economy of, 185, 195-96; education in, 188; energy resources in, 165; environmental problems of, 200-01, 202-04; ethnic diversity in, 152, 175-77, *g 176,* 211; European empires in, 182-83, *m 183,* 186-87; extended family in, 189; forestry in, *m 200,* 200-01, 203, *p 203;* governments in, 183-84; grasslands in, 169; health care in, 187-88; history of, 176, 181-84, 185; housing in, 205; immigrants in, 176; Inca in, 181; independence movements in, 183, 185; industrialization in, 184; industry in, 184, 196-97, 200-01; inland waterways of, 164, 198; interdependence in, 197-98; lakes and waterfalls in, *p 150,* 164; landforms of, *m 154,* 161-64; languages in, 161, 176-77, *m 177;* life and leisure in, 189; literature in, 188-89; Maya in, 181; migrations in, 179; mineral resources of, 155, 165; mining in, 155, 165; mountains of, 154, 161-64; music in, 188; Native American empires in, 181-82; natural resources of, *m 155,* 165, 204; oil resources of, 165; pampas in, 154, 164, 169; plains of, 164; plateaus and hills of, 162-64; population density in, *m 153,* 178, *g 190;* population distribution in, 177-78; population growth in, 204-05; Portuguese in, 182, 186; poverty in, 205; railroads in, 198; rain forests in, 200, *m 200,* 202-04; reforestation in, 203; religions of, *g 186,* 186-87; revolutions in, 183; rivers in, 154, 164; roads in, 198, *p 198,* 202; slavery in, 180; Spaniards in, 182, 186; sports and recreation in, 189, *p 189;* trade in, 185, 197-98; transportation in, 198; vegetation of, 167-68, *p 168, m 169,* 206; viceroys in, 182
latitudes, 5-6, 13, *m 50,* 102, *m 102;* and climate, 48-49; high and middle, 49; low, 48
Latvia, 315
Law of the Return, 350

leach, 427
Lebanon, 382
leeward, 51
Lena River, 294
Lesotho, 412
Lesser Antilles, 161
levees, d 97
Liberia, 410
Libya, 360, 374, 380, 399
Libyan desert, 231
lichens, 663
Liechtenstein, 243
lifestyles. see names of culture regions
light industry, 263
line graph, 20, 506
literacy rate, 74, 318; in Africa South of the Sahara, 445; in East Asia, 562-63; in Europe, 252, 253; in Latin America, 188; in North Africa and Southwest Asia, m 386; in Russia and the Eurasian Republics, 318; in South Asia, 505; in the United States and Canada, 123; literature. see names of culture regions
lithosphere, 28
Lithuania, 315
llanos, 164, 169
location, 5-7; absolute, 5, 6; relative, 6-7
loess, 539, 540
logging. see forestry; lumber industry; names of culture regions
London, England, 215, 242
longhouses, 622
longitude, 6, 13, m 102
Lorraine-Saar district, 263
Los Angeles, California, 109, p 133, 138
Louisiana, 121
Louisiana Purchase, 115, 116
L'Ouverture, Toussaint, 183, p 183
Loyalists, p 114, 115, 119
lumber industry, 38; in Africa South of the Sahara, 427; in the Amazon River basin, p 203; and deforestation, 200-01; in Europe, 233; in Southeast Asia, 630, 638-39; in the United States and Canada, 97, 140, p 140
Lutheranism, 240
Luzon, 591

M

Macao, 537, 538
MacKenzie River, 96
Madagascar, 412, 460
Madrid Protocol Treaty, 677, 697
Maghreb, 371
Magyars, 239
Malacca, Strait of, 615, 633
Malawi, Lake, 420, 437
Malay Peninsula, 592, 598, 619, 621, 632, 633
Malaysia, 592, 593, 597, 598, p 601, 620, 621, 634; agriculture in, 629, 630; population density in, 590, p 610, 611, 612; vegetation in, 604
Maldives, 472, 473, 477
Male Island, m 470
Mali, 410, 411, 438, 443
malnutrition, 187
Malta, 226, 243

mammals, newest, 614
Manchuria, 538, 540, 542
Mandela, Nelson, 440, p 440
mangrove trees, 484, 518, 519
Manila, Philippines, 598, p 632, 633, 634
Manitoba, 115, 130, 131
mantle, of the earth, 29
mantras, 502
manufacturing. see industry
manuka, 663
Maori, 648, 669, p 670, 673, 680
Mao Zedong, 559, 562
Map and Graph Skills, 58, 78, 102, 144, 170, 190, 206, 300, 322, 386, 462, 582, 640, 664
map projections, 17-19; azimuthal, 18; conic, 17; Gall-Peters, 19; Goode's Interrupted Equal-Area, 18; Mercator, 17; polar, 18; Robinson, 19; sinusoidal, 18
maps, 11-22; cartograms, 144, m 144; climate, 234, m 234; comparing with globes, 16; contour, 170, 546; economic activity, 582, m 582; general-purpose, 14, 386; interpreting routes on, 664; land-use, 462; latitude on, 6, 13, 102; longitude on, 6, 13, 102; natural resource, 15; parallels and meridians, 6, 13, 102; physical, 14, 58; political, 14, 58, 300; population density, 566, m 566; relief, 170; road, 11; scale bar, 58; scale of distance, 12, 58; special-purpose, 15, 386; symbols on, 11-12; topographic, 546; vegetation, 206, m 206
maquiladoras, 197
Maracaibo, Lake, 164
Mariana Trench, 28
Marianas, 676
marine west coast climate region, 54, 234; in Australia, 660; in Europe, 230, 232; in New Zealand, 663
maritime powers, 615
market economy, 328
Marmara, Sea of, 224
Marquesas Islands, 673, 676
marsupials, 694, p 695
martial arts, 586-87
Marx, Karl, 313
mass culture, 442
Mato Grosso, 164
Mauryan Empire, 498
Maya civilization, 181
McKinley, Mount, 88
Mediterranean climate region, 54, p 54, 234, 363; in Australia, 660; in Europe, 231, 232; in North Africa and Southwest Asia, 363-64
Mediterranean Sea, 35, 224; islands of, 225; pollution of, 272-73, 274
megalopolis, 109, 554
Mekong River, 591, 592, p 595, 600, 630
Melanesia, 648, 656, 661-62, 673, 678, 688
meltwater, 271
Mercator projection, 17
meridians, 13, 102
Meroë, 438
mesas, 94
Meseta, 230, 231
Mesopotamia, 359, 377, 383
mestizos, 176
meteoroids, 27

metropolitan area, p 4, 109
Mexican Americans, 117, 211
Mexican Plateau, 178
Mexico, 198; arts in, ptg 188, 189; independence of, 183; manufacturing in, 196-97; and the Mexican War, 116; natural resources of, 155, 165; plateaus of, p 162, 178; Spaniards in, 113
Mexico, Gulf of, 35, 89, 96, 113, 165
Mexico City, Mexico, 199; pollution in, 205; population in, 153, 179, p 179
Miami, Florida, 86, 109
mica, 473, 481
Michigan, Lake, 96
Micronesia, 648, 656, 670, 673, 675, 688
Mid-Atlantic Ridge, 40
Middle Ages, 244, 245, 247
Middle East. see North Africa and Southwest Asia
Middle Passage, 440
migrations, 70
military equipment, 117
mineral resources. see names of culture regions
minerals, 37, 38-39
minifundia, 196
mining. see names of culture regions
Mississippi River, m 96, p 96, 96, 109, 113, 116, 135
Missouri River, 96, 109
mistral, 231
mixed farming, 264
mixed forests, 54
mobile society, 122
modernism, 188
Mohenjo-Daro, Pakistan, 496
Moldova, 306, 319, g 322, p 331, 332, 333, 340-41
Mombasa, Kenya, 454
Monaco, 243
monarchies, 380, 499, 676
Mongolia, 533, 552, 553, 559, 563, 575; climate in, 542, 544; landforms of, 532, 537, 538, 539, 540, 572
Mongolian Plateau, 538
Mongols, 312, 530, 552, 558
monotheism, 377
monsoons; in East Asia, 542; in South Asia, p 57, 482-84, 519, m 520; in Southeast Asia, 602
Montreal Protocol, 72, 73
Morocco, 350, 352, 353, 361, 364, 371, 374
mosaics, 188, 189
Moscow, Russia, 291, 309, 312, p 312, 316, 332
mosques, 378, 383, p 383, 503
mountains, 33-34. See also landforms; names of culture regions
movement, 8
Mozambique, 420
mulattoes, 176
multicultural, 120, 239; music; African, 444, 466; blues, 466; calypso, 466; classical, 280; country and western, 82, 280; East Asian, 565; folk, 122; Indian, 495, 503; jazz, 122, 467; Native American, 122; religious, 122; rock and roll, 82, 122, 281, 444, 467; spirituals, 466; in the United States, 82
musical instruments, 281, 565

Muslims, 240, 245, 252, 318, *m 378,* 378-79, 491, 499, 501, 505
Myanmar, 593, 594, 597, 598, 602, 604, 611, 621; agriculture in, 617; houses in, 590; isolationism in, 632
Myanmar River, 599-600

N

NAFTA. *see* North American Free Trade Agreement
Nairobi, Kenya, *p 75,* 444
Namib Desert, 425
Namibia, 425, 434
Nasser, Gamal Abdel, 400
nationalism, 71, 379
nationalities, 305
national parks, 123, 204, 427, 460
Native Americans; in Latin America, 175-76, 181-82, 196; in North America, 37, 87, 107, 111-12, *p 112,* 114, 121
natural gas, 217, *p 228,* 229, 295, 360-61, 392, 481
natural resource maps, 15
natural resources, 37, 39. *See also* resources; names of culture regions
natural vegetation, 31, 52, *m 54, m 101;* chaparral, 54, 232; coniferous forests, 232; deciduous forests, 54, 232; desert, 53, 299; highland, 169, 545; lichens, 663; manuka, 663; mixed forest, 54, 232, 299; of the plains, 101, 112, 232; steppe, 53, 299, 545, 660; subarctic, 56; taiga, 299; tropical, 52, 167-69, 545, *p 545;* tundra, 56, 232, 299. *See also* names of culture regions
Nauru, 670, 676
navigators, 102
Nechako Plateau, 94
neem tree, 495
Nepal, 473, 474, 480, *p 492,* 494, 501, 504, 505; isolation of, 477, 478, 499, 500; tourism in, 515, 518
Netherlands, 215, 228, 263; air pollution in, 271, 274; colonies of, 616; Delta Works Project in, 268-69; explorations by, 674
New Brunswick, *p 114,* 115, 131
New Caledonia, 651, 657
Newfoundland, 115, 141
New Guinea. *see* Papua New Guinea
New Mexico, 86, 87, 113, 115, 117, 121
New Orleans, Louisiana, 7, 109, 115
newspapers. *see* communications networks
New York City, New York, 87, *p 106,* 109
New Zealand, 648, 651, *m 657;* agriculture in, 687-88, *m 689;* British in, 669, 672, 675; cities in, 670; climate regions in, *m 661,* 663; communications in, 691; cultural patterns in, 678-81; economic activity in, *m 689;* environmental problems in, 694-95; ethnic groups in, 648; ethnic origins in, 669-70; ferries in, 691; government in, 675-76; history of, 648, 669, 673-75, *m 674,* 678-79; independence of, 675; islands of, 650, 658, 673; lakes of, 658; landforms of, 658; language in,

679; lifestyles in, 681; manufacturing in, 689; Maori in, 648, 669, *p 670,* 673, 680; mineral resources of, 658; mountains and hills of, 658, 680; natural resources of, *m 649,* 651, *m 651;* population density in, *m 649, m 650;* road and rail systems in, 690; urbanization in, 671; vegetation in, 651, *m 662,* 663; Western lifestyles in, 679. *See also* South Pacific
Nicaragua, 164
Nicaragua, Lake, 164
Nigeria, 411, 413, 454, 456-57
Niger River, 422
Nile River, 359, *p 360,* 422; Aswan Dam on, 400
Nile River Valley, *p 10,* 351, 364, 377
nirvana, 497
Nobel Prize, 189, 444
nomadic life, 673
nomads, 350
nonrenewable resources, 38, 65
North Africa and Southwest Asia, *m 350, m 353, m 360;* Afghanis in, 373; after World War II, 379-80; agriculture in, 353, 359, 364, 373, 391-92; air travel in, 393, *p 393,* 394; American culture in, 406-07; Arabs in, 371, 379; architecture in 379, 383, *p 384;* Armenians in, 373; arts in, 383-84; atlas of, 350-55; birthplace of religions in, 377-79; canals in, 377, 394; cities in, 351, *p 370,* 374, *p 374, p 384,* 384; climate regions in, 231, 357, 358, 361, 362-64, *m 363,* 381, *m 399;* coastal plains of, 357, 358, 363; communications in, 394; conservation in, 381; countries of, 350; Crusades in, 379; Cypriots in, 373; desalination in, 397, 399-400; desert regions of, 357, 359, 362-63, 365, 373; early civilizations in, 376-77, 383; economy of, 391; education in, 385; Egyptians in, 373, 377; environmental problems of, 381, 396-97, 400-01; ethnic diversity in, 371-73; fishing in, 373, 392; foods of, 406-07; governments in, 379-80; health care in, 384; Hebrews in, 377-78; history of, 376-79; housing in, 384; independence in, 379; industrialism in, 392, 393; industries of, 392, 393; inland waterways of, 394; interdependence in, 395; Iranians in, 373; Israelis in, 372-73; Jews in, 377-78, 380; Kurds in, 373; landforms of, 352, 357-59, 381; languages in, 373, 383; leisure time in, 385; lifestyles in, 383-85; literature of, 383-84; livestock in, 392; mineral resources of, 353, 361; mining in, 392; mosques in, 379, 383, *p 383;* mountains in, 358, *p 361;* Muslims in, 378-79; nationalism in, 379-80; natural resources of, *m 351, m 353,* 360-61, 392; oil and natural gas in, 353, 360, 392, 395, *c 395;* overpopulation in, 373-74, 396-97; peninsulas and seas of, 357-58; Persian Gulf War in, 380, 400-01; Phoenicians in, 377; pipelines in, 393, 394, 399; plateaus of, 358; population density in, *m 351, m 352,* 373-74, 381; population distribution in, 373-74; railroads in, 394; religions in, 373, 377-

79, 382, *g 382;* religious holidays in, 385; rivers in, *m 358,* 358-60, 394; service industries in, 393; standards of living in, 350, 384; Sumerians in, 377; tourism in, 393; transportation in, 350, 394; Turks in, 373; universities in, 385; vegetation of, *m 364,* 365; water crisis in, 396-97, 398-400; waterways in, 378, 394. *See also* Africa South of the Sahara
North America, 33, *m 89;* natural resources of, *m 87. See also* Canada; United States
North American Free Trade Agreement (NAFTA), 134
North Atlantic Drift, 231
North Carolina, 142
North China Plain, 539
Northern Hemisphere, 5, 48
Northern Ireland, 252
Northern Territory, 694-95
North European Plain, 227, 232, 291, 297
North Island, 649, 658, 663
North Korea. *see* Korea
North Sea, 217, 223, *p 228,* 229, 273
Northwest Mountains, 226, 227
Northwest Territories, 118, 123
Norway, 217, 223, 231
Nova Scotia, 115
Nubia, 438
nuclear energy, 330, 336-38
nuclear testing, 695
nuclear weapons, 338
Nullarbor Plain, 656
Nunavut, 118

O

oases, 362-63, 374, 425
Ob River, 294
ocean currents, 50-51, 231, 543, 662
Oceania, 648, 650, *m 657;* agriculture in, 680, 688; air travel in, 691; arts in, 680; cities of, 670; climate in, 660, *m 661,* 661-62; cultural patterns in, 679; economic activity in, *m 689;* environmental problems of, 694-95; ethnic groups in, 648; explorations of, 674-75; fishing in, 678, 688; history of, 673-75, *m 674,* 675, 678-79; languages in, 648, 670, 679; lifestyles in, 680-81; logging in, 695; major island groups of, 650, 656; migrations in, 673, 691; mineral resources of, 657, 688, 695; mining in, 688, 695; missionaries in, 675; natural resources of, *m 649, m 651;* population density in, *m 649, m 650,* 670-71; population distribution in, 669; religions in, 675; territories in, 675; trade in, 673, 675, 680, 689; transportation and communications in, 691; vegetation of, 661-62, *m 662;* volcanoes in, 656-57; World War II in, 675. *See also* South Pacific
oceans, 34-35; continental shelf and, 34; currents, 50-51, 543, 662; seamounts, 34
Odessa, 297
Ohio River, 96, 109, 135
oil; in Africa South of the Sahara, 413, 423, 456; in Latin America, 164; in North Africa and Southwest

Asia, 353, 360, 392; in the North Sea, 217, *p 228,* 229; in Russia and the Eurasian Republics, 287, 295, *p 295,* 332-33; in South Asia, 481; in Southeast Asia, 630-31; in the United States and Canada, 39, 135; world production of, *g 395;* world reserves of, *g 394*
O'Keeffe, Georgia, *ptg 122*
Okhotsk, Sea of, 293
Olympic Games, 214
Oman, 353
Ontario, 87, 108, 115, 130, 131, 133
OPEC. *see* Organization of Petroleum Exporting Countries
opinions, 342
oral history, 444
Oregon Country, 116, 117
organic farming, 264
Organization of Petroleum Exporting Countries (OPEC), 395, 453, 631
Ottawa River, 109
Ottoman Turks, 373
outback, 656, *p 663,* 680, 681, *p 690*
outlining, 124
ozone layer, *p 72,* 72-73, 578, 696; CFC destruction of, *d 73;* hole in the, *p 73*

P

Pacific islands. *see* Oceania; South Pacific
Pacific Ocean, 34, 111, 662
pagoda, 565
Pakistan, 470, 477, 481, 491, 499, 501, 504, 514, 521
Palestine, 372-73, 379
Palestinians, 379
Pamirs, 287
pampas, 154, 164, 169
Panama, Isthmus of, 33, 198
Panama Canal, *m 184, p 184,* 198
Pan-American Highway, 198
Pangaea, 420
Papua New Guinea, 598, 649, 650, *c 652,* 670, 695; agriculture in, 673; languages in, 648
paragraphs, 256, 366
Paraguay, 164, 169
Paraguay River, 198
parallels, 6, 13
Paran River, 164, 198
Paris, France, 242
Parliament; Australian, *p 676;* Canadian, 90, 118; English, 248
Pasternak, Boris, 346
pastoralism, 364
Patagonia, 164, *p 178*
patriarch, 318
peat, 229
peninsulas, 34
per capita income, 76, 435
perestroika, 315, 328, 330
permafrost, 55, 231, 297
Persian Empire, 377
Persian Gulf, 358, 360, 401
Persian Gulf War, 380, 400-01, *p 401*
Perth, Australia, 670
Peru, 164, 165, *m 170*
Pescadores, 538
pesticides, 67, 341
Peter the Great, 312
petrochemicals, 392

Philippines, *p 62,* 601, 611, 621, 632; agriculture in, *p 62;* islands of, 538, 591, 592, 597, 598; Spanish rule in, 590; volcanoes in, 538, *m 600, p 600,* 635, 636
Phoenicians, 377
phosphate, 353, 361, 695
physical maps, 14, 58
Picasso, Pablo, 444
pictographs, 21, 86
pidgin English, 680
Piedmont, 94
Pinatubo, Mount, 598, 636
pipelines; in Africa South of the Sahara, 455; in North Africa and Southwest Asia, 394, 399; in Russia and the Eurasian Republics, 333; in the United States and Canada, *p 39,* 136
Pittsburgh, Pennsylvania, 109
place, 7
plains, 34; coastal, 34; interior, 34. See *also* landforms; names of culture regions
planets, 27
Plata River, 198
plateaus, 34. *See also* landforms; names of culture regions
plates; tectonic, 29-30, *m 30,* 597; Pangaea and, 420; Ring of Fire and, 30, 538, 579, 580, *m 581,* 656
Pleistocene Epoch, 31-32
poaching, 460
pogroms, 318
Poland, 233, 255, 265, 267; climate in, 230, 231; manufacturing in, 263, 264; mineral resources in, 263, 271; pollution in, 271, *p 272*
polar areas, 48-49
polar climate. *see* ice cap climate region
polar projection, 18
polders, 228
political maps, 14, 58, 300
political science; and geography, 9-10, 74
political systems. *see* governments; names of culture regions
pollution, 67-68, 310, 338; acid rain, 137-38, 270-71, *p 271,* 577; air, 8, 57, 67, 138, 205, 233, 271, *p 272, p 340,* 341, 577, 635; controlling, 68, 273-75; and eutrophication, 139; industrial, 68, 138, 270-72, 336, 340; land, 142-43; from natural causes, 137, 579; pesticides and, 341; radiation and, 336-37; regulation of, 68, 578; sea, 692-93; smog, 138; soil, 68; thermal, 139; volcanic, 137; waste disposal, 8, 67, 142-43, 272-73, 340, 577-78; water, 8, 67, 138-39, 270, 272-73, 457. *See also* names of culture regions
Polynesia, 656, 673, 676, 680
Pontic Mountains, 358
population; climate and, 241, 308; demography and, 190; world, *m 144. See also* names of culture regions
population density, 65, *g 65,* 308; maps, 566, *m 566;* world, *m 66. See also* names of culture regions
population distribution, 65, 308-09. *See also* names of culture regions
population growth rates, 65; in developing countries, 65; world, *g 65*

population pyramid, 190
Po Basin, 263
Portugal, 224, 247, 253; colony in Brazil, 182, 183; explorations by, 247, 674
potash, 229
prairie, 54
Prairie Provinces, 130
precipitation, 51, 78, *g 78*
prehistory, 6, 249
prevailing winds, 50
primary sources, 276, 624
primate city, 179, 613, 670
prime meridian, 6, 13, 102, 640
prime minister, 118
Prince Edward Island, 115, 131
Protestantism; in Europe, 247, 252; in Latin America, 187; in Russia and the Eurasian Republics, 317; in the United States and Canada, 120
Puerto Rican Americans, 211
Puerto Rico, 118, *p 168*
pyramids, 377, 383
Pyrenees Mountains, 224

Q

qanats, 377
Qatar, 383
Qin dynasty, 556
Quebec, 87, 90, 108, 113, *p 113,* 115, 119, 130, 131
Queensland, 692, 694
quipu, 182
Quito, Ecuador, *p 48,* 50
Quran, 378, 382, 383

R

Rabin, Yitzhak; and West Bank Accord, *p 372;* assassination of, 372
raga, 503
railroads; in Africa South of the Sahara, *p 454,* 454, 455; in Australia and New Zealand, 690; in China, 576; commuter trains, 135; in Europe, 266; in France, 266; high-speed, 266, 576, *p 576;* in Japan, 576, *p 576;* in Latin America, 198; in North Africa and Southwest Asia, 394; in Russia and the Eurasian Republics, 332, *p 332;* in Southeast Asia, 633; in the United States and Canada, 115, *p 116,* 117, 135
rain forests, *m 200,* 234; in Africa South of the Sahara, 427, 453, 460, *p 461;* in Costa Rica, 200-01; deforestation of, 200-01, 202-04, 427, 453, 460, 518-20, 605; in Latin America, 202-04; in Oceania, 661, 695; in South Asia, 484, 518-20; in Southeast Asia, 604-05
rain shadow, 51, *d 51,* 98
Razdan River, 339
realism, 252
recycling programs, 143
Red Sea, 358
redwoods, 110
reforestation, 203, 519
Reformation, 246-47
refugees, 240; Acadian, 110; Cuban, 86; in Europe, 240
regions, 8-9; climate, 48, 52, *m 53;*

culture, *m 71*, 74-77; functional, 9; uniform, 8
reincarnation, 497
relief, 14
relief maps, 170
religions, *m 77*, 76-77, *g 186*, 317-18, *g 318*, *g 443*, *g 502*; art and, 252, 565, 614, 621, 672; birthplace of, 377-79; Buddhism, 497, 501-02, 561, 562, 615, 621; Christianity, 114, 120, 186, 245, 307, 378, 382, 443, 561, 679; Confucianism, 561, 621; Crusades, 246-47; Daoism, 556, 561, 565, 621; Eastern Orthodox, 245, 252, 317-18, *p 318*; freedom of, 120, 252, 317; Hinduism, 246, 497, 499, 501-02, 516-17, 615; Islam, 245, 252, 306, 318, 378-79, 382, 443, 499, 615, 621; Jainism, 502; Judaism, 252, 318, 377-78, 382; Lutheranism, 240; monotheism, 377; Protestantism, 187, 247, 252, 317; Reformation, 246-47; Roman Catholicism, 186-87, 215, 240, 245, 252, 315, 317, 621; shamanism, 562; Shinto, *p 534*, 535, 561; Sikhism, 502; violence and, 252; in the world, *m 76*, 77. *See also* names of culture regions
Renaissance, 71, 246-47, 248, 252
renewable resources, 38
representative democracy, 118
republic, 114, 245
resources, 37-39; distribution of, 39; energy, 97; managing, 38-39; natural, 37, 39; nonrenewable, 38; overuse of, 139-41; renewable, 38; value of, 37-38
revolutions; of the earth, *d 46*, 46-47
Rhine River, 228, 267
Rhodesia, 453
rice, 512, 513, 572, 594, 603, 615, 617, 622, 629-30
Ring of Fire, 30, 538, 579, 598, 635, 656
Rio de Janeiro, Brazil, *p 174*, 189
Río de la Plata, 164
Rio Grande, 96
Rivera, Diego, *ptg 188*, 188
rivers, 35
river systems; headwaters, 96; tributaries, 96. *See also* names of culture regions
road maps, 11
road systems. *see* names of culture regions
Robinson projection, 19
Rocky Mountains, 88, 90, 93-94, 96, 98
Roman Catholicism; in Europe, 215, 240, 245, 252; in Latin America, 186-87; in Russia and the Eurasian Republics, 317; in Southeast Asia, 555, 561, 562, *p 564*, 621; in the United States and Canada, 120
Roman Empire, 244-45
Romania, 224, 231, 251, 265, 271, 306
Romanians, 306, 319
romanticism, 252
Rotterdam, the Netherlands, 228, 266
Royal Flying Doctor Service, 653, 681
Rubal Khali, 363
rubber, 37-38, 473, 617

Ruhr district, 229, 263
Russia and the Eurasian Republics, *m 284*, *m 287*, 291, *m 300*, 312; agriculture in, 291, 299, 329-31, 334-35, 339, 341, *p 341*; air travel in, 332; arts in, 319-20, *p 320*, 346-47; atlas of, 284-289; ballet in, 346, 347; Bolsheviks in, 313-14; canals in, 309, 312, 335; celebrations in, 321; Chernobyl disaster in, 330, 336-37; cities of, 291, *p 304*, 309, *p 312*, *p 313*; climate regions in, 55, 230, 296-98, *g 298*, 316; communications in, 331; communism in, 313-14; countries of, 315; economy in, 315, 327-28, 329, *m 329*; education in, 318-19; energy resources of, 295, *p 295*, 336-38, *p 340*; environmental pollution in, 334-35, 336, 338, *p 340*, 340-41; ethnic diversity in, 284, 285, 305-07, 312; fishing in, 287, 295, 334-35, *p 338*; forests in, 299; government in, 315; history of, 311-23; housing in, *p 321*; industry in, 330-31, 333, 336; interdependence in, 333; lakes in, 286, 293, 338-40; landforms in, 286, 287, 291-93; languages in, 305; life and leisure in, 321; literature in, 320, 346; mineral resources of, 294-95; Mongols in, 312; mountains in, 286, 292-93, *p 292*; musical heritage from, 319-20, *p 320*, 346-47; Napoleon's defeat in, 316, *ptg 316*; natural resources of, *m 285*, *m 287*, 287, 294-95; nuclear power in, 310, 330, 336-37; nuclear weapons in, 338; oil in, 287; perestroika in, 314, 328, 330; pipelines in, 333; plains in, 287, 291-92; plateaus of, 292-93; pollution in, 310; population density in, *m 285*, 308-09; population distribution in, 308-09; railroads in, 332, *p 332*; religions in, 307, 317-18, *g 318*; rivers in, 291, 294, 311; roads in, 332; rule of the czars in, 312-13, 316; russification in, 313; seas and waterways in, 286, 293-94, 309, 311, 331, 332, 334-35, 338-40; serfs in, 312-13; size of, 287; Slavs in, 311-12; socialism in, 312; Soviet era in, 313-14, 327, 329-30; trade in, 311; transportation in, 331-33; and the United States, 314; vegetation of, 292, 298-99; wars in, 313, 314, 316
Russians, 285, 316; ethnic, 306, 307
russification, 313
Ruwenzori Mountains, 420
Rwanda, 411, 434, 460
Ryukyus, 538

S

sadhus, 502
Sahara Desert, *m 53*, 351, 362, 381, 411, 419, 424; climate change in, 381, 438
Sahel, 426, 458, 459
St. Lawrence River, 96, 108, 109, 113, 131, 135
St. Lawrence Seaway, *d 91*, 135
St. Louis, Missouri, 7, 109
St. Petersburg, Russia, 291, *p 304*, 309, 312, *p 313*

samurai, 535, 557
San Marino, 242, 243
Sao Paulo, Brazil, 205
Sarajevo, *p 240*
Sardinia, 226
Saskatchewan, 115, 130
Saudi Arabia, 133, 360, 374, *p 383*, *p 393*, 395, 396; oil exports of, 134
savanna, 234, 426-27
scale, 12, 58, *m 58*
scale bar, 12, 58
scale of distance, 4, 58
Scandinavia, 223, 229, 240; climate in, 230, 231, 233, 241, 270
Scotland, 241
seamounts, 34
seas, 34-35
seasons, 46-47
Seattle, Washington, 109
secondary sources, 276
sedentary farming, 452
seismic, 358
Senegal, *p 434*
Seoul, Korea, 554, *p 564*
Serbs, 240
Serengeti Plains, 427, *p 428*
serfs, 312-13
service industries, 132, 196, 263, 264, 393
Sevan, Lake, 339
shamanism, 562
Shang dynasty, 556
Shanghai, China, 554, 575, 576
Shan Plateau, 602
sheep, 656, 658, 671, *p 686*
shifting cultivation, 381
shifting farming, 452
Shinto, 534, 561
shogun, 557
Shona, 439
Siberia, 284, 293, 294, 297
Sichuan Basin, 533
Sicily, 226
sickles, 629
Siddhartha. *see* Gautama, Siddhartha
Sierra Madre del Sur, 162
Sierra Madre Occidental, 162
Sierra Madre Oriental, 162
Sierra Nevada, 93
Sierra Leone, 442
Sikhism, 502
Silicon Valley, 109
Sinai Peninsula, 358
Singapore, 597, 611, 620, 623; climate in, 593, 605; economic activity in, 615, 619, *m 619*, *p 619*, 632, 633; islands of, 592, 597, 598, 633
Sinhalese, 491-92
sinusoidal projection, 18
siroccos, 231
skyscrapers, *p 82*, 121
slash-and-burn farming, 202
slavery, 113, 116, 176, 182
slave trade, 185, 439, 440
Slavs, 245, 305, 306, 311
Slovakia, 231, 233
slum areas, 205
small-scale maps, 40
smog, 57, 138
social groups, 74-75
socialism, 76, 312
Society islands, 676
sociologists, 10, 74
sociology, and geography, 10
sod, 101, 112, *m 101*
soil pollution, 67-68

solar system, 27, *d 28*
Solomon Islands, 657
solstice, 46-47
Somalia, *g 78*
Songhai, 410, *m 438*, 439, 443
South Africa, 413, 436, 440, 451, 453; apartheid in, 440
South America, 33, 154, 177. *See also* Latin America
South Asia, *m 470, m 479;* agriculture in, *p 483*, 485, 493, 511-13; arts and architecture of, 475, 503-04, 526; atlas of, 470-75; British in, 498, *m 498*, 500, 512; celebrations in, 505, *p 510;* cities of, 475, *p 490*, 494, *p 494*, 517; climate regions of, 474, 482-84, *m 483, g 485*, 500, 519; conservation in, 519-20, 521; cultures in, 495; cyclones in, 484, 519; dams in, 521; dance in, 503; democracies in, 499; early civilizations of, 496; economy of, 514, *m 514;* education in, 505; empires in, 498, *m 498;* energy resources of, 481; environmental problems in, 516-17, 518-20; ethnic groups in, 470, 491-92, 499; fishing in, 480, 514; food needs in, 505, 512-13; forests in, 473, 484, 518-20; governments of, 499, 515, 517; green revolution in, 513; health in, 504; history of, 496-99, 500; industrialization in, 514-15; industry in, 473, 514-15, 526; interdependence in, 521; islands of, 472; landforms of, 472, 477-78; languages in, 470, 501, *m 502;* lifestyles in, 504-05; literature in, 496, 503-04; mineral resources of, 473, 481, *p 481;* mining in, 473, 513-14; monarchies in, 499; monsoons in, *p 57*, 482-83, 519, *m 520;* mountains in, 472, *p 476*, 477-78, 500, *m 519;* music in, 503; natural resources of, *m 471, m 473*, 480-81; plains of, 478, 480; plateaus of, 478; pollution in, 516-17; population density in, *m 471, m 472*, 480, 491, 492-94, *g 493*, 517; population distribution in, 492-94, 513; rain forests in, 518-20; religions of, 491-92, 496-97, 501-02, *g 502, m 503*, 516-17; rivers in, 472, 478-80, 516-17; tourism in, 515, 518; transportation in, 500; vegetation of, *m 484*, 484-85; wildlife in, 520-21, *p 521*
South China Sea, 537
Southeast Asia, *m 590, p 599;* agriculture in, 593, 599, 612-13, 616, 629-30, *p 630;* air travel in, 634; art and architecture of, 621-22; atlas of, 590-95; celebrations in, 623, *p 623;* Chinese influence in, 615, 644-45; cities of, 613, 623, *p 632*, 633-34, 635; climate regions of, *p 8*, 602-05, *m 603*, 636-37; communications in, 634; communism in, 612; countries of, 597, 598; crafts in, 621; cultures of, 620-22; cyclones in, 636; deforestation in, 601, 605, 639; economy of, 623, 630, *m 631*, 638-39; education in, 623; environmental problems in, 635, 638-39; environmental protection in, 630, 639; European colonization of, 616, *m 617;* fish farming in, 601; foods of, 622, 644-45;

forests of, 592, 601, 604-05, 638-39; French in, 240; governments in, 612, 618; health in, 623; history of, 590, 613, 615-18; housing in, 590, 622; importance of rains in, 603; industrialization in, 632, 638-39; interdependence in, 632-33; islands of, 592, 598; Khmer empire in, 615; landforms of, 592, 597-99; languages of, 620; lifestyles in, 622-23; literature of, 621-22; logging in, 630, 638-39; manufacturing in, 632; maritime powers in, 615; mineral resources of, 593, 600-01; mining in, 630-32; monsoons in, 602; mountains of, 598-99; music, dance, and drama in, 622; natural resources of, *m 591, m 593*, 600-01, *p 601;* oil in, 630-31; peninsulas of, 597-98; political conflicts in, 612, 613, 618, 632; population control in, 612; population density in, *m 591*, 611; population growth in, 611-12, *c 612;* railroads in, 633-34; rain forests in, 604-05; religions of, 594, 615-16, 620-21, *g 621*, 622; river deltas in, 592, 600, 629; rivers in, 592, 599-600; roads in, 634; seasonal flooding in, 636; sports and recreation in, 623; Srivijaya Empire in, 615; trade in, 616, *m 616*, 619, 633-34; transportation in, 633-34; typhoons in, 636-37; vegetation of, 603-05, *m 604;* volcanoes in, 598-99, *m 600, p 600*, 635-36, *p 637;* wildlife in, 601
Southern Alps, 658, 663
Southern Hemisphere, 5, 48
South Island, 658, 663
South Korea. *see* Korea
South Pacific, *m 651;* agriculture in, 688, 694; air travel in, *p 691*, 691; animal life in, 694-95; art forms in, 680, 702-03; city life in, 681; climate regions of, 660-63, *m 661*, 670; colonization in, *m 674*, 674-75; communications in, 671, 690, 691; coral reefs in, 656, 692-93; cultural patterns of, 669-70, 678-81; democracies in, 676; early peoples in, 669, 673, 678, 691; environmental problems in, 692-93, 694-97; environmental protection in, 692-93, 696-97; European influence in, 669, 674-75, 678-79, 680, 694, 696; explorations of, 674-75; farming life in, *p 680*, 680, 688; fishing life in, 673, 678; food production in, 687-88; France and, 675, 676, 679; Germany and, 675; governments in, 675-76, *p 676;* Great Britain and, 669, 675, 676, 679; health and education in, 681; history of, 673-75; hunting life in, 673, 678; independence movements in, 675; islands of, 656-57, 658; Japan and, 675; landforms of, *m 648*, 655-59, *p 658;* languages in, 679-80; logging in, 695; manufacturing in, 689; migrations in, 673, 691; military bases in, 675; mining in, 688, 692-93, 695; missionaries in, 675, 679; monarchies in, 676; mountains of, 655, 658; natural resources of, *m 651*, 656, 658, 688; nomadic life in, 673; nuclear testing in, 695; plateaus of, 656; plate movement in, 656; popu-

lation density in, *m 649;* population patterns in, 669-71; ports of, 670, 671; rain forests in, 661, 695; ranching in, 687-88, 691; religious beliefs in, 679, *g 679;* Spanish-American War and, 675; territories in, 675, 676; tourism in, 692-93; trade in, 675, 680, 689; traditional lifestyles in, 673, 678-79, 680-81; transportation in, *p 690*, 690-91; United States and, 675, 676, 679; urbanization in, 670-71; vegetation of, 660-63, *m 662;* volcanic activity in, 656-57; winds and currents in, 662-63; World War II in, 675. *See also* Antarctica; Australia; New Zealand; Oceania
South Pole, 33
Southwest Asia. *see* North Africa and Southwest Asia
Soviet Union, 313-21. *See also* Eurasian Republics; Russia
Spain, 224, 230, 231; colonies of, 86, 113, 182, 185; explorations by, 247, 674; and Latin America, 182
special-purpose maps, 15, 386
spheres of influence, 559, 615-16
sports; ice hockey, 123, 148-49; jai alai, 189; rugby, *p 679;* soccer, 189, 254. *See also* names of culture regions
Sri Lanka, 471, 477, 482, 499, 501, 504, 505, 515; ethnic conflict in, 470, 491-92; natural resources of, 473, 481, 512, 514, 518
Stalin, Joseph, 314
standard of living, 75. *See also* names of culture regions
state farms; in East Asia, 572; in Europe, 264; in Russia and the Eurasian Republics, 329-30
stations, 687-88, 691
steam power, 115
steppe climate region, 53, 234, 364; in Australia, 660; in East Asia, 544; in Latin America, 167; in North Africa and Southwest Asia, 364; in South Asia, 482
steppes, 298
strait, 111
streams, 35
strine, 679
Study and Writing Skills, 124, 256, 366, 624
subarctic climate region, 55, 234; in Europe, 231; in Russia and the Eurasian Republics, 296, 297; in the United States and Canada, 98, 108
subcontinent, 477
subsistence farming, 63-64; in Africa South of the Sahara, 452; in South Asia, 511; in the South Pacific, 680, 688
suburbs, 109
Sudan, 410, 413
Suez, Isthmus of, 33
Suez Canal, 394
sugarcane, 182, 195-96, *p 688, m 688*
Sumatra, Indonesia, 598, *p 613*, 615, 633
Sumerians, 377
sun; effect on climate, 45, 46, 48-51; radiation from, 45
Sunbelt, 87, 108, *p 123*
Suriname, 178

Sweden, 217, 223, 228, 231, 239, 253, 266
Switzerland, 214, 251, 264, 266
Sydney, Australia, *p 668*, 681, 689
symbols; map, 11, 12, 58
Syr Darya, 334
Syria, 374, 396; water supply in, 396-97

T

tables, 22; reading, 682
taiga, 299
Taipei, Taiwan, *p 550*, 554
Taiwan, 530, 551, 559, 562; agriculture in, 541, 572; economy in, 534, 562, 573, 574; landforms of, 532; natural resources of, 533; population density in, 531, 553, 554
Tajikistan, 307
Taj Mahal, 503, *p 504*
Taklamakan Desert, 539, 544
tala, 503
Tamils, 491-92
Tanganyika, Lake, 420
Tang dynasty, 556, 565
Tanzania, 410, 420, 424, 427, 455, 460
tariff, 265
Tarim Basin, 538
Tasmania, 650, 655
Taupo, Lake, *p 658*
Taurus Mountains, 358, 359
Tchaikovsky, Peter, 320, 347
tea, 512, *p 512*
technology; in farming, 116, 131-32, 242, 513; in fishing, 141; in telecommunications, 71, 136, 265, 394
Tel Aviv, Israel, 351
telecommunications systems, 71, 136, 265, 394
temperature, 45; and climate, 51, 78, *g 78*
terracing, *p 3*, 181, 572
Texas, 86, 113, 115
TGV. *see trains á grande vitesse*
Thailand, 590, *p 595*, 597, 598; arts in, *p 622*, 623; industry in, 632, 635, 638-39; logging in, 638-39; natural resources of, 593, 638-39; population density in, 591, 611
Thames River, 229
Thar Desert, 475, 482, 493
Tian Shan, 292, 538
tidal waves, 29-30, 67, 538, 579, 580
tierra caliente, 167, 169, 170
tierra fría, 167, 169, 170
tierra templada, 167, 169, 170
Tigris River, 359
Tikal, 181
timberline, 56, 101
time zones, 640, *m 640*
tin, 155, 165, 197, 600, 631
Titicaca, Lake, 164
Tokyo, Japan, 554, 579
Tonga, 676
tools, 111, 112
topic sentence, 256
topographic maps, 546
topography, 14
tornadoes, 66, *p 67*, 100
Toronto, Canada, *p 128*, 135
tourism, 265, 272, 393
trade, 39; barriers, NAFTA and, 134;

early, 63; fur, 113. *See also* names of culture regions
trading partners, 574
trains á grande vitesse (TGVs), 266, *p 267*
Trans-Alaska Pipeline, *p 39*, 135, 136
Trans-Amazonian Highway, 198, 202
Trans-Andean Highway, *p 198*
Transantarctic Mountains, 659
Trans-Canada Highway, 134
Trans-Canada Pipeline, 136
transportation. *see* names of culture regions
transportation, climate and, 57
Trans-Siberian Railroad, 332, *p 332*, 576
treeline, 545
tree, neem, 495
trekker, 518
tributaries, 96
tropical rain forest climate region, 52; in Africa South of the Sahara, 427; in East Asia, 545; in Latin America, 166, 167-68, 195; in Oceania, 661; in South Asia, 482; in Southeast Asia, 602; in the United States and Canada, 98; tropical savanna climate region, 52; in Latin America, 166; in North Africa and Southwest Asia, 426-27; in South Asia, 482; in Southeast Asia, 602-03; in the United States and Canada, 99
Tropic of Cancer, 5, 46, 49, 424
Tropic of Capricorn, 5, 47, 49, 424
truck farms, 131
trust territory, 675
tsunamis, 29-30, 67, 538, 579, 580
tundra climate region, 55-56, 234, 297; in Antarctica, 663; in Europe, 233; in Russia and the Eurasian Republics, 297; in the United States and Canada, 99, 111
tundra vegetation, 299
tungsten, 533, 631-32
Tunisia, 371, 374
tunnels, 250, 266
Turan Lowland, 291, 292
Turkey, 224, 240, 372, 374, *p 374*; landforms of, 358; water management in, 396-97
Turkic peoples, 285, 305
Turkmenistan, 286, 292, 295, 298, 308
Turks, 306, 373, 396
typhoons, 100, 579, 636-37, 662; in East Asia, 542, 579; in Southeast Asia, 636
Tyumen Field, 295

U

Uganda, 461
Ukraine, 285, 305, *p 306*, 333; agriculture in, 291, 330, *p 330;* education in, 319; ethnic groups in, 305, 306; natural resources of, 295; ports of, 331
Ukrainians, 285
United Kingdom, 215, 217, 264. *See also* Great Britain
United Nations, 400, 675
United Nations Food and Agriculture Organization (FAO), 459

United Nations Mediterranean Action Plan (MAP), 274
United States, *m 95;* acid rain in, 137-38; African influence in, 444, 466-67; Africans in, 113; agriculture in, 89, 97, 101, *m 101*, 112-13, 117, 129-32, *p 131;* arts and architecture in, 121; atlas of, 86-91; borders of, 86, 116; cattle in, 114; celebrations in, 123; cities of, *g 100*, 109, *p 133;* climate regions in, *p 8*, 87, 90, 98-100, *m 99, g 100*, 108, 111, 112, 130; communications in, 134, 135-36; constitution of, 117, 118, 120; crafts in, 121; cultures in, 82-83, 86, 120-22, 375, 466-67, 644-45, 702-03; deserts in, 90; East Asian influence in, 586-87; economy of, 90, 123, 129, *m 130*, 133, 134-35; energy resources of, 97, 115; environmental problems in, 137-39, 142-43; ethnic groups in, 86, 107, *g 108*, 111, 117, 121; European colonization in, 111, 112-14; European influence in, 86, 120, 121, 280; fashion in, 83, *p 83*; fast foods in, 83, *p 83;* fishing in, 89, 96-97, 139, 141; food processing in, 132; foods and dining in, 83, *p 83*, 110, 406-07, 644-45; forests in, 97, 100-01, 140-41; formation of, 114; fur trade in, 113; government of, 90, *p 90*, 114, *d 117*, 118; health care in, 122-23; health insurance in, 123; history of, 86, 111-18; housing in, 121, 122, 180; hurricanes in, 100; immigrants in, 107, 116, 121, 141; independence of, 114-15; industrialization in, 115; industry in, *p 83*, 90, 109, 115-16, 118, 132, 135; inland waterways of, 94-96, 108, 109, 135; interdependence of, 133-34; lakes of, 88, 97, 138, 139; landfills in, 142-43; landforms of, 88-89, 90, 93-94; language in, 120-21; Latin American influences in, 211; levees in, 97; lifestyles in, 122-23, 143; literature in, 121; logging in, 97, 140, *p 140;* Louisiana Purchase and, 115; Mexican War and, 115; Middle Eastern influence in, 406; mineral resources of, 97; mobile society in, 122; mountains of, *m 86*, 88, *p 90*, 93-94; music in, 121, 122, 280, 466; national parks in, 123; Native Americans in, 87, 107, 111-112, 114, 121; natural resources of, 39, *m 87, m 89*, 96-97, 111, 112, 117, 139-41; overuse of resources in, 139-41; plains of, *d 89*, 94, 101; plateaus in, 94; population density in, *m 87, d 87*, 107-08, 308; population distribution in, 107-08; railroads in, 117, 135; refugees in, 86; religion in, 120, *g 121;* rivers of, 88, 94-96, 109, 113; road systems in, *p 133*, 134-35; Russian influence in, 346-47; service industries in, 132; smog in, 138; Southeast Asian influence in, 644-45; South Pacific interests of, 675-76; Spanish influence in, 180; sports and recreation in, 123, 148-49, 586; standard of living in, 122; Sunbelt in, 108, *p 123;* telecommunications in, 136; territories of, 118, 675; thermal pollution in, 139; tornadoes in, 66, *p 67*, 100; trade in,

132-34; transportation in, 117, 134-36; trucking industry in, 135; vegetation of, 100-01, *m 101*; in World War II, 675
universal suffrage, 440
universities, 253
Upper Silesia-Moravia district, 263
Ural Mountains, 33, 286, 292, 294
uranium, 34, *p 696*
urbanization, 75, 178-79, 436; Industrial Revolution and, 242; and poverty, 205. *See also* names of culture regions
Uruguay, 164, 198
Uruguay River, 164, 198
Uzbekistan, 284, 292, *g 322*, 327

V

valleys, 31, 32, 34
Varangians, 311
Vatican City, 215, 241, 243
Vedas, 496, 497
vegetation. *see* natural vegetation
vegetation maps, 206, *m 206*
Venezuela, 165, 197, 395
Venice, Italy, *p 247, m 247*
Verkhoyansk, 296
viceroys, 182
Victoria, Lake, 420, 422
Victoria Falls, 422, *m 422, p 422*
Vietnam, 597, 598, 611, 614, 620, 621; river deltas in, 592, 595; war in, 632
Vindhya Mountains, 478
Virgin Islands, 118
Vistula River, 267
volcanoes, 29, 598-99; in Africa, 420; and climate, 57; in East Asia, 538, 579-80; in Europe, 224, 226; in New Zealand, 658; in Oceania, 30, *p 68;* in Southeast Asia, 598-99
Volga River, 291, *m 292*, 294, *p 294*, 295, 311, 332, 338
Volta, Lake, 420
Vu Quang ox, 614

W

wadis, 360
Wales, 225
Walloons, 240
wastes; disposal of, *p 142*, 142-43, 272-73, 340; hazardous, 8, 68; solid, 68
water bodies, *d 34*, 34-35
water cycle, *d 35*, 36
water pollution, 68, 272-73
water supply, 35, 36, 396-97, 398-400
waterways. *see* names of culture regions
wats, 621
wattles, 660
weather, 45, 78
weathering, 30-31
weather station, *p 44*
welfare states, 253
West Bank Accord, 372
Western Ghats, 478, 484
Western Hemisphere, 33
Western Plateau, 660

Western Samoa, 676, 681
West Indies, 154, 155
West Siberian Plain, 291-92, 295
wheat, 130, 656
Wheat Belt, 130
winds; chinook, 100; and climate, 50, 51, 231; doldrums, 50, 662; foehns, 232; hurricanes, 66-67, 100; mistral, 231; prevailing, 50; siroccos, 231; tornadoes, 66, 100; typhoons, 100, 542, 579, 636, 662; zones, *m 50*
windward, 51, *p 51*
wood-block printing, 565
Wood Buffalo Park, 123

X

Xi River, 540
Xizang, Plateau of, 538, 539, 544-45

Y

Yamato people, 557
Yangon, Myanmar, *p 595*
Yangzi River, 575-76, 578
Yellowstone National Park, 123
Yeltsin, Boris, 315
Yenisey River, 291, 294
Yerevan, Armenia, *p 340*, 341
Yugoslavia, 240
Yugoslav republics, 224
Yukon Territory, 118

Z

Zagros Mountains, 358
Zaire, 412, 433, 453, 455
Zaire River, *m 412*, 422, *p 422*
Zambezi River, 422, 425
Zambia, 413, 455, 461
Zhou dynasty, 556
ziggurats, 383
Zimbabwe, 461

INDEX

Acknowledgments

Cover, ©FBM Photography/Westlight. **iv,** (t) Tony Stone Images, (b) NRSC Ltd./Science Photo Library/Photo Researchers; **v,** (t) ©Craig Aurness/First Light, (b) ©1990 James Randklev/AllStock; **vi,** (l) Frank Wing/Stock Boston, (r) Michael Reagan/FPG International; **vii,** ©1992 G. Cubitt/FPG International; **viii,** (t) ©Stan Way Man/Photo Researchers, (b) ©1990 Travelpix/FPG International; **ix,** (t) ©Ira Kirschenbaum/Stock Boston, (b) ©David R. Austen/Stock Boston; **xvii-A1** © James Westwater; **2-3,** David Doubilet; **4,** ©1992 Jordan Coonrad; **8,** (l) William Johnson/Stock Boston, (r) ©Wolfgang Kaehler; **9,** ©1990 Peter B. Kaplan; **10,** Earth Satellite Corp./Science Photo Library/Photo Researchers; **23,** ©1990 Peter B. Kaplan; **26,** NRSC Ltd./Science Photo Library/Photo Researchers; **32,** (l) ©1991 Chris Noble/AllStock, (r) ©1992 David L. Brown/Tom Stack & Associates; **36,** ©1989 Douglas Faulkner/AllStock; **38,** ©1989 Ray Ellis/Photo Researchers; **39,** ©Tom & Pat Leeson/Photo Researchers; **41,** (t) ©1991 Chris Noble/AllStock, (c) ©1989 Douglas Faulkner/AllStock, (b) ©1989 Ray Ellis/Photo Researchers; **44,** ©Wolfgang Kaehler; **47,** ©Darwin R. Wiggett/First Light; **48,** ©1985 August Upitis/FPG International; **54,** ©Erich Lessing/PhotoEdit; **56,** ©Jim Zuckerman/First Light; **57,** Robert Harding Picture Library; **59,** (t) ©Darwin R. Wiggett/First Light, (c) ©1985 August Upitis/FPG International, (b) ©Eric Lessing/PhotoEdit; **62,** Tony Stone Images; **63,** ©Byron Crader/Ric Ergenbright Photography; **67,** ©Larry Miller/Science Source/Photo Researchers; **68,** ©Peter Boonisar/AllStock; **70,** ©Dallas & John Heaton/Stock Boston; **73,** NASA; **75,** ©1985 Ron Watts/First Light; **79,** (t) ©Byron Crader/Ric Ergenbright Photography, (c) ©Robert Frerck/Odyssey Productions, (b) ©1985 Ron Watts/First Light; **82,** (t) ©Daniel MacDonald/Stock Boston, (c) Aaron Haupt, (b) ©Dallas and John Heaton/Stock Boston; **83,** (tl) ©Stuart Cohen/Comstock, (tr) ©1977 Photoworld/FPG International, (b) ©Ric Ergenbright; **84-85,** ©Annie Griffiths Belt; **90,** (tl) ©Will & Deni McIntyre/AllStock, (tr) ©Dallas & John Heaton/First Light, (b) ©David Barnes/AllStock; **92,** ©1990 James Randklev/AllStock; **96,** ©1993 Dave Gleiter/FPG International; **98,** ©1989 Stacy Pick/Stock Boston; **103,** (t) ©1993 Dave Gleiter/FPG International, (b) ©1989 Stacy Pick/Stock Boston; **106,** ©1993 Rafael Macia/Photo Researchers; **112,** ©1989 Greg Probst/AllStock; **113,** ©Masa Uemura/AllStock; **114,** ©Ken Straiton/First Light; **116,** Culver Pictures, Inc.; **122,** ©1994 The Georgia O'Keeffe Foundation/Artists Rights Society (ARS) NYC, photograph ©1993 Malcolm Varon, NYC; **123,** ©1987 Andy Levin/Photo Researchers; **125,** (t) ©Dallas & John Heaton/First Light, (c) ©Masa Uemura/AllStock, (b) ©1987 Andy Levin/Photo Researchers; **128,** ©Thomas Kitchin/First Light; **131,** ©1992 Inga Spence/Tom Stack & Associates; **133,** ©M. Richards/PhotoEdit; **135,** ©Dorothy Littell Greco/The Image Works; **139,** ©John Shaw/Tom Stack & Associates; **140,** ©1991 Earl Roberge/Photo Researchers; **142,** David Bookstaver/AP/Wide World Photos; **145,** (t) ©1992 Inga Spence/Tom Stack & Associates, (b) ©John Shaw/Tom Stack & Associates; **148,** (t,bl) Hockey Hall of Fame, Toronto, Ontario, (br) ©1980 Paul J. Sutton/Duomo; **149,** (t) ©Bruce Bennett Studios, (b) Steve Reyes/Bruce Bennett Studios; **150-151,** William Franklin; **159,** (tl) ©1991 Travelpix/FPG International, (tr) Telegraph Colour Library/FPG International, (c) Bob Daemmrich/Stock Boston, (b) Luis Villota/Bruce Coleman, Inc.; **160,** ©Manfred Gottschalk/Tom Stack & Associates; **162,** Earth Scenes/Dr. Nigel Smith; **164,** ©Phillip & Karen Smith/Tony Stone Images; **165,** ©Francois Gohier/Photo Researchers; **168,** ©1989 Thomas R. Fletcher/Stock Boston; **171,** (t) ©Phillip and Karen Smith/Tony Stone Images, (b) ©1989 Thomas R. Fletcher/Stock Boston; **174,** Telegraph Colour Library/FPG International; **178,** ©Roland Seitre/Peter Arnold, Inc.; **179,** Earth Scenes/M.P.L. Fogden; **183,** Archive Photos; **184,** Owen Franken/Stock Boston; **185,** ©David R. Frazier Photolibrary; **187,** Bob Thomason/Leo de Wys; **188,** ©Lee Foster/FPG International; **189,** Robert Fried/Stock Boston; **191,** (t) Earth Scenes/M.P.L. Fogden, (c) Archive Photos; (b) Robert Fried/Stock Boston; **194,** ©1988 Dale E. Boyer/Photo Researchers; **196,** ©Carl Frank/Photo Researchers; **198,** Mike Mazzaschi/Stock Boston; **199,** Don Nieman; **201,** ©Wm. Ervin/Comstock; **203,** ©Luiz C. Margio/Peter Arnold, Inc.; **204,** Mike Bacon/Tom Stack & Associates; **205,** Sean Sprague/Lineair; **207,** (t) ©Carl Frank/Photo Researchers, (b) ©Luiz C. Margio/Peter Arnold, Inc.; **210,** (t) ©Bruce Roberts/Photo Researchers, (b) ©Tony Freeman/PhotoEdit; **211,** (tl) ©1992 Marco Corsetti/FPG International, (tr) Chris Brown/Stock Boston, (b) Lois Ellen Frank/Westlight; **212-213,** Christian Sappa, Visa Agence Photographique; **221,** (t) ©Bernard G. Silberstein/FPG International, (b) ©David R. Frazier Photolibrary; **222,** ©1991 David Noble/FPG International; **224,** ©1991 E. Nagele/FPG International; **226,** Frank Wing/Stock Boston; **227,** Earth Scenes/Rocky Jordan; **228,** Telegraph Colour Library/FPG International; **230,** ©1976 Paolo Koch/Photo Researchers; **235,** (t) Frank Wing/Stock Boston, (b) ©1976 Paolo Koch/Photo Researchers; **238,** ©Dallas & John Heaton/Stock Boston; **240,** Boiffin/Photo Researchers; **241,** ©W. Geiersperger/Stock Boston; **246,** (l) Lauros-Giraudon/Art Resource, New York, (r) ©Adam Tanner/Comstock; **247,** ©Vincent J. Modica/Stock Boston; **248,** Margaret Bourke-White, LIFE MAGAZINE ©Time-Warner Inc.; **250,** QA Photos Ltd.; **254,** ©John Eastcott & Yva Momatiuk/The Image Works; **255,** (l) ©Dallas & John Heaton/Stock Boston, (r) Erich Lessing for Art Resource, New York; **256,** ©Wolfgang Kaehler; **257,** (t) Boiffin/Photo Researchers, (c) ©Vincent J. Modica/Stock Boston, (b) ©John Eastcott & Yva Momatiuk/The Image Works; **260,** ©Stuart Cohen/Comstock; **263,** ©David R. Frazier Photolibrary; **266,** ©1985 Karin Reinhard/FPG International; **267,** ©1988 Shinichi Kanno/FPG International; **269,** Lee/Picture Box/Viesti Associates, Inc.; **271,** Earth Scenes/©Richard Packwood, Oxford Scientific Films; **272,** Christopher Pillitz/Matrix; **273,** ©Patrick Walmsley/Envision; **274,** Leo de Wys Inc./J. Tom; **275,** ©1991 Travelpix/FPG International; **276,** ©Ric Ergenbright; **277,** (t) ©David R. Frazier Photolibrary, (b) Earth Scenes/©Richard Packwood, Oxford Scientific Films; **280,** (l) North Wind Picture Archives, ET Archive, London/SuperStock; **281,** (tl) Wide World Photos, (bl) UPI/Bettmann, (r) Rick Weber; **282-283,** Steve Raymer; **289,** (tl) ©Peter Menzel/Stock Boston, (tr) Kaufman Photography/Peter Arnold, Inc., (bl) Galleria Statale Tret'jakov, Moscow/SCALA/Art Resource, New York, (br) ©Dallas & John Heaton/Westlight; **290,** Michael Reagan/FPG International; **292,** L. Sherstenikov, Sovfoto/Eastfoto; **294,** (t) TASS from Sovfoto, (b) Novosti/Sovfoto; **295,** TASS from Sovfoto; **296,** Novosti/Sovfoto; **299,** Ernest Manewal/FPG International; **301,** (t) L. Sherstenikov, Sovfoto/Eastfoto; (b) Ernest Manewal/FPG International; **304,** ©1990 Vadim Sokolov/Sovfoto; **306,** Jeff Greenberg/PhotoEdit; **307,** Rohdan Hrynewych/Stock Boston; **308,** Amanda Merullo/Stock Boston; **309,** Novosti/Sovfoto, **312,** Marcello Bertinelli/Photo Researchers; **313,** Francois Gohier/Photo Researchers; **315,** AP/Wide World Photos; **316,** Musee d'Orsay, Paris/Art Resource, New York; **317,** Jeff Greenberg/Photo Researchers; **319,** Scala/Art Resource; **320,** (t) Helga Lade/Peter Arnold, Inc., (b) Shinichi Kanno/FPG International; **321,** Jim Harrison/Stock Boston; **323,** (t) Amanda Merullo/Stock Boston, (c) Marcello Bertinelli/Photo Researchers; (b) Helga Lade/Peter Arnold, Inc.; **326,** Bruce Gordon/Photo Researchers; **328,** ©Jeff Greenberg/Photo Researchers; **330,** TASS from Sovfoto; **331,** ©Bruno Barbey/Magnum Photos; **332,** Michael Reagan/FPG; **334, 335,** Novosti/Sovfoto; **337, 338,** TASS from Sovfoto; **339,** ©1993 Sarah Leeh/Matrix; **340,** J. Mann, Sovfoto/Eastfoto; **341,** Cary Wolinsky/Stock Boston; **342,** Novosti/Sovfoto; **343,** TASS from Sovfoto; **346,** (tl) Shooting Star, (tr) SuperStock, (bl) Archive Photos; **347,** (tl) Movie Still Archives, (bl) ©1993 Steve Gravano, (r) ©Tretiako Gallery/SuperStock; **348-349,** Mehmet Biber/Ajans Biber; **355,** George Holton/Photo Researchers; **356,** Gordon Gahan/Photo Researchers; **360,** Mikr Malyszko/FPG International; **361,** Victor Englebert/Photo Researchers; **365,** Gianni Tortoli/Photo Researchers; **366,** ©Wolfgang Kaehler; **367,** (t) Victor Englebert/Photo Researchers, (b) Gianni Tortoli/Photo Researchers; **370,** Erika Stone/Peter Arnold, Inc.; **372,** (t) AP/Wide World Photos; (b) ©David R. Austen/Stock Boston; **374,** Robin Laurance/Photo Researchers; **376,** Richard Nowitz/FPG International; **380,** ©ASAP/Aliza Auerbach/Robert Harding Picture Library; **381,** Geraldo Corsi/Tom Stack & Associates; **383,** Nabeel Turner/Tony Stone Images; **384,** (l) Mark D. Phillips/Photo Researchers, (r) Louis Goldman/FPG International; **387,** (t) Robin Laurance/Photo Researchers, (c) ©ASAP/Aliza Auerbach/Robert Harding Picture Library, (b) Nabeel Turner/Tony Stone Images; **390,** Shinichi Kanno/FPG International; **393,** Ray Ellis/Photo Researchers; **396,** Christine Osborne/Photo Researchers; **401,** ©1991 Peter Jordan/Matrix; **403,** (t) Ray Ellis/Photo Researchers, (b) ©1991 Peter Jordan/Matrix; **406,** (t) Elaine Shay, (bl) Bill Aron/PhotoEdit, (br) Amy C. Etra/PhotoEdit; **407,** (t) Peter Johansky/FPG International, (others) Elaine Shay; **408-409,** Frans Lanting; **418,** ©Hubertus Kanus/Photo Researchers; **422,** (t) ©1992 G. Cubitt/FPG International, (b) ©1976 Tom Pix/Peter Arnold, Inc.;